Abnormal Psychology

PERSPECTIVES

David J. A. Dozois
University of Western Ontario

SIXTH EDITION

Dedicated to my kochana,
Dr. Andrea Piotrowski

ᴠɪᴄᴇ Pʀᴇsɪᴅᴇɴᴛ, Eᴅɪᴛᴏʀɪᴀʟ: Anne Williams
ᴇxᴇᴄᴜᴛɪᴠᴇ AᴄQᴜɪsɪᴛɪᴏɴs Eᴅɪᴛᴏʀ: Kimberley Veevers
Mᴀʀᴋᴇᴛɪɴɢ Mᴀɴᴀɢᴇʀ: Lisa Gillis
Cᴏɴᴛᴇɴᴛ Mᴀɴᴀɢᴇʀ: Madhu Ranadive
Pʀᴏᴊᴇᴄᴛ Mᴀɴᴀɢᴇʀ: Susan Johnson
Cᴏɴᴛᴇɴᴛ Dᴇᴠᴇʟᴏᴘᴇʀ: Katherine Goodes
Pʀᴏᴅᴜᴄᴛɪᴏɴ Sᴇʀᴠɪᴄᴇs: Cenveo® Publisher Services

Pᴇʀᴍɪssɪᴏɴs Pʀᴏᴊᴇᴄᴛ Mᴀɴᴀɢᴇʀ: Kathryn O'Handley
Pʜᴏᴛᴏ Pᴇʀᴍɪssɪᴏɴs Rᴇsᴇᴀʀᴄʜ: Integra Publishing Services, Inc.
Tᴇxᴛ Pᴇʀᴍɪssɪᴏɴs Rᴇsᴇᴀʀᴄʜ: Integra Publishing Services, Inc.
Cᴏᴠᴇʀ ᴀɴᴅ Iɴᴛᴇʀɪᴏʀ Dᴇsɪɢɴᴇʀ: Anthony Leung
Cᴏᴠᴇʀ Iᴍᴀɢᴇ: FCSCAFEINE/Shutterstock

978-0-13-442887-1

1   17

Library and Archives Canada Cataloguing in Publication

Abnormal psychology (Toronto, Ont.)
    Abnormal psychology: perspectives / [edited by] David J.A. Dozois, University of Western Ontario.—Sixth edition.

Includes bibliographical references and index.
ISBN 978-0-13-442887-1 (perfect bound)

    1. Psychology, Pathological—Textbooks. 2. Textbooks.
I. Dozois, David J. A., editor II. Title.

RC454.A26 2018   616.89   C2017-907821-6

Brief Contents

Contents

CHAPTER 7

Psychological Factors Affecting Medical Conditions   145

JOSHUA A. RASH   •   KENNETH M. PRKACHIN   •   GLENDA C. PRKACHIN   •
TAVIS S. CAMPBELL

CHAPTER 8

Mood Disorders and Suicide   171

KATE HARKNESS

CHAPTER 9

Schizophrenia Spectrum and Other Psychotic Disorders   202

R. WALTER HEINRICHS   •   FARENA PINNOCK   •   MELISSA PARLAR

CHAPTER 13

Sexual and Gender Identity Disorders 318

CAROLINE F. PUKALL • KATE S. SUTTON

CHAPTER 14

Neurodevelopmental Disorders 350

JESSICA K. JONES • PATRICIA M. MINNES • MARJORY L. PHILLIPS

CHAPTER 15

Behaviour and Emotional Disorders of Childhood and Adolescence 384

TRACY VAILLANCOURT • KHRISTA BOYLAN

Mental Disorder and the Law   482

STEPHEN D. HART • RONALD ROESCH

Focus and Clinical Research

Preface

The subtitle *Perspectives* was chosen for this text because it expresses the essence of its approach. First, since it is a contributed volume, a number of individual perspectives are discussed. Second, we have taken care to present a balance of the psychological perspectives by discussing various relevant paradigms. Although different perspectives are highlighted, we place greater emphasis on the conceptual approaches and therapeutic interventions that have garnered the most empirical support in the research literature. Finally, this text is written by Canadian experts. While it does pay tribute to the best of international research, it does not ignore the world-class scholarship happening in our own country, and this gives the book its uniquely Canadian perspective.

We feel that *Abnormal Psychology: Perspectives* offers a different approach from many of the abnormal psychology texts available:

1. *Canadian content, from the ground up.* Not just an adaptation of an American text, *Abnormal Psychology: Perspectives* was written entirely by Canadian authors with Canadian students in mind. Our universal health care system and relatively high level of secondary education in Canada have resulted in mental health issues that are unique in North America, and they are reflected in this text. As well, a large number of important issues—legal cases, laws governing therapists, ethical issues, prevention programs, ground-breaking research, even the history of abnormal psychology in this country—are considered from the perspective of people who will be studying, living, and working in Canada. Chapter 19 (Mental Disorder and the Law), for example, covers the topic most requested by Canadian instructors tired of having to supplement texts that discuss only the American situation. Each chapter also highlights many of the important contributions that Canadian researchers have made to the understanding and treatment of psychopathology.

2. *Expert contributors.* One of the advantages of a contributed abnormal psychology text is that each disorder chapter can be written by experts in that field, ensuring that the research discussed and the approach taken in each chapter are as accurate and up to date as possible. The panoply of well-known and highly respected contributors to this volume speaks for itself.

3. *A different approach.* The organization of the text has been fine-tuned to reflect the emerging importance of several areas of abnormal psychology. For example, an entire chapter is devoted to prevention and mental health promotion in the community because no matter how adept we become at diagnosing and treating mental disorders, their *incidence* will never decrease without programs designed to prevent them from occurring in the first place. As the familiar adage states, "An ounce of prevention is worth a pound of cure."

4. *Chapter organization.* The chapters in this text provide an excellent flow that we believe progresses well, from general historical and conceptual issues, to an overview of issues related to diagnosis and assessment, to a detailed review of specific disorders, to important issues in the field—such as mental disorders and aging, the efficacy of psychological interventions, prevention of disorders and promotion of mental health, and legal and ethical issues in mental health.

Although the book is multi-authored, we have striven at all times for consistency of level, depth, and format across the chapters. Where applicable, each chapter follows this pattern:

- Learning objectives
- Opening case
- Overview/introduction of the disorder
- Discussion of diagnostic issues (with DSM-5 criteria)
- Historical perspective
- Full description of the disorder
- Etiology (from various theoretical perspectives)
- Treatment (from various theoretical perspectives)
- Within-chapter critical thinking questions ("Before Moving On")
- Within-chapter Applied Clinical Case
- Within-chapter Canadian Research Centre box
- Summary
- Key words

We hope that students and instructors alike will benefit from this collaboration of many individuals who, no doubt like them, will always find the study of abnormal psychology endlessly challenging and utterly absorbing.

What's New in the Sixth Edition

Throughout the text this edition reflects the latest DSM-5 criteria. Our sixth edition was also heavily revised with updated references and statistics, more Canadian research and studies, and five new senior authors (Chapters 7, 10, 12, 14, and 18). To provide you with a brief overview of these changes, we offer some chapter-by-chapter highlights:

CHAPTER 1

- Provides an overview of the strategies used to define abnormality over the course of history, with updated Canadian content
- Covers the developments of the Mental Health Commission of Canada

- Highlights the work of the Canadian Psychological Association's task force on evidence-based practice of psychological treatments and addresses issues related to access to care, including recent government and corporate initiatives for ensuring that Canadians get the right help at the right time.
- Features a Focus box "Treatment and Mistreatment," which examines how Hollywood films depict mental asylums
- Discusses how technology introduces new opportunities and challenges for mental health care.

CHAPTER 2

- Provides an updated overview of the different theoretical perspectives on abnormal behaviour
- Illustrates how theorists from biological, psychodynamic, behavioural, cognitive, humanistic/existential, and socio-cultural perspectives would view a particular case of abnormal behaviour
- Discusses new research on gene–environment interactions
- Highlights research on self-schemas
- Discusses new "third wave" approaches, including Mindfulness-Based Cognitive Therapy and Acceptance and Commitment Therapy
- Addresses the impact of public stigma and self-stigma and recent anti-stigma campaigns

CHAPTER 3

- Describes why we need a classification system, outlines the criteria used to define abnormal behaviour, and provides a history of the classification of mental disorders
- Describes the history of the DSM and the organization of the DSM-5
- Includes a new Focus box on Howie Mandel and his struggles with OCD
- Highlights the Research Domain Criteria initiated by the National Institute of Mental Health
- Discusses the prevalence of mental disorders in Canada

CHAPTER 4

- Updates the literature on psychological and neuropsychological assessment
- Examines the issue of test security in a Focus box on the posting of the Rorschach Inkblot Test on Wikipedia
- Discusses new research on the MMPI-2 and MMPI-2_RF, including a new sample profile
- Updates the literature on cognitive-behavioural assessment
- Highlights new Canadian epidemiological research

CHAPTER 5

- Organizes anxiety and related disorders into three distinct sections within the chapter: Anxiety Disorders, Obsessive-Compulsive and Related Disorders, and Trauma- and Stressor-Related Disorders.
- Updates findings on the etiology of anxiety and related disorders and describes DSM-5 criteria
- Includes a new Focus box highlighting research on OCD, memory confidence, and checking
- Body Dysmorphic Disorder is now included in Chapter 5
- Discusses therapeutic strategies for enhancing exposure therapy
- Features a new Canadian Research Centre box describing the work of Dr. Candice Monson, Ryerson University professor and expert on PTSD
- Discusses the latest treatment and epidemiological research on anxiety and related disorders

CHAPTER 6

- Highlights DSM-5 criteria for dissociative and somatic symptom and related disorders
- Provides updated information regarding the epidemiology of dissociative and somatic symptom and related disorders
- Covers updated research on the etiology and treatment of dissociative amnesia, depersonalization/derealization disorder, and dissociative identity disorder
- Discusses contemporary research concerning the etiology and treatment of somatic symptom disorders

CHAPTER 7

- New authors provide an updated historical review of psychological factors involved in physical illness
- Highlights changes to the classification of psychological factors affecting medical conditions in DSM-5
- Includes a review of alternative systems for measuring and classifying psychological factors affecting medical conditions
- Includes an expanded breadth of coverage of psychological factors affecting medical conditions.
- Includes a balanced and comprehensive review of cardiovascular reactivity, including exaggerated reactivity, blunted reactivity, and cardiovascular recovery
- Updates and expands upon the association between depression and cardiovascular disease
- Details an innovative Canadian research centre

CHAPTER 8

- Provides additional information on historical views of depression

- Highlights changes to the mood disorder diagnoses in DSM-5

- Features work by Dr. Daniel Klein on chronic depression

- New Applied Clinical Case focuses on the difficulties experienced by singer and actor Demi Lovato

- Provides information on the symptoms and causal models of Premenstrual Dysphoric Disorder (PMDD)

- Provides additional information on information-processing biases in unipolar depression and bipolar disorder

- Provides additional information on the role of stress in bipolar disorder

- Provides additional information on the effects of childhood stress on the brain

- Provides additional information on the role of neurotransmitters in bipolar disorder

- Provides information on the role of the immune system and stress in depression

- Examines Mindfulness-Based Cognitive Therapy, developed by Canadian psychologist Dr. Zindel Segal and his colleagues

- Reviews recent data on neurostimulation and neurosurgical treatments

- Highlights the National Suicide Prevention Strategy recently approved by the federal government

- Highlights two psychological models of suicide—the interpersonal model and the motivational-volitional model

- Introduces information on the pharmacological treatment of suicide with ketamine

CHAPTER 9

- Showcases common delusions experienced by individuals with schizophrenia

- Provides updated information on cognitive subtypes and genetic markers of schizophrenia

- Reviews findings from functional and structural imaging research on schizophrenia

- Describes the dopamine hypothesis of psychosis and recent developments in medication

- Clinical Research Centre focuses on the work of Queen's University researcher Dr. Christopher Bowie

- Provides new information on CBT, social skills training, and cognitive remediation programs for schizophrenia

- Introduces a new Clinical Research Centre focusing on the work of Dr. Sean Kidd at Toronto's Centre for Addiction and Mental Health.

CHAPTER 10—NEW

- New additional authors provide updated statistics on the incidence and prevalence of eating disorders

- Contains new information aimed at dispelling myths and stereotypes about eating disorders

- Provides additional information on eating disorders in diverse populations

- Updated research on the role of psychological trauma and other severe adverse experiences has been included in the section on the etiology of eating disorders

- Features updated information on "enhanced CBT" and on family therapy

- Contains new information on integrative etiological models

- New Canadian Research Centre focuses on the newly redesigned Eating Disorder Program at the University Health Network in Toronto

CHAPTER 11

- Provides new prevalence data on substance use and gambling behaviour

- Provides updated information on the etiology of alcohol use disorder

- Supplies new information on the opioid crisis in Canada

- Contains a discussion on the relationship between cannabis and psychosis

- Significant reorganization of hallucinogen and gambling sections

- Provides new information on gambling disorder and its treatment

CHAPTER 12—NEW

- New senior author provides information on the DSM-5 criteria for personality disorders and a fundamentally different diagnostic model being considered for future research

- Presents updated case examples throughout the chapter

- Discusses "The Dark Triad"—a constellation of personality traits deemed to be socially aversive

- Highlights new research on psychopathy, including the "selective impulsivity theory"

- Discusses social media and narcissism

- Introduces psychological autopsies as a means to study suicide

- Discusses non-suicidal self-injury and its relation to, and distinction from, borderline personality disorder
- Discusses borderline personality disorder in adolescence
- Provides an updated overview of borderline personality disorder and its treatment

CHAPTER 13

- Updates prevalence rates for sexual dysfunctions
- Expands information related to the treatments for sexual dysfunctions
- Provides the latest information related to gender dysphoria and gender affirming procedures
- Includes new discussions on hypersexuality and sexual sadism/masochism
- Describes new work on the measurement of sexual arousal
- Includes increased breadth of information about pedophilic disorder and rape

CHAPTER 14—NEW

- New senior author highlights DSM-5 criteria for the diagnosis of neurodevelopmental disorders
- Discusses the new terminology for intellectual developmental disabilities and learning disorders
- Examines changes to genetic testing and the impact of new screening technologies
- Highlights updated profiles of Fetal Alcohol Spectrum Disorder, Down syndrome, and Fragile X Syndrome.
- Describes new developments on the effect of disabilities on the family and issues related to community integration and quality of life
- Examines community inclusion and attitudes toward education and sexuality for individuals with disabilities
- Provides new information and approaches to individuals with dual diagnoses i.e. intellectual disability and mental illness; including issues relating to challenging behaviour and offending behaviour in the community
- Highlights diagnostic changes to Autism Spectrum Disorders and explores advances and challenges in assessment, intervention and treatment
- Provides information about specific learning disabilities and the relationship with mental health, including implications for intervention

CHAPTER 15

- Provides new information on the prevalence of childhood mental disorders

- Discusses the impact of bullying on the brain and on children's mental health
- Details DSM-5 criteria for different disorders
- Provides new discussion of the comorbidity of internalizing and externalizing problems
- Discusses the newly added diagnostic category of Disruptive Mood Dysregulation Disorder
- Provides new discussion of the developmental trajectories of various childhood problems
- Discusses a proposed disorder: Nonsuicidal Self-injury Disorder
- A new Focus box highlights the relation of perfectionism and mental health

CHAPTER 16

- Reviews evidence that mental health tends to improve with age, and explores reasons why
- Highlights ways of preventing mental health problems in older adults
- Compares the efficacy of psychological and drug treatments
- Presents new data on the development and treatment of insomnia in later life
- Updates information on the prevalence and treatment of anxiety disorders
- Focuses on updates concerning cognitive disorders (e.g., delirium) in older adults

CHAPTER 17

- Reviews evidence-based guidelines for the pharmacological treatment of mental disorders
- Highlights the recommendations of the Canadian Psychological Association's Task Force on Prescriptive Authority for Psychologists in Canada
- Discusses recent trends in cognitive-behavioural therapy and other "third wave" approaches
- A new Canadian Research Centre focuses on Dr. Martin Antony from Ryerson University
- Highlights technological advances in the provision of psychological treatments
- Provides new information on the effectiveness of psychological treatments for different disorders
- Discusses modular and transdiagnostic approaches to treatment
- Identifies key issues in the development of evidence-based psychological practice and presents a new model endorsed by the Canadian Psychological Association

CHAPTER 18—NEW

- New senior author discusses updated research on ecological protective factors and cumulative risk

- Describes a school-based approach to public health, prevention, and mental health

- Discusses interactionist and constructionist perspectives on resilience

- Highlights issues related to the implementation and dissemination of prevention programs

- Provides a new subsection on issues related to cultural competence and anti-racism

CHAPTER 19

- Presents a revised and expanded summary of provincial civil mental health laws

- Updates the discussion of risk assessment to include Version 3 of the HCR-20

- Discusses amendments to the *Criminal Code* related to the designation of High Risk Accused

- Incorporates the new fourth edition of the *Canadian Code of Ethics for Psychologists*

Features

Learning Objectives. Each chapter opens with a set of learning objectives. These learning objectives focus on student performance. Each chapter begins with a statement about what the student should be able to learn. Critical thinking questions (titled "Before Moving On") that correspond to the learning objectives are positioned at appropriate locations within the chapter to allow the student to pause and reflect on the material. We believe that this new feature will better allow students to absorb, reflect on, and integrate the course material.

"Before Moving On" Critical Thinking Questions. Throughout each chapter is a series of critical thinking questions positioned within the text so that students can stop and think about the content of the chapter before moving on. Each of these critical thinking questions links to one of the learning objectives identified at the beginning of the chapter, providing students with an excellent way to absorb, integrate, and apply the material. The questions help promote in-class discussions and small group work.

Cases. Cases are, without a doubt, what students find most fascinating about abnormal psychology. Each chapter of this text opens with a case or cases designed to engage student interest. Subsequent cases or clinical examples appear throughout the remainder of the chapter, highlighted in the design by a box, to illustrate nuances between related disorders. Clinical examples are used to illustrate the discussion wherever possible.

Applied Clinical Cases. In addition to the cases that open each chapter, Applied Clinical Cases focus on celebrities or other well-known people. These interesting case examples serve to bring to life some of the concepts outlined in the text.

Focus boxes. These feature boxes present such interesting topical subjects as Depicting Mental Asylums in Movies; The New Classification Framework; OCD; Sex Differences in Depression; Paul Bernardo and Karla Homolka; Measuring Sexual Arousal, and much more!

Canadian Research Centre. These insightful boxes highlight Canadian facilities and Canadian psychologists who have made major contributions in their fields as related to each chapter.

DSM-5 Coverage. A discussion of the DSM-5, its strengths and its limitations, first appears in Chapter 3, Classification and Diagnosis. Thereafter, explanations of the various disorders are always accompanied by tables listing DSM-5 criteria for the disorder.

Key Terms. These are bolded and clearly defined where they are first discussed in the chapter. These definitions also appear in the Glossary at the end of the book.

Summary and Key Terms lists. Each chapter ends with a concise bulleted summary of the important points of the chapter. A list of the key terms for that chapter, with page references, follows.

Instructor Supplements

MyTest from Pearson Canada is a powerful assessment generation program that helps instructors easily create and print quizzes, tests, and exams, as well as homework or practice handouts. Questions and tests can all be authored online, allowing instructors ultimate flexibility and the ability to efficiently manage assessments at any time, from anywhere. MyTest for *Abnormal Psychology: Perspectives*, Sixth Edition, includes over 1900 fully referenced multiple-choice, true/false, and essay questions. Each question is accompanied by a difficulty level, type designation, topic, and answer justification. Instructors can access MyTest at www.pearsonmytest.com.

Test Item File. The MyTest questions in multiple-choice, true/false, and essay formats are also provided in a Word document.

Instructor's Manual. The Instructor's Manual contains chapter summaries, key points, key terms, important names, supplementary lecture material, and questions to provoke class discussion.

PowerPoints. The PointPoint supplement contains a comprehensive selection of 20 to 25 slides per chapter, highlighting key concepts featured in the text. The slides have been specifically developed for clear and easy communication of themes, ideas, and definitions.

The above instructor supplements are available for download from a password-protected section of Pearson Canada's online catalogue (**www.pearson.com/higher-education**). Navigate to your book's catalogue page to view a list of those supplements that are available. See your local sales representative for details and access.

LEARNING SOLUTIONS MANAGERS

Pearson's Learning Solutions Managers work with faculty and campus course designers to ensure that Pearson technology products, assessment tools, and online course materials are tailored to meet your specific needs. This highly qualified team is dedicated to helping schools take full advantage of a wide range of educational resources, by assisting in the integration of a variety of instructional materials and media formats. Your local Pearson Canada sales representative can provide you with more details on this service program.

Acknowledgments

I would like to thank the team at Pearson Canada who provided the initial encouragement to undertake this project and who helped so much in the process of generating the final result. In particular, I would like to thank our Executive Acquisitions Editor, Kim Veevers; our Marketing Manager, Lisa Gillis; our Content Manager, Madhu Ranadive; and our Content Developer, Katherine Goodes, for their hard work on this volume.

In addition, I would like to thank my parents (John and Judy Dozois) for their constant love, support, and encouragement. I would also like to express gratitude to Greg Barrett and Faith Hennessy who have been an incredible source of support, particularly over the past couple of years. A special thanks to Dr. Andrea Piotrowski, who has helped me—to paraphrase Thoreau—to suck the marrow out of life. I would also like to thank my current graduate students who have been an incredible encouragement and source of joy: Katerina Rnic, Monica Tomlinson, Daniel Machado, Lindsay Szota, Jesse Lee Wilde, and Jennifer Gillies. I am also extremely grateful to the chapter authors for their excellent contributions to this text.

Finally, I gratefully acknowledge the comments and suggestions of the many knowledgeable colleagues who reviewed the earlier editions of this text.

About the Editor

David J. A. Dozois, Ph.D., is a Full Professor of Psychology and Director of the Clinical Psychology Graduate Program at the University of Western Ontario in London, Ontario. He completed his undergraduate and graduate studies at the University of Calgary. He is a Fellow of the Canadian Psychological Association (CPA), the Canadian Association of Cognitive and Behavioural Therapies, the CPA Section on Clinical Psychology, the Association for Behavioural and Cognitive Therapies, and the Academy of Cognitive Therapy. He is also a former Beck Institute Scholar at the Beck Institute for Cognitive Therapy and Research. Dr. Dozois' research focuses on cognitive vulnerability to depression and cognitive-behavioural theory/therapy. He has published 162 scientific papers, book chapters and books and has presented over 300 research presentations at national and international conferences. He is editor of *Cognitive-Behavioral Therapy: General Strategies* (2014, Wiley) and co-editor of the *Handbook of Cognitive-Behavioral Therapies* (in press; Guilford), *Prevention of Anxiety and Depression: Theory Research and Practice* (2004, American Psychological Association) and *Risk Factors in Depression* (2008; Elsevier/Academic Press). Dr. Dozois was twice President of the Canadian Psychological Association (2011–12; 2016–17). He is also on the Board of Directors for the Ontario Mental Health Foundation and the International Association of Applied Psychology. Dr. Dozois is a licensed psychologist, and practises cognitive therapy in London, Ontario.

http://dozoislab.com/

http://psychology.uwo.ca/people/faculty/profiles/dozois.html

About the Contributors

Concepts of Abnormality Throughout History

Daniel Machado received his B.A. (Honours) in psychology from the University of Waterloo and his M.Sc. in clinical psychology from Western University. He is currently completing his Ph.D. in clinical psychology at Western University. Daniel's research interests centre on cognitive vulnerabilities to depression, and his current research examines the predictors of relapse/recurrence in the disorder.

Theoretical Perspectives on Abnormal Behaviour

Lindsay Szota received her B.Sc. (Honours) in psychology from the University of Western Ontario and is currently completing her M.Sc. in clinical psychology at the University of Western Ontario. Her research interests focus on cognitive predictors of information-processing biases in depression-prone individuals.

Classification and Diagnosis

Katerina Rnic received her B.A. (Honours) in psychology from Queen's University and her M.Sc. in clinical psychology from the University of Western Ontario. She is currently completing her doctoral degree in clinical psychology at the University of Western Ontario. Her research examines how cognitive and behavioural vulnerabilities relate to the generation of and response to depressogenic life events, particularly those involving rejection or social evaluation.

Psychological Assessment and Research Methods

Monica Tomlinson completed her Bachelor of Arts in Psychology and English at McGill University and her Master's of Science in Clinical Psychology at The University of Western Ontario (UWO). Monica is currently completing her Ph.D. in Clinical Psychology at UWO with Dr. David Dozois. Monica has two major programs of research. Monica's dissertation research, which is funded by the Social Sciences and Humanities Research Council, is looking at the relationship between substance use and depression. She also has a program of research with St. Joseph's Health Care London developing and evaluating rehabilitation programs in forensic psychiatric populations.

Anxiety and Related Disorders

Jesse Lee Wilde received her B.Sc. (Honours) in psychology from the University of Toronto and is currently completing her M.Sc. in clinical psychology at the University of Western Ontario. Her research focuses on cognitive correlates of intimate relationship dysfunction within the context of depression.

Paul A. Frewen completed his Ph.D. in clinical psychology from Western University in London, Ontario, where he is now associate professor in the Department of Psychiatry. Dr. Frewen completed his clinical psychology residency with the Royal Ottawa Health Care Group. His research interests include psychological assessment, and functional magnetic resonance imaging of emotional processing and sense of self in people with mood and anxiety disorders. He received the President's New Researcher Award from the Canadian Psychological Association (CPA) and the Scientist-Practitioner Early Career Award from the Clinical Section of CPA.

Dissociative and Somatic Symptom and Related Disorders

Rod A. Martin completed his Ph.D. in clinical psychology at the University of Waterloo in 1984, and was subsequently a professor in the Department of Psychology at Western University until his retirement in 2016. During his time at Western he served for 12 years as director of the clinical psychology program, and taught courses in abnormal psychology at both the graduate and undergraduate levels for many years. In general, his research has focused on personality variables associated with resiliency and effective coping. A major focus of his research has been on the psychology of humour, particularly as it relates to psychological health and well-being. He has authored numerous journal articles and book chapters on this topic, and his book, *The Psychology of Humor: An Integrative Approach*, has become the leading text in the field. He has also conducted research on depression, Type A personality, and the effects of stress on immunity. He is now a professor emeritus and is enjoying retirement.

Nadia Maiolino is a doctoral candidate in the clinical psychology program at the University of Western Ontario. Nadia also received her M.Sc. in clinical psychology at Western and completed her B.A. (Honours) at Brescia University College. Her research interests include the impact of psychological factors on major mental disorders, and primarily, the role of cognitive and behavioural mechanisms in producing manic symptoms.

Psychological Factors Affecting Medical Conditions

Joshua A. Rash received his Ph.D. in clinical psychology from the University of Calgary in 2017. He is an Assistant Professor of Clinical Psychology at Memorial University of Newfoundland. His research focuses on elucidating the biobehavioural mechanisms involved in the development, progression, and management of chronic disease, including pain, cardiovascular disease, and cancer.

Kenneth M. Prkachin received his Ph.D. in clinical psychology from the University of British Columbia in 1978. Subsequently, he taught in the Department of Psychology at the University of British Columbia and the Department of Health Studies at the University of Waterloo. He is currently professor of psychology and health sciences at the University of Northern British Columbia. His research is in the area of measurement of emotion, psychological determinants of cardiovascular reactivity, and psychological risk factors for heart disease.

Glenda C. Prkachin received her Ph.D. in biopsychology from the University of British Columbia in 1978. Subsequently, she was a Killam Postdoctoral Fellow in the Department of Neuroanatomy at the University of Washington and a Natural Sciences and Engineering Council of Canada University Research Fellow. She has taught at the University of Western Ontario, Mt. Allison University, Wilfrid Laurier University, and the Universities of Guelph and Waterloo. She is currently associate professor of psychology at the University of Northern British Columbia. Her current research is in the perception and neuroscience of emotion.

Tavis Campbell is a Professor of Clinical Psychology and Oncology at the University of Calgary, where he also holds the position of Director of Clinical training. He obtained his Ph.D. from McGill University and completed a Postdoctoral Fellowship at Duke University Medical Centre. His research interests involve identifying and understanding the bio-behavioural mechanisms involved in the development, progression, and management of chronic diseases, such as hypertension, cancer and insomnia. In addition, he is actively involved in the Canadian Hypertension Education Program (CHEP) and is Chair of the Adherence Committee and a member of the Knowledge Translation Committee at Hypertension Canada. Finally, Dr. Campbell is regularly sought out by a variety of healthcare professionals (e.g., physicians, rheumatologists, nurses, dermatologists) to deliver training with a focus on motivating health behaviour change and improving patient-provider communication.

Mood Disorders and Suicide

Kate Harkness, Ph.D., C. Psych., received her Honours B.Sc. in Psychology from the University of Toronto and her M.Sc. and Ph.D. from the University of Oregon. She then completed a residency and post-doctoral fellowship at the Western Psychiatric Institute and Clinic in Pittsburgh. She is a Professor in the Departments of Psychology and Psychiatry at Queen's University. Her research has focused on the role of stress in the onset and recurrence of major depression in adolescents and adults, and she is currently conducting studies examining interactions between biomarkers in the neuroendocrine and neuroinflammatory systems and early life stress in the etiology and syndromal presentation of major depressive disorder. Dr. Harkness's research has been funded by the Canadian Institutes for Health Research, the Canadian Foundation for Innovation, the Ontario Mental Health Foundation, and the Hospital for Sick Children Foundation.

Schizophrenia

R. Walter Heinrichs is Professor in the Department of Psychology at York University in Toronto, Ontario. He became interested in schizophrenia as a student at the Ontario College of Art, where he was exposed to the history of artistic expression in people with serious mental illness. After an

undergraduate degree in psychology, he studied esthetic perception and neuropsychology, obtaining his Ph.D. at the University of Toronto. Dr. Heinrichs then spent several years in hospital practice as a clinical neuropsychologist before embarking on a career in teaching and research. His interests include the history of schizophrenia, meta-analysis of neuroscience evidence, cognition and psychopathology and functional outcome. He is the author of In Search of Madness: Schizophrenia and Neuroscience (2001) published by Oxford University Press.

Farena Pinnock is a Clinical Psychology doctoral student at York University. She completed her Honour's B.A. at Wilfrid Laurier University and M.Sc. at the University of Western Ontario in the Department of Anatomy and Cell Biology. Farena has a passion for clinical research that integrates neurobiological and behavioural techniques and she has benefited from clinical experience in several neuropsychology facilities. Her current research involves examining the neural correlates of cognitive impairment and psychosis among individuals with schizophrenia.

Melissa Parlar received a Ph.D. in Neuroscience at McMaster University, where she conducted research on the interplay between cognitive and emotional processes in psychiatric populations. Melissa is now pursuing doctoral studies in Clinical Psychology at York University where she is combining her clinical and research interests in neuropsychology and schizophrenia. Her current research investigates factors related to functional outcome in patients with schizophrenia.

Eating Disorders

Danielle MacDonald received her Ph.D. from Ryerson University and is currently a staff psychologist (supervised practice) at the University Health Network Eating Disorder Program. Her research has examined rapid response to cognitive behaviour therapy for eating disorders, emotion regulation and eating disorders, and the efficacy and effectiveness of evidence based treatments for eating disorders.

Kathryn Trottier received her Ph.D. from the University of Toronto and is currently a staff psychologist and clinical team leader at Toronto General Hospital's University Health Network Eating Disorder Program and lecturer assistant professor at the University of Toronto, Department of Psychiatry. Her research has examined the interrelationship between eating disorders and posttraumatic stress disorder, as well as socio-cultural influences on eating and body image, the overvaluation of weight and shape in eating disorders, and treatment efficacy and effectiveness in eating disorders.

Substance-Related Disorders

David Hodgins, Ph.D., is a professor in the clinical psychology program in the Department of Psychology, University of Calgary. Dr. Hodgins is a coordinator with the Alberta Gaming Research Institute. He received his B.A. from Carleton University, and his M.A. and Ph.D. from Queen's University.

His research interests focus on various aspects of addictive behaviours, including relapse and recovery from substance abuse and gambling disorders. He has a particular interest in concurrent mental health disorders. He has developed a brief treatment for gambling problems that uses a motivational enhancement model, and research examining its efficacy is funded by the Canadian Institutes of Health Research. Dr. Hodgins teaches in the clinical psychology program and has an active cadre of graduate students. He maintains a private practice in Calgary in addition to providing consultation to a number of organizations internationally.

Magdalen Schluter, B.A., is a master's student in the clinical psychology program at the University of Calgary under the supervision of Dr. David Hodgins. Magdalen received her bachelor's degree in psychology from the University of British Columbia. Her research interests focus on reward-related decision making and executive dysfunction in gambling and substance-related addictive disorders.

The Personality Disorders

Stephen P. Lewis, Ph.D. is an Associate Professor in the Department of Psychology at the University of Guelph. Dr. Lewis completed his doctoral training at Dalhousie University and his clinical residency at the Royal Ottawa Hospital. His areas of expertise are self-injury and youth mental health. His research has been featured in national and international media outlets, including The New York Times, Time, USA Today, ABC, CBS, The Globe and Mail, and the BBC. Dr. Lewis is co-author of the book *Non-Suicidal Self-injury*, which is part of the Advances in Psychotherapy series by the Society of Clinical Psychology (APA Division 12). He is an invited member of the International Society for the Study of Self-Injury (ISSS) and will be taking on the role of ISSS President in June 2017.

Stephen Porter, Ph.D. is a professor of psychology at the University of British Columbia–Okanagan, working as an educator, researcher, and consultant in the area of psychology and law. He is the founding director of the Centre for the Advancement of Psychological Science and Law (CAPSL). He has published numerous research and theoretical articles on forensic issues ranging from personality disorders, credibility assessment, and deception detection to psychopathy, violent crime, and memory for trauma. As a registered forensic psychologist, Dr. Porter has conducted nearly 200 assessments on offenders or accused persons, and has been called as an expert witness in several Canadian legal cases. He has also been consulted by police to aid in detecting deception and strategic interviewing during criminal investigations. In addition, he has provided training to professional groups, including parole officers, private investigators, police, psychologists, psychiatrists, numerous groups of Canadian judges, and other adjudicators. His current research is supported by SSHRC, NSERC, and CFI. Visit the Porter Forensic Psychology Lab website at **https://people.ok.ubc.ca/stporter/Welcome.html**.

Sexual and Gender Identity Disorders

Caroline F. Pukall completed her undergraduate degree in psychology at McGill University, and she received her Ph.D. in clinical psychology from McGill University. She is professor of Psychology at Queen's University, the director of the Sexual Health Research Laboratory (sexlab.ca), and the director of the Sex Therapy Service at the Queen's Psychology Clinic. Her research focuses on vulvodynia (i.e., chronic genital pain in women), persistent genital arousal disorder, and other sexual health issues, as well as diverse relationships. Her work is funded by several organizations, including the Canadian Institutes of Health Research and the National Vulvodynia Association. Dr. Pukall is an associate editor of *Sexual Medicine Reviews* and is on the editorial board of several journals, including *The Archives of Sexual Behavior*.

Katherine S. Sutton, Ph.D., completed her undergraduate degree in Human Sexuality and Gender (Psychology) at the University of Western Ontario. She received her Ph.D. in Clinical Psychology from Queen's University in 2014. She is presently working as a licensed clinical psychologist with sexual offenders in the state of California. Her research has focused on various aspects of health and human sexuality, including vulvodynia, hypersexuality, and paraphilias. She has published numerous articles and book chapters on these topics. Her clinical areas of practice include sex therapy, gender dysphoria, and the assessment and treatment of adult sexual offenders.

Developmental Disorders

Jessica K. Jones is a Professor of Psychiatry and Psychology at Queen's University. Dr. Jones received a doctoral degree in clinical psychology at the University of Wales, Cardiff and her undergraduate psychology degree at University of Ottawa. She completed her specialty training in forensic intellectual disability in Britain and is a registered clinical forensic psychologist in Ontario and a chartered fellow of the BPS in the UK. Dr Jones is the co-chair of the psychiatry Division of Developmental Disabilities and Clinical Director for the dual diagnosis academic-service consulting program. Dr. Jones is an active clinical supervisor for graduate psychology students and residents; and regularly provides invited lectures for scholarly conferences and community engagement workshops. She has authored multiple publications, books, chapters and ministerial briefs relating to individuals with dual diagnosis i.e. intellectual disabilities and/or autism spectrum disorders with psychiatric illness or challenging behaviour. Her research interests include risk assessment, challenging behaviour, sex offending and offenders with autism spectrum disorders/Asperger's syndrome. Dr. Jones has provided expert testimony on a number of cases involving risk assessment and capacity for offenders with intellectual disabilities and autism spectrum disorders. Dr. Jones provides clinical consultation to developmental and mental health partners with a focus on forensics and works alongside policy makers on the service system impact that offenders with disabilities have on the community.

Patricia M. Minnes received a B.A. (Hons.) degree in psychology from Queen's University in Kingston, Ontario, and a master's degree in clinical psychology from the University of Edinburgh, Scotland. She completed her doctorate in psychology at York University, Toronto. Dr. Minnes is a professor emerita in the Departments of Psychology and Psychiatry at Queen's University. Dr. Minnes is a member of the Developmental Disabilities Consulting Program in the Department of Psychiatry at Queen's, serving individuals with dual diagnoses and their families. As part of her clinical responsibilities, Dr. Minnes contributes to the supervision of psychology practicum students and psychology interns.

Dr. Minnes's research focuses on three major areas relating to individuals with disabilities: stress and coping in families and caregivers, community inclusion and quality of life, and attitudes toward persons with disabilities. Within these areas, she has focused primarily on two disability groups: developmental disability and acquired brain injury, as well as issues related to aging and disability. Throughout her career, Dr. Minnes has worked as a scientist practitioner.

Marjory L. Phillips received a doctoral degree in clinical psychology from the University of Waterloo in 1992. Dr. Phillips is the director of clinical services and community education at Integra, the only accredited children's mental health agency in Canada to specialize in providing mental health services to children, youth, and families with learning disabilities. Previously, Dr. Phillips worked with children with disabilities in a children's treatment rehabilitation centre. She joined the Queen's University Psychology Department on a full-time basis in 2004 to establish a psychology training clinic for graduate students. Dr. Phillips also has held cross-appointments as an adjunct assistant professor at Queen's University and York University, and is a clinical supervisor with the University of Toronto.

Behaviour and Emotional Disorders of Childhood and Adolescence

Tracy Vaillancourt is a Canada Research Chair in Children's Mental Health and Violence Prevention at the University of Ottawa, where she is cross-appointed as a full professor in the Faculty of Education (counselling psychology program) and in the School of Psychology, Faculty of Social Sciences. Dr. Vaillancourt is also an adjunct professor in the Department of Psychology, Neuroscience, and Behaviour at McMaster University. She received her B.A., M.A., and Ph.D. from the University of British Columbia (human development), her post-doctoral diploma from the University of Montreal and Laval University (developmental psychology), and post-doctoral re-specialization in applied child psychology (clinical) from McGill University. Dr. Vaillancourt's research examines the links between aggression and children's mental health functioning, with a particular focus on social neuroscience. She is currently funded by the Canadian Institutes of Health Research, the Social Sciences and Humanities Council of Canada, and the Ontario Mental Health Foundation.

Khrista Boylan, MD Ph.D. is a child and adolescent psychiatrist at McMaster Children's Hospital in Hamilton Ontario. She is associate professor in the Departments of Psychiatry and Behavioural Neurosciences and Health Research Methodology at McMaster. Her clinical work and research focuses on emotion dysregulation, suicidal behaviour and personality disorder symptoms in adolescents. She is the editor of the Journal of the Canadian Academy of Child and Adolescent Psychiatry.

Aging and Mental Health

Corey Mackenzie, Ph.D., C. Psych., is a Clinical Psychologist, Professor and Director of Clinical Training in the Department of Psychology, Adjunct Professor in Psychiatry, and a Research Affiliate with the Centre on Aging at the University of Manitoba. His research, clinical, and teaching interests focus on older adults' mental health. Three lines of research, that are being explored in his Aging and Mental Health laboratory (www.coreymackenzie.com), are investigating ways of improving the mental health of older individuals. Using both primary quantitative and qualitative methods, and secondary analyses of national population surveys, research in his lab aims to: (a) understand how age affects mental health, (b) enhance older adults' access to mental health services, and (c) help individuals cope with stress when caring for older adults with dementia. His research is currently funded by the University of Manitoba, the Manitoba Gambling Research Foundation, CIHR, and SSHRC.

Kristin Reynolds, Ph.D., is an Assistant Professor in the Department of Psychology at the University of Manitoba, and a Clinical Psychologist Candidate. As Director of the Health Information Exchange Lab, Dr. Reynolds is interested in decreasing gaps in the translation of health-related knowledge to the public, and increasing access to health-related information and services. Her areas of research and clinical interest and expertise include knowledge translation, mental health literacy, mental health service use, community mental health, geriatric psychology, perinatal health, and health psychology. Dr. Reynolds is passionate about clinical psychology and the advancement of science and practice. She is the Chair-Elect of the Clinical Section of the Canadian Psychological Association and the Communications Director for the Manitoba Psychological Society.

Therapies

John Hunsley is a professor of psychology in the School of Psychology at the University of Ottawa, and is director of the clinical psychology program. He is a registered psychologist who provides psychological services for the treatment of anxiety and mood disorders. He conducts research on evidence-based psychological assessment and the impact of psychological services. Dr. Hunsley has served as editor of the journal *Canadian Psychology* and is a recipient of the Canadian Psychological Association Award for Distinguished Contributions to Education and Training in Psychology.

He is a fellow of the Association of State and Provincial Psychology Boards, the Canadian Psychological Association, and the Canadian Psychological Association's Section on Clinical Psychology.

Catherine M. Lee is a full professor of psychology at the University of Ottawa where she has taught graduate courses in evidence-based services for children and families and an undergraduate course on Clinical Psychology, as well as supervising practicum students and interns at the Centre for Psychological Services and Research. Her research interests focus on the provision of evidence-based services to promote positive parenting. Dr. Lee was President of the CPA in 2008–2009. She is a site visitor for the Canadian Psychological Association Accreditation Panel. She is an accredited trainer and Implementation Consultant for Triple P International.

Prevention and Mental Health Promotion in the Community

Julian Hasford is an assistant professor in the School of Child and Youth Care at Ryerson University. He has a B.A. in environmental studies from York University, a master's degree in health promotion from the University of Toronto, and Ph.D. in community psychology from Wilfrid Laurier University. Julian's scholarly interests are in anti-racism, empowerment, and systems change toward promoting the well-being of racialized youth and communities. He is also interested in community-based mixed method research and evaluation methodologies. Julian's professional experience includes work in child welfare, urban agriculture, and African Canadian community advocacy. He was a recipient of the Donald T. Fraser Award for Academic Excellence at the University of Toronto (2005) and the Council of Canadian Departments of Psychology Teaching Assistantship Award (2007).

Isaac Prilleltensky is dean of the School of Education at the University of Miami in Coral Gables, Florida, where he is also a professor of educational and psychological studies and a professor of psychology. Isaac was born in Argentina and has studied and worked in Israel, Canada, Australia, and the United States. He has lectured widely in South America, Europe, North America, Israel, Australia, and New Zealand. Isaac is concerned with value-based ways of promoting child, family, and community well-being. He is the author, co-author, or co-editor of seven books dealing with psychological and community well-being. He has been involved in community research and action in various countries and is a fellow of the American Psychological Association and of the Society for Community Research and Action. In 2002 he was visiting fellow of the British Psychological Society.

Mental Disorder and the Law

Stephen D. Hart obtained his Ph.D. in clinical psychology from the University of British Columbia. He holds appointments as a professor in the Department of Psychology at Simon Fraser University (SFU) and the Faculty of Psychology at the University of Bergen. His work focuses on forensic assessment, including the assessment of psychopathic personality disorder and violence risk. Outside of SFU, he served as President of the AP-LS and the International Association of Forensic Mental Health Services, as well as a Founding Editor of the *International Journal of Forensic Mental Health* and the *Journal of Threat Assessment and Management*. Among other recognitions, he received the Saleem Shah Award for Early Career Contributions to Psychology and Law from the American Academy of Forensic Psychology and the American Psychology Law Society (AP-LS, Div. 41 of the American Psychological Association), and the Career Contributions Award from the Society of Clinical Psychology (Division 12 of the American Psychological Association).

Ronald Roesch obtained his Ph.D. in clinical psychology from the University of Illinois at Urbana-Champaign. He is a professor in the Department of Psychology at Simon Fraser University. He is director of the Mental Health, Law, and Policy Institute at Simon Fraser University (SFU), and prior to that served for many years as director of clinical training. His research focuses on improving the delivery of mental health services in forensic settings. Outside SFU, he has served as president of the American Psychology-Law Society (AP-LS, Div. 41 of the American Psychological Association) and the International Association of Forensic Mental Health Services; Editor of the journals *Law and Human Behavior* and *Psychology, Public Policy, and Law*; and a Founding Editor of the *International Journal of Forensic Mental Health*. In 2010 he received the Outstanding Contributions to Psychology and Law Award from AP-LS.

DAVID J. A. DOZOIS

•

DANIEL MACHADO

CHAPTER

1

Ranplett/Vetta/Getty Images

Concepts of Abnormality Throughout History

LEARNING OBJECTIVES

AFTER READING THIS CHAPTER, STUDENTS WILL BE ABLE TO:

1 Describe the principles that have been used to define abnormality and then apply them to determine whether a particular behaviour may meet the definition of abnormal behaviour.

2 Understand how the conceptualization of psychological disorders changed from antiquity to the 1800s.

3 Describe at least two treatments that are associated with the biological approach and outline the current status of these treatments.

4 Describe the contributions of at least two influential Canadian individuals in the field of mental health care.

5 Describe two recent significant developments associated with mental health in Canada and discuss implications of recent technological advances on the field of psychology.

Lisa appeared at a clinic saying that her husband and two teenage children had persuaded her to seek treatment for what they saw as dysfunctional behaviour. She told the clinician that after she took a shower (which she did at least three times a day), she felt she had to wash the floor and walls of the bathroom in order to ensure that no dirt or bacteria had splashed off her body and contaminated the room. Lisa also insisted that her family not touch the faucets in the bathroom with their bare hands because she was sure that they would leave germs. The family members agreed to use a tissue to turn the taps on and off. Visits to the house by friends and relatives were not allowed because Lisa felt she could not ask them to follow these instructions and, even if she could bring herself to ask them, she did not believe they would go along with her request. This, of course, meant that her husband and children could never invite friends to their house. This restriction, and various other limits that Lisa imposed upon them, led the family to send her for treatment. Lisa did not consider her problems to be quite as bad as her family saw them.

***

Since childhood, Paul had been sexually aroused by the sight of women's underwear. This had caused him considerable distress as a teenager and young adult. The fact that he could become sexually aroused only in the presence of women's underwear made him feel different from others, and he was afraid that people would find out about his secret desires and ridicule him. When Paul was 26 years old, after years of secrecy, he decided to consult a therapist in an attempt to deal with his unusual desires.

***

Arnold had begun to develop odd ways of perceiving the world and had begun to have unusual thoughts shortly after he entered university. After he graduated from high school, his parents put pressure on him to enrol in an engineering degree program at university so he could earn a large salary. Arnold resisted this pressure for some time, but finally gave in and took up the program. However, he was afraid he would fail and let everyone down. He was afraid they would find out he was really not competent. The pressures from his family, the threat of failure, and the heavy workload of his studies soon became too much for Arnold. He began to develop odd interpretations of world events and of his role in them, and he began to perceive personally relevant messages on the nightly television newscasts. These unusual thoughts and perceptions quickly escalated until finally Arnold went to the local police station requesting a meeting with Canada's prime minister and the American president so he could give them instructions for solving the world's problems. Not surprisingly, Arnold's grades dropped and he had to leave school. He was placed in hospital.

Clearly, Lisa, Paul, and Arnold all have abnormalities of behaviour and thought, but they are also very different from one another. There is no doubt, however, that most people would agree that each of them displayed very unusual, if not bizarre, behaviour. Arnold's problems seriously interfered with his life and his ambitions. Lisa was not as concerned about her problems as her family was, but they nevertheless markedly restricted her social life and interfered with other aspects of her functioning. Paul's case, on the other hand, turned out well. A few months after receiving treatment, he found a partner who apparently could share in his unusual sexual activities, and his life was happy and fulfilled.

What these three cases have in common is that each meets the criteria outlined in current diagnostic manuals for one or another psychological disorder. The current edition of the *Diagnostic and Statistical Manual of Mental Disorders* (DSM-5) of the American Psychiatric Association (2013) is the most broadly accepted system for identifying particular types of disorders, although the *International Classification of Mental and Behavioral Disorders* (ICD-10), issued by the World Health Organization (1992b), is also used by practitioners, primarily outside North America (for details of these diagnostic systems, see Chapter 3). Both of these diagnostic manuals would classify the three cases described above as disordered: Lisa would be classified as manifesting obsessive-compulsive disorder, Paul as having a paraphilic disorder (in this case, a fetishistic disorder), and Arnold as suffering from schizophrenia.

However, there are many people who engage in behaviours or express thoughts that most of us would consider to be strange or deviant, and who may cause distress to others, yet who are not identified in diagnostic systems as disordered. Consider the cases in the following box.

Case Notes

Eileen is a 19-year-old female whose religious beliefs forbid her to wear makeup or colourful clothes, or to listen to the radio or watch television. She must only go out with potential boyfriends in the company of her parents, and she will not attend dances or parties. Along with the rest of the people who attend her church, Eileen believes that the end of the world is imminent, and she has been peacefully preparing herself for that day. In addition, and somewhat contrary to her religious teachings, Eileen believes that the planets and stars control our destiny, and she subscribes to a monthly astrology magazine and consults daily astrological forecasts. Eileen also believes that she can communicate with the spirits of the dead and occasionally participates in seances with her family and their friends.

***

Roger is a professor at a large university. At age 46, he has never married and lives alone in a house whose windows he has painted black to shut out, as he says, "the views of his nosy neighbours." Roger has worn the same tattered suit for years and he wears a rather dirty baseball cap that he says is a family heirloom. He often wears heavy coats in the summer and sandals in the winter. His office is cluttered and he never seems able to find things; in fact, on several occasions he has lost students' essays. In the classroom, Roger wanders about among the desks as he lectures, and his lessons are rambling and difficult for the students to follow. He often introduces odd ideas that seem to have little to do with the topic on which he is lecturing. However, his research is greatly admired, and his colleagues do their best to make up for his teaching inadequacies.

***

James has been a career criminal since his early teenage years. He has broken into many homes and stolen property, he has been convicted of selling marijuana on several occasions, and he has stolen and then sold numerous bicycles and cars. Not surprisingly, James has spent some of his 42 years in prison. Recently, he was living with a woman whom he had met at a bar one week prior to moving in with her and her three children. This was the most recent in a series of relatively short-lived common-law relationships that James had been involved in throughout his adult life. He did not have a job and, despite his promises to his partner, he made little effort to get one. Instead, he stayed home watching television and drinking beer. This led to numerous arguments with his partner and, over time, these arguments became more physical, with each partner hitting the other. Finally, during one of these clashes, James lost his temper and beat his partner with his fists so severely that she lapsed into a coma and died.

Most people would consider Eileen and Roger to be eccentric and, indeed, some students found Roger scary, although he never did anything that would suggest he was dangerous. However, neither Roger nor Eileen has ever been diagnosed as having a psychological disorder. Many people think that anyone who murders is insane, at least temporarily. However, careful examination of James by three independent psychiatrists led them to conclude that, although he had a personality disorder, James was otherwise normal, and the killing resulted from the persistent antagonistic relationship he had with the victim. Therefore, James was held responsible for his actions and duly convicted and imprisoned.

These cases illustrate two problems with defining abnormality. First, eccentric and unusual behaviour or beliefs are not necessarily abnormal according to diagnostic criteria, although the boundary between eccentricity and abnormality is not always clear. Arnold was clearly eccentric but also obviously disturbed. Both Eileen and Roger were eccentric but not so obviously disturbed. Second, behaviours that are repugnant and threatening to others, such as aggression and murder, are not always signs of an underlying psychological disorder. James has acted very badly and in a damaging way to others throughout his life, yet he is not considered to be seriously psychologically disordered. Neither Paul nor Lisa caused distress to other people, but they are judged to be suffering from a disorder.

This book describes our present understanding of the nature of psychological abnormality, the different forms such abnormality takes, how people become abnormal, and what, if anything, can be done to make their functioning normal. A fundamental issue we will have to consider from the outset, then, is just what it is we mean when we say that someone (or a particular behaviour of that person) is psychologically abnormal.

Our notions about abnormality have a long history. From the time of the earliest written records, and no doubt long before that, humans have identified some of their fellow humans as abnormal and offered various explanations and treatments for their behaviours. It is also clear that, over time, definitions of what constitutes abnormal functioning have changed, as have the explanations and treatments for abnormal behaviour. In this chapter, we first consider the various ways in which abnormality has been defined, and then examine the historical developments in the explanations and treatment of abnormality.

First, let us clarify some terms. **Psychological abnormality** refers to behaviour, speech, or thought that impairs the ability of a person to function in a way that is generally expected of him or her, in the context where the unusual functioning occurs. **Mental illness** is a term often used to convey the same meaning as psychological abnormality, but it implies a medical rather than psychological cause. A **psychological disorder** is a specific manifestation of this impairment of functioning, as described by some set of criteria that have been established by a panel of experts. In this book, we will use the term **psychopathology** to mean both the scientific study of psychological abnormality and the problems faced by people who suffer from such disorders. Psychological disorders occur in all societies and have been apparent at all times in history. However, what is considered a disorder varies across time and place.

Attempts at Defining Abnormality

Why is there such confusion about normality and abnormality, and is it possible to resolve the issue? Perhaps the answer to the last part of the question is no, because the concept of abnormality changes with time and differs across cultures and subcultures. However, it is also possible that we cannot easily resolve these problems because, despite the attempts of many writers to provide clear criteria, the concepts of normality and abnormality are so vague.

Several principles are commonly considered in attempts to establish criteria for abnormality. As will become evident, however, no one principle can be considered sufficient to define this elusive concept. Rather, depending on circumstances, the contribution of several criteria may be necessary. The following principles, either alone or in combination, have at one time or another been used to define abnormality.

STATISTICAL CONCEPT

According to this view, behaviour is judged as abnormal if it occurs infrequently in the population. It would, of course, make little sense to describe as abnormal ways of functioning that characterize the majority of people. Relative infrequency, then, ought to be one defining feature of abnormality. However, not all infrequent behaviours or thoughts should be judged abnormal. For instance, innovative ideas are necessarily scarce or they would hardly be original, but most people would not consider the person who had such ideas as displaying abnormality, at least not in its usual pejorative sense. The same is true of athletic prowess. We admire

people like professional hockey player Sidney Crosby, who grew up in Cole Harbour, Nova Scotia, and is currently the captain of the Pittsburgh Penguins (the youngest captain in NHL history). In 2006–07 Crosby became the youngest player in NHL history to win the scoring title and the only teenager in major North American sports leagues to have ever done so. In 2009, he became the youngest captain in NHL history to win the Stanley Cup. Although it is true that individuals like "Sid the Kid" are abnormal in the sense that their athletic skills are rare, we would usually describe such people as exceptional, a term that has no derogatory overtones.

An additional problem with the statistical criterion is that it is not clear how unusual a given behaviour has to be in order to be considered abnormal. For example, a study of Canadian undergraduate students from a small university found that 7 percent of males and 14 percent of females met diagnostic criteria for clinical depression in the preceding year. Thirteen percent of men and 19 percent of women also met criteria for one or more anxiety disorders (Price, McLeod, Gleish, & Hand, 2006). Although the depression rates reported in this study are higher than other one-year Canadian prevalence figures (e.g., Patten, 2009; Pearson, Janz, & Ali, 2013), neither depression nor anxiety can be considered that statistically infrequent—yet both are thought to reflect a disorder in need of treatment. Similarly, the common cold is considered an illness and yet it has a lifetime prevalence of 100 percent (Lilienfeld & Landfield, 2008).

PERSONAL DISTRESS

Many people who are considered to have a psychological disorder report being distressed. Someone who has an anxiety disorder, for example, will report feeling afraid or apprehensive most of the time. Depressed patients are obviously distressed. Yet distress is not present for all people identified as abnormal. An elderly manic patient who was evaluated at a local hospital would persistently pace rapidly around the ward, frequently bumping into people in his rush, despite having no obvious destination. While striding about quickly, he would keep up a constant conversation with no one in particular, and he would leap from topic to unrelated topic. He seemed to be in exuberant spirits, and he described himself as being extremely happy. Obviously, he was not personally distressed and yet, just as obviously, he was suffering from a mental disorder. An individual with antisocial personality disorder, who violates the rights of others, breaks numerous laws, and lacks empathy and remorse is not distressed by his or her behaviour; instead, it is the individuals this person encounters who are distressed by this behaviour.

Some people who outwardly appear happy and successful may reveal to intimate friends that they feel a vague sense of dissatisfaction. They may complain that, despite their apparent success, they feel unfulfilled. There may even be an associated sense of despair at not having achieved something significant, and such people may seek professional help. It is unlikely, however, that they would be labelled abnormal.

In fact, all of us are distressed, or even depressed, at times. When someone we love dies, it is normal to be distressed; indeed, if we do not mourn, our response might be judged to be abnormal. If this distress passes within a reasonable amount of time, our response would be considered normal. However, if our grief did not abate with time, and our depression deepened and persisted for several years, our suffering would be described as abnormal. Distress, then, appears to be a frequent, but not essential, feature of abnormality.

PERSONAL DYSFUNCTION

When behaviour is clearly maladaptive (i.e., it interferes with appropriate functioning), it is typically said to be abnormal. Yet the definition of dysfunction itself is not clear-cut. What is appropriate functioning? What is appropriate functioning in a given context? Many of us responded with feelings of vulnerability, anxiety, anger, and sadness following the terrorist attacks on the World Trade Center and Pentagon on September 11, 2001. Some of us have become increasingly vigilant about possible threats when going through airport security or attending large gatherings such as Canada Day celebrations. Students and faculty have also become more vigilant at universities and colleges following the Dawson College shootings in Montreal (2006) that claimed one life and injured 19 people, and the Virginia Tech massacre (2007) that killed 32. Public schools and religious institutions have also been on higher alert after some were the targets of violent incidents. For example, in 2012, a shooting took place at Sandy Hook Elementary School in Newtown, Connecticut, that killed 27 individuals. In 2017, a shooter in a Quebec City mosque killed six individuals and injured three.

Within reason, such vigilance and anxiety, although distressing, are not abnormal given the circumstances. In fact, scanning the environment for such threats is, to some extent, adaptive as it serves a survival function.

Wakefield (1997, 1999, 2014) has concluded that harmful dysfunction is the key notion—where dysfunctions refer to "failures of internal mechanisms to perform naturally selected functions." To conclude that a given behaviour is disordered "requires both a scientific judgment that there exists a failure of designed function and a value judgment that the design failure harms the individual" (Wakefield, 1999, p. 374). By their functions, Wakefield is referring to what an artifact or behaviour was originally designed to do. For example, the function of a pen is to write—that is the purpose of a pen's design. The fact that we can also use a pen as something to chew on when we are nervous or as a weapon for self-defence does not explain why pens were designed the way they were. Thus, the failure of a pen to help protect an individual would not entail a failure of its function (Wakefield, 1997). Wakefield (1997, 1999) argues that unless there are dysfunctional consequences to the

individual, in that he or she is unable to perform a natural function, it makes little sense to call behaviour abnormal.

Using harmful dysfunction as a potential criterion for abnormal behaviour also creates an interesting link between abnormal and evolutionary psychology. In terms of evolutionary theory, a trait may be dysfunctional if it harms an organism's capacity to reproduce successfully. Antisocial behaviour, for example, may result in being excluded from everyday society, thereby hurting such a person's capacity to reproduce. If the underlying reason for the antisocial behaviour is a lack of inhibition, this may be seen as abnormal. Certain forms of antisocial behaviour, such as unethical business practices, may, however, actually increase an individual's wealth and therefore increase his or her capacity to reproduce (Murphy, 2005).

The boundaries between normal and abnormal and what specifically constitutes "harmful dysfunction" are therefore not clear and are a matter of considerable controversy (e.g., Castel, 2014; Fabrega, 2007; Lilienfeld & Landfield, 2008; Lilienfeld & Marino, 1995). These fuzzy boundaries notwithstanding, categorical distinctions between normal and abnormal can be useful. We discuss this issue further in Chapter 3.

VIOLATION OF NORMS

The behaviour and thoughts of many psychologically disordered individuals run counter to what we might consider appropriate. The thoughts expressed by individuals with schizophrenia, for example, are often so bizarre that observers do not hesitate to declare the ideas irrational and reflecting an extreme departure from what would be expected in the context. Similarly, a man who dresses in women's clothing for the sole purpose of sexual arousal would be judged by most people to be displaying behaviours that are contrary to socially acceptable ideas. On the other hand, criminals clearly engage in behaviours that violate social norms, but few of them meet the criteria for any disorder. No doubt their criminal acts upset others, but discomfort in an observer alone cannot count as the basis for judging someone's behaviour to be disordered. For example, popular Youtube user Felix Kjellberg (a.k.a. Pewdiepie) whose videos have compiled nearly 14.7 billion views as of February 2017, was dropped by Disney following public outcry over anti-Semitic images Kjellberg included in several of his videos (Chokshi, 2017). The lyrics of some songs also make many people uncomfortable. Radio stations were banned from playing the song "Money for Nothing" (performed by Dire Straits) for a period of nine months in 2011, because the song included a word that was deemed to be offensive for homosexual men (CTV, 2011). More recently, rapper Tyler, the Creator was banned from the UK for three to five years based on the claim that his lyrics, which involve the artist taking on a violent alter ego, glamorize abusive and illegal behaviour (Kornhaber, 2015). In a more innocuous example, following the terrorist attacks of 9/11, Clear Channel Communications distributed a list to the 1000+ radio stations under their corporate umbrella of songs that should not be played. The 165 songs on the list contained lyrics Clear Channel deemed to be "question-able" and potentially offensive to American citizens following 9/11, even though many of the songs on the list had links to terrorism that were dubious at best (e.g., "In the Air Tonight" by Phil Collins; It's the End of the World, 2001). These examples show that subjective evaluation of lyrics as containing offensive content would not justify classifying the artists as psychologically abnormal, although that is a characteristic response that people often make to ideas and behaviours they find personally repulsive.

Related to the notion of violating norms is the idea that psychologically abnormal people are unpredictable and somehow dangerous. In fact, very few people suffering from a psychiatric disorder are dangerous to others. Even psychotic patients, who are the most bizarre of all disordered people, rarely attempt to hurt anyone. Most psychologically disordered people are no more dangerous, and no more unpredictable, than are the rest of the population. Conversely, while television and movies like to portray all killers and rapists as "mad", most are not. Apparently, it comforts us to think that someone who would do something as repugnant as maiming or killing another person must be insane.

Perhaps the most serious flaw in this criterion is that social norms vary over time and place. In fact, few disorders are truly universal across different cultures. Depression, for example, has a much higher prevalence rate in Canada (12.6%; Statistics Canada, 2013) and the United States (16.6% lifetime prevalence; Kessler, Petukhova, Sampson, Zaslavsky, & Wittchen, 2012) than in some other parts of the world, such as Taiwan (1.2%; Liao et al., 2012) or Korea (3.3–5.6%; Park & Kim, 2011). Different cultural and ethnic groups also manifest psychopathology differently and exhibit their own strategies for dealing with psychological distress. For example, the lower prevalence of depression in Asian cultures may be due to the emphasis placed on physical symptoms and avoiding the stigma of mental disorders. Neurasthenia is a condition that includes many of the physical symptoms of depression and it is still frequently diagnosed in Asia, but this diagnosis has largely been abandoned in the West. It is important to bear in mind that how we define abnormality is **culturally relative**. The norms of a particular culture determine what is considered to be normal behaviour, and abnormality can be defined only in reference to these norms. Fortunately, the most recent versions of the DSM (e.g., DSM-5) have been far more explicit than previous editions were in encouraging clinicians and researchers to consider cultural diversity.

Society's criteria for defining behaviour as acceptable or unacceptable are also not temporally universal; rather, they reflect the predominant view in society, which changes over time. Thirty-five years ago, when homosexuality was classified as abnormal, it was also considered to be a violation of social norms. Is it a reflection of changing norms that psychologists no longer consider homosexuality to be abnormal? Much earlier, in the late 1800s, masturbation was considered to be a manifestation of a mental

disorder without any consideration of the base rate of this behaviour in the general population (see Mash & Dozois, 2003). To take a more extreme example, in Germany in the 1930s, individuals who were identified as Jews, homosexuals, gypsies, or mentally retarded were persecuted, tortured, or killed on the basis that they represented inferior specimens of human beings. These views, which are repugnant to our society, were apparently sufficiently acceptable to the German populace at the time to allow the Nazis to carry out their so-called ethnic cleansing. Do we conclude that 1930s Germany was an abnormal society—and if so, what does it mean to say that a whole population is abnormal?

DIAGNOSIS BY AN EXPERT

Before we consider this issue, it is an opportune time to identify the professionals involved in the mental health field. **Clinical psychologists** are initially trained in general psychology and then receive graduate training in the application of this knowledge to the understanding, diagnosis, and amelioration of disorders of thinking and behaviour. Psychologists have a thorough grounding in research methods, and some of them spend their careers doing research on abnormal functioning, although many also provide treatment. The treatment methods of clinical psychologists primarily involve psychological interventions of one kind or another. **Psychiatrists** are trained in medicine prior to doing specialized training in dealing with mental disorders. This specialized training focuses on diagnosis and medical treatment that emphasize the use of pharmacological agents in managing mental disorders. Not surprisingly, most psychiatrists attend to the medical aspects and biological foundations of these disorders, although they usually also consider psychological and environmental influences.

The identification of a psychological disorder in any specific individual is ultimately left to a professional to judge. In the final analysis, the opinions of particular mental health workers (usually psychologists and psychiatrists) determine whether a person is said to suffer from a psychological abnormality. In this sense, the DSM-5 (or ICD-10) provides the operational criteria for the various disorders and thereby defines abnormality. This, of course, does not clarify the criteria by which such judgments are made, and an examination of the various criteria for the different disorders suggests that different aspects of the notions outlined above serve to define different disorders. It is hard to discern any clear common thread in the different criteria.

Thomas Szasz (1961), in a book entitled *The Myth of Mental Illness*, suggested that the idea of mental disorders was invented by psychiatry to give control to its practitioners to the exclusion of other people, such as clergymen, who in the past had greater power over the psychologically disordered (see also Schaler, 2004). In addition, Szasz (1970) contended that the institution of the church and the person identified as, for example, a "witch" were replaced by the institution of psychiatry and the patient being treated, respectively. Such criticisms, while perhaps overstating the case (Lilienfeld &

Landfield, 2008), do serve a valuable function by encouraging the generation of evidence to support the existence of mental disorders. There seems to be little doubt today that there is overwhelming evidence of the reality of various disorders. Nevertheless, the power held by mental health professionals remains an issue.

SUMMARY OF DEFINITIONS

As we have seen, not one of the various criteria that have been offered for defining abnormality seems satisfactory on its own. There are many ways to approach defining a person's functioning as normal or abnormal, and the criteria discussed above do not exhaust all possible approaches. Nevertheless, together they represent the core defining features of abnormality. To identify a person or a behaviour as abnormal, no single criterion is either necessary (i.e., must be present) or sufficient (enough on its own). Typically, some combination of these criteria is used, with one or more features having greater relevance depending upon the specific circumstances or features of the client. Our purpose in discussing various criteria for abnormal psychological functioning is to alert the reader to the rather elusive nature of the concept and to suggest that, while such a notion may have some general value, it has little practical application. In practice, most diagnosticians avoid the use of the term *abnormality* and simply prefer to match their clients' symptoms to a set of criteria appearing in the latest edition of the diagnostic manual. While this approach does not clarify the nature of abnormality, it works effectively in practice. Defining specific behaviours, thoughts, and feelings as representing particular disorders, as does the fifth edition of the *Diagnostic and Statistical Manual of Mental Disorders* (DSM-5), is useful because then we can plan the management and treatment of the person displaying such problems. Searching for criteria that will define any and all instances of disordered functioning (or abnormality), however, may be pointless. Nevertheless, throughout the ages people have held quite different views, not only about what abnormality is, but also about its causes.

 BEFORE MOVING ON

How do you determine when someone's behaviour is abnormal? What are the strengths and weaknesses of the *four* general attempts at defining abnormality?

Historical Concepts of Abnormality

We now turn to an examination of the different notions that have, over time, guided approaches to dealing with abnormality. Looking at changes in the conceptualization of abnormal psychological functioning can provide a basis for understanding how we arrived at our current formulations and responses to abnormality. We will see how societal concepts are shaped by the prevailing views of the time concerning all manner of phenomena. Indeed, as Erwin Ackerknecht, a historian of psychiatry, has suggested, "The criterion by which a person in any society is judged to be mentally ill is not primarily the presence of certain unvarying and universally occurring symptoms. It depends rather on whether the affected individual is capable of some minimum of adaptation and social functioning within his [or her] society" (Ackerknecht, 1968, p. 3).

Revolutions in philosophy and science, such as the Renaissance and the era of Enlightenment, generally had profound effects on all aspects of society, including a change in the way that mad people were seen. For example, Darwin's radical conceptualization of the mechanism of evolution, which he called natural selection, had an immediate influence not only on all the biological sciences but also on psychology, politics, and economics. Modern evolutionary biologists have since rejected the implications that were drawn from Darwin's theory by eugenicists (Gould, 1985). Proponents of this view, who included Darwin's cousin Sir Francis Galton (1822–1911), interpreted Darwin's work to mean that those whose intellectual, social, or economic functioning was seen as inferior were defective, or maladaptive. Many further argued that because society and the advancement of medicine now protected these deficiencies from the forces of natural selection, they ought to be selected by society for sterilization in order to eliminate their defective genes. In the hands of the Nazis, eugenics led to the extermination of millions of people. Our own Canadian history was also affected by this type of thinking. In 1928, Alberta passed the *Sexual Sterilization Act* under which individuals who were deemed "feebleminded," "mentally deficient," or "mentally ill" were to be involuntarily sterilized to prevent deterioration of the intellectual level of the general population. A total of 2832 individuals were sterilized in Alberta alone (British Columbia passed a similar act in 1933). One case involved a 17-year-old woman from Edmonton who was diagnosed as a "moron." The rationale for her sterilization was that she was "rather bossy and bad tempered" and had a tendency to go "out alone a lot" and "pick up with anyone and talk and chat with them" (Park & Radford, 1998, p. 327). In 1999, the government of Alberta publicly apologized for the suffering experienced by those who were sterilized under this *act* and negotiated a financial settlement with victims (Government of Alberta, 1999).

An examination of the historical development of our ideas about abnormality, then, will reveal that such ideas are simply one aspect of the general views of the time. This is important for another reason. When we consider some past notions about abnormality, we might tend to scoff and treat them as absurd, and so they may be from the perspective of the present day. However, they must have seemed correct at the time because they matched the general ideas of the day. Reflecting on this may help us to recognize that perhaps our own conceptualization of abnormality seems so right to us only because it fits with our current world views and beliefs (see Mash & Dozois, 2003). Remember that earlier ideas about abnormality were accepted not only by those who made decisions about the insane, but also by many of the sufferers and their families. Treatments that seem bizarre or even cruel to us today may have helped sufferers because they believed that the procedures would be effective. Perhaps the same is true to some degree of our current ideas and treatments (Kirsh et al., 2008). We encourage the student of psychopathology to be a critical consumer of research—it is possible, after all, that at some point in the future we will view our current ideas as archaic and ill-founded.

Throughout recorded history, and no doubt long before that, people have been concerned with identifying and treating psychological dysfunction. What has been seen as evidence of madness or of other disturbed thinking or behaving, however, has changed over the course of evolving societies. For many years, people who claimed to be able to foretell the future were revered and frequently given jobs in royal courts to assist kings and queens in their decision making. Today, most people regard with skepticism the claims of soothsayers and may even doubt the sanity of people who repeatedly say that they can foresee future events. Not only have the notions about what constitutes abnormality changed over time, so too have explanations for the causes of such behaviour. Likewise, treatments have also differed across time. They have ranged from compassionate care to brutal torture, depending upon the type of abnormality and the accepted account of its origin.

All these changes in the acceptability, treatment, and theories of etiology of abnormal behaviour have reflected, and continue to reflect, the values of society at a particular time. A society that explains everyday events (e.g., weather, seasons, war, and so on) as a result of **supernatural causes**—causes beyond the understanding of ordinary mortals, such as the influence of gods, demons, or magic—will view madness similarly. Psychological dysfunction in various historical periods was thought to result from either possession by demons or the witchcraft of evil people. Treatment involved ridding the mad person of these influences by exorcism or other magical or spiritual means. When worldly events are seen to have **natural causes** (i.e., causes that can be observed and examined), so too are mental afflictions, and they are treated in a way that addresses these presumed natural causes.

EVIDENCE FROM PREHISTORY

Paleoanthropologists have discovered Stone Age human remains that were originally interpreted as providing evidence of supernatural beliefs as early as half a million years ago. Skulls have been found with circular sections cut out of them. Since there are clear signs of bone regeneration around these holes, it was concluded that the operations (called **trephination**) were done while the person was still alive. Apparently a stone tool was used to cut the holes, and it was originally presumed that this was done to let out evil spirits that were causing the victim to engage in severely abnormal behaviour. There may, however, be simpler explanations. Maher and Maher (1985), for example, suggest that

trephination may have been intended to remove bone splinters or blood clots caused by blows to the head during warfare. Piek, Lidke, and Terberger (2011) presented evidence consistent with this medical explanation. Whatever the reason for these neat circular holes in the skulls of Stone Age people, we know from early written records that demonic possession was popularly accepted in early human societies as the cause of madness. Egyptian papyri from almost 4000 years ago describe supernatural explanations for various disorders and the use of magic and incantations as treatment procedures. These early Egyptians recognized that the brain was the site of mental activities, although they believed that demonic possession disrupted its functioning in mad people. Thus, their belief was something of a mixture of natural and supernatural assumptions.

Hunter-gatherer societies that have been examined over the past 100 years may provide clues to how our own prehistoric ancestors viewed madness. These societies characteristically do not distinguish mental from physical disorders; both are seen as having supernatural causes. Sadly, the belief in a demonological view of abnormality still exists even today. In February 2001, the CBC program *The National* broadcast a documentary entitled "The Mentally Ill of Africa's Ivory Coast." This documentary featured a man named Koffi and his struggle with schizophrenia. The people in Koffi's community believed that he was possessed by demons and chained him to a tree outside of the village for more than 10 years. Many more people are incarcerated in a similar way in this area of the continent. Food and water are provided on occasion, but often such individuals are forced to go for days without eating anything.

GREEK AND ROMAN THOUGHT

With the rise of Pericles (495–429 BCE) to the leadership of Athens, the Golden Age of Greece began. Temples of healing were soon established that emphasized natural causes for mental disorders and that developed a greater understanding of the causes and treatment of these problems. The great

Trephination, the prehistoric practice of chipping a hole into a person's skull, was an early form of surgery, possibly intended to let out evil spirits.

National Museum, Denmark/ Munoz-Yague/Science Photo Library

physician Hippocrates (460–377 BCE), who has been called the father of modern medicine, denied the popular belief of the time that psychological problems were caused by the intervention of gods or demons. This represented the first recorded instance of a rejection of supernatural causes for mental illness. Hippocrates did not distinguish mental diseases from physical diseases. Instead, he thought that all disorders had natural causes. Although he emphasized the primacy of brain dysfunctions, Hippocrates argued that stress could influence mental functioning. He also thought that dreams were important in understanding why a person was suffering from a mental disorder, and in this he predated Freud and the psychoanalysts of the twentieth century. As for treatment, Hippocrates advocated a quiet life, a vegetarian diet, healthful exercise, and abstinence from alcohol. If these procedures did not work, and sometimes as a supplement to them, Hippocrates considered induced bleeding or vomiting to be of value.

This latter claim for the value of vomiting or bleeding arose primarily as a result of Hippocrates' idea that psychological functioning resulted from disturbances of bodily fluids, or **humours**, as they were then called. Both vomiting and bleeding were thought to reduce excesses of one or another of the humours. Cheerfulness, so Hippocrates thought, was caused by an excess of blood; ill-temper by an excess of yellow bile; gloom by an excess of black bile; and listlessness by an excess of phlegm. Hippocrates was the first to describe what he called *hysteria*, which is now known as *conversion disorder*: psychologically induced blindness, deafness, or other apparent defects in perceptual or bodily processes (see Chapter 6). Hippocrates claimed that hysteria occurred only in women and was due to a "wandering" uterus. While Hippocrates' ideas seem absurd to us now, at the time they represented a significant advance because they pointed to natural causes rather than demonic possession and other supernatural events. As a consequence, Hippocrates' theories encouraged the beginnings of a scientific understanding of disordered behaviour and thought.

Many of Hippocrates' ideas were taken up by the Greek philosophers Plato (427–347 BCE) and Aristotle (384–322 BCE). However, Plato placed more emphasis on sociocultural influences on thought and behaviour. Elaborating on Hippocrates' notions about dreams, Plato suggested that they served to satisfy desires because the inhibiting influences of the higher faculties were not present during sleep. This view foreshadows Freud's theory of dreams. Plato declared that mentally disturbed people who commit crimes should not be held responsible, since they could not be said to understand what they had done. In this respect, he anticipated modern notions of not being criminally responsible by reason of mental disorder (Bill C-30; see Chapter 19). Plato also suggested treatment responses that presaged current approaches. For example, he said that in most cases, the mentally ill should be cared for at the homes of relatives, anticipating the present trend toward community care. For those who must be hospitalized, Plato said their thinking must be rationally challenged in a conversational style of

Hippocrates (460–377 BCE).

therapy that was remarkably like some forms of present-day psychotherapy.

Aristotle wrote extensively on mental disorders and on other aspects of psychological functioning. He accepted Hippocrates' bodily fluids theory and denied the influence of psychological factors in the etiology of dysfunctional thinking and behaving. In keeping with Greek tradition, Aristotle advocated the humane treatment of mental patients.

After Alexander the Great founded Alexandria, Egypt, in 332 BCE, the Egyptians adopted and expanded the medical and psychological ideas of the Greeks. They established temples to Saturn, which came to be sanatoriums for people who were psychologically unwell. These temples provided pleasant and peaceful surroundings, the opportunity for interesting and calming activities, healthful diets, soothing massages, and education. The priests who attended to these disturbed clients also employed bleeding, purges, and restraints, but only when all other attempts had failed.

After 300 BCE, there emerged in ancient Greece various schools of thought that rejected Hippocrates' theories of mental illness. The most important and best known of these was Methodism, its principal advocate being Soranus of Ephesus (circa CE 100). Methodism regarded mental illness as a disorder that resulted either from a constriction of body tissue or from a relaxation of those tissues due to exhaustion. The head was seen as the primary site of this affliction. Mania, Soranus said, resulted from overexertion, licentiousness, or alcoholism. Ordinarily, so Soranus thought, natural bloodletting (e.g., by hemorrhoids or menstruation) would provide an avoidance of the disorder, but in cases where this did not happen, mania or some other mental illness would result. Soranus rejected the mind–body distinction so common among Greek thinkers and maintained instead that there was no difference between mental and physical disorders; they all arose from problems in the body. The Greek physician Aretaeus (CE 50–130), however, considered emotional factors to be primary in causing disturbances of mental functioning and advocated using psychological, rather than strictly medical, methods.

The Greeks were first and foremost empirical. They provided the first clinical observations of disorders and made the first attempts at classification. Treatment, for the Greeks, was primarily physical, but some psychological and social components were typically included. Even though their theories were rarely accurate, and their treatments were sometimes unsuccessful, the Greeks remained devoted to naturalistic explanations and responsive to the world as they saw it.

After the Romans assumed control of the ancient world, their physicians carried on the work of the Greeks. Galen (CE 129–198), a Greek physician living in Rome, continued the work of Hippocrates. He thought there were two sources of mental disorder: physical and psychological. Physical causes included head injuries, alcohol abuse, and menstrual disturbances; whereas psychological factors included stress, loss of love, and fear. The Romans thought it was necessary for effective treatment to provide comfortable surroundings for patients; even when they employed physical treatments, Romans did not use any stressful procedures, preferring things like warm baths. Galen suggested that having people talk about their problems to a sympathetic listener had value in treating the mentally disordered. Apparently, this was an another early form of what we now call psychotherapy.

THE ARAB WORLD

With Galen's death in CE 198, the enlightened period of mental health research and treatment that had begun with Hippocrates in the fifth century BCE came to an end in Europe, but it was carried on by the Arab world. While the Dark Ages descended on Europe, the Arabs continued the Greco-Roman traditions of investigation and humane treatment of the mentally ill. In Egypt, the gentle methods used in the temples of Saturn persisted into the Mohammedan period. These generally supportive and kindly approaches to the mentally ill continued to characterize the Arab world's approach throughout the period, during which the writings of the Greek scholars were lost to Europeans. The Quran itself reflects compassionate attitudes toward the mentally ill, and it is interesting that, despite Western assumptions to the contrary, Arab societies in general continue to hold to these admirable views and practices. Today, the mentally disordered are treated with sympathy in the Arab world, as they were in the period beginning in the eighth century CE. Units for the mentally ill within the great Arab hospitals were established in Baghdad in CE 800,

and asylums were created in other Arab cities in the years thereafter—some 500 years before Europeans built their first asylums. In these Arab **asylums** (a word meaning place of refuge and protection), treatment followed the tradition of care, support, and compassion (Polvan, 1969).

Persian philosopher and physician Avicenna (CE 980–1037) developed an astonishing understanding of medicine and psychological functioning, which he described in his remarkable volume *The Canon of Medicine*. This book is considered to be one of the most widely read and authoritative medical texts in the history of medicine (see Dols, 2006), and the work's prominence in the Arab world led to Avicenna's approach becoming emblematic of Islamic medicine (Moosavi, 2009). Avicenna's analyses of mental disorders reflect a practical approach characterized by an emphasis on natural causes, particularly environmental and psychological factors. His treatment recommendations followed the Greco-Roman emphasis on care and compassion, but he also employed procedures not unlike early behaviour therapy methods of the twentieth century. For example, Browne (1921) describes Avicenna's way of dealing with a prince who believed himself to be a cow and repeatedly asked to be killed and made into a stew. When Avicenna first examined the case, the young man had stopped eating altogether; a cause for great concern. Avicenna began by sending a message to the prince telling him that a butcher would arrive soon to slaughter him. Shortly thereafter, Avicenna appeared brandishing a knife, saying, "Where is this cow that I may kill it?" He then felt the patient's body all over and declared, "He is too lean, and not ready to be killed; he must be fattened." The attendants then offered the prince food, which he enthusiastically ate. As he gradually regained his strength, the prince's delusion disappeared.

EUROPE IN THE MIDDLE AGES

After the fall of the Roman Empire at the end of the fifth century, Europe entered a period, approximately CE 500 to 1500, when the teachings of the Greeks and Romans were either lost or suppressed. It is often claimed that the natural theories of Greco-Roman times were entirely replaced during this period by supernatural explanations, while the compassionate and practical treatment of the mentally disturbed was supplanted by quite unpleasant procedures meant to free the afflicted person of possession by the devil or his minions. However, this is not entirely true and, in fact, some of Galen's theories survived and were expressed in naturalistic approaches to treatment (Schoenman, 1984). Whereas demonological theories of insanity attributed disorders to sin on the part of the sufferer, Kroll and Bachrach (1984), in an examination of cases recorded in the fifteenth and sixteenth centuries, note that in very few cases was sin considered to be an etiological factor. Kroll and Bachrach point out that the notion of "possession," so popular in the writings of authors during the Middle Ages, may have meant much the same as our own current expression "nervous breakdown." It may simply have been a colloquial descriptor applied to a vague and general set of problems without necessarily implying, in all cases, that the afflicted person had been taken over by the devil or some other supernatural force.

Perhaps the issue to which earlier historians most frequently misapplied these demonological ideas was witchcraft (Zilboorg & Henry, 1941). Until the 1980s, it was generally held that people identified as witches during the late Middle Ages were mad and that their madness was considered to result from possession by the devil. There was some truth to this notion. For example, some of the most eminent physicians of the early sixteenth century firmly believed that mad people were possessed and in need of exorcism. Furthermore, Martin Luther (1483–1546) claimed that when people sinned in particularly bad ways, God would deliver them over to Satan, who could possess them either corporally (i.e., bodily) or spiritually. According to Luther, if the devil possessed them corporally, they would become mad, but if he possessed them spiritually, they should be considered witches. Luther, then, made a clear distinction between madness and witchcraft. Despite earlier historical interpretations that the many thousands of so-called witches who were tortured or killed during the fifteenth and sixteenth centuries were insane, it appears that most were not, nor were they considered to be insane at the time. The majority of these unfortunate victims were accused of exercising evil powers over others by people who simply wanted to be rid of them, and the accusations were all too often eagerly accepted by those who were appointed to seek out witches for punishment.

Throughout the Middle Ages in Europe, people suffering from psychological disorders for the most part received treatment and care from the clergy, as they were the only ones with sufficient concern and resources to provide assistance. For a long time, the insane were provided refuge from the world in monasteries and convents. The treatment they were given was typically mild, and emphasized prayer and a generally caring approach. As the idea of possession by the devil became more popular, exorcism replaced these gentle approaches. Exorcism, meant to drive out the evil forces that possessed the afflicted, was itself initially mild, but over time became more and more vigorous. To rid the person of the possession, exorcists would curse and insult the devil. If this did not succeed, they would attempt to make the body uncomfortable for him by subjecting the disordered individual to all manner of bodily insults. In some cases, these bodily insults amounted to torture, becoming progressively more severe until the person was either cured or had died—which was also considered a cure.

Such approaches to mental illness were not without critics, who also opposed the idea of witchcraft and vehemently protested the torture and killing of those identified as witches. This opposition grew with the onset of the Renaissance, when Greco-Roman thought was rediscovered and passed into the hands of secular scholars. Paracelsus (1493–1541), a famous Swiss alchemist and physician, was one of the first to attack the beliefs about supernatural possession. He was determined to develop a new approach to mental disorders and attempted to create a new system of classification. Paracelsus rejected the four-humours theory of the Greeks and Romans and instead claimed that all mental illness resulted from disturbances of the *spiritus vitae* (breath of life). In some cases, the *spiritus vitae* was upset by the stars, in others it was disturbed by vapours arising in various parts of the body. Although we would today consider

This picture illustrates the practice of exorcism, which was used to expel evil spirits that had possessed people.

The Miracle of the Holy Sacrament, from the predella of the Altar of the Holy Eucharist, 1423 (tempera on panel), Sassetta (Stefano di Giovanni di Consolo) (c.1392-1450) / The Bowes Museum, Barnard Castle, County Durham, UK/Bridgeman Images

This fifteenth-century engraving shows peasant women overcome by St. Vitus' dance.

Granger/REX/Shutterstock

these ideas false, they do represent an attempt to offer naturalistic rather than magical or demonic origins to madness.

During the waning years of the Middle Ages, there arose in Europe what came to be known as **St. Vitus' dance**. This was an epidemic of mass hysteria, where groups of people would suddenly be seized by an irresistible urge to leap about, jumping and dancing, and sometimes convulsing. Some of these dancers claimed to have been bitten by tarantula spiders, apparently in order to excuse their behaviour so it would not be attributed to possession by evil spirits. Thus the behaviour was originally called the Tarantella, which subsequently became the name of a dance. However, the more general explanation at the time was that these people were possessed. Paracelsus denied this assertion and instead declared the problem to be a disease; in fact, he was among the first to suggest that psychic conflicts might cause mental illness, and he treated disordered people with what appears to have been an early version of hypnotism.

The efforts of Paracelsus were followed by Johannes Weyer (1515–1588), who, despite still accepting that the devil was the cause of some cases of mental illness, advocated natural and physical treatments while rejecting exorcism. Weyer also observed that mental illness could arise from natural causes. For instance, he claimed that "fantasies" (by which he probably meant delusions or hallucinations) could be traced in some patients to their use of belladonna ointments. He based this claim on both clinical observation and experiments carried out by two earlier physicians, Cardona and Della Porta. Weyer's views are quite interesting because they reflect a characteristic of Renaissance thought—that is, the mixture of traditional ideas (such as possession by the devil), theological concerns, and original observations. His views represented a significant move toward a more scientific and naturalistic attitude about the insane.

This new humane attitude was most apparent in Spain due to the influence of the Moors. The Moors, Muslims from North Africa, had conquered the Iberian peninsula in the eighth century and had brought with them the knowledge and attitudes of the Arab world. Although the Moors were finally expelled from Spain in 1614, their influence remained. During the Renaissance, Spain had enjoyed a golden era of medicine. Mental institutions were established in Valencia in 1409, in Seville in 1436, and in Toledo in 1430. In fact, the first mental institution in North America was built by the Spaniards at San Hippolyto in Mexico.

THE BEGINNINGS OF A SCIENTIFIC APPROACH

While Paracelsus's analysis of St. Vitus' dance represents a far more scientific view of mental disorders than had existed in Europe for centuries, he also enthusiastically held that the moon influenced emotional and mental processes (the term *lunatic* stems from the Latin for moon, *luna*). Accordingly, Paracelsus did not have the influence on scientific thinking he might otherwise have had. This was left to others, the most significant of whom was Teresa of Avila in Spain, the head

Teresa of Avila (1515–1582).

of a group of nuns at the time of the Spanish Inquisition (sixteenth century). When her charges began to display hysterical behaviours and were in danger of being accused of possession by the devil, St. Teresa (she was later canonized) defended them by claiming that they were sick (actually, "as if sick," *comas enfermas*); her argument was so convincing that she saved them from the Inquisition (Radden, 2004). Another eminent religious teacher, St. Vincent de Paul (1576–1660), who is today widely recognized for his compassion, also challenged heterodoxy by claiming that mental disease and bodily disease are not different. He advocated the protection of people suffering from mental disorders and declared that it was society's responsibility to develop means to relieve such individuals of their suffering. St. Vincent was, therefore, arguing for the development of a scientific and humane approach to dealing with the problems of the insane.

As a result of this movement toward a more caring and naturalistic way of construing psychological dysfunctions, asylums began to be established in Europe. While the intentions of those who created these institutions may have been compassionate, the reality was that most asylums were places where the residents were treated cruelly and lived in appalling conditions. Perhaps the most famous of these early European asylums was the one established by Henry VIII in 1547 when he had the monastery of St. Mary of Bethlehem in London converted to a place where mentally disordered individuals could be housed. Although it has been moved to several locations since then, the Bethlem Royal Hospital (as it is now known) still exists, although it is now an exemplary mental hospital in the pleasant countryside south of London. While Henry VIII provided an institutional setting, he did not satisfactorily fund the asylum. Those in charge had to raise funds by whatever means they could. One procedure was to invite the public to visit the asylum and charge them a small sum. The entrance fee provided the tourists with the opportunity to tease and poke with sticks the hapless residents who, not surprisingly, screamed and moaned, much to the visitors' pleasure. This noise and disruption among the residents prompted the use of the word **bedlam** (the local corruption of "Bethlem") to describe any form of rowdy, chaotic behaviour.

Other asylums in Europe followed a form similar to that of Bethlem, with the treatment of the insane being much the same. La Bicêtre in Paris was one of the most notorious. There, patients were shackled to the walls in unlit cells, unable to lie down even to sleep. Their food was inadequate, they were not permitted to wash regularly, and they were essentially treated like animals. In North America, the conditions of mental asylums were no better, and the treatments offered were harsh, including electric shocks, bleeding, and plunging the patients into ice-cold water (see Focus box 1.1). Bennett (1947) examined historical records from these institutions in the United States dating from the early 1800s. These records revealed that patients were placed in unlit cells, had their heads shaved, and were given a restricted diet, often accompanied by purgatives. They were often isolated from all other patients, apparently to "cure" their frenzied behaviour. Not surprisingly, the success rates of these procedures were quite low.

In the midst of these otherwise dreadful approaches, there was at least one shining example of a distinctly humanitarian attempt to deal more effectively with these unfortunate people. A legendary tale, dating from the thirteenth century, tells of the flight of a young princess who had escaped from her incestuous father and fled to Belgium. Her father caught up with her just outside the town of Gheel, whereupon he killed her. She was said to have attended to the insane prior to her escape from her father. Some years after her death, five lunatics slept one night under the tree where she was slain. When they awoke in the morning, their insanity had disappeared; thereafter, the place became a shrine visited by the mentally ill seeking a cure. These pilgrims frequently stayed on in Gheel, where the townsfolk took them into their houses and allowed them to live comfortably, which seems to have produced remarkably beneficial results (Karnesh & Zucker, 1945). In fact, the tradition lives on today, with as many as 1000 patients living with families in Gheel and working in local community centres. Although this unusual program is effective, it receives little recognition and has had little influence on the general approach to dealing with the mentally ill.

While there was significant progress toward a more humane and rational approach to understanding and managing the mentally ill during the sixteenth century, the trend did not continue in the following century. The large number of poor was seen as a serious social problem that the absolutist governments of the day wanted to get rid of. Their solution was to establish what the English called "workhouses," where the poor, the old, orphans, and others, including the insane, were incarcerated in dreadful conditions. Mad people were chained to the walls, flogged regularly, and given only the bare minimum of care; physicians were rarely, if ever, consulted. In Paris, men were sent to La Bicêtre and women to the Saltpêtrière.

As a result of the European philosophical movement known as the Enlightenment, the eighteenth century saw radical changes in the way in which abnormal behaviour was conceptualized. The basic ideas of the Enlightenment concerned the superiority of reason in the analysis of problems, the idea that progress was an inevitable and desirable feature of human society, and the belief that it was both appropriate and necessary to challenge traditional ideas, including religious doctrine. One of the many consequences of such thinking was a re-examination of the ways in which society dealt with the insane. One of the leaders of this movement was Philippe Pinel (1745–1826), who was appointed by the French revolutionary government as director of La Bicêtre in 1792.

In response to seeing the appalling conditions at La Bicêtre, Pinel ordered that the inmates' chains be removed. He had the institution cleaned and the windows replaced to let in full sunlight, encouraged healthful exercise on the grounds, and instructed staff to treat the patients with kindness rather than giving them regular beatings. Although evidence (Weiner, 1979) indicates that it was the institution's manager, Jean-Baptiste Pussin, who in fact had begun these reforms, Pinel carried on these dramatic changes at a time when it was clear that, had the experiment failed, he would likely have been led off to the guillotine along with other failed revolutionaries. Pinel's actions were those of a courageous and compassionate human being, and he is properly remembered as one of the leaders of the humanitarian reforms that swept through Europe in the late eighteenth and early nineteenth centuries. What brought an end to this approach was not its failure (for it was in fact quite effective) but the remarkable increase in mental patients, primarily as a result of the proliferation of patients suffering from general paresis of the insane (see below) and those affected by alcoholism. This overcrowding of mental institutions made it all but impossible to treat every patient in the way that Pinel recommended.

Pinel should be remembered for his humanity but also for the influence he exerted on psychiatry as a whole. He developed a systematic and statistically based approach to the classification, management, and treatment of disorders. Pinel emphasized the role of psychological and social factors in the development of mental illness, and he elaborated clear descriptions of the symptomatology of the various disorders. He saw the asylum as therapeutic, a place where patients could be separated from their families and from the stresses of their everyday lives. Patients were to be treated

Treatment and Mistreatment: The Depiction of Mental Asylums in the Movies

FOCUS
1.1

The conditions that existed in asylums and reports of maltreatment made mental health treatment during the asylum era a popular subject for Hollywood films. In the 2010 movie *Shutter Island* (Scorsese, 2010), U.S. Marshal Teddy Daniels (played by Leonardo DiCaprio) is sent to investigate the escape of a patient from an asylum for criminally insane patients. Teddy is soon confronted by rumours of people being drugged against their will, lobotomies being performed, patients being experimented on, and torture. It is eventually revealed that Teddy is actually an inpatient who murdered his wife and is now suffering from delusions and hallucinations. His psychiatrist and other staff members play along with his delusion in the hope of being able to confront him with the reality of what he had done. Although most of the rumours Teddy hears about turn out to be false, the treatment he receives is still conducted without his approval, which would raise ethical concerns in a modern treatment environment.

The rumour that Teddy Daniels hears about patients being experimented upon is, however, not without any foundation in historical reality. Perhaps the worst instance of abuse of psychiatric power in Canada is the well-documented story of Dr. Ewen Cameron's brainwashing experiments at Montreal's Allen Memorial Hospital during the late 1950s and early 1960s (Collins, 1988). Cameron's work was funded, at least in part, by the American Central Intelligence Agency (CIA), which apparently hoped to discover ways both to overcome the effects of brainwashing by its enemies and to brainwash captured enemies. None of the unfortunate participants in these studies, most of whom were psychiatric patients seeking Cameron's help, were ever informed that they were part of a research project, let alone that such research was funded by the CIA. Under the guise of therapy, Cameron subjected his patients to massive and repeated doses of electroconvulsive therapy (ECT), prolonged sensory deprivation, and chemically induced sleep. This last procedure was employed for days on end, during which time audiotapes telling the patients how awful they were and how

they must change were played under their pillows. Patients were also repeatedly injected with lysergic acid diethylamide (LSD), a hallucinogenic drug, without ever being told what it was or how it would affect them. Of course, most of them experienced terror.

The abuse of psychiatric power is also vividly portrayed in the Oscar-winning movie *One Flew over the Cuckoo's Nest* (Forman, 1975). In the movie, Randle McMurphy (portrayed by Jack Nicholson) fakes a mental disorder in order to obtain a transfer from prison to an asylum. He soon incurs the wrath of the head nurse, Nurse Ratched, who runs the ward with an iron fist. After a series of confrontations that culminate in an attack upon Nurse Ratched, she uses her psychiatric power to force McMurphy to receive drug treatment and ECT as punishment, and eventually suggests that he should be lobotomized. These forms of biological intervention were usually used as an attempt to cure or reduce harm rather than to punish, but, as we discuss later, these interventions may have been overused.

A more benign and more modern portrayal of mental health institutions can be found in the 2001 movie *K-Pax* (Softley, 2001). A man (portrayed by Kevin Spacey) who claims to be an alien called Prot from the planet K-Pax is being treated in a mental health facility by Dr. Mark Powell (portrayed by Jeff Bridges). The facility has many windows, adequate lighting, a garden that is open to patients, and meaningful daily activities for patients. Client consent is obtained for all procedures that are performed, and institutional personnel are reserved in their use of force to control patients. The movie is guilty of overdramatizing the process of hypnosis and suggesting that trauma is the primary cause of psychotic behaviour, but overall it is a fairly realistic portrayal of current institutionalized care.

Mental asylums were established throughout the world in the nineteenth century in response to the deplorable conditions in which the mentally disordered were kept (Porter & Wright, 2003). Individuals with mental disorders were often forced to wander from town to town or to fend for themselves in the countryside. Turned out of their homes, they became part of the cavalcade of beggars across Europe. Conditions were no better for those allowed to stay at home.

The conditions in which the mentally disordered were forced to exist led many reformers to demand that proper hospitals be established to care for the mentally disordered. Dorothea Dix (1802–1887), a Boston schoolteacher who taught at the local prison, was shocked by what she saw there and became a crusader for better conditions for offenders. Her concern quickly spread to mental patients, and she launched an effective nationwide campaign to improve the lot of individuals with mental disorders. Her campaign resulted directly in the opening of 32 state hospitals, including two in Canada, and many more indirectly.

In *The Shame of the States*, journalist Albert Deutsch (1948) reported on a 1946 tour of U.S. mental institutions. He described "hundreds of patients sleeping in damp, bug-ridden basements." One doctor complained to Deutsch, "I know I should see many more patients individually. But how can I when I have five hundred patients under my care?" The furor that resulted from this book along with the advent of antipsychotic drugs in 1954 led to a massive deinstitutionalization of mental patients. ●

AF archive/Alamy Stock Photo

respectfully so as to inspire their confidence, and they were given activities to stimulate them. Pinel did not discard physical approaches to treatment, but rather saw the humane management of patients as the basis on which physical treatments could have their effects. Pinel was thoroughly scientific and looked only to natural explanations for the origins of mental disorders. In Britain, William Tuke (1732–1822) followed Pinel's example by establishing similar approaches in psychiatric hospitals, and Benjamin Rush (1745–1813) brought **moral therapy** to North America.

These efforts came to be known as the **mental hygiene movement**, which was characterized by a desire to protect and to provide humane treatment for the mentally ill. Despite noble aims to alleviate human suffering, the movement of enormous numbers of individuals with mental disorders into large asylums did not, in fact, improve their lot. The asylums were overcrowded, custodial, and countertherapeutic, and the staff had no time to do more than warehouse patients (Sussman, 1998). Restraints such as straitjackets were more refined than the old fetters but no less cruel (Bockoven, 1963). In addition, the average population within asylums in North America increased dramatically over the years, resulting in the construction of even more institutions. Hunter, Shannon, and Sambrook (1986) argued that one reason for the increase in patient numbers was that the responsibility for the care of the insane shifted from the family and local community to the states and provinces.

② BEFORE MOVING ON

In what way does our world view today influence the understanding and treatment of mental health problems? When you look back through history you may view the so-called treatments for mental health problems as barbaric. Indeed, many of these interventions were inhumane by our standards. How do you think we will view our current treatments in 50 or 100 years?

Development of Modern Views
BIOLOGICAL APPROACHES

Toward the end of the eighteenth century, theorists had abandoned the notions of Hippocrates and Galen that stated that disruptions in the four humours cause people to become mentally ill. As a result of anatomical examinations of the cadavers of mad patients, and the concurrent discoveries regarding the functioning of the nervous system, mental disorders came to be viewed as disruptions in nervous system functioning. The culmination of this line of thought was expressed most clearly by Cabanis (1757–1808), who combined psychological and somatic factors in his account of mental disorders. His theories were particularly influential and encouraged the development of psychological approaches to treatment. Cabanis provided the first clear theoretical basis for moral therapy. The eighteenth century can be seen as the first flowering of what later became known

as psychotherapy, and it more generally set the stage for a move toward a thoroughly rational and scientific approach to abnormal behaviour.

HEREDITY Benedict Augustin Morel (1809–1873), a Viennese physician, was the first to introduce "degeneration" theory. This idea proposed that deviations from normal functioning are transmitted by hereditary processes and that these deviations progressively degenerate over generations. Morel's final version of this theory appeared in 1857, just one year before the publication of Charles Darwin's remarkable *The Origin of Species*. Darwin's notion of the inheritance of advantageous features and the disappearance of disadvantageous features by natural selection lent support to theories like Morel's that proposed an inherited basis for human functioning. The possibility that human behaviour (both normal and abnormal) could be seen as being passed on genetically from generation to generation inspired many theorists to suggest that it might be possible to identify people as potential madmen or criminals before they developed such problems. Cesare Lombroso (1836–1909) concluded from his observations that criminality was inherited and could be identified by the shape of a person's skull. While phrenology (as this study was called) enjoyed a good deal of popularity for a time, it did not withstand more careful scrutiny. However, the idea that disorders of functioning could be passed on genetically not only survived, but now enjoys widespread acceptance in psychiatry and psychology.

SYNDROMES AND THE BEGINNING OF CLASSIFICATION Perhaps the most influential person in the latter part of the nineteenth century, however, was Emil Kraepelin. In 1883, he published a very important textbook, *Clinical Psychiatry*, that attempted to classify mental illness. Classification is, as we will see in Chapter 3, the foundation from which research is generated. It also attempts to guide the selection of treatment and to indicate the likely course and outcome of the disorder. In any case, without some form of classification, research would be markedly restricted, since it would be impossible to group people according to their common disorder. Kraepelin, however, was not interested in treatment, because he believed that all mental disorders were the result of biological problems for which, at that time, there were no treatments available. Accordingly, he focused on diagnosis and classification as ends in themselves. Kraepelin noted that certain groups of symptoms tended to occur together, and he called these groupings **syndromes**. These different syndromes, Kraepelin observed, could serve as a way of grouping patients who shared certain features into categories that identified specific disorders. He was the first to recognize that the different disorders not only had distinct features, but also differed in their age of onset and their typical course over time. As a result, Kraepelin suggested that the different disorders probably had different causes, although he thought that these different causes were all biological in one way or another.

Kraepelin's efforts led to an interest in classification that lives on in the current versions of DSM-5 and ICD-10. Although these more recent classification systems owe much to Kraepelin's innovative work, they have evolved into a considerably different, far more detailed and research-driven system of classifying mental disorders.

INFECTION AS A CAUSE OF MENTAL DISORDER Following Kraepelin's view that mental disorders were the result of biological processes, Richard von Krafft-Ebing (1840–1902) became interested in the possibility that patients with **general paresis of the insane (GPI)** might have acquired this disorder by an infection. GPI (or neurosyphilis) is now known to result from untreated infections by the syphilis spirochete (a coil-shaped bacterium). Initial infection results in a sore on the genitals and sometimes swollen lymph glands of the groin. Untreated, the spirochete does not disappear but remains in the bloodstream; after about one year, it enters the meningeal lining of the brain and spinal cord, although it does not affect functioning at this stage. The immune system sometimes overcomes the infection at this point, but if it does not, then a decade or so later the affected person becomes symptomatic. Mania, euphoria, and grandiosity are the first marked features of this delayed response, followed by a progressive deterioration of brain functioning (called *dementia*) and paralysis. In the latter part of the nineteenth and early part of the twentieth century, patients with GPI filled most of the beds in psychiatric hospitals (Shorter, 1997).

Louis Pasteur had established the germ theory of disease in the 1860s, and Krafft-Ebing noted that it had been observed that some patients with GPI had previously had syphilis. His guess was that GPI was a long-term consequence of syphilis. To test this theory, Krafft-Ebing infected GPI patients with syphilitic material (Valenstein, 1986). If his theory was correct, then his injected patients would not develop syphilis since they had already been infected. Although the ethics of his procedures are repugnant to modern readers, Krafft-Ebing's guess turned out to be correct. Subsequently, the spirochete that causes syphilis was discovered, and it was shown that there was a link between infection and later destruction of particular areas of the brain that produced the mental and physical deterioration shown by patients with GPI.

This confirmation of the idea that such a widespread and serious mental disorder as GPI was the result of an infectious agent encouraged confidence in the view that all mental disorders would soon be found to be caused either by infections or by some other biological factor. **Somatogenesis** (the idea that psychopathology is caused by biological factors—*soma* meaning "body" in Latin) not only gained prominence as a result of the success in identifying the cause of GPI but also followed quite logically from the remarkable successes that occurred in the middle and latter half of the nineteenth century in science in general and in medicine more specifically. It seemed at the time that all disorders (physical as well as psychological) would be solved quite soon as a result of applying biological science. While such

optimism proved unfounded, these views did encourage a scientific approach to abnormal functioning that became progressively more sophisticated.

The discovery that GPI had an organic cause not only led to a search for the somatic bases of other mental illnesses, but also encouraged trials of various physical approaches to treatment (see Valenstein, 1986). Because GPI was now known to result from an infection, it was thought that deliberately inducing a fever in such patients would cause the increased body temperature to kill the infectious agent. In 1890, Julius von Wagner-Jauregg injected GPI patients with a vaccine in order to induce a fever. Shorter (1997) said it was tuberculin, a vaccine for tuberculosis, whereas Ackerknect (1968) said it was typhus vaccine. Whichever it was, Wagner-Jauregg got reasonably good results, but the unreliability of the approach encouraged him to try infecting these patients with malaria to induce a fever more reliably. This actually worked to kill off the syphilitic spirochete and prevent further progress of the disease. In fact, it proved so successful that Wagner-Jauregg was awarded the Nobel Prize in 1927.

SHOCK THERAPY Since antiquity, it has been known that shocks could produce recovery from mental illness. For example, sudden submersion in water had been shown to alleviate the symptoms of some people suffering from disturbances of mental functioning (Ackerknect, 1968). It occurred to Manfred Sakel, a German physician, that shock treatments might, therefore, be effective in treating the insane (Valenstein, 1986). He had used insulin in the late 1920s to manage the withdrawal symptoms of morphine addicts. When insulin was occasionally given in an accidentally high dose, it induced a coma in the patient. Sakel observed that after the coma passed, the patient's desire for morphine disappeared and patients who were previously agitated became tranquil. Soon after these observations, Sakel began examining the value of insulin-induced comas for individuals with schizophrenia. He reported that 70 percent of these patients fully recovered and a further 18 percent were able to at least function well. Sakel's procedure was taken up enthusiastically by others and, by 1944, Eliot Slater and William Sargent's influential English psychiatric textbook listed insulin coma as the first choice in treating the mentally ill. This physical procedure was appealing not only for its effectiveness, but also because it allowed asylum psychiatrists to become more than just custodians and it aligned them with physical medicine (Shorter, 1997).

Insulin administrations not only induced a coma, but also occasionally produced convulsions, and some theorists thought these might be the main active feature of the treatment. In 1934, Ladislas von Meduna suggested that deliberately provoking convulsions, by the administration of Metrazol (a drug similar to camphor), might ameliorate the symptoms of schizophrenia. Meduna noted that the brains of epileptic patients (i.e., patients who suffered from chronic convulsions or seizures) were quite different (or so he thought) from those of individuals with schizophrenia, and it was also reported about the same time that epileptics who developed schizophrenia thereafter experienced fewer seizures. Meduna deduced that producing seizures in people with schizophrenia might eliminate their disorder. He tried his procedure with 110 patients and 50 percent completely recovered from their illness. As a result, a series of Metrazol-induced convulsions became reasonably popular in the treatment of psychotic patients. However, there were undesirable side effects, including a terror of dying, such that many patients refused a second injection. With the discovery that electricity applied to the head could induce convulsions, other forms of coma or convulsive therapy disappeared.

The first individual to employ electricity to induce a seizure in mental patients was Ugo Cerletti in 1938. After a series of animal studies established the difference between convulsive and lethal shock intensity, and the optimal placement of electrodes on the skull, Cerletti and his assistants began to use the procedure on human patients. The device they developed delivered a shock of 80 to 100 volts to the temples for a fraction of a second. After 11 treatments, Cerletti's first patient, an individual with severe schizophrenia, was able to be discharged, although he did return one year later. **Electroconvulsive therapy (ECT)**, as this treatment was called, was enthusiastically welcomed by the psychiatric community and very soon replaced most other physical treatments. Although ECT was initially used only for the treatment of schizophrenia, it was found to be most effective with patients suffering from major depression, on whom it is still used to this day (see Chapter 8).

One problem with the initial uses of ECT was that during the bodily convulsion produced by the brain seizure, some patients suffered broken limbs or cracked vertebrae. These were obviously very undesirable side effects. However, the finding that curare (a poison extracted from the South American vine *Strychnos toxifera* and applied by natives to the tip of their arrows), in very small doses, produced relaxation of the limbs of spastic children suggested that it could be useful in preventing the bodily reactions to ECT. It proved effective, but was risky, so it was replaced by the less dangerous drug succinylcholine that, when combined with a fast-acting barbiturate, allowed patients undergoing ECT to avoid pretreatment anxiety and the within-treatment risk of fractures.

THE BEGINNINGS OF PSYCHOPHARMACOLOGY In the 1950s, pharmacological agents for the treatment of psychiatric disorders became widely available and began what the Canadian psychiatric historian Edward Shorter (1997) calls "the second biological psychiatry." The view of this period, which continues to the present, was that mental illness results from disordered brain chemistry. The widespread acceptance of this view led to the rejection by much of psychiatry of psychological perspectives, including psychoanalysis. Interestingly, this point in time corresponds to the revival, among psychologists, of the application of behaviourism to the amelioration of psychological disorders.

The first neurotransmitter was isolated in 1926 by Otto Loewi at the University of Graz in Austria. He identified the action of acetylcholine (a neurotransmitter) as mediating the transmission of nerve impulses within the brain (see Chapter 2 for a discussion of neurotransmission). Although this finding might have suggested a possible way to change brain functioning in mental patients by introducing an *agonist* (something that facilitates the production of acetylcholine) or an *antagonist* (something that inhibits its production), such approaches did not develop until the 1950s. Some of the early work on the effects of drugs derived from these ideas was done by Heinz Lehmann at Montreal's Verdun Protestant Hospital. His experiments, while unsuccessful, nevertheless paved the way for further research.

In an attempt to calm soldiers before surgery, Henri Laborit in 1949 examined the value of some recently developed antihistamines of the phenothiazine group of drugs. He found these drugs to be very effective in inducing a calm and relaxed state in his patients. Following this, Laborit obtained the latest drug in this series, called chlorpromazine, and persuaded some psychiatrist friends to try it with their patients. It virtually eliminated one manic patient's problems. Subsequently, it was evaluated in more systematic trials and chlorpromazine soon enjoyed widespread popularity. In her book on the history of psychopharmacology, Anne Caldwell (1978) provides a dramatic description of the benefits and changes resulting from the adoption of this drug as a treatment for patients with mental disorders:

> The atmosphere in the disturbed wards of mental hospitals in Paris was transformed: straitjackets, psychohydraulic packs, and noise were a thing of the past! Once more Paris psychiatrists, who long ago unchained the chained, became pioneers in liberating their patients, this time from inner torments, and with a drug: chlorpromazine. It accomplished the pharmacological revolution of psychiatry. (Caldwell, 1978, p. 30)

Due to the success of antipsychotic medications (and the advent of tricyclic antidepressants in the 1960s), the patients' rights movement (which suggested that patients can better recover if they are integrated into the community), and U.S. President Kennedy's community mental health movement, a process of **deinstitutionalization** was set in motion. Beginning in the 1950s, hundreds of thousands of institutionalized patients were discharged. However, because the closure of psychiatric institutions had not been balanced by a strengthening of community resources, many mentally disordered individuals were homeless and lacked adequate support (Sussman, 1998). In 1988, the government of Canada published *Mental Health for Canadians: Striking a Balance*, which was intended to promote mental health and improve community care.

Chlorpromazine had remarkable advantages over other forms of treatment and management at the time. Not only did it do away with physical restraints and make psychiatric management an easier task, it was less dangerous than ECT and more easily tolerated by patients.

Thereafter, the pharmaceutical industry began to produce a plethora of neurotransmitter-affecting drugs to treat patients with schizophrenia, mania, and depression. The era of psychopharmacology had arrived. However, psychological or environmental explanations of mental disorders did not simply disappear throughout the twentieth century. Indeed, it was one of the strongest periods for such theorizing. Somatic and psychological explanations and treatments of psychiatric patients, often seen by their proponents as antithetical to one another, proceeded to develop somewhat independently. It has only been in recent years that they have been seen by many as complementary and interactive.

❸ BEFORE MOVING ON

> There was great hope for biological therapies in the early 1900s, and a recent revival in the application of these interventions, particularly drug treatments, has occurred. Is this renewed usage because the evidence about their effectiveness is convincing, or is it because they offer an easy, but limited, solution to problems?

PSYCHOLOGICAL APPROACHES

Psychological accounts of the etiology of mental disorders had been popular throughout history and obtained some eminence in the latter part of the eighteenth century. An increased interest in psychological explanations was sparked by the work of Anton Mesmer (1734–1815) with hysteria (see Chapter 6 for a description of this disorder, now called *conversion disorder*), although Mesmer's explanation was physiological. Mesmer thought that hysteria was the result of a disturbed distribution of the magnetic fluid present in all bodies. His procedure involved a good deal of mystery and required that the patients be touched by Mesmer with various rods that were said to transmit, from Mesmer directly to the patients, a magnetic force he called "animal magnetism" that would rearrange their fluids and cure the disorder. These procedures obviously required Mesmer to present his treatment very convincingly, using various tactics to suggest strongly to his patients that they would recover. In fact, a subsequent study, conducted by Benjamin Franklin, indicated that mesmerism was essentially due to the "power of suggestion." Mesmer's approach was a predecessor of hypnotism and, in fact, it was called this by James Braid, a British surgeon in the mid-1800s, who saw great promise in the technique.

HYPNOTISM AND THE BIRTH OF PSYCHOANALYSIS

Although Mesmer was generally viewed by his contemporaries as a charlatan, the popularity of his procedure and his numerous apparent successes prompted an interest in the powers of suggestion. The Parisian neurologist Jean Charcot (1825–1893), in particular, came to believe that hypnotism might have value in treating hysterics and, accordingly, he revised his earlier somatogenic view to suggest that psychological factors caused hysteria. One of his students, Pierre Janet (1859–1947), elaborated this view

into an account that claimed hysteria resulted from a break in the organized system of thought and emotion. Hysteria, in fact, became a focus of interest in itself, particularly among Viennese physicians. Josef Breuer (1842–1925) and his younger colleague Sigmund Freud (1856–1939) not only elaborated complex psychological conceptualizations of mental disorders (see Chapter 2 for an account of Freud's approach), but also developed specific treatment methods. Breuer's approach employed hypnosis in order to have the patient talk freely about, and relive, unpleasant past events that he believed caused the hysteria. He thought that vividly reliving these past experiences would somehow exhaust the emotional problems that resulted from them. Breuer called this treatment the *cathartic method*. Freud's approach was similar, although he also used procedures other than hypnosis, and his treatment came to be called *psychoanalysis*.

BEHAVIOURISM Another psychological approach to understanding abnormal behaviour emerged in the early part of the twentieth century. John B. Watson (1878–1958) produced a revolution in psychological thought (and, for that matter, in philosophical thought) with the publication in 1913 of a provocative article entitled "Psychology as the Behaviorist Views It." This, and subsequent work by Watson, established what became known as **behaviourism**. This viewpoint declared that if psychology were to become a science, it must be restricted to the study of observable features: namely, the behaviour of organisms. From this perspective, Watson considered abnormal functioning to be learned and, consequently, he believed it could be unlearned. His model for learning was derived from Ivan Pavlov's (1849–1936) studies of classical conditioning. All problematic functioning, Watson claimed, was the result of unfortunate conditioning experiences. Although this theory had a profound impact on thinking about mental disorders, it has not quite lived up to Watson's rather grand expectations. Nevertheless, behavioural approaches to the understanding and treatment of psychological disorders were reintroduced in the late 1950s and early 1960s and enjoyed considerable success and acceptance. In various forms, they have become established and empirically supported parts of the overall approach to dealing with mental disorders.

Throughout the twentieth century, conceptualizing and theorizing about abnormal behaviour have followed one of the paths initiated by the earlier thinkers. Somatogenic theories remain very popular and have enjoyed better success in the analysis of some problems than others, although it is fair to say that the research generated by such views has contributed to a better understanding of all mental disorders. Similarly, psychogenic theories (e.g., Freudian, behavioural, and numerous others) and the research their advocates have produced have expanded our knowledge and treatment of all disorders—although, again, psychological approaches have proven to be more valuable with some disorders than with others. The various models derived from these two views are the subject of the next chapter.

The Growth of Mental Health Services in Canada

The history of the development of proper places of care for individuals with mental disorders in Canada is well documented in a very detailed account by Hurd and colleagues (1916). It reveals a reluctance on the part of the various provinces (except for Quebec) to deal with the issue during the early days of settlement. The early British, and then provincial, leaders were content to place the insane in prisons along with criminals (Bartlett, 2000). Of course, they offered little or no treatment to these unfortunate citizens.

The Hôtel Dieu in Quebec was the first asylum anywhere in what would become Canada to house the mentally ill. This institution was founded by the Duchess d'Aiguillon, niece of the powerful Cardinal Richelieu, who was at that time First Minister of France and the effective ruler of the country. The Hôtel Dieu housed not only so-called idiots, who included patients suffering from all types of mental disabilities and dysfunctions, but also indigents and cripples. Similar hospitals were built in Quebec throughout the latter part of the seventeenth century. However, asylums were not established in other parts of Canada until the nineteenth century (Sussman, 1998).

The delay in establishing proper housing for the insane in places outside Quebec was not due simply to the fact that Quebec was the first area to be extensively settled. After all, the British were well entrenched in North America in the seventeenth century. The area that became known as Ontario was a British territory by the middle of the eighteenth century, and Upper Canada was officially constituted in 1791. Yet it was not until 1841 that a mental asylum in Toronto first took in patients (Wright, Moran, & Gouglas, 2003). This was followed shortly thereafter by the opening of the Rockwood asylum in Kingston, which was directed by Dr. J. P. Litchfield, an Australian who had at best minimal experience with the mentally ill. A tardy and rather careless approach, with little real concern for how these institutions were operated, characterized the early efforts of various provincial governments to provide care for the insane. In the latter part of the nineteenth century, the Dominion government began to pressure provinces to remove lunatics from their prisons; this became an order in 1884. Some provinces had already done so and others followed suit. Asylums were first established in the various provinces in the following years: New Brunswick, 1835; Prince Edward Island, 1847; Newfoundland, 1853; Nova Scotia, 1858; Manitoba, 1871; British Columbia, 1872; Alberta, 1907; and Saskatchewan, 1913. The first textbook printed in Canada dealing with the care and housing of the mentally ill was published in 1840 under the authorship of J. F. Lehman. Lehman's views were harsh and certainly did not reflect the approach referred to as moral therapy in other countries. He strongly advocated a regimen of severe discipline to rid the afflicted of their disorder, and he suggested that recalcitrant individuals should be flogged. Lehman deplored indulgence toward the insane, believing that it simply worsened their problems. Fortunately, his views did not receive popular support, although later treatments employed in Canada were equally harsh. For example, psychosurgery was widely used in Canada from the mid-1940s until the mid- to late 1960s. During this time, tens of thousands of Canadians had **lobotomies** (surgical removal, or disconnection, of the frontal lobes of the brain) intended to relieve all manner of mental and emotional disorders (Simmons, 1987; Valenstein, 1986). Fortunately, in the early 1970s, legislation was enacted requiring review boards to be established in all mental hospitals with the responsibility to decide in each individual case whether psychosurgery was justified. Thereafter, psychosurgery was rarely done. According to Simmons (1987), archival evidence reveals that, prior to 1970, most of the early lobotomies were performed primarily to alleviate hospital management problems or to advance research rather than out of a concern to benefit the patient. It is also interesting to note (Simmons, 1987) that in Ontario during this period, the majority of lobotomies were performed on women (well over 60 percent of all psychosurgery patients were women). The same was true of mandatory sterilization in Alberta (Park & Radford, 1998).

By no means has all mental health care in Canada been reprehensible. As the reader will discern in subsequent chapters of this text, Canada has had its share of dedicated, helping professionals, including many on the cutting edge of research. For example, Dr. Ruth Kajander, who now practises in Thunder Bay, Ontario, was one of the first psychiatrists in North America to recognize the potential value of a major tranquilizer in the treatment of schizophrenia (Schuck, 1999). Originally from Germany, Dr. Kajander came to Canada in 1952 to train at the psychiatric hospital in London, Ontario. During her time there, she observed an anaesthesiologist using a recently introduced drug to prepare patients for surgery, and she recognized it as the same drug (chlorpromazine) that was used in Europe to reduce anxiety in patients prior to surgery. Later in the same year, it occurred to Kajander that chlorpromazine might be useful in the treatment of overactive schizophrenia. Her ideas, apparently formed quite independently and without knowledge of the developments occurring in Europe at the same time, matched Laborit's similar steps in discovering the value of chlorpromazine. Kajander obtained permission from the hospital superintendent to run a trial with the drug on 25 patients over a period of several months. The results were very encouraging: the drug calmed the patients' restlessness, reduced their activity, allowed them to discuss their problems, and made them able to eat and sleep without the difficulties they had previously shown. Kajander's subsequent presentation of the results at the Ontario Neuropsychiatric Association's conference in late 1953 represents what appears to be the first scientific report of the use of chlorpromazine with psychiatric patients in North America. At about the same time, Heinz Lehmann began using it with his patients in Montreal. Kajander received an Order of Canada for her work in mental health care on May 26, 2011. Interestingly, she has spoken out against an overreliance on psychopharmacological treatment, noting that many alternative therapies are being ignored in favour of drug treatment (Miner, 2009).

Over the years, many other Canadians have made significant contributions, in terms of both theory and new treatment approaches. Albert Bandura, who now lives and works in the United States but was raised in Canada, developed one of the most influential theories of human functioning to emerge in recent times. Social learning theory (see Chapter 2) was originally developed by Bandura and Richard Walters (who taught at the University of Waterloo in Ontario) to explain how aggressive behaviour is acquired as part of the learning process that occurs mostly in childhood (Bandura, 1973; Bandura & Walters, 1963). Bandura's analysis of aggression was so successful that he subsequently extended it to human behaviour in general (Bandura, 1973, 1977, 2000a, 2000b) and generated a variety of very effective treatment techniques for numerous disorders.

One of the most significant treatment developments of the 1970s was the extension of behavioural approaches to include the modification of cognitions (e.g., thoughts, feelings, beliefs, and attitudes). This approach, which came to be called *cognitive-behaviour therapy* (CBT; see Chapter 17), was led by a handful of researchers; prominent among them was Canadian psychologist Donald Meichenbaum (2003). Meichenbaum's early work provided a significant impetus to the growth of CBT (Meichenbaum, 1974), and his subsequent efforts have led to the development of very effective treatments for various problems, including impulsivity (Meichenbaum & Goodman, 1971); pain, anxiety, and anger (Meichenbaum, 2002; Meichenbaum & Turk, 1976); stress (Meichenbaum, 1985, 2007); and post-traumatic stress disorder (Meichenbaum, 1997). An important extension of CBT has involved mindfulness training, which was developed by Zindel Segal (Centre for Addiction and Mental Health, Toronto; see Chapter 8) and his colleagues as a strategy for preventing relapse in depression (Piet & Hougaard, 2011; Segal, Williams, & Teasdale, 2013; Williams & Kuyken, 2012).

A number of other Canadian researchers who have made significant contributions will be mentioned throughout this book. Canadian scientists are at the forefront of developments in the mental health field and will remain so for the foreseeable future.

Recent Developments

The **Mental Health Commission of Canada (MHCC)** was established in 2007. The goal of the MHCC is to develop an integrated mental health system that encourages better co-operation among governments, mental health providers, employers, the scientific community, and Canadians who live with or care for those with mental disorders. Some specific goals of the MHCC are to

- be a catalyst for the reform of mental health policies and improvements in service delivery;

- act as a facilitator, enabler, and supporter of a national approach to mental health issues;

- work to diminish the stigma and discrimination faced by Canadians living with mental disorders; and

- disseminate evidence-based information on all aspects of mental health and mental illness to governments, stakeholders, and the public. (MHCC, 2011)

At a Collaboration for Change forum in Vancouver in April 2008, the Honourable Michael Kirby (then chair of the MHCC) spoke about the stigma associated with mental health problems:

Half a century ago, a report on mental illness in Canada began with these words: "In no other field, except perhaps leprosy, has there been as much confusion, misdirection and discrimination against a patient as in mental illness ... Down through the ages, they have been estranged by society and cast out to wander in the wilderness. Mental illness, even today, is all too often considered a crime to be punished, a sin to be expiated, a possessing demon to be exorcised, a disgrace to be hushed up, a personality weakness to be deplored or a welfare problem to be handled as cheaply as possible. Those words were written 50 years ago. In many ways they are still true today" (Kirby, 2008).

An important step toward fulfilling the mandates of the MHCC involved the publication of a national mental health strategy in 2012 that included recommendations to improve community access and public funding to mental health care, as well as strategies to reduce stigma and to better promote well-being.

4 BEFORE MOVING ON

In your opinion, is mental health stigma changing and in what ways? What do you think would further help reduce stigma?

A second major development pertaining to mental health services in Canada is an increased focus on encouraging evidence-based practice for psychologists. **Evidence-based practice (EBP)** refers to the integration of scientific evidence with individual expertise in order to inform optimum client care (American Psychological Association Presidential Task Force on Evidence-Based Practice, 2006). The purpose of EBP is to bolster the efficacious treatment of mental disorders, to maintain the competitiveness of psychologists in the mental health market, and to increase accountability and reduce liability. In practising EBP, psychologists could be expected to consider the use of treatments that research has shown to be effective. The promotion of EBP would therefore preclude psychologists from prescribing and administering treatments that are without a sound scientific basis and ensure that research findings are relevant to real-world environments.

In 2011 the Canadian Psychological Association initiated a task force on the EBP of psychological treatments.

This task force operationalized what constitutes EBP in psychology, made recommendations about how psychologists can best integrate evidence into practice, and suggested strategies for dissemination (see Dozois et al., 2014; also see Chapter 17). A significant gap exists between scientists and practitioners: we need more evidence-based practice and more practice-based evidence. Practitioners need to be competent consumers of research, and researchers need to ensure that their findings apply to real-world environments (Dozois, 2013; Dozois et al., 2014).

ACCESS TO CARE

Access to mental health care is a significant concern in Canada, having been described as "a silent crisis" (Peachey, Hicks, & Adams, 2013, p. 3) due to inconsistent and inadequate access to services. As society's understanding and acceptance of mental health challenges has progressed, we have moved away from institutionalized care toward community-based treatment (see Focus box 1.2). However, a significant gap between need and access remains, and is, arguably, the greatest threat to public health in this country. Evidence-based psychological interventions are considered the treatment of choice for most mental disorders, but Canada's public health care system does not currently provide sufficient access. As a result, primary care physicians tend to be over-burdened by treating mental health concerns (Peachey et al., 2013). Additionally, corporate insurance plans are typically heavily limited, usually covering only several sessions of therapy. Many individuals are then left to pay out of pocket, which is not financially feasible for many Canadians. Recently, the Canadian Psychological Association (CPA) commissioned an independent economic analysis of access to mental health care (Peachey et al., 2013). The CPA and the Council of Professional Associations of Psychologists have been advocating that federal and provincial governments ensure all Canadians have efficient and equitable access to psychological services.

Peachey et al. (2013) recommended an increase in government funding for psychological services, more employer support for psychological treatments, and increased benefits offered by private insurance providers. The Peachey et al. (2013) report, and the recommendations of the CPA task force on evidence-based practice of psychological treatments reinforce the importance of providing services that are rooted in the best available empirical evidence for improving the quality of available care, as well as the necessity of further increasing awareness of EBP for both professional psychologists and the public.

FOCUS 1.2 Governmental and Corporate Initiative

As the figures on funding indicate, global expenditures in mental health prevention and treatment range from paltry to thoroughly inadequate. Fortunately, there is growing recognition and awareness of a need for change. However taking the steps required to meet the imperative for improving access to care will take a significant investment. Chisholm et al. (2016) estimated that the cost of bringing treatment coverage for depression and anxiety disorders up to standard would be $147 billion. However, a return on investment analysis determined that effective treatment coverage would produce a $310 billion gain owing to extra years of healthy life, and another $230 billion and $169 billion in economic productivity benefits associated with improved treatment for depression and anxiety disorders, respectively (Chisholm et al., 2016).

It will be interesting to see how the global community responds to the challenge of improving mental health infrastructure, and implements needed changes in how mental health services are funded and disseminated. There is some reason for optimism within our own borders: Prime Minister Justin Trudeau, has pledged to work with the provinces—which have jurisdiction over health care in Canada—to increase funding for mental health services and reduce the costs of prescription medication. It is hoped that a new federal government that recognizes the importance of investing in mental health care will bring much-needed change to the public system and remove the long-standing barriers many Canadians face to receiving appropriate care.

In the province of Ontario, mental illness is responsible for 10% of the burden of disease, yet it is allotted only 7% of the health care budget; this amounts to an estimated shortfall of $1.5 billion in funding (Brien et al., 2015; Institute for Health Metrics and Evaluation, 2015). Even when faced with potentially long wait times and an over-taxed public system, turning to expensive private care is also often not a palatable option. Socioeconomic status is negatively correlated with mental health, with those in the lowest income bracket several times more likely than those in the highest income bracket to report poor to fair mental health (Mawani & Gilmour, 2010). Employers increasing coverage for workers seeking therapy would go a long way to helping fill the void.

Starbucks Canada announced in October 2016 that they would offer employees $5000 per year in mental health

Day Owl/Shutterstock

(Continued)

insurance coverage (a 1250% increase). Employees seeking treatment previously only received enough benefits to cover far fewer than the 10 to 20 sessions needed to effectively treat most common mental health concerns (CPA, 2017). The decision was applauded by mental health advocates and business analysts alike, with the latter pointing out that the costs could be largely recouped through fewer disability claims and missed work days, and increased employee satisfaction (Anderssen, 2016). Moreover, the average Starbucks employee is 24 years old, and young people aged 15 to 24 are at a higher risk for the onset of mental disorders than any other age bracket (Mawani & Gilmour, 2010; Statistics Canada, 2013).

Another company, Manulife Canada, has since pledged $10 000 per year in mental health benefits to its employees and their families (CPA, 2017). Manulife's new benefits package is one of the most extensive corporate plans in Canada. Mental health and adequate access to psychological care via evidence-based treatments are pressing issues facing many Canadians. The role of the employer in the workplace is evolving, as it has become clear that organizational success relies on the well-being of employees. Thus, an investment in mental health prevention and timely remediation of mental illness is a sound decision for any employer.

Do you think employers have a duty to offer mental health coverage to their employees, or is this something that should be fully provided by the government? ●

Torontonian/Alamy Stock Photo

Funding shortfalls and access to effective treatment options are not challenges restricted to Canada. Low- and middle-income countries fare the worst, with most spending less than US$2 per person on mental health prevention and treatment, compared to the $50 per person that high-income countries spend (Chisholm et al., 2016). Overall, an estimated U.S.$2.5 to $8.5 trillion in productivity losses were incurred worldwide in 2010 due to mental disorders, a figure that is expected to as much as double within the next 15 years (Bloom et al., 2011).

A CHANGING LANDSCAPE

The proliferation of technology has brought new opportunities and challenges for psychologists in recent years (Drapeau, Holmqvist, & Piotrowski, 2016). For example, there are new and exciting ways to bring psychological services to individuals who may not previously have had access to them, because of geographic or other limitations (e.g., Campbell et al., 2016; Johnson, 2014). Technology also offers novel ways of data collection and analysis, such as through smartphone applications or online crowdsourcing marketplaces. With the ubiquity of online communication and the potential to leave a cyber fingerprint with every interaction you have comes a new set of ethical challenges for today's professionals. This changing landscape was typified in 2014 when the Facebook scandal at Dalhousie University played out in the public eye (see Task Force on Misogyny, Sexism and Homophobia in the Faculty of Dentistry, 2015). Social media has brought new and nuanced meaning to the term "professional discretion," as mental health professionals must consider carefully the potential consequences of sharing photos and personal opinions online, and how such actions may impact relationships with potential clients or the workplaces they represent.

⑤ BEFORE MOVING ON

Do you think that employers and institutions should establish guidelines for their employees on how to conduct themselves online? At what point would this involve too much control?

SUMMARY

- According to the statistical view, abnormal behaviour can be determined by how frequently it occurs in the population.

- Personal distress can indicate the presence of abnormal behaviour.

- The personal dysfunction viewpoint emphasizes that abnormal behaviour interferes with appropriate functioning in a particular situation or environment.

- Abnormal behaviour could be defined in terms of whether it violates societal norms and values.

- Experts may determine what qualifies as abnormal behaviour.

- None of these principles is necessary or sufficient in defining abnormal behaviour; therefore, our definition of psychological disorders includes elements of all these principles.

- Evidence from prehistoric times suggests that supernatural explanations for psychological disorders may have been dominant.
- Greek and Roman philosophers and physicians held surprisingly modern views and emphasized biological and psychological causes and treatments of disorders.
- In the Arab world, treatment was humane and environmental and psychological factors were emphasized.
- During the Middle Ages in Europe, attributing supernatural causes to psychological disorders became more common again, although some individuals continued to explore other potential causes. Asylums were established around the 1500s, but treatment was often harsh and ineffective.
- During the Enlightenment, social and psychological factors became increasingly emphasized and treatments became more humane, although resources for caring for the mentally ill were still scarce.
- Abnormal behaviour may be caused by medical problems such as syphilis. These problems are normally treated pharmacologically and potential medical causes are often ruled out before diagnosing a mental disorder.
- Surgical procedures such as lobotomies were used to remove areas of the brain that were implicated in mental disorders.
- Electroconvulsive therapy employs electricity in order to induce a seizure in patients. This treatment has become much safer over the years and is still used for severe depression.
- Pharmacological treatments for psychological disorders usually target neurotransmitters and are currently a popular treatment method.
- Dr. Ruth Kajander was one of the first psychiatrists to use major tranquilizers to treat schizophrenia.
- Albert Bandura developed a theory of learning of aggressive behaviour in childhood and generated a number of treatment approaches emphasizing learning theory.
- Donald Meichenbaum played a key role in the development of cognitive-behavioural therapy, which is now used as a treatment for a variety of psychological disorders.
- The Mental Health Commission of Canada was established to improve access to mental health care and to reduce the stigma of mental illness. An emphasis on the potential for recovery is characteristic of the MHCC's approach to reducing stigma.
- Practitioners are now being encouraged to engage in evidence-based practice, i.e., to consider and integrate research evidence into their decisions regarding the best treatment for their clients.

KEY TERMS

asylums (p. 10)

bedlam (p. 13)

behaviourism (p. 18)

clinical psychologists (p. 6)

culturally relative (p. 6)

deinstitutionalization (p. 17)

electroconvulsive therapy (ECT) (p. 17)

evidence-based practice (EBP) (p. 20)

general paresis of the insane (GPI) (p. 16)

humours (p. 9)

lobotomies (p. 19)

Mental Health Commission of Canada (MHCC) (p. 20)

mental hygiene movement (p. 15)

mental illness (p. 4)

moral therapy (p. 15)

natural causes (p. 8)

psychiatrists (p. 6)

psychological abnormality (p. 4)

psychological disorder (p. 4)

psychopathology (p. 4)

somatogenesis (p. 16)

St. Vitus' dance (p. 12)

supernatural causes (p. 8)

syndromes (p. 15)

trephination (p. 8)

DAVID J. A. DOZOIS

·

LINDSAY SZOTA

CHAPTER

2

Bram Janssens/123RF

Theoretical Perspectives on Abnormal Behaviour

LEARNING OBJECTIVES

AFTER READING THIS CHAPTER, STUDENTS WILL BE ABLE TO:

1 View behaviour and thinking (disordered or not) as arising from the interaction between biological and environmental experiences.

2 Define neurotransmitters and describe the four ways in which they can influence abnormal behaviour, using examples.

3 Describe the role of the id, ego, and superego as personality structures and explain how they influence an individual's defence mechanisms.

4 Explain how classical and operant conditioning can influence an individual's behaviour and provide examples.

5 Define schemas and describe how they come to influence an individual's thoughts, beliefs, information processing, and behaviours.

6 Understand how close others (e.g., partners, friends, family) can influence the development and maintenance of mental health disorders through stigma or social support.

7 Identify how gender, race, and poverty influence mental health disorders.

Hailey suffered from major depressive disorder. Shortly after Hailey's birth, her mother experienced an episode of postpartum depression and was often physically or psychologically unavailable to her daughter. As a result, Hailey learned that caregivers were often inconsistent when responding to her needs and feared that she would be abandoned. Her parents noted that, from a young age, Hailey was very reactive to stressful situations and overly responsive to changes in her environment.

When Hailey was 16, she began dating her first boyfriend. Although her boyfriend was supportive and would often tell her that he loved her, Hailey found herself constantly asking for reassurance of his affection because she feared that he would abandon her. Frustrated by her behaviour, Hailey's boyfriend eventually broke up with her.

Following the breakup Hailey began to experience low mood and started to withdraw from her friends, family, and participation in school. As a result, she lacked the necessary support from others to overcome her disorder, and her low mood worsened. By the time she sought treatment a few months later, Hailey was having difficulty sleeping, had no appetite, had lost interest in things she used to enjoy doing, and lacked energy.

The General Nature of Theories

Chapter 1 traced the development of ideas about abnormal behaviour from the ancient Greeks to the present. Beginning in the early twentieth century, there have been two main streams of thought concerning mental disorders: one focusing on the biological aspects of disorders and the other focusing on environmental influences, roughly following the nature/nurture distinction that is made in so many areas of human functioning. Although a number of variations exist within each stream, biological approaches tend to dismiss or downplay the influence of experience, whereas psychological or environmental approaches tend to emphasize external factors (e.g., poverty, parenting style) in the development of disorders. Indeed, some behavioural theories (e.g., Skinner, 1953) attribute no effects at all to biology, assuming that, as British philosopher John Locke (1632–1704) put it, humans are born *tabula rasa* (a blank slate upon which experience writes all that is meaningful in thought and behaviour).

As we discuss in this chapter, biological and psychodynamic formulations view dysfunctional behaviour as the product of forces beyond the individual's control, whereas humanistic and existential approaches lay the responsibility for action and choices squarely on the shoulders of the individual. In contrast, behavioural and cognitive theories imply that a mixture of external and internal factors produce dysfunctions.

The perspective taken when examining the cause of psychopathology determines many things. It directs research, guides diagnostic decisions, and defines treatment responses.

The acceptance of the biological model, for example, encourages researchers to seek a physical basis for disorders, leads to the formulation of a diagnostic system that classifies people as disordered, and implies that physical interventions should be the treatments of choice. The behavioural perspective, on the other hand, leads researchers to seek environmental events that shape specific dysfunctional responses and emphasizes the classification of behaviours rather than of people. From the behavioural perspective, treatment involves either manipulating the environment or (for those who adopt a cognitive-behavioural perspective) modifying the perceptions people have regarding their experiences and themselves.

As an example of how different perspectives would shed light on a disorder, let's look at what might have caused Hailey's depression. Biological and psychodynamic formulations view dysfunctional behaviour as the product of forces beyond the individual's control. In Hailey's case, a biologically oriented theorist would point out the fact that Hailey's mother also suffered from depression, supporting a genetic basis for Hailey's problem. A Freudian, or psychodynamic theorist, would want to examine Hailey's childhood relationship with her mother. Behavioural and cognitive theories, on the other hand, suggest that a mixture of internal and external factors produce dysfunction. For example, in Hailey's case, a behaviourist would examine Hailey's reassurance seeking and her withdrawal behaviours resulting from her depression. A cognitive theorist would examine how Hailey's schemas or beliefs (her fear of abandonment), automatic thoughts, and the way she processes information influence her disorder.

Humanistic and existential approaches lay the responsibility for action and choices on the individual suffering from the disorder. These two approaches would focus on Hailey's personal decisions, level of acceptance, and perceptions of her experience with depression. A socio-cultural formulation would examine factors such as whether or not Hailey has good social supports to help her handle her disorder, how being female influences her depression, or how being labelled as being depressed affects her life. Someone who took an integrative perspective would look at the dynamic and reciprocal relationships among all these factors.

In the rest of this chapter, we will look more closely at these various theoretical approaches. In fact, throughout this book we will see confirmation of the theme illustrated by Hailey's case: that the origins of psychological disorders are complex, with no one factor providing a complete explanation.

Interestingly, the adoption of a perspective is far more influenced by the prevailing social belief system and by an individual's disposition to see human behaviour as determined by factors beyond or within the control of the individual, than by the weight of evidence. Indeed, theorists often stubbornly hold on to a view in spite of evidence to the contrary. This tenacious clinging to a specific theory is not necessarily a bad thing, since it allows that theory to be fully explored. A theory is useful not so much because it is true, but because it generates research that leads to an increase in knowledge. A theory should be abandoned only when there is a better one available (that is, one that does a better job of integrating current knowledge and that generates more research). Thus, the scientific theories of the past should be judged not by how well they match current information, but rather by how much new information they generated.

LEVELS OF THEORIES

To state that a genetic defect or a single traumatic experience causes a mental disorder is to accept a **single-factor explanation**, which attempts to trace the origins of a particular disorder to one factor. For example, a single-factor explanation of social anxiety may be that it runs in families. It is important to point out that most single-factor models reflect the primary focus of the researcher, theorist, or clinician rather than the belief that there really is a single cause. For instance, a cognitive therapist would emphasize the modification of negative automatic thoughts and core beliefs in the treatment of depression. However, this therapist would not ignore or discount other contributing causes and might, in fact, suggest that a patient receive a trial of antidepressant medications as a useful complement to cognitive therapy. However, human behaviour, in all its complexity, is unlikely to be the product of a single defect or experience. **Interactionist explanations**, which view behaviour as the product of the interaction of a variety of factors, generally make more satisfactory theories in describing mental disorders. As knowledge of any single disorder increases, so, characteristically, does the complexity of theories offered to account

for its development and maintenance. Single-factor theories, then, often simply reflect the lack of current comprehensive knowledge of disorders. Interactionist explanations take into account the biology and behaviour of the individual, as well as the cognitive, social, and cultural environment, given that any one component inevitably affects the other components.

Theories may also be classified according to their level of explanation (Marshall, 1982; Mash & Dozois, 2003). Some theories try to explain all human behaviour (for example, Maslow's [1954] theory of self-actualization), some try to explain all abnormal behaviour (for example, Freud, 1917/1971), and others try to account for all disorders within a particular category, such as all types of personality disorders (e.g., Hopwood, Wright, Ansell, & Pincus, 2013). Even more specifically, there are theories that endeavour to reveal the causes of a particular problem such as generalized anxiety disorder (e.g., Lissek et al., 2014). Finally, there are theories that attempt to elucidate the influence of a single factor within a more general theory. For example, our own work has tested the organization of the self-schema within the broader context of cognitive vulnerability to depression (Dozois, 2007; Dozois et al., 2014; Dozois & Dobson, 2001a, 2001b; Dozois & Rnic, 2015; Evraire & Dozois, 2014; Evraire, Dozois, & Hayden, 2015).

Single-factor theories, however, should not be considered valueless simply because they may later be discarded for more complex explanations. The history of science is replete with the rejection of theories that at one time were broadly accepted and seemed to explain phenomena. To expand on an earlier point, scientific theories are judged to be valuable not because they describe the enduring truth about an issue, but rather because they embody three essential features:

1. They integrate most of what is currently known about the phenomena in the simplest way possible (parsimony);
2. They make testable predictions about aspects of the phenomena that were not previously thought of; and
3. They make it possible to specify what evidence would deny the theory.

TESTING THEORIES: THE NULL HYPOTHESIS

Theories are replaced in science not because the evidence against them is significant (although that is a good reason to search for alternatives), but rather because another theory comes along that is open to being disproved and that does a better job of integrating knowledge and generating novel predictions.

This latter notion often puzzles students; however, it is the cornerstone of science. Experiments are *not set up to prove the worth of a theory* but rather *to reject (or fail to reject)* what is called the null hypothesis. The **null hypothesis** essentially proposes that the prediction made from the theory is false. Let us look at a simple example. Suppose we claim that low self-esteem causes and maintains depression. A prediction from this claim would be that patients suffering from depression should have lower self-esteem than do non-depressed patients. If we compare these two groups of patients and find that the depressed group scores significantly lower than does the non-depressed group, we may have offered some support for the theory, but we have not proved it to be true: some other, as yet unknown, factor may produce both depression and low self-esteem. However, these results allow us to reject the null hypothesis, which, in this case, says there are no differences in self-esteem between the depressed and non-depressed groups. This at least eliminates an alternative possible theory; namely, that low self-esteem is characteristic of all people regardless of whether or not they are suffering from depression.

Theories gain strength not just because the evidence supports their predictions, but primarily because alternative explanations are rejected. Despite popular belief to the contrary, scientists do not set out to prove their theories to be true and, in fact, no amount of evidence can ever prove the truth of a theory. Theories are not facts. They are simply the best approximation we have at any moment, so that current theories are almost inevitably going to be replaced as knowledge accumulates. It is the very process of trying to prove our theories wrong that generates the new knowledge that will one day lead to their rejection.

Some accounts of abnormal behaviour, or indeed of psychological functioning more generally, do not in fact meet the criteria of scientific theories because they are essentially immune to disproof. For example, many critics have maintained that the theories of Sigmund Freud are not open to disproof.

The Search for Causes

The general aims of theories about mental disorders are to (1) explain the **etiology** (that is, the causes or origins) of the problem behaviour, (2) identify the factors that maintain the behaviour, (3) predict the course of the disorder, and (4) design effective treatments. Of course, theories of abnormal behaviour are chosen presumably because they fit with theorists' more general sentiments about human nature. Some people feel uncomfortable attributing causes of behaviour to factors over which a person has little or no control (for example, biological causes or unconscious processes). Such theorists are likely to be attracted to accounts of human dysfunction that attribute causation to environmental influences. These theorists are, therefore, optimistic about the potential for environmental manipulations to produce behaviour change. Other people are more attracted to biological explanations because they hold similar hopes for effective medical treatment.

It is important to note that factors involved in the etiology of a problem may not be relevant to its maintenance. For example, as was the case with Hailey, an individual may become depressed as a result of the termination of a significant relationship (e.g., the end of an intimate relationship or death of a family member). However, once depressed, the individual may withdraw from others or frustrate close others by continuously trying to gain acceptance and approval, leading to an environment of social isolation in which the individual with depression cannot receive the necessary support to overcome his or her disorder (Evraire & Dozois, 2011). Similarly, the factors that determine the course of a disorder may have more to do with the lifestyle of the sufferer than with the factors that caused the disorder in the first place. For example, a frightening experience with a dog may cause a person to become phobic. However, subsequent careful avoidance of all dogs will maintain the disorder in some individuals, whereas others may force themselves to interact with the animals and thereby overcome their irrational fears.

Even in disorders where there is a clear biological cause, environmental manipulations may alleviate or even prevent the development of the most serious symptoms. For example, phenylketonuria (PKU) is an inborn metabolic defect that causes the body to be unable to metabolize phenylalanine, a substance present in many foods. This metabolic problem is genetically transmitted as a recessive autosomal trait, meaning that both parents must have the gene that carries the disorder for the child to develop PKU. Untreated PKU will markedly raise blood levels of phenylalanine, resulting in a decrease in various neurotransmitters in the brain, thereby producing severe intellectual developmental difficulties, microencephalopathy, seizures, and other behavioural disturbances (Hellekson, 2001). However, when PKU is detected in newborns (screening tests for PKU are now routine) the infant is given a diet low in phenylalanine, and most of the disastrous consequences are avoided, allowing the child to live a relatively normal life. In this way, environmental influences (that is, diet) affect the development of a biologically driven disorder.

Along these lines, a modified version of Aaron T. Beck's cognitive formulation of depression and anxiety (discussed later in this chapter) has been proposed to describe how cognitive therapy (CT) can not only alter an individual's cognitive processes in order to reduce symptoms of depression or anxiety, but also affect his or her neurobiology (Clark & Beck, 2010a). In this model, depressive and anxious symptoms result from the activation of negative schemas, or core beliefs, and negative emotions, which are associated with increased activation in the amygdalohippocampal subcortical region of the brain. Depression and anxiety are also associated with restricted access to reflective processes or cognitive control (e.g., the control of negative emotion) associated with the anterior cingulated cortex (ACC), medial and lateral prefrontal cortex (PFC), and orbitofrontal cortex (OFC). Cognitive therapy directly seeks to reduce symptoms by modifying maladaptive thoughts, attitudes, and beliefs, as well as information processing biases. However, the literature has recently demonstrated that CT is also associated with reduced activation of the amygdalohippocampal subcortical region along with increased activation of the brain regions listed above involved in the cognitive control of negative emotion (Gotlib & Joormann, 2010). While more recent reviews indicate that the evidence for these findings is mixed (Franklin, Carson, & Welch, 2016), this research nevertheless shows that external factors such as CT can affect biological functioning quite dramatically (see also Frewen, Dozois, & Lanius, 2008); no doubt the converse is also true.

Many theories have been advanced regarding the etiology of mental disorders. We limit ourselves here to a description of the most popular, grouped by the primary proposed cause: (1) biological, (2) psychodynamic (derived from the theories of Freud or his followers), (3) behavioural or cognitive-behavioural theories, (4) cognitive theories examining dysfunctional thoughts or beliefs, (5) humanistic or existential theories that examine interpersonal processes, and (6) socio-cultural influences. Of course, it is reasonable to assume that these various influences interact to produce mental disorders. Even within each of these models, various causes are seen as primary by one or another theorist. For example, within the biological category, some theories emphasize abnormal brain functioning, whereas others place the site of the problem in the autonomic nervous system, in genetic endowment, or in a dysfunctional endocrine system.

Strict biological determinism all too often leads to the dismal conclusion that psychological or environmental interventions will do no good. Well-intentioned clinicians may assume that disorders that are difficult to treat are completely biological. For instance, schizophrenia has traditionally been viewed as predominantly biologically based. However, recent studies suggest that cognitive therapy and other psychosocial interventions are effective supplements to antipsychotic medication (see Kurtz, 2015, and Mueser, Deavers, Penn, & Cassisi, 2013, for reviews) and are now recommended aspects of routine care.

Frequently, cultural or environmental determinists feel obliged to deny the influence of biological disadvantages. However, no amount of devoted training, expert guidance, or determination would ever make a person who is 1.5 metres tall into a world-class high jumper. Lifestyle and education may ease the life of someone who inherits the defective gene that causes Huntington's disease but will not prevent the development of dementia, jerky body movements, depression, and psychosis.

In fact, all of these systems (that is, biological, behavioural, and so on) work in concert and it is almost impossible (if not meaningless) to disentangle their influence. Dividing this interrelated system of theories into its presumed components all too often has the effect of convincing some theorists that one or another aspect is causally more important than all other features. This type of thinking, which may attribute primary causation to biological problems (biological determinism), or to socio-cultural or environmental influences (cultural or environmental determinism), is a form of reductionism, in that the actions of the whole are said to be caused by (that is, reduced to the influence of) one or other of the component parts. This is akin to saying that body temperature is entirely determined by our internal thermal regulatory system, or alternatively by our external environment, when, of course, it is a product of the dynamic interaction of the two, each of which is complexly determined. Reductionist thinking ignores the rather obvious possibility that human behaviour in all its forms is a product of an array of features (biological, developmental, environmental, personal choice, cultural, and so on) interacting. For example, being able to run a marathon in world-record time requires not only a biologically appropriate body, but also a devoted training schedule and the right footwear (environmental features), and a culture that allows or encourages such long-distance running (cultural or social influences).

To understand the various theoretical approaches to abnormal behaviour, we will have to consider them separately, as that is the way they have always been described. This separation, however, should not be taken to mean that we agree with any one model that assumes the prior causal control of behaviour. We view behaviour and thinking (whether normal or disordered) as arising from the integrated dynamic and essentially inseparable interactions between multiple biological and environmental experiences.

 BEFORE MOVING ON

> Pharmaceutical advertisements and other media often portray the message that psychological problems are caused by chemical imbalances. How convinced are you that this is true? What are the advantages and disadvantages of adopting this belief?

Biological Models

Biological theorists of human behaviour typically not only borrow their model from medicine, but also co-opt the language of medicine, calling clients "patients" and their problems "symptoms" or "syndromes," and describing the response to these problems as "treatment." Thus, adopting a biological model has implications for the way in which people with problems are treated. The same, of course, is true for all theoretical perspectives, and it is necessary to consider the ramifications of these, often unnoticed, implications when deciding on a particular point of view about abnormal behaviour. A model may be appealing because it fits with current thinking, but it also may have less obvious features that are not so attractive.

To appreciate the meaning of the various biological explanations of disordered behaviour or thinking, it is necessary to have some understanding of relevant aspects of bodily functioning. Biological theories have primarily implicated dysfunctions in or damage to the brain (the central nervous system, or CNS), problems of control of one or another aspect of the peripheral nervous system (that is, the autonomic nervous system or the somatic nervous system), or malfunctioning of the endocrine system.

For purposes of exposition, the nervous system is divided into the CNS and the peripheral nervous system, although in normal functioning the activities of these two complex systems are integrated, and their actions are further coordinated with activity in the endocrine system.

THE ROLE OF THE CENTRAL NERVOUS SYSTEM

The average adult male brain contains approximately 86 billion neurons, and an approximately equal number of non-neuronal (glial) cells (Azevedo et al., 2009). Glial cells were originally presumed to be support cells, although new evidence suggests that they exert more of an active role in the brain function and information processing (Allen & Barres, 2009). These cells group together into anatomically distinct areas, which appear to have somewhat distinctive functions, although active interconnections throughout the brain indicate that no one area exclusively performs any one function. It is perhaps better to think of brain activity associated with particular functions as the product of interactions among neuronal networks that produce domain-general functions, rather than due to activity located within one single area of the brain.

Figure 2.1 depicts the anatomical areas of the brain. The hindbrain primarily directs the functioning of the autonomic nervous system, which in turn controls primarily internal activities such as digestion, cardiovascular functioning, and breathing. The midbrain is the centre of the reticular activating system, which controls arousal levels (often called the sleep–wake centre) and thereby attentional processes.

The forebrain controls thought, speech, perception, memory, learning, and planning—indeed, all the processes that make us sentient, self-conscious beings. Obviously, damage to any of these parts of the brain will cause proportionate dysfunction in many areas, including psychological functioning.

Some disorders have been shown to be directly linked to brain damage. Dementia (a deterioration in all cognitive processes, particularly memory and learning) that occurs in disorders such as Parkinson's or Alzheimer's is linked to the loss or ineffective functioning of brain cells. These losses of brain cell functioning can be transitory, but in many cases

they are irreversible, and may result from various sources such as direct head injuries, diseases, or toxins. Sophisticated methods are now available for detecting even quite small areas of damage or dysfunction in the brain. Various imaging techniques, such as computerized axial tomography (CAT scans), magnetic resonance imaging (MRI), and positron emission tomography (PET scans), have all enabled the detailed, although expensive, examination of brain functioning. However, current theories about the brain bases of abnormal behaviour have given more weight to the role of neurotransmitters than to actual neuronal damage.

Neurotransmitters are the chemical substances that carry the messages from one neuron to the next in the complex pathways of nervous activity within the brain. Nerve cells are not connected to one another, so activity in one neuron does not directly stimulate activity in other neurons. There is a gap (called a synapse or synaptic cleft) between the axons (which carry the nerve impulse to the synapse) of one neuron and the dendrites (which pick up the activity from the first neuron) of neighbouring neurons. The transmission of the electrical activity in the axon to the neighbouring dendrites occurs as a result of the release of chemicals called neurotransmitters (see Focus box 2.1). There are numerous neurotransmitters, but to date the majority of research attention has been given to the role of dopamine, serotonin, norepinephrine, and, more recently, gamma aminobutyric acid (or GABA). These neurotransmitters act either on their own, or more likely, in concert with others, in the spread of nerve impulses throughout the brain. Different types seem to be concentrated in different areas of the brain and, therefore, are thought to play a role in different functions. For example, pleasure-seeking and exploratory behaviours seem to be associated with dopamine activity, whereas serotonin activity appears to be related to the constraint or inhibition of behaviour. These two neurotransmitters, then, seem to act to create a balance in behaviour (see Depue, 2009, for review).

When neurotransmitters are released into the synapse, some will be taken up at the receptor sites on the dendrites and thereby activate or inhibit (depending upon the action of the transmitter) an impulse in the post-synaptic neuron. However, within the synaptic cleft are substances that deactivate neurotransmitters, so some of the released transmitters will be destroyed before they can act on the dendrites. Furthermore, many of the released neurotransmitters are quickly drawn back into the releasing axon by a process called reuptake. Thus, abnormal behaviour can result from disturbances in neurotransmitter systems in various ways: (1) there may be too much or too little of the neurotransmitter produced or released into the synapse, (2) there may be too few or too many receptors on the dendrites, (3) there may be an excess or a deficit in the amount of the transmitter-deactivating substance in the synapse, or (4) the reuptake process may be too rapid or too slow. Any or all of these problems can cause either too much excitation or too much inhibition in the particular brain circuits, and this excessive or reduced activity may result in abnormal functioning. Schizophrenia, for example, is thought

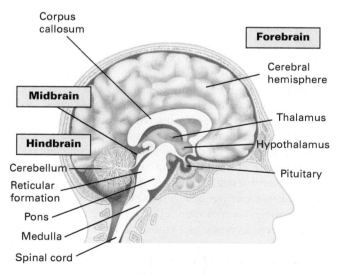

FIGURE 2.1   The Human Brain (Side View)

Source: Baron, R. A., *Psychology*, 2nd ed., ©1992. Reprinted and Electronically reproduced by permission of Pearson Education, Inc., Upper Saddle River, New Jersey.

FOCUS 2.1

Neurotransmission

Nerve impulses are electrochemical discharges that are received by the dendrites of one neuron, thereby activating (or inhibiting) that neuron, and then travel down the axons of that neuron to activate (or inhibit) the electrochemical activity in the dendrites of another neuron. At the point of contact between the axon of the neuron propagating the nerve impulse (called the presynaptic neuron) and the dendrite of the receiving neuron (called the post-synaptic neuron) is the synapse. This is a minute space through which strictly chemical messengers (neurotransmitters) pass from the axon terminals to the receiving dendrites, where they either activate or inhibit electrochemically generated impulses.

The neurotransmitters (of which there are several kinds, all serving apparently different activating or inhibiting functions) are held in vesicles within the axon terminals. When these vesicles are stimulated by the neural impulse, which travels down the axon, they move to the releasing site and emit the neurotransmitters into the synapse. Some of the released transmitters are reabsorbed (a process called reuptake) by the axon, some are deactivated by substances in the synapse, and the remainder are taken up at receptor sites on the dendrites of the post-synaptic neuron. These receptor sites are highly specialized and can take up only transmitters whose structure exactly fits into the structure of the receptor so that each receptor can absorb only particular neurotransmitters. This makes it possible to create drugs whose chemical structure is an exact match for particular transmitters, so that when they are released into the synapse these drugs block the action of the transmitters by taking their place in the receptors. Other drugs can be made to accelerate or inhibit the action of the deactivators, again specifically affecting particular neurotransmitters, or they can stimulate or reduce the release of particular neurotransmitters. ●

Anatomy of a Neuron

Transmission of Neural Impulses across the Synapse

1. Within the axons of the neuron are neurotransmitters, which are held in storage-like vesicles until they are released when the neuron is stimulated.

2. The small space between the axon terminal and the dendrite of the next axon is called the *synapse*. The action potential stimulates the release of neurotransmitters across the synapse.

3. The neurotransmitter binds itself to the receptor sites on dendrites of the next neuron, causing a change in potential.

by some theorists to result from too much activity in the brain circuits (the dopamine system) that mediate the importance we attach to stimuli in our environment; this causes individuals with schizophrenia to over-assign importance to irrelevant stimuli, so that they experience the world as overwhelming (Maia & Frank, 2017). However, most researchers now believe that many aspects of brain functioning are much more complex than this. Disturbances in neurotransmitter systems are currently thought more likely to have general rather than specific effects, and it is the interaction of various neurotransmitters and their subtypes that is related to behaviour (e.g., Mittal et al., 2016).

The logic involved in inferring a causal relationship between disturbances in neurotransmitter functioning and abnormal behaviour depends to some extent on the methods used in examining this claim. For example, it is now known (with reasonable certainty) that drugs that ameliorate the symptoms of schizophrenia exert their action primarily (but not exclusively) by decreasing activity in the dopaminergic system (Dimitrelis & Shankar, 2016). This is taken as supportive evidence for the hypothesis that schizophrenia is caused by excessive dopamine, but this may be a false inference. For example, the administration of quinine relieves the symptoms of malaria, but it is not the absence of quinine that causes malaria; rather, malaria is caused by the bite of the *Anopheles* mosquito, which introduces the *Plasmodium* protozoa into the body. At a more basic level, it is important to note that the processes connecting behaviour and the neurochemical bases of brain activity do not represent a one-way street. No doubt neurotransmitter activity affects behaviour, but behaviour also affects neurotransmitter activity. Dr. Bryan Kolb, a distinguished neurophysiologist at the University of Lethbridge in Alberta, reviewed the incredible capacity of the brain to reorganize its circuitry—**brain plasticity**. Brain plasticity can be influenced by a number of experiences that occur pre- and postnatally through hormones, diet, aging, stress, disease, and maturation (for a review, see Kolb, Mychasiuk, & Gibb, 2014;

Kolb & Teskey, 2011). In one experiment, the offspring of rats that were raised in a complex environment exhibited increased synaptic space on the neurons in their cerebral cortex. Kolb, Gibb, and Robinson (2003) argue that "virtually any manipulation that produces an enduring change in behavior leaves an anatomical footprint in the brain" (p. 3). At present, it remains a possibility, although not one supported by many theorists, that environmental events cause schizophrenia and that the behavioural response to these events results in increased activity in neurotransmitter systems. Much more likely is the possibility that environmental events, the person's response to them, and biological substrates all play a part in causing abnormal functioning.

2 BEFORE MOVING ON

Antidepressants take several weeks to take effect and decrease symptoms of depression. Explain why this might be the case, considering what you know about how neurotransmitters influence abnormal behaviour.

THE ROLE OF THE PERIPHERAL NERVOUS SYSTEM

The peripheral nervous system includes the *somatic nervous system*, which controls the muscles, and the *autonomic nervous system (ANS)*. The ANS has two parts: the sympathetic nervous system and the parasympathetic nervous system (see Figure 2.2). These two systems typically function co-operatively to produce homeostatic (that is, balanced) activity in a variety of bodily functions such as heart rate, digestive and eliminatory processes, sexual arousal, breathing, perspiration, and so on. In times of stress, however, they function antagonistically. During stress, or when a person feels threatened, the sympathetic nervous system readies the body for action (fight or flight) by, for example, increasing heart rate, pupil size (making vision more acute), and breathing (which becomes faster and deeper to take in more oxygen). At the same time, the parasympathetic nervous system shuts down digestive processes, since energy given to this function would be wasted in a time of emergency.

Since humans display variability in all other response systems, it would not be surprising to find that, in some people, the ANS response to stress or threat is either

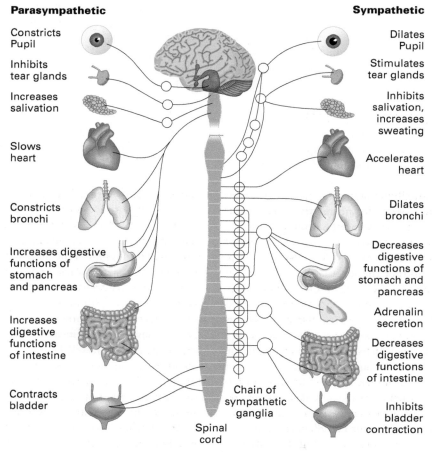

FIGURE 2.2 The Sympathetic and Parasympathetic Divisions of the Autonomic Nervous System

Source: Baron, R. A., *Psychology*, 2nd ed., ©1992. Reprinted and Electronically reproduced by permission of Pearson Education, Inc., New York, NY.

exaggeratedly strong or remarkably weak. Canadian physician Hans Selye studied responses to stress, beginning in 1936 and continuing until his death in 1983. Selye's work established the area of study now known as *stress physiology*. It has become clear that individuals differ in both the strength and the duration of their response to threat, and this variability has been related to the person's propensity to develop psychophysiological disorders (Friedman & Booth-Kewley, 1987). The ANS (more particularly, the sympathetic nervous system) is involved in fear and anxiety reactions. Thus, an overreactive ANS may increase readiness to acquire phobias or other anxiety or trauma-related disorders. That is, the strength of an individual's ANS response to a "frightening experience" may determine whether he or she acquires a conditioned phobic reaction. Such differences in responsivity may explain why one person exposed to a traumatic experience develops a severe and enduring conditioned emotional response while another person exposed to exactly the same experience does not (Bryant, Harvey, Guthrie, & Moulds, 2000).

Individual differences in the *regulation* of various ANS and somatic nervous system functions may also play a part in disordered behaviour. For example, irregular functioning in the respiratory and cardiovascular systems can be observed up to 47 minutes prior to the onset of a naturally occurring panic attack (Meuret et al., 2011). Further, individuals with panic appear to take longer to unlearn a conditioned fear response (as shown using physiological measures) compared to healthy controls (Michael, Blechert, Vriends, Margraf, & Wilhelm, 2007). These examples highlight how abnormalities in ANS functioning can contribute to psychological disorders.

THE ROLE OF THE ENDOCRINE SYSTEM

Aspects of the CNS interact with the endocrine system in a feedback loop that maintains appropriate levels of hormones circulating in the bloodstream. Hormones are chemical messengers that are secreted by various glands. These secretions maintain adequate bodily functioning and play an important role in the development of the organism; they also appear to be involved in the activation of some behaviours.

The relationship of the endocrine glands both to each other and to the CNS is complex. For example, in response to feedback indicating that the circulating levels of sex hormones (or sex steroids) are low, the CNS activates the hypothalamus (a small CNS structure located in the lower central part of the forebrain). In response, the hypothalamus secretes what are called "releasing" hormones that, in turn, activate the pituitary gland. Increased levels of circulating sex steroids alert the hypothalamus and pituitary to shut down this activity. The hormones secreted by the pituitary influence hormonal production in the adrenal gland and the testes (in males) and the ovaries (in females). The pituitary (which is often called the "master gland" because it plays such a controlling role in activating the other endocrine glands) releases many hormones, some of which, as we have seen, activate other glands whereas others have a more direct action. Growth hormone promotes and regulates muscle, bone, and other tissue growth; prolactin stimulates milk production in women; and adrenocorticotropic hormone helps the body handle stress. Obviously, the endocrine system has many and complex effects on behaviour.

Two disorders are known to be related to malfunctioning endocrine glands. Cretinism, a disorder involving a dwarflike appearance and intellectual deficits is a result of a defective thyroid gland. Hypoglycemia, which results from the pancreas failing to produce balanced levels of insulin or glycogen, produces experiences that mimic anxiety, and some patients who report to anxiety disorder clinics are in fact suffering from hypoglycemia. Similarly, thyroid dysregulation has been associated with a variety of psychiatric symptoms including anxiety and depression (Ittermann, Völzke, Baumeister, Appel, & Grabe, 2015).

One system that has also been studied extensively with regard to depression and anxiety is the hypothalamic-pituitary-adrenal (HPA) axis (see Chapter 7). The HPA axis is activated in response to stressors and involves an intricate system of communication among the hypothalamus, the pituitary gland, and the adrenal cortex. An important action of the HPA axis involves the release of the stress hormone cortisol into the bloodstream by the adrenal cortex. This hormone facilitates an individual's response to short-term threat by producing a number of changes in the body. For example, it causes an increase in intracellular glucocorticoid receptors, which leads to anti-inflammatory effects and other survival benefits.

Sensitivity to stress (as in the case of Hailey at the beginning of the chapter) has been strongly implicated in the etiology of major depression and anxiety disorders (Farb, Irving, Anderson, & Segal, 2015; Harkness, Hayden, & Lopez-Duran, 2015; Morris & Rottenberg, 2015). Consistent with this idea, altered functioning of the HPA axis is seen in many individuals with depression and anxiety (Jarcho, Slavich, Tylova-Stein, Wolkowitz, & Burke, 2013; Zorn et al., 2016), although the specific nature of these changes appears to vary across disorders (Gray & McEwen, 2014).

GENETICS AND BEHAVIOUR

The idea that human behaviour is inherited has a long history. This idea is part of the more general concept of biological determinism: that what a person is is determined largely by inherited characteristics. Thomas Hobbes, a seventeenth-century English philosopher, thought that aggression and self-interest were inborn features of all humans and that it was the business of political systems to restrain and usefully channel these impulses. By the nineteenth century, it was widely believed that all people took their biologically allotted place in society (that is, the destitute were condemned by their inherited characteristics to be poor, whereas the wealthy and the aristocracy were simply displaying their hereditary advantages). Cesare Lombroso (1836–1909) declared that criminals could be identified by the physiological features they had inherited from their degenerate parents. The eminent neuroanatomist Paul Broca (1824–1880) claimed that males were born with brains superior to those of females. Similar claims were made with respect to racial differences—with Europeans being seen as the supreme race.

It is good to keep in mind that claims about the inheritance of defective features can easily be used by those who would treat these individuals in a prejudicial manner. While these criticisms should make us cautious, they should not blind us to the possibility of genetic contributions to psychological disorders. Rejecting the idea that genes completely determine behaviour does not require us to accept that society, culture, or personal experience wholly account for human thought and action. It seems more reasonable to expect that most, if not all, behaviours are the product of an interaction between these sources of influence. **Behavioural genetics** offer us an insight into the biological bases of abnormal functioning.

In the case of psychopathology, however, "genes confer a liability not a certainty" (Wallace, Schneider, & McGuffin, 2002, p. 179). Recent research has emphasized the **gene–environment (genotype environment) interaction** (Manuck & McCaffery, 2014). It appears as though genes may influence behaviours that contribute to environmental stressors, which, in turn, increase the risk of psychopathology. This type of reciprocal relationship between genetic predisposition and environmental risk factors has been found in both animal models and human studies (Lesch, 2004). In one study, Caspi and colleagues (2003) examined the interactive effects of a genotype associated with depression and stressful life events (SLEs). The genotype of interest in their study was a gene that influences the transmission of serotonin (a neurotransmitter implicated in depression and other disorders) in the brain. This gene that Caspi et al. were studying comes in two versions or alleles: the long allele (L) and the short allele (S). Prior work with animals suggested that individuals with at least two copies of the long allele (LL) would better cope. All participants in the study reported experiencing SLEs, but the relationship between SLEs and depression was much stronger among adults who also had two S alleles. For example, people with two copies of the S allele were twice as likely to experience a major depressive episode if they had at least four SLEs, compared with people who experienced the same amount of stress but had two L alleles. Importantly, there was no direct link between the genotype and depression. In other words, adults with two S alleles developed depression *only* if they also experienced SLEs. Although some studies have failed to replicate this genotype-environment interactions (Zammit & Owen, 2006), a meta-analysis of 54 studies found strong evidence for this interaction effect (Karg, Burmeister, Shedden, & Sen, 2011). Clearly neither genes nor environmental events alone can explain the onset of a disorder such as depression. Rather, a complex interaction of the two factors is required.

Behavioural research into the genetic bases of psychiatric disorders typically takes one of three forms: family (or pedigree) studies, twin studies, and adoption studies. In all such studies, a person with a disorder is identified (called the index case or proband) and other people (family or non-family members) are examined to see if there is a match for the disorder. When the problem that characterizes the index case also occurs in the comparison person, the two are said to be *concordant* (or to display **concordance** for the problem). The degree of concordance is thought to reveal the influence of genetics. However, this assumption is not altogether accurate, since concordance can reveal environmental influences, depending on the circumstances.

More recent techniques for studying genetic influences include **genetic linkage studies** and research methods in **molecular biology**. In genetic linkage studies, researchers examine families that have a high incidence of a particular psychiatric disorder. Within these extended families, researchers look for the presence of particular traits (called genetic markers) that can be linked to the occurrence of the disorder. Common among these genetic markers are features like hair or eye colour, colour blindness, and the presence of medical disorders that have a known genetic basis. If all members of the family who have the mental disorder also have the genetic marker, but the unaffected family members do not, the conclusion is that the mental disorder has a genetic origin. These sorts of genetic linkage studies have provided strong evidence of a genetic basis for schizophrenia, although a number of studies have failed to replicate these findings (Cariaga-Martinez, Saiz-Ruiz, & Alelu-Paz, 2016).

Researchers in molecular biology have been able to compare specific DNA segments and identify the genes that determine individual characteristics. Based on the human genome project, researchers have been able to pinpoint the defective genes that contribute to various medical and psychological disorders (e.g., Ament et al., 2015; Glausiusz, 1997; Sullivan, 2008). In most of these cases, multiple gene defects appear to interact with environmental factors to produce the disorder. A detailed description of the research strategies involved in attempting to determine genetic influences in psychopathology, and the potential interpretations of the data derived from these studies, is provided in Chapter 4.

Psychosocial Theories

Case Notes

"Little Hans" was a five-year-old boy whose father brought him to the attention of Sigmund Freud (1905). The boy was so fearful of being bitten by a horse that he would not leave the house. The father told Freud that one day he and Hans had boarded a streetcar (pulled, in those days, by horses). At some point during the trip, the horses, frightened by a loud noise, reared up, pushing the streetcar backwards, and then bolted, dragging the careening car after them. When they finally stopped, the boy was very frightened and distressed, and his father took him home. Freud apparently analyzed this case without ever seeing Hans. He dismissed the experience with the bolting horses as a cause, considering the fear to have hidden, unconscious origins.

Many theorists have ignored, or relegated to a lesser role, the influence of biological processes on behaviour and thought. Psychodynamic theorists, like Freud, have suggested that behaviour is motivated by unconscious processes acquired during the formative years of life. In the Case Notes on previous page, Hans' phobia was seen as a symbol of underlying psychic conflict. Hans' apparent fear of being bitten by a horse, Freud said, was a symbolic representation of his dread of being castrated by his father. Freud cast the story in terms of his famous Oedipus complex (explained later in this chapter). Other theorists believe that behaviours are learned responses to environmental stimuli. This belief characterizes behavioural, cognitive-behavioural, and social learning theorists. For example, Little Hans' case has been seen as clear evidence of a behavioural or conditioning explanation for phobias. Strictly cognitive theorists claim that it is the way people think about or perceive their world that causes them to develop disorders. (No doubt they would argue that it was the way in which Little Hans viewed and remembered the experience that caused him to become fearful.) Humanists and existentialists suggest that personal experience provides the basis for the development of self-directed behaviour. Finally, socio-cultural theorists suggest that the surrounding society or culture exerts powerful influences on people; that such influences may cause a disorder to occur; and, moreover, that a particular society may define a person as abnormal because it suits the ends of that society. What all of these different theories have in common is that they stress experience.

PSYCHODYNAMIC THEORIES

Sigmund Freud (1856–1939), a Viennese neurologist, was the founder of the **psychodynamic** school of thought. Psychodynamic theories claim that unconscious forces of which the person is unaware control behaviour. In this sense, psychodynamic theories, like biological theories, see the person as having little control over his or her actions. However, psychodynamic theorists consider the origins of unconscious controls to reside in the individual's personal experience (albeit during the very early formative years).

Freud's analysis of a patient known as "Anna O" provided the insights he needed to develop his theory. Anna O had quite complex symptoms, including paralysis, deafness, and disturbances of vision, which apparently were psychologically induced rather than a result of physical damage. During hypnosis, Anna O revealed traumatic past experiences associated with deep emotional responses. Memories of these experiences were apparently repressed, since the patient could not recall them during her waking state, but after she had expressed them during hypnosis, Freud and his mentor, Josef Breuer (1842–1925), judged Anna O to have improved. This led Freud to conclude that traumatic experiences early in life become repressed (that is, inaccessible to awareness) because they are too distressing to contemplate. Freud further assumed that these repressed or unconscious memories influence current functioning.

Discharging the emotional responses attached to these unconscious memories, by identifying the original traumatic experiences during hypnosis, was called *catharsis* by Breuer and Freud, and they saw this as the effective element in treating such problems.

Interestingly, Anna O (whose real name was Bertha Pappenheim) continued to suffer from intermittent recurrence of her problems for some years after being discharged as effectively treated, and she subsequently became quite hostile toward what she called "the talking cure" (what Freud came to call *psychoanalysis*). Pappenheim finally recovered completely and became not only Germany's first social worker, but also a leading feminist. She would not allow any of the girls in the home she ran to be psychoanalyzed despite their often considerable problems.

In Freud's theory, four features together determine current behaviour and thinking, both normal and abnormal. The different levels of consciousness determine the accessibility of thoughts and desires; the structures of personality represent the embodiment of the various controlling forces; the stages of psychosexual development indicate the points in experience where problems can arise; and, finally, defence mechanisms are the means by which people channel their psychic energy in functional or dysfunctional ways.

LEVELS OF CONSCIOUSNESS Freud distinguished what he believed to be three levels of awareness:

- the **conscious**, which contains information of which we are currently aware;
- the **preconscious**, which holds information not presently within our awareness but that can readily be brought into awareness; and
- the **unconscious**, which, according to Freud, contains the majority of our memories and drives that, unfortunately, can only be raised to awareness with great difficulty and typically only in response to particular techniques (that is, by psychoanalytic procedures).

Sigmund Freud (1856–1939), founder of the psychoanalytic movement.

Hulton Deutsch/Corbis Historical/Getty Images

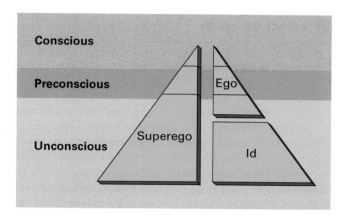

Conscious

Preconscious

Unconscious

Ego

Superego

Id

FIGURE 2.3 Levels of Awareness and Structures of Personality, According to Sigmund Freud

For Freud, the unconscious was the most important level of the mind. All of our biological drives, particularly sexual and aggressive drives, reside at this level, as do our traumatic memories. Freud thought that sexual and aggressive drives, which he considered to be instinctual, upset people so much that they could not face the fact that they had such urges. These unacceptable drives and the traumatic memories were kept out of awareness by what Freud called *defence mechanisms*.

STRUCTURES OF PERSONALITY According to Freud, three structures of personality (see Figure 2.3) are in constant conflict. Whether Freud really meant these to be understood as actual structures or as metaphors for different psychic forces is not altogether clear, but there is no doubt that he thought they represented the sources that determined personality.

The **id** is the structure present at birth and it contains, or represents, the biological or instinctual drives. These drives demand instant gratification without concern for the consequences either to the self or to others. In this sense, the id acts according to what Freud called the *pleasure principle*.

In the first year of life, the ego begins to develop. The **ego** develops to curb the desires of the id so that the individual does not suffer any unpleasant consequences. There is no concern here for what is right or wrong, but only for the avoidance of pain or discomfort and the maximization of unpunished pleasure. As the individual learns what expressions of desires are practical and possible, the ego comes to be governed by the *reality principle*. Early in life, then, there is a constant clash between the id and the ego, which is reduced over time so long as the ego develops normally.

As the child gets older, the **superego** begins to develop. The superego is the internalization of the moral standards of society inculcated by the child's parents. The operating guide of the superego is the *moral principle*, and it serves as the person's conscience by monitoring the ego. The ego, therefore, attempts to satisfy the id while not offending the principles of the superego. The more strongly developed the ego, the better able it is to handle these often opposing pressures.

PSYCHOSEXUAL STAGES OF DEVELOPMENT Freud thought that sexual drives were the most important determinants of behaviour, and that even the most innocent actions might be driven by sexual desires. Sexual drives were seen as the major life instinct, which Freud called *eros*, the energy for which was libido. Sexual pleasure, or the expression of libidinal energy, was focused on different body parts, which Freud called *erogenous zones*, and the focus of these zones differed at different stages of psychosexual development (see Table 2.1). Failure to resolve a stage would result in a fixation on the erogenous zone associated with that stage. For example, individuals fixated at the oral stage (that is, those who failed to have their oral desires fully satisfied) were thought to produce later behaviours that are either directly oral (for example, smoking, alcoholism, or overeating) or symbolically so (for example, constantly talking).

The **phallic stage** has received the greatest attention from psychoanalysts. In this stage, boys are presumed to develop sexual desires for their mother and to see their father as a competitor for their mother's love. This is described as the **Oedipal complex**, in reference to the character of Oedipus in the play by the Greek tragedian Sophocles. In Sophocles' play, Oedipus unwittingly kills his father and marries his mother, Jocasta. At the same time that a boy recognizes his father as a threat to the fulfillment of his desire for his mother, he also fears reprisal from his father. In Freud's view, the boy fears that his father will mutilate the boy's genitals to prevent any union with the mother. This fear is called *castration anxiety*—an odd choice of term, since castration denotes removal of the testicles, not the penis, and would not prevent intercourse. Because this fear is not consciously recognized, it can manifest itself as fear of something apparently unrelated, as in the case of Little Hans.

Similarly, girls are thought to desire their father—not to win their father's love, but rather, by seducing him, to gain what they truly desire: a penis. In girls, this desire for the father is called the **Electra complex**, again by analogy to a character who appears in several Greek tragedies (Electra, in fact, did not desire her father, but rather

TABLE 2.1 SUMMARY OF PSYCHOSEXUAL STAGES OF DEVELOPMENT

Stage	Duration	Manifestations
Oral	Birth–18 months	Focus on oral activities (for example, eating and sucking)
Anal	18 months–3 years	Toilet training—child may co-operate or resist by soiling or withholding
Phallic	3–6 years	Oedipal or Electra complex
Latency	6–12 years	Consolidation of behavioural skills and attitudes—relatively quiescent stage
Genital	Adolescence–death	Achievement of personal and sexual maturity

helped her brother, Orestes, to kill their mother, who had murdered their father).

DEFENCE MECHANISMS Remember that the function of the ego is to restrain the direct expression of the libidinal desires of the id. It does so by employing, at an unconscious level, a kind of censoring system. The ego uses **defence mechanisms** to allow the expression of libidinal desires in a distorted or symbolic form. The id, however, does its best to break through these defences, so that psychic energy is used up in this almost constant conflict between the ego and the id. The weaker the ego (that is, the less resolved the individual's psychosexual stages), the greater the conflict and, thereby, the greater the exhaustion of psychic energy. This exhaustion of psychic energy leads to a breakdown of psychological functioning, with the particular symptoms of this breakdown reflecting the unresolved stage of psychosexual development. Table 2.2 describes some of the more commonly identified defence mechanisms. Among clinicians, this aspect of Freud's theory has witnessed the greatest acceptance of any of his ideas.

TABLE 2.2   SOME TYPICAL DEFENCE MECHANISMS

Defence Mechanism	Description	Example
Repression	Burying in the unconscious the unacceptable impulses of the id	Inability to recall being sexually abused as a child
Regression	Employing behaviours typical of an earlier stage of development	Petulance or tantrums in response to frustration
Projection	Attributing one's own desires to others	Someone who cheats on an exam, or is tempted to cheat, claiming everyone cheats
Intellectualization	Hiding the real issues behind a screen of abstract analyses	A criminal appealing his conviction, despite admitting guilt, on the grounds of improper trial procedures
Denial	Refusal to acknowledge an unpleasant reality	A person, told she has two months to live, planning a holiday in a year's time
Displacement	The transfer of feelings from one person to another, less threatening person	A person humiliated by her employer directing her anger toward her spouse
Reaction formation	Repressing unacceptable desires by expressing the opposite viewpoint	A man who has strong sexual desires toward most women berating people who are promiscuous
Sublimation	Transformation of sexual or aggressive energy into some more acceptable activity	Freud thought that artists who painted nudes were sublimating their sexual desires

3 BEFORE MOVING ON

> Do you use defence mechanisms? How accurate do you think Freud was in his conceptualization of defence mechanisms?

Freud thought that sexual desires were often unwelcome to the ego or superego and, accordingly, were repressed or channelled into other activities. This repression, however, frequently led to problems for the person, although these problems would not be manifestly sexual and would be disguised from the person's own awareness by unconscious defences. When the ego was not strong enough to contain or rechannel the libidinal desires of the id, it was because one or another of the stages of psychosexual development had not been resolved satisfactorily, which would produce symptoms associated with that stage. By interpreting the symbolic nature of the symptoms, the psychoanalyst could focus on the particular period of the person's formative years (that is, the particular psychosexual stage) to reveal to the patient the origin of his or her problem. The patient's acceptance of the analyst's account of the origin of the problem was called *insight*, and it was expected that this would result in an alleviation of the problem.

FREUD'S INFLUENCE Freudian theory is largely speculative and has little empirical support. Attempts to test Freud's ideas experimentally have run into the problem that no matter what the results are, they can be explained within the theory. Yet some aspects of Freud's thinking have been valuable to psychology. He legitimized discussion and research on sexual matters, he encouraged a concern with processes beyond our awareness, and he recognized that the motives for human behaviour were not always the obvious ones. In short, no single psychological theorist has been more influential than Freud, even though psychoanalysis is much less popular today than it was in the early and middle parts of the twentieth century. Some of Freud's followers (e.g., Carl Jung, Alfred Adler, Melanie Klein) have developed or modified Freud's theories and treatment approach. These modified theories have enjoyed greater acceptance in recent years. Unlike Freud's original theory, these newer perspectives in psychodynamic thought generate testable hypotheses and have led to novel and apparently effective treatments.

BEHAVIOURAL THEORIES

CONDITIONING ACCOUNTS As noted in Chapter 1, behaviourism was first introduced as a perspective on human behaviour by John B. Watson. Early behaviourists such as Watson were environmentalists in that they assumed that all (or almost all) human behaviour, including abnormal behaviour, was learned. Watson (1913) took the view that **classical conditioning**, as described by the Russian physiologist Ivan Pavlov (1849–1936), was the basis for this learning. Pavlov demonstrated classical conditioning in his famous experiment with dogs (see Figure 2.4). Every time the dogs were

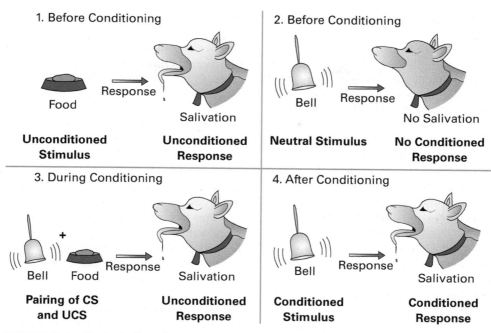

FIGURE 2.4 Pavlov's Experiment: The Process of Classical Conditioning

fed, a bell was rung. At first, the dogs salivated when they saw and smelled the meat. After a number of conditioning trials, they would salivate at the sound of the bell alone. To put it in Pavlov's terms, initially, a bell (that is, the conditioned stimulus, or CS) elicited an orienting response; that is, the dog looked toward the sound and listened. The meat (the unconditioned stimulus, or UCS) elicited an unconditioned response, salivation. Repeated pairings of the CS and UCS result in the CS eliciting some degree of salivation (the conditioned response, or CR). What is learned in classical conditioning, then, is the transfer of a response (that is, the UCR or its practical replication, the CR) from one stimulus (UCS) to another (CS). This process is called *stimulus–stimulus learning*.

Watson's most famous application of this type of analysis was to the acquisition of phobias: unrealistic fears of usually harmless things, such as cats or dogs. According to Watson, people with a phobia of dogs must have had a frightening experience with a dog at one time. The case of Little Hans' horse phobia, described at the beginning of this section, has been interpreted as an example of classical conditioning (Wolpe & Rachman, 1960). Prior to the frightening experience, a horse was a neutral stimulus (that is, a CS) in that it did not elicit fear. The bolting horses and careening streetcar represent the UCS, and automatically elicited a fear response (the UCR). Watson believed that an unconditioned response to pain or threat was inborn, and served, along with other similar inborn UCS–UCR connections, as the basis for all subsequently acquired responses (CRs). The frightening experience with the horses invoked the conditioning processes that would instill a fear response (CR) to the sight, or even the thought, of a horse (CS).

Watson and Rayner (1920) demonstrated that classical conditioning could instill a fear of a white rat in an 11-month-old boy identified as Little Albert. This boy was first shown a white rat, to which he displayed no fear; in fact, he appeared to enjoy trying to play with it. After several presentations like this to ensure that Little Albert was not fearful of the rat, Watson and Rayner followed the rat's appearance by making a sudden loud noise close behind the boy. This loud noise startled and upset Little Albert. After seven presentations of the rat (the CS) paired with the sudden loud noise (the UCS), Little Albert displayed a conditioned fear response to the rat. Watson and Rayner had indeed demonstrated that conditioning procedures could instill a phobic response to a harmless animal. On the basis of this single demonstration, Watson concluded that all phobias resulted from classical conditioning experiences. This, of course, was an overgeneralization.

4 BEFORE MOVING ON

> Ever since Phil was bitten by a dog at a young age he has been afraid of all dogs. Describe how classical conditioning could have played a role in the development of Phil's phobia of dogs.

However, this study has served as a model for demonstrating conditioning possibilities in humans, and was for a long time taken as the basis for a conditioning account of human fears. As we will see in Chapter 5, classical conditioning alone cannot explain many facets of phobias, most particularly their persistence. For instance, when the UCS is removed from classical conditioning studies, extinction (that is, the loss of response to the CS) occurs quite rapidly. In Pavlov's study, for example, withdrawal of the meat followed by repeated presentations of the bell causes the bell to cease eliciting salivation. Most people with phobias repeatedly encounter their phobic stimulus without any dreadful consequences occurring. Under these conditions (that is, the CS occurs repeatedly in the absence of the UCS), they should lose their fears (that is, CRs should cease to occur when the CS is presented). Yet, in fact, phobias display remarkable persistence.

Faced with this problem, Mowrer (1947) developed what came to be known as the **two-factor theory** of conditioning. He suggested that two types of learning take place in the acquisition and maintenance of phobias: (1) classical conditioning establishes the aversive response to a previously neutral stimulus (the CS), and (2) thereafter, the organism avoids the CS in order to prevent feeling afraid. Avoiding the CS, of course, effectively prevents extinction from occurring. This latter component of Mowrer's theory is derived from the work of Burrhus F. Skinner (1904–1990), who developed the ideas involved in **operant conditioning**. In Skinner's operant conditioning, the consequences of behaviour are important. All actions are followed by consequences of one kind or another. Some consequences encourage the repetition of the behaviour that produces them, whereas other consequences result in the opposite effect. When behaviour increases in frequency as a result of consistent consequences, **reinforcement** is said to occur; when a behaviour decreases in frequency as a result of its consequences, this is described as **punishment**. Some behaviours (for example, opening a refrigerator door) lead to pleasant consequences or rewards

(for example, eating ice cream), and the behaviour of going to the refrigerator increases; this is called *positive reinforcement*. Other behaviours (for example, taking an aspirin) result in a reduction of distress (that is, the headache goes away); this is called *negative reinforcement*. When a behaviour is reduced by the consequent occurrence of an unpleasant experience, it is called *positive punishment*, and when the behaviour is reduced following the removal of something desirable, *negative punishment* is said to have occurred. (Note that "positive" and "negative" are not used to mean good and bad; rather, positive refers simply to the presence of something and negative to the absence of something.) Table 2.3 summarizes these consequences and their effects.

Two-factor theory explains the persistence of phobias, in a way that simple classical conditioning cannot, by adding a negative reinforcement component to the process. Once a person has acquired a classically conditioned fear of a harmless stimulus, he or she begins to escape from the stimulus whenever it appears. Escape behaviour is negatively reinforced by the consequent reduction in fear, and the person soon learns that avoiding the stimulus altogether eliminates the distress. Thus, the person never experiences the CS (that is, phobic stimulus) in the absence of the UCS (for example, an attack by a dog), and therefore extinction cannot occur.

Burrhus F. Skinner (1904–1990) developed the ideas involved in operant conditioning.

TABLE 2.3 OPERANT CONDITIONING: CONSEQUENCES AND THEIR EFFECTS

Examples	Condition	Effects
Reinforcement		
(a) Rat presses lever and gets food	Positive	Lever pressing increases
(b) Child imitates mother's speech and mother smiles		Imitation increases
(a) Rat escapes from white side of box to black side and shock terminates	Negative	Escape behaviour increases
(b) Student quits seminar course and feels relief from speech anxiety		Avoidance of seminar courses increases
Punishment		
(a) Rat gets shocked for exploratory behaviour	Positive	Exploratory behaviour decreases
(b) Bully starts a fight and is badly beaten		Attempts to start fights decrease
(a) Food tray is removed when a pigeon pecks a red key	Negative	Pecking red key decreases
(b) Child is rude and is not allowed to have ice cream		Rudeness decreases

Various other elaborations on basic learning paradigms have been developed to explain a variety of pathological behaviours, and behaviour therapists have had significant successes in treating numerous problems with procedures derived from learning principles. Perhaps the most influential of these more recent learning-based approaches is **social learning theory**, which was initially developed in Canada by Albert Bandura and Richard Walters.

SOCIAL LEARNING THEORY As originally outlined by Bandura and Walters (1959), social learning theory suggested that, although classical and operant conditioning experiences are important, the majority of these experiences occur within a social context and are primarily acquired vicariously—that is, by observation of others rather than by direct personal experience. Accordingly, it was shown that children could learn to be aggressive by observing others being rewarded for aggression (Bandura, Ross, & Ross, 1961, 1963), or they could learn to be fearful by watching their phobic parents (Bandura & Menlove, 1968). Subsequently, this theory has been extended to include not only direct observation of others but also information derived from books, movies, and television.

Because Bandura's theory (1976) emphasized the importance of cognitive processes, such as perceiving the behaviour of others and storing such information in memory, it gave rise to the notion that other mediational processes play a part in learning. The idea underlying mediation is that a simple stimulus-response model does not account for the acquisition of all human behaviour. Rather, a number of individual characteristics (expectations, abilities, appraisals, feelings, and so on) appear to influence different responses to stimuli. The loss of a job, for example, does not invariably trigger depression; an individual's appraisal of the situation also contributes to his or her feelings and responses. Some individuals might view this unemployment with excitement as they see it as a new opportunity to do something different. Others might be relieved because they have detested the work that they do. Still others may be saddened because they believe that their sense of achievement is an important defining feature of self. Eventually, this idea of mediation led to the development of what became known as cognitive-behavioural theory (Dozois, Dobson & Rnic, in press).

Cognitive-behavioural theory reflects the view that both thinking and behaviour are learned and, therefore, can be changed. This approach assumes that the way in which people view the world, including their beliefs and attitudes toward the world, themselves, and others, arises out of their experience and that these patterns of thinking and perceiving are maintained by consequences in the same way that overt behaviour is maintained.

COGNITIVE THEORIES

There are many clinically oriented cognitive theories, all of which share three principles: (1) thinking affects emotion and behaviour, (2) thoughts can be monitored and changed, and (3) by altering one's thoughts, a person will experience desired behavioural and emotional change (Dozois et al., in press).

Two pre-eminent cognitive theorists have offered accounts of the etiology and treatment of abnormal behaviours: Albert Ellis and Aaron Beck.

RATIONAL-EMOTIVE BEHAVIOUR THERAPY Albert Ellis developed **rational-emotive behaviour therapy** more than four decades ago (Ellis, 1962, 2004). Ellis (1962) has argued that, when faced with unfavourable life circumstances, human beings tend to make themselves feel frustrated, disappointed, and miserable; and behave in self-defeating ways, mainly because they construct irrational beliefs about themselves and their situations. Ellis (1999) argued that adaptive feelings and behaviours stem from rational and functional thoughts. At the crux of this conceptualization is the ABC model of human disturbance, which states that the consequences (C) of life events (e.g., symptomatology, negative affect) are not contingent upon the activating event (A) per se, but are mediated by one's beliefs (B) about these experiences (Ellis & Ellis, 2014).

Ellis (1991) identified a number of distinctive irrational beliefs that may contribute to emotional disturbance (e.g., things must always go right; I must be loved and have approval at all times). These beliefs are considered maladaptive because they are expressed in absolutist terms and held on to rigidly as needs, demands, and evaluative statements rather than as more flexible preferences, wishes, or desires (Bishop & Fleming, 2015; Dryden 2012, 2013).

Since his original proposal (Ellis, 1962), Ellis has made some modifications to his theory. For example, he now acknowledges that it is not simply the irrational propositions (e.g., words, phrases) that people use that contribute to feelings of dysphoria and negative affect, but the "basic meaning" and "core philosophy" that underlie each of these statements that are the prime denigrator of their sense of self-worth (Ellis, 1999).

COGNITIVE THEORY AND THERAPY Aaron Beck's cognitive model (Beck, 1963; Beck & Dozois, 2011, 2014; Beck, Rush, Shaw, & Emery, 1979; Clark, Beck, & Alford, 1999; Dozois & Beck, 2012) states that emotions and behaviours are heavily influenced by individual perceptions or cognitive appraisals of events. Three main levels of cognition are emphasized in this theory: (1) schemas; (2) information processing and intermediate beliefs (including dysfunctional rules, assumptions, and attitudes); and (3) automatic thoughts (Beck & Dozois, 2014; Dozois & Beck, 2008; Dozois, Frewen, & Covin, 2006).

Schemas refer to internal representations of stored information and experiences. Schemas are used to organize new information in a meaningful way and help to determine how we perceive and understand what goes on around us (Clark & Beck, 1999). Many of the core beliefs that are indicative of psychopathology (e.g., "I am incompetent," "I am bad," "I am unlovable," "I am defective") stem from an individual's self-schema. Young (1999) described a set of core beliefs, which he has labelled Early Maladaptive Schemas (EMS), that originate from repetitious, aversive experiences

TABLE 2.4 EARLY MALADAPTIVE SCHEMAS

1. Disconnection and rejection
   a. Emotional deprivation
   b. Mistrust/abuse
   c. Emotional inhibition
   d. Defectiveness/shame
   e. Social isolation/alienation
2. Impaired autonomy and performance
   a. Dependence/incompetence
   b. Abandonment/Instability
   c. Vulnerability to harm or illness
   d. Enmeshment/undeveloped self
   e. Failure
   f. Subjugation/Invalidation
3. Impaired limits
   a. Entitlement/grandiosity
   b. Insufficient self-control/self-discipline
4. Excessive Responsibility and Standards
   a. Self-sacrifice
   b. Unrelenting Standards/Hypercriticalness
5. Unclassified Schemas
   a. Approval seeking/recognition seeking
   b. Negativity/Pessimism
   c. Punitiveness

Source: Updated by the first author from the original source: Young, J. E., Klosko, J. S., & Weishaar, M. E. (2003). Schema therapy: Conceptual model. In *Schema therapy: A practitioner's guide* (p. 7). New York: Guilford Press. ©2017 Jeffrey Young, Ph.D.

in childhood. These EMSs are broad, pervasive themes or patterns that are composed of memories, emotions, cognitions, and bodily sensations regarding the self and one's relationships with others (Young, Klosko, & Weishaar, 2003). EMS act as a priori truths and influence how an individual processes later experiences, and thinks, acts, feels, and relates to others throughout life. The five sets of EMS and their constituents are listed in Table 2.4.

According to Beck, the development and organization of a maladaptive self-schema occurs during early childhood, but the schema does not become active until it is triggered by negative life events. For example, an individual who is vulnerable to depression may fundamentally believe that he or she is worthless and unlovable. This belief, however, may not affect this individual until he or she experiences rejection from a peer or partner. Once this belief is active in an individual's mind, he or she may start to selectively attend to and recall information that is consistent with this negative view of self. For instance, this person might start to pay attention to cues that are suggestive of unlovability and disqualify information that does not fit that expectation and belief. For example, Hailey's core belief that close others are inconsistent and may abandon her caused her to doubt the reassurance that her boyfriend provided. Different types of beliefs are considered to be related to different kinds of abnormal behaviour—what Beck referred to as **content-specificity** (Beck & Dozois, 2014; Dozois & Beck, 2008, 2012). Individuals who are depressed are theorized to have negative automatic thoughts that focus on themes of personal loss, deprivation, and failure (Beck et al., 1979). Anxiety tends to be related to thoughts about the world

being dangerous, the future uncertain, and the self inadequate (Beck & Emery, 1985). Paranoia is associated with cognitions that people cannot be trusted and that others are malevolent, abusive, and deceitful, whereas excessive dependency is related to a view of self as weak, helpless, and incompetent (Beck & Dozois, 2014).

Information processing biases and intermediate beliefs compose the next level of cognition (Clark et al., 1999; Ingram, Miranda, & Segal, 1998). These biases often take the form of selective attention or enhanced memory for information that is schema-consistent. For example, compared to individuals with low levels of anxiety, those with high levels of anxiety have been shown to pay more attention to threatening stimuli (Dudeney, Sharpe, & Hunt, 2015), although the relation between attentional biases and anxiety is likely bidirectional (Van Bockstaele et al., 2014). In addition, there is some evidence to suggest that such attention biases in anxiety disorders are disorder specific (Pergamin-Hight, Naim, Bakermans-Kranenburg, Ijzendoorn, & Bar-Haim, 2015). Individuals with anxiety also appear to negatively interpret ambiguous stimuli (Cabrera, Montorio, & MacLeod, in press), and to show enhanced memory for stimuli related to their fears (Ashbaugh & Radomsky, 2009, 2011). This pattern of information processing is consistent with an anxious individual's schema, in that he or she tends to view the world as dangerous and the self as vulnerable.

Information processing biases are also represented as "if–then" statements and inaccurate causal attributions. For example, a person may engage in "all-or-nothing thinking" in which he or she evaluates personal qualities or situations

Dr. Aaron T. Beck, the founder of cognitive therapy.

in absolutist terms (e.g., an "A" student receiving a lower-than-expected grade may regard him- or herself as a complete failure). Recent research has demonstrated that these types of "cognitive errors" are associated with anxious and depressive symptoms in children and adolescents (Schwartz & Maric, 2015;Weems, Costa, Watts, Taylor, & Cannon, 2007), and are found at elevated rates in individuals who have recently attempted suicide, compared to other psychiatric controls (Jager-Hyman et al., 2014). Further research suggests that these negative cognitive errors tend to improve in individuals who respond to cognitive therapy for depression (Blake, Dobson, Sheptycki & Drapeau, 2016).

Finally, *automatic thoughts* refer to the frequent thoughts that pop into our minds and that are not accompanied by conscious appraisal. An analogy is that of learning how to drive a car. When an individual first learns to drive, he or she is acutely aware of how much pressure is being placed on the gas or the brakes, whether the radio is on or off, whether the window is open or closed, and what is happening on the other side of the windshield. Every skill involved in driving becomes a conscious and sometimes frightening task for the young driver. As people become more adept at driving, however, these skills become easier to carry out and the processes become increasingly automated such that individuals are able to sing along to music, carry on a conversation, and enjoy the landscape as they perform the multiple tasks involved with manipulating their vehicle. Every day, each of us experiences hundreds of automatic thoughts, but people who experience psychopathology have a greater number of negative and threat-related automatic thoughts.

Automatic thoughts are considered to be cognitive by-products because they stem directly from an individual's core beliefs, or schemas, in interaction with the environment. For example, an individual who is passed in the corridor at work without a colleague's salutation may have the automatic thought "She doesn't like me," perhaps stemming from a core belief of being unlovable or undesirable. Similarly, someone with a self-schema focused on incompetence may have the thought "I will never be able to do this" when faced with a novel task.

Cognition is the primary focus of Beck's theory; however, the model does not simply state that cognitions *cause* emotions and behaviours. Instead, it is acknowledged that these variables are interrelated and that many other factors (e.g., biological predispositions) are involved (Alford & Beck, 1997; Beck & Dozois, 2011).

Consistent with the major tenets of this cognitive theory of psychological functioning, cognitive therapy aims to help clients shift from unhealthy appraisals to more realistic and adaptive ones. Treatment is highly collaborative and involves designing specific learning experiences to teach clients how to monitor automatic thoughts; understand the relationships among cognition, affect, and behaviour; examine the validity of automatic thoughts; develop more realistic and adaptive cognitions; and alter underlying beliefs, assumptions, and schemas (Dozois et al., 2006). The primary assumptions of Beck's theory have been well supported by the research

literature (Beck & Dozois, 2011; Dozois & Beck, 2008, 2012). As we will see in later chapters, cognitive therapy has also enjoyed success in the treatment of many disorders, most particularly anxiety and mood disorders.

⑤ BEFORE MOVING ON

In what ways do you think your early childhood experiences have influenced your schemas? How do your schemas influence your thoughts, beliefs, information processing, and behaviour?

NEWER (THIRD WAVE) APPROACHES TO CBT

Over the past few decades, research has focused on the investigation of mindfulness as a form of clinical intervention. Mindfulness is defined as the awareness that arises through "paying attention in a particular way: on purpose, in the present moment, and nonjudgmental" (Kabat-Zinn, 1994, p. 4). The components of mindfulness, particularly awareness and acceptance of one's experiences in the moment, have been shown to be effective against worry, fear, anxiety, anger, and other forms of psychological distress (for a review, see Keng, Smoski, & Robins, 2011). There are four major forms of mindfulness-based interventions: Mindfulness-Based Stress Reduction (MBSR), Mindfulness-Based Cognitive Therapy (MBCT), Dialectical Behaviour Therapy (DBT), and Acceptance and Commitment Therapy (ACT). A growing body of research supports the effectiveness of these mindfulness-based interventions in treating a number of disorders, including depression, substance abuse, borderline personality disorder, anxiety disorders (Keng et al., 2011), binge-eating (Katterman, Kleinman, Hood, Nackers, & Corsica, 2014), and for reducing stress in nonclinical populations (Sharma & Rush, 2014). Mindfulness-based interventions have a positive impact on an individual's psychological health through various mechanisms. Changes in cognitive and emotional reactivity are viewed as some of the strongest mechanisms underlying mindfulness-based interventions (Gu, Strauss, Bond, & Cavanagh, 2015). For example, mindfulness training causes individuals to view their thoughts and emotions as passing mental events rather than identifying with them or believing thoughts to be an accurate representation of reality (Segal, Williams, & Teasdale, 2013; Semple, Lee, & Miller, 2014). Furthermore, as a result of attending to all experiences in a nonjudgmental manner, mindfulness training desensitizes individuals such that distressing situations that may otherwise have been avoided, along with accompanying thoughts and emotions, become less distressing (Carmody, Baer, Lykins, & Olendzki, 2009).

HUMANISTIC AND EXISTENTIAL THEORIES

Humanistic and existential theories can be considered to be variants on the phenomenological approach to understanding human behaviour. Phenomenology as a philosophical position had many antecedents, but Edmund Husserl (1859–1938) is generally considered the first to clearly formulate this viewpoint. Husserl's account was subsequently elaborated by French philosopher Maurice Merleau-Ponty (1908–1961). According to this view, it is through experience that people form their sense of themselves and of the world. However, experience is not the objective observation of external events, but rather the accumulation of perceptions of the world. The way in which an individual perceives the world is a product of the personal experiences that have produced his or her sense of self. This sense of self guides, and is formed by, the person's perception of his or her experiences. Life is said to involve a continuous synthesis of experience that progressively refines our sense of self and develops our values. This sense of self, along with our values and our accumulated experience, provides the basis for our choices of action. Behaviour is not determined by experience alone, since experience simply provides the basis for choice. These choices represent the expression of our free will.

From this perspective of human experience, phenomenologists developed theories about all manner of psychological functioning, including, of course, perception, but also the development of human values Most importantly, phenomenologists generated accounts of personal development.

HUMANISTIC VIEWS The two most eminent advocates of humanistic psychology were Carl Rogers (1902–1987) and Abraham Maslow (1908–1970). Both individuals emphasized the dignity and potential of humans and saw experience (as perceived by the individual) as providing the basis for improving oneself. Rogers's position has been called a *person-centred* theory of personality because he considered the person to be of central importance in understanding behaviour. According to Rogers, self-fulfillment is achieved by accepting oneself, being honest in all interactions, trusting experience (which he said is the highest authority), and relying on oneself for personal evaluations. People who can do so will be able to accept others for who they are, thus encouraging both themselves and others to be more honest, and such honesty will help accumulate experiences that will lead them to realize their potential.

According to Rogers (1961), distressing life events (or the perception of events as distressing) distort a person's perception of his or her subsequent experiences. These distressing life events and resulting distortions are thought to result in an inability to trust experiences. Such lack of trust causes an individual to view him- or herself in a distorted way, thereby causing abnormal behaviour. These distorted perceptions impact future choices and cause behaviours that are detrimental to personal development, further entrench the distorted views of self and experience, and perpetuate dysfunctional behaviour.

Maslow (1954) essentially believed that people are good and that they behave dysfunctionally or nastily only as a result of experience (or their interpretation of it) that has diverted them from the path of **self-actualization**. He described a hierarchy of needs that, when fully satisfied, result in the actualization of the person's potential. It is toward this realization

FIGURE 2.5   Maslow's Hierarchy of Needs

Source: Maslow, Abraham H.; Frager, Robert D.; Fadiman, James, *Motivation and Personality*, 3rd ed., ©1987. Reprinted and Electronically reproduced by permission of Pearson Education, Inc., New York, NY.

of personal potential that all persons should strive. Maslow's hierarchy of needs can be visualized as a pyramid (see Figure 2.5). At the base of the pyramid are biological or survival needs, including food, water, and shelter; safety occupies the next level. Unless these are met, the person will not survive, and if they are unsatisfactorily met, the person will not be able to move up the hierarchy toward self-actualization. The need to belong represents the next step up in the hierarchy and refers to needs for friendship and affiliation. When these are met, the individual seeks an assurance of self-worth, which comes from giving and receiving love and from an internalized sense of self-esteem derived from experience. From this base of self-confidence, self-actualization becomes possible. In Maslow's view, abnormal or dysfunctional behaviour results from a failure to attain the self-esteem necessary to achieve self-actualization.

Both of these humanists have an optimistic view of people and consider human behaviour to result from personal decisions and perceptions of their experience and of themselves. Thus, they hold the individual to be responsible, rather than forces beyond the individual's control (for example, biological determinants, unconscious processes, or actual external events). Obviously, then, if dysfunctional behaviour is derived from people's view of themselves and their experiences, they can be helped to change their perspective and, thereby, overcome their problems.

EXISTENTIAL VIEWS Existentialists see the individual's awareness of his or her own existence as a critical feature of human functioning. This awareness brings with it the realization that we could, and obviously eventually will, cease to exist. However, it is not just the possibility of death that existentialists consider to be a threat, but also the loss of direction and meaning in our lives. Existentialists also stress our responsibility for our choices and, therefore, for our actions. We make free choices and must necessarily take responsibility for them.

Abraham Maslow (1908–1970), who developed the theory of self-actualization.

According to the existentialist point of view, this awareness of the possibility of nonbeing (whether death or the emptiness of no meaning) and the acceptance of responsibility for our actions makes us anxious. It is this existential *angst* (a German word that means something more than the English "anxiety" and conveys a sense of more severe distress) that causes people problems, so life becomes a search for meaning. Making the effort to seek meaning is said to reflect the "courage to be" (Tillich, 1952), whereas the alternative is to give up the struggle and become full of despair. This is a somewhat gloomier view of the human condition than the humanistic view, since the struggle to "be" is very difficult and few actually display the necessary courage. However, like humanistic psychology, existentialism sees the individual as responsible and as potentially capable of dealing effectively with life.

The leading exponents of the existential view, as applied to human problem behaviour, have been Rollo May (1961) and Viktor Frankl (1962). Both of these theorists see the struggle to find meaning in our lives and our acceptance of responsibility for our choices as critical in understanding human behaviour. Treatment, therefore, is directed at confronting clients with their responsibility for their actions and assisting them in finding meaning in their lives. Until recently, very little research has evaluated either this interesting approach or the humanistic approach to understanding and treating human problems.

SOCIO-CULTURAL INFLUENCES

Various theorists and researchers have considered the role that society or close others (e.g., friends, parents, partners) play in the etiology and maintenance of mental health disorders.

STIGMA Stigma surrounding mental health issues plays an important role in the maintenance of a number of mental health disorders, since it is one of the largest barriers to individuals seeking treatment (Clement et al., 2015; Corrigan, Druss, & Perlick, 2014; Lally, O'conghaile, Quigley, Bainbridge, & McDonald, 2013). Despite the fact that one in five Canadians will experience a mental health problem or illness in a given year (Smetanin et al., 2011), about one-third of those with a mental health care need report that their need was unmet or only partially met (Sunderland & Findlay, 2013). Differences between a person's preferred way of viewing the self and negative stereotypes about mental illness (e.g., that mental illness means you're "crazy" or weak) cause one to anticipate negative consequences of disclosing their symptoms (e.g., being labelled, having a record, experiencing stigma and shame). Consequently, people avoid disclosing their mental health concerns and are deterred from seeking help (Clement et al., 2015).

Research has distinguished between two main types of stigma (Corrigan, 2004): **public stigma** refers to the "perception held by a group or society . . . that a person who seeks psychological treatment is undesirable or socially unacceptable" whereas **self-stigma** is the "reduction of an individual's self-esteem or self-worth caused by the individual self-labeling herself or himself as someone who is socially unacceptable" (Vogel, Wade, & Haake, 2006, p. 325). Research supports the contention that the internalization of public stigma can lead to self-stigma (Vogel, Bitman, Hammer & Wade, 2013), and that self-stigma leads individuals to have negative attitudes towards help-seeking (Bathje & Pryor, 2011).

The importance of reducing mental health stigma and increasing the use of mental health services in Canada is beginning to be realized. A number of anti-stigma campaigns have recently been launched throughout the country (see the Applied Clinical Case on page 44). These anti-stigma interventions appear to yield short-term positive changes in attitudes, and to a lesser extent, improve knowledge regarding mental illness (Thornicroft et al., 2016). Further, interventions that involve social contact with an afflicted individual are the most effective in terms of improving stigma-related attitudes and knowledge. If you are interested in reading more about initiatives and projects being run throughout Canada, visit the Mental Health Commission of Canada website at *www.mentalhealthcomission.ca*.

6 **BEFORE MOVING ON**

What are some of the ways in which each of us can work to reduce mental health stigmas?

SOCIAL SUPPORT There is clear evidence that **social support** from close others is a significant factor in preventing or reducing the intensity of psychological problems, and that the absence of such support is a factor in the causal chain leading to dysfunction (Cohen & Wills, 1985; Marver et al., in press).

Bettmann/Getty Images

An Olympian Speaks out about Mental Health

A six-time Olympic games medal winner, and the only person to have won multiple medals in both the Summer and Winter Olympics, Canadian athlete Clara Hughes is a success story and a role model to many. In 2010, Clara publicly revealed her longstanding struggle with depression. Clara engaged in early alcohol and drug use to escape a difficult home life as an adolescent, but when she witnessed Gaeten Boucher win in speed skating at the 1988 Winter Olympics, Clara was inspired to pursue sports. However, after the elation of winning two bronze medals at the 1996 Olympics, Clara gradually began to feel lonely and exhausted, and experienced crying spells and feelings of self-loathing and worthlessness, regardless of her many wins she achieved. At the time, Clara reportedly knew something was wrong, but was unsure of what it was and felt that she needed to fix herself alone. She began to gain weight, sleep for most of the day, and lost motivation to train, leaving her feeling guilty. It was not until the following year that a national team doctor at a training camp suggested to Clara that she may be suffering from depression and that help was available. After deciding she just needed to train harder, Clara discovered that she could not focus, and sustained an injury from overtraining. Eventually, she began to take steps to better care for herself, became involved in a larger set of activities, and sought therapy. Today, Clara is the national spokesperson for the Bell

Canada Let's Talk campaign in support of mental health services and reducing stigma around mental health. She is a recipient of the Order of Manitoba and the Order of Canada for her success in sports and her humanitarian work. Clara's story underscores that an individual with a mental illness is so much more than his or her diagnosis; he or she can be an athlete, a caring partner, a charismatic speaker, and so much more. Clara's story also tells us that anyone can experience depression or other mental disorders, even when they are excelling, and that there is no shame in struggling with mental health.

For example, lack of social support has been associated with longer recovery times in individuals with depression (Fuller-Thomson, Battiston, Gadalla, & Brennenstuhl, 2014) and with suicidal ideation (Handley et al., 2012). Conversely, individuals who experience higher levels of perceived social support following disclosure of past childhood abuse report better mental health (Lueger-Schuster et al., 2015), and perceived support is a protective factor for common mental illnesses (Charavustra & Cloitre, 2008; Smyth, Siriwardhana, Hotopf, & Hatch, 2015).

Increasingly, research is examining the influence of social media on perceived social support and mental well-being. In a recent study, Cole, Nick, Zelkowitz, Roeder, and Spinelli (2017) surveyed undergraduate students regarding their self-esteem, depressive symptoms, and in-person and online social support (e.g., "How often does someone say something nice to you online?") and victimization (e.g., "How many people have posted something online just to hurt you?"). This research yielded three major findings: (1) social media served as a unique form of social support for individuals with low levels of in-person social support. Conversely, for individuals who already had high levels of in-person social support, the support provided by social media was largely redundant; (2) online social support and in-person social support were each uniquely negatively associated with depressive thoughts, suggesting that each has incremental

utility over and above the other. Importantly, these correlations were larger for in-person social support compared to online, which suggests that in-person support may be a more influential form of support; and, (3) the benefits attained from online and in-person social support outweigh some of the negative influences of peer victimization. With these findings, the researchers concluded that the strategic use of social media in addition to in-person social relations can be beneficial in improving social support systems.

Finally, more recent research has examined the detrimental effects that loneliness can have on one's well-being. A meta-analytical study found that social isolation, loneliness, and living alone result in increases in the likelihood of mortality by 29%, 26%, and 32%, respectively (Holt-Lunstad, Smith, Baker, Harris, & Stephenson, 2015). These results were obtained even when controlling for initial health status and other factors. The researchers concluded that "the risk associated with social isolation and loneliness is comparable with well-established risk factors for mortality" (p. 235), including but not limited to physical activity, obesity, mental health, immunization, and access to health care. Clearly, social connection plays an important role in maintaining our overall health.

GENDER The influence of societies' stereotypes and people's consequent reaction to specific groups also seems to play a role in the development of disorders, as do poverty and social class. There are very obvious differences in male and female rates for several disorders (e.g., Slaunwhite, 2015), and it may be that gender-specific socialization processes render males and females differentially likely to acquire one or another disorder. For example, eating disorders such as anorexia nervosa and bulimia nervosa are more common in females, with an approximately 10:1 female-to-male ratio (American Psychiatric Association, 2013). In Western cultures, including Canada and the United States, internalization of the ideal of thinness (that female beauty is synonymous with a lean body), and media exposure have been shown to predict increases in body dissatisfaction, dieting, and symptoms of bulimia in females (Culbert, Racine, & Klump, 2015). These sociocultural factors are hypothesized to account for the gender differences in rates of eating disorders, although empirical examinations of this hypothesis are limited (Culbert et al., 2015).

In addition, Canadian psychologists Pantony and Caplan (1991) point out that certain personality disorders appear to reflect exaggerated features of either female or male stereotyped behaviours. For example, dependent personality disorder is characterized by dependency and submissiveness, whereas antisocial personality disorder involves aggressiveness and self-interest. Very few men are diagnosed with dependent personality disorder and very few women are considered to have antisocial personality disorder. This sharp difference may be due to biases in the diagnostic criteria or clinicians' gender-related expectations (see Millon, Grossman, Millon, Meagher, & Ramnath, 2004). There is also evidence that expectations parents have regarding sex-appropriate behaviour (e.g., aggressiveness in males, passivity in females) can influence whether parents refer their child for treatment of "abnormal" behaviour (Oakley, 2015). Clearly, gender roles have an influence on the identification of disorders, but it is not clear yet exactly what form this influence takes.

7 BEFORE MOVING ON

> To what extent do you think altering gender stereotypes might change the prevalence rates of mental health problems for males and females?

RACE AND POVERTY Race and poverty have also been linked to the prevalence of psychiatric disorders. However, because ethnic minorities tend to be concentrated in poorer areas, it is difficult to disentangle these two influences. Members of ethnic minorities are the victims of various forms of prejudice that exclude them from many opportunities available to the dominant group (for example, consider President Trump's 2017 attempted travel ban targeting refugees from six Muslim-majority countries preventing them from entering the United States). These prejudices, and lack of opportunities, create stress in the lives of minorities in the same way that poverty does. When minority ethnicity and poverty go together, as they so often do, we can expect a number of psychological and social problems.

Poverty is a significant risk factor for mental disorders (Lepiece, Reynaert, Jacques, & Zdanowicz, 2015; Lund et al., 2010; Wang, Schmitz, & Dewa, 2010). Children and adolescents from socio-economically disadvantaged families are two to three times more likely to develop a mental health problem (Reiss, 2013). The poverty dimensions of education, food insecurity, housing, social class, socio-economic status, and financial stress demonstrate the strongest and most consistent associations with a variety of mental illnesses (Lund et al., 2010). These findings may reflect similar effects noted for racial prejudice. The resentment at being poor, in an otherwise reasonably wealthy society, may generate behaviours that are viewed by others as antisocial or dysfunctional. Of course, it may be that because being poor produces such high levels of stress (Haushofer & Fehr, 2014), higher rates of psychological dysfunction are to be expected. However, it might also be that dysfunctional people gravitate to the lower end of the socio-economic spectrum. Finally, it may be that professionals from the privileged classes are more apt to apply denigrating diagnoses (for example, antisocial personality disorder or schizophrenia) to patients from the lower classes, while reserving more acceptable diagnoses (for example, chronic fatigue syndrome) for the upper classes.

Integrative Theories

Throughout this text, we will see evidence for the influence of various biological factors in the onset of many psychological disorders. Environmental influences (psychological as well as socio-cultural) have an important role to play. In fact, it is only through the interaction of all of these various influences that disorders emerge. Three models have been proposed that attempt to integrate these diverse influences.

SYSTEMS THEORY

Systems theory proposes that the whole is more than the sum of its parts, whereas reductionism says that the whole is the sum of its parts. A systems theory approach has had profound influences on many areas of science, including biology, engineering, and computer science (Davidson, 1982). This view of the way things behave sees causation as the combined effect of multiple factors that are likely to be bidirectional. For example, persistent misbehaviour of a child appears to influence parental behaviour such that the parents' actions worsen the child's behaviour (Paschall & Mastergeorge, 2016). This is an example of bidirectional causation unlike the unidirectional causation so dear to the hearts of reductionists.

Not only does systems theory suggest that causation is the result of multiple factors interacting, and that causation is a bidirectional process, it also points out that the same end result can arise from one of many possible causes. In medicine it is clear that the same disease can have different causes in different people. As will be shown in Chapter 7, heart disease can result from stress, a particular behavioural style, smoking, poor diet, lack of exercise, and constitutional factors. Systems theory, therefore, would seem to have something significant to offer theorists and researchers who study abnormal human behaviour.

THE DIATHESIS-STRESS PERSPECTIVE

According to the **diathesis-stress perspective**, a predisposition to developing a disorder (the diathesis) interacting with the experience of stress causes mental disorders. According to this view, this interaction underlies the onset of all disorders, although either the predisposition or the stress may be more important in a particular disorder, or in a particular person.

Note that this perspective cannot be categorized as either a biological or a psychological model. A diathesis may be either biological or psychological—as may a stressor. One example of a biological diathesis is the role played by genetics in schizophrenia, mood disorders, and alcoholism. Dysfunctions of the central or peripheral nervous system or of the endocrine system may have a genetic basis or may be caused by events such as problems during gestation or birth, but in either case would be seen as a biological diathesis.

Psychological diatheses may arise as a result of temperament, childhood abuse, inappropriate parenting, or social and cultural pressures. For example, a readiness to acquire dissociative identity disorder appears to come from childhood sexual abuse. A series of unpredictable and unpleasant events may produce a sense of resignation that predisposes a person to depression (Dozois, Dobson, & Westra, 2004). Socio-cultural standards of an attractive body shape seem to create a diathesis for eating disorders (Culbert et al., 2015).

However, a predisposition will not produce a disorder without the trigger of some stress, whether biological (such as physical illness), psychological (such as breakdown of a relationship), or social (such as perceived pressure from others to meet certain standards). In the case of Hailey, described at the beginning of the chapter, her high reactivity to stress, along with the fact that depression runs in her family, could be considered the diathesis; her breakup with her boyfriend was likely the stressor that triggered her disorder.

The advantage of this perspective is that it encourages us to look at a range of possible influences rather than fixing our attention on a single factor. This perspective also allows the possibility that different individuals may develop disorders through the influence of different diatheses and different stressors.

THE BIOPSYCHOSOCIAL MODEL

Like the diathesis-stress perspective, the **biopsychosocial model** declares that disorders cannot be understood as resulting from the influence of one factor, be it biological, psychological, or social. Each of these factors must be taken into account, again with differing emphases depending on the disorder in question.

Several lines of research indicate the importance of the interaction among multiple biological and environmental processes for human functioning (Price & Zwolinski, 2010). For example, Plomin and Neiderhiser (1992) have integrated research findings to strongly suggest that genetics and environment interact to determine human behaviour, although these findings require replication (Plomin, DeFries, Knopik, & Neiderhiser, 2016). In addition, brain functions have been shown both to influence and to be influenced by psychological and social processes; the relationship is reciprocal (Cacioppo & Berntson, 1992).

There is increased recognition of the need to integrate existing models to provide a more comprehensive understanding of abnormality. Such integration often requires interdisciplinary research and a general openness to relating concepts from diverse theoretical perspectives. In recent years, such integration has become more commonplace. For example, research by Elizabeth Hayden, currently at the University of Western Ontario, and her colleagues has investigated the relationships between genotype, personality, cognition, and behaviour in childhood vulnerability to mood and anxiety disorders (Hayden, Dougherty, Maloney, Durbin et al., 2008; Hayden, Dougherty, Maloney, Olino et al., 2008; Hayden et al., 2010a, 2010b; Hayden et al., 2013). Attachment theory has also been integrated with cognitive models (Ingram, Atchley, & Segal, 2011). Another related shift that has occurred over the years has been the movement away from conceptualizing psychopathology as "within the individual" to examining contextual factors that operate "outside of the individual" (Mash & Dozois, 2003).

SUMMARY

- There has been a consistent move toward viewing the etiology of mental health problems from an integrative perspective.
- Biological, psychological, and socio-cultural factors interact in complex ways to produce psychiatric disorders.
- Single-factor theories are unlikely to explain the etiology of any disorder, and are gradually falling into disuse.

- Theories gain strength not because the evidence supports their predictions but rather because alternative explanations are rejected.
- Biological views propose that brain dysfunction, neurotransmitters, hormonal or peripheral nervous system problems, or genetic errors cause psychological problems.
- Neurotransmitters are chemical substances that carry messages from one neuron to the next. Disturbances in

neurotransmitter systems can often result in abnormal behaviour.

- Recent research emphasizes the importance of the genotype–environment interaction, which describes how features that are inherited interact with the environment to produce behaviour.

- Freud and other psychodynamic theorists suggested that behaviour is controlled by unconscious forces.

- Freud discussed three levels of consciousness that determine the accessibility of thoughts and desires: the conscious, which contains information of which we are currently aware; the preconscious, which holds information that is not presently in awareness but can be brought into awareness; and the unconscious, which contains the majority of an individual's memories and drives that can be raised into awareness only with difficulty or particular techniques.

- The three personality structures of psychodynamic theories include the id, which represents biological or instinctual drives; the ego, which develops to control the desires of the id; and the superego, which is the internalization of the moral standards of society.

- The ego develops defence mechanisms in an attempt to control the desires of the id.

- Freud also described stages of psychosexual development, which indicate points in experience where problems can arise.

- Behavioural theorists argue that all or almost all human behaviour, including abnormal behaviour, is learned.

- In classical conditioning, a neutral stimulus (the CS) comes to elicit a conditioned response (CR) through its being paired with another stimulus (UCS) that already elicits that reflexive response (UCR).

- In operant conditioning, when a behaviour increases in frequency in response to consistent consequences, reinforcement is said to occur; when the behaviour decreases in frequency as a result of its consequences, this is described as punishment.

- Cognitive theorists believe that mental health problems stem from dysfunctional beliefs, attitudes, or ways of thinking.

- Three main levels of cognition are emphasized in cognitive theory: schemas, information processing and intermediate beliefs, and automatic thoughts.

- Schemas, or internal representations of stored information and experiences, influence an individual's thoughts, beliefs, information processing, feelings, and behaviour.

- Being stigmatized for having a mental health disorder can cause an individual to experience a decrease in self-esteem and fail to seek treatment for the disorder or the support of close others.

- Reducing the stigma of mental illness is essential so that individuals suffering with mental health issues can feel comfortable reaching out to others and receive the necessary support to overcome their disorders.

- Having high-quality relationships with close others (e.g., partner, friends, family) prevents or reduces the intensity of psychological distress following stressful events, while the absence of such support is a factor in the causal chain leading to dysfunction.

- There are clear differences between male and female rates for several disorders.

- Race and poverty have also been linked to the prevalence of psychiatric disorders.

KEY TERMS

behavioural genetics (p. 33)

biopsychosocial model (p. 46)

brain plasticity (p. 30)

classical conditioning (p. 36)

cognitive-behavioural theory (p. 39)

concordance (p. 33)

conscious (p. 34)

content-specificity (p. 40)

defence mechanisms (p. 36)

diathesis-stress perspective (p. 46)

ego (p. 35)

Electra complex (p. 35)

etiology (p. 27)

genetic linkage studies (p. 33)

genotype–environment interaction (p. 33)

id (p. 35)

interactionist explanation (p. 26)

molecular biology (p. 33)

neurotransmitters (p. 29)

null hypothesis (p. 26)

Oedipal complex (p. 35)

operant conditioning (p. 38)

phallic stage (p. 35)

preconscious (p. 34)

psychodynamic (p. 34)

public stigma (p. 43)

punishment (p. 38)

rational-emotive behaviour therapy (p. 39)

reinforcement (p. 38)

schemas (p. 39)

self-actualization (p. 42)

self-stigma (p. 43)

single-factor explanation (p. 26)

social learning theory (p. 39)

social support (p. 43)

superego (p. 35)

systems theory (p. 45)

two-factor theory (p. 38)

unconscious (p. 34)

DAVID J. A. DOZOIS

•

KATERINA RNIC

CHAPTER

3

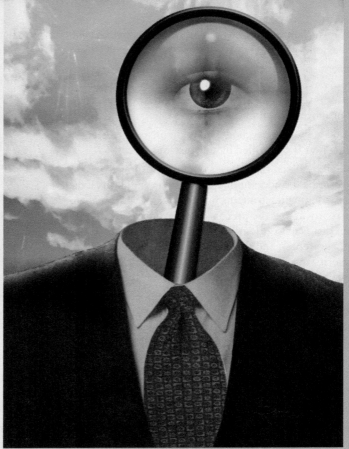

Bruce Rolff/123RF

Classification and Diagnosis

LEARNING OBJECTIVES

AFTER READING THIS CHAPTER, STUDENTS WILL BE ABLE TO:

1 Describe why we need a classification system for mental disorders.

2 Outline what criteria can be used to evaluate a system of classification.

3 Describe the history of classification of mental disorders.

4 Describe the system of classification of mental disorders.

5 Identify the key reasons why the system of classification was revised to create the DSM-5.

6 Describe the benefits of going beyond the DSM by using a new classification framework for research that examines psychopathology.

7 Outline the major criticisms of the current and past systems of classification of mental disorders.

Nick is a 30-year-old single man who lives with his widowed mother. Although his mother has repeatedly encouraged him to move out in order to gain his independence, Nick is comfortable residing with his mother and very resistant to these suggestions. Every time he thinks about living on his own, Nick becomes overwhelmed by feelings of anxiety and uncertainty regarding the possibility of having to take care of himself. He has suffered from diabetes and high blood pressure for the past five years, at least partially as a result of weight issues. Given that his medical conditions require strict and regimented medical care, Nick is convinced that he requires his mother's assistance to ensure that he is properly medicated.

In addition to his medical conditions, Nick has had a lifelong history of anxiety. His panic attacks have increased in frequency over the past year, often occurring twice a day. Nick's first panic attack occurred when he was 22 years of age. He recalls being in a movie theatre with a friend, and suddenly becoming paralyzed by an intense feeling of terror. He began to tremble and sweat while feeling helpless in gaining control over the anxiety. Following this incident, Nick became afraid of social situations or places where he might experience another attack and be unable to leave.

Although Nick began to limit his time spent in social settings with friends, he was still able to work full time as a computer technician for a small business located close to his home. His job entailed minimal contact with others, and allowed Nick to work from home most of the time. He found this job appealing not only because he could avoid having to work among others, but also because he could work in the comfort of his own home with his mother present to prepare his meals and keep him on task. However, just over a year ago, Nick was laid off from his job as a result of company cutbacks. Since this setback, he has rarely worked up the nerve to leave the house. At the urging of his mother, Nick went to a psychologist for an assessment and received the following diagnoses:

- Panic Disorder
- Agoraphobia
- Dependent Personality Disorder

In the realm of medicine and abnormal psychology, a **diagnosis** consists of a determination or identification of the nature of a person's disease or condition, or a statement of that finding. In Nick's case, the psychologist who assessed him determined, based on information that he gathered, that Nick's symptoms were consistent with a diagnosis of panic disorder, agoraphobia, and dependent personality disorder. In Chapter 5, we will review the specific symptoms that have to be present for such a diagnosis to be made. In order to make Nick's diagnosis, the psychologist relied on a **diagnostic** (or classification) **system**, a system of rules for recognizing and grouping various types of abnormalities (Glanze, Anderson, & Anderson, 1985).

Why Do We Need a Classification System for Mental Disorders?

Classification is a fundamental activity of all humans. From a very early age we learn to classify objects by their colours, shapes, and sizes. As we get older, our understanding of these objects becomes more sophisticated and we refine our taxonomy. The term *bird* may have been used initially to refer to "all things that fly." As we develop, however, we start to make more specific distinctions among these objects, identifying them as robins, crows, butterflies, airplanes, and so on. Classification is also of vital importance to science. The ability to categorize information allows scientists to better identify and understand various phenomena, from molecular structures, to personality, to galaxies.

A diagnostic system for mental disorders serves a number of important functions, including providing a description of different mental disorders. For example, what are the features of a panic disorder, and how does this disorder differ from depression or schizophrenia? By describing and organizing different mental disorders, a diagnostic system gives us a vocabulary for communicating about mental disorders with others. Let's say that the psychologist who worked with Nick had to refer him to someone else for treatment; in his referral he would note "panic disorder," and this diagnosis would provide the other mental health professional with information about what type of symptoms Nick is experiencing. In research, too, diagnostic systems serve a critical function. For example, psychopathology researchers rely on diagnostic systems to identify individuals who meet criteria for a particular disorder and to exclude individuals who do not meet the criteria for that disorder. Research findings, in turn, help us to refine and improve our diagnostic systems. This feedback loop is vital for the continued improvement of our diagnostic systems. Accurate diagnosis also provides important information for effective clinical intervention. Nick's diagnosis of "panic disorder" should inform the type of treatment he receives. Diagnostic systems are also needed for surveying population health and for understanding the prevalence and etiology (i.e., causes) of particular mental health problems (Hyman, 2010).

To gather all the information required for a proper diagnosis, a thorough assessment is required. Students often confuse assessment and diagnosis. An **assessment** is a procedure through which information is gathered systematically in the evaluation of a condition; this assessment procedure yields information that serves as the basis for a diagnosis. A mental health assessment may include interviews with the patient or the patient's family, medical testing, psychophysiological or psychological testing, and the completion of self-report scales or other report rating scales (see Chapter 4). A diagnostic system provides a number of criteria for a disorder. If a certain number of these criteria or indications are present, the person is diagnosed as having that particular disorder. Therefore, information from each of the assessment procedures contributes to the formulation of a diagnosis.

 BEFORE MOVING ON

> In psychology, who are some of the stakeholders in having a useful and effective system of classification of mental disorders?

The Perfect Diagnostic System

The perfect diagnostic system would classify disorders on the basis of a study of presenting symptoms (pattern of behaviours), etiology (history of the development of the symptoms and underlying causes), prognosis (future development of this pattern of behaviours), and response to treatment. In the development of this diagnostic system, a large number of people would have been thoroughly assessed psychologically and physically, in terms of feelings, thoughts, behaviours, and various other important features (e.g., laboratory tests and physical examination findings; see Kapur, Phillips, & Insel, 2012). A thorough history would have been taken in order to understand how various features developed. These people would then have been observed over a long period of time to assess the natural progression of their problems. In addition, various treatments would have been tried on groups of these patients, in a controlled fashion, to assess their effectiveness. Diagnostic categories would then be established by determining exactly which patterns of presenting problems, with what kind of history, developed in which particular manner and responded differentially to various treatments. Presumably, different symptom clusters, with dissimilar histories and differing normal progression, would signal different syndromes. In the resulting perfect system, each sign or symptom would be found in only one diagnostic category; there would be no overlap in the symptom profiles presented by patients. Furthermore, treatment modalities would be so thoroughly developed that we would have at our disposal a perfect cure for each diagnostic category, which would alleviate suffering for people who fit that category with pinpoint accuracy.

Unfortunately, scientific research is not so neat; nor are human beings. Practicalities preclude us from being able to systematically observe and measure many aspects of functioning in large numbers of people, in a controlled way, over long periods of time. Even if we knew which symptoms were important to note, human beings are incredibly complex, rapidly changing, and socially embedded organisms, and multiple interacting events and processes contribute to both adaptive and maladaptive behaviour (Mash & Barkley, 2014). The history of therapeutic interventions has also revealed how difficult it is to implement procedures following strict scientific principles.

Characteristics of Strong Diagnostic Systems

Most researchers and clinicians believe that a good diagnostic system is very useful, if not essential (see Table 3.1). What criteria are used to determine whether a diagnostic system is

TABLE 3.1   FUNCTIONS OF A GOOD CLASSIFICATION SYSTEM

1. Organization of clinical information	It provides the essentials of a patient's condition coherently and concisely.
2. Shorthand communication	It enhances the effective interchange of information, by clearly transmitting important features of a disorder and ignoring unimportant features.
3. Prediction of natural development	It allows accurate short-term and long-term prediction of an individual's development.
4. Treatment recommendations	It allows accurate predictions of the most effective interventions.
5. Heuristic value	It allows the investigation and clarification of issues related to a problem area. It also enhances theory-building.
6. Guidelines for financial support	It provides guidelines to services needed, including payment of caregivers.

useful or not? The first criterion is **reliability**. To be useful, a diagnostic system must give the same measurement for a given thing every time. For example, let's say that when you get home tonight, you decide to weigh yourself. You are surprised by the reading and you decide that you want to check again, just to be sure. This time, when you weigh yourself, your scale reading suggests that you are two kilos heavier! A little annoyed, you stand on the scale again, and this time you are back to the original reading. You might think to yourself, "Time to throw out the scale." It is difficult to trust the reading on the scale because it's not reliable. You certainly wouldn't use it any longer if accurate measurement of weight was important to you. A type of reliability that is particularly relevant when evaluating the value of a diagnostic system is inter-rater reliability. **Inter-rater reliability** refers to the extent to which two clinicians agree on the diagnosis of a particular patient. For example, if a system does not allow clinicians to agree on the signs and symptoms that constitute a specific disorder, inter-rater reliability will remain low. A classic study on the reliability of the diagnostic process was carried out many years ago (Beck et al., 1962). In this investigation, four highly experienced psychiatrists interviewed 153 new inpatients in a psychiatric hospital. Each patient was interviewed first by one psychiatrist and then a few hours later by a second psychiatrist. The psychiatrists were asked to formulate a diagnosis based on the interviews. The overall percentage agreement between pairs of raters was rather low, at 54 percent. That is, just over half of the time, the two psychiatrists agreed on a given patient's diagnosis.

One might speculate that this disagreement arose because the patient did not give the same report to both psychiatrists. A patient might, for example, mention domestic

violence during one interview and not the other. Indeed, such discrepancies did occur, but when the authors of the study analyzed the data, they found this to be the least important contributor to poor reliability. A more significant cause was differences between the interviewers, such as different interview techniques or differences in interpretation and in the importance given to certain symptoms. However, the factor most responsible by far for poor inter-rater reliability was the inadequacy of the diagnostic system itself.

The second criterion is **validity**. In a diagnostic system, validity is determined by whether a diagnostic category is able to predict behavioural and psychiatric disorders accurately. The two most important types of validity for diagnostic systems are concurrent validity and predictive validity. **Concurrent validity** refers to the ability of a diagnostic category to estimate an individual's present standing on factors related to the disorder but not themselves part of the diagnostic criteria. For example, although significant academic underachievement and a downward drift in socioeconomic status are not diagnostic items for schizophrenia, they are clearly found in most people with schizophrenia. If an assessment of siblings without schizophrenia of people diagnosed with schizophrenia revealed that they had better education and higher income, this would be an indication of concurrent validity. A major criticism of the DSM is that it sheds little light on the non-symptom attributes of people with a given diagnosis.

Another essential requirement of a good diagnostic system is **predictive validity**, the ability of a test to predict the future course of an individual's development. The key to a clear understanding of a disorder is its progression. As we will see in Chapter 15, a diagnosis of conduct disorder in early adolescence has been found to be highly related to a diagnosis of antisocial personality disorder as an adult. If all children with conduct disorder were reassessed at 20 years of age, and achieved a diagnosis of antisocial personality disorder, the predictive validity of conduct disorder would be perfect. As we shall see later, this is certainly not the case.

2 BEFORE MOVING ON

Why is it important to have a classification system that helps us understand the prognosis of disorders?

The History of Classification of Mental Disorders

As we learned in Chapter 1, an interest in the classification of psychopathology dates back at least to the Middle Ages. Modern efforts at classification owe much to Kraepelin's work in the nineteenth century, but even his categories and descriptors bear little resemblance to contemporary systems.

A milestone in the modern development of a comprehensive diagnostic scheme was the World Health Organization's decision to add mental health disorders to the

International List of the Causes of Death. In 1948, the list was expanded to become the International Statistical Classification of Diseases, Injuries, and Causes of Death (ICD), a comprehensive listing of all diseases, including abnormal behaviour. In response to perceived inadequacies of the ICD system, the American Psychiatric Association published its own classification system, the *Diagnostic and Statistical Manual* (DSM), in 1952. However, the original DSM, and its second edition (DSM-II; American Psychiatric Association [APA], 1968), proved highly unsatisfactory. These two volumes were very brief and contained only vague descriptions of the diagnostic categories. For example, DSM-I contained 106 categories of disorders that fell under the rubric of three major categories (organic brain syndromes, functional disorder, and mental deficiency). The current system contains more than three times that number of separate categories (Grohol & Tartakovsky, 2013). DSM-I and DSM-II were also greatly influenced by psychoanalytic theory, focused on internal unobservable processes, were not empirically based, and contained few objective criteria. Such influences are illustrated by an excerpt from the preamble to the specific diagnostic categories in DSM-II (APA, 1968, p. 39), describing "Neuroses":

> Anxiety is the chief characteristic of the neuroses. It may be felt and expressed directly, or it may be controlled unconsciously and automatically by conversion, displacement and various other psychological mechanisms. Generally, these mechanisms produce symptoms experienced as subjective distress from which the patient desires relief.

Not surprisingly, the system proved wholly unreliable, and as a result it was not unusual for clinicians to come up with widely differing diagnoses for the same person.

In 1980, the American Psychiatric Association published a newly revised and transformed diagnostic manual, DSM-III, which was followed by a more modest revision in 1987, DSM-III-R. DSM-III introduced several significant differences. In an attempt to improve reliability, field trials were conducted, substantiating the content of the manual by placing greater emphasis on empirical research. Some 12 500 patients and 550 clinicians were involved in these trials (Widiger & Trull, 1991). Furthermore, these versions of the manual became **atheoretical**; that is, they moved away from endorsing any one theory of abnormal psychology, becoming more pragmatic as they moved to more precise behavioural descriptions. To increase precision, they operationally defined the required number of symptoms and specified how long the symptoms had to last in order to meet diagnostic criteria. DSM-III-R was developed to be **polythetic**, meaning that an individual could be diagnosed with a certain subset of symptoms without having to meet all criteria. It also introduced a multiaxial requirement. In addition to a primary diagnosis, diagnosticians were required to provide substantial patient information, evaluating and rating patients on five different axes, or areas of functioning. This system was retained with the publication of DSM-IV (APA, 1994), which was developed based on a series of extensive literature reviews and multisite field trials over a span of six years. A minor text revision of the manual was released in 2000 (DSM-IV-TR).

In 1999, the APA launched an evaluation of the strengths and weaknesses of the DSM-IV-TR and, after several conferences, charged a task force to begin work on DSM-5 to improve on its previous work. Thirteen work groups were established to cover each major diagnostic category, and eight additional work groups investigated issues relevant to specific aspects of DSM-5 development and issues that cut across the diagnostic categories (e.g., the notion of impairment and disability, gender, and cross-cultural issues). Professionals from all fields related to mental health were consulted. In addition to comprehensive literature reviews, old data sets were reanalyzed, and an additional 11 field trials (which included one Canadian site) were conducted to collect new data. These field trials, which evaluated approximately 2000 patients, were constituted to ensure that participants represented diverse socio-economic, cultural, and ethnic backgrounds. A second set of data from routine clinical, private, and small-group practices was also acquired. In addition to reliability of the diagnoses, these field trials assessed the validity and clinical utility of the diagnoses, and set out to establish improved criteria. Clinicians used several draft versions of proposed diagnostic categories in their work and reported to the work groups on their findings. Representatives from all over the world, including several Canadian psychiatrists and psychologists, sat on the committees or consulted with them. Furthermore, the APA posted draft diagnostic criteria and proposed organizational changes to the DSM on its website. They invited feedback from the professional and public community, and work groups reviewed the comments and petitions for and against proposed changes that they received. The result of this mammoth 12-year undertaking was DSM-5 (APA, 2013).

Currently, DSM-5 is widely used in Canada and the United States; it is also the most-used classification system worldwide for research in psychopathology. Clinicians in the European Union more commonly use the tenth edition of the World Health Organization's (WHO, 1992) *International Classification of Diseases* (ICD-10). The ICD is currently undergoing revision, with a release date scheduled for 2018 (Boerma, Harrison, Jakob, Mathers, Schmider, & Weber, 2016; see WHO, 2016a). It is important to appreciate, however, that due to the considerable consultation among mental health researchers around the world, these latest revisions reflect increasing similarities between two modern classification systems for mental disorders (Kupfer, Kuhl, & Regier, 2013; Regier, Kuhl, & Kupfer, 2013). For instance, to facilitate the use of DSM-5 internationally, its appendix contains diagnostic criteria with ICD-10 codes.

3 BEFORE MOVING ON

One of the major limitations of DSM-I and DSM-II is that these systems were based on psychoanalytic conceptualizations of psychopathology. Why was this a problem?

DSM-5: Organizational Structure

SECTION I: INTRODUCTION AND USE OF THE MANUAL

Section I of DSM-5 provides a historical background of the DSM and a summary of its development, as well as an introduction to relevant issues and guidelines for proper use of the diagnostic system.

SECTION II: DIAGNOSTIC CRITERIA AND CODES

Included in Section II are the psychological disorders that have been recognized for centuries because of their bizarre nature (e.g., schizophrenia) or the difficulty they pose in the everyday life of individuals (e.g., mood disorders). Also included are the personality disorders, which are generally less severe long-term disturbances that nevertheless may interfere with a person's life. Usually, individuals with these problems can function in jobs and relationships, albeit with significant difficulty. In our opening case, Nick was found to have a dependent personality disorder; this diagnosis is not his most obvious problem, but it is still significant.

Section II also collects information on the patient's life circumstances, recognizing that individuals live within a social milieu and that stressful social circumstances might contribute to symptom onset. Suppose that two women have an anxiety disorder; one is single, and the other has an abusive husband and three children. Although their primary diagnosis is the same, the course of their disorder and response to treatment might be quite different.

SECTION III: EMERGING MEASURES AND MODELS

Section III contains optional measures and models and diagnoses that are in need of further study before possibly being placed in Section II as official diagnoses. One of the optional measures is the WHO Disability Assessment Schedule 2.0 (WHODAS), a self-report questionnaire that assesses how well a person is able to cope with the circumstances related to his or her problem(s). This information can be indicative of the need for treatment and of the person's coping mechanisms, and can assist in planning interventions. Suppose that two people both saw children die in a terrible school bus accident, and both are suffering from acute stress disorder (a severe stress response lasting three days to one month following the exposure to one or more traumatic events). One individual finds him- or herself unable to work and is having suicidal thoughts. The other is somewhat depressed and experiencing mild insomnia, but generally functioning satisfactorily. The first person may be given a fast-acting psychotropic medication or cognitive-behavioural therapy to ensure that he or she does not deteriorate psychologically or attempt suicide; the other may need only short-term psychological counselling.

Section III also includes the Outline for Cultural Formulation, which provides a framework for assessing the cultural features of an individual's clinical presentation, and the Cultural Formulation Interview (CFI), which assesses the influence of culture on an individual's mental health problem(s).

Finally, Section III provides an alternative model of personality disorders that uses a more dimensional perspective and focuses on pathological personality traits. It also includes dimensional symptom-based assessment tools for measuring the severity of a disorder.

Categories of Disorder in DSM-5

Section II groups all the disorders into 19 categories on the basis of broad similarities in how the disorders affect people, or how people experiencing these problems may appear to the clinician. The disorders are also grouped according to research evidence that may suggest similar underpinnings and etiologies. Furthermore, categories are grouped together in terms of whether they represent internalizing symptoms (behaviours that are harmful to the individual who engages in them) or externalizing symptoms (behaviours that directly harm others), and are arranged in order of when they tend to manifest in the lifespan.

NEURODEVELOPMENTAL DISORDERS

Included in this broad-ranging category are the intellectual, emotional, and physical disorders that typically begin before maturity (discussed in Chapters 14 and 15). There is *attention deficit/hyperactivity disorder*, in which the individual displays maladaptive levels of inattention, hyperactivity, or impulsivity, or a combination of these. Other diagnostic categories include *intellectual disability*, deficits in intellectual and adaptive functioning with impairments in social adjustment, identified at an early age; *autism spectrum disorder*, in which the child shows severe impediments in several areas of development, including social interactions and communication; *learning disorders*, in which the person's functioning in particular academic skill areas is significantly below what is expected based on his or her intelligence; *communication disorders*, in which the individual experiences significant difficulty with the reception, expression, or social use of language; and *motor skills disorders*, in which the individual experiences developmental problems with coordination and which include the *tic disorders*, in which the body moves repeatedly, quickly, suddenly, and/or uncontrollably (tics can occur in any body part, or can be vocal).

SCHIZOPHRENIA SPECTRUM AND OTHER PSYCHOTIC DISORDERS

The disorder known as *schizophrenia* is marked by severe debilitation in thinking and perception. People with schizophrenia suffer from a state of *psychosis*, often characterized by *delusions* (false beliefs, such as believing that people are trying to hurt them when there is no evidence of this) and *hallucinations* (false perceptions, such as hearing voices that comment on ongoing activity). People suffering from schizophrenia often lose the

Children may develop disorders most commonly seen in adults, such as depression or schizophrenia. These are diagnosed according to the same basic criteria as those used for adults.

Compulsive handwashing is one possible manifestation of an anxiety disorder.

ability to care for themselves, relate to others, and function at work. Thought disorder is often prominent, demonstrated by *incoherent speech*, *loose associations* (unconnected pieces of thought), *inappropriate affect* (such as smiling and laughing while watching an upsetting or violent scene in a movie), and *disorganized behaviour* (such as public masturbation). Essentially, people in a psychotic state have lost contact with the world and with others. Schizophrenia is discussed in Chapter 9.

MOOD DISORDERS

The most prominent and prevalent mood disorder is **major depressive disorder**, which is characterized by the occurrence of depressive mood episodes in which a person is extremely sad and discouraged, and displays a marked loss of pleasure in usual activities (see Chapter 8). Individuals with clinical depression often have severe problems sleeping; experience weight loss or gain; lack energy to do things; have difficulty concentrating; and feel worthless, hopeless, and sometimes suicidal. **Mania** is another type of mood episode, in which a person is extremely elated, more active, and in less need of sleep, and displays flights of somewhat disconnected ideas, grandiosity (an illusion of personal importance), and impairment in functioning. In **bipolar disorders**, mania, and often depression, is exhibited. Moreover, severity of mood disorders can vary. Less severe variants of these mood disorders include Persistent Depressive Disorder (or *dysthymia*), which is a more chronic low-grade depression, and *cyclothymia*, in which the person fluctuates between more mild bouts of mania and less severe depressive symptoms. Bipolar and related disorders (e.g., bipolar disorders, cyclothymia) are categorized in a separate chapter in DSM-5 than are depressive disorders (e.g., *major depressive disorder* and *dysthymia*).

ANXIETY AND RELATED DISORDERS

Anxiety is the predominant disturbance in this group of disorders (discussed in Chapter 5). Individuals who suffer from an anxiety disorder experience excessive fear, worry, or apprehension; the excessive fear usually produces a maladaptive pattern of avoidance. A person can have an intense fear of a specific object or situation, which is referred to as a *phobia*. Some individuals have an extreme fear of social situations (*social phobia*); experience panic attacks and fear that they will go crazy, have a heart attack, or die (*panic disorder*); or have difficulty controlling excessive worry (*generalized anxiety disorder*). Obsessive-compulsive disorder is characterized by *obsessions* (recurrent, unwanted, and intrusive thoughts) and *compulsions* (strongly repetitive behaviours), which, when not performed, cause overwhelming distress. People with *body dysmorphic disorder* are overly preoccupied with an imagined defect in their appearance. Individuals may also experience long-standing anxiety subsequent to extraordinarily traumatic events (*acute stress disorder* and *post-traumatic stress disorder*). Although we cover them together in the chapter on Anxiety, Obsessive-Compulsive, and Trauma-Related Disorders (Chapter 5), DSM-5 technically categorizes different anxiety disorders in three separate sections: Anxiety Disorders (e.g., *specific phobia, social anxiety disorder, panic disorder, agoraphobia, generalized anxiety disorder*), Obsessive-Compulsive and Related Disorders (e.g., *obsessive-compulsive disorder, hoarding disorder, body dysmorphic disorder*), and Trauma- and Stress-Related Disorders (e.g., *post-traumatic stress disorder, acute stress disorder, adjustment disorder*). Anxiety disorders and mood disorders are often diagnosed in the same individuals at the same time (see Focus box 3.1 for a discussion of comorbidity).

DISSOCIATIVE DISORDERS

Dissociation is characterized by a sudden and profound disruption in consciousness, identity, memory, and perception. People with *dissociative amnesia* may forget their entire past or, more selectively, lose their memory for a particular time period and may suddenly and unexpectedly leave their home and travel to a new locale, start a new life, and forget their previous identity. Individuals with *dissociative identity disorder* possess two or more distinct personality states, each with unique memories, behaviour patterns, preferences, and social relationships. *Depersonalization/derealization disorder* involves a severe and disruptive feeling of self-estrangement or unreality (see Chapter 6).

SOMATIC SYMPTOM AND RELATED DISORDERS

The physical symptoms of somatic disorders have no known physiological cause, but seem to serve a psychological purpose. Somatic symptom disorder is characterized by the experience of one or more persistent physical symptoms accompanied by excessive thoughts, feelings, or behaviours related to the symptom(s). In *conversion disorder*, the person reports the loss of motor or sensory function, for example, a paralysis or blindness. *Illness anxiety disorder* involves extreme anxiety about health in the absence of somatic symptoms; individuals become preoccupied with the fear that they have a serious illness. *Factitious disorders* are diagnosed when individuals intentionally produce or complain of either physical or psychological symptoms, due to a psychological need to assume the role of a sick person. If a person's medical illness appears to be in part psychological, or exacerbated by a psychological condition, the diagnosis is "psychological factors affecting other medical conditions." Somatic disorders are discussed in Chapter 6.

FEEDING AND EATING DISORDERS

Eating disorders (discussed in Chapter 10) are characterized by disturbances in eating behaviour. This can mean eating too much, not eating enough, or eating in an extremely unhealthy manner (such as repetitively bingeing and purging). In *anorexia nervosa*, the individual refuses to maintain a minimally normal weight for her or his age and height. Such people avoid eating and become emaciated, often due to an intense fear of becoming fat. In *bulimia nervosa*, there are frequent episodes of binge eating coupled with compensatory activities such as self-induced vomiting or the use of laxatives. In *binge-eating disorder*, there are frequent episodes of eating large amounts of food in a discrete period of time. Also included in this category (although not covered in Chapter 10) are other feeding disorders. For example, *Pica's disorder* involves eating substances that have no nutritional value, such as sand and feces, on a persistent basis.

ELIMINATION DISORDERS

These disorders are usually diagnosed in childhood or adolescence. *Enuresis* involves the repeated voiding of urine in inappropriate places, and *encopresis* is the repeated passage of feces in inappropriate places. Both can occur voluntarily or involuntarily.

SLEEP–WAKE DISORDERS

Insomnia (not getting enough sleep), *hypersomnolence* (excessive sleepiness), *narcolepsy* (suddenly lapsing into sleep), and *breathing-related sleep disorders* are those disorders relating to the amount, quality, and timing of sleep. *Parasomnias* relate to abnormal behaviour or physiological events that occur during the process of sleep or sleep–wake transitions (for example, *sleep terror disorder* or *sleepwalking disorder*).

SEXUAL DISORDERS AND GENDER DYSPHORIA

The DSM-5 includes the broad categories Sexual Dysfunctions, Paraphilic Disorders, and Gender Dysphoria. These disorders are discussed together in Chapter 13. Individuals who suffer from a *sexual dysfunction* are characterized by

---

FOCUS 3.1

Comorbidity

One of the limitations of the DSM is that it is characterized by high levels of comorbidity. In broad terms, **comorbidity** is defined as the presence of more than one disorder in the same individual (Markon, 2014). We know that rates of comorbidity for certain psychological disorders tend to be very high (Gadermann, Alonso, Vilagut, Zaslavsky, & Kessler, 2012). One concrete illustration of comorbidity is that approximately 50 percent of people suffering from anxiety disorders also have mood disorders (e.g., Hofmeijer-Sevink et al., 2012).

One of the principles that form the basis of a categorical system of classification is the idea that any one specific disorder is distinct from another disorder. However, when disorders co-occur at a much greater frequency than would be expected by chance, it suggests that the lines between disorders may be fuzzy, and in some cases, artificial and arbitrary. Yet the architects of the DSM-5 argue that it is a rationally based system that groups disorders based on their shared phenomenological features (APA, 2013).

A phenomenological approach to classification is one that places emphasis on observed similarities and differences rather than the underlying structure or nature of mental disorders. Watson (2005) argues that "we now have sufficient knowledge to eliminate this rationally based system and replace it with an empirically based structure that reflects the actual—not the apparent—similarities among different disorders" (p. 524). Watson views comorbidity not necessarily as a liability, but rather as an empirical basis on which to improve the existing system of classification. As an example, given the high comorbidity of anxiety and depressive disorders, Watson and colleagues recommended that we have one category representing both depression and anxiety rather than two distinct categories. Although DSM-5 did not incorporate this change, it did include a new structure that groups disorders with similar phenomenology that co-occur at a high rate. This was done with the hope that it would encourage researchers to investigate processes common to disorders in a diagnostic class, possibly leading to an improved delineation of diagnostic boundaries. We are optimistic that each iteration of the DSM will do a better job of incorporating empirical evidence so that we are able to develop a classification system that represents an empirically based structure of psychopathology. ●

disturbance in sexual desire or in the psychophysiological changes that accompany the sexual response cycle. Inability to maintain an erection, premature ejaculation, and inhibitions of orgasm are some examples of their problems. Individuals with *paraphilic disorders* are characterized by sexual urges, fantasies, or behaviours that involve unusual objects or activities, such as exhibitionism, voyeurism, sadism, and masochism; and that cause significant distress or impairment. People with *gender dysphoria* feel extreme and overwhelming distress associated with their anatomical sex and an incongruity between their biological sex and expressed gender.

DISRUPTIVE, IMPULSE-CONTROL, AND CONDUCT DISORDERS

This category involves disorders characterized by failure or extreme difficulty in controlling impulses, despite the negative consequences. For example, in *intermittent explosive disorder*, the person has episodes of violent behaviour that result in the destruction of property or injury to others. In *oppositional defiant disorder*, there is a recurrent pattern of negativistic, defiant, disobedient, and hostile behaviour toward authority figures. In *conduct disorder*, children persistently violate societal norms, rules, or the basic rights of others. Oppositional defiant disorder and conduct disorder are described in Chapter 15. Furthermore, persons suffering from *trichotillomania* experience intense urges to pull out their own hair. Although trichotillomania was included with the *impulse control disorders* in previous editions of the DSM, research suggests that it fits better with the Obsessive-Compulsive and Related Disorders, where it is now grouped in DSM-5.

SUBSTANCE-RELATED AND ADDICTIVE DISORDERS

These disorders are brought about by the excessive use of a substance, which can be defined as anything that is ingested in order to produce a high, alter one's senses, or otherwise affect functioning. When the use of these substances results in social, occupational, psychological, or physical problems, it is considered a mental disorder. Individuals with such diagnoses may be unable to control or stop their use of substances and may have become physically addicted to them. Included in the group of substance abuse disorders are *alcohol-related disorders*, *hallucinogen-related disorders*, *opioid-related disorders*, *sedative-, hypnotic-,* or *anxiolytic-related disorders*, and *stimulant-related disorders* among others. DSM-5 also includes *gambling disorder*, a behavioural addiction, in this category. Substance-related disorders are discussed in Chapter 11.

NEUROCOGNITIVE DISORDERS

The Neurocognitive Disorders refer to conditions in which there is a decline in cognitive functioning (APA, 2013). *Delirium* is a clouding of consciousness, wandering attention, and an incoherent stream of thought. It may be caused by several medical conditions as well as by poor diet and substance abuse. Major and mild neurocognitive disorders are a deterioration of mental capacities, are typically irreversible, and are usually associated with Alzheimer's disease, stroke, several other medical conditions, or substance abuse. Mild neurocognitive disorders are less severe but may progress to become major neurocognitive disorders.

PERSONALITY DISORDERS

These disorders (discussed in Chapter 12) are characterized by an enduring, pervasive, inflexible, and maladaptive pattern of behaviour that has existed since adolescence or early adulthood, markedly impairs functioning, and/or causes subjective stress. One common example of personality disorder is *antisocial personality disorder*, in which the person displays a history of continuous and chronic disregard for and violation of the rights of others. In *dependent personality disorder* a person manifests a pattern of submissive and clinging behaviour and fear of separation. The DSM-5 includes 10 distinct personality disorders.

OTHER CONDITIONS THAT MAY BE A FOCUS OF CLINICAL ATTENTION

This broad category is used for conditions that are not considered to be mental disorders but may still be a focus of attention or treatment. Conditions in this category include academic problems, marital problems, occupational problems, and being physically or sexually abused. For example, a student's academic performance may decrease for a significant period of time, even though the student is not suffering from an anxiety disorder, clinical depression, a learning disability, or any other mental disorder that would account for the underachievement.

4 **BEFORE MOVING ON**

> "DSM-5 sufficiently takes into account the social and interpersonal context of mental disorders." Provide one argument supporting this position and one argument against this position.

INNOVATIONS OF DSM-5

There are a number of reasons why the DSM was recently revised. As researchers gather new empirical evidence about mental disorders (e.g., how different disorders are related to and distinct from each other), it becomes necessary to revise and update our classification system to reflect the new knowledge and understanding. This is consistent with the principle of evidence-based practice, which means that the assessment and treatment of psychological disorders should be based on the most current and valid research findings (Dozois et al., 2014; Hunsley & Elliott, 2014; Hunsely & Mash, 2011).

One example of a change that was introduced in DSM-5 to reflect new scientific evidence involves the addition of *hoarding disorder.* Individuals with this disorder experience distress related to discarding possessions, regardless of their value, and accumulate excessive amounts of objects and items as a result. In previous editions of the DSM, hoarding was listed as a possible symptom of, or subtype of, obsessive-compulsive disorder (OCD). However, over time, research showed that the presentation of hoarding was distinct from OCD in a number of ways, such that it made sense to make hoarding a disorder in its own right. For example, hoarding disorder has a higher prevalence than OCD; people with hoarding show less insight into their problem; hoarding behaviours tend to worsen over time; hoarding is not accompanied by obsessive thoughts; and people who hoard show a poorer response to medication and psychological treatments for OCD. The APA (2013) refers to DSM-5 as a living document, and states that updates and revisions will be introduced as new discoveries are made.

A major criticism that has been levelled against DSM-5 (as well as earlier versions of the DSM) is its **categorical approach** to the classification of mental disorders. That is, an individual is deemed to either have a disorder or not have a disorder, with no in-between. One reason for this approach is historical. Psychiatrists have developed mental health classification systems for the most part, and, being physicians, they have used the same approach taken in physical health. For example, if a person reports pain in the lower right abdomen, vomiting, and fever; and if a blood sample reveals an elevated white blood cell count, the physician makes a categorical decision: Does this person need surgery for appendicitis or not? There is no in-between. However, is this a reasonable model for assessing mental function? After all, a categorical system does not recognize the continuum between normal and abnormal.

Consider the case of a teenager who engages in significant bullying and cruelty to animals. Would one conclude that because he falls short of the required criteria for conduct disorder, he has *no* problems? Does this mean that the large body of research on children with conduct disorder is completely irrelevant to this youngster? It is troubling, but undeniably true, that people are denied help because they fall just short of diagnostic criteria. Several investigations have demonstrated that these subthreshold syndromes are not only highly prevalent but also result in substantial impairment. Balázs et al. (2013), for instance, found that 53.7% of adolescents in a sample drawn from 11 countries experienced symptoms of depression or anxiety, and of these, 12.6% experienced clinically diagnosable levels of these disorders. However, both individuals with subthreshold (not quite meeting diagnosis) and threshold-level symptoms experienced significant functional impairment and suicidality. Furthermore, critics allege, a categorical approach does not provide a meaningful description of an individual's psychological problems. For these reasons, some researchers (e.g., Carragher, Krueger, Eaton, & Slade, 2015) have advocated a **dimensional approach** to diagnosis, based on a continuum for mental disorders from non-existent or mild to severe.

Another goal of the development of DSM-5 was to enhance its clinical utility. *Clinical utility* refers to the extent to which a diagnostic system assists clinicians in performing functions such as communicating clinical information to patients, their families, and other health care providers; selecting effective interventions; and predicting the course of a disorder (First et al., 2007). Consistent with this goal, the DSM-5 introduces a scale for assessing the severity of psychotic symptoms to help clinicians determine a prognosis.

5 BEFORE MOVING ON

DSM-5 lowered the threshold for certain disorders. There is a lot of controversy about this, with one vocal group arguing against any proposed changes that would reduce the threshold for any diagnosis and others vociferously backing such changes. Identify two or three problems with reducing the diagnostic threshold for certain disorders and two or three reasons why reducing diagnostic thresholds is necessary and important.

Issues in the Diagnosis and Classification of Abnormal Behaviour

Despite the long history and widespread use of the DSM and other diagnostic systems for mental health, considerable controversy still surrounds them (Welch, Klassen, Borisova, & Clothier, 2013). There are two main arenas of controversy. One body of opinion objects to classification per se, and suggests that any classification system for mental disorders is irrelevant at best and inappropriate at worst. The second type of opposition targets the DSM in particular.

AGAINST CLASSIFICATION

MEDICAL MODEL A substantial number of professionals argue that the whole diagnostic endeavour is flawed because of its adherence to the medical model. Medical disorders are legitimate, they argue, because they have a clear indication, such as a lesion, that serves as a recognizable deviation in anatomical structure, whereas most mental disorders involve no such anatomical deviations. Diagnosis of "mental illness," these critics suggest, is simply a de facto means of social control (Szasz, 1961). In a succinct rejection of this position, Wakefield (1992) pointed out that there are many medical disorders for which there are no known lesions or anatomical abnormalities. Trigeminal neuralgia, for example, is classified on the basis of associated dysfunction alone; furthermore, it is possible that at some future point we may discover anatomical anomalies associated with some mental health disorders.

STIGMATIZATION Another argument against diagnosis is that it unfairly stigmatizes individuals. A person diagnosed with schizophrenia, for instance, is often seen simply as a "schizophrenic," rather than as a complex individual with skills and interests. Such a label might have a major impact both socially and occupationally because the individual may not fit in or may have difficulty seeking employment; he or she may also come to identify with the label, leading to further deterioration or impeding rehabilitation (i.e., a self-fulfilling prophecy). Stigmatization also discourages individuals with mental disorders from seeking help (Clement et al., 2015). Wakefield (1992) argues that the flaw lies not in the classification system but in people's reactions to mental disorders. Professionals must guard against discouraging or belittling people with mental disorders, and must help to educate the public appropriately. There is encouraging evidence that interventions, such as providing education about mental health or contact (either in person or recorded) with people who have experienced mental health issues can reduce stigma in the general population (Botha, Shamblaw, & Dozois, 2017; Thornicroft et al., 2016). As mentioned in Chapter 1, reduction of stigmatization and discrimination is a primary mandate of the Mental Health Commission of Canada (MHCC, 2011).

LOSS OF INFORMATION A frequent charge against diagnosis is that inherent in any label is a loss of information. You have probably already learned in your statistics courses what happens when you dichotomize a continuous variable: there

is a loss of statistical power and a resultant loss of information. How can anyone's uniqueness be summarized in a word or two, whether the label is favourable (e.g., "beautiful" or "smart") or unfavourable (e.g., "lazy" or "aloof")? Similarly, an individual with depression is characterized by many other qualities, not just her or his depression. The label alone can give us a false sense of confidence in understanding the person and making assumptions about his or her personhood and life that are not valid. How can we reconcile this drawback with the need to be able to discuss a patient's symptoms in an efficient and clear manner? As discussed earlier, such information is often needed for mental health professionals to speak to each other and to provide health care in a coordinated fashion. Also, patients often report that knowing the name of a disorder helps them understand their experiences and may even provide some relief. Perhaps the take-home message from this is not that diagnostic labels should be abandoned but that they should be used in an educated, informed, and nuanced manner. As the study by the psychologist Rosenhan, discussed below, illustrates, our diagnostic system is fallible.

Rosenhan (1973) conducted an influential study that highlighted many of the problems associated with diagnosis of mental disorders and raised important questions about the validity of psychiatric diagnoses. Rosenhan recruited pseudo-patients (individuals instructed to fake the symptoms of a mental illness), who faked auditory hallucinations

APPLIED CLINICAL CASE

Howie Mandel

Howie Mandel is an actor and comedian, and is known for being a judge on *America's Got Talent*, a talent competition show on TV, and the host of *Deal or No Deal*, a game show. Mandel, who was born and raised in Canada, is very open about his diagnosis of obsessive-compulsive disorder (OCD). His fear of germs has led him to shave his head to feel clean and prevents him from shaking hands with people, which explains why he is often seen bumping fists instead. During an interview on the NFL Network in 2007, former football player Marshall Faulk shook Mandel's hand as a surprise. Mandel looked upset and responded by walking away. Presumably, this handshake stimulated a succession of obsessions dealing with thoughts and feelings of being contaminated and unclean. To manage and eliminate these feelings, Mandel probably felt compelled to wash his hands repeatedly. In 2010 when a contestant on *America's Got Talent* performed a routine involving sneezing, Mandel hit the 'X' button, ran to the aisle, and shouted for the other judges to do the same. Despite his problems with OCD, Mandel has functioned very effectively in life. In May 2007, he was invited to Washington, D.C., as an honourable speaker for National Children's Mental Health Awareness Day. He is also a spokesperson for the Bell Canada Let's Talk Campaign, which aims to destigmatize mental health and raise funding for mental health programs. Mandel has spoken about the challenges of mental health stigma, which prevented him from seeking help

Nancy Kaszerman/ZUMAPRESS.com/Alamy Stock Photo

for his disorder as a child, and has encouraged those with mental health problems to seek treatment. He is not only an entertainer, but also a husband, father, and charismatic speaker, and is so much more than his diagnosis. His story highlights that even the most successful among us are not immune to mental health disorders, and there is no shame in experiencing psychological symptoms or seeking help.

in order to gain admission to psychiatric hospitals. After admission, the pseudo-patients stopped displaying any psychotic symptoms and informed hospital staff that they were no longer experiencing hallucinations. Despite this, many of the pseudo-patients were confined as inpatients for significant periods of time and all were discharged with the diagnosis of a psychiatric disorder. One of the important lessons of this study is that it demonstrates how powerful the process of labelling can be. Once the pseudo-patients were seen as having the label of a psychiatric disorder, all their subsequent behaviour was seen through the prism of this diagnosis. Thus, if the pseudo-patients did not display symptoms, the mental health professionals working with them interpreted this to mean that their symptoms were being managed well, not that there might have been a mistake in the original diagnosis or that the diagnosis may no longer apply.

Few would argue that all forms of classification of mental disorders should be abandoned. However, what the critics of the current classification system state, and studies such as the one conducted by Rosenhan highlight, is that mental health professionals need to be aware of the biases and fallibility in our systems of diagnosis and classification. Similarly, mental health professionals need to be aware of the power differential that is inherent in clinician–patient relationships and that a system of classification can be used incorrectly to perpetuate and establish that power differential. Furthermore, there have to be parallel efforts to bring about changes in the public's perception of mental disorders and to reduce the stigma of having a mental health problem.

CRITICISMS SPECIFIC TO THE DSM DIAGNOSTIC SYSTEM

GENDER BIAS IN THE DSM The late 1960s saw poignant criticisms of gender bias and sexism in the mental health system (Chesler, 1972). DSM-I and DSM-II were strongly influenced by psychoanalytic theory, which has been charged with sexism (Kaschak, 1992). In 1974, the American Psychological Association set up a task force to investigate gender bias and sex-role stereotyping in mental health assessment and therapy. The first step was to survey female clinicians to determine what practices indicate gender bias or sexism. Four categories were developed: fostering traditional gender roles, bias in expectations and devaluation of women, sexist use of psychoanalytic concepts, and treating women as sex objects, including the seduction of a female patient (which was not specifically labelled unethical by a professional body until 1978). Nonetheless, DSM-III was in no way free of gender bias.

Some writers have claimed that the DSM describes many psychiatric disorders in a fashion that makes a diagnosis more probable for women, even when no pathology is involved (APA, 2007). They contend that diagnostic categories in the DSM are based on professional assumptions regarding the nature of psychopathology, which are in turn influenced by societal norms that value stereotypical masculine behaviour, such as assertiveness and goal-directed behaviour, over stereotypical feminine behaviour, such as co-operation and nurturing others. These feminine behaviours

are considered secondary to mental health and may even be seen as signs of emotional immaturity and psychopathology (APA, 2007).

Another criticism of the DSM is that it does not take life circumstances sufficiently into account, assuming that psychological problems can be attributed largely to the individual. Although recent years have seen increased acknowledgment of the extent to which women may be oppressed in Western society, there is still insufficient recognition of these factors in the diagnostic assessment (Ussher, 2011).

The personality disorders have also come under fire because some seem to correspond to exaggerated female stereotypes (e.g., histrionic personality disorder and dependent personality disorder), and thus may be diagnosed more frequently in women than in men. Investigations suggest that gender bias in diagnoses is not merely an artifact of the experimental procedure employed. For example, Braamhorst and colleagues (2015) presented clinicians with case summaries of patients who met the criteria for several personality disorders. They found that clinicians tended to diagnose these patients in accordance with gender stereotypes. Furthermore, even when males and females were diagnosed with the same personality disorder (histrionic personality disorder and antisocial personality disorder, in this particular experiment), women were judged to be more pathological (Hamilton, Rothbart, & Dawes, 1986). Sampling bias represents another problem that has confounded this issue. Hartung and Widiger (1998) argued that many clinical studies fail to obtain a representative sample of individuals with a given disorder. For example, much of the research on conduct disorder is confined to boys. Such an unrepresentative sample not only will affect our understanding of prevalence differences but also might inadvertently contribute to further biases (e.g., in this case, researchers may develop a male-biased description of the disorder).

CULTURAL BIAS IN THE DSM Just as mental health professionals have learned to recognize gender bias, they have been led by recent developments to grapple with similar concerns related to culture. More than 220 000 immigrants from all over the world have moved to Canada annually over the past 10 years. The North American milieu now includes a great variety of religions and languages, and has seen a tremendous increase in the diversity of cultural practices. More than ever, clinicians must be aware of cultural factors that might influence the diagnostic process.

DSM-5 has striven to be atheoretical and to take cultural differences into account. It stresses that an individual's primary social and cultural reference group, as well as his or her unique personal experience, must be taken into account during an assessment (Kupfer, Kuhl, & Regier, 2013). Despite these improvements to the DSM-5, the designation of behaviour as normal or abnormal is fraught with cultural and professional assumptions, especially considering that disorders in the DSM are determined largely by the consensus of English-speaking scientists trained primarily in the United States and, to a lesser extent, in Canada.

It is important to note that some behaviours considered abnormal in white North American culture may not be considered abnormal in other cultures. For example, hallucinations should not necessarily be considered abnormal during North American Aboriginal religious ceremonies (e.g., Crowe-Salazar, 2007). In addition, since many in Hispanic nations such as Puerto Rico believe that evil spirits can possess an individual, such reports should not always be considered a sign of schizophrenia in individuals from this culture.

A related area of controversy has to do with cultural bias in intelligence testing. In reviewing the literature on intelligence test scores and later outcomes, such as school achievement, Baydala and colleagues (2009) note that the link between intelligence scores and subsequent academic and career outcomes tends to be weaker for indigenous children in the United States and Canada, calling into question the validity of these tests for these individuals. Similarly, it has been noted that Indigenous culture instills a sense of co-operation, valuing the group more than the individual. The same has been reported with other cultures (see Saklofske, van de Vijver, Oakland, Mpofu, & Suzuki, 2015). Furthermore, North American Indigenous people are overrepresented in the lower socio-economic strata, and several studies have shown that IQ tests underestimate the intelligence of people in these strata (Croizet, & Dutrévis, 2004).

Certain syndromes appear only within a particular culture. The DSM-5 lists nine syndromes that appear to be culture-bound. *Taijin kyofusho*, a syndrome found primarily in Japan and Korea, is characterized by an excessive fear that one will embarrass or offend others. This syndrome afflicts 7 to 36 percent of people treated by psychiatrists in Japan and primarily affects young Japanese men. In contrast to typical Western presentations of social anxiety disorder characterized by fear for oneself, individuals with *taijin kyofusho* fear that they may present themselves or behave in a way that will discomfort others, such as blushing, having a deformed body, making an inappropriate facial expression, making too much eye contact, or emitting a foul body odour. Some of these subtypes may share some overlap with body dysmorphic or delusional disorder. DSM-5 discusses *taijin kyofusho* as a culture-bound syndrome, however, DSM-5 also includes fear of offending others in its newly revised diagnostic criteria for social anxiety disorder (Heimberg et al., 2014). Thus, it is not entirely clear whether *taijin kyofusho* is truly a cultural syndrome.

Research in the United States has suggested that emotional difficulties may be diagnosed differently in African-American and Hispanic populations than in white populations. Several studies found that clinicians shown a case summary were more likely to diagnose the patient with schizophrenia if told the patient was black. Hospital-based studies have also suggested that blacks were overdiagnosed with schizophrenia and underdiagnosed with mood disorders (Garb, 1997). Alternatively, there is also some evidence to suggest that psychopathology has been underestimated in Hispanics as a result of their reluctance to disclose information to non-Hispanics (Rastogi, Massey-Hastings, & Wieling, 2012; Shattell, Hamilton, Starr, Jenkins, & Hinderliter, 2008).

The developers of the DSM-5 attempted to address some of the concerns about cultural bias that were voiced about earlier versions of the DSM. For example, the DSM-5 has encouraged clinicians to be culturally sensitive in their assessments and diagnoses of persons from diverse ethnic backgrounds. Within the description of each disorder is included a list of cultural and ethnic factors to consider. In addition, Section III of DSM-5 contains important information related to conducting a systematic review of an individual's culture and determining the influence of a patient's culture on the expression and evaluation of symptoms. As previously mentioned, a list of cultural syndromes is also provided.

⑥ BEFORE MOVING ON

> What are the benefits of adopting a new classification framework for research examining psychopathology rather than relying exclusively on the DSM?

POLITICS AND THE DSM Another criticism of the DSM is that the decisions about diagnostic criteria are too often influenced by factors other than pure empiricism. For example, students might be surprised to learn that homosexuality was included as a diagnostic category in the DSM until the release of DSM-III in 1980; it was removed not due to accumulated empirical evidence, but because the members of the APA were asked to vote on the matter. Concerns have also been voiced about the individuals selected for the panels responsible for revising previous editions of the DSM, because many had ties to the pharmaceutical industry. In an effort to avoid conflicts of interest, task force and work group members involved in the development of DSM-5 were required to disclose all sources of income, with limits imposed on how much income could come from industry sources. Given the above issues with the DSM, researchers are working toward a new classification framework (see Focus box 3.2).

⑦ BEFORE MOVING ON

> Why should we be concerned about the possible influence of pharmaceutical companies on the development and evolution of the DSM?

THE PREVALENCE OF MENTAL DISORDERS

In 2002, Health Canada published *A Report on Mental Illnesses in Canada*. The purpose of this report was to collate existing data on prevalence rates of mental disorders in Canada in an effort to start building a more complete picture of the mental health needs of Canadians. The report concluded that one out of five Canadians will experience a mental illness in their lifetime (Health Canada, 2002). An updated report, which incorporated new data on mental health from the 2002 Statistics Canada survey, the Canadian

Research Domain Criteria: A New Classification Framework

The National Institute of Mental Health (NIMH), a major funding body in the United States, recently published the Research Domain Criteria (RDoC) as a more biologically valid alternative to researching and understanding mental disorders. RDoC is a matrix of constructs and levels of analysis that the NIMH is encouraging researchers to use as a framework when designing empirical studies that assess psychopathology. Constructs fit into four broad areas of functioning: negative valence systems (acute threat/fear, potential threat/anxiety, sustained threat, loss, and frustrative nonreward); positive valence systems (approach motivation, initial responsiveness to reward attainment, sustained responsiveness to reward attainment, reward learning, habit); cognitive systems (attention, perception, declarative memory, language, cognitive control, working memory); social processes (affiliation and attachment, social communication, perception and understanding of self, perception and understanding of others); and arousal and regulatory systems (arousal, circadian

rhythms, sleep-wakefulness). Levels of analysis for examining constructs are genes, molecules, cells, brain circuits, physiology, behaviour, self-report, and paradigms (i.e., tasks and tests used to examine phenomena). The goal of RDoC is to stimulate research that examines the underlying mechanisms of dysfunction in order to better understand psychopathology, particularly given the huge amount of comorbidity and heterogeneity in the clinical presentation, etiology, and pathophysiology within diagnostic groups defined using current classification systems such as DSM-5. By focusing on particular functional processes and not on syndromes, researchers may learn more about abnormal psychology, as they are no longer confined by the limitations and biases of the DSM. The hope is that research designed using RDoC will help to create a new taxonomy of mental disorders, such that clinicians could go beyond questionnaires and clinical interviews about symptoms, and use laboratory and behavioural data to examine dysfunctional processes in an individual to inform better and more targeted treatment. ●

Community Health Survey Cycle, the 2002–2003 Hospital Mental Health Database, and the 2004 Health Behaviours of School Children Survey (Government of Canada, 2006), also reported a 20 percent lifetime prevalence of mental disorders. Mental disorders represent the second leading cause of disability and premature death in Canada (Canadian Medical Association, 2008). Statistics Canada reported that in 2012, 10.1% of Canadians ages 15 and older reported symptoms consistent with a major depressive episode, bipolar disorder, generalized anxiety disorder,

and/or substance misuse. In 2014, 6.3% of Canadians rated their mental health as fair or poor (Statistics Canada, 2016). Global data on prevalence rates of mental disorders are even more sobering. Globally, it is estimated that one-third of the world's population has some form of mental disorder and, of those individuals, about two-thirds receive no treatment, even in high-income countries (WHO, 2000). Depression is now the leading cause of disability worldwide (WHO, 2016b), and yet only 1% of the global health workforce works in mental health (WHO, 2015).

SUMMARY

- A diagnostic system for mental disorders serves a number of important functions, such as providing a description of mental disorders, distinguishing among different types of mental disorders, providing a vocabulary for communicating about mental disorders, and facilitating research in psychopathology. Furthermore, accurate assessment and diagnosis, as well as effective treatment of mental disorders, rely on a system of classification. Diagnostic systems are also needed for surveying population health and for understanding the prevalence and etiology of particular mental health problems.

- Every science includes a system for categorizing information. In abnormal psychology, the perfect diagnostic system would be based on etiology, presenting symptoms, prognosis, and response to treatment. This diagnostic system would also enhance the organization of clinical factors and provide a shorthand to help professionals communicate easily.

- Although attempts to classify mental disorders date back to at least the Middle Ages, modern efforts at classification owe much to Kraepelin's work in the nineteenth century. A milestone in the modern development of a comprehensive diagnostic scheme was the World Health Organization's decision to add mental health disorders to the International List of the Causes of Death. In 1948 the list was expanded to become the International Statistical Classification of Diseases, Injuries, and Causes of Death (ICD), a comprehensive listing of all diseases, including abnormal behaviour. In response to limitations of the ICD system, the American Psychiatric Association published its own classification system, the Diagnostic and Statistical Manual (DSM), in 1952. Both of these systems of classification (ICD and DSM) have undergone numerous revisions, in efforts to address inadequacies of previous editions (e.g., poor reliability) and to ensure that research evidence informs our classification of mental disorders. Currently, the system of classification used most commonly in North America is the DSM-5.

- The editions of the DSM have progressed considerably in arriving at DSM-5 and recognize the importance of psychosocial features in the development and maintenance of psychological problems.

- To address some of the limitations of the diagnostic system, the DSM is periodically revised. The guiding principles behind the revisions are to update the diagnostic system, based on the most current available scientific evidence, and to enhance the clinical utility of the diagnostic system.

- Many professionals feel that current and past versions of the DSM remain too closely aligned with the medical model, and that this leads to excessive stigmatization and loss of information about individuals. The whole enterprise of diagnosis of mental disorders is also criticized for using categories that do not do justice to the complexity of human behaviour and for displaying gender and cultural biases.

- As we have seen, the DSM-5 is far from perfect. However, as the history of classification in the natural

sciences has demonstrated, the development of a diagnostic classification system is an ongoing process that requires continual refinement. Classification is an accepted procedure in all sciences, and it is very likely that the field of mental health will continue to use it. It is encouraging to note that the field of mental health is continually looking to efforts to improve and validate the diagnostic system using empirical evidence. This scientific attitude should allow the detection of flaws in the present system and lead to an improved diagnostic system in the future. An example of this is the NIMH's adoption of RDoC as a way of encouraging researchers to examine underlying processes across domains of functioning and at various levels of analysis to better understand psychopathology, and eventually, to develop a more biologically valid classification system and better treatments. Gradually, diagnostic categories in any mental health taxonomy should be refined as we fill in the present gaps in our knowledge and come to recognize how culture, politics, and social norms have influenced professional concepts of mental health. This refinement process is well under way.

KEY TERMS

assessment (p. 50)

atheoretical (p. 52)

bipolar disorders (p. 54)

categorical approach (p. 57)

comorbidity (p. 55)

concurrent validity (p. 51)

diagnosis (p. 49)

diagnostic system (p. 49)

dimensional approach (p. 57)

inter-rater reliability (p. 51)

major depressive disorder (p. 54)

mania (p. 54)

polythetic (p. 52)

predictive validity (p. 51)

reliability (p. 51)

validity (p. 51)

DAVID J. A. DOZOIS

·

MONICA F. TOMLINSON

CHAPTER

4

Anson0618/Shutterstock

Psychological Assessment and Research Methods

LEARNING OBJECTIVES

AFTER READING THIS CHAPTER, STUDENTS WILL BE ABLE TO:

1 Differentiate between psychological testing and psychological assessment and describe the importance of this distinction.

2 Explain the importance of reliability and validity in clinical assessment.

3 Describe the strengths and weaknesses of clinical versus actuarial prediction.

4 Compare and contrast structured versus unstructured interviews and describe circumstances in which you might favour one format over the other.

5 Define what an "experiment" is and explain what differentiates it from non-experimental research methods.

6 Explain why it is important to consider clinical significance in addition to statistical significance.

Aidan was a boy, aged 5 years and 10 months, whose parents had requested a psychological assessment because his teachers had reported that he was disruptive in class and performing below his peers. His teachers wondered whether Aidan's mediocre academic achievement and disruptive behaviour might be caused by family or emotional problems.

The psychologist addressed this assessment on three fronts. First, he interviewed Aidan's family, starting with the whole family together: Aidan, his parents, and his brother, who was three years older. Then he spoke to the parents alone, to each of the boys alone, and to the two boys together. The psychologist also asked the teachers to complete the Vineland Adaptive Behavior Scales (Sparrow, Cicchetti, & Balla, 2005), a measure widely used to assess children's behavioural development and skills as well as the Child Behavior Checklist (Achenbach & Rescorla, 2001), a checklist widely used to assess classroom behaviour. Finally, Aidan's IQ was assessed using the Wechsler Intelligence Scale for Children (Wechsler, 2014).

The psychologist did not find evidence of marital problems or family issues beyond the normal strains of raising two young boys. The behaviour checklist showed a problem only on the scales that measure attention/impulsivity, on which Aidan scored at approximately the 71st percentile for his age group. On the adaptive behaviour scales, his scores suggested that had difficulty following rules and playing with others. Aidan scored within normal limits on scales that measure anxiety, depression, and antisocial behaviour. Aidan's IQ was very high. His overall score placed him in the 98th percentile, with excellent performance in all areas.

The psychologist's report, which was provided to both the parents and the school, included the following interpretations:

- There was no evidence of family issues leading to Aidan's problem behaviour.
- Aidan's problem behaviour in class was largely a result of difficulty with concentration and impulsivity.
- Aidan's personality assessment suggested that he was a bit immature.
- Aidan's IQ was in the gifted range. His academic performance was indeed below his potential.

The report noted that because Aidan was born in the winter, just before the school's January cut-off for registration, he was the youngest boy, and one of the youngest children, in his class. Some of his impulsive actions and inattention might reflect his youth, and may no longer be a problem in a year. His intellectual abilities may have allowed him to function as well as he did despite this immaturity. The report suggested that since Aidan was only in Grade 1 and his problems were not severe, the school should monitor his behaviour for another year. The only action recommended was that both the parents and the school be firm in response to Aidan's aggressive behaviour to ensure that Aidan knows what is considered acceptable.

In the following school year, Aidan was placed in an accelerated class containing only 12 children. Aidan did very well academically with the increased structure and supervision, and his classroom behaviour improved dramatically.

Assessment

As mentioned in Chapter 3, an accurate diagnosis provides a shorthand description of many important attributes of a patient and allows some predictions about the individual's development. This diagnosis usually results from a **psychological assessment**, a systematic gathering and evaluation of information pertaining to an individual with suspected abnormal behaviour. This assessment can be carried out with a wide variety of techniques to appraise social, psychological, and/or biological factors.

A diagnosis is only as good as the assessment on which it is based, and the assessment, in turn, is only as good as the tools used to carry it out. Therefore, good diagnosis hinges on the development of accurate assessment tools. Think of your car, for example. If the gas gauge is faulty, you cannot easily tell whether problems with your engine or a lack of gas caused you to come to a sudden, grinding halt.

Psychological assessment is not a single score but a series of scores placed *within the context* of the history, referral information, behavioural observations, and life of an individual to provide a comprehensive understanding of that individual (Meyer et al., 2001). It is important to remember that a test is only a sample of behaviour—a tool to be used in this process of assessment. A good medical analogy is that of a blood sample; the medical assessment takes the blood work information from the lab and integrates it with other information (e.g., symptoms, age, history) to arrive at a comprehensive understanding of the client's presenting complaints and problems. Unfortunately, many individuals fail to appreciate the differences between testing and assessment and, particularly with the advent of computerized testing, the process of comprehensive assessment may be overlooked.

Although assessments are usually thought of in relation to diagnosis, they may also have other specific purposes. An IQ test may be used to guide school placement, a neuropsychological test to assess the natural progression of a disorder, or a symptom checklist to facilitate case formulation or gauge the success of treatment.

A good assessment tool depends on two things: an accurate ability to measure some aspect of the person being assessed, and knowledge of how people in general fare on such a measure, for the purposes of comparison. Because this knowledge is derived from research, in the second half of this chapter we turn our attention to research methods. You will also notice that assessment and research often use similar methods—sometimes even the same tools—and must deal with similar issues of reliability and validity.

① BEFORE MOVING ON

> What is the difference between psychological testing and psychological assessment? Why is it important to distinguish between them?

ASSESSMENT TOOLS: STRIVING FOR THE WHOLE PICTURE

A diagnostician trying to understand someone is attempting to piece together a puzzle. The patient may be able to present a partial description of issues related to the suspected psychological abnormality, from his or her unique perspective. This report gives one piece of the puzzle, but the clinician needs a more objective perspective. Glimpses of the past, revealing the patient's behaviour and experiences at various ages and in various settings, will provide a few more pieces. Missing at this point from the overall picture are accounts of the patient's emotional, cognitive, and physiological states. Sometimes patients cannot report on their own internal states, even when they can accurately describe their observable behaviour. Fortunately, psychological methods are available to fill in many of the missing pieces. The most useful understanding of a patient comes from a combination of techniques to shed light on the individual's overall functioning.

RELIABILITY AND VALIDITY

Of course, to be useful, any test must be both reliable and valid, as discussed in Chapter 3. Several types of reliability are particularly important for psychological tests.

Test-retest reliability refers to the degree to which a test yields the same results when it is given more than once to the same person. For example, if your score on an IQ test is dramatically different from one day to the next, the test does not provide a good measure of intelligence. Test-retest reliability can be evaluated by correlating a person's score on the same test at two different time points. The higher the relationship between the two scores (expressed as a correlation coefficient), the greater the reliability. One obvious problem is that a person may improve on a test the second time around because of practice with the procedures or familiarity with the questions. To circumvent this problem, behavioural scientists often attempt to ascertain a test's **alternate-form reliability**. To do this, the test designers prepare two forms of the same test—that is, they decide what construct they want their test to measure, develop questions (or items) that would test that construct, and then word those questions in a slightly different way to create a comparable second version of the test that correlates highly with the first test.

Internal consistency refers to the degree of reliability within a test. That is, to what extent do different parts of the same test yield the same results? One measure of internal consistency is **split-half reliability**, which is often evaluated by comparing responses on odd-numbered test items with responses on even-numbered test items. If the scores for these responses are highly correlated, then the test has high split-half reliability. Another method for evaluating internal consistency, **coefficient alpha**, is calculated by averaging the intercorrelations of all items on a given test. The higher the coefficient alpha, the higher the internal consistency of the test.

Clearly an unreliable measure is useless. However, as discussed in Chapter 3, a reliable measure may be of little value if it is not *valid*. As we shall see later in this chapter, there are several measures of intelligence that have excellent reliability quotients. However, their usefulness is still hotly debated. What exactly do they measure? How well do they predict future functioning? In addition to concurrent validity and predictive validity, discussed in Chapter 3, there are several other types of validities related to psychological tests.

Face validity means that the user of a test believes that the items on that test resemble the characteristics associated with the concept being tested. For example, suppose that a test for assertiveness asks questions like "How do you react when you are overcharged in a store? When someone cuts in front of you in a line?" Because such behaviours seemingly relate to the general concept of assertiveness, the test would have face validity.

Content validity goes one step further and requires that a test's content include a representative sample of all behaviours thought to be related to the construct (i.e., the concept or entity) that the test is designed to measure. For example, the construct of depression includes features such as lack of energy, sadness, and negative self-perception. To have content validity, an instrument designed to assess depression should address such features. A test that focused only on sadness without considering other features would not have good content validity.

The concept of **criterion validity** arises because some qualities are easier to recognize than to define completely. Suppose you wanted to know whether a calculator was working properly; you could input a problem to which you already know the answer: say, "6 × 5." If the calculator gives an answer of 368, you know it is not a valid instrument. Now suppose you wanted to develop a test for artistic ability. You design an instrument that asks many questions about creative behaviour and activities. You then give the test to a large group of well-known and highly regarded artists and to a control group of people not identified as artistic. If the artists' test scores are much higher than the non-artists' scores, your test has good criterion validity. Note that this large survey is not an assessment of the people involved; you started with the assumption that the artists are artistic. It is the test instrument that is being evaluated.

Construct validity refers to the importance of a test within a specific theoretical framework and can only be understood in the context of that framework. This type of validity is especially useful when the construct to be measured is abstract, such as self-esteem. To design a measure of self-esteem, for example, you could draw from theories that predict self-esteem. Developmental psychologists suggest that children who come from emotionally supportive families have higher self-esteem than those from neglectful or abusive families. Therefore, the measure of self-esteem could be given to groups of children from either background to see how much the construct validity of the self-esteem measure was related to the backgrounds of these children.

2 BEFORE MOVING ON

Issues of reliability and validity are obviously important in the context of research. Why do you think they are important for clinical assessment?

CLINICAL VERSUS ACTUARIAL PREDICTION

How can one best take all the information available about a patient and put it together? Two very different approaches to this question have been developed. People who endorse the **clinical approach** argue that there is no substitute for the clinician's experience and personal judgment. They prefer to draw on all available data in their own manner; they are guided by intuition honed with professional experience rather than by formal rules. Those who endorse the **actuarial approach** argue that a more objective standard is needed—something primarily based in empirical data. They rely exclusively on statistical procedures, empirical methods, and formal rules in evaluating data.

Which method is superior? Decades of research have suggested that the actuarial approach tends to be much more efficient in making predictions in a variety of situations (e.g., relapse, dangerousness, improvement in therapy, success in university), especially when many predictions must be made and the base of data is large (Meehl, 1954, 1959; see Dozois, 2013).

In spite of the research evidence (which has favoured actuarial methods unequivocally), clinicians still tend to rely on the clinical method (Grove & Lloyd, 2006). Statistical rules (e.g., regression equations) do outperform clinical hunches, but there are two basic problems with them. First, many of the equations and algorithms found in the literature do not generalize to practice settings. Second, there are no prediction rules for the bulk of our decisions.

3 BEFORE MOVING ON

What are the strengths and weaknesses of clinical versus actuarial prediction?

Biological Assessment

In trying to determine the cause of abnormal behaviour, it is important to be aware of any medical conditions that may be causing or contributing to such behaviour. For example, it has been well established that one form of psychosis may be caused by syphilis (see Chapter 1), which is readily diagnosed with a simple blood test. We also know that disruptions in the functioning of the thyroid may mimic anxiety and depression in previously psychologically stable individuals. When medication stabilizes the thyroid functions, their psychological symptoms abate. Many other medical conditions can also affect behaviour. Further, sufficient exposure to certain illicit substances (such as cocaine and cannabis) can induce, usually transient, psychotic-like symptoms that mimic symptoms of psychotic spectrum disorders (Kraan et al., 2016; Willi et al., 2016). Therefore, it is important that a general physical examination be conducted as part of an assessment for psychological disorders.

BRAIN IMAGING TECHNIQUES

One of the oldest and most well-established brain imaging techniques is the electroencephalogram (EEG). The EEG uses electrodes placed on various parts of the scalp to measure the brain's electrical activity. These electrical impulses are carried to special electronic equipment that is able to amplify and record the activity in many parts of the brain. On occasion, patients may be asked to carry out a variety of visual or auditory tasks to see how their brains respond. Since we know so much about normal brain patterns, deviations in a particular part of the brain might be considered an indication of a problem for further investigation. Many seizure disorders, brain lesions, and tumours can be detected through EEG examinations.

Neuroimaging techniques can provide both structural and functional information concerning the physiological health of the central nervous system. Prior to the 1970s, brain imaging was done through radiography. This method could identify problems with the cerebral vasculature, but could not identify differences in tissue density.

COMPUTED TOMOGRAPHY (CT) At the beginning of the 1970s, rapid developments in computer technology made possible a revolutionary brain imaging technique known as **computerized axial tomography (CAT)**, or CT scan. In this procedure, a narrow band of X-rays is projected through the head and onto scintillation crystals, which are much more sensitive than X-ray film. The X-ray source and detector then rotate very slightly and project another image; to complete the scan, the source rotates a total of 180 degrees, producing a number of images at predetermined angles. Each separate exposure produces a matrix of dark and light areas, which are later combined by a computer to produce a highly detailed *tomography*, a two-dimensional image or cross-section of the brain. The resolution of this image can be further improved by injecting an iodinitic radiopaque substance to enhance the contrast between different sorts of tissue. The resolutional capability of a CT scan is in the range of about 1 millimetre in soft tissue, and it can resolve structures such as cerebral vasculature, ventricles, grey and white matter, and some subcortical structures such as the thalamus and basal ganglia. This provides a wealth of information about an individual, living brain.

CT scans have confirmed a number of ideas about how the brain works in abnormal psychology. CT scans can be used to look at changes in structural abnormalities before and after the treatment of a disorder. For example, stem cell transplants are being increasingly used to help treat the symptoms of autism. The stem cell transplants have been shown to improve immune functioning and increase the amount of oxygen and nutrients being transferred to

Case Notes

A physician referred Michael, a seven-year-old boy, to a psychologist. Michael's mother, a registered nurse, told the psychologist that Michael had experienced eight short, unpredictable seizures over a period of three months. Michael could not remember having them and no one but his mother had witnessed them. On one occasion, Michael had a seizure while in the car with his mother, only 10 minutes from a hospital. By the time they reached the hospital, there was no medical evidence of any seizure activity. Michael had been given a full medical and neurological examination and declared healthy. The referring physician suspected that Michael may have been faking the seizures to get attention or sympathy from his parents. The psychologist spent several sessions with each family together and alone. Once, while the parents were in the psychologist's office at the hospital, Michael fell and had what appeared to be a very short seizure while in the neurology waiting area. This was the first time that someone other than his mother had been present. Once again, there were no medical signs of a seizure. According to the psychologist, there were no psychological reasons for the seizure either. About six months later, the psychologist saw Michael being pushed in a wheelchair by his mother. A few weeks after that, Michael had deteriorated rapidly. Only at that point were physicians able to diagnose a very rare and progressive brain disorder that would lead to death within a year. The disorder could not be diagnosed in its early stages with the technology available at that time.

This is not the only case we have seen—though it was certainly the most dramatic—in which what appeared to be a psychological disorder was the first sign of some medical problem.

different areas of the brain. A group of researchers in India performed stem cell transplants on 32 patients with autism and followed them up for over two years. Not only did these patients' speech, language, communication, social interactions, and emotional responsiveness improve in many cases, but their brains showed changes too. CT scans were conducted on 8 of the 32 patients, and researchers found changes in glucose metabolism, primarily in the frontal and parietal lobes (Sharma et al., 2013).

MAGNETIC RESONANCE IMAGING (MRI) Nuclear magnetic resonance imaging, or simply **magnetic resonance imaging (MRI)**, is a non-invasive technique, developed in the early 1980s, that reveals both the structure and the functioning of the brain. A strong homogeneous magnetic field is produced around the patient's head. This field causes atoms with odd atomic weights (especially hydrogen) to align their electrons parallel to the direction of the field. Brief pulses of radio waves are subsequently introduced, causing these electrons to move in a characteristic gyroscopic manner. When the radio waves are turned off, the electrons return to their original configuration and, in doing so, emit radio waves of their own at a characteristic frequency, which can then be detected outside a patient's head. By adding a small magnetic gradient to the field, the frequency of radio wave transmission by atoms within the brain is altered to correlate with the gradient, allowing scientists to determine the location of the radio source. The information gathered is then integrated into a computer-generated image of the brain (see Figure 4.1). MRI techniques are capable of discriminating extremely small differences in water concentration. MRI is also a safe technology: because it uses neither high-energy radiation (X-rays) nor injections, it avoids the risks of overexposure and neurological complications. Studies using MRI have now corroborated results found in previous imaging studies, including the decreased grey matter volume in the frontal lobes of individuals with schizophrenia (Brent, Thermenos, Keshavan, & Seidman, 2013).

Functional magnetic resonance imaging (fMRI) is a more recent modification (early 1990s) of MRI. fMRI provides a dynamic view of metabolic changes occurring in the active brain (Seibyl, Scanley, Krystal, & Innis, 2004). A recent study conducted by researchers at the University of Western Ontario (Penner et al., 2016) helps to illustrate what kinds of information can be gleaned from fMRI investigations. This research looked at whether individuals with different mental disorders had anomalies in the connections between different brain regions. The researchers hypothesized that disruptions in the connections between different brain regions could impair cognitive processes and contribute to distorted thinking patterns, such as those seen in schizophrenia and depression.

FIGURE 4.1 An Image of the Brain Produced through Magnetic Resonance Imaging

Interestingly, they found that patients with schizophrenia had reduced connectivity between the medial prefrontal cortex and the dorsal anterior cingulate cortex. These regions are often implicated in individuals' sense of control over their thoughts (which is related to the symptomatology of schizophrenia; see Chapter 9). Among patients with depression, reduced connectivity was found between the medial prefrontal cortex and the ventral prefrontal emotional encoding regions. Both patient groups were compared to healthy controls. Reduced connectivity in these areas is associated with a reduced accuracy in encoding and interpreting emotional information—a common symptom among individuals with depression. fMRI scans have also been used to determine how patients respond to therapy. Structural brain changes correlated strongly with changes in symptoms of depression (Sankar et al., 2015), showing that biological changes can impact changes in patients' thoughts and feelings or vice-versa.

MRI research is also being enhanced by scalp recordings of electrical activity (event-related potentials, or ERPs) and magnetic fields (e.g., magnetoencephalography, or MEG). ERP methodology has been widely used but, because the brain is not electrically homogeneous, finding the source of the electrical potential is difficult and the spatial resolution is low. MEG, in contrast, allows for a more precise determination of the source of activation (Hari, 2015). Recent studies have used this advanced technology to look at dynamic changes in individuals' response to stimuli over a period of time. Wessing, Romer, and Junghöfer (2016), for example, found that children with anxiety disorders initially process threatening stimuli (e.g., angry faces) with more vigilance than do healthy children, but avoid threating stimuli more than healthy children at later time intervals.

POSITRON EMISSION TOMOGRAPHY (PET) **Positron emission tomography (PET)** is a combination of computerized tomography and radioisotope imaging. As in MRI, radiation is detected outside the head. In the case of PET, the radiation is generated by injected or inhaled *radioisotopes*—that is, common elements or substances that have had the atom altered to be radioactive (Matusch & Kroll, 2017). Isotopes with half-lives of minutes to hours are required for a PET scan. As the substance is used in brain activity, radiation is given off and detected by the PET equipment. This process allows the scientist to measure a variety of biological activities as the processes occur in the living brain. Recall from Chapter 2 the importance of neurotransmitters in brain activity. Providing a radioactive version of a *ligand*—a common molecule present in the chemical bonding that characterizes neurotransmission—allows the PET scan to show the distribution of various neurotransmitters within the brain. Similarly, glucose with a radioactive "label" (so called because it can be detected by the equipment) allows the rate of metabolic activity to be measured. Thus, while CT scans and MRIs can produce a static image of the brain's anatomy, PET scans and fMRIs produce a dynamic image of the functioning brain (see Figure 4.2).

Clinicians often use CT or MRI in addition to PET scans to determine the cause of structural abnormalities,

Photo Researchers/Science History Images/Alamy Stock Photo

FIGURE 4.2 PET Scan Images of a Brain of a Patient with Schizophrenia and a Brain of Someone Without a Psychiatric Disorder

such as reduced blood flow. PET scans have confirmed that there are abnormal patterns of metabolic activity in people with seizures, tumours, autism spectrum disorders, stroke, Alzheimer's disease, schizophrenia, bipolar disorder, and obsessive-compulsive disorder; they also show atypical patterns of cortical blood flow as they perform cognitive tasks. (Altamura et al., 2013; Morioka et al., 2007; Zipursky, Meyer, & Verhoeff, 2007; Zürcher, Bhanot, McDougle, & Hooker, 2015). A group of researchers from the Rotman Research Institute at Baycrest Centre and the Centre for Addiction and Mental Health, both in Toronto, used PET to study brain changes in individuals who were receiving cognitive-behaviour therapy (CBT) for depression (Goldapple et al., 2004). The findings from these patients were compared to an independent sample of individuals who had responded to a serotonin-based antidepressant (paroxetine). These researchers found a distinct pattern of metabolic changes (in limbic and cortical regions) in patients who received CBT, but not among those who received antidepressants who received antidepressants (also see Franklin, Carson, & Welch, 2016; Frewen, Dozois, & Lanius, 2008). The future of neuroimaging rests in the integration of various techniques to provide a comprehensive understanding of both normal and abnormal brain functioning (e.g., Bandettini & Wong, 2015; Lequin & Hendrikse, 2017).

NEUROPSYCHOLOGICAL ASSESSMENTS

Neuropsychological assessments are used to determine relations between behaviour and brain function. These assessments are often conducted by neuropsychologists, who are specially trained to assess and diagnose

neurological impairment. Many psychometrically rigorous psychological tests can be used within the context of a neuropsychological assessment. Screening tools are most often used in neuropsychological assessments to provide a brief evaluation of whether neurological impairment may be present. Some well-known neuropsychological screening tests are the **Bender Visual-Motor Gestalt Test** (Bender-Gestalt II; Brannigan & Decker, 2003), **Repeatable Battery for the Assessment of Neuropsychological Status** (RBANS; Randolph, Tierney, Mohr, & Chase, 1998), the **Montreal Cognitive Assessment** (MoCA; Nasreddine et al., 2005), and the screening elements of the **Halstead-Reitan Neuropsychological Test Battery** (Reitan & Wolfson, 1985).

The Bender Visual-Motor Gestalt Test is the oldest neuropsychological screening test (Piotrowski, 2016; see Figure 4.3). The second (and most recent) version of this test, referred to as the Bender-Gestalt II, was created in 2003 (Brannigan & Decker, 2003). The Bender-Gestalt II has 16 designs, a subset of which are selected based on the individuals' age.

Respondents are asked first to copy the designs onto another card and then to draw them from memory. The copied and recalled designs are scored using The Global Scoring System, which evaluates the representation of each design on the basis of its overall quality using a 5-point (0 to 4) rating scale (Brannigan & Decker, 2003). The main problem with this test is that it produces many false negatives; that is, some people with neurological impairment can complete the test with few errors.

The RBANS (Randolph et al., 1998) addresses many of the concerns raised by critics of the Bender-Gestalt by assessing a range of abilities (beyond visuo-constructional and memory abilities). The RBANS is a brief screening tool of 12 subtests that cover a wide range of domains relevant to neurological impairment. This test takes approximately 20 to 30 minutes to administer and is exclusively used with adults. The subtests cover five major domains of functioning: immediate memory, visuo-spatial/constructional ability, language, attention, and delayed memory (Groth-Marnat, 2016). This screening tool has strong psychometric properties, is simple to administer, and is age-normed, that is, results can be compared to individuals who are a similar age to the patient (Strauss, Sherman, & Spreen, 2006).

The MoCA is another commonly used, psychometrically valid, brief, and very rapid screening tool for mild cognitive impairment (Nasreddine et al., 2005). Created in 1996 in Montreal, this test assesses a broad range of domains, including attention and concentration, memory, executive functioning, visuo-constructional skills, and orientation in approximately 10 minutes, thus making it a more practical tool than the RBANS in busy hospital settings.

The screening components of the Halsted-Reitan Neuropsychological Test Battery include many similar measures to the MOCA and the RBANS. This measure also includes tests of sensory perceptions, such as sound and touch perception (Groth-Marnat, 2016). This test can take several hours to complete and is not generally recommended as a screening test.

When neurological impairment is suspected, comprehensive assessments are used. Neuropsychological assessments involve a review of the patient's developmental and medical history as well as the administration of standardized comprehensive neuropsychological tests (Strauss et al., 2006). Typically, the tests administered cover the domains of *cognitive functioning* (e.g., the Wechsler Adult Intelligence Scale, fourth edition; Wechsler, 2008), *executive functioning* (e.g., The Delis-Kaplan Executive Functioning System; Delis, Kaplan, & Kramer, 2001), *attention/concentration* (e.g., Trail Making Test; Reitan & Wolfson, 1985), *memory* (e.g., the Wechsler Memory Scale; Wechsler, 1997) *motivation* (the Test of Memory Malingering; Tombaugh, 1996), *language* (Peabody Picture Vocabulary Test; Dunn & Dunn, 2007), *visual functioning* (the Beery-Buktenica Developmental Test of Visual-Motor Integration (Beery & Beery, 2010), *motor functioning* (Finger Tapping Test, Grooved Pegboard Test), *somatosensory/olfaction* (Smell Identification Test), *academic achievement* (the Wechsler Individual Achievement Test; Wechsler, 2009) and *personality/emotional functioning* (e.g., Personality Assessment Inventory; Morey, 2007).

A full neuropsychological battery of tests can take several hours to administer, depending on the patient and on the reason for the assessment. Given how demanding these assessments are for the patient, it is important to complete them when the patient is functioning at his or her optimal state in order to achieve the most valid results possible. Therefore, the assessment should take place when the patient is relatively stable medically and emotionally.

FIGURE 4.3   The Bender Visual-Motor Gestalt Test

Note: Part A shows the nine images that respondents are asked to reproduce. Part B shows the drawings of a person known to have brain damage.

Psychological Assessment

CLINICAL INTERVIEWS

The clinical interview is the most common assessment tool, and is used by almost every clinician. This method allows the clinician to better understand what symptoms are occurring, what they look like, under what circumstances they are occurring, and how they are affecting the individual. As mentioned earlier in this chapter, a psychological test is meaningless unless it is placed within the context of an individual's life. The clinical interview provides this valuable contextual information. Practitioners ask about many aspects of the individual's life: medical history, psychiatric history, age, marital status, family, education, and lifestyle, as well as the reason the person is seeking consultation.

Not all interviews are the same. Different types of interviews are often used to provide different kinds of information.

UNSTRUCTURED INTERVIEWS As the name implies, unstructured interviews tend to be open-ended, allowing the interviewer to pursue a specific line of questioning or to follow the patients' lead. Patients are often under considerable stress, and are being asked to reveal very personal and sometimes embarrassing information to a stranger. In an unstructured interview, it is relatively easy to avoid a sensitive topic until a patient is more at ease. Thus, the main advantage of unstructured interviews is that they facilitate **rapport**, mutual trust, and respect between clinician and patient.

The major criticism of this type of interview is its poor reliability and validity. The clinician's own theoretical orientation and personality greatly influence the type of information sought. For example, a behavioural therapist might focus on immediate circumstances surrounding a patient's problem, whereas a psychodynamic therapist might focus on childhood memories and dream content. Thus, clinicians may tend to uncover only the information that fits their theoretical orientation and confirms their hypotheses.

STRUCTURED INTERVIEWS How can an interview get away from the subjectivity of the interviewer and become a reliable procedure? A number of *structured interviews* have been developed that strictly prescribe the wording of questions and the interpretation of responses. The Diagnostic Interview Schedule, Version IV (DIS-IV; Robins et al., 2000), is a highly structured interview that can be administered by both mental health professionals and trained lay interviewers. The DIS-IV was developed for large-scale epidemiological research. Because of the large number of participants required for epidemiological studies, the cost of paying for professional diagnosticians is often prohibitive. By increasing the standardization of a diagnostic interview, and requiring that each question be read aloud verbatim, researchers are able to obtain the information they need without having to rely on the judgments of individual lay interviewers (Compton & Cottler, 2004). Although highly structured interviews might increase reliability, they tend to jeopardize rapport.

4 BEFORE MOVING ON

What are the advantages and disadvantages of structured and unstructured interviews? In what circumstances might you want to favour one format over another?

SEMI-STRUCTURED INTERVIEWS To reap the benefits of unstructured and highly structured approaches while simultaneously avoiding their pitfalls, *semi-structured interviews* have been developed. As in the unstructured interview, the clinician has considerable leeway about what questions to ask, in what order, and with what wording. The questions are guided, however, by an outline that lists certain dimensions of the patient's functioning that need to be covered. The most frequently used semi-structured interview in psychiatric settings is the **mental status examination** (see Table 4.1), which screens for patients' emotional, intellectual, and

TABLE 4.1 DIMENSIONS ASSESSED BY THE MENTAL STATUS EXAMINATION

1. *Appearance.* Is the patient clean and well groomed?
2. *Behaviour.* Are there any peculiar aspects to the patient's behaviour, such as atypical speech patterns (speed or cadence), odd mannerisms or tics, strange posture or gait? Do they appear cooperative or defensive?
3. *Sensorium* (sensory apparatus). Do the five senses appear to be intact?
4. *Affect* (expressed emotional responses). Has the patient expressed anger, anxiety, or any other general state during the interview? Has the patient's affect been inappropriate to the topic (e.g., laughing or smiling when sad things were being discussed)?
5. *Risk.* Does the patient appear to be a risk to him- or herself? Has the patient harmed him- or herself in the past? Has the patient had any thoughts of harming or killing him- or herself? Is the person at risk of harming another person?
6. *Orientation.* Is the patient aware of who he or she is; where he or she is; the time, date, and year?
7. *Thought content.* Does the patient describe hearing or seeing things whose existence is questionable? Does the patient seem to have delusions of persecution, grandeur, or the like?
8. *Memory.* How intact is the patient's memory for long-past events and recent events?
9. *Intelligence.* How sophisticated is the patient's vocabulary? How well does the patient express thoughts and ideas, use and understand abstractions and metaphors? Is the patient able to express and understand sophisticated concepts?
10. *Thought processes.* Is thought logical and coherent, or is there evidence of a loosening of associations, apparently unconnected ideas that are joined together?
11. *Insight.* Is the patient aware of his or her situation, and able to appreciate its severity and the necessity for clinical assistance?
12. *Judgment.* Has the patient shown the ability to make sound and well-thought-out decisions, in the past and presently?

neurological functioning. It is used in formal diagnosis or to plan treatment.

Many semi-structured interviews are designed to look for specific problems, such as behaviour problems of childhood (Mash & Barkley, 2007), depression (Dozois & Dobson, 2010), anxiety disorders (Summerfeldt, Kloosterman, & Antony, 2010), and personality disorders (Widiger & Lowe, 2010). The most used semi-structured interview to assess psychopathology is the Structured Clinical Interview for DSM Disorders (SCID-5; First, Williams, Karg, & Spitzer, 2015b). The SCID-5 follows the same approach as the decision trees for differential diagnoses found originally in DSM-III and now in DSM-5. At each point, the interviewer is instructed to ask a specific question. Patient responses are rated, and the interviewer is instructed to carry on with another set of questions depending on the patient's response. A "yes" response from the patient leads to a very different set of questions than a "no" response. The developers have also created a SCID for personality disorders (SCID-5-PD; First, Williams, Benjamin, & Spitzer, 2015) to assess for personality disorders according to the criteria in the DSM-5. The SCID-5 is also used commonly in research studies to screen for patients with different mental disorders (or to screen out patients with certain disorders). To facilitate the use of the SCID in research studies, versions of the SCID for general research (SCID-5-RV; First, Williams, Karg, & Spitzer, 2015c) and for clinical trials, specifically (SCID-5-CT; First, Williams, Karg, & Spitzer, 2015a), have also been developed.

RATING SCALES As in the case of interviews, the use of rating scales in clinical observation and in self-reports helps both to organize information and to encourage reliability and objectivity (McDowell, 2006). That is, the formal structure of a scale is likely to keep observer inferences to a minimum. The most useful rating scales are those that enable a rater to indicate not only the presence or absence of a trait or behaviour but also its prominence or degree. Ratings scales

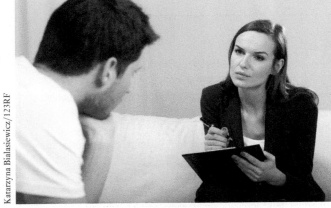

During an assessment interview, a clinician obtains information about various aspects of a patient's situation, behaviour, and personality makeup. The interview is usually conducted face-to-face and may have a relatively open structure or be more tightly controlled, depending on the goals and style of the clinician.

can be made not only as part of an initial evaluation but also to check on the course or outcome of treatment.

ASSESSMENT OF INTELLIGENCE

Intelligence tests were the first assessment tools developed by psychologists to win widespread acceptance; by now, virtually everyone in our society has heard of them. The first scientific study of intellectual functioning was conducted by the biologist Sir Francis Galton (1822–1911) in 1883, to test the hypothesis that intelligence has a hereditary aspect, a concept still being explored today. Galton believed that pure intelligence could best be measured by studying physiological cues—for example, the speed of response to a flash of light—an attribute later known as *sensory intelligence.* This was the first attempt to demonstrate the biological correlates of intelligence.

The first widely accepted and successful test of intelligence was designed to predict academic performance. The French psychologist Alfred Binet (1857–1911) was commissioned by the Paris school board to develop a means of determining which children should receive a public school education and which required special education. He did so by developing separate tests of judgment, comprehension, and reasoning. Binet was the first to use a large sample of participants to establish norms for the purpose of describing intelligence. His approach was to take a child's mental age, which was determined by the child's successful performance on age-grouped tests that had been normed, divide it by the child's chronological age, and multiply the quotient by 100. This would result in an **intelligence quotient,** or IQ. Theoretically, at least, an individual's IQ was always a reflection of that person's performance compared with the population of others of the same age. Therefore, a person aged 14.8 years who received a mental age score of 15.6 would achieve an IQ of $(15.6 / 14.8) \times 100 = 105$. Binet's work developed into the **Stanford-Binet Intelligence Scales**, which have been revised over the years and are now in their fifth edition (Roid, 2003). The most recent Stanford-Binet assesses five general kinds of ability: fluid reasoning, knowledge, visual-spatial processing, quantitative reasoning, and working memory (Becker, 2003; Kamphaus & Kroncke, 2004). It produces separate scores for each of these functions as well as a global IQ score that summarizes the child's ability.

Virtually all contemporary, standardized tests of intelligence, as well as other types of psychological tests, share Binet's basic principle of comparison. A person's IQ is a function of how his or her score compares to others of the same age. Convention has dictated that the average be set at 100: those who perform more poorly have lower IQs; those who perform better have higher IQs.

The most popular IQ tests were developed by David Wechsler (1896–1981). In 1939, he published the first widely used intelligence tests for adults. The most recent version of the **Wechsler Adult Intelligence Scale** was published in 2008 and is called the **WAIS-IV** (Wechsler, 2008). This test was designed to measure diverse aspects of intelligence

Katarzyna Bialasiewicz/123RF

and consists of 10 core subtests and five supplementary subtests: four verbal comprehension, three working memory, five perceptual reasoning tests, and 3 processing speed tests.

Figure 4.4 shows examples of two of the perceptual reasoning tasks. Average intelligence on this scale is an IQ of 100. The standard deviation (a measure of how far from the mean

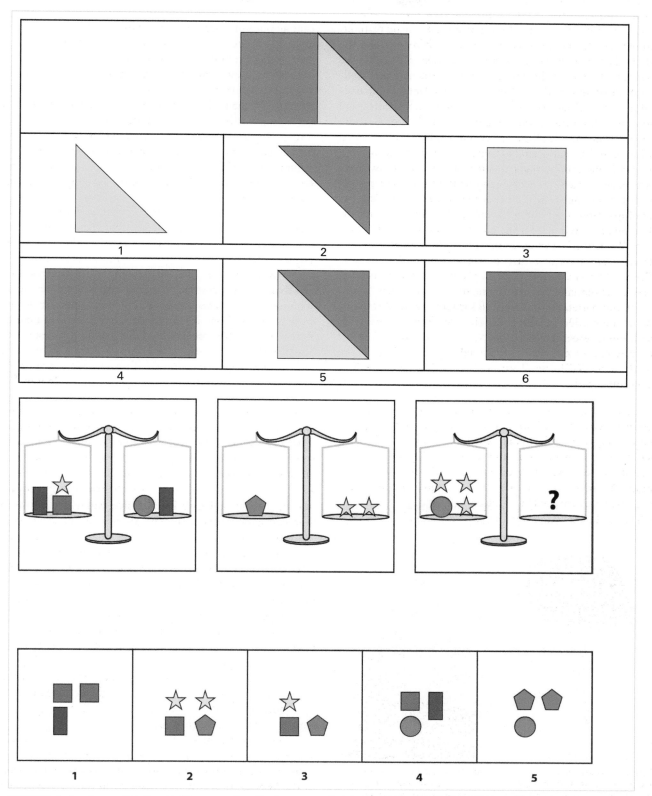

FIGURE 4.4   Items Similar to Those on the Performance Subtests of the Wechsler Adult Intelligence Scale IV

an average score will fall) on this instrument is 15, so scores below 70 fall in the lower extreme and scores above 130 indicate exceptional intelligence. In 1974, the Wechsler Intelligence Test for Children (WISC) was published. The most recent version is the WISC-V, published in 2014 (Wechsler, 2014). The Wechsler Preschool and Primary Scale of Intelligence (WPPSI) was originally published in 1967 and the WPPSI-IV was released in 2012 (Wechsler, 2012). These Wechsler scales are the epitome of well-designed and well-researched assessment tools. They have very good test-retest and split-half reliability and concurrent validity, and readily distinguish between the intellectually gifted, those with learning disabilities, and individuals with intellectual disabilities (Gordon, 2004; Groth-Marnat, 2016; Sattler, 2008). In the last few years, many of the Wechsler tests have become available in a web-based format through a system called Q-Global. Through this system, psychologists can administer and score these tests using two iPads, one for the administrator and one for the client. This web-based system helps to further standardize the administration and scoring of these tests, significantly shortens that amount of time spent scoring these tests, and facilitates the rapid distribution of test updates, such as revised norms.

Of all psychological traits, IQ shows the most stability. As demonstrated in Table 4.2, the correlation diminishes with time, but a correlation of 0.78 from 8 to 15 years of age is quite remarkable. It should be noted, however, that more than half of all children show a variation of 10 points or more between early school years and adolescence. Some children have shown as much as a 40-point change in IQ within the same time period (Bukatko & Daehler, 2012).

What does IQ really predict? The typical correlation between IQ scores and academic performance is about 0.50-0.70, suggesting that 25 to 49% of the variance in academic achievement can be accounted for by IQ, depending on the tests being studied, the age of the individuals assessed, and how academic performance is measured (Bornstein & Lamb, 2010; Gagné & St. Père, 2002). In fact, IQ has consistently been considered the strongest predictor of academic performance,

even after accounting for other social, economic, genetic, and personality-related factors (Gagné & St. Père, 2002; Spinath, Spinath, Harlaar, & Plomin, 2006). Naturally, personality-related factors are extremely important. Studies have shown that both motivation and self-discipline account for a significant amount of variance in individual's school performance, and some argue that self-discipline is an even better predictor of school performance than IQ. However, the researchers making these claims used less rigorous measures of IQ, which may limit the interpretation of these findings (Duckworth & Seligman, 2005). As expected, education also affects IQ. Children who attend high quality schools, regularly, for longer periods of time have higher IQs than children who have fewer years of school, attend school intermittently, and attend lower quality schools (Bornstein & Lamb, 2010; Wang, Ren, Schweizer, & Xu, 2015). Beyond academic achievement, IQ also predicts occupation (Strenze, 2007), job performance (Drasgow, 2012; Ones, Dilchert, & Viswesvaran, 2012), health (Gottfredson & Deary, 2004), income (Kura, 2013; Lynn, 2010; Strenze, 2007), and general life satisfaction (Bukatko & Daehler, 2011).

The use of IQ tests has become quite controversial. Do they really measure innate capacities or achievement? The issue of fairness is perhaps the most sensitive. Critics have argued that the IQ differences that have been found in North America between Whites, Blacks, and people of Asian background are actually a function of poor test construction; others argue that these differences are a function of respondents' socio-economic environments (Groth-Marnat, 2016), and others still argue that IQ is highly genetic and differences in IQ scores may represent real differences in IQ among different populations (Uzzell, Ponton, & Ardila, 2007). Certainly, IQ scores have to be evaluated within the context of ethnic, age, gender, and culturally appropriate norms. Dr. Donald Saklofske at the University of Western Ontario has been instrumental in developing Canadian norms for the Wechsler intelligence scales (e.g., Bowden, Saklofske, & Weiss, 2011; Weiss, Saklofske, Coalson, & Raiford, 2010).

PERSONALITY ASSESSMENT

The early success of intelligence tests in predicting academic performance stimulated research on the measure of personality. While intelligence tests tend to produce total scores, personality assessments usually describe various characteristics that make up an individual's unique personality. A wealth of tests, questionnaires, and rating scales are available that offer shortcuts to understanding an individual and to predicting behaviour. These formal personality tests and other assessment methods are widely used for a variety of tasks including research, personnel selection, and diagnosis in clinical settings.

PROJECTIVE TEST Projective tests have the longest history in modern personality assessment, and are generally rooted in psychoanalytic principles. The theory behind a **projective test** is that a person presented with an ambiguous

TABLE 4.2 CORRELATIONS OF INTELLIGENCE FROM 3 TO 15 YEARS OF AGE

Age	3	4	5	6	7	8	9	15
2	.74	.68	.63	.61	.54	.58	.56	.47
3		.76	.72	.73	.68	.67	.65	.58
4			.80	.79	.72	.72	.71	.60
5				.87	.81	.79	.79	.67
6					.86	.84	.84	.69
7						.87	.87	.69
8							.90	.78
9								.80

Source: Intelligence, vol. 2, 1992, by Nathan Brody, page 232, with permission from Elsevier.

Test Security: Posting of the Rorschach Inkblot Test

The Rorschach inkblot test made headlines in 2009 when an emergency room physician from Moose Jaw, Saskatchewan, posted the entire set of 10 inkblots along with a listing of possible responses to the test on the Wikipedia website (*http://en.wikipedia.org/wiki/Rorschach_test*). The doctor believed that such information should be available to anyone interested and not held in secrecy by psychologists and psychiatrists (Cohen, 2009). At the same time, information about the Rorschach test is already available in books at your neighbourhood library or bookstore (Exner, 2002; Exner & Erdberg, 2005).

Both professional psychologists/psychiatrists and the company that owned the rights to Hermann Rorschach's seminal book were outraged by the Wikipedia post. Dr. Karen Cohen, Chief Executive Officer of the Canadian Psychological Association, stated that, "the test becomes meaningless. If someone has all the questions and the answers, you can't administer the test." (Canadian Psychological Association, 2009; White, 2009). They pleaded for Wikipedia to remove the diagrams and answers, stating that the public posting would jeopardize one of the oldest continually used psychological tests. Regrettably, nothing could be done to remove these pictures as the copyright for the test has now expired and the pictures are public domain. There are growing fears that the images will be distributed widely through other internet sources, such as YouTube, Facebook, Instagram, Twitter, and LinkedIn.

In the last few years, research has turned to better understanding the impact of this Wikipedia exposure. Schultz and Loving (2012) found that, in only a few years, sensitive information about the Rorschach has rapidly spread. These researchers found 88 search results using the keywords "Rorschach" and "inkblot test" on popular search engines, and 19% of these included sensitive information on the Rorschach (e.g., pictures of the inkblots, lists of common responses, information on scoring the test, and recommendations for "faking" it). In a follow-up study, Schultz & Brabender (2013) found that people who had been exposed to this information tended to use this information to "fake healthy" on the test. These researchers concluded that this leaked information has the potential to compromise the validity of this test. Considering that projective tests, like the Rorschach, are used in high stakes court cases (e.g., to determine parental custody, legal responsibility), these findings warrant considerable concern. At the same time, there have been longstanding concerns about whether projective tests should ever be used in these high-stakes situations, regardless of whether individuals are exposed to them before testing (Wood et al., 2010). ●

---

stimulus will project onto that stimulus his or her unconscious motives, needs, drives, feelings, defences, and personality characteristics. Thus, the test reveals information that the person cannot or will not report directly. Projective tests are used to help clinicians form hypotheses about an individual's personality. Although the use of these tests remains controversial, they are still frequently adopted by clinicians (Basu, 2014; Frick, Barry, & Kamphaus, 2010).

Rorschach Inkblot Test. The oldest and probably best-known projective test is the **Rorschach inkblot test** (see Focus box 4.1). Hermann Rorschach (1884–1922), a Swiss psychologist, was intrigued as a child by the game of dripping ink on paper and folding the paper to make symmetrical figures. He noticed that people saw different things in the same inkblot, and he believed that their "percepts" reflected their personality. In high school, his friends gave him the nickname "Klecks," meaning "inkblot" in German. As a professional, he continued to experiment with hundreds of inkblots to identify those that could help in the diagnosis of psychological problems. At the age of 38, the year following the publication of these inkblots, he died of complications from a ruptured appendix. Figure 4.5 shows inkblots similar to those on the Rorschach test. Each inkblot is presented on a separate card and is handed to the respondent in a particular sequence. Initially, most clinicians used their own clinical approach to interpreting the results of a Rorschach examination. They would generally use the content of a patient's responses to the inkblots (e.g., "I see two people fighting"), as

well as colour, shading, texture, and movement in the interpretation of results. The **Exner system** was developed in an attempt to increase reliability and validity by standardizing the scoring of responses (Exner, 1993). Dr. John Hunsley at the University of Ottawa and Dr. Eric Mash at the University of Calgary have closely reviewed the scientific literature about the Rorschach and suggest that its weak psychometric properties make its clinical utility questionable (Hunsley & Mash, 2011). To improve the scoring of the Rorschach

xpixel/Shutterstock

FIGURE 4.5   Inkblots Like Those on the Rorschach Test

inkblot test, the Rorschach Performance Assessment System was recently developed (Meyer, Erard, Erdberg, Mihura, & Viglione, 2011). Research is still needed to determine whether this system is a reliable improvement from the Exner system (Lindh, 2015).

Unfortunately, the Rorschach test, as well as other projective instruments, tends to be used in ways that extend beyond what is warranted based on the empirical literature, and remains highly popular with some clinicians (Butcher, 2010; Widiger & Boyd, 2009; Wood et al., 2010).

Thematic Apperception Test. The **thematic apperception test (TAT)** was developed by psychologists Henry Murray (1893–1988) and Christiana Morgan (1897–1967) at Harvard University. *Apperception* is a French word that can be translated as "interpreting (new ideas or impressions) on the basis of existing ideas (cognitive structures and past experience)." The TAT consists of drawings on cards depicting ambiguous social interactions (see Figure 4.6). Individuals are asked to construct stories about the cards. Respondents are asked what they believe is happening in the scenes, what led up to these actions, what thoughts and feelings the character is experiencing, what happens next, and so on. Psychodynamically oriented clinicians assume that respondents identify with the protagonist or victims in their stories, and project their psychological needs and conflicts into the events they apperceive. On a more superficial level, the stories also

suggest how respondents might interpret or behave in similar situations in their own lives. The validity and reliability of scoring techniques are open to the same criticisms as the Rorschach inkblot test.

In general, advocates of projective tests argue that they may yield meaningful material not easily obtained by self-report questionnaires or interviews. Because people want to be judged favourably, many people will give socially desirable responses to questionnaires; that is, consciously or unconsciously, they try to answer according to what they think they ought to be rather than what they are. Projective tests avoid this problem by presenting an ambiguous picture and by not asking directly about the subject. However, research has not been very supportive of the reliability and validity of many of the projective techniques (Groth-Marnat, 2016; Hunsley & Mash, 2011). Rather, it appears that clinicians tend to interpret responses in a way that confirms their own clinical assumptions, without empirical validation of their accuracy. It appears that the degree of comfort professionals have with projective methods depends more on their acceptance of the underlying theories than on the reliability and validity of the techniques.

PERSONALITY INVENTORIES A range of instruments have also been developed that use scientifically accepted procedures such as standardization, establishment of norms, clinical and control groups, and statistically validated methods of interpretation.

Minnesota Multiphasic Personality Inventory. The most widely used objective test of personality is probably the **Minnesota Multiphasic Personality Inventory,** or **MMPI.** It was originally published in 1943 by Hathaway and McKinley. The revised and updated versions, the MMPI-2 for adults and the MMPI-A for adolescents, were published by Butcher, Dahlstrom, Graham, Tellegen, and Kaemmer (1989), and Butcher, Williams, Graham, Archer, Tellegen, Ben-Porath, and Kaemmer (1992), respectively. It is multiphasic because it assesses many aspects of personality. The MMPI-2 contains 567 questions grouped to form 10 content scales plus additional scales to detect sources of invalidity such as carelessness, defensiveness, or evasion (see Table 4.3). Each item is a statement; the respondent is asked to check "True," "False," or "Cannot Say." Many items appear to have little face validity—it is difficult to infer what the question is supposed to measure. In 2008, Ben-Porath and Tellegen published the MMPI-2 Restructured Form (MMPI-2-RF). This version has 338 true-false statements and was designed to provide a more nuanced assessment of symptom over-reporting (Ben-Porath & Tellegen, 2008). Issues of symptom over-reporting are particularly important to consider in legal cases, where individuals may be motivated to appear more psychologically unwell than they are to either receive mental health resources or to reduce their level of criminal responsibility for an offence. Dr. Michael Bagby from the Centre for

FIGURE 4.6 A Drawing Similar to Those on the Thematic Apperception Test

TABLE 4.3   THE MMPI-2 SCALES

The list below is a description of the Validity Indicators and Clinical Scales.	
Validity Indicators	
Cannot say (CNS) (?)	Measures the total number of unanswered items
Lie (L)	Measures the tendency to claim excessive virtue or to try to present an overall favourable image
Infrequency (F)	Measures the tendency to falsely claim or exaggerate psychological problems in the first part of the booklet; alternatively, detects random responding
Back F (F)	Measures the tendency to falsely claim or exaggerate psychological problems on items toward the end of the booklet
Infrequency-Psychopathology (Fb)	Measures the tendency to intentionally falsely claim or exaggerate psychological problems among individuals who have psychopathology
Correction (K)	Measures the tendency to see oneself in an unrealistically positive way
Variable Response Inconsistency (VRIN)	Measures the tendency to endorse items in an inconsistent or random manner
True Response Inconsistency (TRIN)	Measures the tendency to endorse items in a fixed manner.
Superlative Self-Presentation (S)	Measures the tendency to appear excessively good. Improves upon the K scale
Clinical Scales		
Scale 1	Hypochondriasis (Hs)	Measures excessive somatic concern and physical complaints
Scale 2	Depression (D)	Measures symptomatic depression
Scale 3	Hysteria (Hy)	Measures hysteroid personality features such as "rose-colored glasses" view of the world and the tendency to develop physical problems under stress
Scale 4	Psychopathic Deviate (Pd)	Measures antisocial tendencies
Scale 5	Masculinity/femininity (Mf)	Measures gender-role reversal
Scale 6	Paranoia (Pa)	Measures suspicious, paranoid ideation
Scale 7	Psychasthenia (Pt)	Measures anxiety and obsessive, worrying behaviour
Scale 8	Schizophrenia (Sc)	Measures peculiarities in thinking, feeling, and social behaviour
Scale 9	Hypomania (Ma)	Measures elated mood state and tendencies to yield to impulses
Scale 0	Social Introversion (Si)	Measures social anxiety, withdrawal, and overcontrol

Source: University of Minnesota Press.

Addiction and Mental Health in Toronto, with his American colleague, Dr. Martin Sellbom, found preliminary evidence that the added validity scales included in this restructured form can accurately differentiate between individuals who are intentionally trying to over-report their symptoms and individuals who actually have significant psychopathology (Sellbom & Bagby, 2010). This version also helps resolve a major limitation of the MMPI-2—its (sometimes prohibitive) length.

To establish the categories and items, the creators of the test compared the responses of a large number of patients with well-diagnosed disorders like depression, anxiety, antisocial disorders, paranoia, schizophrenia, and mania to each other and to the responses of non-diagnosed individuals. The MMPI is based on the *contrasted-groups* method of ascertaining validity: items were chosen only if people known to have the characteristic the scale is intended to measure responded differently to the item than did people who did not have that characteristic. For example, a question would appear on the depression scale only if there was a clear difference between the responses of a group of depressed people and a group of people who were not depressed. This technique establishes concurrent validity, with group membership as the criterion by which the validity of the test is gauged.

As is common with the new breed of actuarially based personality assessments, raw scores are converted into standard scores with a mean of 50 and a standard deviation of 10. An individual's personality profile is depicted as an elevation on a graph, which facilitates interpretation. Results of an MMPI-2 assessment do not constitute a diagnosis, but rather a profile of personality characteristics compared to psychiatric and non-psychiatric groups that may assist in forming a diagnosis. As an example, a standard score of 65 or higher on a particular scale places an individual at approximately the

92nd percentile or higher of the revised normative sample, and is considered to be clinically significant. The higher a score, the more likely is the presence of a disorder. Although a single scale may be informative, MMPI experts typically interpret the pattern of relative scores from the entire profile. In the hands of a trained clinician, this profile can provide considerable insight into the functioning of an individual. Focus box 4.2 gives an example of how an individual's scores can be analyzed.

Many items on objective tests like the MMPI-2 are clearly indicative of disturbed thoughts and feelings. The transparency of these items opens the opportunity for faking. MMPI-2 validity scales include the L (lie) scale, the F (infrequency) scale, and the K (defensive) scale, among others. The L scale contains items that refer to minor foibles or flaws in character that nearly all of us possess and admit

to readily. People who disavow these foibles may also deny items with more serious clinical implications. The lie scale identifies individuals who are trying to "fake good." The F scale contains items that were endorsed by fewer than 10 percent of the normal sample. A high F score may suggest random or careless responding, difficulty in reading or comprehending the test items, or an effort to "fake bad" to exaggerate complaints. An irony that clouds interpretation of the MMPI-2 is that abnormal validity scale scores do not necessarily invalidate the test for highly disturbed respondents such as individuals with schizophrenia. The K scale measures a subtler form of distortion, called psychological defensiveness or guardedness—respondents' tendency to conceal genuine feelings about sensitive issues to create a favourable impression. The K scale is used as a correction factor; scores on clinical scales that may be biased by

FOCUS 4.2   The MMPI-2: A Sample Profile

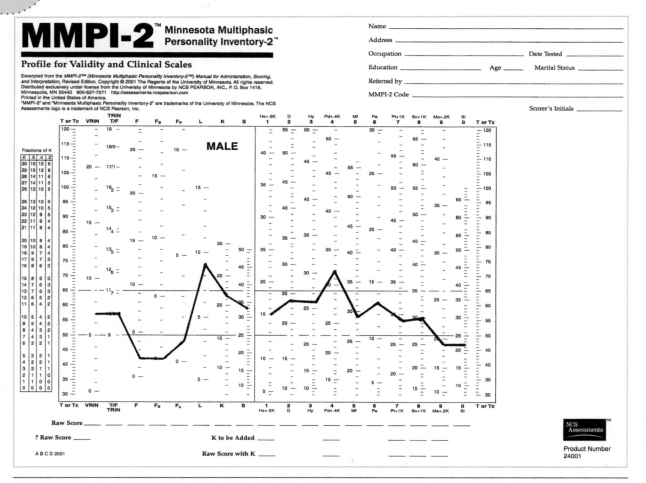

Source: Excerpted from the MMPI®-2 (Minnesota Multiphasic Personality Inventory®-2). Manual for Administration, Scoring and Interpretation, Revised Edition. Copyright © 2001 by the Regents of the University of Minnesota. Used by permission of the University of Minnesota Press. All rights reserved. "MMPI" and "Minnesota Multiphasic Personality Inventory" are trademarks owned by the Regents of the University of Minnesota.

Legend

VRIN	Response inconsistency scale
TRIN T/F	True Response Inconsistency Scale
F	Infrequency scale
F_b	Infrequency scale (changes in response pattern)
F_p	Infrequency scale (intentional over-reporting)
L	Lie scale
K	Defensiveness scale
S	Superlative self-presentation
1 (Hs+.5K)	Hypochondriasis
2 (D)	Depression
3 (Hy)	Hysteria
4 (Pd+.4K)	Psychopathic deviate
5 (Mf)	Masculinity-femininity
6 (Pa)	Paranoia
7 (Pt+1K)	Psychasthenia
8 (Sc1K)	Schizophrenia
9 (Ma+.2K)	Hypomania
0 (Si)	Social introversion

MMPI Form

The above is a profile of an individual who was referred as part of the selection process to become a police officer in the Royal Canadian Mounted Police (RCMP). This assessment was carried out following broader personnel and general medical screening, a polygraph, and security clearance. The purpose of this assessment was to determine whether the candidate shows any signs of psychopathology, symptoms, personality traits, or interpersonal tendencies that could deem this person unsuitable for the role of general duty constable.

Report

The validity of the candidate's MMPI-2 profile was questionable due to a marked elevation on the L scale, moderate elevation on the K scale and low scores on the F scales. Based on these results, it appeared as though this individual was providing a self-description in an overly favourable light. This pattern of responding may have been due to conscious deception or, alternatively, might reflect an unrealistic view of self. Such individuals may be inflexible, lack insight and be unaware of the impressions they make on others, may experience difficulties in future relationships, and may perceive their world in a rigid, self-centred manner. Such individuals may not make good law enforcement officers as they tend to engage in problematic behaviours later on when hired as police officers (Weiss & Weiss, 2010). They may be attempting to hide negative characteristics or may be relatively dishonest people. Regardless, these scores indicate that the client was not being frank in answering questions on the inventory. Notwithstanding the likely denial of symptomatology, the candidate also produced an elevated score on scale 4. Such persons often have difficulty with authority and tend to be unreliable, egocentric, and irresponsible. They may be unable to learn from past experience or to plan ahead. Although such individuals may create a good first impression, the problematic features of their interpersonal style may surface over longer interactions or under stress. The candidate showed a moderate elevation on scale 2, indicative of potential problems with depression or dissatisfaction with self or the current situation.

Although presenting oneself in a favourable light is common in personnel screening situations, the candidate's scores were marked and suggested potential problems with honesty or with self-deception. The elevations on the clinical scale 4 and was also potentially problematic. In addition to the irregularities on the MMPI-2 profile and past experiences, the writer found evidence in the interview that indicated that this person would not be suitable to serve with the RCMP. ●

defensive tendencies are augmented (corrected) by a fraction of the K scale score.

A concern about the original edition of the test (MMPI) was the narrowness of the group of participants on whom it was standardized. All were White, and most were young married people living in small towns or rural areas near Minneapolis. With the revision (MMPI-2), the test was standardized on a much more representative sample based on census information and modernized in other ways as well. The MMPI-2 and MMPI-A have been validated in a wide number of studies (Archer, 2016).

Millon Clinical Multiaxial Inventory. Whereas the MMPI-2 focuses primarily on mental disorders, the **Millon Clinical Multiaxial Inventory (MCMI)** was developed to help clinicians make diagnostic judgments about personality disorders and other clinical syndromes. The most recent version of this instrument is the MCMI-IV (Millon, Grossman, & Millon, 2015) The MCMI-IV consists of 195 self-reported true-false items that yield scores for 25 clinical scales (divided into 15 personality and 10 clinical syndrome scales), associated with DSM categories, and 5 validity indices. The normative sample used to validate the instrument consisted of 1547 clinical patients, including males and females and representing a wide variety of diagnoses. Past versions of the MCMI have been criticized for underestimating the severity of depressive disorders and overestimating the presence of personality disorders (Millon & Meagher, 2004). Although data on the validity and reliability of this version are still being collected, preliminary data are encouraging. The internal consistency of the MCMI-IV, for example, exceeds 0.80 for 20 of the 25 clinical scales, and reaches 0.93 for the Persistent Depression Scale (Millon et al., 2015). Generally, the MCMI-IV has been shown to be a well-constructed psychometrically-sound instrument thus far (Groth-Marnat, 2016).

Personality Assessment Inventory. The **Personality Assessment Inventory** (PAI; Morey, 2007) is a self-administered, objective inventory of adult personality.

This instrument provides information relevant for clinical diagnosis, treatment planning, and screening for psychopathology. It is a fairly sophisticated instrument that uses the most recent techniques in test construction and psychometrics and shares many of the positive features of the MMPI-2 and MCMI-IV and arguably fewer of their limitations.

In contrast to the MMPI-2 and MCMI-IV, which use true-false response options, the 344 PAI items are each scored using a 4-point Likert scale. This continuum in scoring is intentional and reflects the purpose of the PAI to assess symptoms that range from mild to severe. There are 4 validity scales, 11 clinical scales (much like the previous personality tests we have discussed), 5 treatment-consideration scales (e.g., suicidality, aggressiveness), and 2 interpersonal scales. The PAI also has 27 critical items that serve as indicators of potential crisis situations. These items are important for clinicians to note and follow-up on during their assessment of the individual. The reliability and validity of this instrument are well supported (Blais, Baity, & Hopwood, 2010; Kurtz & Blais, 2007; Morey, 2007).

A major limiting factor in any self-report test is that many people do not give accurate reports about themselves. Some will lie, and others will fall into *response sets*, or test-taking attitudes that lead them to shade their responses in one way or another, on the basis of their own personal traits (e.g., some people like to say "yes"), cognitive traits, or *demand characteristics* (i.e., answering as the person thinks the tester would desire). A common response set is *social desirability*—answering to make yourself look good (Jackson & Messick, 1961). Despite control scales designed to detect such distortions, no professional assumes that the problem is eliminated.

Walter Mischel (1968) eloquently argued, with considerable empirical support, that personality tests are flawed by an inherent basic assumption common to all of them: that an individual's personality, or behavioural characteristics, are stable traits, generalizable across situations and over time. Many researchers supported Mischel's view, arguing that predicting a person's behaviour requires knowledge of both the person's typical behaviour patterns and the characteristics of the setting, sometimes called the **person by situation interaction** (Endler & Magnusson, 1976).

In addition to general psychopathology- and personality-based instruments are symptom-specific self-report measures that are useful for diagnostic assessment, case formulation, treatment planning, and outcome assessment (Dozois & Dobson, 2010). For example, when assessing an individual with panic disorder, a clinician may decide to administer a measure of panic symptoms, an index that taps into fear of bodily sensations, and a questionnaire that asks patients questions about what situations they avoid. There are literally several hundred measures that can be used to assess anxiety (Antony, Orsillo, & Roemer, 2001 and depression (Nezu, Ronan, Meadows, & McClure, 2000) alone.

BEHAVIOURAL AND COGNITIVE ASSESSMENT

The development of the DSM from DSM-I to DSM-5 has been marked by an increased reliance on behaviour that is readily observable and quantifiable. This has been a response, in part, to the rejection of older theories of personality that stressed the importance of underlying traits in predicting behaviour. Led by social learning theorists (Mischel, 1968), many working in the field of psychopathology have concluded that the underlying personality structures and traits assessed by more traditional psychological tests (such as hostility, rigidity, paranoia, or obsessiveness), while interesting, are of limited usefulness in predicting behaviour. They have suggested that the best predictor of future behaviour is past behaviour. As a result, a number of techniques arose to assess behaviour itself.

OBSERVATIONAL TECHNIQUES Behavioural clinicians try, whenever possible, to observe their patients' troubled behaviours directly. Techniques have been developed for observing the behaviours of a wide range of clinical populations. One form of behavioural observation employs behaviour rating scales—a preprinted sheet on which the observer notes the presence, absence, and/or intensity of targeted behaviours, usually by checking boxes or by filling in coded terms. This form of assessment is particularly popular when working with children and adolescents, because they all attend school. Consequently, parents and teachers can rate a child's behaviour independently and in different environments. One such rating scale, the Child Behaviour Checklist (Achenbach & Rescorla, 2001), is considered an excellent tool that can detect a broad array of problems in children, including aggressive behaviour, delinquent behaviour, attention problems, social problems, anxiety, and somatic complaints. It has undergone rigorous and sophisticated research for more than a decade, with parents, teachers, and the youths themselves using various versions of the rating scales. The development of these scales has included boys, girls, men, and women from all over the world, resulting in excellent norms based on age and sex.

However, behaviour therapists are often interested in more focused rating scales developed for particular populations, in which behaviour problems are already known to exist. Raters are required to respond only to a small number of items, most of which are present in all individuals with this problem. These types of rating scales are particularly useful as before-and-after assessments in treatment programs.

Behaviourally oriented therapists often observe children's problem behaviours in relation to the *antecedents* (what happens before the behaviour) and *consequences* (what happens after the behaviour). To determine why particular behaviours are maintained, clinicians might gather observational data about sequences of behaviours to determine the function of the behaviour. For example, Table 4.4 presents an illustration of a child who misbehaves at school. The antecedent-behaviour-consequence (ABC) chart helps the clinician to determine why the child behaves in the way he does—in this case, to escape or avoid the situation or demand being placed on him.

TABLE 4.4   ANTECEDENT-BEHAVIOUR-CONSEQUENCE (ABC) CHART

Time	Activity	Antecedent	Behaviour	Consequence	Response	Function
9:03 am	Circle Time/Letter Activity	Children sitting on rug pointing to letters	Nicky lay down	Teacher verbally redirected, "Sit up and point to your letters, please"	Nicky continued to lie on the rug	Escape from letter activity
9:25 am	Transition to Playground	Peer swinging on swing	Nicky began to follow peer and demand the swing	Teacher verbally redirected, "Go play with your friends for a little bit and then you can have a turn on the swing"	Nicky continued to stand behind peer and demand swing	Access to preferred item (swing)
10:20 am	Centres	Ms. Jane (Teacher) helping other students	Nicky lay down on empty chairs at table	Teacher Verbally redirected, "Sit up, please"	Nicky verbalized "Oh, sorry" and sat up	Ms. Jane's attention
11:15 am	Waiting for Snack	Teacher giving verbally direction "Wash your hands, please"	Nicky ran around into the closet and slammed door	Teacher Ignored the behaviour	Nicky remained in the closet until hand-washing time elapsed, before returning to his seat	Avoidance of hand washing
1:30 pm	Vocabulary Worksheet	Working independently at desk	Nicky clapped his hands in a quick repetitive fashion	Teacher ignored the behaviour	Nicky clapped his hands in a quick repetitive fashion	Avoidance of work

Note: Actual data but the names of those mentioned have been changed for the purposes of confidentiality.

Source: Freeman, R. L., Britten, J., McCart, A., Smith, C., Poston, D., Anderson, D., Edmonson, H., Sailor, W., Baker, D., Guess, D., & Reichle, J. (1999). Functional Assessment (Module 2) [Online]. Lawrence, KS: University of Kansas UAP, Center for Research on Learning. Available: http://www.uappbs.lsi.ku.edu.

How do environmental variables—perhaps the actions of parents, siblings, and friends—affect a behaviour of concern? When this is an important question, a clinician may go into a person's everyday environment to record a running narrative of events, using pencil and paper, video, or camera. This is called **in vivo observation** (literally, "in the living being"). More commonly, observations are made by *participant* observers—key people in the client's environment—and reported to the clinician. However, observation in the natural environment is often impractical because of time constraints and the unpredictability of modern family life. Therefore, clinicians sometimes create an **analogue observational setting**, an artificial setting in an office or laboratory constructed to elicit specific classes of behaviour in individuals. Observations from in vivo or analog observational settings can be used to formulate a conceptualization of the child's behaviour problems and to develop a treatment plan.

Although useful, such observational methods are fraught with difficulty. Validity may be undermined by **reactivity**, the change in behaviour often seen when people know they are being observed or recorded. Moreover, because behaviour is often specific to particular situations, observations in one setting cannot always be applied to other settings (Sattler, 2008). Methodological issues include inconsistency between observers, which can be avoided by training them properly. Frequent monitoring of observers is also important to avoid *observer drift*, a steady deterioration in accuracy as a result of fatigue or of a gradual, inadvertent change in the

criteria over a long period of observation (Sattler, 2008). Any assessment requiring observation of individuals, in natural or analogue situations, is fraught with logistical concerns, and is often expensive in terms of time, equipment, and scoring procedures.

Partly in response to such difficulties, clinicians or researchers may use challenge tests tailored to an individual's problem. This technique is particularly popular when dealing with phobias. We have brought spiders to our office, for example, to gauge the severity of a patient's spider phobia: How close to the spider can the patient stand? Of course, this technique would hardly be possible with a phobia of thunder.

COGNITIVE-BEHAVIOURAL ASSESSMENT The thoughts that precede, accompany, and follow maladaptive behaviour are sometimes very important to a clinician's understanding of an individual (Beck & Dozois, 2011). The way in which individuals process information and think about it can tell psychologists a lot about how maladaptive behaviour develops and is maintained (Dozois et al., 2009). How do we measure the way people think and process information? Cognitive assessment tools are used in cognitive-behavioural assessment to help determine (1) how biases in information processing are related to the development of mental disorders, (2) who might be at risk for processing information in a biased, or possibly pathological, way, and (3) how much cognitive behavioural treatments eliminate or reduce information processing biases (Clark & Brown, 2014).

In both research and clinical practice, cognitive assessment tools can be used to measure how "dysfunctional" ways of thinking affect maladaptive behaviour. For example, The Dysfunctional Attitudes Scale (Beevers, Strong, Meyer, Pilkonis, & Miller, 2007; Weissman & Beck, 1978) and the Automatic Thoughts Questionnaire (Hollon & Kendall, 1980) are both commonly used, short, easily administered questionnaires that assess thought patterns related to the development and maintenance of mental disorders, such as depression. In recent years, there has been some criticism over clinicians' over-reliance on questionnaires. In response, clinicians are now beginning to take advantage of technological advances by asking their patients to record their ongoing thoughts on smartphone apps in addition to completing questionnaires. These "real-time" assessments of people's thoughts can provide a useful sample of how people are processing events in their daily lives (Clark & Brown, 2014).

Measures such as the Leiden Index of Depression Sensitivity (LEIDS; Van der Does, 2002) can be used to help determine who is more vulnerable to developing disorders, such as depression, and who is more likely to experience another depressive episode after a period of remission. This measure has been shown to reliably distinguish between people at risk for depression and those who are not (Solis, Antypa, Conijn, Kelderman, & Van der Does, 2016). Measures of individuals' vulnerability to disorders such as depression are invaluable in creating prevention programs for individuals at risk and for monitoring at risk people over time.

Researchers have also advocated for the use of theoretically appropriate measures to assess treatment outcome. Because CBT emphasizes the modification of unhelpful automatic thoughts and dysfunctional attitudes, the measurement of cognition is an important component of outcome assessment in this modality of treatment. A number of self-report measures are available to assess cognitive change in treatment (e.g., Dozois, Covin, & Brinker, 2003). Researchers have also tested changes in information processing (e.g., attention and memory biases) and other forms of cognition that are associated with clinical improvement (e.g., Dozois et al., 2014; Joormann & Stanton, 2016; Quilty, Dozois, Lobo, Ravindran, & Bagby, 2014).

SELF-MONITORING As its name implies, self-monitoring converts a patient into an assessor. Patients are usually asked to note the frequency with which they perform various acts, and sometimes the circumstances surrounding these occurrences and their response to them. Self-monitoring–type tasks have also been used with other, less overt "behaviour" such as thoughts and feelings (Piasecki, Richardson, & Smith, 2007; Simpson, Kivlahan, Bush, & McFall, 2005). For example, behaviour therapists treating people who are depressed may ask them to monitor their own thoughts and feelings to help them become aware of the sequence of events leading to their self-defeating or self-damaging cognitions. Obviously, this technique depends on a competent, diligent, and motivated person to monitor him- or herself. Self-monitoring is useful and cost-effective in many types of

behavioural intervention programs (Kratochwill, Sheridan, Carlson, & Lasecki, 1999).

Behaviour rating scales and systems may be categorized as ranging from direct to indirect, depending on how closely the observational setting approximates the setting in which the behaviour naturally occurs. Time, resources, and privacy should be considered in choosing an assessment technique. Another distinction is between *broad-band* instruments, which seek to measure a wide variety of behaviours, and *narrow-band* instruments, which focus on behaviours related to single, specific constructs such as hyperactivity, shyness, or depression (Skinner, Freeland, & Shapiro, 2003). Narrow-band tests are appropriate when the psychological problems of a patient are fairly well known.

Behaviourally oriented therapists will often require patients to keep a diary, in which they record factors related to their problems. For example, clinicians may have clients keep track of their panic attacks, along with the associated bodily sensations, thoughts, and behaviours. As shown in Figure 4.7, a panic attack record can provide the clinician and the client with information about events that occurred outside the therapy session. By recording such data as soon as possible after a panic attack, more accurate information about the frequency, duration, and context of the panic attacks may be gleaned (Craske & Barlow, 2014). Applications for smart phones and tablets now make self-monitoring much easier (Kauer et al., 2012). For example, eCBT Mood, Worry Watch, T2 Mood Tracker, Mood Journal Plus, Thought Diary Pro, and Mood & Anxiety Diary allow people to track their symptoms and thoughts on their electronic personal devices without needing to write things down. This can make it much easier for people to comply with their therapists' requests for gathering information for an assessment.

We often think of psychological assessment as falling under the rubric of the "soft sciences" as opposed to being able to examine a piece of tissue under a microscope, as is the case in the harder sciences. Interestingly, however, a meta-analytic review indicated not only that the validity of many psychological tests is compelling, but also that these tests yield validity coefficients similar to many medical tests (Meyer et al., 2001). Of course, these tests must be supplemented with other information about patients to provide a thorough understanding of their difficulties, their context, and the appropriate targets for intervention.

Research Methods

Psychological assessment and diagnosis are inextricably entwined with research. Research validates the tools used in assessment. Conversely, psychological assessment and diagnosis provide the descriptive and measurement tools used by researchers in examining the attributes of clinical populations. To the extent that diagnostic criteria are impaired or the tests are undependable, research results are doomed to be erroneous.

One of the primary goals of clinical research is the **description** (defined as the specification and classification

Date: _____   Time Began: _____

Triggers: _____

Expected: _____   Unexpected: _____

Maximum Fear: 0____1____2____3____4____5____6____7____8____9____10
               None   Mild   Moderate   Strong   Extreme

Check all symptoms present to at least a mild degree:

Chest pain or discomfort	_____	Sweating	_____
Heart racing/palpitations/pounding	_____	Nausea/upset stomach	_____
Short of breath	_____	Dizzy/unsteady/lightheaded/faint	_____
Shaking/trembling	_____	Chills/hot flushes	_____
Numbness/tingling	_____	Feelings of unreality	_____
Feelings of choking	_____	Fear of dying	_____
Fear of losing control/going crazy	_____		

Thoughts: _____

Behaviours: _____

FIGURE 4.7   A Panic Attack Record

Source: "A Panic Attack Record", Author: David H. Barlow © 2007, in *Clinical Handbook of Psychological Disorders*, Fourth Edition: A Step-by-Step Treatment Manual, ISBN: 9781606237656

of an event) of clinical phenomena. The other is the prediction of behaviour. The two are linked; without some descriptive strategies and subsequent classification scheme it would be difficult to predict the likelihood of future events.

In this section, we will review some of the science required in the study of abnormal behaviour. The word **science** comes from the Latin *scientia* ("knowledge") and is defined as "knowledge ascertained by observation and experimentation, critically tested, systematized, and brought under general principles." Behavioural investigators strive to explore human behaviour in the same manner as scientists explore physical phenomena. The assumption is that the scientific method and principles are immutable, whether one is studying the path of the sun, why water turns to ice, or why some people become depressed and others do not. Those studying human behaviour have obstacles different from the ones faced by material scientists, while clinical researchers, those who study abnormal psychological behaviour, face their own unique challenges.

All scientific research can be divided into two broad categories: experimental methods and non-experimental methods.

Experimental Methods
CONTROLLED EXPERIMENTAL RESEARCH

One of the distinguishing features of all science is that questions must be posed in a manner that allows clear and precise answers. To allow this clarity, investigators must have as much control as possible over all aspects of the research, but this proves most difficult in clinical studies. The flagship of research into psychopathology is the **experiment**.

In an experiment, variables are manipulated and the effects of these manipulations on other variables are gauged. Large groups of participants are generally used, and the results are analyzed with proven statistical techniques. In a true experiment, participants are randomly assigned to experimental and control groups. **Random assignment** is a procedure that ensures that each participant has an equal probability of being in either the experimental or the control group, guaranteeing the equivalence of these groups. Both groups are then assessed on traits of interest. The **experimental group** is the one that is exposed to a variable that is manipulated, the **independent variable**. Then, the groups are given an assessment on measures the researchers hypothesized would be affected by the manipulation. These behavioural responses constitute the **dependent variables**. The **control group** experiences all aspects of the experiment, including assessments, in a manner identical to the experimental group, except for the manipulation of the independent variable. An **experimental effect** is obtained when differences in a dependent variable are found to occur as a function of manipulation of the independent variable. Acceptable statistical methods are employed to determine the probability that differences in the dependent variable reflect an experimental effect rather than the influence of chance. The results are then interpreted and discussed.

A common question in psychopathology is which treatment is most effective for a certain type of patient. An experiment can address this question. Some of the issues associated with this type of research can be seen in a clinical experiment with adolescents with depression (Kennedy et al., 2009; Treatment for Adolescents with Depression Study [TADS] Team, 2003).

The Treatment for Adolescents with Depression Study (TADS) was designed to compare the relative effectiveness and combined effectiveness of two common treatment procedures for depression: medication (in this case, fluoxetine) and cognitive-behavioural therapy. One of the most important requirements of a good experiment is participant selection. To ensure that others can replicate the study, participants should meet well-defined criteria and be well described in terms of any features that may be important. In the TADS experiment, the results would have been meaningless if the adolescents did not actually have depression. Therefore, the TADS research team used only adolescents who met the criteria for a diagnosis of a current major depressive disorder. In addition, the adolescents were required to score above cut-offs on both a well-known clinician rating scale completed by clinicians after they interviewed the adolescents and a test of intellectual ability. As well, adolescents were required to be free of other significant psychological or medical disorders, concurrent treatment with another psychotropic medication, or psychoses (see TADS Team, 2003, for the full list of inclusion and exclusion criteria).

Once a suitable sample was obtained, participants were randomly assigned to treatment groups. If participants had been allowed to choose, it might have turned out that the families who chose one treatment over another were those with a higher (or lower) education level, a higher (or lower) income, a bias against medication, or some other factor that could influence the outcome. It would then be impossible to say whether any difference in outcome between the groups was caused by the different treatments or by the differences among the families. To prevent this type of bias, adolescents were randomly assigned to treatment groups. Adolescents were put into one of four groups: (1) fluoxetine (Prozac) alone (F), (2) cognitive-behavioural therapy alone (CBT), (3) placebo medication (P), or (4) combination of fluoxetine and cognitive-behavioural therapy (F+CBT).

In this experiment, the types of treatment being compared (F, CBT, P, and F+CBT) were the independent variables. For descriptive purposes, participants were assessed on many measures prior to treatment. This is often referred to as a **pretest**. To get a comprehensive picture of the effects of manipulating the independent variable, adolescents were assessed on several dependent variables judged to be important to their functioning (rating scales filled out by parents and adolescents). This is often called a **post-test**.

Research experience has revealed that individuals in treatment programs expect to get better, or report improvement to please the experimenter (Kazdin, 2003b). This has been called the **placebo effect**. To avoid having results reflect this effect, all participants should have, as nearly as possible, the same expectations. Thus, in TADS, adolescents who were not receiving fluoxetine were given placebo medication. A **placebo** is a substance that looks and feels like the substance being tested, but does not contain the active ingredient. Although originally used in medication research, this approach has also been adopted to include placebo psychological treatments, such as spending time talking generally with the individual. It is also known that experimenters can unwittingly influence the results. If the experimenter expects that participants receiving the treatment will show more improvement than the controls, this expectation can be subtly communicated to the participants. Therefore, to further ensure that expectations would not influence the outcome of the study, a **double-blind** procedure was used; that is, neither the participants nor the experimenters knew who was getting medication and who was getting a placebo. In a perfect experiment, one would have provided a placebo to match the cognitive-behavioural therapy in the CBT condition. However, resources and ethics precluded this.

A key issue in any experiment is validity. The first type of validity to consider is **internal validity**, the degree to which the changes in the dependent variables are a result of the manipulation of the independent variable; this reflects the internal integrity of the study. If no alternative explanations are possible, one has strong internal validity. The other is **external validity**, the generalizability of the findings, or the degree to which the findings in the investigation apply to other individuals in other settings. How well do you think TADS controlled for internal and external validity? Are there any problems that you can think of?

PROS AND CONS The strength of the controlled experiment is that it allows inference concerning causes and effects, the prime goal in all research. However, the controlled experiment is arguably the most difficult research strategy to implement, because of the need to control for so many factors. If strict control cannot be achieved, the internal validity of any experiment is threatened. Profound ethical dilemmas can arise relating to random assignment. For example, early in the development of a treatment for AIDS, research required that some participants be provided with active medication, which was withheld from the control group of patients. Is it ethical to withhold treatment, no matter how speculative, from a seriously ill population? If so, for how long is it ethical? A similar question arose in the TADS experiment. Adolescents had agreed to stay in their assigned treatment condition for 12 weeks before being informed of their medication status (placebo versus fluoxetine). It would have been ethically unacceptable to keep adolescents who were doing poorly on the placebo for longer than that given that there are two empirically supported treatments available in the study (medication and CBT). On the other hand, to keep only those adolescents who showed an improvement on the placebo medication would compromise the validity of the experiment. Finally, the rigorous requirements of participant selection and the intervention procedures required in many controlled experiments limit the generalizability of findings.

Findings from this trial have indicated that the combined CBT and fluoxetine is most effective at reducing depression (TADS Team, 2007) and increasing protective factors, or factors that improve individuals' outcomes for depression (e.g., problem solving; Gottlieb, Martinovich, Meyers, & Reinecke, 2016). However, other findings have shown that suicide risk was higher among individuals who took fluoxetine compared to the placebo medication, and compared to those who were in CBT (Högberg, Antonuccio, & Healy, 2015).

QUASI-EXPERIMENTAL METHODS

Many important questions in abnormal psychology cannot be addressed in a pure experiment, since it is impossible—or, where possible, highly unethical—to create psychological disturbance in individuals in order to carry out investigations. Quasi-experimental studies, which do not face some of the challenges of controlled experiments, have therefore been essential in the development of various classification systems, including the DSM-5. A **quasi-experimental study** is one in which the participants in the experimental group are not randomly assigned but selected on the basis of certain characteristics, and in which there is no manipulation of independent variables.

Some of the issues arising in quasi-experimental investigations can be seen in an investigation of teenagers with migraine headaches led by Dr. Pat McGrath of Dalhousie University, a well-known specialist in the study of pain (Cunningham et al., 1987). The study grew out of a notion that people with certain types of personalities—those who were anxious, depressed, and had a poor self-concept—were prone to headaches. A group of adolescents who experienced significant migraine headaches was selected. In a quasi-experimental design, this group is designated the experimental group. The control group in a quasi-experimental study is selected not through random assignment but through matching; that is, attempting to ensure that the participants in all conditions are comparable on all variables that might be important to the research except for the key variable: in this case, the presence of migraine headaches.

Selecting the control group in this project presented a particularly intriguing problem. The normal control group was constituted by finding other children attending the same hospital who were the same age and sex as the participants with migraines. These control participants were included if they had similar social and medical histories, but did not suffer from disorders that involved prolonged pain. Unfortunately, because the experimental group experienced prolonged pain and the control group did not, the study was confounded. A **confound** occurs when two or more variables exert their influence at the same time, making it impossible to accurately establish the causal role of either variable. In the migraine study, if psychological differences emerged between the experimental and control groups, two interpretations would be possible. First, it could be that these psychological differences *led* to the

migraines; however, it could also be that the psychological differences *resulted* from the pain endured by the participants with migraines. To control for this problem in interpretation, the researchers included a *clinical control group* as well: a group similar to the control group but possessing some pathology similar to that of the experimental group. In this study, the clinical control group was made up of teenagers who suffered from chronic musculoskeletal pain such as rheumatoid arthritis.

The results revealed that the experimental group did demonstrate more psychological problems than the normal controls. However, when the three groups were compared, it was clear that it was the level of pain, not the source of pain, that was associated with personality and behavioural differences. In the end, the results did not support the hypothesis that personality and behavioural styles put one at risk for developing migraines. Rather, it seemed that people who suffer pronounced and prolonged pain respond by becoming anxious and depressed.

PROS AND CONS The quasi-experimental study allows for meaningful analysis of many aspects of psychological disorders that cannot be studied by experiment. In fact, the development of DSM-5 was based largely on such quasi-experimental procedures. Nevertheless, the assignment of participants on the basis of their personal characteristics limits the cause-and-effect inferences that are possible. In addition, experience has demonstrated that it is difficult to match participants on all factors but the one in question.

Non-Experimental Methods
CORRELATIONAL RESEARCH

The **correlational method** measures the degree of relationship between two variables and generally requires a large number of participants. It is not invasive; behaviour is not manipulated, just measured quantitatively and then analyzed statistically. The resulting correlation coefficient statistic describing the relationship between two variables is analyzed by a test of statistical significance to determine whether it is likely that the observed relationship could have occurred simply by chance. *Correlation coefficients* are represented by the symbol r and range in value from -1.00 to 1.00. A *positive correlation*, such as $r = 0.68$, indicates that an increase in one variable is associated with an increase in the other. A *negative correlation*, such as $r = -0.63$, indicates that an increase in one variable is associated with a decrease in the other. When the correlation coefficient is close to zero, there is no significant relationship between the two variables. Generally, psychologists are interested in correlation coefficients greater than or equal to ±0.30.

Correlational research is frequently carried out where experimental manipulation is impossible or unethical. For example, in studying the effects of maternal smoking on a developing fetus, it would be unacceptable to randomly assign expectant mothers to groups and ask some of them to smoke. However, a common misconception is that if two variables are reliably correlated, a causal relationship must exist. Actually, a significant correlation may have one of three interpretations. First, it is possible that variable A caused variable B. Second, it is possible that variable B caused variable A. Finally, a third variable may be responsible for the occurrence of both A and B.

One way to reduce the ambiguity regarding the direction of correlational relationships is to conduct longitudinal studies. **Longitudinal studies** permit an examination of early factors that precede the onset of a disorder. However, longitudinal studies are generally extremely demanding in terms of resources (i.e., money, time, sample size, and so on), especially when the disorder or outcome of interest has a low base rate in the general population. Thousands of people would have to be studied and followed up over several years just to have an acceptable sample size of people who actually develop the disorder of interest. One variation on the longitudinal approach considers only people who have an elevated likelihood of developing the disorder of interest. This is referred to as the *high-risk method*. In this longitudinal design, a sample of people who will more likely experience the desired outcome compared to the more general population (e.g., children of depressed mothers who are at greater risk for developing depression themselves) is selected.

PROS AND CONS Correlational research is a relatively inexpensive method of studying the relationship between naturally occurring phenomena. It can indicate whether a meaningful relationship exists between two variables. This knowledge may be of value even if the reasons for the relationship are not evident. Furthermore, it can also be used to illuminate areas that might benefit from more rigorous research strategies. Nevertheless, it is impossible to make cause-and-effect inferences with this design.

THE CASE STUDY

The **case study** is a description of the past and current functioning of a single individual. Variables such as family history, education, employment history, medical history, social relationships, and the patient's level of psychological adjustment are described within the case study. This information is collected primarily by interview, but may be supplemented by test scores, archival records, consultations with family members, and actual observation during the clinical interview (e.g., behavioural tics, emotional state, posture). The goal of the case study is a description of an individual's current problem, and its relation to his or her past. Ultimately, it seeks to provide a theory concerning the etiology of a patient's problem or psychological makeup, and/or a course of treatment and outcome.

Pros and Cons. As a method of investigating abnormal psychology, the case study possesses definite, albeit limited, advantages. Its approach is classified as *idiographic* in that it offers rich detail and vividness concerning a particular individual that is frequently lost in large studies. In contrast, the *nomothetic* approach, more favoured by scientists, studies large groups of participants to uncover the basic principles governing behaviour. The case study can be an excellent source for the generation of new hypotheses concerning the etiology and treatment of psychological disorders that may later be tested under more rigorous statistical controls. In addition, the case study is useful in the description of particularly rare disorders and in their treatment. Finally, the case study can be used to supply a counter-example to universally accepted principles, since the existence of only one exception can render a proposition false. As an example, it has often been asserted that all sex offenders have themselves been victimized as children. If one is able to find any sex offender who has not been victimized, this assertion is incorrect. The exception to the rule does not, however, preclude the suggestion that there may be a higher incidence of sexual victimization in the history of sex offenders than in that of normal controls.

These advantages notwithstanding, the case study has limited use in the study of psychopathology. It does not employ the scientific method or control for rival hypotheses, and so cannot demonstrate cause and effect. Thus, the case study cannot prove a theory. In addition, one cannot be certain of the generalizability of the findings. Finally, the clinician's theoretical background has been shown to influence the questions asked and therefore skew the information gleaned. Thus, although the case study method has an assured position within the field of abnormal psychology, its usefulness will always be limited.

Case Notes

Peter was a four-year-old with attention deficit/hyperactivity disorder (ADHD), enrolled in a regular preschool program, who was often both physically and verbally aggressive toward other children, using commands, threats, teasing, and verbal conflicts. Children and parents complained regularly about his conduct. He had been told by staff and parents many times not to act in this fashion, to no avail. It was decided to target his physical aggression first. The teachers and researchers first agreed on what constituted physical aggression. For the next five days, all adults working in the school, including the researchers, were asked to surreptitiously record every aggressive incident on a prepared chart and to deal with it as they had previously. This generally consisted of separating Peter from the other child, reprimanding him verbally, and sending him to play in another part of the room. At the end of each day, all adults gave their charts to the researcher. As expected, and as demonstrated in Figure 4.8, the talk with Peter did little to change his physical or verbal aggression. This constituted the A1 phase of the intervention.

Peter was then told that every time he was aggressive toward another child, he would be placed in "timeout": that is, he would have to sit in a chair facing the corner in an unused part of the room until he was quiet for two minutes. As the figure demonstrates, Peter's aggressive behaviour rapidly diminished. This constituted the B1 phase of intervention.

After five days in phase B1, it was decided to stop putting Peter into timeout and return to the approach used before the study started (A2). Within three days, his aggressive behaviour returned to nearly pre-intervention levels. At the request of the parents and teachers, it was decided to reinstate the timeout after day 3 of this condition (B2). This time, Peter's aggressive behaviour appeared to decrease even more rapidly than it had the first time. Interestingly, his activity level did not change.

SINGLE-SUBJECT RESEARCH

Like the case study, **single-subject designs** are based on the intense investigation of an individual participant. However, this approach avoids many of the criticisms of the case study by using experimentally accepted procedures. The

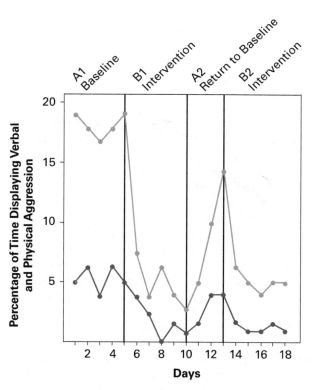

FIGURE 4.8   The Effect of Timeouts on Aggressive Behaviour: A Single-Subject Design

variations of this design have several common elements: they use observable behaviours that are quantifiable; they quantify the presence of the behaviour prior to any intervention; they systematically apply readily observable and quantifiable interventions; and they measure the effects of the intervention on the behaviours of the participant. The **ABAB** design, also called the **reversal design**, requires the quantification of behaviour in its naturally occurring environment prior to any intervention. This constitutes the *A* phase or the baseline of the procedure. Next, in the *B* phase, the treatment is introduced in a controlled manner. The next *A* phase constitutes the reversal, during which time the treatment is removed and the participant returns to the original baseline conditions. Finally, the treatment is provided once again and represents the final *B* (Firestone, 1976).

Pros and Cons. Peter's case (see page 86) demonstrates how a single-subject design differs from a case study. The single-subject design has the advantage of being relatively inexpensive. Moreover, the variables in question are clearly defined, observable, and quite accurately measured, removing the element of personal bias from the observations. An individual's performance can be judged more accurately than in even a well-executed group design, where performance is based on group means.

One problem inherent in this research strategy was demonstrated in Peter's case. While his undesirable behaviour improved dramatically in response to the first intervention, the behaviour did not immediately return to pre-study levels when the intervention was withdrawn. Peter's initial state was not recoverable within the time constraints of the present study. We assume that this was a result of some permanence in the change of Peter's behaviour pattern—which is the goal of most treatment. The other, perhaps more important, problem with the ABAB design is an ethical one: Can one justify reinstating contingencies that don't work in order to demonstrate that others do? More practically, participants are often unwilling to give up treatment that works just to preserve the integrity of the research design. Finally, results are not generalizable; there is clear support that timeouts are effective with Peter, but we cannot say whether they will be effective for other children. Therefore, single-subject designs can be used to demonstrate whether interventions warrant further study with larger sample sizes.

EPIDEMIOLOGICAL RESEARCH

Epidemiology is the study of the incidence and prevalence of disorders in a population. **Incidence** refers to the number of new cases of a disorder in a particular population over a specified time period, usually a year. **Prevalence** is the frequency of a disorder in a population at a given point or period of time. Epidemiological research also identifies risk factors that, if present, increase the probability of developing the disorder. In psychopathology, epidemiological research can help to identify the frequency, development, progression, and maintenance of disorders in various populations, which can assist with intervention and prevention strategies.

Perhaps the most famous epidemiological study occurred during a cholera outbreak in London, England, in the nineteenth century. At that time, John Snow noted that most people coming down with cholera congregated at or drank water from one source, the Broad Street Pump. He also noted that rates of cholera were lower upstream from London, where the water was less contaminated. He was thus able to demonstrate that the cholera was being spread by contaminated water.

We have no example in psychopathology of an epidemiological study that was able to prevent a disorder. However, Statistics Canada is consistently implementing epidemiological studies to better understand mental health issues in Canada. Currently, the Canadian government is collecting information on a number of prospective epidemiological studies, including the Canadian Health Survey on Children and Youth (CHSCY), assessing the physical and psychological development of Canadian children; and the Canadian Community Health Survey (CCHS), following health status, health care utilization, and health determinants for the Canadian population.

Statistics Canada also recently conducted an epidemiological survey of seven mental health disorders affecting Canadians (major depressive disorder, bipolar disorder, generalized anxiety disorder, alcohol abuse or dependence, cannabis abuse or dependence, and other drug abuse or dependence). In 2012, the Canadian Community Health Survey: Mental Health collected data from 25 113 respondents aged 15 years and older from households in every province of Canada (Statistics Canada, 2013) with one-on-one interviews using computer assisted personal interviewing (CAPI) software. Once data were collected, survey sampling weights were applied to the data so that they could be representative of the Canadian population as a whole (Pearson, Janz, & Ali, 2013).

Of note, this survey excluded individuals who were living on reserves and other Indigenous settlements, full-time members of the Canadian Forces, and anyone living in an institutionalized setting (which includes individuals in inpatient psychiatric facilities and correctional facilities). This excluded population represents about 3% of the target population. Unfortunately, given the disproportionately high rates of mental disorders, especially substance use disorders, in institutionalized settings, these statistics may somewhat underrepresent the actual prevalence estimates of these disorders across Canadians.

According to the 2012 survey, one in three Canadians met the criteria for at least one of these six selected mental or substance use disorders at some point in their lifetime. Approximately 21.6% of Canadians met the criteria for at least one of the selected substance use disorders (18.1% for an alcohol use disorder, 6.8% for a cannabis use disorder, and 4% for other substance use disorders). Approximately 12.6% of Canadians met criteria for a mood disorder (11.3% for major depressive disorder, and 2.6% for bipolar disorder).

The lifetime prevalence for generalized anxiety disorder was 8.4%. From 2011–2012, approximately 4.4% of Canadians met criteria for at least one of the substance use disorders, 5.4% for at least one of the mood disorders, and 2.6% for generalized anxiety disorder.

These statistics can be used to implement intervention programs in areas with higher rates of these disorders, and can be used to track the availability and use of mental health resources. Dr. Scott Patten and his colleagues at the University of Calgary have been instrumental in using these data to better understand who is suffering from these disorders and what their access to mental health services is (e.g., Patten et al., 2015).

PROS AND CONS The advent of epidemiological research strategies allowed for the detailed collection of information concerning the incidence and prevalence of disorders in large populations. Such information is essential to the understanding of factors that contribute to the health of a population and the design of intervention strategies. However, this research strategy does not easily allow inferences concerning cause and effect. The final hindrance to epidemiological research is that it requires very large numbers of participants in order for relationships between factors to be recognized. This means that these types of studies can be very time-consuming and financially costly to conduct.

STUDIES OF INHERITANCE

Is a person born with a disorder, or a tendency to a disorder, or is it developed through environmental influences? As a general question, this may be termed the nature/nurture debate, and the short answer is that there is no simple answer: both factors are important. However, the question still remains for particular disorders and particular cases: Is the source of a problem genetic or environmental? (In this discussion, *genetic* refers to inherited traits. In fact, some genetic disorders are not inherited but caused by mutation; for example, in Down syndrome, genetic damage occurs to the cells produced by parents whose own cells are normal. Such disorders are not, of course, tracked through family studies.)

FAMILY STUDIES Researchers often examine the incidence of a disorder among family members, frequently including distant as well as close relatives. Genetic similarity between family members is greater than between non-family members. Furthermore, genetic similarity is greater between parents and their children, and between siblings, than it is between cousins, aunts/uncles, or grandparents. Table 4.5 shows the genetic relationships between family members and non-family members. (Note that the genetic relationship between a parent and child is not exactly the same as between siblings. A child gets half of his or her genes from each parent; therefore, parent and child always have 50 percent of their genes in common. Siblings each get half of their genes from the mother and half from the father, but it is not known which of a parent's genes each child will get. Therefore, two siblings could in theory have anywhere from 0 to

TABLE 4.5   GENETIC RELATIONSHIPS

Relationship to Proband	Genes Shared (%)
Non-family member	0.0
Spouse	0.0
Cousin	12.5
Grandparent	25.0
Grandchild	25.0
Aunt or uncle	25.0
Niece or nephew	25.0
Parent	50.0
Child	50.0
Non-twin sibling (brother or sister)	50.0
Non-identical twin (dizygotic twin)	50.0
Identical twin (monozygotic twin)	100.0

100 percent of genes in common; the average genetic similarity between siblings is 50 percent.)

In family studies, the patient, or the person who has come to the attention of the clinician or researcher, is called the index case or **proband**. If the proband and a comparison person are alike on the characteristic of interest (if, for example, they show the same abnormal behaviour), the two are said to be *concordant* (or to display **concordance**). If the concordance rate for the disorder increases with increasing genetic similarity, this will offer support for, but will not confirm, a genetic basis for the problem. After all, families typically live in, and create, far more similar environments than are found between people from different families. Heredity and environment are thus confounded in family studies. For these reasons, behavioural geneticists have turned to other methods of studying these influences.

ADOPTION STUDIES Adoption studies offer researchers an opportunity to determine the separate effects of genetics and environment on the development of psychological disorders (Charney et al., 2002). In the prototypical investigation, a group of individuals who were adopted away from their biological parents at an early age and who demonstrate a psychological disorder are studied. The rates of disorder in the biological and adoptive parents are then compared. This allows researchers to control for environmental effects, assuming that the children were adopted at birth. Presumably, if there is greater agreement between adoptees and biological parents than there is between adoptees and adoptive parents, then a genetic link likely exists. Unfortunately, this type of research has demonstrated how difficult it is to match parent groups. For example, groups of parents who adopt children tend not to be a random representation of the community at large, and this may unduly influence the results. They tend to come from higher socio-economic strata and tend to have fewer problems such as alcoholism or substance abuse. This is not surprising, since in most jurisdictions parents wanting to adopt children are screened by agencies for suitability.

Cross-fostering is a great improvement on the traditional adoption study. In this case, one group comprises adopted children whose biological parents have a disorder and whose adoptive parents demonstrate no psychopathology. The other group comprises adopted children whose biological parents have no disorder but whose adoptive parents develop psychopathology. The comparisons available in this design allow statements concerning the relative impact of genes and environment.

There are several limitations to adoption studies as a research tool. It is very difficult to obtain full, accurate information concerning the biological parents of adoptees. Frequently, only the mothers are considered in this research, since it is not possible to verify who the fathers are. It is also difficult to control for the contact adoptees have had with their biological parents. Researchers may have difficulty in acquiring samples large enough to permit inferences. Furthermore, adoption studies do not control for the effects of prenatal exposure to toxins, maternal illness, or perinatal trauma; such factors can have significant physiological effects on the fetus, but are not transmitted genetically (Blackburn, 2014).

TWIN STUDIES Examination of the concordance rates among twins has been seen as a more accurate basis from which to infer genetic contributions to disorders, because the genetic similarity between twins is known. For example, identical twins share exactly the same genotype (they have inherited exactly the same genes from their parents), whereas non-identical twins share only half of their genotype. Identical twins, also known as **monozygotic (MZ) twins** (from *mono* meaning "one," and *zygote* meaning "fertilized egg"), result from the fertilization by a single sperm of a single ovum. This is followed by an unusual extra division into exactly matched zygotes, which subsequently develop into genetically identical fetuses. Thus, MZ twins have 100 percent of their genes in common. Non-identical (or *fraternal*) twins, also known as **dizygotic (DZ) twins** (from *di* meaning "two"), result when two independent sperm separately fertilize two independent ova at approximately the same time. Thus, DZ twins, like non-twin siblings, have, on average, just 50 percent of their genes in common. If there is greater concordance for a disorder among MZ twins than among DZ twins, so the argument goes, we can infer a genetic basis for the disorder.

It is not easy, however, to amass a large number of participants for such studies, because only a little more than 1 percent of all children are twins, and only one in three of these are monozygotic. For any particular disorder, there will be even fewer twins to select from, since most disorders occur in only a very small percentage of the population. For example, schizophrenia, a disorder that has been persistently examined for a genetic basis, occurs in only 1 percent of the population. Researchers are going to have to search far and wide to find enough monozygotic twins where at least one has schizophrenia. Typically, this challenge has forced researchers to examine hospital records spanning many years. The difficulty is that, since diagnostic procedures have changed over the years, it is hard to be sure what the sample truly includes.

Other important criticisms attack the basic assumption of twin studies. For example, it is assumed that environmental influences are held constant in these comparisons between MZ and DZ twins and that, therefore, only genotypic differences can account for differential concordance rates. Lewontin, Rose, and Kamin (1984) point out that the environment of MZ twins is remarkably more similar than that of DZ twins. After all, MZ twins look alike, they are almost invariably dressed the same by their parents, and most everyone, including their parents, has great difficulty telling them apart. Lewontin and colleagues argue that these facts suggest that MZ twins will be treated almost identically; that is, the environmental responses to them will be the same. For DZ twins, however, who do not look the same (or at least no more alike than non-twin siblings), environmental responses can be expected to differ from one twin to the other. Therefore, according to Lewontin and colleagues, different concordance rates between MZ and DZ twins could readily be accounted for in terms of environmental rather than genetic influences. Moreover, identical twins have been found to exert greater influence over each other than do fraternal twins (Carey, 1992).

It is interesting to examine the differences in concordance rates between DZ twins and non-twin siblings. Since fraternal twins and non-twin siblings are equally similar genetically, what is one to make of differences in concordance rates between these two groups? Studies of schizophrenia consistently show that DZ twins have higher concordance rates than do non-twin siblings. Given that DZ twins are born at the same time, go through the same temporal changes, attend the same school, and often share the same friends, it is likely that environmental similarities play a significant role. Even more to the point, same-sex fraternal twins can be assumed to share far more environmental experiences in common than opposite-sex fraternal twins, although these two different sorts of fraternal twins have exactly the same genetic relationships. Six studies (Lewontin et al., 1984) have shown greater concordance among same-sex DZ twins than among opposite-sex DZ twins, a further indication of environmental influence. Recent research has demonstrated that the mother's health, perinatal trauma, viral infections, and environmental toxins, all interacting with the sex of the fetus, may be implicated in the long-term development of children through non-genetic, physiological processes. These elements may contribute, at least in part, to the higher concordance rates reported in DZ, same-sex twins than in DZ, opposite-sex twins (Blackburn, 2014)

Obviously, it would be ideal to combine twin and adoption strategies by studying large numbers of MZ and DZ twins who suffer from the disorders of interest and were adopted early in life. However, finding sufficient numbers of such individuals who are willing to participate is a demanding task. Nevertheless, there has been a great deal of converging research, using a wide variety of research strategies, with several pathological groups, including individuals with schizophrenia, those with bipolar disorders, and substance abusers. Such studies have generally revealed higher concordance rates for disorders in MZ than in DZ twins. Some scientists have developed statistical procedures to calculate the degree to which genetics, as opposed to environmental factors, are responsible for psychological characteristics, using correlational data obtained with the twin study method. In one procedure, the correlation coefficient for DZ twins is subtracted from the correlation coefficient for MZ twins, and the result is then multiplied by 2 (Falconer, 1960). Using this formula, Plomin (1990) has suggested that height is correlated 0.90 among MZ twins and 0.45 among DZ twins. One could therefore conclude that height is 90 percent inherited, and by subtraction determine that 10 percent may be due to environmental factors. However, this simple calculation must be viewed with caution. It is only an estimate of the average contribution of genetics to the development of disorders, and, under extreme circumstances, the environment can exert a greater influence than is suggested by this simple computation. For example, factors such as extreme malnutrition or prenatal exposure to toxins may result in the genetic propensity of a trait not manifesting itself.

We have examined a number of different research designs in this chapter, each with particular strengths and weaknesses. Table 4.6 summarizes the pros and cons of all of these methods.

GENE–ENVIRONMENT INTERACTIONS Genes guide individuals to their maturation, but do not fully determine their development. Each person's **phenotype**, or the observable expression of his or her genetic contribution, is more accurately determined by the interaction of one's genes and the environment. That is to say that genetic factors influence one's sensitivity to environmental effects, or that environmental exposure to situations moderates the effect of genetic risk factors. Studies examining these **gene–environment interactions** (G × E) have become plentiful in the literature, as researchers search to discover why only certain individuals react to environmental circumstances in particular ways (Caspi et al., 2003; Gunter, Vaughn, & Philibert, 2010). Since gaining popularity in the early 2000s, hundreds of studies have now examined gene–environment interactions in various psychological disorders (Dick et al., 2015; Manuck & McCaffery, 2014).

Unfortunately, we cannot consider genes and environment to be two independently functioning influences on developmental outcomes. Instead, there is a correlation between individuals' genotypes and the properties of their environmental experience. In general, there are three different ways that genotypes and environments are related and can influence development (Scarr & McCartney, 1983). They are not mutually exclusive, but rather all three can influence one's development.

1. *Passive gene–environment correlation.* In this situation, one's biological parents determine not only one's genotype, but also the quality of one's early experiences created

TABLE 4.6   PROS AND CONS OF DIFFERENT RESEARCH DESIGNS

Research Design	Pros	Cons
Controlled experiment	1. Cause and effect can be established	1. Difficult to implement because of control required (internal validity) 2. Ethical problems due to required manipulation of variables 3. External validity problematic
Quasi-experimental	1. Allows research when manipulation of variables is not possible 2. Provides information on pathological groups	1. Cause-and-effect statements compromised by lack of random assignment 2. Difficult to match participants in different groups
Correlational study	1. Relatively easy and inexpensive to implement 2. Allows study of relationships and between common phenomena variables	1. Cause and effect cannot be established
Case study	1. Very easy to implement 2. Idiographic approach provides rich detail 3. Allows some insight into infrequently occurring disorders 4. Provides for generation of new hypotheses	1. Cause and effect cannot be established 2. Highly biased by clinician's perspective 3. Cannot generalize to other patients or populations
Single-subject design	1. Relatively easy and inexpensive to implement 2. Allows cause-and-effect statements 3. Allows some insight into infrequently occurring disorders	1. Ethically and practically difficult to implement some reversals 2. Impossible to generalize results to other settings or participants
Twin and adoption study	1. Allows insight into genetic and environmental contributions to pathology	1. Generally cause and effect cannot be established (some diseases such as Tay-Sachs are the exception)
Epidemiological study	1. Provides information on the incidence and prevalence of problems 2. Provides information on factors related to the occurrence of problems	1. Impossible to make cause-and-effect statements 2. Large numbers of participants required

by those biological parents. For example, parents with higher intelligence may pass this genetic predisposition to their offspring. As well, because of their higher intelligence and potentially higher-than-average salaries, these parents may have better access to more nutritious meals, have access to better child care and schools, and provide a more stimulating environment for their children. Children in these situations passively receive genotypes and early environmental experiences contributing to high intelligence.

2. *Evocative (reactive) gene–environment correlation.* In this situation, individuals' heritable behaviours evoke an environmental response. Continuing with the example used above, children who, like their parents, begin to show signs of above-average intelligence may behave in particular ways. They may show better verbal skills, learn more quickly, or work more independently in class. All of these behaviours will elicit certain responses from others, such as school personnel labelling them as "gifted," schools providing them with a more enriched educational experience, and prestigious universities offering them academic scholarships.

3. *Active gene–environment correlation.* In this situation, individuals possessing particular heritable propensities by virtue of their genotype will be more likely to actively select certain environments. For example, highly intelligent children may be more likely to develop friendships with other bright children with similar interests, join clubs or associations that satisfy their curiosity in a particular subject field, or choose demanding majors in university. This tendency to select environmental experiences based on genotype is sometimes referred to as "niche-picking."

Beyond this, research now examines **epigenetics**, or the study of modifications of gene expressions that are caused by mechanisms other than changes in the underlying DNA sequence. There is now evidence to suggest that environmental and psychosocial factors can change one's underlying genes to some degree (Masterpasqua, 2009; Chen, Li, Subramaniam, Shyy, & Chien, 2017).

⑤ BEFORE MOVING ON

What is an experiment, and how is it different from non-experimental methods of research?

Statistical Versus Clinical Significance

In experimental research, the concept of **statistical significance** is crucial, since it is the standard by which most research is judged as valuable or worthy of being published. Basically, experimental results are deemed statistically significant if it is extremely unlikely that the obtained results could have occurred purely by chance. The convention in psychological research is to set a significance level of 0.05 (often written as $p = 0.05$, where p stands for "probability"), meaning that if the independent variable exerted no effect whatsoever, the obtained findings would be observed no more than 5 percent of the time, solely by chance. Thus, if $p = 0.05$, it seems reasonable to assume that the independent variable is exerting an effect. However, there is a big difference between demonstrating statistical significance and finding a treatment that works in real life.

Suppose that a psychologist has developed a treatment for depression and has found, through careful quantitative research using large groups of participants, that the intervention significantly decreases symptoms of depression. As a result, she offers this new treatment to a few patients outside the study. Some show no symptom relief. Others score somewhat lower on a scale of depression, or report that some symptoms have decreased but their lives have not improved in any meaningful way; they still feel depressed. Assuming that the clinician correctly administered the treatment, why did a seemingly promising therapy fail to ameliorate the patients' quality of life?

At issue is the concept of **clinical significance**, which refers to a treatment's practical utility, and which does not follow automatically from statistical significance (Kazdin, 2003a). In a study with a large number of participants, statistically significant results may demonstrate that small changes are not due to chance. However, it is possible that only a minority of participants in the group experienced improvement, or that the improvement was measurable but small. Unless change is sufficient to be of value to a patient, the treatment has little merit. In fact, the cost in terms of time and money, and possible side effects, may render the treatment worse than useless. Moreover, some interventions work better in controlled circumstances than in the everyday world. Suppose, for example, that a medication worked only if administered eight times a day at precisely the same time. It might work fine when administered by a nurse in a hospital, but once home, the patient would be unable to stick to the schedule, and the treatment would become ineffective.

To control for the potential irrelevance of statistical significance in research, it has been suggested that it is equally important to evaluate the social validity of a treatment and attend to the qualitative changes in patients' functioning. This might be accomplished by collecting subjective input on therapy results from patients and significant others in their lives. Another meaningful approach, called **normative comparison**, compares treatment results to non-disturbed samples (Dozois et al., 2003; Ingram, Nelson, Steidtmann, Bistricky, 2007; Jacobson & Truax, 1991; Kendall, Marrs-Garcia, Nath, & Sheldrick, 1999). Concern with clinical significance has now grown to the point that many journals will not accept articles (especially those dealing with interventions that have already been well studied) unless the authors can provide data showing meaningful, practical outcomes. Recently, there has been growing interest in also measuring *how much* a given intervention is effective. This information is best captured by a statistic called an **effect size**. Effect size is a measurement of the degree to which an effect exists. That is, effect sizes give you a measurement of how "strong" of an effect your intervention has. There has recently been a push to report effect sizes in addition to clinical significance statistics (Gignac & Szodorai, 2016).

⑥ BEFORE MOVING ON

Why do you think it is important to consider clinical significance in addition to statistical significance?

SUMMARY

- Psychological testing involves gathering a sample of behaviour to determine a set of scores on a given measure. Psychometrically strong (i.e., reliable and valid) psychological tests contribute to a well-rounded psychological assessment. Psychological assessment plays an important role in abnormal psychology, providing a comprehensive system for describing an individual's psychological profile. A psychological test provides a piece of information that must be integrated and evaluated *within the context* of other information to create a thorough psychological assessment.

- Reliability and validity are important for both research and clinical assessment. Having measurement tools that are reliable and valid helps ensure that clinicians can consistently measure what they are hoping to, and are measuring what they think they are measuring.

- The debate between clinical and actuarial prediction has continued for years. It involves the contrast between clinicians' professional experience and intuition versus statistical procedures and empirical methods in clinical decision making. Both clinical and actuarial prediction have benefits and limitations.

- Biologically based procedures used in the study of psychological problems include EEG, CT scan, MRI, and PET. Although the results of most brain imaging assessments cannot be used to help in diagnoses, aside from circumstances in which there is obvious neurological impairment, they have contributed greatly to research.

- A number of neuropsychological tests are used to study brain–behaviour relationships, including the Montreal Cognitive Assessment, Halstead Reitan Neuropsychological Test Battery, the Repeatable Battery for the Assessment of Neuropsychological Status, and the Bender Visual-Motor Gestalt Test.

- Clinical interviews have always been an integral part of any psychological assessment, and more structured components have been recently developed to reduce bias. Both structured and unstructured interviews have advantages and disadvantages. Semi-structured interviews provide a nice balance between facilitating rapport with clients while affording standardization and reliability.

- IQ tests were the first psychological tests to gain wide acceptance, and they do a fairly good job of predicting school performance. IQ tests with good psychometric properties also readily distinguish between individuals who are intellectually gifted, individuals who have learning disabilities, and individuals with intellectual disabilities.

- Projective tests, initially based on psychoanalytic theory, were the first personality tests. The Rorschach inkblot test and Thematic Apperception Test are two examples of projective tests. However, actuarial personality tests like the MMPI-2, MCMI-IV, and PAI, based on more psychometrically sound procedures, have become more favoured among clinicians. Behavioural and cognitive-behavioural assessment techniques have become widely accepted. Most of these tests focus on specific behaviour problems (e.g., risk of suicide, level of depression, ability to concentrate) rather than on the whole range of personality functioning.

- The controlled experiment is not always possible in human research for ethical and logistical reasons. However, quasi-experimental and correlational research can provide a great deal of insight into human behaviour. Although not as scientifically rigorous, case studies and single-subject research designs can raise important questions and may point the way to more controlled research. Family, adoption, twin, and gene–environment interaction studies offer valuable insight into the relative contribution of heredity and the environment. Experiments differ from these other forms of non-experimental research in that they manipulate variables, randomly assign participants to experimental and control groups, and can draw clear inferences about cause and effect.

- Recently, researchers have stressed that it is not enough to simply demonstrate statistically significant results of an intervention. The more important question is whether the treatment offers meaningful relief of the distress or difficulty of people with psychopathology. Research now recognizes the importance of examining *both* statistical and clinical significance when determining if a treatment is effective and will be useful in the real world.

KEY TERMS

ABAB (p. 87)

actuarial approach (p. 66)

alternate-form reliability (p. 65)

analogue observational setting (p. 81)

Bender Visual-Motor Gestalt Test-II (p. 69)

case study (p. 86)

clinical approach (p. 66)

clinical significance (p. 92)

coefficient alpha (p. 65)

computerized axial tomography (CAT) (p. 67)

concordance (p. 89)

confound (p. 85)

construct validity (p. 66)

content validity (p. 66)

control group (p. 83)

correlational method (p. 85)

criterion validity (p. 66)

cross-fostering (p. 89)

dependent variable (p. 83)

description (p. 82)

dizygotic (DZ) twins (p. 89)

double-blind (p. 84)

effect size (p. 92)

epidemiology (p. 87)

epigenetics (p. 91)

Exner system (p. 75)

experiment (p. 83)

experimental effect (p. 83)

experimental group (p. 83)

external validity (p. 84)

face validity (p. 66)

gene–environment interactions (p. 90)

Halstead-Reitan Neuropsychological Battery (p. 69)

incidence (p. 87)

independent variable (p. 83)

intelligence quotient (IQ) (p. 72)

internal consistency (p. 65)

internal validity (p. 84)

in vivo observation (p. 81)

longitudinal studies (p. 86)

magnetic resonance imaging (MRI) (p. 67)

mental status examination (p. 71)

Millon Clinical Multiaxial Inventory (MCMI) (p. 79)

Minnesota Multiphasic Personality Inventory (MMPI) (p. 76)

monozygotic (MZ) twins (p. 89)

Montreal Cognitive Assessment (p. 69)

normative comparison (p. 92)

Personality Assessment Inventory (PAI) (p. 79)

person by situation interaction (p. 80)

phenotype (p. 90)

placebo (p. 84)

placebo effect (p. 84)

positron emission tomography (PET) (p. 68)

post-test (p. 84)

pretest (p. 84)

prevalence (p. 87)

proband (p. 89)

projective test (p. 74)

psychological assessment (p. 65)

quasi-experimental study (p. 85)

random assignment (p. 83)

rapport (p. 71)

reactivity (p. 81)

Repeatable Battery for the Assessment of Neuropsychological Status (p. 69)

reversal design (p. 87)

Rorschach inkblot test (p. 75)

science (p. 83)

single-subject designs (p. 87)

split-half reliability (p. 65)

Stanford-Binet Intelligence Scales (p. 72)

statistical significance (p. 92)

test-retest reliability (p. 65)

thematic apperception test (TAT) (p. 76)

WAIS-IV (p. 72)

Wechsler Adult Intelligence Scale (p. 72)

DAVID J. A. DOZOIS

•

JESSE LEE WILDE

•

PAUL A. FREWEN

CHAPTER

5

Kheng Ho Toh/123RF

Anxiety, Obsessive-Compulsive, and Trauma-Related Disorders

LEARNING OBJECTIVES

AFTER READING THIS CHAPTER, STUDENTS WILL BE ABLE TO:

1 Describe the characteristics of anxiety.

2 Discuss various etiological factors involved in anxiety and related disorders.

3 Identify and describe the methods involved in the assessment of anxiety and related disorders.

4 Differentiate the anxiety and anxiety-related disorders from one another.

5 Summarize and discuss common treatments for anxiety and related disorders.

On the morning of her abnormal psychology exam, Crystal is experiencing a number of noticeable but mild symptoms of anxiety. Her body is tense, her heart is beating a little faster than usual, and she has a few worried thoughts coursing through her mind (e.g., "Did I study enough to do well on this exam?"). Sitting next to Crystal is Greg, whose symptoms are more severe. Greg's heart is pounding in his chest, his breathing is quick and shallow, and he too has a number of worried thoughts, although they are different in content and more distressing than Crystal's. Greg is worried that he is going to have a panic attack during the exam, and he is frantically scanning the examination room to mark all the exits should he feel the need to escape. Furthermore, he is very worried that others will notice his anxiety symptoms and that this will be embarrassing. To top it all off, he also has the exam to worry about!

Both Crystal and Greg are experiencing symptoms of anxiety. Crystal's anxiety is fairly typical of what many undergraduates experience before an important exam. However, Greg's symptoms are much more severe, cause him extreme discomfort, and impair his ability to concentrate. Greg may even get up and leave before the exam begins.

The Characteristics of Anxiety

Before we discuss anxiety and two other related emotional states (panic and fear), we must distinguish among three distinctive components of emotion: physiological, cognitive, and behavioural. The physiological component involves changes in the autonomic nervous system that result in respiratory, cardiovascular, and muscular changes in the body (e.g., changes in breathing rate, heart rate, and muscle tone). The cognitive component includes alterations in consciousness (e.g., in attention levels) and specific thoughts a person may have while experiencing a particular emotion. For example, it is common for individuals experiencing a panic attack to think "I'm going to die," or for someone with social anxiety to think "I'm going to embarrass myself in front of everyone." Finally, specific behavioural responses tend to be consequences of certain emotions. For example, if Greg experiences a panic attack during his exam, he may feel compelled to leave the situation. It is important to remember that the three components of emotional states are highly interrelated, and that each affects the other two.

There are also important theoretical distinctions between anxiety, fear, and panic (Barlow, 2002; Clark & Beck, 2010b). **Anxiety** is an affective state whereby an individual feels threatened by the potential occurrence of a future negative event. In the examples above, both Crystal and Greg are concerned about the possibility of something "bad" happening in the immediate future. Thus, anxiety in general is "future oriented." In contrast, **fear** is a more "primitive" emotion and occurs in response to a real or perceived current threat. Therefore, fear is "present oriented" in

the sense that this emotion involves a reaction to something that is believed to be threatening at the present moment. From an evolutionary perspective, fear is a very important emotion because of the behavioural response that it elicits. This behavioural response is popularly known as the **"fight or flight" response**, so named because fear prompts a person (or organism) to either flee from a dangerous situation or stand and fight. When one considers the physiological symptoms involved in the emotion of fear, which include increased heart rate, muscle tension, and breathing rate, it is easy to see that this reaction is the body's method of preparing to respond to danger. **Panic** is very similar to fear, making these two emotional states difficult to distinguish in terms of their physiological and behavioural components. However, whereas fear is an emotional response to an objective, current, and identifiable threat, panic is an extreme fear reaction that is triggered even though there is nothing to be afraid of (it is essentially a "false alarm"; Barlow, 2002).

Historical Perspective

References to anxiety or fear have been made since the beginning of recorded history. Fear, for instance, is mentioned in ancient Greek writings and in biblical accounts. One of the earliest examples is from Hippocrates (see Chapter 1), who described a man who was terrified of flute music (Moehle & Levitt, 1991).

Until 1980, anxiety disorders were classified together with the somatoform and dissociative disorders (see Chapter 6) under the heading of **neurosis**. In the eighteenth century, people who were not psychotic but who still had emotional problems were labelled "neurotic." This term implied that the cause was presumed to be due to a disturbance in the central nervous system. Freud was one of the earliest theorists to focus on anxiety. His theories of anxiety can be traced to several of his works, including his 1895 paper "Obsessions and Phobias," his 1895 book *Studies in Hysteria*, and his 1926 text *Inhibitions, Symptoms and Anxiety*. Freud theorized that there was an important difference between objective fears and neurotic anxiety. He proposed that neurotic anxiety is a signal to the ego that an unacceptable drive (mainly sexual in nature) is pressing for conscious representation. Anxiety was viewed as a signal to ensure that the ego takes defensive action against these internal pressures. If anxiety rose above a certain level of intensity (e.g., beyond what the psychological defences can handle), symptoms ensued. In other words, anxiety was thought to occur because defence mechanisms failed to repress painful memories, impulses, or thoughts.

Research conducted over the past few decades has greatly expanded our understanding of the nature of anxiety and its treatment. The major models of anxiety today are behavioural and cognitive behavioural, although it is recognized that the causes of anxiety are complex and require an integrative understanding of biological, psychological, and interpersonal processes.

 BEFORE MOVING ON

> What are the primary differences among anxiety, fear, and panic? Give an example of how each can be adaptive and maladaptive.

Diagnostic Organization of Anxiety and Anxiety-Related Disorders

In DSM-5, anxiety-related disorders are categorized into three distinct chapters: Anxiety Disorders, Obsessive-Compulsive and Related Disorders, and Trauma- and Stressor-Related Disorders. In earlier versions of the DSM, these disorders were grouped together under the broad heading of anxiety disorders. For the sake of simplicity, we continue to cover these disorders as a group in this chapter. Although there are distinguishing characteristics, these disorders also share many similarities in their origins, etiologies, and treatments. In this chapter, we review features of the most common disorders in these categories, beginning with what DSM-5 refers to as anxiety disorders (including panic disorder, agoraphobia, specific phobia, social anxiety disorder, and generalized anxiety disorder). We then move on to obsessive-compulsive and related disorders (including obsessive-compulsive disorder and body dysmorphic disorder), and trauma- and stressor-related disorders (including post-traumatic stress disorder). We use the term anxiety disorders to refer to any of the psychological problems discussed in this chapter.

Etiology

BIOLOGICAL FACTORS

GENETICS Evidence of a genetic influence in the etiology of anxiety disorders comes from epidemiological studies of families and twins, which demonstrate that virtually all of the anxiety disorders show at least a moderate level of concordance within family members. Individuals who have a family member who is diagnosed with an anxiety disorder are four to six times more likely to have an anxiety disorder than are those without a family history. The estimated heritabilities range from 30 to 50 percent, depending on the specific anxiety disorder studied (Shimada-Sugimoto, Otowa, & Hettema, 2015). In addition, studies reveal that environmental factors particular to specific individuals account for a greater degree of the non-genetic variation in risk for anxiety disorders than do shared family factors (e.g., place of living; Hettema et al., 2001).

The genetic risk associated with anxiety disorders, however, appears to be fairly nonspecific. Rather than inheriting a risk for a specific type of anxiety disorder, the genetic risk for anxiety disorders is more likely passed on in terms of broader temperamental and/or dispositional traits, such as behavioural inhibition (the tendency of some children to respond to new situations with heightened arousal) and neuroticism (the dispositional tendency to experience negative emotions; see Minelli & Maffioletti, 2014). Individual differences in these dimensions likely serve as early risk factors for the later development of full-scale anxiety disorders when co-occurring with particular types of stress.

Although family and twin studies clearly demonstrate that genetic factors are involved in the etiology of anxiety disorders, the specific genetic basis of this risk remains to be understood. A number of preliminary studies have provided evidence of specific genetic abnormalities, but none of the findings has been sufficiently replicated to allow any firm conclusions.

NEUROANATOMY AND NEUROTRANSMITTERS The majority of what is known about the neurobiology of fear, anxiety, and panic comes from research with animals, although recent neuroimaging studies are rapidly increasing our knowledge concerning the neural underpinnings of anxiety disorders in humans (Mincic, 2015; Wessing, Romer, & Junghöfer, 2017).

The neural fear circuit as studied in animals is thought to begin with the registry of sensory information at the thalamus; this information is then sent to the amygdala. From the amygdala, information is sent to areas in the hypothalamus, and then through a midbrain area (the periaquaductal grey) to the brain stem and spinal cord. The brain stem and spinal cord connect with the various autonomic (e.g., increased heart rate, blood pressure, body temperature) and behavioural (e.g., freezing or flight) output components that are involved in the expression of fear. Direct electrical stimulation of this circuit at low levels causes subjective anxiety in humans and freezing in rats, whereas stimulation at high levels provokes feelings of terror and flight behaviour

(Panskepp, 1998). Human neuroimaging studies also suggest a role for the insular cortex, which may represent some of the somatic manifestations of anxiety (Etkin & Wager, 2007).

It is therefore important to note that higher cortical areas are not directly involved in the fear circuit. Instead, the fear system principally involves a subcortical network that can be aroused without the influence of complex cortical input. For example, the amygdala can effectively process external stimuli and determine its survival relevance without the influence of higher brain functioning (Fox, Oler, Tromp, Fudge, & Kalin, 2015). However, cortical and subcortical areas of the brain interact. These higher cortical areas are necessary for extinguishing conditioned fears (i.e., for learning that something that was previously feared no longer need be; Kim et al., 2011).

Information transfer between the neuroanatomical structures involved in fear, anxiety, and panic is mediated by a complex and interacting number of neurotransmitter systems. However, no neurotransmitter system has been found to be solely dedicated to the expression of fear, anxiety, or panic. Rather, each of the neurotransmitters involved in fear, anxiety, and panic is also involved in an assortment of general cognitive, affective, and behavioural functions. For example, gamma-aminobutyric acid (GABA) is the most pervasive inhibitory neurotransmitter in the brain, and receptors for this transmitter are well distributed along the neural fear circuit described above. Benzodiazepines are a class of anti-anxiety medications that operate primarily on GABA-mediated inhibition of the fear system. Other neurotransmitter systems are also involved, the most studied of which are the serotonin and norepinephrine systems. These systems serve general arousal regulatory functions in the central nervous system, and many of the medications used in the management of anxiety disorders have serotonin- and/or norepinephrine-based modes of action.

PSYCHOLOGICAL FACTORS

BEHAVIOURAL FACTORS The idea that anxiety and fear are acquired through learning has a long history. The origins of this proposal stem from Pavlov's discovery of classical conditioning, an idea that was expanded upon by Watson and Rayner (1920) and the case of Little Albert (see Chapter 2). In 1947, Mowrer proposed his **two-factor theory** that attempted to account for the acquisition of fears and the maintenance of anxiety. Mowrer suggested that fears develop through the process of classical conditioning and are maintained through operant conditioning. In the first phase, a neutral stimulus (the conditioned stimulus, or CS) becomes paired with an inherently negative stimulus (e.g., a frightening event, the unconditioned stimulus, or UCS). The individual later learns to lessen this anxiety by avoiding the CS, a behaviour that is negatively reinforced through operant conditioning. In the case of Little Albert, for example, Watson and Rayner (1920) showed how the fear of a rat (the CS) became conditioned through pairings with a sudden loud noise (the UCS). If Albert subsequently avoided rats, he

would probably feel less anxious (at least in the short term), which would increase the probability that he would continue this avoidance behaviour. As we discuss later in this chapter, avoidance can be effective in reducing a person's anxiety in the short term, but can serve to increase anxiety over the long haul. Imagine what would happen if you had a fear of dogs and tried to avoid them altogether. As long as you were able to avoid them, your anxiety would be fairly low; however, you would inevitably have to confront a dog at some point in the future and, during these moments, your anxiety would increase. Moreover, by avoiding dogs you would miss many opportunities for learning that they are usually not harmful. In other words, avoidance feeds the belief that there is something to fear.

Although there is support for Mowrer's two-factor theory, it does not do an adequate job of explaining the development of all phobias. Subsequent research has demonstrated, for instance, that not all fears develop through classical conditioning. For example, it is possible to develop fears by observing the reactions of other people (**vicarious learning** or modelling). Some people also develop fears by hearing fear-relevant information. For example, one of the authors heard a mother calling her son. This little boy was standing in some tall grass paying little attention to his mother's increasing demands to "come when he is called." Exasperated, the mother resorted to scaring her son, stating, "Come over here quickly. There are snakes in there and you will be bitten." There is also evidence that we are biologically prepared to fear certain types of stimuli (Seligman, 1971), a topic that is discussed in the section on the etiology of specific phobias.

COGNITIVE FACTORS Although there are many specific cognitive theories that pertain to each of the anxiety disorders, the main cognitive model for anxiety stems from the work of Dr. Aaron T. Beck (Beck & Emery, 1985; Clark & Beck, 2010b). Beck proposed that people are afraid because of the biased perceptions that they have about the world, the future, and themselves. Anxious individuals often see the world as dangerous, the future as uncertain, and themselves as ill-equipped to cope with life's threats (Beck & Emery, 1985). Individuals who are susceptible to anxiety often have core beliefs that they are helpless and vulnerable. These individuals also selectively attend to and recall information that is consistent with their views of self as helpless and the world as threatening (e.g., paying special attention to information suggestive of uncontrollability while ignoring information that does not fit with that expectation).

Numerous studies have demonstrated that anxious individuals tend to focus on information that is relevant to their fears (Clark & Beck, 2010b). For example, individuals who are phobic of spiders tend to orient toward words like *crawl* or *hairy* relative to positive or neutral words, whereas individuals with social anxiety show this effect for words such as *boring* or *foolish* (Williams, Mathews, & MacLeod, 1996). Individuals who are highly anxious may also filter out or ignore information that contradicts the presence of an objective danger. For example, individuals with recurrent panic attacks often have fears that focus on bodily (e.g., "I am going to have a heart attack"), mental ("I am going to go crazy"), or interpersonal ("I am going to be embarrassed") danger when less threatening interpretations of their symptoms are far more likely.

Although cognitive models are considerably more complex than what we describe (e.g., Beck, 1996; Beck & Dozois, 2014; Dozois & Beck, 2008), schemas, information processing biases, and automatic thoughts (see Chapter 2) are believed to be relevant to the development and maintenance of anxiety.

INTERPERSONAL FACTORS Parents who are anxious themselves tend to interact with their children in ways that are less warm and positive, more critical and catastrophic, and less granting of autonomy when compared to non-anxious parents. Such parenting styles may foster beliefs of helplessness and uncontrollability in children that contribute to a general psychological vulnerability to anxiety.

The early attachment relationship may be important in the development of anxiety. Attachment theorists have postulated that early parent–child interactions can lead to the development of general belief systems (or "internal working models") for how relationships operate in general (Bowlby, 1973; Thompson, 2008). Children who develop an "anxious-ambivalent" attachment style learn to fear being abandoned by loved ones. This attachment style may develop from interactions with parents who are inconsistent in their emotional caregiving toward the infant. Later in life, these individuals may be wary of the availability of significant others and become chronically worried about negative interpersonal events. Although anxious-ambivalent attachment is presumed to predict anxiety problems in adulthood, few longitudinal studies have tested this hypothesis (Bar-Haim, Dan, Eshel, & Sagi-Schwartz, 2007). The available research offers some support. Warren, Huston, Egeland, and Sroufe (1997) found that an anxious-ambivalent attachment style in infancy predicted anxiety problems when the children were 17.5 years old.

COMMENT ON ETIOLOGY

Clearly, no single factor causes anxiety. Instead, there is a complex and dynamic interplay among biological, psychological, and interpersonal factors. Barlow (2002) advanced a "triple vulnerability" etiological model of anxiety in which generalized biological (e.g., a genetic predisposition to being high-strung, behaviourally inhibited, nervous), nonspecific psychological (e.g., diminished sense of control, low self-esteem), and specific psychological (i.e., experiencing a real danger, false alarm, or vicarious exposure) vulnerabilities interact to increase risk (see; Payne, Ellard, Farchione, Fairholme, & Barlow, 2014). While it is likely that some individuals have a generalized biological tendency to be high-strung or nervous (Barlow, 2002), a generalized psychological vulnerability to anxiety can also develop as a result of learning experiences and interactions with parents

and peers. Over time, individuals may come to believe that the world is dangerous and threatening and that they have few resources to deal with it. Therefore, various combinations of biological, psychological, and interpersonal vulnerabilities contribute to anxiety.

② BEFORE MOVING ON

> Briefly describe three factors that are involved in the etiology of anxiety disorders and describe an experiment that might test the role of each of these factors.

Anxiety Disorders

Anxiety disorders represent the most common of all mental disorders (Kessler et al., 2009; Kessler, Chiu, Demler, & Walters, 2005). For example, epidemiological studies conducted in the United States suggest that this rate may be as high as 31 percent (Kessler, Petukhova, Sampson, Zaslavsky, & Wittchen 2012).

Without treatment, anxiety disorders tend to be chronic and recurrent, and are associated with significant distress, suffering, and impairment across multiple domains of functioning (Dozois & Westra, 2004; Panayiotou & Karekla, 2013). The reduced quality of life reported among individuals with anxiety disorders is comparable to and in some instances worse than other major medical illnesses (Penner-Goeke et al., 2015).

The Scream was painted by Edvard Munch, a Norwegian expressionist. Munch suffered from a number of psychological problems, including panic disorder. In 2012, this painting sold for $119.9 million at a New York auction.

Munch, Edvard (1863-1944)/Album/Art Resource, NY

Anxiety disorders are also costly, in terms of both treatment and lost productivity (Hendriks et al., 2015). In Europe, anxiety disorders have been estimated to cost approximately $548 million for every million people (Konnopka et al., 2009). Although comparable data in Canada are not currently available, the cost per capita is estimated to be similar (Koerner et al., 2004).

PANIC DISORDER

DESCRIPTION Individuals with panic disorder experience recurrent and unexpected panic attacks. **Panic attacks** involve a sudden rush of intense fear or discomfort during which an individual experiences a number of physiological and psychological symptoms. To be considered a true panic attack, at least 4 of the 13 symptoms outlined in Table 5.1 must be present. According to DSM-5, the attack must also develop suddenly, reaching a peak within minutes (American Psychiatric Association [APA], 2013). Individuals with panic disorder usually experience numerous bouts of panic, but at least two unexpected attacks are required for this diagnosis.

Panic attacks themselves are not atypical. Twenty-one percent of Canadians aged 15 years or older (roughly 7.5 million people) will experience at least one panic attack in their lifetime (Ramage-Morin, 2004). In contrast, only about 1.5 percent of the Canadian population meets the criteria for panic disorder (Caron & Liu, 2010). Panic attacks

are a common feature of other anxiety disorders. For example, it is not uncommon for an individual with social anxiety disorder to experience a panic attack when initiating social contact or for an individual with arachnophobia to have a panic attack when he or she confronts a spider. In panic disorder, however, the attacks occur (at least initially) "out of the blue" and are not cued by obvious triggers.

Diagnostically, at least one of the panic attacks must be followed by persistent concerns (lasting at least one month) about having additional attacks or by worry about the ramifications of the attack (e.g., worry that the person will lose control, go "crazy," have a heart attack, or die). Alternatively, panic disorder is diagnosed when at least one panic attack results in a significant alteration in behaviour. Panic disorder is not an appropriate diagnosis, however, if the onset of an individual's panic attacks is judged to be due to a general medical condition or to the ingestion of a substance (APA, 2013).

Most people who develop panic disorder do so in the late teenage years or early adulthood, although treatment is usually sought somewhat later, around 34 years of age (Craske & Barlow, 2014). Women are twice as likely as men to be affected by panic disorder, a finding that has been replicated across countries (Weissman et al., 1997). As illustrated in the case of Judy (see Case Notes on next page), panic disorder is often comorbid with other mental disorders, most notably depression, substance abuse problems, and other anxiety conditions, including agoraphobia.

TABLE 5.1 PANIC ATTACK SPECIFIER

Note: Symptoms are presented for the purpose of identifying a panic attack; however, panic attack is not a mental disorder and cannot be coded. Panic attacks can occur in the context of any anxiety disorder as well as other mental disorders (e.g., depressive disorders, post-traumatic stress disorder, substance use disorders) and some medical conditions (e.g., cardiac, respiratory, vestibular, gastrointestinal conditions). When the presence of a panic attack is identified, it should be noted as a specifier (e.g., "post-traumatic stress disorder with panic attacks"). For panic disorder, the presence of panic attack is contained within the criteria for the disorder and panic attack is not used as a specifier.

An abrupt surge of intense fear or intense discomfort that reaches a peak within minutes, and during which time four (or more) of the following symptoms occur:

Note: The abrupt surge can occur from a calm state or an anxious state.

1. Palpitations, pounding heart, or accelerated heart rate.
2. Sweating.
3. Trembling or shaking.
4. Sensations of shortness of breath or smothering.
5. Feelings of choking.
6. Chest pain or discomfort.
7. Nausea or abdominal distress.
8. Feeling dizzy, unsteady, light-headed, or faint.
9. Chills or heat sensations.
10. Paresthesias (numbness or tingling sensations).
11. Derealization (feelings of unreality) or depersonalization (being detached from oneself).
12. Fear of losing control or "going crazy."
13. Fear of dying.

Note: Culture-specific symptoms (e.g., tinnitus, neck soreness, headache, uncontrollable screaming or crying) may be seen. Such symptoms should not count as one of the four required symptoms.

AGORAPHOBIA

DESCRIPTION Agoraphobia (literally meaning "fear of the marketplace") is anxiety about being in places or situations where an individual might find it difficult to escape (e.g., being in crowds, standing in lines, going to a movie theatre, being on a bridge, travelling in a car) or in which he or she would not have help readily available should a panic attack occur (e.g., being outside of home alone, travelling). Panic disorder and agoraphobia are highly comorbid, and the occurrence of panic attacks often instigates agoraphobia. When this avoidance is persistent and pervasive, the diagnosis of agoraphobia is made. This diagnosis is made only when feared situations are actively avoided, require the presence of a companion, or are endured only with extreme anxiety; and is made irrespective of whether panic disorder is present. If an individual meets the criteria for both panic disorder and agoraphobia, then both diagnoses are assigned (APA, 2013).

DIAGNOSIS AND ASSESSMENT A number of additional issues are relevant to diagnostic practice. Conducting a differential diagnosis can be tricky at times because panic attacks themselves are not unique to panic disorder and occur in other anxiety disorders (Craske & Barlow, 2014). The cardinal feature of panic disorder is that individuals initially experience unexpected panic attacks and have marked apprehension and worry over the possibility of having additional panic attacks. In contrast, panic attacks associated with other anxiety disorders are usually cued by specific situations or feared objects. To illustrate, although an individual with social phobia may experience a panic attack during a social function, it might be brought on by the fear of being humiliated or embarrassed. People with a phobia of flying may be concerned that their plane will crash, but those with panic disorder may fear getting on a plane because they might have a panic attack and not be able to escape. There are also a number of medical conditions that create symptoms that mimic panic disorder (e.g., hypoglycemia, hyperthyroidism). Therefore, it is important for clinicians to ensure that a patient has received a proper medical examination before diagnosing panic disorder (Baker-Morrissette, Bitran, & Barlow, 2010).

Case Notes

Judy was a 29-year-old from Burnaby, British Columbia, who began to experience unexpected panic attacks five months ago. These panic attacks persisted for approximately three weeks, at which time she sought treatment and was prescribed a benzodiazepine. Secondary to her anxiety, Judy also experienced a number of symptoms of depression. She had moved to Canada a few years ago and had difficulty adjusting to this change. She became increasingly isolated and lonely. Judy described her upbringing as psychologically abusive. While growing up, she worked hard at the family-owned store and achieved good grades at school. She thought that by working hard

enough she might gain the approval of her father, but this approval never materialized and she was instead humiliated publicly and criticized. After completing university, Judy worked in a government job in her country of origin. She married shortly thereafter and terminated her employment to devote time to raising her children. When Judy first met her psychologist, she continued to experience a significant number of panic attacks, although the severity of these episodes had decreased somewhat subsequent to taking anti-anxiety medication. Initially, these panic attacks came "out of the blue" and occurred frequently. During these panic attacks she experienced tachycardia (increased heart rate), perspiration, hyperventilation, facial flushing, feelings of dizziness and unsteadiness, shaking, chest pressure and pain, nausea, and peripheral numbness and tingling sensations. She also worried that she was going to die, have a heart attack, or go crazy.

As is the case for all the anxiety disorders, a multimethod assessment that includes a clinical interview, behavioural measurement, psychophysiological tests, and self-report indices is the ideal assessment strategy (Baker-Morrissette et al., 2010). The Structured Clinical Interview for DSM-5 (First, Williams, Karg, & Spitzer, 2015) is a semistructured interview that covers the main clinical disorders, including panic disorder and agoraphobia (see Chapter 4). Another popular semi-structured interview is the Anxiety and Related Disorders Interview Schedule for DSM-5 (ADIS-5; Brown, & Barlow, 2014), which is used to establish differential diagnosis among the anxiety disorders.

Behavioural assessment is also frequently used to assess avoidance and severity. For example, a clinician may decide to observe individuals in their naturalistic environments to assess their degree of agoraphobic avoidance. One strategy is the **behavioural avoidance test (BAT)**. In this test, patients are asked to enter situations that they would typically avoid. They provide a rating of their degree of anticipatory anxiety and the actual level of anxiety that they experience. Another behavioural assessment strategy for panic disorder is the symptom induction test. For example, a patient may be asked to hyperventilate, to shake his or her head from side to side, or to spin in a chair in order to bring on symptoms of panic. Such exercises can be useful both as a way of assessing symptom severity and as a strategy for exposure treatment.

Psychophysiological assessment strategies can include the monitoring of heart rate, breathing, blood pressure, and galvanic skin response while a patient is approaching a feared situation or experiencing a panic attack (see Baker, Patterson, & Barlow, 2002). Finally, at least 30 empirically supported self-report questionnaires are available that specifically assess panic-related thoughts, behaviours, and symptoms (Antony et al., 2001; Baker et al., 2002). One popular instrument is the Anxiety Sensitivity Index (Peterson & Reiss, 1993), which measures an individual's fear of anxiety-related symptoms. Dr. Steve Taylor (University of British Columbia) and his colleagues developed an expanded version of this instrument (Taylor et al., 2007).

ETIOLOGY Panic disorder and agoraphobia are rooted in both biological and psychological factors. First, these disorders tend to run in families. The biological relatives of individuals with panic disorder, for instance, are about five times more likely to develop panic disorder than are individuals who do not have panic-prone relatives (Hettema et al., 2001). Attempts to find specific genetic markers, however, remain inconsistent (Bastiaansen et al., 2014; Howe et al., 2016). Second, there is evidence that biological challenges induce panic attacks in individuals with panic disorder more frequently than they do in non-psychiatric controls (Barlow, 2002; McNally, 1994). A biological challenge refers to the presentation of a stimulus (e.g., breathing in certain levels of CO2, hyperventilating) intended to induce physiological changes associated with anxiety. However, as Barlow (2002) pointed out, there does not appear to be an underlying biological mechanism that can account for the fact that the same basic physiological and psychological responses are displayed across these many diverse types of challenge procedures. In addition, between 44 and 71 percent of individuals with panic disorder report **nocturnal panic** (Craske & Barlow, 2014)—attacks that occur while sleeping (most often during the lighter stages of sleep, between one and three hours of falling asleep)—and some people experience panic when they are attempting to relax. A sense of losing control elicited by a somatic response may underlie the panic-inducing properties of many biological challenge procedures. In the case of nocturnal or relaxation-induced panic attacks, the cognitive experience may be similar—a fear of letting go. These findings have led to the development of cognitive theories of panic.

Cognitive theories focus on the idea that individuals with panic disorder experience **catastrophic misinterpretations** of their bodily sensations (Clark, 1986, 1996; see Gellatly & Beck, 2016). Most of us experience variability in our bodily sensations throughout the day. For example, we may get up too quickly and feel dizzy, our heart may beat quickly, or we may feel shortness of breath. Those of us who do not have panic disorder often ignore these sensations or attribute them to something benign. An individual with panic disorder, on the other hand, may quickly misinterpret these symptoms as a sign that something must be wrong (e.g., "I am going to have a heart attack"). This reaction may then cause even more apprehension such that the person worries about additional symptoms. Although the intention is to reduce these sensations, they paradoxically increase because of the response of the autonomic nervous system (the fight or flight response) to real or perceived threat. This process continues until the person feels out of control and experiences another panic attack (see Figure 5.1). People may then begin to avoid situations or bodily sensations that become associated with having panic attacks. A related theory

FIGURE 5.1 Cognitive Model of Panic

contends that there is a trait-like tendency to be anxiety sensitive. **Anxiety sensitivity** has to do with the belief that the somatic symptoms related to anxiety will have negative consequences that extend beyond the panic episode itself (see Taylor, 2014, for review).

Barlow and his colleagues (Barlow, 2002; Bouton, Mineka, & Barlow, 2001) have proposed an "**alarm theory**" of panic. As mentioned earlier, unexpected panic attacks are not uncommon in the general population. When a real danger is present, a "true alarm" occurs and our bodies kick in an incredibly adaptive physiological response that allows us to face the feared object or flee from the situation. If you were just about to be hit by a bus, you would be grateful for this alarm system—it means that your blood is circulating to the main muscle groups to help you escape, your breathing is increasing in anticipation that you will be burning off the carbon dioxide, and so on. In some instances, however, this system can be activated by emotional cues (e.g., the perception of threat rather than objective threat). The same response occurs but in this instance it is a "false alarm." The panic attack, or the situation that triggered it, then becomes associated with neutral cues through classical conditioning and the person may begin to fear internal sensations or external stimuli. Individuals with panic disorder develop apprehension about experiencing further panic attacks and they associate weak bodily sensations with the experience of a full-blown panic attack. Because of this anxiety, they focus intensely on their bodily sensations (and on other environmental cues that may have been present during the attack) to prepare for and prevent future panic attacks. However, these individuals also perceive these experiences as uncontrollable and unpredictable. Bouton et al. (2001) argue that most people who experience panic attacks do not go on to develop panic disorder and that numerous biological, cognitive, and experiential factors come into play.

③ BEFORE MOVING ON

List and describe four methods that are integral to a multi-method assessment of anxiety disorders.

SPECIFIC PHOBIA

DESCRIPTION Many of us have specific fears, such as a fear of spiders, snakes, or lightning. However, these fears tend not to be significant enough to interfere with our day-to-day activities. Many people may momentarily cringe and become scared upon seeing a spider, but most of us do not go about our day worrying about spiders. However, for some people like Donna in the case on the next page, such fears cause marked distress and significantly disrupt their daily lives. When an individual's fears are this extreme, we refer to them as specific *phobias*. Fears are adaptive reactions to threats in the environment, but phobias are excessive and unreasonable fear reactions.

Kessler and his colleagues found that 12.1 percent of the population had a diagnosable specific phobia in a given year, and that 18.4 percent of the population could expect to develop a specific phobia at some point in their lives (Kessler et al., 2012). The prevalence rates are higher among females, with a lifetime prevalence rate of 15.7 percent compared to 6.7 percent for men (Kessler, Berglund, et al., 2005).

The frequency of normal fears varies dramatically, with some fears more common than others (Depla, ten Have, van Balkom, & de Graaf, 2008). The prevalence of fears also varies across gender. Women typically report a greater number of animal (e.g., snakes and spiders) and situational (e.g., closed spaces, lightning, flying) fears than do men. However, men and women report an equal number of fears related to injections and dental procedures. When asked to rate *how much* they fear various stimuli, women report experiencing a greater degree of fear than do men across all types of fear stimuli. In terms of specific phobias, fear of animals appears to be the most prevalent (Becker et al., 2007).

DIAGNOSIS AND ASSESSMENT For the diagnosis of a specific phobia, there must be marked and persistent fear of an object or situation. Furthermore, exposure to the feared object or situation must invariably produce an anxiety reaction that is excessive and unreasonable. As with all of the anxiety disorders, a diagnosis is given when the symptoms interfere with everyday functioning (e.g., spending excessive amounts of time avoiding or worrying about encountering the feared object or situation) or cause considerable distress.

The DSM-5 outlines five specifiers of specific phobia:

Animal Type: The phobic object is an animal or insect.

Natural Environment Type: The phobic object is part of the natural environment (e.g., thunderstorms, water, heights).

Blood Injection–Injury Type: The person fears seeing blood or an injury, or fears an injection or other type of invasive medical procedure.

Situational Type: The person fears specific situations, such as bridges, public transportation, and enclosed spaces.

Other Type: Used for all other phobias not covered in the other categories, such as extreme fears of choking, vomiting, and clowns. This category also includes what is known as

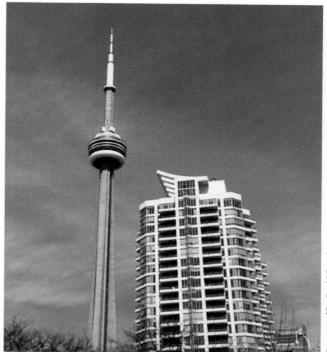

Individuals with a natural environment phobia fear such things as heights, storms, and water.

Courtesy of Dr. David Dozois

illness phobia, which involves an intense fear of developing a disease that the person currently does not have. Illness phobia is different from hypochondriasis, where people believe that they *currently have* a disease or medical condition (see Chapter 6).

Having a phobia from one of these subtypes increases the probability of developing another phobia within the same category (APA, 2000; Hofmann, Lehman, & Barlow, 1997; LeBeau et al., 2010). For example, if someone has a phobia of spiders, he or she is also more likely to be afraid of snakes, and more likely to be afraid of other animals than of thunderstorms.

ETIOLOGY The classical conditioning theory of fear, based on the work of Watson and Rayner (1920), was described earlier in this chapter. One of the main criticisms of this conditioning model is that it assumes that all neutral stimuli have an equal potential for becoming phobias. This is known as the **equipotentiality premise** (Rachman, 1977). In other words, the chances of being afraid of a lamp and a snake are presumed to be equal. However, it is not the case that people have phobias for pretty much everything; rather, a select number of stimuli seem to be consistently related to phobias.

Contrary to the associative (conditioning) model of phobias is the **nonassociative model** (Menzies & Clarke, 1995; Poulton & Menzies, 2002). The nonassociative model proposes that the process of evolution has endowed humans to respond fearfully to a select group of stimuli (e.g., water, heights, spiders), and thus no learning is necessary to develop these fears (Forsyth & Chorpita, 1997). Essentially, the types of stimuli that elicit fear do so because it is too dangerous for humans *to have to learn* to fear the stimuli with personal experience. For example, a biological predisposition to fear heights is very useful when you consider that one bad experience with falling could be deadly (Menzies & Clarke, 1995).

Evidence for nonassociative theories also comes from the finding that babies seem to be born with certain kinds of "prewired" anxiety that is elicited at various developmental stages. For example, between the ages of four and nine months, infants develop stranger anxiety, whereby they appear to instinctively fear strangers. This type of anxiety has been found across numerous countries regardless of rearing practices (Skuse, Bruce, Dowdney, & Mrazek, 2011).

Based on the underpinnings of this theory, why don't all adult humans have phobias? If we are biologically prepared to fear snakes, then shouldn't we fear snakes for the rest of our lives once we've encountered one? Menzies and Clarke (1995) argue that most of us eventually habituate to the feared stimulus over time. For instance, even though most of us may have initially feared heights as an infant, our fear likely dissipated over time after repeated exposure to heights. However, some people may fail to habituate to certain stimuli. This failure to habituate may occur because they did not have appropriate opportunities for exposure during development, or because of individual differences in the rate of habituation (Poulton & Menzies, 2002).

Case Notes

Donna is a 42-year-old woman who lives in southwestern Ontario. She has an intense fear of thunderstorms. Although she was always warned about the dangers of thunderstorms during childhood, this fear did not fully develop until she was pregnant with her first daughter at the age of 21. She recalled falling asleep on the couch and being awakened abruptly by a loud crash of thunder; she was frightened for her daughter's safety and could only think of protecting her. Since that time, she has been extremely frightened of thunderstorms and worries that they will turn into tornados and result in utter catastrophe. For large parts of the day, Donna pays close attention to any alterations in the weather and she regularly monitors the weather channel, even when the forecast is good. Her fear has increased drastically over the years, causing considerable distress and interfering with her daily functioning. For example, she avoids booking any appointments during the summer months because she is afraid to leave her house due to the possibility of a storm. When a thunderstorm does occur, Donna experiences panic attacks.

Additional support for nonassociative theories includes the fact that researchers have identified a genetic contribution to fears (Distel et al., 2008). A study of 5465 twins and their siblings found that the heritability of select specific phobias was between 35 and 51 percent. However, there are also problems with nonassociative theories. For example, not all fears entail major threats to the species. For instance, of the 35 000 varieties of spiders in the world, only 0.1 percent of them are dangerous, yet spider phobias constitute a large proportion of phobias (Diaz, 2004). In contrast, mushrooms are rarely the focus of specific phobias but can be fatally poisonous; indeed, vastly more people die of mushroom poisoning in North America than die from spider bites (Langley, 2005; Trestrail, 1991).

Another theory of etiology combines elements of both the associative and the nonassociative models. In 1971, when learning was the primary etiological model of phobias, Seligman (1971) argued that there has to be more to their etiology than classical conditioning. He suggested that people are more likely to fear certain types of stimuli because of **biological preparedness**. Similar to the nonassociative model, it is believed that the process of natural selection has equipped humans with the predisposition to fear objects and situations that represented threats to our species over the course of our evolutionary heritage. However, unlike the nonassociative model, associative learning is still necessary to develop a phobia. This helps to obviate problems with the equipotentiality premise discussed earlier, as associative learning experiences will produce phobias for those stimuli that represent threats in an evolutionary sense. Hence, this explains why learning to fear snakes is easier than learning to fear lamps.

Research has focused on the role not only of fear but also of disgust sensitivity in the formation and maintenance of phobias. **Disgust sensitivity** refers to the degree to which people are susceptible to being disgusted by a variety of stimuli such as certain bugs, types of food, and small animals (Woody & Tolin, 2002). The main hypothesis is that people develop some phobias because the phobic object is disgusting and possibly contaminated. For example, in a classic study on phobias, Mulkens, de Jong, and Merckelbach (1996) asked two groups of women (a group with a spider phobia and a control group) to do something pretty simple—choose a cookie they would like to eat and then eat it. However, there was one catch; before they ate the cookie, they had to watch an actual spider walk across it. Few of the women with a spider phobia (25 percent) were willing to eat at least some of the tasty cookie, unlike a majority of women not afraid of spiders (70 percent). Women tend to have a higher degree of disgust sensitivity than do men, and recent evidence suggests that this gender difference might partly explain the higher prevalence of specific phobias for women (Connolly, Olatunji, & Lohr, 2008). Overall, there appears to be growing support for the role of disgust sensitivity in phobias, including findings that individuals with spider and blood injection-injury phobias have higher levels of disgust sensitivity and fears of contamination than individuals without these phobias (Bianchi & Carter, 2012). These studies support the notion that the cause of phobias may not always involve only fear of danger, but other emotions, such as disgust and possibly fear of contamination.

FOCUS 5.1   Cultural Differences in Anxiety

Cross-national epidemiological research confirms that anxiety disorders occur worldwide, but the experience and prevalence of anxiety may vary across different cultures (APA, 2000). The prevalence of social anxiety disorder, for example, is lower in Asian countries (0.5 percent) than in countries such as France and Switzerland, where the rate is closer to 4 percent (Lépine, 2001). Another study revealed that the prevalence rate of anxiety disorders is lower in Japan than in Western cultures (Tsuchiya et al., 2009).

Even the interpretation of anxiety symptoms may vary widely. Culture provides the rules and the context for how we interact and express complex emotions such as anxiety (Norasakkunkit & Kalick, 2009). The culturally bound syndrome of *taijin kyofusho* in Japan and Korea, for example, shares many symptoms of social anxiety disorder. However, this syndrome is related to concerns about embarrassing or offending others rather than just being personally embarrassed or humiliated. This focus on others is consistent with the cultural emphasis on showing deference and attentiveness to where one fits in the social hierarchy (Norasakkunkit & Kalick, 2009).

The DSM-5 includes an appendix that outlines various "culture-bound syndromes" related to anxiety disorders. The following are some examples:

Ataque de nervios—this expression refers to a sense of being out of control and is recognized among many Latinos from the Caribbean. The symptoms include uncontrollable shouting, bouts of crying, trembling, heat in the chest, and verbal or physical aggression.

Dhat—this term is used in India to refer to extreme anxiety and fears related to the discharge of semen, discoloration of the urine, and exhaustion.

Taijin kyofusho—this is a culturally distinctive phobia that resembles DSM-5 social phobia. This syndrome is included in the Japanese diagnostic system and refers to an intense fear that one's body (appearance, odour, facial expressions) will displease, embarrass, or offend others.

Khyâl cap, or "wind attacks," is a syndrome found among individuals of Cambodian descent. Individuals with Khyâl cap experience panic-attack–like symptoms (e.g., dizziness, palpitations, shortness of breath) and catastrophic cognitions centred on concerns that a windlike substance that may rise in the body will cause a range of serious problems, such as asphyxia, tinnitus, and blurry vision.

Kufungisisa is a term of distress expressed by the peoples of Shona in Zimbabwe. (The term means "too much thinking" in the Shona language.) Too much thinking is thought to cause anxiety, depression, and somatic problems, and to be damaging to the mind. Kufungisisa involves ruminating on upsetting thoughts and worrying (APA, 2013).

Kirmayer (2001), a scientist at the Culture and Mental Health Research Unit in Montreal, reports that in many areas of the world people do not view symptoms of anxiety as problematic and may even reject psychological explanations and treatments. He argues that a clinician's objective should be to understand, from the patient's point of view, how his or her symptoms are experienced and to derive a treatment strategy that will be acceptable to that patient. ●

SOCIAL ANXIETY DISORDER

Case Notes

Tony found it extremely difficult to open up or relate to others and claimed that he was constantly anxious, particularly in social situations. He stated that his problems with anxiety dated back to when he was a young child. Tony claimed that he felt extremely uncomfortable in most social situations, especially when he was around unfamiliar people. His anxiety was not restricted only to speaking in front of others but also extended to eating and writing in the presence of others and using public washrooms. Tony feared that others were looking at him and that he might do something that would be embarrassing or humiliating. Because of this nervousness, he avoided most interpersonal interactions. As a child, Tony avoided school and felt extremely anxious when he did attend class. His anxiety and avoidance increased over the years, to the point where he was only able to go to five locations (the homes of close friends and relatives). As a result of his anxiety, Tony "self-medicated" with alcohol. He reported that he drank an average of 36 beers per week. "It's not the drinking that's the problem," he said, "but dealing with people when I'm not drunk."

DESCRIPTION People like Tony suffer from *social anxiety disorder (social phobia)*, a marked and persistent fear of social or performance-related situations. Often their anxiety focuses on the fear of acting in a way that will be humiliating or embarrassing. People with social anxiety have an underlying fear of being evaluated negatively and frequently worry about what others might be thinking about them. This may include fears that they will expose their inner-felt anxiety to others by not making eye contact, by blushing, or by being awkward in their speech or posture during social interactions. One of the most prototypical fears is being the "centre of attention." Table 5.2 lists the DSM-5 diagnostic criteria for social anxiety disorder.

TABLE 5.2 DSM-5 DIAGNOSTIC CRITERIA FOR SOCIAL ANXIETY DISORDER

A. Marked fear or anxiety about one or more social situations in which the individual is exposed to possible scrutiny by others. Examples include social interactions (e.g., having a conversation, meeting unfamiliar people), being observed (e.g., eating or drinking), and performing in front of others (e.g., giving a speech).

   Note: In children, the anxiety must occur in peer settings and not just during interactions with adults.

B. The individual fears that he or she will act in a way or show anxiety symptoms that will be negatively evaluated (i.e., will be humiliating or embarrassing; will lead to rejection or offend others).

C. The social situations almost always provoke fear or anxiety.

   Note: In children, the fear or anxiety may be expressed by crying, tantrums, freezing, clinging, shrinking, or failing to speak in social situations.

D. The social situations are avoided or endured with intense fear or anxiety.

E. The fear or anxiety is out of proportion to the actual threat posed by the social situation and to the sociocultural context.

F. The fear, anxiety, or avoidance is persistent, typically lasting for 6 months or more.

G. The fear, anxiety, or avoidance causes clinically significant distress or impairment in social, occupational, or other important areas of functioning.

H. The fear, anxiety, or avoidance is not attributable to the physiological effects of a substance (e.g., a drug of abuse, a medication) or another medical condition.

I. The fear, anxiety, or avoidance is not better explained by the symptoms of another mental disorder, such as panic disorder, body dysmorphic disorder, or autism spectrum disorder.

J. If another medical condition (e.g., Parkinson's disease, obesity, disfigurement from burns or injury) is present, the fear, anxiety, or avoidance is clearly unrelated or is excessive.

Source: Reprinted with permission from the *Diagnostic and Statistical Manual of Mental Disorders, Fifth Edition.* (Copyright © 2013). American Psychiatric Association. All Rights Reserved.

Individuals with *social anxiety disorder* fear interacting with others in most social settings. In contrast, those individuals with *performance only social phobia* fear specific social situations or activities, which may include casual speaking, eating or writing in public, or giving formal speeches. As one would predict, the former condition tends to be more disabling. Although probably everyone has experienced social or performance anxiety at one time or another, social anxiety is not merely synonymous with shyness or the "social butterflies." Exposing individuals with social anxiety to their feared situation almost invariably provokes intense anxiety, which may take the form of situationally predisposed panic attacks.

Individuals with social anxiety are generally well aware of the fact that their fears are excessive and unreasonable. Thus, one of the keys to understanding their condition is that their fears persist despite this knowledge (Hirsch & Clark, 2004).

Individuals with social anxiety disorder find most social gatherings terrifying.

Outside the anxious situation they may be fully cognizant of the extreme nature of their fears, although somehow this adaptive and logical perspective holds less force relative to the overwhelming anxiety they experience during actual social encounters. Consequently, these individuals frequently avoid social situations; those situations they cannot avoid are otherwise endured with intense anxiety and distress. In these latter situations, they may manage their anxiety by taking refuge in the periphery of the situation, where their anxiety may be less prominent. For example, at a large social gathering, they might converse only with long-familiar friends, as opposed to acquainting themselves with other people. Alternatively, in a large group discussion, they may listen quietly but contribute nothing to the dialogue themselves. Even more subtle methods of avoidance may be present as well. For example, when needing to entertain company at their home, individuals with social anxiety may busy themselves with preparations (e.g., cooking, cleaning) so as to covertly avoid having to engage in conversation with guests.

Over time, these patterns of *overt* and *covert avoidance* may result in individuals with social phobia becoming considerably lonely and isolated (Teo, Lerrigo, & Rogers, 2013). Added to this are frequent self-critical thoughts about their social performance and hopelessness that they will ever overcome their social inhibition. Accordingly, individuals with social anxiety often have low self-esteem, and are at increased risk for mood problems such as depression (Ohayon & Schatzberg, 2010).

Based on the Canadian Community Health Survey (Health Canada, 2002), the one-year prevalence of social anxiety in Canada is approximately 3 percent, with rates almost identical in females (3.4 percent) and males (2.6 percent). Higher rates (approximately 7 percent, across both sexes) have been observed in epidemiological studies in the United States (Kessler et al., 2012). As such, social anxiety is one of the most prevalent psychiatric disorders, with a prevalence rate comparable to unipolar depression. The majority of individuals with social anxiety have one or more additional psychiatric diagnoses. In the National Comorbidity Survey, 63 percent of individuals were diagnosed with comorbid conditions, with the most common co-occurring disorders involving anxiety, mood, and substance disorders (Ruscio et al., 2008). For most individuals with comorbid social anxiety disorder, the onset of their social anxiety predates the onset of the comorbid disorder (Kessler, Berglund, et al., 2005).

DIAGNOSIS AND ASSESSMENT Assessment of social anxiety usually takes the form of a structured or semi-structured interview combined with completion of various self-report measures. These methods allow clinicians to examine an individual's thoughts, feelings, and behaviours associated with social situations. Certain diagnostic considerations are particularly relevant to social anxiety. One of these is distinguishing between social anxiety and agoraphobia. Although individuals with both social anxiety and agoraphobia may experience anxiety in public places, the reason for this fear is fundamentally different in the two disorders. The fear that characterizes social anxiety involves being negatively evaluated or embarrassed in social situations.

ETIOLOGY The etiology of social anxiety includes genetic-biological, environmental, and cognitive factors (Rapee & Spence, 2004). Genetic factors appear to account for approximately 40 percent of the variance in risk for social anxiety (Scaini, Belotti, & Ogliari, 2014). What seems largely to be inherited, however, is a predisposition to develop anxiety about social situations rather than the disorder itself. Behavioural inhibition is an early marker of risk for social anxiety disorder. Toddlers who are behaviourally inhibited are more than twice as likely to develop social anxiety by the end of adolescence when compared with non-inhibited toddlers (Rapee, 2014).

Research is beginning to identify the neurocircuitry involved in social anxiety, although most studies have investigated social anxiety in general rather than ensuring that participants met diagnostic criteria for social anxiety disorder specifically. It is likely that interactions among structures involved in fear recognition and conditioning (e.g., amygdala), arousal, and stress (e.g., hypothalamic-pituitary-adrenal axis), and the regulation and areas of the brain that monitor negative affect (e.g., anterior cingulate cortex, prefrontal and orbitofrontal cortex) play an important role. In addition, dysregulation of serotonin, norepinephrine, and other neurotransmission systems during stress responses are likely associated with socially anxious behaviour.

Early psychosocial experiences play a large role in shaping an individual's risk for social anxiety. A Hamilton, Ontario, study revealed that 92 percent of an adult sample of individuals with social anxiety reported that they were bullied or severely teased during childhood; this was at least twice as frequent in social anxiety as it was in obsessive-compulsive disorder or panic disorder (McCabe, Antony, Summerfeldt, Liss, & Swinson, 2003). In addition, individuals with social anxiety report being exposed to a greater level of parental criticism, overprotection, and control as a child (Alden & Taylor, 2004; Boelen & Reijntjes, 2009). As a result of these negative peer and family influences, individuals may develop a lack of confidence and a negative self-focus that creates and reinforces the anxiety they experience in social situations (Alden & Taylor, 2004; Rapee & Spence, 2004).

Cognitive factors associated with social anxiety involve both negative beliefs and judgments about self and others, as well as abnormal processing of social information (Norton & Abbott, 2016). For example, people with social anxiety exhibit greater concern about making mistakes in general, and are more doubtful about the accuracy of their decision making and behaviour than non-psychiatric controls (Antony, Purdon, Huta, & Swinson, 1998). In addition, individuals with social anxiety tend to judge themselves as inferior to others and to engage in negative thinking about self (Mitchell & Schmidt, 2014). As a result of their perfectionistic and self-critical tendencies, individuals with social anxiety may develop a negative view of self that is similar to individuals with depression (Dozois & Frewen, 2006). In addition, the self-concept of socially anxious individuals may be further eroded over time by repeated *dishonest self-disclosure* (Orr & Moscovitch, 2015). This refers to a self-protective strategy wherein individuals assert inauthentic or dishonest opinions to try to "tell others what they want to hear" instead of expressing their own genuine opinion.

Individuals with social anxiety also display elements of abnormal social information processing (Bögels & Mansell, 2004). For example, these individuals tend to avoid looking directly at other people's faces, although they exhibit vigilance for signs of social threat (e.g., angry expressions of others; Liang, Tsai, & Hsu, 2017). Consistent with these attentional biases, individuals with social anxiety show increased brain activity in the amygdala when viewing others' facial expressions, suggesting increased threat monitoring (Birbaumer et al., 1998; Stein, Goldin, Sareen, Zorrilla, & Brown, 2002). Socially anxious individuals also have a tendency to engage in *self-focused attention*, and place excessive attention inward on the self. Self-focused attention has been linked to increased activity in brain structures responsible for introspection and self-referential processes (Boehme, Miltner, & Staube, 2015). Paradoxically, this excessive self-focused attention may diminish important cognitive resources, thereby interfering with their ability to accurately interpret social cues (Judah, Grant, Mills, & Lechner, 2013). Individuals with social anxiety also tend to be high in *public self-consciousness*, which refers to the awareness of the self as an object of attention, or the tendency to see the self's actions from the perspective of an outside observer rather than through the person's own eyes (Bögels & Mansell, 2004).

Interestingly, while people generally tend to prefer interacting with warmer and less dominant others, socially anxious individuals may be more willing to interact with others who are colder and more submissive. This may be because socially anxious individuals see themselves similarly and prefer interacting with others who they perceive to be more like them (Rodebaugh, Bielak, Vidovic, & Moscovitch, 2016). University of British Columbia researchers Lynn Alden and Charles Taylor (2004) make the important point that social anxiety entails more than simply the presence of anxiety symptoms. Instead, they characterize social anxiety as an *interpersonal disorder*—a condition that is commonly associated with marked disruption in the ability to relate with other people. These theorists call attention to the importance of "self-perpetuating interpersonal cycles" in the onset and maintenance of social anxiety, whereby excessive social anxiety leads to avoidance and eventual peer rejection, with further social anxiety and possible depression as a consequence.

GENERALIZED ANXIETY DISORDER

Case Notes

Elizabeth was a "worrier" for as long as she could remember. Her worry became worse, however, when she experienced a work-related injury that bruised her chest wall. Following this injury, she began to experience health-related anxiety and presented at the emergency room on two occasions complaining of chest pain. Elizabeth reported that she experiences far more than just health anxiety. She worries constantly about the safety and well-being of her loved ones. For example, when her daughter is ill, she cannot bring herself to provide medicine because she fears that the dose she gives will be too much or too little and that harm will come to her daughter. She also worries about family members who live out of town and phones them regularly to ensure their safety. Elizabeth worries, as well, about finances, about getting into an accident whenever she drives, and about the safety of gas appliances. She even avoids pumping gas at a service station for fear that an explosion may result. She recognizes that her worry is excessive but finds it difficult to control, and she experiences symptoms of fatigue, muscle tension, restlessness, and sleep difficulties.

DESCRIPTION Elizabeth's symptoms are characteristic of generalized anxiety disorder (GAD), in which the central difficulty involves uncontrollable and excessive worry (also called *pathological worry*). We all worry to some degree, but it becomes pathological when it is chronic, excessive, uncontrollable, and essentially takes the joy out of life (Borkovec, Ray, & Stober, 1998). Although significant negative life events have the capacity to create feelings of distress and anxiety even in the most resilient of individuals, the anxiety experienced by people with GAD is far in excess of what would be

naturally elicited by a given set of life stressors. For individuals with GAD it is often not the amount of stress in their lives that is the clinical problem, but rather the amount of anxiety and worry they experience as a result of a relatively normal level of life stress. An estimated 2 percent of the population has GAD in any 12-month period, whereas almost 9 percent of the general population can be expected to develop this disorder at some point in their lives (Kessler et al., 2012). As with many of the other anxiety disorders, women make up the majority of those diagnosed with GApD. This disorder is twice as common in females as it is in males (APA, 2013).

DIAGNOSIS AND ASSESSMENT

The primary criterion for GAD, in DSM-5, is the presence of excessive worry, which must be present for more days than not for a period of at least six months (see Table 5.3). Three or more other symptoms of anxiety must also be present, such as restlessness, muscle tension, and sleep problems. One of the challenges in making the diagnosis of GAD involves determining that the source of a person's anxiety and worry is not confined to another clinical disorder. This sometimes makes diagnosis difficult because worry is a prominent feature in many of the anxiety disorders. For example, individuals with panic disorder often worry about future panic attacks, and those with social anxiety disorder tend to worry about upcoming social interactions. Worry can also be a prominent symptom in other "non-anxiety" disorders. For example, individuals with hypochondriasis (see Chapter 6) often spend a lot of time worrying about the possibility that they might have a disease or medical condition. Therefore, it is important for the clinician to make sure that worry is fairly ubiquitous in the sense that it is not specific to one content area. In contrast to the worries of individuals with other anxiety disorders, which tend to be restricted to a single domain or theme, individuals with GAD "worry about everything." They often worry about several things at once and report a long history of worrying.

ETIOLOGY Given that worry is the central symptom in GAD, it is not surprising that many of the etiological models are primarily cognitive in nature. Tom Borkovec and his colleagues have proposed that individuals with GAD use worry primarily as an avoidance strategy. One thing that individuals with GAD appear to "avoid" by worrying is physiological arousal. The physical feeling of anxiety can be quite discomforting and bothersome, and therefore avoidance of arousal is reinforcing to the individual. Interestingly, then, the process of worry tends to *decrease* somatic arousal (Borkovec, Lyonsfields, Wiser, & Deihl, 1993; Thayer, Friedman, & Borkovec, 1996). For example, Borkovec and Hu (1990) had participants worry before exposing them to a phobic image. Results showed that worrying decreased their physiological reaction to the phobic stimulus by inhibiting cardiovascular activity. Physiological changes in response to worry may also be influenced by characteristics of the individual. For instance, individuals with less *tolerance for uncertainty* (discussed in more detail below) display greater reductions in

TABLE 5.3   DSM-5 DIAGNOSTIC CRITERIA FOR GENERALIZED ANXIETY DISORDER

A. Excessive anxiety and worry (apprehensive expectation), occurring more days than not for at least 6 months, about a number of events or activities (e.g., work, school performance).

B. The person finds it difficult to control the worry.

C. The anxiety and worry are associated with three (or more) of the following six symptoms (with at least some symptoms present for more days than not for the past 6 months). **Note:** Only one item is required in children.

   (1) restlessness or feeling keyed up or on edge

   (2) being easily fatigued

   (3) difficulty concentrating or mind going blank

   (4) irritability

   (5) muscle tension

   (6) sleep disturbance (difficulty falling or staying asleep, or restless unsatisfying sleep)

D. The anxiety, worry, or physical symptoms cause clinically significant distress or impairment in social, occupational, or other important areas of functioning.

E. The disturbance is not attributable to the physiological effects of a substance (e.g., a drug of abuse, a medication) or another medical condition (e.g., hyperthyroidism).

F. The disturbance is not better explained by another mental disorder (e.g., anxiety or worry about having panic attacks in panic disorder, negative evaluation in social anxiety disorder [social phobia], contamination or other obsessions in obsessive-compulsive disorder, separation from attachment figures in separation anxiety disorder, reminders of traumatic events in posttraumatic stress disorder, gaining weight in anorexia nervosa, physical complaints in somatic symptom disorder, perceived appearance flaws in body dysmorphic disorder, having a serious illness in illness anxiety disorder, or the content of delusional beliefs in schizophrenia or delusional disorder).

heart rate variability during a worry-inducing task compared to those with greater tolerance of uncertainty (Deschênes, Dugas, & Gouin, 2016).

How does worry decrease physiological arousal? The answer seems to relate to the fact that worrying is primarily accompanied by verbal thought and very little imagery. When the majority of people are asked to report the content of their thoughts while in a relaxed state, they tend to report a preponderance of imagery over verbal thoughts. In contrast, those with GAD report an equal balance of imagery and verbal thoughts. However, when both groups are induced to worry, imagery soon disappears and verbal statements dominate thinking (Borkovec & Inz, 1990). It appears that anxious images elicit arousal, whereas verbal thoughts decrease arousal. Hence, worrying is negatively reinforced because it can lead to a reduction in anxiety symptoms.

Another purpose of worry is to avoid future threat. For many people with and without GAD, worry is considered to be a very useful way of preparing for the future. Indeed, there are a number of reasons why people report worrying, some of which are listed in Table 5.4. Many people believe that worry is an effective way of preventing or preparing for future threat (Borkovec & Roemer, 1995; Freeston, Rheaume, Letarte, Dugas, & Ladouceur, 1994). For example, at certain times during the semester, when your work piles up, you may start to worry. This process may lead you to work hard and to do well. However, getting a good grade may reinforce the habit of worry—you may not, for example, want to take a chance and see how you would do with hard work alone (i.e., without worrying). You may come to mistakenly believe that worrying prevented you from failing, even though you may never have failed in the first place and it was your hard work that allowed you to do well.

TABLE 5.4   REASONS FOR WORRYING AND SAMPLE ITEMS FROM THE WHY WORRY II SCALE

Reason	Example (sample items)
Enhances motivation	"The fact that I worry motivates me to do the things I must do."
Facilitates problem solving	"I worry because I think it can help me find a solution to my problem."
Protects against negative emotions	"If I worry in advance, I will be less disappointed if something serious occurs."
Prevents negative outcomes	"The act of worrying itself can prevent mishaps from occurring."
Reflects a positive personality traits	"If I did not worry, I would be careless and irresponsible."

Individuals with GAD tend to worry so much that it significantly disrupts their life and causes more problems than benefits.

Drs. Michel Dugas and Robert Ladouceur are two Canadian researchers who have had a tremendous impact on the field of GAD research. Together with their colleagues, they have proposed their own theory of GAD, which primarily focuses on a cognitive vulnerability factor they call intolerance of uncertainty (Dugas, Gagnon, Ladouceur, & Freeston, 1998; Gentes & Ruscio, 2011). **Intolerance of uncertainty (IU)** refers to an individual's discomfort with ambiguity and uncertainty. Everyone has a different threshold for accepting and dealing with life's uncertainties; individuals with GAD tend to have lower thresholds for these uncertainties, leading to anxiety and distress. IU is responsible for creating and exacerbating "what if . . . " questions, which are questions we all ask ourselves at some point in time. The following is a list of "what if . . . " questions asked by many undergraduate students:

- "What if I don't do well on my next exam?"
- "What if I don't get a good job after I graduate?"
- "What if my boyfriend (or girlfriend) is cheating on me?"

Notice that each of these questions addresses uncertainty about the future. Fortunately, many of us are forced to deal with only a limited number of such questions. However, individuals with GAD are constantly grappling with these questions because they have a selective bias for uncertainty. For example, individuals with high levels of IU tend to pay more attention to threatening and uncertain information and to interpret ambiguous information as more threatening than do those with low IU (Dugas et al., 2005). Therefore, not only does IU lead to the identification of more uncertainty in both daily life and the future, but this uncertainty is also considered to be more threatening. Several studies have supported IU as an etiological risk factor for GAD (e.g. Dugas, Marchand, & Ladouceur, 2005). This construct consistently correlates with pathological worry and anxiety (Gentes & Ruscio, 2011) and distinguishes between individuals with GAD and those without the disorder (Dugas et al., 1998).

While not a necessary diagnostic criterion of GAD, elevated levels of anger appear to be an associated feature and often characterize individuals with this disorder (Deschênes, Dugas, Fracalanza, & Koerner, 2012). Certain beliefs related to IU may be important in understanding the link between anger and GAD. In particular, the belief that uncertainty is unfair appears to contribute to feelings of anger in individuals with symptoms of GAD (Fracalanza, Koerner, Deschênes, & Dugas, 2014), and feelings of anger in turn result further reinforce the belief that uncertainty is unfair (Deschênes, Dugas, Anderson, & Gouin, 2015). In addition, a state of uncertainty may be especially likely to lead to anger when an individual perceives the instance of uncertainty as being avoidable (Anderson, Deschênes, & Dugas, 2016).

④ BEFORE MOVING ON

Sara is constantly worried that she is going to die in a car accident. When she was a child, her father died in a car accident on his way to pick her up from school. However, her fear of dying in a car accident didn't occur until she went away to university at the age of 18. Sara reports that she often has intrusive thoughts of being involved in a motor vehicle accident and that these thoughts persist no matter how much she tries to ignore them. Sara avoids driving or being in a car whenever possible. If she has to ride in a car, Sara spends more than an hour checking it over before she gets in. Sara understands that these thoughts and her avoidance are negatively affecting her life. Based on this information, which anxiety disorder do you think Sara most likely has?

Obsessive-Compulsive and Related Disorders

Obsessive-Compulsive and Related Disorders include the diagnoses of obsessive-compulsive disorder (OCD), body dysmorphic disorder (BDD), hoarding disorder, trichotillomania (hair-pulling disorder) and excoriation (skin-picking disorder). In this section, we focus on OCD and BDD. The primary features of OCD are recurrent obsessions and compulsions that cause marked distress for the individual. BDD is characterized by a preoccupation with perceived defects in one's own physical appearance, often accompanied by repetitive behaviours (e.g., mirror checking) in response to appearance concerns. Kessler and colleagues (2012) have estimated that the one-year prevalence rate for OCD in the general population is about 1 percent, with approximately 3 percent of the population expected to develop the disorder at some point in their lifetime. OCD and the related disorders often occur together; for example, approximately 8% of individuals seeking treatment for OCD also have BDD (Torresan et al., 2013; Lochner et al., 2014).

OBSESSIVE-COMPULSIVE DISORDER

Case Notes

Scott experienced a number of bizarre and disturbing thoughts that he would be contaminated by germs. He responded to these fears by engaging in a number of cleaning rituals. For instance, he washed his hands two to three times before eating. He reported that the extent to which he washed varied depending on the situation. When he was at a friend's house, he washed an average of two to three times; at a public washroom, this increased to six or more times. Scott worked in the shipping and receiving department at The Bay in downtown Montreal. At work, he wore gloves during the day and kept his own bars of soap in his desk drawer. He washed his hands at every occasion possible. At home, Scott scrubbed his walls with bleach, going through eight litres per week. He thoroughly washed the walls in his house three times a week and spot cleaned twice a day. He also vacuumed his home a few times a day. His dishes and the countertop were washed numerous times every day. These washing and cleaning rituals would consume several hours of each day. Scott was also unsure as to whether he had locked the doors or turned off the stove; consequently, he checked these multiple times before leaving his house. These symptoms interfered greatly with his work performance and he received a number of verbal and written warnings from his employer that he was wasting too much time at work.

DESCRIPTION Obsessions are defined as recurrent and uncontrollable thoughts, impulses, or ideas that the individual finds disturbing and anxiety-provoking. Common obsessions include thoughts related to uncertainty (e.g., doubting if one has locked the door or turned off the stove), sexuality (e.g., homosexual imagery), violence (e.g., harming a child), and contamination (e.g., believing one is dirty and covered with germs). Individuals with OCD often consider their obsessions to be so disturbing that they try to conceal them from others (Newth & Rachman, 2001), fearing that others will react negatively to their thoughts. Because their obsessions are a source of personal shame and embarrassment, patients with OCD may be reluctant to reveal the exact nature of these obsessions even to their therapists. Yet a Canadian study revealed that intrusive thoughts are common. Clark and Purdon (2009) found that 80 percent of students reported intrusive worry thoughts. Hence, some therapists attempt to reduce distress about these cognitive symptoms by sharing this information with their patients and "normalizing" the occurrence of obsessional thinking.

As demonstrated in the case of Scott, individuals with OCD often attempt to cope with their feelings of discomfort by engaging in compulsions. **Compulsions** are repetitive behaviours or cognitive acts that are intended to reduce anxiety. Examples of repetitive behaviours include handwashing, checking, and rigidly maintaining order and organization (e.g., placing ornaments around the house in a particular order). Cognitive acts include things like counting numbers, praying, and repeating words or phrases over and over. Thus, compulsions involve observable behaviour or mental acts that are used to reduce anxiety. Approximately 80 percent of patients exhibit both behavioural and mental compulsions (Foa & Kozak, 1995).

A related way that patients deal with anxiety is through neutralizations. **Neutralizations** are behavioural or mental acts that are used by individuals to try to prevent, cancel, or "undo" the feared consequences and distress caused by an obsession (Rachman, 1997; Salkovskis, 1985). Rachman, Shafran, Mitchell, Trant, and Teachman (1996) tested undergraduates' use of neutralization in an experiment. The researchers induced a discomforting and intrusive thought by having participants complete the following sentence: "I hope ____ is in a car accident" by inserting a friend's name in the blank space, and imagining that the situation had actually

happened. Following this manipulation, the research participants were told that they could do whatever they wanted to do to cancel the effects of writing the sentence. All the students engaged in some neutralizing activity. For example, some students inserted the word *not* in the sentence, others crossed out the sentence, and some students scrunched up the paper and threw it away. One participant even asked to take the paper home to burn it! Two important things are noteworthy with regard to this experiment. First, the participants tended to feel better after engaging in a neutralizing act. Second, the participants were undergraduate students and not OCD patients. This shows that neutralizing is a normal and common activity.

One of the more striking aspects of individuals with OCD is their excessive beliefs about personal responsibility and feelings of guilt (Lawrence & Williams, 2011; Rachman, 1993). Individuals with OCD are often quite concerned with making sure their behaviour will not lead to negative consequences, particularly to others. In addition to an excessive sense of responsibility for their behaviours, there can be an inflated sense of responsibility for their thoughts. Having an unwanted thought such as hitting a child can make people feel immoral—and the more responsible they feel for the content of their thoughts, the worse they feel (Rachman, 1993). In fact, one of the more interesting findings with OCD patients is their tendency to fuse thoughts and behaviours together (Shafran & Rachman, 2004). **Thought-action fusion (TAF)** refers to two types of irrational thinking: (1) the belief that having a particular thought increases the probability that the thought will come true (e.g., "If I think about getting hit by a car, I'm more likely to get hit by a car"); and (2) the belief that having a particular thought is the moral equivalent of a particular action (e.g. having a thought about harming someone is the moral equivalent of actually doing it). While TAF is related to OCD symptoms (Bailey, Wu, Valentiner, & McGrath, 2014), studies suggest that we all tend to engage in some form of TAF from time to time (Rassin, Merckelbach, Muris, & Schmidt, 2001; Shafran & Rachman, 2004). Have you ever felt so superstitious about something that you didn't want to think about it just in case you might jinx the outcome?

DIAGNOSIS AND ASSESSMENT The diagnostic criteria for OCD are presented in Table 5.5. The first criterion for a diagnosis of OCD is the presence of either obsessions or compulsions. Although they may occur in isolation, obsessions co-occur with compulsions most of the time (96 percent; Foa & Kozak, 1995). When assessing for the presence of obsessions, it is important to distinguish obsessions from excessive worries about everyday problems. This may be difficult given that obsessions and pathological worry have a number of similarities (e.g., intrusiveness and uncontrollability of thoughts). However, there are characteristics that distinguish obsessions from worries, including the fact that obsessions tend to be more bizarre and involve more imagery than do worries (Comer, Kendall, Franklin, Hudson, & Pimental, 2004). As with most disorders, the diagnostic criteria also require that the symptoms cause marked distress or significantly interfere with the person's life.

TABLE 5.5   DSM-5 DIAGNOSTIC CRITERIA FOR OBSESSIVE-COMPULSIVE DISORDER

A. Presence of obsessions, compulsions, or both:

Obsessions are defined by (1) and (2):

1. Recurrent and persistent thoughts, urges, or images that are experienced, at some time during the disturbance, as intrusive and unwanted, and that in most individuals cause marked anxiety or distress.

2. The individual attempts to ignore or suppress such thoughts, urges, or images, or to neutralize them with some other thought or action (i.e., by performing a compulsion).

Compulsions are defined by (1) and (2):

1. Repetitive behaviors (e.g., hand washing, ordering, checking) or mental acts (e.g., praying, counting, repeating words silently) that the individual feels driven to perform in response to an obsession or according to rules that must be applied rigidly.

2. The behaviors or mental acts are aimed at preventing or reducing anxiety or distress, or preventing some dreaded event or situation; however, these behaviors or mental acts are not connected in a realistic way with what they are designed to neutralize or prevent, or are clearly excessive.

   Note: Young children may not be able to articulate the aims of these behaviors or mental acts.

B. The obsessions or compulsions are time-consuming (e.g., take more than 1 hour per day) or cause clinically significant distress or impairment in social, occupational, or other important areas of functioning.

C. The obsessive-compulsions symptoms are not attributable to the physiological effects of a substance (e.g., a drug of abuse, a medication) or another medical condition.

D. The disturbance is not better explained by the symptoms of another mental disorder (e.g., excessive worries, as in generalized anxiety disorder; preoccupation with appearance, as in body dysmorphic disorder; difficulty discarding or parting with possessions, as in hoarding disorder; hair pulling, as in trichotillomanis [hair-pulling disorder]; skin picking, as in excoriation [skin picking] disorder; stereotypies, as in stereotypic movement disorder; ritualized eating behavior, as in eating disorders; preoccupation with substances or gambling, as in substance-related and addictive disorders; preoccupation with having an illness, as in illness anxiety disorder; sexual urges or fantasies, as in paraphilic disorders; impulses, as in disruptive, impulse, impulse-control, and conduct disorders; guilty ruminations, as in major depressive disorder; thought insertion or delusional preoccupations, as in schizophrenia spectrum and other psychotic disorders; or repetitive patterns of behavior, as in autism spectrum disorder).

It is also often useful to distinguish between certain OCD subtypes. Given the fact that OCD is a relatively heterogeneous disorder, subtyping may provide a greater understanding of the condition and lead to more effective treatments. Researchers have found that obsessions and compulsions can be divided into several common subtypes or content areas. For example, many individuals with OCD have obsessions and compulsions specifically related to themes of contamination and washing or cleaning. These individuals may experience discomfort or distress because they feel contaminated or "dirty", or they may be concerned about germs harming themselves or others. Individuals with contamination concerns often engage in washing or cleaning behaviours to reduce the distress of feeling "dirty," or reduce the perceived risk of spreading germs to others. Other subtypes include those with a need for order or symmetry (because it "feels" right), and those with a strong tendency to engage in checking behaviours to relieve anxiety associated with thoughts of harm.

ETIOLOGY There is no fully accepted model of what causes OCD, and over 20 different theories exist (Jenike, 1998; Taylor, Afifi, Stein, Asmundson, & Jang, 2010). In this section, we focus on two of the more prominent models: the neurobiological model and the cognitive-behavioural model.

There has been limited conclusive research on the role of genetics and OCD, although over 30 potential genes have been investigated (Stewart & Pauls, 2010). However, based on the available evidence, there does appear to be a mild genetic risk factor for the disorder. For example, Taylor and colleagues

(2010) found that heritability accounted for 32 to 40 percent of the variance in dysfunctional beliefs that give rise to OCD.

Most neuropsychology models of OCD implicate the basal ganglia and frontal cortex (Baxter et al., 1987; Rauch, Whalen, Dougherty, & Jenike, 1998; Rosenberg & Keshavan, 1998). One of the primary functions of the basal ganglia is to control motor behaviours, whereas the frontal cortex is responsible for a wide range of higher cognitive functions such as abstract reasoning, inhibition, planning, and decision making. These two areas of the brain are connected and form a looped system through which information travels back and forth. Structural and/or functional abnormalities in this brain system may be responsible for compulsions and obsessions. For example, Pujol and his colleagues (2004) found that patients with OCD have less brain volume in parts of the frontal cortex and more brain volume in parts of the basal ganglia than do individuals without OCD.

Neurochemical theories of OCD have also been proposed. The leading neurochemical theory is the serotonin hypothesis, which is based on the notion that abnormalities in the serotonin system are responsible for OCD symptoms (Abramowitz, 2008). For example, the success of selective serotonin reuptake inhibitors (SSRIs) in alleviating OCD symptoms has led many researchers to implicate abnormalities in serotonin neurotransmission in the pathophysiology of OCD (Denys, van Nieuwerburgh, Deforce, & Westenberg, 2007). However, this kind of logic has been criticized by researchers as flawed; in fact, evidence that serotonin is causally related to OCD has been inconclusive (Abramowitz, 2008).

FOCUS 5.2
OCD and Checking: Poor Memory or Poor Memory Confidence?

OCD is often characterized by recurrent doubts (e.g., doubts about whether or not you have remembered to lock the door) and repeated checking behaviours (e.g., checking whether the door is indeed locked). Some researchers have speculated that these symptoms may be the result of memory deficits in individuals with the disorder (e.g., compulsive checkers actually cannot remember if they locked the door; Greisberg & McKay, 2003; Savage et al., 1999). Research suggests, however, that this may not be the case, and that people with OCD are more likely to be affected by poor memory confidence, as opposed to poor memory accuracy (Coles, Radomsky, & Horng, 2006; Radomsky & Alcolado, 2010; Radomsky, Gilchrist, & Dussault, 2006).

Adam Radomsky and his colleagues (2014) at Concordia University conducted an interesting study to further examine the link between doubt, compulsive checking, and memory in OCD. Participants included a sample of individuals diagnosed

with OCD, and a control sample of undergraduate students without the disorder. The researchers instructed participants to repeatedly turn on, turn off, and check a real kitchen stove or kitchen faucet in a standardized, ritualized manner. Participants were then asked to identify which three of six kitchen knobs they had checked in the most recent trial; and to rate the confidence, vividness, and detail of their memory of which knobs they had checked. Results indicated that following repeated checking, both clinical and nonclinical participants reported significantly reduced memory confidence, vividness, and detail. In other words, repeated checking caused individuals with and without OCD to doubt their memory of completing a task. These findings are consistent with models of OCD suggesting that checking behaviours represent a self-perpetuating, vicious cycle, wherein checking increases doubt, which subsequently results in further desire to engage in checking behaviours (Rachman, 2002). ●

The cognitive-behavioural conceptualization of OCD posits that problematic obsessions are caused by the person's *reaction* to intrusive thoughts (Salkovskis, 1985). Many people have intrusive thoughts but most do not go on to develop abnormal obsessions. Rachman (1998) argued that abnormal obsessions arise from **"catastrophic misinterpretations"** of these intrusive thoughts. Individuals with OCD have high levels of personal responsibility and believe that their thoughts can influence the probability that others will be harmed. When they have thoughts of harming another, for example, people with OCD tend to conclude: "This must mean I'm actually a dangerous person" or "There's a greater chance I might actually harm someone."

Obsessions are believed to persist because of the person's maladaptive attempts to cope with them. Because misinterpretations often involve serious consequences (e.g., "I could contaminate or hurt another person"), the person feels compelled to take action. These actions include suppression of thoughts, avoidance behaviours, and neutralizations. Unfortunately, each of these responses can unintentionally serve to perpetuate obsessional thinking. For example, trying to suppress obsessional thoughts can have the paradoxical effect of increasing their frequency—known as the *rebound effect* (Wenzlaff & Wegner, 2000). Also, if people use avoidance behaviour (e.g., avoiding children for fear of harming them) or neutralizations to combat their obsessions, they may never learn that their assumptions and beliefs are incorrect. In fact, engaging in compulsive behaviours may serve to strengthen irrational beliefs. Consider individuals who have obsessive fears about germ contamination. Each time they wash their hands they momentarily feel less anxious, their obsessive concerns about germs temporarily settle, and they fail to develop any serious physical illness. These consequences are rewarding and serve to maintain the use of compulsions in the long term. Compulsions are believed to persist because they tend to (1) lower the severity of anxiety,

(2) lower the frequency of obsessions, and (3) "prevent" obsessions from coming true. However, this short-term relief comes at the expense of failing to learn that the feared illness likely would not occur anyway and that their anxiety would have eventually decreased on its own.

BODY DYSMORPHIC DISORDER

DESCRIPTION Many people express some dissatisfaction with certain aspects of their physical appearance. In **body dysmorphic disorder (BDD)**, however, there is excessive preoccupation with an imagined or exaggerated body disfigurement, sometimes to the point of a delusion. For example, individuals may become preoccupied with a perceived defect in their face, the shape or size of their nose, or other parts of their body. If a slight physical anomaly is actually present, the diagnosis is made only if the individual's concern is markedly excessive. When considering this diagnosis, clinicians look not only for this preoccupation, but also for significant distress or impairment in social, occupational, or another important aspect of life. The excessive preoccupations are described as being difficult to control, and sufferers typically spend many hours of each day dwelling on their "defect," to the detriment of work, family, or other social situations. Patients with BDD often face intense suffering and they tend to describe their preoccupations as "tormenting" or "devastating." In fact, approximately 25 percent of these patients attempt suicide (Phillips, 2007). Table 5.6 provides a list of imagined defects of patients with body dysmorphic disorder. BDD usually begins in adolescence, reflecting the concern for body image that often emerges at that age, and usually persists throughout the lifespan.

DIAGNOSIS AND ASSESSMENT Many experts have pointed out similarities between BDD and obsessive-compulsive disorder (OCD). Individuals with BDD have prominent obsessions and compulsive behaviours, similar to

TABLE 5.6 LOCATION OF IMAGINED DEFECTS IN 30 PATIENTS WITH BODY DYSMORPHIC DISORDER*

Location	n	%
Hair[a]	19	63
Nose	15	50
Skin[b]	15	50
Eyes	8	27
Head/face[c]	6	20
Overall body build/bone structure	6	20
Lips	5	17
Chin	5	17
Stomach/waist	5	17
Teeth	4	13
Legs/knees	4	13
Breasts/pectoral muscles	3	10
Ugly face (general)	3	10
Ears	2	7
Cheeks	2	7
Buttocks	2	7
Penis	2	7
Arms/wrists	2	7
Neck	1	3
Forehead	1	3
Facial muscles	1	3
Shoulders	1	3
Hips	1	3

Source: Reprinted with permission from the *American Journal of Psychiatry*, (Copyright ©1993). American Psychiatric Association. All Rights Reserved.

* Total is greater than 100% because most patients had "defects" in more than one location.
[a] Involved head hair in 15 cases, beard growth in 2 cases, and other body hair in 3 cases.
[b] Involved acne in 7 cases, facial lines in 3 cases, and other skin concerns in 7 cases.
[c] Involved concerns with shape in 5 cases and size in 1 case.

patients with OCD. Research comparing individuals with the two disorders has found many similarities, including a tendency for the two to occur together in families. However, there are also some differences between the two disorders. Notably, individuals with BDD tend to be more severely disturbed than those with OCD, with higher rates of suicidal ideation, delusions, major depression, substance abuse, and social phobia. Phillips and colleagues (2007) concluded that, although the two disorders have many common features, BDD should not be viewed simply as a subtype of OCD. Another disorder that seems quite similar to BDD is anorexia nervosa, an eating disorder (discussed in Chapter 10) that also involves strong dissatisfaction with and misperception of one's body size and shape. However, Grant and Phillips (2004) reviewed the relevant research and concluded that, despite their similarities, these two disorders are quite distinct. In particular, they do not show the same gender distribution, familial patterns, or response to treatments.

Trauma- and Stressor-Related Disorders

Trauma and stressor related disorders are those in which exposure to a traumatic or stressful life event is listed explicitly as a diagnostic criterion. The diagnoses in this category include reactive attachment disorder, disinhibited social engagement disorder, post-traumatic stress disorder (PTSD), acute stress disorder, and adjustment disorders. In this section, we focus on PTSD (see Table 5.7). This disorder is characterized by a profile of psychological symptoms that are experienced following a traumatic incident. The event must have involved actual or threatened death or serious injury, or a threat to the physical integrity of self or others, and have been experienced with intense fear, helplessness, or horror. To qualify for a diagnosis of PTSD, the individual must display the symptoms for longer than one month after the event.

POST-TRAUMATIC STRESS DISORDER

Case Notes

Raúl was born in Cuba. His parents separated when he was a young child and he lived with his grandparents for a number of years. At the age of 12, he enrolled in military school. He later became a paratrooper in the Cuban army and was posted in various locations around the world. While engaged in military combat, he saw several of his friends shot to death or killed by shrapnel. He was later "grounded" because of high blood pressure and assigned to work on naval ships. After hearing rumours that the authorities were after him due to suspected anti-government activities, he fled from Cuba on a ship that was headed to Germany. He jumped ship while the vessel was docked in Nova Scotia, and showed up at one of the city's hospitals a few months later, complaining of flashbacks, recurrent nightmares, and feeling easily startled and always on edge.

DESCRIPTION A central feature of PTSD is that the individual continues to re-experience intrusive, unwanted recollections of a past traumatic event. For example, individuals with PTSD may repeatedly have intrusive and distressing thoughts, images, and dreams about the traumatic event. They may also experience emotional and physiological distress when exposed to internal (i.e., bodily) or external cues that remind them of some aspect of the trauma. These cues may include certain sights, sounds, or smells that resemble those around them when the trauma occurred. The link between the trauma and a cue or trigger may be fairly direct and obvious to the individual with PTSD (such as when a car accident victim revisits the site of the collision). Alternatively, individuals with the disorder may be less consciously aware of some of their triggers (such as when an assault victim smells a cologne similar to the one worn by her assailant),

TABLE 5.7   DSM-5 DIAGNOSTIC CRITERIA FOR POST-TRAUMATIC STRESS DISORDER

Note: The following criteria apply to adults, adolescents, and children older than 6 years. For children 6 years and younger, see corresponding criteria below.

A. Exposure to actual or threatened death, serious injury, or sexual violence in one (or more) of the following ways:
  1. Directly experiencing the traumatic event(s).
  2. Witnessing, in person, the event(s) as it occurred to others.
  3. Learning that the traumatic event(s) occurred to a close family member or close friend. In cases of actual or threatened death of a family member or friend, the event(s) must have been violent or accidental.
  4. Experiencing repeated or extreme exposure to aversive details of the traumatic event(s) (e.g., first responders collecting human remains; police officers repeatedly exposed to details of child abuse).
     Note: Criterion A4 does not apply to exposure through electronic media, television, movies, or pictures, unless this exposure is work related.

B. Presence of one (or more) of the following intrusion symptoms associated with the traumatic events(s), beginning after the traumatic event(s) occurred.
  1. Recurrent, involuntary, and intrusive distressing memories of the traumatic event(s).
     Note: In children older than 6 years, repetitive play may occur in which themes or aspects of the traumatic event(s) are expressed.
  2. Recurrent distressing dreams in which the content and/or affect of the dream are related to the traumatic event(s)
     Note: In children, there may be frightening dreams without recognizable content.
  3. Dissociative reactions (e.g., flashbacks) in which the individual feels or acts as if the traumatic event(s) were recurring. (Such reactions may occur on the continuum, with the most extreme expression being a complete loss of awareness of present surroundings.)
     Note: In children, trauma-specific reenactment may occur in play.
  4. Intense or prolonged psychological distress at exposure to internal or external cues that symbolize or resemble an aspect of the traumatic event(s).
  5. Marked physiological reactions to internal or external cues that symbolize or resemble an aspect of the traumatic event(s).

C. Persistent avoidance of stimuli associated with the traumatic event(s), beginning after the traumatic event(s) occurred, as evidenced by one or both of the following:
  1. Avoidance of or efforts to avoid distressing memories, thoughts, or feelings about or closely associated with the traumatic events(s).
  2. Avoidance of or efforts to avoid external reminders (people, places, conversations, activities, objects, situations) that arouse distressing memories, thoughts, or feelings about or closely associated with the traumatic event(s).

D. Negative alternations in cognitions and mood associated with the traumatic event(s) (typically due to dissociative amnesia and not to other factors such as head injury, alcohol, or drugs).
  1. Inability to remember an important aspect of the traumatic event(s) (typically due to dissociative amnesia and not to other factors such as head injury, alcohol, or drugs).
  2. Persistent and exaggerated negative beliefs or expectations about oneself, others, or the world (e.g., "I am bad," "No one can be trusted," "The world is completely dangerous," "My whole nervous system is permanently ruined").
  3. Persistent, distorted cognitions about the cause or consequences of the traumatic event(s) that lead the individual to blame himself/herself or others.
  4. Persistent negative emotional state (e.g., fear, horror, anger, guilt, or shame).
  5. Markedly diminished interest or participation in significant activities.
  6. Feelings of detachment or estrangement from others.
  7. Persistent inability to experience positive emotions (e.g., inability to experience happiness, satisfaction, or loving feelings).

E. Marked alterations in arousal and reactivity associated with the traumatic event(s), beginning or worsening after the traumatic event(s) occurred, as evidenced by two (or more) of the following:
  1. Irritable behavior and angry outbursts (with little or no provocation) typically expressed as verbal or physical aggression toward people or objects.
  2. Reckless or self-destructive behavior.
  3. Hypervigilance.
  4. Exaggerated startle response.
  5. Problems with concentration.
  6. Sleep disturbance (e.g., difficulty falling or staying asleep or restless sleep).

F. Duration of the disturbance (Criteria B, C, D, and E) is more than 1 month.

G. The disturbance causes clinically significant distress or impairment in social, occupational, or other important areas of functioning.

H. The disturbance is not attributable to the physiological effects of a substance (e.g., medication, alcohol) or another medical condition.

As such, the onset of certain re-experiencing episodes may seem to arise at random when individuals are triggered by cues that are more subtly associated with their trauma.

Some individuals with PTSD may experience *flashbacks*, which are transient breaks from reality wherein an individual acts or feels as if the traumatic event is recurring in the present moment. The experience of a flashback is very different from simply remembering what happened to them because individuals actually feel as if they are *reliving* the event. During a flashback, individuals may experience visual and auditory

Survivors of traumatic events, such as the terrorist attack on the World Trade Center, may experience symptoms of PTSD.

Lieutenant-General Roméo Dallaire was the commander of the UN peacekeeping forces in Rwanda until he retired as a result of PTSD. In 2008, he received the Humanitarian Award from the Canadian Psychological Association.

hallucinations that "replay" the traumatic event (Brewin, 2011). Not surprisingly, the majority of individuals experience flash-backs with intense fear. However, some individuals who dissoci-ate display a relative absence of physiological reactivity, appear to be "spaced out," and seem momentarily non-responsive to their environment. Research increasingly suggests that the neurobiological basis of hyperarousal responses versus hypoarousal responses, involving becoming "shut down," "detached," and "numb," may be different (Lanius et al., 2010).

Partly as a result of their susceptibility to re-experiencing episodes, individuals with PTSD display a hallmark symptom of anxiety disorders: avoidance. Specifically, they commonly attempt to avoid thinking or talking about their traumatic event, as well as avoid places, people, or activities that may remind them of the trauma. These symptoms can be classified as *cognitive avoidance* and *behavioural avoidance*, respectively, and they often co-occur as prototypical features of anxiety-spectrum behaviour.

Individuals with PTSD may be unable to remember aspects of the traumatic event, or have exaggerated feelings of guilt and self-blame. Mood alterations may occur and include a markedly diminished interest or participation in pre-trauma daily-living activities, feeling detached or estranged from others, and being unable to experience certain feelings (especially positive affect). This set of symptoms represents an inability to experience emotions, and has been referred to as **emotional numbing** (Frewen & Lanius, 2015; Orsillo, Theodore-Oklota, Luterek, & Plumb, 2007). Individuals with PTSD also experience sleep difficulties, concentration

problems, irritability, significant anger problems, and other symptoms of elevated arousal. These individuals are fre-quently *hypervigilant* to threatening stimuli and exhibit an exaggerated startle response to unexpected stimuli.

DIAGNOSIS AND ASSESSMENT The diagnosis and assess-ment of PTSD generally involves the combination of a semi-structured clinical interview and the results of psychometric scales. One of the most well-used and validated interview measures of PTSD is the *Clinician Administered PTSD Scale* (CAPS; Blake et al., 1990). Several questionnaire measures of PTSD symptoms and associated problems are also avail-able. Additionally, an essential component of PTSD diagno-sis and assessment involves determining whether additional disorders are present. As a rule, most individuals with PTSD tend to have other disorders, including depression, anxiety disorders, and personality disorders (Sareen et al., 2007).

ETIOLOGY By definition, exposure of an individual to a trau-matic life event plays a role in the development of PTSD. However, traumatic events are relatively common, and not every individual who has experienced a traumatic event develops PTSD. For example, a study with undergraduate stu-dents found that 85 percent reported experiencing a traumatic event in their lifetime and 21 percent reported experiencing such an event in the last two months (Frazier et al., 2009). In one study, it was estimated that in a sample of natural disaster survivors, only 40% of individuals met the criteria for symp-toms of PTSD (Carmassi et al., 2013). Certain risk factors may predispose individuals to be more likely both to be exposed to traumatic events and to develop PTSD in response to these events. A number of these risk factors are outlined below.

Women are approximately two times as likely to develop PTSD following exposure to a traumatic event than are men (risk rates are 20 percent and 8 percent, respectively; Kessler et al., 1995). There are also gender differences in the types of traumatic experiences to which men and women are exposed. Men more often reported witnessing someone badly injured or killed; being exposed to fires, floods, and/or natural disasters; being involved in life-threatening accidents, physical attacks, or war-related combat; being threatened with weapons; or being held captive or kidnapped. In contrast, women more often reported being raped, sexually molested, neglected by their parents as children, and physically abused as children. Although men are exposed to a greater number of traumatic events on average than are women, women are exposed to more events particularly likely to be associated with the development of PTSD, such as rape (APA, 2013; Tolin & Foa, 2006). This at least partly explains the increased risk of PTSD that is associated with being female (Olff, Langeland, Draijer, & Gersons, 2007).

A number of risk factors for the development of PTSD have been identified, including both *pre-event* and *post-event* factors (Cougle, Resnick, & Kilpatrick, 2009). Pre-event risk factors for adult PTSD include being low in socio-economic status, education, and tested intelligence; having a previous psychiatric history; and experiencing childhood adversity, including being abused as a child. Post-event risk factors are somewhat more powerful predictors of PTSD than are pre-event factors, and include the severity of the traumatic event, lack of social support, and whether or not additional stressful experiences occur after the traumatic event. Also, exposure to *interpersonal traumas* (e.g., related to physical violence or sexual abuse) is generally more likely to provoke PTSD than exposure to *non-interpersonal traumas* (e.g., natural disaster, car accident). Certain genetic factors may also predispose individuals to be more likely both to be exposed to traumatic events and to develop PTSD in response to these events (Broekman, Olff, & Boer, 2007).

Neuroimaging and endocrinology studies are beginning to uncover physiological markers of PTSD. Research suggests that individuals with this disorder have dysfunctional neurocircuitry in areas of the brain implicated in processing and responding quickly to threat. These brain regions include the brainstem, amygdala, and frontotemporal cortex, and have been collectively conceptualized as part of the *Innate Alarm System* (IAS; Steuwe et al., 2014). PTSD has been associated with greater activity and connectivity between IAS brain regions (Lanius et al., 2017). In addition, an important biological component of the stress response is the functioning of the hypothalamic-pituitary-adrenal (HPA) axis (see Chapter 7). Several studies of male combat veterans and Holocaust survivors have found *decreased* cortisol and/or *enhanced* negative feedback of adrenal function (Metzger et al., 2008; Yehuda, Golier, Halligan, Meaney, & Bierer, 2004; Yehuda, Halligan, Golier, Grossman, & Bierer, 2004). Another consistent finding is that the volume of the hippocampus is less in individuals with PTSD than in those without the disorder (van Rooij et al., 2015). What remains unclear, however, is whether these reductions in hippocampal volume represent a cause or effect of PTSD.

Cognitive theories of PTSD emphasize the multiple levels upon which traumatic experiences can affect the mind (Dalgleish, 2004). For example, Dual Representation Theory details differences in the way that traumatic memories and non-traumatic memories may be stored and retrieved (Brewin, 2011; Brewin, Dalgleish, & Stephen, 1996). Traumatic memories may be initially stored and retrieved in a nonverbal sensory-based form, whereas non-traumatic memories are typically encoded and retrieved in a verbal form. Therefore, sensory-based memories may need to be transferred into verbal form in order for the individual to effectively process the traumatic experience. This theory is consistent with the results of much of the brain-based evidence reviewed above (Brewin, 2011) and with the beneficial effects of therapies that involve repeated writing or talking about one's traumatic experiences (e.g., Hijazi, Lumley, Ziadni, Haddad, Rapport & Arnetz, 2014; Zang, Hunt, & Coz, 2013).

Additional cognitive theories focus on the individuals' perceptions of meaning that a traumatic event has for themselves, others, and their environment. Individuals who have experienced trauma are forced to integrate conflicting previous beliefs (e.g., "the world is a safe place"; "people are generally good") with the discrepant realities of the trauma they have just faced (such as rape). As a result, individuals may alter pre-existing beliefs to reflect their traumatic experience (e.g., "the world is not safe"; "all men are dangerous".) These new beliefs may be maladaptive and lead to a sense of *current and generalized threat*, subsequently contributing to symptoms such as chronic arousal, distress, and hypervigilance (Ehlers & Clark, 2000). For example, an individual who is robbed in a back alley late in the evening who comes to believe that "the world is dangerous" as opposed to "back alleys are dangerous places especially at night" is much more likely to experience chronic arousal and hypervigilance when going about his daily routine.

Treatment of Anxiety and Anxiety-Related Disorders

Although the management of anxiety disorders often includes medication, psychological interventions have received tremendous empirical support. When considering both short- and long-term outcomes, exposure-based behavioural interventions and cognitive-behavioural therapy are the most effective treatments for anxiety disorders. In fact, various treatment guidelines now recommend that the cognitive-behavioural interventions be administered as first-line treatments (Anxiety Review Panel, 2000; Department of Health, 2001; Hunsley, Elliot, & Therrien, 2013; National Institute for Health and Clinical Excellence, 2011; Norton & Price, 2007). The main components of these psychological treatments are highlighted after a description of pharmacotherapy. We then briefly summarize the literature on treatment effectiveness.

PHARMACOTHERAPY

Canadian researchers Hoffman and Mathew (2008) reviewed the effectiveness of various medicinal treatments for different anxiety disorders. Before the development of antidepressants, benzodiazepines were the most widely prescribed psychiatric medication. These drugs are appropriately referred to as *minor tranquilizers*; they provide rapid, short-term relief from physiological symptoms of acute anxiety such as heart palpitations, muscle tension, and gastrointestinal distress. Benzodiazepines bind to receptor sites for the neurotransmitter gamma-aminobutyric acid (GABA), which functions to temporally inhibit activity broadly across neural sites, including brain systems that are involved in generating fear and anxiety.

However, being the brain's primary inhibitory neurotransmitter, GABA is involved at least to some extent in virtually all cognitive, affective, and behavioural functions (i.e., including those that are not particular to fear and anxiety). Thus benzodiazepines have many side effects, which include psychomotor (e.g., dizziness and drowsiness) and cognitive (e.g., attention and memory) impairments, depending on the dosage and type of benzodiazepine used. Accordingly, these drugs are most appropriately used for temporary relief of subjective distress associated with infrequently encountered anxiety-provoking situations. They are less suitable as a long-term treatment for anxiety disorders, especially because they have a significant addictive potential and are associated with withdrawal symptoms in long-term users who try to discontinue the drug. In fact, patients typically find that their anxiety symptoms return, often in a worsened form, upon discontinuing benzodiazepines after long-term use.

Drs. Henny Westra (York University) and Sherry Stuart (Dalhousie University) have made a strong case against the use of benzodiazepines as a long-term treatment for anxiety. These researchers argue that exposure therapies seek to increase clients' self-efficacy by demonstrating to them that physiological symptoms of anxiety are not harmful in themselves, and that anxiety-provoking situations can be managed despite anxious feelings. In contrast, pharmacological therapies may teach patients that their anxiety symptoms themselves are "pathological" and can be controlled only by medication. This may focus patients' attention even more on their anxiety symptoms rather than on finding solutions to the life problems that give rise to them (Westra & Stewart, 1998). Indeed Westra, Stewart, and their colleagues have shown that use of benzodiazepines on an as-needed basis is associated with increased hypervigilance for signals of threat (Stewart, Westra, Thompson, & Conrad, 2000) and decreased memory for psychoeducational material presented during cognitive-behavioural therapy (Westra et al., 2004). Additional research is needed to understand the effects of long-term benzodiazepine use on cognitive functioning (Perna, Alciati, Riva, Micieli, & Caldirola, 2016).

Antidepressant drugs are currently the most well-used and effective medications for the treatment of anxiety disorders. As the name implies, these medications were first used in treating depression, and their efficacy in the treatment of both anxiety and depression suggests that there may be some level of overlap in how these two conditions are neurologically expressed. The monoamine oxidase inhibitors (MAOIs) are so called because they interfere with the action of monoamine oxidase, an enzyme that degrades certain neurotransmitters (including norepinephrine and serotonin) after being released by neurons, thus increasing the number of these transmitters in the brain generally. Although once widely used in the treatment of anxiety disorders, research has revealed that these drugs can have significant adverse effects on the digestive and cardiovascular systems, especially when taken in combination with foods prepared by fermentation (e.g., alcohol), and their use has decreased accordingly. However, this medication type is effective in the treatment of social phobia (Schneier, 2011). In contrast, the tricyclic antidepressants (TCAs) are in more widespread use, and function to block the reuptake of the neurotransmitters norepinephrine and serotonin. These drugs (especially clomipramine) have been found to be particularly effective in the treatment of OCD, although they too are associated with significant side effects, which include possible weight gain, blurred vision, dry mouth, and constipation. The selective serotonin reuptake inhibitors (SSRIs) are the most well-prescribed anxiolytic medications. As their name implies, these drugs have a particular affinity for serotonin receptors. Patients usually tolerate the side effects of SSRIs better.

Two categories of medications have been introduced more recently. One of these, azapirones, appears to elicit its anxiolytic effects primarily through serotonergic effects, in addition to altering dopamine levels in the brain. Venlafaxine hydrochloride is a newer antidepressant medication that is particularly effective in the treatment of GAD. This medication acts not only to increase serotonin but also to increase both norepinephrine and dopamine levels in the brain, and is generally associated with fewer side effects than traditional SSRI medications. With increasing research, the pharmacology of different existing anxiolytic medications is becoming better understood.

COGNITIVE RESTRUCTURING

Cognitive restructuring is based on the idea that anxiety and other emotional disorders are, at least in part, due to faulty, maladaptive, or unhelpful thinking patterns (Beck & Dozois, 2011; Clark, 2014; Dozois & Beck, 2008; Dozois, Seeds, & Collins, 2009). In the case of anxiety, these thoughts are future-oriented and involve themes of imminent or looming threat. Individuals with anxiety problems often overestimate the probability and severity of various threats (risk) and underestimate their ability to cope with them (resources). The goal of cognitive restructuring is to help patients develop healthier and more evidence-based thoughts—to help them adjust the imbalance between perceived risk and resource (Beck & Emery, 1985; Clark & Beck, 2010b). Patients learn to become better scientists of their own thoughts by monitoring and identifying automatic thoughts and underlying beliefs, examining the validity of these cognitions, and developing more balanced appraisals.

A number of strategies are used to help facilitate this process. One commonly used technique involves the thought record. An example of a thought record is shown in Table 5.8.

TABLE 5.8   EXAMPLE OF A THOUGHT RECORD

Situation	Moods (intensity in %)	Automatic Thoughts	Supporting Evidence	Contradictory Evidence	Alternative Thoughts	Re-rate Emotion (intensity in %)
Starting to relax while watching my favourite TV show and my heart started to pound for no apparent reason	Panic (98%)	My heart is beating faster than normal. I am shaking and sweating. (I am going to have a heart attack.)	My heart is beginning to race. I am shaky and sweaty.	I do not have any family history of heart disease. I take care of myself physically. As my therapist warned, I may be experiencing anxiety because I am relaxing and I fear letting go. The heart is supposed to beat fast at times and it can handle the strain—it is a muscle after all. A quick heartbeat does not mean that I am having a heart attack; there could be other explanations.	Although I am experiencing physical sensations, the odds are good that I am not having a heart attack.	Panic reduced to 30%
Driving from London to Toronto on Highway 401	Worry (80%)	There are so many trucks on this highway. I am getting nervous. (I am going to get into an accident and die.)	The 401 is a more dangerous highway than many others.	Just because I fear getting into an accident doesn't mean I am going to. Even if I do get into an accident, it doesn't mean I will die (many, even serious, accidents are non-fatal). I am doing what I can to protect myself—I wear my seatbelt, I drive carefully, I am not tired.	Although accidents do occur, the chance is not as high as I feel it is. Besides, most accidents are not fatal. I am a careful driver, which improves my odds of being safe.	Worry reduced to 25%

Note: The patient circled the thought that he or she recognizes contributes most to the negative emotion.

The thought record serves many purposes. Early on in therapy, it is used to help patients understand the important relationship between what they are thinking and how they are feeling. Whenever their anxiety increases, patients learn to ask themselves, "What was I thinking just before I started to feel this way?" Patients also learn to monitor and "catch" their automatic thoughts and beliefs systematically, so that they can examine the utility and validity of them. With the help of a therapist, patients examine the evidence for or against various beliefs and are taught strategies for developing more balanced thinking styles. Throughout this process, therapists use a style of Socratic questioning to elicit and test a patient's beliefs. The Socratic approach involves asking a number of questions to query and evaluate the beliefs and behaviours that contribute to anxiety. Therapists also engage in collaborative empiricism, meaning that the therapist and patient operate as a team to conceptualize a patient's difficulties and modify his or her beliefs (e.g., "What is the evidence for and against this belief?"; "Are there different ways of looking at this situation?"; "Are you confusing a low probability event with a high probability one?"; see Beck & Emery, 1985). Patients are also encouraged to conduct "behavioural experiments" to test certain beliefs and assumptions. For example, the belief that one will be rejected if one initiates a social interaction can be tested behaviourally.

Usually, deeper cognitive change occurs when the elicited cognitions are also connected to significant emotionally charged responses. Greenberger and Padesky (2015) refer to these thoughts as "hot cognitions." Thus, an important component of cognitive restructuring involves probing the patient to find out what deeper beliefs and schemas are triggering his or her automatic thoughts.

EXPOSURE TECHNIQUES

Few researchers would disagree that exposure is the main therapeutic ingredient across all psychological interventions for anxiety. Although the specific focus of exposure differs depending on the disorder being treated, the principle is the same: by facing anxiety-provoking stimuli, one's fears become extinguished, new coping skills are developed, and significant cognitive change occurs. The change in threat-related cognitions occurs as new evidence is accumulated that is discrepant from one's beliefs, thereby providing an opportunity for new learning to take place (see Focus box 5.3).

One of the earliest forms of exposure was **systematic desensitization**, initially developed by Joseph Wolpe (1958). With the assistance of a therapist, the patient develops a

FOCUS 5.3

Therapeutic Strategies for Enhancing Exposure Therapy

Researchers are still examining the exact mechanisms through which exposure reduces anxiety. It is possible that exposure is effective through several different processes, such as *habituation* or *inhibitory learning*. Historically, exposure was theorized to work primarily through the behavioural mechanism of habituation. That is, exposure therapy works because repeated exposure to the feared stimulus eventually results in a diminished behavioural response to that stimulus. More recent research in the field by Dr. Michelle Craske and her colleagues suggests that a key ingredient in exposure therapy is the cognitively rooted mechanism of inhibitory learning, wherein anxiety is reduced because individuals learn, through repeated exposure, that the feared stimulus no longer predicts the feared consequence. This challenges the notion of exposures as purely behaviour-based interventions by emphasizing the role of cognitive factors, such as expectancy violation. Based on this assertion, Craske and her colleagues (2014) outline eight therapeutic strategies for enhancing inhibitory learning during exposure. ●

Strategy	Description
Expectancy violation	*Test it out* – Design exposures that violate the client's expectations about the frequency or intensity of the feared outcome. For example, an individual who fears dogs because he/she believes they will bite should use exposures as a way to disconfirm this belief and learn that dogs will probably not bite him/her.
Deepened extinction	*Combine it* – Whenever possible, expose the individual to multiple feared situations simultaneously after at least one has been successfully "mastered". For example, if drinking coffee and entering a shopping mall are two separate situations that trigger an individual with panic's feared bodily sensations (e.g., heart palpitations), exposure to both situations simultaneously may enhance learning.
Remove safety behaviours	*Throw it out* – Decrease the use of safety behaviours while completing exposure exercises. Examples of safety behaviours include carrying around medication to take in the event a panic attack occurs, rehearsing a conversation before interacting with someone to prevent "saying the wrong thing" and feeling socially anxious, or bringing a friend or therapist along for reassurance in a feared situation.
Variability	*Vary it up* – Vary stimuli and contexts in which exposures to the feared situation are experienced. This will increase the number of retrieval cues and enhance the ability to make and access newly learned responses to the feared situation.
Reinforced extinction	*Face your fears* – Occasionally present the feared outcome during exposures. For example, if a socially anxious individual avoids interacting with others for fear of rejection, deliberate experiencing of rejection can enhance exposure effects.
Attentional focus	*Stay with it* – Maintain attention on the target stimulus during exposure.
Affect labelling	*Talk it out* – Encourage the clients to describe their emotional experience during exposures.
Mental reinstatement/ retrieval cues	*Bring it back* – Imagining previous successful exposures may help maintain the effectiveness of exposure therapy.

Source: Based on Craske et al. (2014). Maximizing exposure therapy: An inhibitory learning approach. *Behaviour and Research Therapy, 58*, 10–23.

fear hierarchy. A fear hierarchy is a list of feared situations or objects that are arranged in descending order according to how much they evoke anxiety. Often therapists use the term *subjective units of distress*, or SUDS, which is a rating that patients provide from 0 (meaning that there is no anxiety at all) to 100 (meaning that the anxiety is the worst the individual has ever experienced). Systematic desensitization starts by having patients imagine the lowest feared stimulus and combining this image with a relaxation response. Patients gradually work their way up the fear hierarchy so that they can learn to handle increasingly distressing stimuli.

The rationale underlying systematic desensitization is that anxiety is a learned or conditioned response. By pairing a relaxation response with the feared stimulus,

counter-conditioning or extinction is believed to occur. That is, because relaxation is an incompatible response to anxiety, the patient learns to be less anxious in the presence of the feared object or situation. Systematic desensitization has frequently been used to treat specific phobias. However, this approach is used less frequently now because research has indicated that **in vivo (meaning real life) exposure** itself is more effective than imaginal exposure and that the inclusion of relaxation provides no better response than exposure alone (Antony & Barlow, 2002; Vortstenbosch, Newman, & Antony, 2014). One area where imagery tends to be useful is in the treatment of GAD. Because many of the worries in GAD are not amenable to exposure, coupled with the fact that pathological worry is used as a means of avoiding intense negative emotions and arousal, patients are sometimes encouraged to engage in **worry imagery exposure** (Waters & Craske, 2005). This involves systematic exposure to feared images that are related to an individual's worries. After holding a worry image in their minds for 25 to 30 minutes (which helps individuals with GAD to tolerate and habituate to their fearful images), patients may be encouraged to think about a number of possible outcomes other than the worst-case scenario that was initially envisioned.

Exposure that is in vivo is effective for a wide range of anxiety problems. In gradual exposure, the patient approaches the items in his or her fear hierarchy beginning at a lower level of intensity and working up, over time, to face higher-intensity stimuli. We often tell our patients that exposure works optimally when they try to increase its frequency, duration, and intensity. In other words, they should do it as often as they can and for as long as they can handle it, and move up their hierarchy in increments of increased intensity. Imagine, for instance, that you have a fear of elevators. You could overcome this fear much faster by going into an elevator numerous times a day than by facing this fear only once a week. Another variation of exposure is called **flooding or intense exposure**. This involves starting at a very high level of intensity rather than working gradually through the fear hierarchy. Graduated and intense exposure are both effective; which approach is taken sometimes simply depends on what the patient is willing to tolerate.

There are many variants of exposure. Individuals who suffer from social phobia, for example, are asked to engage in social interactions like initiating a conversation, going to a party, and asking for directions. People with PTSD are instructed to write about, describe, and recall the details of the traumatic event (imaginal exposure) so they can learn that the event—although horrific—is a memory rather than an ongoing occurrence. In the treatment of panic disorder, individuals are often exposed to both external feared situations and internal sensations. For example, they may be encouraged to go into a grocery store or a movie theatre. Exposure to internal cues (i.e., bodily sensations) is called **interoceptive exposure** and is also effective for panic disorder. Interoceptive exposure involves the induction of physical sensations (e.g., dizziness) by means of hyperventilating, spinning in a chair, exercising, and so on (Craske & Barlow, 2014).

The main treatment for OCD involves exposure and **ritual prevention** (also called response prevention). Ritual prevention involves promoting abstinence from rituals that, while reducing anxiety in the short term, only serve to reinforce the obsessions in the long run (Franklin & Foa, 2014). Scott, the individual with obsessions and compulsions described earlier, was treated with exposure exercises, response prevention, and cognitive restructuring. After identifying a specific hierarchy of fears, he engaged in gradual exposure. Exposure began within the hospital by having him eat from cafeteria plates that he did not wash personally. Several sessions were also spent in the hospital washroom, because that is where his main fears of contamination were triggered. Exposure eventually moved to outside the

hospital setting in order to generalize therapy to other settings. Following each of these exposure exercises, Scott was encouraged to refrain from washing his hands or engaging in other cleaning rituals.

An important component of exposure also involves helping individuals to reduce their **subtle avoidance** (Abramowitz, Deacon, & Whiteside, 2011). An individual with agoraphobia might be willing to go to a movie theatre as part of an exposure exercise. However, this individual would not get the full benefit of exposure if he or she used distraction strategies or engaged in other "safety behaviours," which are covert avoidance strategies that only serve to reinforce anxiety in the long run (e.g., sitting on the aisle, checking where the emergency exits are, or going to the movie with a "safe" person). Similarly, exposure would not be very effective if, during the course of facing his or her fears, an individual engaged in distraction. Canadian researchers Stanley (Jack) Rachman (University of British Columbia) and Adam Radomsky (Concordia University) have argued that whereas the *judicious* use of safety behaviours may be helpful early in treatment by making exposure less threatening and fostering a sense of control, as treatment continues, these safety behaviours should be reduced or eliminated (Rachman, Radomsky, & Shafran, 2008; Levy, Senn, & Radomsky, 2014).

PROBLEM SOLVING

Problem solving is based on the assumption that by generating and implementing effective solutions to problems, patients will experience less anxiety (Epp & Dobson, 2010; Nezu & Nezu, 2014). This approach begins with a problem-orientation phase, in which individuals are encouraged to approach and deal with their problems constructively rather than worry about, avoid, or deny them. This phase involves teaching an individual to accept that the occurrence of problems is an inevitable part of life rather than being due to a personal deficiency, to view problems as challenges rather than as sources of threat or harm, and to view anxiety as a signal of a problem that needs to be dealt with rather than as a feeling to get rid of. The basic problem-solving strategy involves defining a specific problem, generating a wide range of alternative solutions, deciding on and implementing one or more of the solution-focused strategies, and evaluating the outcome (Nezu & Nezu, 2014).

RELAXATION

Relaxation strategies aim to reduce anxious arousal directly, and can be classified into two general types: mental relaxation and physical relaxation. Training in mental relaxation often takes the form of guided imagery exercises. During guided imagery, the client and therapist work together to develop a personalized description of positive thoughts and images that promote a calm and peaceful state. The scripted scenes may involve images of walking along the shore of a warm sandy beach or climbing a majestic mountain range.

Progressive muscle relaxation involves tensing and then releasing various muscle groups and noting the difference in sensations between the two. Muscle groups where the client particularly experiences tension (e.g., neck, shoulders, back) are especially targeted, although the full body is relaxed, including the facial muscles. Given that the sensations involved in tension and relaxation are incompatible, the individual learns how to reduce his or her anxiety by deliberately relaxing the tension in his or her muscles. In addition, focusing on the body often distracts from the influence of negative thinking (e.g., worry and rumination), at least temporarily.

Another common relaxation method is breathing retraining, which involves teaching patients how to breathe using their diaphragm rather than their thoracic (chest) muscles. Research shows that different breathing patterns are associated with different emotional states, and that a pronounced thoracic breathing style can produce hyperventilation symptoms that eventually lead to panic attacks in some individuals. In contrast, diaphragmatic breathing is a more relaxing natural respiration pattern. Although training in relaxation strategies often produces some immediate benefit, research generally shows that exposure is the more important treatment component (Craske & Barlow, 2001).

OTHER TECHNIQUES

The majority of the therapeutic strategies previously discussed have a long history and strong empirical basis in the effective treatment of anxiety disorders. However, a number of additional strategies are also beginning to be applied in anxiety treatment. Mindfulness-based strategies combine the practice of sitting and moving (e.g., yoga, walking) meditation with a number of principles intended to promote psychological well-being, physical health, and stress management (see Woodruff, Arnkoff, Glass, & Hindman, 2014). Mindfulness-based strategies seek to cultivate a state of present-focused "being," often contrasted with various forms of "thinking" (e.g., worrying) and "doing." Research suggests that mindfulness-based approaches are effective therapies for anxiety disorders (Hofmann, Sawyer, Witt, & Oh, 2010).

An additional emerging trend in the treatment of anxiety involves the use of virtual reality technology (Wiederhold & Wiederhold, 2004). These strategies use virtual environments to expose individuals to the objects they fear. These technologies are able to create vivid environments for use in exposure therapies that are otherwise too difficult to conjure in real life (e.g., battlefields in the treatment of combat-related PTSD) or too expensive for repetitive in vivo exposure (e.g., riding airplanes during flight disturbance). A somewhat controversial treatment is Eye Movement Desensitization and Reprocessing (EMDR; Shapiro, 2001), which is primarily used for the treatment of post-traumatic stress disorder. In EMDR, an individual remembers an actual or imagined negative life event while simultaneously focusing his or her attention on a stimulus that oscillates from left to right. Although EMDR is an effective method for treating PTSD, it has no clear advantage over traditional exposure or cognitive-behavioural therapy (CBT; Cloitre, 2009).

⑤ BEFORE MOVING ON

Select three exposure treatments that you might use in treating an anxiety disorder. Describe each treatment and explain how you would employ it.

Treatment Efficacy

In the absence of treatment, anxiety disorders are chronic and recurrent. Fortunately, a number of effective treatments have been developed over the years. In this final section of the chapter, we summarize the main approaches to treatment that have been supported in the research literature.

TREATMENT OF PANIC DISORDER

Many of the techniques described in the previous section are key elements of cognitive-behavioural therapy (CBT) for panic disorder (Sánchez-Meca, Rosa-Alcázar, Marín-Martínez, & Gómez-Conesa, 2010). Barlow's panic control treatment, for example, involves psychoeducation (i.e., education about the nature and physiology of anxiety), cognitive restructuring, breathing retraining, applied relaxation, interoceptive exposure, and in vivo exposure (Craske & Barlow, 2014). CBT is the most well-studied and empirically supported treatment for panic disorder. A number of studies have shown that CBT is as effective as benzodiazepines and antidepressants in the short term. CBT also produces more powerful long-term results (e.g., Barlow, Gorman, Shear, & Woods, 2000). Whereas patients receiving pharmacotherapy have to continue to take drugs in order to maintain therapeutic gains, 70 to 80 percent of CBT patients are panic-free at the end of treatment, and these gains tend to be maintained (Craske & Barlow, 2014). As such, CBT is a cost-effective treatment option (Kar, 2011), particularly when administered in a group setting. In a meta-analysis of 43 controlled studies, CBT showed the largest effect sizes and the smallest drop-out rates compared to medication or the combination of drug and psychological treatments (Gould, Otto, & Pollack, 1995). Similarly, in a more recent meta-analysis of 60 studies, Pompoli and colleagues (2016) concluded that CBT was most often superior to other forms of psychotherapy.

TREATMENT OF SPECIFIC PHOBIAS

Pharmacological interventions offer little benefit for the treatment of specific phobias and in fact can interfere with exposure-based treatments by dampening anxiety during these exercises (Antony & Barlow, 2002). The main form of treatment for specific phobias is in vivo exposure (Nowakowski, Rogojanski, & Antony, 2014). The results have been encouraging: approximately 80 to 90 percent of individuals are effectively treated with exposure (Choy, Fyer, & Lipsitz, 2007). More short-term (e.g., one-day) but intensive treatment approaches have also been successful (Antony & Barlow, 2002). Martin Antony and his colleagues from Toronto and Hamilton, Ontario, for example, administered a two-hour session of exposure to a group of individuals with a specific phobia of spiders. Patients improved significantly, as indicated by physiological, self-report, and behavioural measures (Antony, McCabe, Leeuw, Sano, & Swinson, 2001). Exposure via virtual reality seems to be effective for a number of specific phobias, including fear of heights, public speaking, and flying (Parson & Rizzo, 2008; Wallach, Safir, & Bar-Zvi, 2009). Moreover, a meta-analysis by Morina, Ijntema, Meyerbroker, and Emmelkamp (2015) using data from 14 clinical trials revealed that virtual reality exposure therapy for specific phobias may be just as effective as in vivo exposures in producing behaviour change in real life at post-treatment and follow-up.

TREATMENT OF SOCIAL ANXIETY DISORDER

The most popular treatment for social anxiety disorder, cognitive-behavioural group therapy (CBGT), integrates both cognitive restructuring and exposure (Heimberg, & Magee, 2014). In some cases, social skills training and relaxation training are incorporated into the treatment package as well. The group setting itself provides ample opportunities for exposure. After working together as a group on various cognitive restructuring exercises, participants practise social interactions and role-play situations that are associated with social anxiety. Researchers have examined whether adding cognitive interventions improves treatment efficacy over and above exposure alone for social anxiety. One meta-analysis suggested that cognitive interventions may be more important than exposure in the treatment of social anxiety (Ougrin, 2011); however, more research is needed to support this. Regardless, data continue to support the effectiveness of CBGT for the treatment of social anxiety disorder (Bruce & Heimberg, 2014; Wersebe, Sijbrandij, & Cuijpers, 2013).

CBGT has also been compared to medications in several studies. Overall, few differences exist between CBGT and medication in terms of treatment response (Ledley & Heimberg, 2005). However, individuals in CBGT appear to be better protected against relapse than are individuals in pharmacotherapy alone (Canton, Scott, & Glue, 2012; Hofmann & Barlow, 2002). At present, the data are not conclusive as to whether combined CBGT and medication is superior to either treatment alone (Bruce & Heimberg, 2014), though some evidence suggests a combination may be more effective than either strategy alone (Canton, Scott, & Glue, 2012). Researchers have previously demonstrated that D-Cycloserine (an antibiotic drug used to treat tuberculosis) can enhance the learning that takes place in exposure treatment for social anxiety (Morissette, Spiegel, & Barlow, 2008; Mataix-Cols et al., 2017) by working on glutamatergic receptors (N-methyl-D-aspartate, or NMDA) in the amygdala (Hofmann, Pollack & Otto, 2006). Future research will determine whether this pharmacological agent reliably augments exposure treatment; however, research has been inconsistent (Ori et al., 2015; Rodrigues et al., 2014).

TREATMENT OF GENERALIZED ANXIETY DISORDER

Benzodiazepines are commonly used to treat GAD. Studies have shown that this class of medications is effective in reducing 65 to 70 percent of symptoms in the short term (Roemer, Orsillo, & Barlow, 2002). The long-term outcome data are not encouraging, though. Many patients experience an increase in symptoms while on these medications, and relapse following treatment is common. In addition, the long-term use of benzodiazepines can result in the development of tolerance, physical dependence (Ashton, 2005), and a decline in cognitive functioning over time (Federico et al., 2016). Other pharmacological treatments (e.g., antidepressants and azapirones) are also used with some positive results. CBT is the most highly recommended psychological therapy for GAD (Ouimet, Covin, & Dozois, 2012; Bolognesi, Baldwin, & Ruini, 2014), and a number of variants of CBT have been developed for treating this disorder. Michel Dugas (Concordia University), for example, has been instrumental in developing the notion of intolerance of uncertainty (IU) and in testing new approaches aimed at reducing it in treatment (e.g., Dugas & Robichaud, 2007; Robichaud & Dugas, 2015). Research suggests that improving tolerance to uncertainty appears to be effective at alleviating anxiety symptoms by reducing worry (Donegan & Dugas, 2012). A meta-analysis conducted by researchers at the University of Western Ontario found that CBT results in a significant reduction of pathological worry (the core symptom of GAD), with the largest effects stemming from the intervention developed by Dugas and his colleagues (Covin, Ouimet, Seeds, & Dozois, 2008).

TREATMENT OF OBSESSIVE-COMPULSIVE AND BODY DYSMORPHIC DISORDERS

The main psychological treatment approach for obsessive-compulsive disorder (OCD) has involved exposure and ritual prevention (ERP). Recently, there has been a growing interest in more cognitively oriented strategies that also appear to be effective for this population (Whittal, Thordarson, & McLean, 2005; Wilhelm & Steketee, 2006). Without question, ERP alters the faulty appraisals and beliefs of individuals with OCD. In fact, cognitive change may be an important mechanism of improvement in these behavioural interventions. Not surprisingly, then, cognitive therapy and ERP have both yielded impressive results in therapy outcome trials. Considerable research has also tested the efficacy of medications (especially serotonin-based medications like clomipramine, fluvoxamine, and fluoxetine) for the treatment of OCD, with supportive results. Studies that have investigated the combination of medication and ERP, although not conclusive, indicate that it is no better than ERP alone (Franklin & Foa, 2014). In a report developed for Health Canada, Antony and Swinson (1996) suggested that, all things considered, cognitive-behavioural interventions are the treatment of choice for OCD.

Similarly, emerging evidence suggests that cognitive-behavioural interventions are efficacious for BDD (Wilhelm, Phillips, Fama, Greenberg, & Steketee, 2011). CBT for BDD includes components of cognitive restructuring and exposure and response prevention (Wilhelm, Phillips, & Steketee, 2013). In a meta-analysis of seven studies, Harrison and colleagues (2016) found that CBT is effective for BDD, and that symptom improvements are maintained for up to several months after treatment. Currently, however, pharmacotherapy with SSRIs is regarded as the front-line treatment for BDD (Phillips, 2009). Medication and CBT for BDD can be combined, but further research is required to understand the additive effects of both.

TREATMENT OF POST-TRAUMATIC STRESS DISORDER

The treatment of PTSD typically involves facing the trauma (using imaginal exposure) and discussing it in detail. By doing so, patients begin to realize that these are indeed memories rather than ongoing events and can make sense of them and integrate them with other aspects of their lives. Ehlers and Clark (2000, pp. 336, 337) suggest that a useful analogy is to "compare the trauma memory to a cupboard in which many things have been thrown in quickly and in a disorganized fashion, so it is impossible to fully close the door and things fall out at unpredictable times. Organizing the cupboard will mean looking at each of the things and putting them into their place. Once this is done, the door can be closed and remains shut." An underlying assumption of cognitive processing theories is that a traumatic event creates a discrepancy between new information (e.g., witnessing a homicide) and a person's prior schemas (e.g., that the world is a safe place). Overall, imaginal exposure and cognitive reprocessing strategies are effective for the treatment of PTSD.

Given the negative effects PTSD can have on intimate relationships, Canadian researcher Dr. Candice Monson (Ryerson University) and her colleagues have developed a promising new couples-based approach to the disorder. Cognitive-behavioural conjoint therapy for PTSD (CBCT for PTSD; Monson & Fredman, 2012) aims to improve symptoms of the disorder by improving the quality of intimate relationships. More research is needed to confirm the efficacy of this approach and understand its mechanisms, however, the evidence thus far is promising (Macdonald, Pukay-Martin, Wagner, Fredman, & Monson, 2016).

Another approach that has been used for a considerable period of time is psychological debriefing. Often a critical incident stress debriefing team will meet with individuals shortly after a traumatic event (e.g., after the Dawson College shootings in Montreal on September 13, 2006). This brief intervention is intended to help survivors of trauma express their feelings related to the trauma and normalize their reactions. Although the purpose of psychological debriefing is to prevent PTSD, Ehlers and Clark (2003) have found that intervening too early (i.e., within one month of the trauma) is not effective and can in fact make matters worse, increasing rather than decreasing the likelihood that individuals will develop PTSD.

COMMENT ON TREATMENTS THAT WORK

CBT is regarded as a highly effective treatment for anxiety and related disorders. Evidence also suggests that it may be more effective than pharmacotherapy in producing long-term gains and preventing relapse. Unfortunately, the majority of individuals who suffer from anxiety do not seek psychological treatment, and those who do often do not receive referrals for the most effective treatments (Collins, Westra, Dozois, & Burns, 2004; Stein et al., 2011). In addition, most individuals who do seek help receive treatment from a primary care practitioner. Research suggests that more than half of patients receiving treatment in primary care received poor quality pharmacologic or psychological therapy; only 21% received high quality CBT-based therapies (Stein et al., 2011). As such, although there are highly effective treatments for anxiety disorders, individuals who seek treatment do not always receive quality interventions from highly trained professionals. Therefore, it is imperative that we enhance awareness among the public, physicians, and other mental health providers that psychologists have a number of effective evidence-based treatments for anxiety disorders (see Collins et al., 2004).

CANADIAN RESEARCH CENTRE

Dr. Candice Monson

Dr. Candice Monson is Professor of Psychology at Ryerson University, where she served as Director of Clinical Training from 2009 to 2015. She is one of the foremost experts on the role of interpersonal factors such as social support in understanding and promoting trauma recovery. She is also well known for developing, testing, and disseminating front-line recommended psychotherapies for PTSD in multiple treatment guidelines world wide. She has co-authored six books, including *Cognitive Processing Therapy: A Comprehensive Manual* and *Cognitive-Behavioral Conjoint Therapy for PTSD*, and has published over 100 peer-reviewed publications.

Courtesy of Dr. Candice Monson

How did you become interested in the study of post-traumatic stress disorder?

My interest in the study of PTSD was sparked while I was a Pre-doctoral Psychology Intern at the Boston VA Medical Center. I had not previously assessed or treated veterans, and was compelled by the stories they shared—they were harrowing stories of extraordinary human circumstances and the possibility of resilience and growth. I also saw firsthand the havoc that PTSD had wreaked on their families and loved ones, and the promise of including them in treatment to facilitate recovery beyond the individual. At that time, PTSD was considered a chronic and disabling condition, and most of the care being offered was focused on relieving suffering and making them as comfortable as possible in the face of their illness. Yet, there was some promising work being done, showing that cognitive-behavioural therapies could help them overcome PTSD. The hope of those therapies, and the idea that psychological interventions would be the treatment of choice, inspired me to a career of creating, testing, and ultimately training therapists to deliver these treatments. To this day, watching survivors (and their loved ones) overcome, transform, and often times become stronger than they were before as a result of therapy maintains my passion for studying trauma.

What is your general approach to the treatment of trauma and stressor related disorders?

My general approach to treating trauma- and stressor-related disorders is grounded in a cognitive-behavioural approach that emphasizes recovery. Most North Americans will be exposed to some type of traumatic event (e.g., motor vehicle accident, sexual assault, natural disaster); however, only about 10% will go on to develop a trauma-related disorder like PTSD in their lifetime. In this way, something has impeded the natural recovery that occurs for most people who are diagnosed with a trauma-/stressor-related disorder. My job is to work collaboratively with clients to help them overcome those impediments to recover. I specifically use "trauma-related" interventions that are designed to address the causes, and thereby, the symptoms of these disorders. In other words, I join with clients to discover how they have been thinking about, or making sense of the traumatic events that they have experienced (cognitions), to form a more realistic narrative about the trauma—a story with which they can live better. Avoiding trauma memories and reminders of traumas in clients' daily lives serves to reinforce the symptoms of these disorders. Thus, behavioural interventions are used to help clients face what they fear in order to no longer fear them. This includes the memories themselves, as well as the places, people, situations, and feelings that are reminiscent of their traumas.

What is your perspective on the importance of cognitive versus behavioural approaches in treating PTSD and anxiety disorders?

For me, the importance of cognitive versus behavioural approaches to treating PTSD is a practical one: cognitive interventions seem to be more acceptable to clients. For many years, behavioural interventions were the mainstay approach to treating PTSD and anxiety disorders. In the case of PTSD, this includes having clients repeatedly expose themselves to their trauma memories through retelling the events with high levels of sensory detail (i.e., images, smells, tastes) and putting themselves in here-and-now situations that serve as reminders of those trauma, until their anxiety is habituated. A behavioural orientation is highly effective in treating PTSD symptoms. However, research documents that clients are less inclined to this type of treatment if given the choice, and drop-out rates are higher if they receive it. A cognitive approach to trauma processing, which involves correcting people's appraisals about their traumas (e.g., "I should have or could have done something different at the time") and the consequences of them (e.g., "I can't trust anyone"), offers an alternative and seemingly more tolerable avenue to recovery. In the end, behavioural approaches change cognitions, and cognitive approaches change behaviour. Giving clients a choice about the road chosen is most important to me.

What are some of the most interesting trends in research on trauma and stressor related disorders? Where do you see the treatment of PTSD heading in the future?

I think one of the most interesting trends for research in this area relates to the decision to make these disorders their own class of disorders in the most recent version of the DSM. Removing PTSD, for example, from the Anxiety Disorders has major implications for understanding post-traumatic reactions to be beyond problems with anxiety. I think we will better understand the range of emotional reactions that flow from trauma exposure (e.g., guilt, shame, anger), which will innovate our approach to treatment. Also, expanding the spectrum to include a range of trauma- and stress-related disorders is going to have major implications for better understanding the various clinical problems people can have from exposure to chronic stress, and not just classically defined traumatic stressors. Fortunately, we are beyond whether or not PTSD can be treated; now, we can focus on which treatment, for whom, when, and how. We are beginning to test how to facilitate our existing evidence-based psychotherapies with adjunctive medications (e.g., MDMA, d-cycloserine, beta blockers) and also how to improve delivery to make these therapies accessible to a larger number of suffering individuals by using technology (e.g., online, teletherapy), paraprofessionals (e.g., rape crisis counsellors, peers support workers), and in family practice settings.

Are there any controversies in the literature on the treatment of PTSD?

The field of traumatic stress more generally is rife with controversy, in part because the sources of trauma are often very political in nature (e.g., combat/peacekeeping, interpersonal violence). Specific to treatment, one of the biggest controversies facing the field right now is the whether or not there is "Complex PTSD". Those promoting the construct argue that the developmental stage in which trauma occurs (e.g., childhood versus adulthood), the number of traumas, or prolonged exposure to a traumatic event results in a different constellation of clinical problems, and consequently is in need of different treatments. The committee creating the criteria for PTSD for DSM-5 voted down this construct, concluding that there was insufficient evidence for it to be included. There is also some controversy about when it is safe to use trauma-focused therapies, with some arguing that they can be delivered while individuals remain at risk for re-exposure (e.g., combat theatre, domestic violence shelters), and others believing that there is always risk for re-exposure and treating PTSD decreases the likelihood of re-exposure or clinical problems upon re-exposure.

SUMMARY

- There are three distinctive components of emotion: physiology, cognition, and behaviour. When anxiety occurs, we might expect to see increased heart rate and breathing (physiology). The individual may also experience thoughts such as "Something terrible will happen" (cognition), and avoid the anxiety-provoking trigger (behaviour). Anxiety is distinct from panic and fear. Although these are all emotional states, in anxiety the individual feels threatened by a potential future event. In fear, the individual responds to a present or perceived threat. Panic is similar to fear but, in contrast to fear, which is often in response to an objective threat, panic is extreme and can be triggered in the absence of an actual threat.

- Three main etiological factors are known to be involved in anxiety disorders: biological, psychological, and interpersonal. Biological factors encompass genetic heritability and the role of brain systems, including the amygdala and neurochemicals such as GABA. Learning (a psychological factor) and attachment influences (interpersonal factors) are also contributing factors.

- Methods of assessment include the use of structured and semi-structured interviews to establish if the individual meets diagnostic criteria for a particular disorder.

- Behavioural and psychophysiological indices are sometimes used to measure severity and to determine how the disorder is manifested. For example, the clinician could measure heart and breathing rates in an individual who describes having panic attacks or behavioural avoidance in an individual with social phobia. Self-report measures are also an invaluable part of assessment. These reports can measure each individual's self-reported behaviour, symptoms, and emotions.

- Etiological models of anxiety disorders include the two-factor theory, the equipotentiality premise, and the nonassociative model. Concepts important to understanding anxiety disorders include panic attacks, compulsions, and obsessions.

- This chapter highlighted descriptions of the major anxiety disorders listed in DSM-5: panic disorder with and without agoraphobia, specific phobia, social anxiety disorder, GAD, OCD, BDD, and PTSD.

- Interventions include pharmacotherapy, cognitive restructuring, exposure techniques, problem solving, relaxation, and other techniques such as exercise and mindfulness strategies.

KEY TERMS

agoraphobia (p. 101)

alarm theory (p. 102)

anxiety (p. 96)

anxiety sensitivity (p. 102)

behavioural avoidance test (BAT) (p. 101)

biological preparedness (p. 104)

body dysmorphic disorder (BDD) 113

catastrophic misinterpretation (p. 102)

compulsions (p. 111)

disgust sensitivity (p. 104)

emotional numbing (p. 116)

equipotentiality premise (p. 103)

fear (p. 96)

fear hierarchy (p. 120)

"fight or flight" response (p. 96)

flooding (intense exposure) (p. 121)

illness phobia (p. 103)

interoceptive exposure (p. 121)

intolerance of uncertainty (IU) (p. 110)

in vivo exposure (p. 120)

neurosis (p. 96)

neutralizations (p. 111)

nocturnal panic (p. 102)

nonassociative model (p. 103)

obsessions (p. 111)

panic (p. 96)

panic attack (p. 100)

ritual prevention (p. 121)

subtle avoidance (p. 121)

systematic desensitization (p. 119)

thought-action fusion (TAF) (p. 111)

two-factor theory (p. 98)

vicarious learning (p. 98)

worry imagery exposure (p. 121)

ROD A. MARTIN

•

NADIA MAIOLINO

CHAPTER

6

SensorSpot/Vetta/Getty Images

Dissociative and Somatic Symptom and Related Disorders

LEARNING OBJECTIVES

AFTER READING THIS CHAPTER, STUDENTS WILL BE ABLE TO:

1 Describe the symptoms and clinical features of the major dissociative disorders.

2 Compare and contrast two competing theories of the etiology of dissociative identity disorder.

3 Describe the symptoms and clinical features of the major somatic symptom and related disorders.

4 Explain how biological, psychological, and social-environmental factors can work together to cause somatic symptom and related disorders.

5 Discuss the goals and methods of contemporary psychological treatments for somatic symptom and related disorders.

Kathy is 35 years old and has been in and out of the mental health system for approximately 15 years. Her previous therapists have given her a number of diagnoses, including generalized anxiety disorder and borderline personality disorder. During an initial assessment, her current psychotherapist learned that Kathy had an extensive history of sexual abuse perpetrated by her father and grandfather. Kathy told the therapist that when she was a child she often felt like a robot, and described herself as feeling "dead from the neck down" when she was repeatedly raped by these family members. The psychologist noted that there were sizable gaps in Kathy's memory of her psychosocial history and that she was better able to recount her history on some days compared to others. Her therapist also began to notice dramatic changes in Kathy's appearance from one day to the next. For example, on one day she would be dressed provocatively, wearing a great deal of makeup, and on other days she would be dressed conservatively, with little makeup and her hair pulled into a bun. The psychologist decided to work with Kathy to help her cope with her history of sexual abuse, beginning very slowly by helping her build her trust until she felt comfortable in the therapy sessions. After a year of working together, Kathy felt comfortable enough with her psychologist to tell her about the other personalities she experiences, something she had not been able to do previously.

***

Casey is a 30-year-old man who is very afraid that he might die of cancer, as his mother did several years ago. He has made frequent visits to different doctors, complaining of a pain in his left leg. He began checking for lumps in his leg several times a day and reading about cancer on the internet. He went to the emergency room complaining of pain in his leg, thinking this a sure sign that a tumour was growing. After conducting several tests, the doctors found nothing wrong with his leg, and reported that he was in excellent physical condition. After a year without a diagnosis, Casey found that he was experiencing chest pain in addition to the pains in his leg. He went to the emergency room three times, certain that he was dying of a vicious cancer that had now spread to his lungs. Each time, the doctors assured him that, although his pains might be real, they could find no physical cause. Casey decided that the doctors were simply not competent enough to find his disease. He became increasingly frustrated and began to stay at home as much as he could to learn more about his perceived condition and to chat with cancer patients on Facebook and Twitter. His relationships with family and friends have become strained, and he is becoming increasingly socially isolated.

Kathy's and Casey's cases are clinical examples of two fascinating groups of disorders known as the dissociative and somatic symptom and related disorders. Kathy has one of the most severe types of dissociative disorders, dissociative identity disorder, in which an individual's sense of self is fragmented and resembles two or more personality states. As a group, the dissociative disorders include a wide range of symptoms that involve severe disruptions in consciousness, memory, and identity (Kihlstrom, 2005). Casey has somatic symptom disorder, in which people have long-standing beliefs that they have a serious illness, resulting in excessive anxiety and dysfunction. As a group, the somatic symptom and related disorders include conditions involving bodily symptoms associated with significant distress and impairment.

Many clinicians and researchers believe that these disorders result from maladaptive ways of coping with extreme stress. However, as we will see, there is a great deal of debate among experts concerning the nature and causes of these disorders. Although a large body of clinical literature of case studies and observational reports has accumulated over more than a century, more systematic research has only begun to accumulate in recent years, and our knowledge about these two groups of disorders is still quite limited.

Although the dissociative and somatic symptom and related disorders are classified as two separate diagnostic categories in DSM-5, they are strongly linked historically and share common features. In early versions of the DSM, these groups of disorders were classified together with the anxiety disorders under the general category of neuroses. It was assumed that anxiety was the predominant underlying feature in the etiology of these disorders, whether or not anxiety could be observed overtly. With DSM-III, however, the classification of psychological disorders shifted in emphasis from etiology to observable behaviour, a trend even more evident in DSM-5. This shift resulted in the dissociative and somatic symptom disorders being separated into two groupings independent of the anxiety disorders, due to their different symptom presentations.

Historical Perspective

The dissociative disorders and some of the somatic symptom disorders were once viewed as expressions of **hysteria**. Dating back to ancient Greece, *hysteria* was a term used to describe a symptom pattern characterized by emotional excitability and physical symptoms (e.g., convulsions, paralyses, numbness, loss of vision) in the absence of any evident physiological cause. Hippocrates believed that these symptoms were caused in women by a wandering womb (*hysteros*). He thought the womb was like an animal that desired to reproduce; if it remained inactive for too long, it became angry and wandered around the body, blocking the channels of respiration and causing illness (Merskey, 1995).

With the rise of Christianity, organic theories of hysteria were replaced by supernatural explanations: dissociation and related complaints were now seen as the result of demonic possession, and exorcism was the favoured treatment (Ross, 1989). Only after the decline in acceptance of possession as an explanation for abnormal behaviour did more psychologically based theories develop. Over time, the components of hysteria were examined as separate processes, and many of the pioneers of modern psychological theories, such as Alfred Binet, Jean-Martin Charcot, and Carl Jung, wrote about dissociative and somatizing processes. Pierre Janet, a French philosophy professor who trained with Charcot, was the first to systematically study the concept of dissociation, which he viewed as a pathological breakdown in the normal integration of mental processes, occurring as a result of exposure to traumatic experiences (van der Kolk & van der Hart, 1989).

Around the same time, Josef Breuer and Sigmund Freud, in their classic 1895 publication *Studies in Hysteria*, posited that trauma, often of a sexual nature, was a predisposing factor for hysteria and established a relationship between dissociation and hypnotic-like states. They described in some detail the usefulness of hypnosis in the treatment of such patients. The book consisted primarily of case studies of female patients suffering from dissociation, most of whom had been sexually abused. Several of these patients also suffered from somatic symptom and related disorders. For example, the first case described "Anna O," a 21-year-old woman treated by Breuer who developed visual and hearing problems, total paralysis of both legs and her right arm, partial paralysis of her left arm, a nervous cough, and periods of disturbed consciousness in which she seemed to be quite a different person. The classic Freudian view of somatic symptom and dissociative disorders began with such cases and was modified over several years. Freud eventually began to doubt the accuracy of his patients' retrospective reports of traumatic sexual abuse and decided instead that their memories of trauma were fantasized and not real. He believed that dissociation and other intrapsychic defences developed in order to protect individuals from their unacceptable sexual impulses, not from real traumatic memories.

Freud also viewed conversion symptoms as expressions of unconscious psychological conflicts. He suggested that "conversion" of anxiety to more acceptable physical symptoms relieved the pressure of having to deal directly with the conflict. This avoidance of conflict was termed *primary gain*, and was viewed as the primary reinforcement maintaining the somatic symptoms. Freud also recognized that hysterical symptoms could help a patient avoid responsibility and gain attention and sympathy, referring to these reinforcements as *secondary gains* of the symptoms. The term *secondary gain* is still commonly used today to refer to the benefits a patient may either unknowingly or knowingly seek by adopting the sick role.

The Granger Collection

"Anna O" (Bertha Pappenheim; 1859–1936) developed a bizarre range of physical and psychological symptoms. Her case was influential in the development of Freud's ideas.

The study of dissociation has followed a particularly interesting course through history. After a peak of interest in the last two decades of the nineteenth century, interest in dissociative processes dropped off exponentially during the early part of the twentieth century (Goettman, Greaves, & Coons, 1994). This decrease in interest has been attributed to many factors, including the rise of behaviourism and biological approaches within psychology, which did not allow for the study of internal states such as consciousness (Ross, 1996). However, a resurgence of interest in dissociative processes took place from the 1970s to the 1990s. This renewal of interest was shaped by several events, including the publication of popular accounts of cases of multiple personality, the inclusion of dissociative identity disorder in the DSM-III (published in 1980), and new research into consciousness and hypnosis (Hilgard, 1986). More recently, though, interest in dissociative disorders appears to have waned once again, with the annual number of scientific publications on this topic dropping in the first few years of the twenty-first century to only about 25 percent of its peak level in the 1990s (Pope, Barry, Bodkin, & Hudson, 2006). Many researchers now believe that dissociative disorders were overdiagnosed in recent decades when they enjoyed a brief "bubble" of fashion that has now declined. Others attest that this research area is "alive and relatively healthy," drawing attention to ongoing investigations that continue to be conducted on the dissociative disorders despite markedly diminished interest (Boysen & VanBergen, 2013a, p. 441).

❶ BEFORE MOVING ON

> Why were dissociative and somatic symptom and related disorders traditionally grouped together in early diagnostic systems, and why were they divided into separate diagnostic groups with the publication of DSM-III?

Dissociative Disorders

Dissociative disorders are characterized by severe maladaptive disruptions or alterations of identity, memory, and consciousness that are experienced as being beyond one's control. The defining symptom of these disorders is **dissociation**, the lack of normal integration of one or more aspects of psychological functioning, such as identity, memory, consciousness, emotion, sensorimotor functioning, and behaviour (Spiegel et al., 2011). Normally, there is a unity in our consciousness that gives rise to our sense of self. We know who we are. We know our names, where we live, and what we do for a living. But for individuals with dissociative disorders, these simple aspects of daily living are bizarrely disturbed and remain unintegrated, so that a coherent sense of self does not always exist.

Dissociation itself is not necessarily a pathological process. In fact, a certain degree of dissociation can be harmless and, in some cases, even adaptive (Barlow & Freyd, 2009). If you have ever become lost in a daydream or become so absorbed in a book or movie that you forgot about your surroundings and the passage of time, you have had a mild dissociative experience. Dissociative experiences of this sort are commonly reported in the general population (Gershuny & Thayer, 1999; Ross, 1996). If normal functioning is not impaired by these occasional lapses and if the person can "snap out of it," there is no concern about pathological dissociation. However, a problem exists when the person is unable to control these drifts of consciousness or behaviour and they affect his or her ability to function in everyday life.

There are also fairly stable individual differences in the degree to which individuals tend to have dissociative experiences: some people dissociate more frequently than others (Carlson, Yates, & Sroufe, 2009). Dissociative tendency is related to other personality traits such as hypnotizability and absorption. Research by Waller, Putnam, and Carlson (1996) indicates that dissociative experiences fall into two groups. The first group involves mild, non-pathological forms of dissociation, such as absorption and imaginative involvement, that are normally distributed on a continuum across the general population. The second group involves more severe, pathological types of experiences, such as amnesia, derealization, depersonalization, and identity alteration, that do not normally occur in the general population and that form a discrete category or *taxon*.

The three major dissociative disorders classified in DSM-5 will be discussed in this chapter: dissociative amnesia (which includes dissociative fugue as a subtype), depersonalization/derealization disorder, and dissociative identity disorder (formerly known as multiple personality disorder). Table 6.1 outlines the characteristics of these three disorders.

TABLE 6.1 TYPES OF DISSOCIATIVE DISORDERS

Disorder	Description	Comments
Dissociative amnesia	Inability to recall important personal information	Includes dissociative fugue, a rare condition in which individuals unexpectedly leave home and may turn up in a distant city with no memory of their past.
Dissociative identity disorder	Presence of two or more personality states	Formerly known as multiple personality disorder. The classic case is *The Three Faces of Eve* (Thigpen & Cleckley, 1957).
Depersonalization/derealization disorder	Feeling of being detached from oneself and one's physical and social environment	Depersonalization experienced for a short period of time is very common and not pathological.

FOCUS 6.1

Repressed Memory or False Memory?

At the age of 23, Alana sought help from a therapist because of feelings of depression and difficulty establishing meaningful relationships. After several sessions of therapy involving the use of hypnosis to help her recall her early relationship with her father, Alana remembered, in a vague way at first but subsequently in increasing detail, that her father had sexually abused her during her childhood. She was shocked but learned from her therapist that these traumatic memories had been **repressed** so that she could survive in her family for all these years. Although Alana had been somewhat distant from her father, she had not remembered this abuse for 17 years. She confronted her parents, and both her father and her mother vehemently denied any sexual abuse. With support from her therapist, Alana took her accusation to the police, who, after some investigation, charged her father with sexual abuse.

Alana's father claimed total innocence. After he was charged, he consulted a lawyer and learned about **false memory syndrome** (Loftus & Davis, 2006), a proposed condition in which people are induced by therapists to remember events that never occurred. Loftus and other researchers posit that some therapists unwittingly implant these memories by using leading questions and repeated suggestion while patients are under hypnosis. Several experiments have been conducted to demonstrate the existence of illusory or distorted memories and the idea that false memories can successfully be produced. For example, a study by Loftus and Pickrell (1995) showed that adults could be convinced that they had been lost for an extended period of time when they were about five years old, after a trusted companion was recruited to "plant" this memory.

On the other side of this debate, proponents of recovered memory therapy point to research evidence indicating that early traumatic experiences can cause selective dissociative amnesia (Gleaves, 1996; Kluft, 1999), although critics have noted methodological weaknesses in these studies (Kihlstrom, 2005). The concept of repressed memory derives from Freudian theory, which suggests that very traumatic events can be entirely forgotten in order to protect the child from the severe anxiety associated with the event. Research examining the effects of stress on the neurobiology of memory supports a link between trauma and amnesia. Studies have shown that extreme stress can have long-term effects on memory, by alter-

ing brain regions and neurochemicals responsible for memory functions (Bremner, 2001).

However, critics of the trauma–repression hypothesis have noted that it is based on the faulty assumption that the mind records memories of childhood accurately, and that these recorded memories can be repressed and then recovered at a later time through psychotherapy or hypnosis. These assumptions are contradicted by a considerable amount of memory research indicating that most experiences are not recorded as with a video camera, but are distorted by various life events (Paris, 1996). Furthermore, most memories are far from factually correct. In fact, as Loftus (1993) has pointed out, experimentally implanted false memories, once they are accepted as true by participants, are reported as fact with enormous conviction and are often embellished over time.

A further complicating factor is that it is generally not possible to establish the accuracy of a recovered traumatic memory. Over the past decade, a growing number of functional magnetic resonance imaging (fMRI) studies have attempted to determine whether differences between true and false memories can be detected by means of brain scans (e.g., Baym & Gonsalves, 2010). Despite promising results, the available evidence is far from conclusive (see Schacter & Loftus, 2013). At present, there is no objective way to determine whether a memory elicited in psychotherapy is true or false, aside from corroborating evidence, which is often not available. On the other hand, there is considerable evidence that hypnosis can implant highly detailed but untrue memories.

The highly controversial issue of repressed memory is not likely to be resolved soon. Because false memories can be created through strong repeated suggestions, therapists need to be very careful about making suggestions of early abuse when patients do not raise the topic themselves. On the other hand, it is also possible that people who have experienced extreme abuse or trauma could have dissociated these memories from awareness. Advocates on both sides of this issue agree that clinical research needs to focus on identifying the conditions under which the implantation of false memories is likely and to define markers that indicate real traumatic amnesia. In the meantime, mental health professionals must be extremely careful not to cause unnecessary suffering to either victims of actual trauma or victims falsely accused as abusers. ●

Similar to other diagnostic classes in DSM-5, there is also an "other specified dissociative disorder" category to aid in the description of clinically significant symptoms that do not meet diagnostic criteria for any of the above disorders. One presentation that could be specified is "identity disturbance due to prolonged and intense coercive persuasion," which could follow from acts of torture or brainwashing (APA, 2013, p. 306). By contrast, the "unspecified dissociative disorder" category applies when there is insufficient information to specify why syndromes do not meet diagnostic criteria for any of the major dissociative disorders.

PREVALENCE

Not surprisingly, dissociation is more common among psychiatric patients than the general population. Studies of the prevalence of dissociative disorders in adult psychiatric inpatient populations suggest that as many as 15 to 21 percent of inpatients in Canada have some kind of dissociative disorder (Horen, Leichner, & Lawson, 1995; Ross, Anderson, Fleisher, & Norton, 1991). A study of adult outpatients at an inner-city psychiatric facility found that as many as 29 percent met the criteria for diagnosis of a dissociative disorder (Foote,

Smolin, Kaplan, Legatt, & Lipschitz, 2006). To determine the prevalence of dissociative disorders in the general population, Johnson and colleagues (2006) conducted structured clinical interviews with a representative sample of 658 adults from New York State. They found that 9.1 percent of these individuals could be diagnosed with dissociative disorders, including 0.8 percent with depersonalization/derealization disorder, 1.8 percent with dissociative amnesia, 1.5 percent with dissociative identity disorder, and 5.5 percent with dissociative disorder not otherwise specified. No cases of dissociative fugue were found in this sample. There were no differences between men and women in the prevalence of these disorders, and they were slightly more common in younger than in older adults. This study also found high rates of comorbidity with other psychological disorders, including anxiety, bipolar, depressive, and personality disorders.

Dissociative Amnesia

The primary symptom of **dissociative amnesia** is the inability to recall significant personal information in the absence of organic impairment. Typically, this amnesia occurs following a traumatic event, such as an automobile accident or battlefield experiences during wartime. Afflicted individuals usually have no memory of the precipitating traumatic event; and may be unable to recall their own name, occupation, and other autobiographical information, even though they may still retain general knowledge of world events, such as the name of the current prime minister of Canada. There is a large degree of variability concerning the chronicity and reoccurrence of amnestic episodes, as well as the level of functional impairment associated with cases of dissociative amnesia. In most instances, the amnesia remits spontaneously within a few days after the person is in a safe environment, and may only be detected once memories are recovered. In other cases, amnesia can be more chronic, recurrent, and debilitating.

Five patterns of memory loss characteristic of dissociative amnesia are described in DSM-5, including (1) *localized amnesia,* wherein the person fails to recall information from a very specific time period (e.g., the events immediately surrounding a trauma); (2) *selective amnesia,* wherein only parts of the trauma are forgotten while other parts are remembered; (3) *generalized amnesia,* wherein the person forgets all personal information from his or her past; (4) *continuous amnesia,* wherein the individual forgets information from a specific date until the present; and (5) *systematized amnesia,* wherein the individual only forgets certain categories of information, such as certain people or places. The latter three patterns of memory loss are less common, usually associated with more significant psychopathology, and are more commonly associated with a diagnosis of dissociative identity disorder.

Dissociative Fugue is included in DSM-5 as a subtype of dissociative amnesia. **Dissociative fugue** is an extremely rare type of amnesia for autobiographical information that is so profound that individuals also travel unexpectedly away from home (*fugue* derives from the Latin word meaning "flight"). Some individuals travel thousands of miles from their home before they recall their personal history. The fugue is usually brief in duration, lasting from a few days to a few weeks, but there are rare cases where the individual disappears for a prolonged period of time. The behaviour of individuals presenting with dissociative fugue is not all that unusual; they are able to function reasonably well and may even successfully adopt a new identity and occupation if the disorder is prolonged. Dissociative fugue may end either abruptly or gradually with persistent confusion or amnesia about identity. Often, those who have recovered from the disorder report no memory of what occurred during the fugue state.

Our understanding of dissociative fugue is limited, largely due to the fact that it is so rare and because most of these patients do not present for treatment (Coons, 1998). Precipitating factors include life stressors, such as severe marital and financial distress. Accordingly, the incidence of dissociative fugue has been reported to increase during times of greater stress, such as during war or following a natural disaster. Dissociative fugue is relatively common in dissociative identity disorder, and comorbid diagnoses of depressive and bipolar disorders and substance abuse are also frequently found (APA, 2013; Coons, 1999).

❷ BEFORE MOVING ON

> Amnesia can also result from brain damage due to various causes (e.g., car accident, Alzheimer's disease). How might clinicians distinguish between these types of organic amnesia and dissociative amnesia?

Depersonalization/Derealization Disorder

Depersonalization/derealization disorder is a dissociative disorder in which the individual has persistent or recurrent experiences of depersonalization and/or derealization. **Depersonalization** is a condition in which individuals have a distinct sense of unreality and detachment from their own thoughts, feelings, sensations, actions, or body. Fleeting experiences of depersonalization are relatively common, with approximately half of the general population reporting such symptoms, often during times of stress (Reutens, Nielsen, & Sachdev, 2010). As a symptom, depersonalization can also occur in several different disorders. In fact, it is the third most commonly reported clinical symptom among psychiatric patients, after depression and anxiety. Depersonalization/derealization disorder is diagnosed only when severe depersonalization is the primary problem, and when the symptoms are persistent and cause clinically significant impairment or distress. Individuals with this disorder experience recurrent episodes of depersonalization, in which they feel as though they are living in a dream, observing their own mental processes or body from the outside, or as if time is moving slowly. They commonly describe feeling like a robot that is able to respond to their environment, but without feeling connected to their actions (Simeon, 2009).

Derealization is similar to depersonalization, but it involves feelings of unreality and detachment with respect to one's surroundings rather than the self. Individuals who have this symptom experience other people or objects in their environment as unreal, dreamlike, foggy, or distant. They may even have subjective visual distortions in which they see objects as distorted, blurred, flattened, or larger or smaller than they actually are.

Unlike the other dissociative disorders, depersonalization/derealization disorder is not characterized by memory impairment or identity confusion. This disorder typically begins in adolescence and tends to be chronic in nature. High rates of comorbidity with anxiety, depression, personality disorders, and other dissociative disorders have been found (Simeon, Knutelska, Nelson, & Guralnik, 2003). Laboratory research suggests that individuals with depersonalization/derealization disorder have reduced emotional reactivity to stressful or emotionally arousing stimuli (Sierra et al., 2002; Simeon, Guralnik, Knutelska, Yehuda, & Schmeidler, 2003; Stanton et al., 2001), as well as cognitive disruptions in perceptual and attentional processes (Guralnik, Giesbrecht, Knutelska, Sirroff, & Simeon, 2007). Neuroimaging research has begun to identify specific brain regions involved in the experience of depersonalization/derealization. For example, the inferior longitudinal fasciculus (ILF) may be critical for integrating visual and emotional information, since damage to this area has been associated with diminished responses to emotionally evocative images (Fischer et al., 2016).

Dissociative Identity Disorder

We all wear many hats or play different roles. For example, many of us could describe ourselves as students, siblings, Canadians, employees, partners, or spouses. In addition, it is not unusual to behave quite differently depending on the role we are playing. For example, you might appear to be a more patient person when dealing with difficult customers at your job than you are at home when your roommate fails to take out the trash. For most of us, it is not difficult to juggle these multiple roles or identities and adopt the behaviour most appropriate to a particular setting. We remain conscious of these shifts and, no matter how many different roles we must play within a particular day, we continue to have the experience of being a single person with one consciousness.

Dissociative identity disorder (DID) (formerly known as *multiple personality disorder*) is one of the most controversial and fascinating disorders recognized in clinical psychology. This unusual disorder is diagnosed when the patient presents with two or more distinct personality states, wherein a disruption of identity is indicated by discontinuities in one's sense of self and corresponding changes in psychological functioning (e.g., altered emotional displays and behaviour). The presence of alternative personality states leads to recurrent gaps in memory for everyday events, trauma, and/or important autobiographical information. The DSM-5 diagnostic criteria for DID are listed in Table 6.2.

In classic examples of DID, alternative personality states resemble different identities or personalities that periodically intrude into the consciousness and assume control of a person's behaviour. Historically, in DID, one of the personality states is identified as the "host," whereas subsequent personality states are identified as **alters**. Each of the "personalities" is distinct and presents with different memories, personal histories, and mannerisms. Different alters may identify themselves as men or women, as adults or children, or more rarely as animals. Some researchers have reported differences between alters in eyeglass prescriptions, EEG patterns, allergies, and other physical parameters (Nijenhuis & den Boer, 2009). Although the number of alters can range from one additional personality state to more than a thousand, the average number appears to be somewhere between 10 and 16 (Acocella, 1999; Coons, 1998).

The process of changing from one personality to another has been referred to as **switching**. Switching often occurs in response to a stressful situation, such as an argument with a spouse, or physical or sexual abuse, and may also occur if the therapist makes a request while the individual is hypnotized. The switch may or may not be dramatic enough to grab the attention of others, and may involve eye

TABLE 6.2   DSM-5 DIAGNOSTIC CRITERIA FOR DISSOCIATIVE IDENTITY DISORDER

A. Disruption of identity characterized by two or more distinct personality states, which may be described in some cultures as an experience of possession. The disruption in identity involves marked discontinuity in sense of self and sense of agency, accompanied by related alterations in affect, behaviour, consciousness, memory, perception, cognition, and/or sensory-motor functioning. These signs and symptoms may be observed by others or reported by the individual.
B. Recurrent gaps in the recall of everyday events, important personal information, and/or traumatic events that are inconsistent with ordinary forgetting.
C. The symptoms cause clinically significant distress or impairment in social, occupational, or other important areas of functioning.
D. The disturbance is not a normal part of a broadly accepted cultural or religious practice. **Note:** in children, the symptoms are not better explained by imaginary playmates or other fantasy play.
E. The symptoms are not attributable to the physiological effects of a substance (e.g., blackouts or chaotic behaviour during alcohol intoxication) or another medical condition (e.g., complex partial seizures).

blinking or eye rolling (Coons, 1998). The presence of a new alter may also lead to a change in the tone of voice, demeanour, or posture of the individual.

In contrast to previous versions of DSM, the diagnostic criteria in DSM-5 are more flexible and emphasize less dramatic presentations of DID. Individuals are no longer required to display distinct "identities" that appear to "take control" of behaviour in order to receive a diagnosis of this disorder. Instead, it is recognized that alternative personality states may vary according to their level of overtness, and signs of identity disturbance may be quite subtle. For example, the emergence of an alternative personality state could correspond with the sudden occurrence of emotions or behaviours that individuals find perplexing and not within their control. DSM-5 acknowledges that highly overt personality states are more likely to occur in so-called "possession-form" cases of DID, which "typically manifest as if a 'spirit', supernatural being, or outside person has taken control, such that the individual begins speaking or acting in a distinctly different manner" (APA, 2013, p. 293).

The average age at diagnosis of DID is 29 to 35 years and this disorder is diagnosed three to nine times more frequently in women than in men (APA, 2000). Self-destructive behaviour is common among people with DID, including self-inflicted burns, wrist slashing, and overdosing. About 75 percent of patients with DID have a history of suicide attempts and more than 90 percent report recurrent suicidal thoughts (Ross, 1997). DID is chronic by nature and patients often spend six to seven years seeking help from a variety of therapists for other problems, such as depression or anxiety, before they are diagnosed with the disorder. Not surprisingly, given the severity of this condition, patients with DID often have multiple diagnoses, including depression, post-traumatic stress disorder, borderline personality disorder, substance abuse disorders, eating disorders, and various anxiety disorders (Rodewald, Wilhelm-Gossling, Emrich, Reddemann, & Gast, 2011). The clinical picture is complex, and these patients have developed a reputation for being notoriously difficult to treat. Once diagnosed, most specialists in the area agree that several years of therapy are required before integration of the host and alter personalities is possible (Kluft, 2001).

There is a great deal of debate among mental health professionals about the prevalence of DID, and even about the legitimacy of this diagnosis. Only about 200 cases of dissociative identity disorder were reported in the entire world literature prior to 1980 (Greaves, 1980). Over the next two decades, however, diagnoses of this disorder increased exponentially. By 1986, it was estimated that 6000 cases had been diagnosed in North America (Coons, 1986), and many thousands more appeared in subsequent years. Recently, however, the number of diagnoses has dropped precipitously (Pope et al., 2006). This dramatic rise and fall in prevalence has led some practitioners to believe that the disorder was overdiagnosed in highly suggestible people by well-intentioned but overly zealous clinicians. This view will be explored further in the next section.

Etiology

Our knowledge of the causes of the dissociative disorders is minimal compared to many other clinical disorders, such as depressive and anxiety disorders. As noted previously, this issue has generated a great deal of debate, particularly with regard to the etiology of DID. Two competing explanatory models have been proposed: the trauma model and the sociocognitive model (also referred to as the fantasy model). The **trauma model**, which is a diathesis-stress formulation, has a long history and continues to be widely accepted by many clinicians and researchers (Dalenberg et al., 2012, 2014; Gleaves, 1996; Ross, 1997). According to this model, dissociative disorders are a result of severe childhood trauma, including sexual, physical, and emotional abuse, accompanied by personality traits that predispose the individual to employ dissociation as a defence mechanism or coping strategy. Initially, dissociation may be an adaptive response to traumatic events that helps individuals cope with their trauma. For a chronically abused child, for example, dissociation offers a means of escape when no other means is possible. If the child can escape into a fantasy world and become somebody else and if this escape blunts the physical and emotional pain temporarily, he or she will likely do it again. However, this defence mechanism is no longer adaptive when it is maintained as a habitual way of coping throughout adulthood.

Not all people who are abused as children or who experience other types of trauma develop dissociative disorders. According to the trauma model, certain personality traits, such as high hypnotizability, fantasy proneness, and openness to altered states of consciousness, may represent a diathesis, predisposing some individuals to develop dissociative experiences in the face of trauma. These personality traits themselves do not lead to dissociative disorders (Rauschenberger & Lynn, 1995). However, they may increase the risk that people who undergo severe trauma will develop dissociative processes to cope with this trauma. In contrast, people who are low in dissociative tendencies may develop anxious, intrusive thoughts rather than a dissociative reaction (Kirmayer, Robbins, & Paris, 1994).

There may also be a genetic heritability component to these personality traits that makes some individuals more vulnerable to dissociative disorders. Some studies comparing identical and fraternal twins have found that genetic factors account for approximately 50 percent of the variance in dissociative symptoms (Becker-Blease et al., 2004; Jang, Paris, Zweig-Frank, & Livesley, 1998). There is also evidence for heritability of the related traits of hypnotizability, absorption, and fantasy proneness (Morgan, 1973; Tellegen et al., 1988). However, at least one study has failed to find evidence for heritability of pathological dissociative tendencies (Waller & Ross, 1997).

Some researchers have advanced the notion that attachment theory can also help to explain why some people are more vulnerable to dissociative disorders (Harari, Bakermans-Kranenburg, & van Ijzendoorn, 2007; Liotti, 2009). According to attachment theory, sensitive responding by the parent to an infant's needs results in a child who demonstrates secure attachment, developing the skills and confidence necessary to relate to others later in adult life. The lack of such sensitive responding by the caregiver results in insecure attachment, wherein children lack confidence in relations with others. One type of insecure attachment style observed in infants has been labelled the "disorganized pattern," which is characterized by inconsistent, contradictory behaviours when faced with stress, including stereotypical and anomalous movements or postures, freezing, and trance-like states. Attachment researchers have noted similarities between these behaviours and dissociative states, and have proposed that disorganized attachment may be a risk factor for the development of pathological dissociation in adult life (Liotti, 2009; Main & Morgan, 1996). Disorganized attachment by itself does not necessarily lead to the development of dissociative disorders, but when individuals with this attachment style also experience overwhelming trauma, they may be particularly vulnerable to developing a dissociative disorder (Lieberman, Chu, van Horn, & Harris, 2011).

In contrast to the trauma model, the **socio-cognitive model** represents a very different etiological position that is taken by many mental health professionals who do not accept DID as a legitimate disorder (Lynn et al., 2014; Piper & Merskey, 2004a; Spanos, 1994, 1996). Nick Spanos, who was a professor of psychology at Carleton University in Ottawa, was a leading proponent of this model of DID. According to this perspective, multiple personality is a form of role-playing in which individuals come to construe themselves as possessing multiple selves and then begin to act in ways consistent with their own or their therapist's conception of the disorder. Spanos (1996) did not suggest that these individuals were faking or malingering their illness, but did assert that it is entirely possible to alter a person's personal history so that it is consistent with the belief that he or she has DID. Spanos believed that therapists' leading questions, cues, and other demand characteristics play an important role in the generation and maintenance of this disorder.

Harold Merskey, a psychiatrist and professor emeritus at the University of Western Ontario, has also championed this view (Merskey, 1992; Piper & Merskey, 2004a, 2004b). Merskey (1992) argued that DID is an **iatrogenic** (literally meaning "caused by treatment") condition, which means that it is largely caused by therapists themselves during the course of therapy. While treating emotionally troubled individuals by means of hypnosis, therapists may plant suggestions in their patients that they have multiple personalities. Highly hypnotizable patients, who have grown up in a culture in which stories of DID are widely reported in the media, may then develop the symptoms of DID as a learned social role. In support of this view, Merskey (1992) pointed to the sharp increase in diagnosed cases of DID following the release of films that portrayed this disorder, such as *The Three Faces of Eve* and *Sybil*. Furthermore, until approximately 20 years ago, the diagnosis of DID appeared to be limited to North America, and was quite rare in many other parts of the world before increasing global media attention. In addition, most cases of DID have been reported by a relatively small number of clinicians who are strong believers in the legitimacy of this diagnosis, whereas many other clinicians who work with severely disturbed and abused patients never encounter it (Boysen & VanBergen, 2013b). These arguments have led to a considerable amount of skepticism about the trauma model of DID among many mental health professionals. Surveys of psychiatrists in Canada and the United States at the beginning of the twenty-first century showed that less than one-quarter of these clinicians believed that DID has strong scientific validity (Lalonde, Hudson, Gigante, & Pope, 2001; Pope, Oliva, Hudson, Bodkin, & Gruber, 1999).

A critical issue dividing these two theories is whether or not DID actually develops in childhood as a result of abuse. Proponents of the socio-cognitive model point out that DID is usually diagnosed in adults and almost never observed during childhood, when it is supposed to begin (Piper & Merskey, 2004a).

Although a number of mental health professionals continue to question the legitimacy of DID as a psychiatric diagnosis (Paris, 2012), others vehemently disagree (Brand, Loewenstein, & Spiegel, 2013; Martinez-Taboas, Dorahy, Sar, Middleton, & Krüger, 2013). The debate between trauma and socio-cognitive models continues and, if anything, is more contentious than ever. Proponents of the trauma model point to a considerable amount of research evidence linking dissociative disorders with a history of trauma. In a widely cited meta-analysis, Dalenberg and colleagues (2012) reported a moderately strong relationship between trauma and dissociation, even when the analysis was restricted to studies that relied on objective indicators of trauma. Additionally, provocative results of prospective studies suggest that highly aversive events are linked to later experiences of dissociation (Dalenberg et al., 2012).

Critics of the trauma model respond by citing several methodological flaws and inconsistencies in research used to support this model (Lynn et al., 2014). Many relevant studies that document severe childhood physical and/or sexual abuse are based on adult patients' retrospective reports, which are very difficult to corroborate (Kihlstrom, 2005). In addition, more robust studies utilizing prospective designs and well-corroborated cases of trauma have at times failed to find the expected relationship between trauma and dissociation (Lynn et al., 2014). Another source of information has been studies that contrast diagnosed cases of DID with individuals feigning symptoms of this disorder. A systematic review conducted by Boysen and VanBergen (2014) suggests that there is a lack of meaningful differences between these two groups, lending support to the socio-cognitive model. However, these authors also cite several methodological flaws limiting the interpretability of research in this area.

❸ BEFORE MOVING ON

The trauma model and the socio-cognitive model represent two very different ways of explaining DID. What types of evidence have been used to support each of these explanations?

Dissociative Amnesia with Fugue

On September 10, 2006, a man appeared in the emergency room of a hospital in Denver, Colorado, in obvious distress. He said he did not know his name or where he came from. Since waking up on the sidewalk with no memory of his previous life, he had been wandering the streets in confusion. Doctors at the hospital diagnosed him with dissociative fugue, and over the following weeks they tried unsuccessfully to recover his memory by means of hypnosis and sodium amytal (truth serum) treatments. After more than six weeks with no improvement, he appeared on national television, pleading for someone to recognize him. Within hours, a woman telephoned from Olympia, Washington, saying that he was her fiancé, Jeff Ingram, a 40-year-old man originally from Canada. He had disappeared after leaving on a trip to visit his parents in northern Alberta, and his family and friends had been searching frantically for him for nearly two months. When he was reunited with his fiancée and family, Jeff did not recognize them, and six months later he still had no memory of his past, although he and his fiancée were making plans for their wedding. The mystery of how he ended up in Denver was never solved.

Treatment

PSYCHOTHERAPY

Most psychotherapies for dissociative disorders focus on helping patients resolve emotional distress associated with past traumas and learn more effective ways of coping with stress in their lives (Harper, 2011). Treatment of DID tends to be a quite prolonged and arduous process, going through a series of stages leading to the eventual integration of the various personalities (Kluft, 1999). The first stage of therapy involves the establishment of a trusting, safe environment for the patient to discuss emotionally charged memories of past trauma. The next stage begins by helping patients develop new coping skills that will be required when discussions of past history of abuse take place. Agreements for open communication between alters may be necessary to establish these new patterns of responding to stress. Therapy can then focus on remembering and grieving the abuse that the patient experienced at the hands of those who should have protected him or her. Once the patient develops more effective coping strategies and has reached a certain level of acceptance of his or her past history of abuse, therapy can move on to the final stage: integration of the personalities. Here the goal is for the alters to merge into a single personality or at least a group of alters that are working together and are aware of each other.

Recent research on the effectiveness of psychotherapy for dissociative disorders includes a large-scale naturalistic study of patients who received therapy in the community for DID (Brand et al., 2013). Main findings included lower levels of dissociation, depression, general distress, and post-traumatic stress disorder symptoms at the 30-month follow-up. Despite these promising results, it should be emphasized that very little systematic research has been conducted to date, and most of the existing studies on the effectiveness of psychotherapy for dissociative disorders have methodological flaws.

HYPNOSIS

Hypnosis has been a popular treatment method for many clinicians working with patients with DID to confirm the diagnosis, to contact alters, and to uncover memories of traumatic childhood abuse (Kluft, 1999). However, others have criticized the use of hypnosis in this patient population because of the potential of retrieving confabulated memories and personalities.

MEDICATION

Medication is generally not useful in the direct treatment of the dissociative disorders (Somer, Amos-Williams, & Stein, 2013). However, psychopharmacology may be helpful in treating comorbid disorders, such as depression and anxiety. "Truth serum" or sodium amytal, a barbiturate causing drowsiness, has sometimes been used to help the individual recall previously forgotten memories or identify additional alters. However, other psychotherapies are typically used at the same time because the chemical does not always work or the individual does not remember what was reported while under the influence of this drug.

NEUROSURGICAL TREATMENTS

Emerging evidence points to the effectiveness of repetitive transcranial magnetic stimulation (rTMS) in the treatment of dissociative disorders, particularly in cases of depersonalization/derealization disorder. This noninvasive procedure involves the generation of a magnetic field at the level of the scalp using a metal coil, which in turn influences the electrical activity in nearby regions of the brain. A recent study of patients with depersonalization/derealization disorder reported that 20 sessions of rTMS to the right ventrolateral prefrontal cortex significantly improved symptoms of depersonalization in six out of seven cases (Jay et al., 2016). However, the results also suggest that general symptoms of dissociation are relatively unaffected by this procedure.

Somatic Symptom and Related Disorders

The word *somatic* derives from the Greek *soma*, meaning "body." The **somatic symptom and related disorders** are a group of disorders in which individuals present with

TABLE 6.3   SOMATIC SYMPTOM AND RELATED DISORDERS

Disorder	Description
Somatic symptom disorder	One or more somatic symptoms (e.g., chronic pain, fatigue) that are distressing or cause significant disruption of daily life, accompanied by disproportionate concerns about seriousness, anxiety, and/or excessive time and energy devoted to health concerns; a diagnosed medical illness may or may not be present
Illness anxiety disorder	Preoccupation, anxiety, and worry about having or acquiring a serious illness in the absence of significant somatic symptoms and despite the fact that thorough evaluation fails to identify a serious medical condition
Conversion disorder	Symptoms affecting voluntary motor or sensory functions (e.g., blindness, paralysis, loss of feeling) that are incompatible with recognized neurological or medical conditions
Psychological factors affecting other medical conditions	The individual has a medical condition (e.g., asthma, heart disease, diabetes) that is adversely affected by psychological or behavioural factors (e.g., anxiety exacerbating asthma symptoms, stressful work environment causing high blood pressure)
Factitious disorder	Faking or inducing symptoms of illness to gain sympathy, medical care, and attention (e.g., taking excessive laxatives, contaminating urine samples, intentionally injuring oneself)

physical symptoms suggestive of medical illnesses, along with significant psychological distress and functional impairment. The physical symptoms can take a number of different forms. In dramatic cases, they involve substantial impairment of a sensory or muscular system, such as a loss of vision or paralysis in one arm. In other disorders, individuals become unduly preoccupied with the belief that they may have a serious disease; and become disabled by constant worry, anxiety, and excessive time and energy devoted to their health concerns. Not surprisingly, individuals with these disorders tend to view themselves as having a medical disease or illness rather than a psychological disorder, and they are much more likely to seek help from a physician in general medicine than from a psychologist or psychiatrist.

In earlier versions of the DSM, these disorders were called *somatoform disorders* and an important criterion for diagnosis was that the bodily complaints of these individuals did not have a physiological basis or medical explanation. Instead, it was assumed that these symptoms were caused by psychological factors such as early traumatic experiences or unresolved emotional distress. Because of the implication that their physical symptoms were "all in their head," many patients viewed these diagnoses as demeaning and pejorative. These disorders have therefore been reconceptualised in DSM-5 so that medically unexplained symptoms are no longer such a central criterion for diagnosis. They may be present to varying degrees, particularly in conversion disorder, but they are not necessary for a diagnosis of somatic symptom and related disorders. Thus, an individual could have a diagnosed medical condition and still meet the criteria for one of these disorders. The key point is that psychological factors are causing excessive worry, distress, and impairment, or are contributing to the onset or severity of the medical condition.

The somatic symptom and related disorders comprise several disorders, all of which involve a predominant focus on bodily concerns. The major diagnoses are *somatic symptom disorder, illness anxiety disorder, conversion disorder, psychological factors affecting other medical conditions,* and *factitious disorder* (see Table 6.3). In this chapter, we will discuss each of these except psychological factors affecting other medical conditions, which is the focus of Chapter 7.

PREVALENCE

Because these disorders in DSM-5 represent a major reconceptualization of the diagnostic group formerly called the somatoform disorders, little prevalence information is available to date. To obtain an estimate of their prevalence, we need to extrapolate from existing studies using the previous somatoform diagnoses. For example, the newly defined somatic symptom disorder subsumes the previous diagnosis of somatization disorder as well as most cases of hypochondriasis. Past epidemiological studies assessing the prevalence of somatization disorder found an average prevalence of 0.4 percent in the general population, whereas the prevalence of hypochondriasis was about 5 percent (Creed & Barsky, 2004). The prevalence of somatic symptom disorder is therefore likely to be about 5 percent as well. Since the DSM-5 diagnosis of illness anxiety disorder comprises a smaller subset of hypochondriasis, the prevalence of this disorder is likely to be somewhat less than 5 percent. Epidemiological findings suggest that conversion disorder is rarely found in the general population, with the estimated prevalence being lower than 0.1% (Akagi & House, 2001). However, this disorder appears to be more common in neurological treatment settings; a recent study conducted in Iran found that 8.2% of patients referred to an outpatient epilepsy clinic have non-epileptic seizures with no identifiable organic basis (Asadi-Pooya, Emami, & Emami, 2014). The prevalence of factitious disorder is largely unknown due to inherent difficulties in studying this disorder. However, one investigation conducted within a pediatric hospital setting reported that approximately 1.8% of persons involved in patient cases qualified for a diagnosis of this disorder (Ferrara et al., 2013).

Conversion Disorder

Conversion disorder, also called *functional neurological symptom disorder*, is the most dramatic of the somatic symptom and related disorders. Individuals with this disorder have a loss of functioning in a part of their body that appears to be due to a neurological or other medical cause, but without any underlying medical abnormality to explain it. They may have motor deficits such as paralysis or localized weakness, impaired coordination or balance, inability to speak, difficulty swallowing or the sensation of a lump in the throat, and urinary retention. Behaviour resembling seizures or convulsions may also occur. In other cases, individuals have sensory deficits such as loss of touch or pain sensation, double vision, blindness, or deafness. Psychological factors, such as conflict or stress, are presumed to be associated with the onset or exacerbation of the condition. Patients with conversion disorder often have other diagnosable psychological disorders, such as depression and anxiety (Aybek, Kanaan, & David, 2008; Stone, Warlow, & Sharpe, 2010).

Careful medical evaluation of these patients is always essential to ensure that a genuine medical condition is not misdiagnosed as a conversion disorder. Indeed, DSM-5 criteria stipulate that this disorder can be diagnosed only after thorough medical testing provides clear evidence that the symptoms are not compatible with a neurological disease. In the past, a number of studies suggested that many people diagnosed with conversion disorder were actually suffering from a medical condition that diagnostic tests could not identify. For example, early studies found that one-quarter to one-half of all patients thought to have conversion disorders ultimately were diagnosed with medical conditions (Slater & Glithero, 1965). However, growing evidence indicates that rates of misdiagnosis have improved substantially over recent decades, likely due to improved knowledge and diagnostic techniques (Stone et al., 2005, 2009). For instance, a follow-up study of neurology outpatients reported that a potential organic cause of medically unexplained symptoms was later discovered in only 0.4% of cases (Stone et al., 2009).

In making a diagnosis of conversion disorder, clinicians often look for particular signs that help to distinguish these symptoms from those with an organic origin (Daum, Hubschmid, & Aybek, 2014). For example, electroencephalographic recordings might show that a patient's seizures are not accompanied by the distinctive brainwave activity seen in epilepsy (Marchetti, Kurcgant, Neto, Von Bismark, & Fiore, 2009). Patients may also show inconsistencies over time (e.g., inadvertently moving a "paralyzed" limb when attention is directed elsewhere) or unusual symptom patterns (e.g., unusual head movements during seizures). A careful physical exam may indicate substantial strength in muscles that have supposedly been immobilized for a long time.

FIGURE 6.1 Glove Anaesthesia

People with glove anaesthesia lose sensation in the entire hand (A), not the area affected by the ulnar nerve which is where the loss would be expected to a person with nerve damage (B).

Another indicator that symptoms are likely due to conversion disorder is when they are clearly inconsistent with known physiological mechanisms. A classic example is **glove anaesthesia**. This involves a loss of all sensation (e.g., touch, temperature, and pain) throughout the hand, with the loss sharply demarcated at the wrist (see Figure 6.1A) rather than following a pattern consistent with the sensory innervation of the hand and forearm (Figure 6.1B). Another classic sign that was previously thought to identify conversion symptoms was **la belle indifférence**, a nonchalant lack of concern about the nature and implications of one's symptoms. However, recent research indicates that this is found in only a minority of cases and it does not reliably distinguish between conversion symptoms and symptoms of organic disease (Stone, Smyth, Carson, Warlow, & Sharpe, 2006).

Several studies have employed brain imaging techniques such as fMRI to examine the brain regions involved in conversion disorders (see Ejareh dar & Kanaan, 2016). These studies suggest that conversion symptoms result from a dynamic reorganization of the brain circuits that link volition, movement, and perception, leading to an inhibition of normal cortical activity (Black, Seritan, Taber, & Hurley,

2004). Interestingly, these mechanisms are not observed in individuals who are instructed to feign conversion symptoms, suggesting that individuals with conversion disorders are not simply faking their symptoms.

As discussed earlier, prior to the publication of DSM-III, conversion and dissociative disorders were grouped together under the concept of hysteria. Some experts have suggested that conversion disorder might best be viewed as a form of dissociative disorder (Brown, Cardena, Nijenhuis, Sar, & van der Hart, 2007). According to this view, conversion disorders involve a process of dissociation in which there is a lack of integration between conscious awareness and sensory processes or voluntary control over physical symptoms. This argument is supported by findings that individuals with conversion disorders also frequently meet the criteria for diagnoses of dissociative disorders, tend to have high scores on measures of dissociative experiences and hypnotizability, and frequently have a history of childhood abuse and trauma (Roelofs et al., 2002; Yayla et al., 2015).

 BEFORE MOVING ON

> When diagnosing a conversion disorder, what steps should be taken by a clinician to rule out possible physiological causes for the symptoms?

Somatic Symptom Disorder

Somatic symptom disorder is a new diagnosis in DSM-5, which subsumes the former *somatization disorder* as well as most individuals who would previously have been diagnosed with *hypochondriasis*. Individuals with somatic symptom disorder typically have multiple, recurrent somatic symptoms such as pain, fatigue, nausea, muscle weakness, numbness, or indigestion. These symptoms, which may or may not be due to a diagnosed medical disease or illness, must be very distressing to the individual and result in significant disruption of daily life. Individuals with this disorder have a great deal of anxiety about their health, worry excessively about their symptoms, and devote excessive time and energy to thinking about them. Their personal identity may become wrapped up with their perceived physical illnesses, and they may restrict their activities, avoiding social events, frequently taking sick days from work, and even quitting work completely and staying at home on disability.

Not surprisingly, these individuals frequently go to the doctor to seek medical treatment for their bodily concerns. Sometimes a medical examination leads to the discovery of a genuine illness or disease, but the individual's level of anxiety and functional impairment continues to far exceed what is normal or realistic for their particular health problem. More often, however, no serious medical problem is found, but these individuals are not reassured and may become resentful that the doctor is not taking their symptoms seriously enough. Patients also tend to strongly resist suggestions that psychological or social

factors might contribute to their illness or disability, and they become quite upset at the suggestion to see a psychologist or psychiatrist.

Patients with somatic symptom disorder often describe their problems in a colourful or exaggerated manner, but without specific factual information. Their accounts can be very persuasive and potentially expose them to danger as a result of invasive or risky diagnostic procedures (e.g., X-ray examinations or invasive probes), surgery, hospitalization, side effects from potent medications, or treatment by several physicians at once, perhaps leading to complicated or even hazardous care (Woolfolk & Allen, 2010). Multidisciplinary assessment is often required. On the one hand, physicians need to test for the possible presence of medical conditions for which there can be vague, multiple, and confusing somatic symptoms (e.g., systemic lupus, multiple sclerosis, or chronic parasitic disease). On the other hand, psychologists need to assess emotional, cognitive, behavioural, and social issues.

These patients are often prone to periods of anxiety and depression that they cannot express or cope with adaptively (Löwe et al., 2008). In addition, these individuals often report histories of substance abuse and personality disorders (Bornstein & Gold, 2008; Noyes et al., 2001).

Individuals with somatic symptom disorder often display an excessive sensitivity to relatively minor bodily symptoms. The patient may be alarmed by his or her heartbeat, breathing, or sweating; become apprehensive about a small sore; or worry about a minor cough. These symptoms are attributed to some serious disease and serve to confirm the patient's fears that an illness is indeed present, resulting in a great deal of time spent thinking about the meaning, authenticity, or etiology of the somatic experiences. If you have read Chapter 5 on anxiety disorders, you may have noticed a similarity between somatic symptom disorder and panic disorder, in that both disorders involve excessive concern with and misinterpretation of bodily symptoms (Deacon & Abramowitz, 2008). A difference, however, is that those with panic disorder typically fear *immediate* symptom-related disasters that might occur during the panic attack itself, whereas individuals with somatic symptom disorder focus on the *long-term* process of illness and disease.

Pain is one of the most frequent bodily symptoms associated with somatic symptom disorder. In previous versions of DSM, *pain disorder* was a separate diagnosis, but in DSM-5 it has been subsumed within somatic symptom disorder, and affected individuals receive the diagnosis of **somatic symptom disorder with predominant pain**. Pain as a consequence of injury or disease is a very common experience. Fortunately, it is usually self-limiting, and most sources of pain can be identified and eliminated. However, pain can also be extraordinarily severe and distressing, and it can persist long beyond the span of time one would expect necessary for damaged tissue to heal. These experiences of pain are not infrequent. An epidemiological survey of 18 countries suggests that between 37 and 41 percent of the general population suffers with chronic or recurrent pain of varying

People with somatic symptom and related disorders often become frustrated with physicians and embark on an intense search for the drug or device that will solve their problems.

severity (Tsang et al., 2008). When pain persists beyond its expected time span, a patient can often benefit from a consideration of the role of psychosocial factors. Pain is an individual and subjective experience, and both its onset and course are known to be affected by a number of psychological factors, including stress, anxiety, and depression. These psychological dimensions of pain establish an important role for psychologists in understanding and controlling pain (Wiech & Tracey, 2009).

Overall, the DSM-5's reconceptualization of somatic symptom disorder has been met with resistance from some researchers and clinicians who fear that changes will result in greater stigmatization of individuals with legitimate medical conditions, such as chronic pain (Katz, Rosenbloom, & Fashler, 2015). Now that this disorder can be diagnosed within the context of physical illness, there is concern that individuals with medical issues will be over-diagnosed with mental disorders (Frances & Chapman, 2013). However, findings of a recent study indicate that the DSM-5 diagnostic criteria are more restrictive than previously thought. Claassen-van Dessel and colleagues (2016) reported that fewer patients with medically unexplained symptoms were diagnosed with a somatic symptom disorder when assessment was based on DSM-5 criteria (45.5%) compared to DSM-IV requirements for somatoform disorders (92.9%).

Illness Anxiety Disorder

Illness anxiety disorder is another new diagnosis in DSM-5, which applies to a subset of the individuals who would previously have been diagnosed with *hypochondriasis*. People with illness anxiety disorder are preoccupied with the fear that they may have a serious medical disease, despite the fact that thorough medical examination reveals that there is nothing seriously wrong with them. The main difference between this disorder and somatic symptom disorder is that individuals with illness anxiety disorder do not have any significant bodily symptoms and are primarily concerned with the idea that they are ill, whereas those with somatic symptom disorder have significant symptoms such as pain and may actually have a diagnosed medical illness.

People with illness anxiety disorder tend to be highly anxious about their health and become easily alarmed about illness-related events, such as hearing that a friend has become ill or watching a health-related news story on TV. They tend to examine themselves frequently (e.g., taking their temperature or examining their throat in a mirror), and they search the internet excessively to research their suspected disease. Illness becomes central to their self-identity, affecting their daily activities, and a major focus of their conversations with friends and family. Like those with somatic symptom disorder, these individuals are far more likely to seek help from a general medical practitioner than from a psychologist or psychiatrist, and they tend to become quite upset when it is suggested that they might benefit from psychological intervention. To be diagnosed with this disorder, the illness preoccupation must have been present for at least six months, although the particular illness that is feared may have changed during that time.

Since anxiety is the predominant symptom of this disorder, some researchers believe that illness anxiety disorder would be more appropriately categorized as an anxiety disorder than a somatic symptom disorder (Olatunji, Deacon, & Abramowitz, 2009).

5 BEFORE MOVING ON

If you were suffering from a somatic symptom disorder, how might you identify any secondary gains that might be reinforcing the disorder?

Factitious Disorder

Individuals with **factitious disorder** (also called *Munchausen syndrome*) deliberately fake or generate the symptoms of illness or injury to gain medical attention. For example, they might surreptitiously take excessive amounts of laxatives, contaminate urine samples with fecal matter, or inject cleaning fluids into their skin to make it appear that they have a serious illness. Besides physical symptoms, factitious disorders can involve faking psychiatric symptoms, such as hallucinations or delusions. A recent analysis of 372 studies suggests that most patients choose to self-induce illness or injury, rather than falsely report or simulate symptoms (Yates & Feldman, 2016). To be diagnosed with this disorder, there must not be any obvious external rewards for this behaviour, such as receiving insurance money, evading military service, or avoiding an exam. Instead, the motivation of these individuals seems to be to gain sympathy, care, and attention that accompany the sick role. A particularly troubling variant of this disorder is **factitious disorder imposed on another**, in which an individual falsifies illness in another person, most commonly the person's own child. The news media occasionally report tragic cases of mothers producing life-threatening symptoms in their children, such as injecting them with a noxious substance or smothering them with a pillow to induce unconsciousness. Needless to say, this disorder is typically associated with a significant level of psychological distress and impairment.

Etiology

The somatic symptom and related disorders are a rather disparate group of disorders that have little in common except the fact that they all involve bodily symptoms in one way or another. In view of the heterogeneity of these disorders, it is likely that somewhat different etiological processes are involved in each of them. Traditional psychoanalytic explanations proposed that these disorders resulted from conversion of the anxiety associated with unconscious conflicts and unacceptable sexual drives into somatic symptomatology and distress. However, this view is not widely held today. Kirmayer and Looper (2007) have proposed an integrative biopsychosocial model to explain the development of somatic symptom and related disorders. According to this theory, a number of physiological, psychological, and social factors may interact in a series of vicious cycles, with different somatic symptom disorders resulting from different patterns of interaction.

Although genetic factors likely have some role in the development of somatic symptom and related disorders (Kendler et al., 1995), more is known about the influence of *physiological* factors. For example, chronic stress produces activation of the hypothalamic-pituitary-adrenal (HPA) axis, producing high levels of cortisol, which can adversely affect the immune system and also produce feelings of fatigue, pain, and general malaise (Kirmayer & Looper, 2007). These feelings in turn can cause individuals to perceive themselves as having a physical illness when they are actually experiencing stress.

Cognitive factors also seem to play an important role in the development of these disorders. We all experience many bodily sensations arising from various aches and pains, common viral infections, and feelings of apprehension or dysphoria arising from stressful life experiences. However, individuals with somatic symptom disorders spend substantial time monitoring their bodies and thus they are more likely to notice the various changes that take place. People with these disorders also tend to interpret bodily sensations in a distorted manner, magnifying their seriousness or importance and attributing them to serious illnesses, leading to increased distress and further physiological arousal (Barsky, 1992; Vervoort et al., 2006).

Abramowitz, Deacon, and Valentiner (2007) have proposed a cognitive-behavioural model of health anxiety that encapsulates many of the previously described cognitive mechanisms and bears resemblance to models of other anxiety-related disorders. They theorize, as others have (Salkovskis, 1996; Salkovskis & Warwick, 1986), that we all develop beliefs and attitudes about our physical well-being through personal experiences with illness and information from others about their experiences. The development of dysfunctional beliefs about illness leads an individual to become attentionally biased to misinterpret information in a self-alarming and personally threatening manner. Distorted and catastrophic interpretation of bodily symptoms produces anxiety and uncertainty, which prompts a person to engage in various safety-seeking behaviours. Specifically, individuals with health-related anxiety often avoid illness-related information, frequently check symptoms, and repeatedly seek help from medical professionals to receive reassurance regarding their concerns (Hadjistavropoulos, Craig, & Hadjistavropoulos, 1998). It is proposed that these behaviours impede corrective learning about a patient's health and reinforce dysfunctional beliefs about illness, thereby completing a vicious cycle and maintaining anxiety (Abramowitz et al., 2007).

Individual differences in various *personality traits*, such as negative affectivity and emotion regulation deficits, have also been proposed as contributors to the development of somatic symptom and related disorders (e.g., Zunhammer, Eberle, Eichhammer, & Volker, 2013). As we have seen, recent research also suggests that many people with conversion disorders, like people with dissociative disorders, are highly hypnotizable (Roelofs et al., 2002), and that conversion symptoms result from spontaneous self-hypnosis, in which sensory or motor functions are split off from consciousness in reaction to extreme stress.

Early life experiences and social learning also likely play a role in the etiology of somatic symptom and related disorders. A good deal of evidence has been offered for a relationship between trauma and these disorders. A significant degree of childhood physical or sexual abuse or other severe childhood adversity has been reported in many patients with somatic symptom and related disorders (Şar, Akyüz, Kundakçı, Kızıltan, & Doğan, 2004).

Individuals who report medically unexplained symptoms in adulthood often also report early experiences of illness and/or observing serious illness in others (Hotopf, Wilson-Jones, Mayou, Wadsworth, & Wessely, 2000). From a social learning perspective, children observe and internalize the health-related opinions and behaviours of close others, such as how parents perceive illness and respond to bodily symptoms (Marshall, Jones, Ramchandani, Stein, & Bass, 2007). Moreover, illness-related behaviours and the "sick role" can be positively reinforced by the care, concern, and attention received from others, and negatively reinforced by allowing the individual to avoid burdensome work activities or uncomfortable social situations. This does not mean that individuals with these disorders are consciously faking their symptoms to obtain rewards, but rather that people learn to adopt roles as a result of their reinforcement history.

Treatment
MEDICATION

Existing research suggests that antidepressant medication is likely helpful for addressing primary symptoms of these disorders (Somashekar, Jainer, & Wuntakal, 2013). However, the evidence supporting its efficacy is low in quality, and the number of adverse effects reported in the available studies is concerning (Kleinstäuber et al., 2014). Future research is necessary to evaluate the utility of medication for the somatic symptom disorders. However, identification and treatment of comorbid anxiety and depressive disorders is a vital part of treatment, for which pharmacotherapeutic interventions are often prescribed.

PSYCHOTHERAPY

Generally, treatment of the somatic symptom and related disorders has shifted away from traditional psychodynamic therapy, which viewed somatic symptoms as masked expressions of psychological conflict and focused on helping individuals acquire insight into the origins of their difficulties. Current treatments focus on the cognitive, affective, and social processes that maintain excessive or inappropriate behaviour (Woolfolk & Allen, 2007). Because patients with somatic symptom and related disorders are usually very reluctant to view their symptoms as having a psychological cause, establishing a co-operative therapeutic environment is crucial when treating these disorders. Simon (2002) notes the important features of developing such an environment, including establishing the position that all symptoms are "real" and distressing, negotiating a mutually acceptable treatment goal (e.g., tolerance of reasonable uncertainty about health), shifting attention from somatic symptoms to life stresses or affective states that may provoke or exacerbate symptoms, and focusing on symptom management and rehabilitation rather than medical diagnosis and cure.

The cognitive-behavioural approach to treating somatic symptom and related disorders involves restructuring morbid thoughts and preoccupations, and works to bring dysfunctional behaviour patterns under control. Many reviews of the existing research indicate that cognitive-behavioural therapy (CBT) is an effective method for treating patients with these disorders. For example, Olatunji and colleagues (2014) conducted a meta-analysis to examine the effectiveness of CBT for hypochondriasis/health anxiety, based on the previously discussed cognitive-behavioural model (Abramowitz et al., 2007). Patients who were randomly assigned to CBT exhibited diminished symptoms of health anxiety and also depression at post-treatment and follow-up compared to those who received a control treatment, which often consisted of routine medical care or being placed on a waitlist for CBT (Olatunji et al., 2014). Unfortunately, despite the fact that effective cognitive-behavioural treatments have been developed for several somatic symptom and related disorders, many patients do not seek psychological treatment, insisting that their problems are physical, even after extensive medical testing indicates otherwise.

⑥ BEFORE MOVING ON

In recent years, clinicians and researchers have begun to conceptualize somatic symptom disorder as a form of anxiety disorder. How might cognitive-behavioural methods for treating anxiety disorders be applied to the treatment of somatic symptom disorder?

CANADIAN RESEARCH CENTRE

Dr. Laurence J. Kirmayer

Dr. Kirmayer is a professor of psychiatry at McGill University, where he is the director of the Division of Social and Transcultural Psychiatry and editor-in-chief of the journal *Transcultural Psychiatry*. Following undergraduate studies in physiological psychology, he obtained a doctorate in medicine at McGill and completed a residency in psychiatry at the University of California, Davis. Since childhood, he has had a strong interest in cultural diversity and identity, and this has profoundly influenced his approach to understanding and treating psychological disorders. He is now an internationally renowned clinician and researcher in cultural psychiatry, a field that cuts across anthropology, sociology, and other social sciences. He has authored numerous research articles and co-edited several books on this topic. Dr. Kirmayer is particularly interested in

the way that cultural factors influence the symptomatology and treatment of psychological disorders. A major focus of his research is on mental health, healing, and resilience among Indigenous peoples in Canada and other countries.

Dr. Kirmayer's research has made particular contributions to our understanding of somatization and dissociation, both of which are key issues in cultural psychiatry. His studies of somatization in primary health care have led to the development of an influential theoretical model of somatic symptom disorder as illness behaviour triggered by psychosocial stress and emotional distress, emphasizing the role of causal attributions and interpersonal processes. His interest in dissociation stems from his earlier work with clinical hypnosis in behavioural

Courtesy Dr. Laurence J. Kirmayer

medicine, and dissociation continues to be a topic of interest in his more recent cross-cultural research on trauma and healing processes.

SUMMARY

- Dissociative disorders are characterized by severe disturbances or alterations of identity, memory, and consciousness.

- The primary symptom of dissociative amnesia is the inability to recall significant personal information, usually of a traumatic or stressful nature, in the absence of organic impairment.

- Dissociative fugue is an extremely rare subtype of dissociative amnesia in which individuals forget who they are and suddenly and unexpectedly travel away from their home.

- The key feature of depersonalization/derealization disorder is a persistent feeling of unreality and detachment from one's self or surroundings, often described as feeling like one is in a dream.

- Dissociative identity disorder (DID) is diagnosed when the patient presents with two or more distinct personality states, wherein various symptoms indicate a disruption in sense of self and sense of agency.

- According to the trauma model, DID results from a combination of (1) severe childhood trauma, including sexual, physical, and emotional abuse; and (2) particular personality traits that predispose the individual to employ dissociation as way of coping with that trauma. Although dissociation may initially be an adaptive way of coping with traumatic events, it becomes maladaptive when it is maintained as a habitual way of coping throughout adulthood.

- In contrast, proponents of the socio-cognitive model argue that DID is an iatrogenic condition that results from well-intentioned but misguided therapists inadvertently planting suggestions in the minds of their patients that they have multiple personalities. Highly hypnotizable patients may then develop the symptoms of DID as a learned social role.

- Individuals with somatic symptom and related disorders complain about bodily symptoms suggestive of medical illnesses, along with significant psychological distress and functional impairment.

- In conversion disorder, symptoms are observed in voluntary motor or sensory functions (e.g., paralysis or seizures) that suggest neurological or other medical etiologies, but these cannot be confirmed by medical tests.

- Somatic symptom disorder involves one or more somatic symptoms (e.g., chronic pain, fatigue) that are distressing or cause significant disruption of daily life, accompanied by disproportionate concerns about seriousness, anxiety, and/or excessive time and energy devoted to health concerns; a diagnosed medical illness may or may not be present.

- People with illness anxiety disorder have long-standing fears, suspicions, or convictions about a serious disease, despite medical reassurance that the disease is not present.

- According to the integrative biopsychosocial model (Kirmayer & Looper, 2007), somatic symptom and related disorders result from a series of vicious cycles involving physiological, psychological, and social factors.

- Physiological factors include stress-related increases in cortisol, which can adversely affect immunity and produce feelings of fatigue, pain, and general malaise, causing individuals under stress to perceive themselves as having a physical illness.

- Psychological factors include excessive attention to and misattribution of bodily symptoms, somatic amplification, and high levels of health anxiety.

- Social factors include early childhood abuse and social learning comprising both positive and negative reinforcement of illness behaviours and the "sick role."

- Establishing a co-operative therapeutic relationship between therapist and patient is a particular challenge and a vital first step in psychotherapy for somatic symptom and related disorders.

- Identification and treatment of comorbid anxiety and depressive disorders is also important.

- Cognitive interventions for somatic symptom and related disorders involve restructuring dysfunctional thoughts, interpretations, and preoccupations relating to bodily symptoms and illness.

KEY TERMS

alters (p. 133)

conversion disorder (p. 138)

depersonalization
(p. 132)

depersonalization/derealization disorder
(p. 132)

derealization (p. 133)

dissociation (p. 130)

dissociative amnesia
(p. 132)

dissociative disorders (p. 130)

dissociative fugue (p. 132)

dissociative identity disorder (DID) (p. 133)

factitious disorder imposed on another (p. 140)

factitious disorder (p. 140)

false memory syndrome (p. 131)

glove anaesthesia (p. 138)

hysteria (p. 129)

iatrogenic (p. 135)

illness anxiety disorder (p. 140)

la belle indifférence (p. 138)

repressed (p. 131)

socio-cognitive model (p. 135)

somatic symptom and related disorders (p. 136)

somatic symptom disorder (p. 139)

somatic symptom disorder with predominant pain (p. 139)

switching (p. 133)

trauma model (p. 134)

JOSHUA A. RASH

•

KENNETH M. PRKACHIN

•

GLENDA C. PRKACHIN

•

TAVIS S. CAMPBELL

CHAPTER

7

Sebastian Kaulitzki/Shutterstock

Psychological Factors Affecting Medical Conditions

LEARNING OBJECTIVES

AFTER READING THIS CHAPTER, STUDENTS WILL BE ABLE TO:

1 Describe the history of the study of medical conditions linked to psychological/behavioural factors and differentiate the fields contributing to it.

2 Articulate the concept of a "mechanism" and describe four biologically plausible pathways in which psychological factors or behaviours contribute to "physical" disease.

3 Explain what is meant by "psychological stress," distinguish three different approaches to conceptualizing it, and describe how it is measured and studied.

4 Describe the disease processes resulting in gastric ulcer and coronary heart disease.

5 Explain the psychosocial processes thought to contribute to infectious, ulcer, and coronary disease, using evidence from empirical studies.

6 Characterize psychological/behavioural treatment techniques used with people suffering from psycho-physiological disorders and explain how they relate to the psychosocial etiological mechanisms identified in this chapter.

George, a 32-year-old high school music teacher, was referred for psychological evaluation by his family physician. For 16 months, George had been consulting his doctor about chest pains that had caused him great anxiety. He was convinced he was having a heart attack. Within the last year, George had consulted his doctor 37 times and had undergone extensive medical tests, none of which had provided an explanation for his symptoms. Although there was no unusual history of heart problems in his family and he was normal weight for his height, George was a smoker, sat most of the day at work and did not exercise regularly.

Psychological evaluation revealed a man who was obviously distressed over his physical condition, but whose agitation extended beyond that. George readily expressed grievances with other people in his life: his principal for being demanding and incompetent, his wife for her sexual aloofness, his father for his coolness, and numerous other individuals or classes of individuals for a litany of reasons. He described his daily life as "going all out." He was up at 5:00 a.m., at work for early band practice, and usually finished at 6:30 each night. On his way home, he would pick up a six-pack of beer and a sandwich to eat on the fly. Once at home, he would prepare his lessons for the next day, finish the six-pack, and go to sleep.

George was an effective music teacher. His bands were always competitive in provincial championships and for the preceding two years had been judged the best in the province. Yet these achievements gave George no pleasure; he was always preoccupied with the deficiencies in his students' performances.

George's case is representative of many people who are referred for psychological or psychiatric evaluation. The presenting problem (recurrent chest pain) is ordinarily dealt with in clinical medicine, yet there are behavioural (drinking, smoking, being sedentary), psychological (inability to experience pleasure, hard-driven, hostile, and agitated), and social (isolation) characteristics that seem relevant to the symptoms he is experiencing. Moreover, a substantial scientific literature suggests that George's symptoms may be explained, at least in part, by psychological and behavioural variables that were identified in his psychological evaluation. Perhaps even more importantly, there is reason to believe that psychological therapies that target the psychological and behavioural characteristics George has displayed may alleviate his distress and enhance his physical health.

Historical Perspective

This chapter focuses on the role of psychological factors in physical illness. The idea that psychological processes can affect bodily states, even to the extent of producing physical disease, has a long history in Western intellectual tradition and may be even more deeply embedded in other cultures (Harrington, 2008). For example, Cannon (1942) discussed the phenomenon of voodoo death. A member of a culture in which voodoo is practised may die as a consequence of learning that he or she has been cursed. Cannon attributed this phenomenon to physiological processes elicited by extreme threat and fear. As Western medicine evolved during the first half of the twentieth century, diminishing attention was paid to these ideas. However, advances in scientific methods, combined with the emergence of interdisciplinary approaches, often involving the simultaneous examination of psychological and physiological variables, led to a powerful rebirth of the field toward the end of the twentieth century.

In the early years of psychopathology, this field of study came to be referred to as *psychosomatic medicine* and the health problems as *psychosomatic disorders*. People often incorrectly use this term to describe imaginary illnesses, or the experience of symptoms (headaches, for example) with no known pathophysiological cause. Yet the disorders in question involve identifiable disturbances in bodily structures and functions and are in no way feigned. The term also implies a **dualistic** view of mind and body as separate entities, subject to different laws. To avoid such implications, in DSM-II (American Psychiatric Association [APA], 1968) the terminology was changed to *psychophysiological disorders*.

For many years, there was a set of "classic psychosomatic disorders," such as gastrointestinal ulcers, ulcerative colitis, hypertension (high blood pressure), asthma, and arthritis. These disorders were probably considered together for a number of reasons. First, because evidence available at the time could not identify a specific pathophysiological cause, dualistic thinking suggested that the roots of the disorders must be psychological. Second, there was evidence suggesting distinct psychological features in patients suffering from these disorders. Such thinking could be seen in early work of psychodynamically oriented theorists who posited specific psychological etiologies for each of the classic psychosomatic disorders. For example, Helen Flanders Dunbar (1935) theorized that specific disorders were the natural consequence of specific emotions and personality traits. The psychoanalyst Franz Alexander (1950) argued that the causes of classic psychosomatic disorders lay in characteristic intrapersonal conflicts. According to this theory, people who were prone to high blood pressure had a chronic sense of rage, but inhibited its expression. Consequently, they appeared unassertive and overly compliant. This conflict was thought to have physiological consequences that led to clinical disease. The specific symptomatology was seen as symbolic of the underlying conflict. Such ideas persist to this day. For example, there is considerable evidence that the experience or expression of anger contributes to the pathophysiology of heart disease (Chida & Steptoe, 2009; Myrtek, 2007; Smith et al., 2008).

In the late 1970s, a new perspective emerged from the realization that many, perhaps all, disease states are influenced directly or indirectly by social and psychological factors. The psychiatrist George Engel (1977) argued that the biomedical model of disease should be expanded to a "biopsychosocial" model (see Chapter 2). Engel's argument was based on evidence that psychological characteristics and societal forces must be invoked to explain the origins of many diseases and the nature of health.

At about the same time, psychologists uncovered increasing evidence of the important role that psychological factors and behaviour play in health and illness. For example, health care around the world began to incorporate the idea that pain is in large part a psychological phenomenon (Melzack & Wall, 1982) and can be treated using psychological techniques (Fordyce, 1976). A number of behaviours, for example, smoking, poor diet, and lack of exercise, had already been identified as increasing risk of disease. Interest intensified as it became understood that such risk factors were the major determinants of the leading causes of death in Western societies. Behavioural therapy techniques offered apparently successful methods for controlling such behaviours. Increasing evidence justified the belief that other psychological variables, such as stress and characteristic styles of behaviour, were also associated with physical disease.

All of these developments converged in a new branch of psychology called behavioural medicine, or health psychology. **Behavioural medicine** usually refers to application of the methods of behaviour change to the treatment or prevention of disease—for example, the use of psychological techniques to control pain in patients undergoing medical procedures, or interventions to improve a person with diabetes an ability to control his or her blood glucose or adhere to complex medical regimens. The broader term, **health psychology**, refers to any application of psychological methods and theories to understand the origins of disease, individual responses to disease, and the determinants of good health. In this chapter, we shall highlight a number of key concepts, findings, and issues that health psychology has contributed to the study of psychopathology, focusing on those disorders that reflect the impact of psychophysiological variables.

① BEFORE MOVING ON

The Greeks and their descendants in the Western intellectual tradition viewed disease as a consequence of the imbalance of four bodily fluids (blood, phlegm, and yellow and black bile), excesses in any of which were thought to be correlated with particular temperaments. Traditional Chinese medicine attributes certain diseases to imbalance of the life forces Yin and Yang. In thinking about contemporary views of psychophysiological disorders, people sometimes see parallels with these and similar conceptions. How do you think current conceptualizations are likely to differ from these earlier ideas?

Diagnostic Issues

DSM-5 specifies the diagnostic criteria for a group of Somatic Symptom and Related Disorders. Within this broad grouping of conditions is a specific category: *psychological factors affecting other medical conditions.* People who suffer or experience medical conditions apart from mental disorders, but whose medical conditions are evidently affected in one of several ways by psychological factors, are given this diagnosis under the DSM-5 principles. To be diagnosed with psychological factors affecting another medical condition requires the presence of a diagnosed medical condition. The key criterion for this diagnosis is evidence that the medical condition is adversely affected by some identifiable psychological or behavioural factor. DSM-5 specifies four ways in which a psychological or behavioural factor might be ruled in. One way is that the identified factor has influenced the course of the condition. This requires evidence that there is a correlation between the occurrence of the psychological or behavioural factor on the one hand and the development, exacerbation of, or delay of recovery from the medical condition on the other. Another is that the psychological or behavioural factor interferes with the treatment of the medical condition; something that is frequently observed when patients do not adhere to a prescribed course of treatment, for example. A third way is if an identifiable psychological or behavioural factor poses an additional risk to the health of the individual. This would be the case for a person with cancer who persists in smoking cigarettes. Finally, this diagnostic category can be ruled in when an identified psychological or behavioural factor influences the pathophysiology of the disorder. It is this latter circumstance that most of this chapter is devoted to. An exclusion criterion specifies that the psychological or behavioural factors at issue are not better explained by some other recognized mental disorder, such as major depressive disorder. Clinicians employing this diagnosis must specify the severity of the condition on a scale ranging from "mild" to "extreme." A mild disorder would be one in which the medical risk to the patient is increased; for example, when a patient with high blood pressure is inconsistent in his or her use of medication. An extreme disorder would be one in which there is imminent risk to the patient's survival; for example, a patient who is experiencing pain in the chest and arm, crushing sensations, and perspiration, ignores these symptoms.

The International Classification of Diseases - 10 (ICD-10; currently undergoing revision with an expected release date for ICD-11 of 2018) also specifies a category "*psychological or behavioural factors affecting disorders or diseases classified elsewhere.*" This category allows for the classification psychological factors that increase the risk of suffering, disability, or death, and represent a focus of clinical attention. Similar to DSM-5, these factors may influence the course or treatment of the medical condition, by affecting treatment adherence or care seeking, or by influencing the underlying pathophysiology and precipitating or exacerbating symptoms.

While informative, it has been argued that the category of psychological factors affecting other medical conditions lacks specificity and results in virtually no impact on clinical practice (Fava & Wise, 2007). It is important to note that alternative diagnostic systems have been developed to supplement DSM-based classification of psychological factors that affect medical conditions and provide operational tools that may better inform clinical practice. One such system is the *Diagnostic Criteria for Psychosomatic Research (DCPR)* that was introduced in 1995 by an international group of investigators (Fava, Freyberger et al., 1995). The DCPR encompasses 12 psychosomatic syndromes, four of which (alexithymia, type A behaviour, demoralization, and irritable mood) refer to the domain of psychological factors affecting medical conditions (Fabbri, Fava, Sirri, & Wise, 2007; Sirri & Fava, 2013).

Imagine a 55-year-old woman, Cindy, who has recently suffered a myocardial infarction (heart attack) resulting from underlying atherosclerosis. She is a partner in a law firm and has a recent history of uncontrollable and ruminative worry, sleep loss, fatigue, and restlessness, meeting the criteria for generalized anxiety disorder. In the past year, these symptoms have diminished her job performance, leading to considerable conflict with her firm's other partners. The symptoms of chest pain and shortness of breath that indicated the onset of her heart attack occurred right after a partners' meeting in which she had had to defend herself against other partners' criticisms of her handling of her caseload. Under DSM-5, Cindy would qualify for the diagnosis of a psychological factor affecting another medical condition, the other condition being myocardial infarction, because of the close temporal association between her anxiety symptoms and the onset of her heart attack. Comorbid generalized anxiety disorder would also be diagnosable. Under the DCPR, Cindy would qualify for illness denial that would supplement DSM-5 diagnosis and be used to aid case conceptualization and treatment planning.

② BEFORE MOVING ON

> Imagine Mark, an adolescent boy with asthma, which is a chronic and occasionally fatal respiratory illness that causes the airways to constrict, leading to the inability to breathe. Now consider the DSM-5 criteria that must be met in order to justify use of this disorder. What might be some of the psychological factors that contribute to Mark's asthmatic condition?

Psychosocial Mechanisms of Disease

What are the mechanisms by which psychological factors might influence body systems? To answer this, we must understand the ways in which body tissues may be affected by behaviours and psychological processes. For the purposes of this discussion, *behaviour* is a discrete and potentially observable act, such as eating, being physically active, exercising, smoking cigarettes, and so on. A *psychological process* is not observable directly, but may be inferred reasonably on the basis of other phenomena that are. For example, we cannot see another's depression, but we can see evidence—in facial expression, in the way the individual speaks, in changes in sleeping, and even in responses to a questionnaire—that allows us to infer with some confidence that depression is present.

Psychological influences on body tissues can be the effects of behaviours, particularly if those behaviours are repeated frequently over weeks, months, or years. For example, there is no longer any reasonable doubt that the effects of smoking are deadly. This is not because the act of smoking is inherently pathogenic, but because it repeatedly exposes body tissues to tar and nicotine, which are known causes of disease. There are many other examples of behaviours that promote disease by exposing body tissue to pathogenic substances. Conversely, there are also behaviours that have beneficial effects, for example, exercise.

Pathological influences on body tissues can also be a consequence of psychological processes. A host of such influences have been postulated, ranging from perceptual schemata (the ways in which people characteristically interpret experience) to emotions (Hereafter, we will use the term *psychosocial variables* to refer to this broad class of influences). How could such influences affect body tissue?

Three body systems are responsive to psychosocial variables: the endocrine system, the autonomic nervous system, and the immune system. Although we will discuss them separately, all three interact with the brain and with each other.

FIGURE 7.1   The Endocrine System

THE ENDOCRINE SYSTEM

The endocrine system consists of organs that manufacture hormones and, when the occasion is right, secrete them into the bloodstream. Hormones are biologically active substances that circulate in the blood until they reach a "target" organ such as the heart, the liver, or the bones, where they will cause certain changes. Figure 7.1 displays some of the endocrine organs in the human body.

Several endocrine organs are known to be highly responsive to psychosocial variables. Perhaps the best known is the hypothalamic-pituitary-adrenal (HPA) axis (an axis is a system of several organs that act together in a cascade of effects). This system, depicted in Figure 7.2, begins with the hypothalamus, a brain structure that controls a large number of body functions and is responsive to psychosocial influences. When activated it can cause the pituitary gland, with which it is connected by nerve fibres, to secrete a substance called adrenocorticotropic hormone (ACTH) into the circulation. The targets for ACTH are the cells in the adrenal cortex, the outer layer of the adrenal glands, located above the kidneys. When these tissues are stimulated they secrete a well-known "stress" hormone, the glucocorticoid cortisol,

FIGURE 7.2   The HPA Axis

into the circulation. Cortisol is a highly active hormone that produces a variety of effects. It suppresses inflammation, mobilizes glucose from the liver, increases cardiovascular tone, produces immune system changes, and inhibits other endocrine structures (Herman, Prewitt, & Cullinan, 1996). These features of glucocorticoid response are a defence mechanism. In the short term they promote immediate survival and inhibit unnecessary activity. However, they are maladaptive when prolonged or exaggerated. In particular, there is evidence that glucocorticoids suppress immune system function, enhance the development of atherosclerosis (discussed later), and contribute to neuronal damage in the brain (Becker, Breedlove, Crews, & McCarthy, 2002; Chrousos & Kino, 2007; Miller, Chen, & Zhou, 2007) in a way that may contribute to the intellectual decline associated with dementia. It is also increasingly recognized that cortisol released during stress plays an important role in the development of abdominal obesity, a major risk factor for cardiovascular disease (see below). Fat cells in the abdominal region have a high concentration of receptors for glucocorticoids. When activated by glucocorticoid release, this has the effect, among other things, of activating enzymes that increase the storage of fat within these cells (Bjorntorp, 2001). Complicating the matter, cortisol also plays a role in increasing the production of fat cells (Warne & Dallman, 2007). These and other known effects of cortisol release implicate the HPA axis in a wide variety of disease states.

THE AUTONOMIC NERVOUS SYSTEM

The second major body system that is responsive to psychosocial influences is the autonomic nervous system (ANS; see Chapter 2). Most people have found themselves perspiring before some important event like an examination, or blushing after doing something embarrassing. Most people are also aware of body changes that take place during other emotional states: the heart pounding, butterflies in the stomach, dryness in the mouth, and so on. Many of these immediate changes result from the activity of the ANS. The term *autonomic* comes from the same root as "autonomous," and reflects the belief that this system operates outside of consciousness and control. Although this is not totally correct, ordinarily it is true that we have little awareness or direct control of the ANS. Refer back to Figure 2.2 on page 31 for a diagram of the main structures in this system. As described in Chapter 2, the ANS consists of two anatomically distinct parts. The *sympathetic branch* consists of nerve fibres that emanate from the thoracic and lumbar (or middle) regions of the spinal cord and make contact with several organs: the heart, the stomach, blood vessels, and so on. Notice, however, that most organs that are innervated by the sympathetic system are also innervated by the *parasympathetic branch*, whose fibres emanate from the cranial and sacral (or end) regions of the spinal cord.

For many of the organs that are innervated by both, the sympathetic and parasympathetic systems tend to act as accelerator and brakes. When the sympathetic system is aroused, it tends to produce changes that prepare the body for vigorous action, such as increased blood pressure, heart rate, and perspiration and decreased digestive activity. Many of the effects of the sympathetic system would be dangerous if they were prolonged. For example, sustained increases in blood pressure could damage brain or vascular tissues. The parasympathetic branch can "apply the brakes" to such changes to return the body to a more quiescent state that is within the body's tolerance. This is somewhat of an oversimplification, however, as many of the daily changes in physiological processes may result from an increase or decrease in parasympathetic or sympathetic arousal. For example, momentary fluctuations in heart rate are often due to either decreased parasympathetic (resulting in increased heart rate) or increased parasympathetic (resulting in decreased heart rate) influences on the sino-atrial node of the heart. Similarly, increased and decreased myocardial contractility (changes in the ability to produce force during the contraction of the heart) are associated with increased and decreased sympathetic nervous system activation of the left ventricle of the heart. The level of activity of such systems is determined by the relative balance of input from the sympathetic and parasympathetic systems.

In comparison to endocrine effects, which rely on the bloodstream to convey hormones to target organs, ANS effects are rapid because they are based on the speed of nervous conduction. The sympathetic system itself, however, is part of a second endocrine subsystem whose effects involve release of hormones into the bloodstream: the *sympathetic-adrenal medullary* (SAM) axis. Nerve fibres from the sympathetic system stimulate the cells of the inner region of the adrenal gland, the adrenal medulla, to secrete the hormones epinephrine and norepinephrine (also known as adrenalin and noradrenalin). These belong to a broader class of hormones known as catecholamines. When they are released into the bloodstream, epinephrine and norepinephrine circulate to a variety of target organs where they can have powerful effects. Most of us are aware of these: we refer to exciting events as producing an "adrenalin rush" and describe risk-takers as "adrenalin junkies." Such descriptions convey the idea that catecholamines increase energy and activate the body. Notice that the effects are complementary to the direct effects of the sympathetic system.

THE IMMUNE SYSTEM

A third mechanism that is responsive to psychosocial factors is the immune system. The immune system comprises a network of cells and organs that defends the body against external, disease-causing forces (e.g., bacteria, viruses, fungi) or internal pathogens (e.g., cancerous cells) known as antigens. The immune system performs this function through the complex actions of a variety of white blood cells (Guyton, 1991).

Immune cells are produced and stored in several organs, including the thymus gland, the lymph nodes, the bone marrow, and the small intestines. They exert their effects as they circulate in the bloodstream. As shown in Figure 7.3, there are

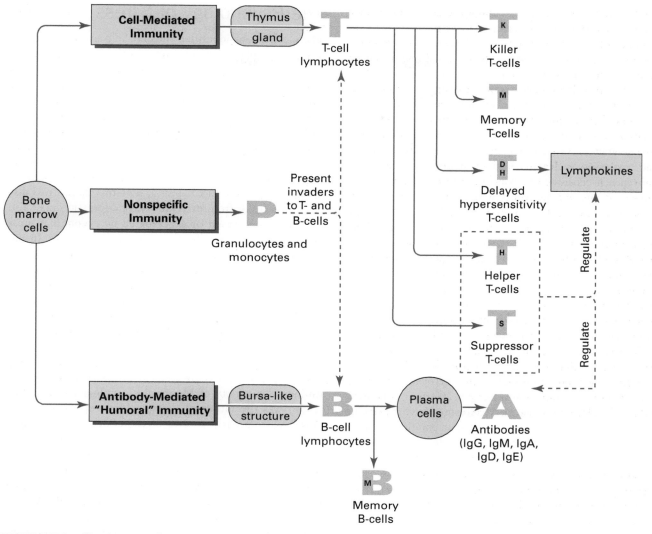

FIGURE 7.3 The Immune System

Source: Sarafino, E. P. (1997). Reprinted with permission of John Wiley & Sons, Inc.

three general categories of immune response, *nonspecific, cellular,* and *humoral,* each of which depends on different cell types and courses of action. In **nonspecific immune responses,** circulating white cells, called granulocytes and monocytes, identify invading antigens (an antigen is a substance that is recognized as foreign to the body) and destroy them by a process of engulfing and digesting called phagocytosis. **Cellular immunity** is based on the action of a class of blood cells called T-lymphocytes. The "T" designation refers to their site of production, the thymus gland. Cellular immunity results from a complex cascade of actions of various types of T-lymphocytes. In an initial episode of invasion by a foreign substance, an antigen is presented to T-lymphocytes by other cells, called macrophages (the antigen is recognized as such by biochemical markers on its cell surface). This causes the T-cells to proliferate (reproduce) and then circulate in the body. Several other types of T-cells participate in an immune episode. *Helper T-cells* secrete substances called *lymphokines* (e.g., the interleukins, interferon) that control the responses

of other types of T-cells. One group of these, the so-called *killer (K) T-cells,* attack foreign or mutated cells directly. *Suppressor T-cells* inhibit the actions of both the helper cells and the natural killer cells, thereby providing a negative feedback mechanism to control the immune episode and prevent it from continuing indefinitely. In the course of an immune episode, certain T-cells become permanently altered and are transformed into *memory T-cells,* which are stored in the body in anticipation of the next time it needs to counter the same threat. This process is responsible for our "building up immunity" to certain kinds of microbes. In this way, we may become sick with a particular disease, such as chicken pox, only once. And, of course, it is this process that is taken advantage of when people are vaccinated against infectious diseases.

In **humoral immunity,** invading antigens are also presented by macrophages to *B-lymphocytes* ("B" stands for bursa, an organ in which such cells are produced in birds; in humans they come from the liver and bone marrow; Guyton, 1991). This causes the B-cells to reproduce, a process that is reinforced by lymphokine secretion from the helper T-cells. Some of the activated B-cells remain as *memory B-cells*. Others go on to be plasma cells, secreting antibodies called immunoglobulins that neutralize antigens by clumping, rupturing, or presenting them to phagocytic cells.

In the 1980s, scientists became aware that the immune system responds to psychosocial influences, giving rise to the new field of **psychoneuroimmunology**, the study of mind–brain–immune system interactions (Ader, Felten, & Cohen, 2001; Kendall-Tackett, 2010). For example, exposure of people to acute stressors, such as making them perform an extemporaneous speech, consistently produces changes such as increased numbers of natural killer and suppressor T-cells and reduced T-cell proliferation (Cohen & Herbert, 1996). Cohen and colleagues (1992) studied immune function in Cynomolgus (macaque) monkeys exposed to stable or unstable social conditions. Blood samples taken from animals exposed to social disruption (by changing the monkeys in the experimental colony every month) showed impairment of the ability of T-cells to proliferate, indicating a suppression of immune system functioning. Interestingly, impaired immune functioning was most pronounced in animals that showed less affiliative behaviour, such as contacting or grooming other animals, suggesting that such social behaviours have important stress-modifying effects.

There have been many demonstrations of similar effects of psychological conditions in humans (Herbert & Cohen, 1993). For example, Zakowski, McAllister, Deal, and Baum (1992) exposed healthy people to either an emotionally neutral film (of African landscapes) or a film depicting unpleasant surgical procedures such as amputation. They collected blood samples periodically during exposure to and recovery from the stressor. The ability of lymphocytes taken from the blood samples to proliferate in response to an immune challenge was measured. The results indicated a decrease in proliferation of the lymphocytes taken from participants shown the gruesome film, compared with an increase among participants shown the neutral film (see Focus box 7.1 for a discussion of the effects of marital conflict on immunity).

Cohen and Herbert (1996) have described three pathways through which psychosocial variables can influence immune activity: (1) by the direct action of the central nervous system on organs and structures of the immune system, (2) as a secondary consequence of the hormonal changes discussed above, and (3) by changes in behaviour (e.g., poor dietary habits) that reflect personal characteristics or adaptations to changing life conditions.

③ BEFORE MOVING ON

> The bodily changes mediated by the endocrine, autonomic, and immune systems are the products of evolution. Evolved characteristics are generally adaptive—they contribute to survival of the individual and reproductive advantage. However a process that contributes to the development of early disease and death could hardly support either advantage. How could the responses produced by neuroendocrine, autonomic, or immune systems be both adaptive *and* pathogenic?

The Psychology of Stress

The mechanisms identified thus far help us to understand some of the physiological processes that can mediate disease. But how might they be activated by psychological influences? The study of psychological stress has provided answers.

Stress has become one of the most pervasive ideas in psychology. Most of us implicitly understand the term. As you are reading this text, you may be cramming for final exams, the outcome of which may have an important influence on the rest of your life. If so, you know something about stress. As discussed in Chapter 5, post-traumatic stress disorder can result from extreme stress; depression may also sometimes be caused or exacerbated by events that most of us would call stressful (see Chapters 8 and 16). In the case that opened this chapter, one of the salient features of George's life was that he was constantly "on edge," largely because of his own attributes.

How can we understand the impact of stress on health? The term stress has been used to refer to (1) a *stimulus*, or a property of the external world, (2) a *response*, or (3) to a *transaction* that mediates stimulus and response.

The earliest views on stress emphasized its role as a response, particularly as a set of physiological changes. Eminent University of Montreal physiologist Hans Selye (1956) was the father of the stress concept. His theory emerged from early studies of the effects of an ovarian extract in rats. He noticed, at first, that animals treated with regular injections of an extract showed characteristic changes: enlarged adrenal glands, degenerated immune system organs, and ulcers in their stomach linings. To his surprise, however, rats injected with a simple saline solution showed the same changes! Legend has it that Selye was a bit of a klutz at injecting rats, and his clumsiness caused the observed reactions. To his credit, he realized that the critical determinant of the effects he observed must have been something common to both conditions, namely change, unpleasantness, and a need to adapt. Later experiments confirmed that physiological changes could be produced by a wide variety of conditions involving both physical and psychological challenges. Integrating the results of many experiments and observations, Selye proposed that they reflected a common underlying process, which he called stress.

Selye proposed that stress was a consequence of adaptation to demands placed on the body and argued that it followed a natural trajectory. In the first phase, **alarm**, the body mobilizes its defences. If the challenge persists, the body then enters the **resistance** phase, during which it actively copes with the challenge through immune and neuroendocrine changes. In the short term, these adaptive responses enhance the body's ability to ward off threats. If the challenge persists, however, **exhaustion** follows: energy is depleted and resistance can no longer be maintained. At this point, the characteristic tissue changes described above occur and the organism may succumb to a disease of adaptation, such as an ulcer. This **general adaptation syndrome**

Putting It All Together: Stress, Marriage, Physiological Changes, and Health

FOCUS 7.1

Advances in research and technology have made it possible to study the effects of stress in realistic human contexts. One of the most interesting examples is the study of stress and physiology in the context of marital relationships. Marriage is obviously one of the most important of human relationships. It is entered into by a majority of people, it is a source of great pleasure for many, but it can also be a source of profound emotional distress. Virtually all marriages have points of tension; and issues of dominance, control, and social status. This has led investigators to study what happens psychologically and physiologically to couples during difficult marital situations. To do this kind of research, investigators identify couples who are willing to participate in controlled observations in a laboratory. Typically, they are asked to discuss specific topics for a designated period of time. Of greatest interest is what happens during conflict, so the researchers must find a way of inducing it. To do so, the couple may be interviewed or given questionnaires to identify areas of disagreement (e.g., finances, friendships). These points of disagreement then become the focus of discussion during the experiments. To evaluate the emotional tone of the discussions, participants are videotaped and the tapes are coded for different types of emotional behaviour.

Malarkey, Kiecolt-Glaser, Pearl, and Glaser (1994) studied 90 newlywed couples in this manner. Participants were admitted to a hospital research unit for a 24-hour period. Husband and wife had catheters implanted in their arms. The catheters were connected to plastic tubing that allowed nurses to draw samples of blood periodically without the participants' knowledge. The samples were stored and then tested for a variety of pituitary and adrenal hormones. The findings revealed interesting changes associated with the behaviours displayed by the participants during the conflict interviews. Some couples engaged in high levels of hostile behaviour during the interviews, such as criticizing, interrupting, and disapproving; others did not. Among couples who displayed these high rates of hostile behaviour, epinephrine, norepinephrine, and ACTH levels tended to be elevated during conflict or to remain high after conflict; in contrast, changes indicative of less arousal or enhanced recovery characterized the couples who displayed lower levels of hostility. The researchers suggested that this profile of changes is consistent with *downregulation*, or reduced effectiveness, of the immune system, which may play a role in long-term health consequences. More recently, Kiecolt-Glaser and colleagues (2005) showed that the expression of hostility in marital interactions was associated with slower wound healing and a profile of inflammatory cytokine release that is known to promote a variety of age-related chronic conditions, including cardiovascular disease, diabetes, and some cancers.

These studies demonstrate the value of investigating meaningful interpersonal relationships using rigorous observational and biological methods. Clearly, specific behavioural processes that occur during marital conflict are associated with a range of biological consequences. Although the studies by themselves do not establish etiology, they do add detailed knowledge that advances our understanding of disease mechanisms. ●

(GAS) was the first formal description and definition of stress. Note that, according to this model, stress is inferred from a set of bodily changes; that is, it is defined by a response. Note, as well, that by this definition any event that can bring about the characteristic set of changes is a *stressor*. This implication of the "stress as response" perspective has been controversial.

Others have taken the position that stress may be viewed as a kind of stimulus. Even in the GAS model, it is implicit that some event must take place to set off adaptation effects. Perhaps it would be helpful to characterize those events, or their psychological consequences, as stress. In another well-known line of research, investigators have attempted to characterize the stimuli that elicit stress through identifying more or less universally challenging events. The earliest and most famous of these attempts was the Social Readjustment Rating Scale by Holmes and Rahe (1967). These investigators developed a list of life events that required change. These events, such as death of a spouse, divorce, trouble with the law, all the way through to minor inconveniences such as holiday stress and traffic infractions, were rated according to expert consensus of the relative degree of threat they entailed and assigned points through a process of psychophysical scaling (marriage served as the standard against which all other changes were assessed and was assigned an arbitrary change value of 50). Implicit in this approach is the idea that stress is a property of the environment—that is, a stimulus.

Scores of studies have shown that experiencing such events increases the likelihood of psychological disorders and physical diseases (Holmes & Masuda, 1974). Nevertheless, the approach has also been sharply criticized. One criticism is that there is tremendous variability in the outcomes of studies examining prospective associations between life event stress and health outcomes, with a sizable minority demonstrating no clear association. Another concern is that major events are not representative of the common sources of stress in our lives. Kanner, Coyne, Schaefer, and Lazarus (1981) suggested that people's day-to-day lives are more affected by smaller events, or "hassles," such as troubling thoughts about the future, too many responsibilities, or fear of rejection. They developed a scale to assess the frequency of such events and how upsetting people found them. There is some evidence that a measure of the intensity of hassles predicts symptoms of physical illness (Weinberger, Hiner, & Tierney, 1987).

Neither the stress-as-response nor the stress-as-stimulus approach has been embraced by contemporary students. Defining stress by its physiological dimension forces us to consider very different processes as identical. For example, your heart rate will increase if you are frightened or if you walk up a flight of stairs. If we view stress only as a set of physiological responses, we are at risk of glossing over fundamental distinctions and of paying insufficient attention to other determinants of physiological responses. Defining stress as a stimulus is equally inadequate because people vary dramatically in what stimuli or events provoke physiological arousal or subjective distress. For example, divorce is probably a disturbing event for most people; yet for some it may be liberating. It is essential to take into account the individual's perspective when accounting for stress and its effects.

This view, which has been articulated forcefully by Richard Lazarus and his colleagues (e.g., Lazarus & Folkman, 1984), is called the **transactional model** of stress. It conceives of stress as a property of neither stimulus nor response, but rather as an ongoing series of transactions between an individual and his or her environment. Central to this formulation is the idea that people constantly evaluate what is happening to them. The eminent stress researcher Robert Sapolsky (1994, pp. 1–2) provides the following example:

> It's two o'clock in the morning and you're lying in bed. You have something immensely important and challenging to do the next day . . . You have to get a decent night's rest, but you're still wide awake. . . [S]omewhere around two-thirty, when you're lying there clammy and hyperventilating, an entirely new, disruptive chain of thoughts will no doubt intrude. Suddenly, . . . you begin to contemplate that nonspecific pain you've been having in your side, that sense of exhaustion lately, that frequent headache. The realization hits you—I'm sick, fatally sick! . . . When it's two-thirty on those mornings, I always have a brain tumor. They're very useful for that sort of terror, because you can attribute every conceivable nonspecific symptom to a brain tumor and convince yourself it's time to panic.

In the transactional model, such evaluations are called **appraisals**. Appraisals can take different forms, but one of the most critical is the appraisal of threat (see Chapter 5 for a discussion of appraisal as an element in the development of anxiety). When faced with an event that may have adaptational significance, such as the experience of symptoms of illness or a final examination worth half of your grade, it is *as if* the individual poses the following question: "Is this a threat to me?" (Note the italics. Lazarus's view is that such appraisals may occur quite unconsciously so that they can be described only metaphorically). This evaluative process is called **primary appraisal**, and it sets the stage for further events that may or may not lead to stress. If the individual concludes that the event poses no threat, the process comes to an end and the person continues to evaluate subsequent events. If the individual concludes that there is an element of threat, **secondary appraisals** then take place, characterized by the question: "Can I do anything?" The individual may have a number of options available, such as seeking the advice of a physician or trying to discern what will be on the final examination. Such approaches have been termed *problem-focused coping* because they attempt to identify and rectify the threat. Alternatively, the individual may focus on mollifying the bad feelings associated with the perception of threat. Such *emotion-focused coping* might involve engaging in diverting thoughts or activities or taking drugs to induce a different-feeling state. The individual will then evaluate the effectiveness of such coping activities. If the individual concludes that his or her coping is effective, stress will be minimized. If not, the appraisal of threat will be reconfirmed. Thus, the transactional model views stress as emanating from the balance between primary and secondary appraisals of threat and coping, respectively.

The transactional model is popular and has intuitive appeal. However, we must ask how it helps account for the relation between psychosocial factors and bodily processes that contribute to disease states. The first answer to this question is empirical. The transactional model grew out of evidence that the way a person perceives a potentially threatening event plays an important role in the physiological response to it. In a series of classic studies, Lazarus and colleagues demonstrated this by measuring autonomic reactions to films that many people would find gruesome or uncomfortable to watch. In one study, people watched a film depicting a coming-of-age rite among Australian Aborigines (Speisman, Lazarus, Mordkoff, & Davidson, 1964). In this film, young males undergo a procedure called subincision, in which the underside of the penis is cut open in public and without pain relief. People who view this film often show substantial autonomic arousal. However, people shown this film after instructions based on an "intellectualization" (emphasizing the importance of the ritual in its cultural context and minimizing the discomfort of the ceremony) or a "denial" strategy (downplaying the pain) showed less arousal than people whose instructions accentuated the discomfort and risks of the ritual. Thus, the way that one appraises events can modify the physiological response to them. Such findings have a direct implication for intervention: if one can manipulate the way people make stress-related appraisals, then presumably one can alter physiological responses to treat or prevent stress-related disease.

A second answer to the practical utility of the transactional model is that it can help us organize the way we think about psychosocial influences on disease. Shortly, we will review evidence that social conditions, personality characteristics, emotions, and perceptions are associated with disease states. Many of these variables are thought to exert their effects through the processes proposed within the transactional model. The model, then, encourages us to ask such questions as "How would having a supportive social network affect appraisal or coping processes?" or "What are the likely consequences of a particular coping process to a depressed person?" An organizing model that guides thinking about the processes elicited by potentially threatening conditions can be very valuable.

Psychosocial Factors That Influence Disease

Beginning with Selye's work, hundreds of studies of the effects of stress on bodily responses and health outcomes have been done. For example, Boscarino (1997) studied approximately 1400 Vietnam War–era United States Army veterans approximately 17 years after their service. Respondents were divided into those who had high and those who had low levels of combat exposure. Veterans with high combat exposure had higher rates of circulatory, digestive, musculoskeletal, nervous system, respiratory, and infectious diseases over the follow-up interval than those with low combat exposure. These differences remained even after the influence of potentially confounding variables was taken into account. In a more recent analysis of these veterans, Boscarino (2008) showed that those who met the criteria for post-traumatic stress disorder were more than twice as likely to have died from heart disease some three decades after their wartime experience. Exposure to combat is one of the most stressful experiences humans can undergo; consequently, these findings provide strong evidence for long-term effects of stress on a variety of health outcomes. The effects can be quite complex, however, and other variables can play mediating roles. Of the mediating variables studied to date, social status, controllability, and social support are three of the most important.

SOCIAL STATUS

Social status refers to an individual's relative position in a social hierarchy. Many human systems are organized hierarchically—some people occupy high positions that accord them status and power, others occupy low positions, and most fall somewhere in between. Social status may be represented by economic status, occupational prestige, dominance within a social group, or comparable variables. Differences in social status are also observed in other species, where they may be studied with respect to their implications for human differences. Sapolsky (1990), for example, has studied stress responses among baboons, a species organized in distinct dominance hierarchies.

The influence of social status on health should come as no surprise. Marmot and colleagues (Marmot, 1986; Marmot, Kogevinas, & Elston, 1987; Marmot & Theorell, 1988) have reported on one of the most extensive studies to address this issue. The Whitehall study collected information on the habits and health of 10 000 British civil servants over approximately 20 years (Whitehall is the district in London that houses the British government's main offices). Participants in the Whitehall study could be ordered along a gradient of occupational and income status from clerical workers at the bottom end to administrators at the top. The study established the importance of social status as an influence on health and suggested that its effects are subtle and pervasive. For one thing, 40- to 64-year-old men in the lowest-status positions were between three and four times more likely to die in a 10-year period than men in the highest positions. This was not just a difference between the highest- and the lowest-status individuals; there was a *gradient* to this effect that applied across the range of social status (see Figure 7.4). This observation is extremely important. It implies that whatever is responsible for the differences varies quantitatively; there is no "threshold" below which one observes high mortality and above which one observes low mortality. Moreover, as Evans (1994) has pointed out, none of the people in the Whitehall study would be considered to be impoverished. Thus, something other than material deprivation must be responsible for the differences. One suggestion as to what that might be comes from Sapolsky's (1995) studies of baboons.

In baboons, social status can be assessed by observing such things as which animals will defer to others when competing for food, avoid eye contact, or make submissive gestures. The physiological correlates of social status can be studied by analyzing blood samples. Dominant and submissive baboons differ on a number of measures (Sapolsky, 1989). Dominant males show reduced concentrations of cortisol, higher levels of high-density lipoprotein cholesterol (the so-called good cholesterol that is associated with reduced risk of heart disease in humans), lower blood pressure, and higher levels of circulating lymphocytes than submissive baboons under resting conditions. In other words, dominance is associated with changed neuroendocrine, autonomic, and immune profiles. When stressed, for example in

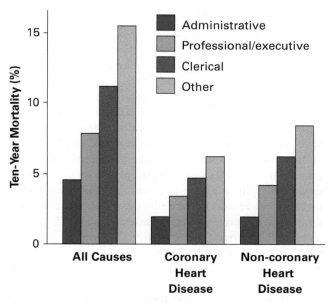

FIGURE 7.4   Mortality in Whitehall

Source: Marmot & Mustard (1994, p. 206).

Andrew Macaskill/Wildlife Pictures Online

The big adult male is demonstrating his dominance. Baboons make good subjects for the effects of status because their hierarchies are clearly marked and fairly consistent. In this way, these animals resemble members of highly structured human hierarchies, such as feudal systems and the civil service.

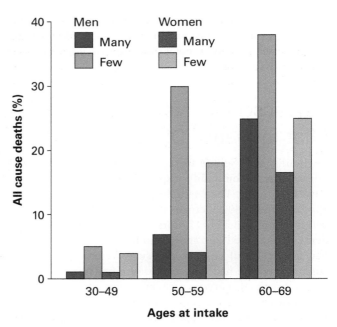

FIGURE 7.5 Deaths from All Causes among Residents of Alameda County over Nine Years

Participants who had many social connections were more likely to be alive at follow-up than participants who had few social connections.

Source: Based on Berkman, L. F., & Syme, S. L. (1979). Social networks, host resistance, and mortality: A nine-year follow-up study of Alameda County residents. *American Journal of Epidemiology*, 109, 186–204.

a fight, dominant baboons show a larger response on many of these parameters, but a faster return to resting conditions, suggesting that they are better at recovering from provocation. There is a parallel between these findings and further observations that have been made of the Whitehall civil servants. Marmot and Theorell (1988) found that although all grades of civil servants showed elevated blood pressure during the workday, the blood pressures of administrators dropped significantly more than that of lower-grade workers when they went home.

Thus, social status may have an effect on longevity through some of the stress-related physiological effects with which it correlates. These effects, in turn, probably depend on other psychosocial factors.

SOCIAL SUPPORT

One psychosocial variable that has been consistently related to health status is social support: the extent to which an individual feels connected to other people in meaningful ways. It is usually assessed by asking people about the number of others with whom they have frequent contact, whether there is anyone they feel comfortable confiding in, and so on. The classic study of social support was performed in Alameda County, California. Berkman and Syme (1979) investigated the health outcomes of some 7000 residents, followed for nine years. At the beginning of the study, participants responded to a questionnaire that assessed their social ties with other people by asking questions about marital status, interpersonal relationships, and involvement in community organizations. At follow-up, through an intensive process of investigating health records and death certificates, researchers discovered that there were significantly fewer deaths among people with many social affiliations—people who were highly "connected" with others—than among people with few connections (see Figure 7.5). Social support appears to be associated with effects on a remarkably wide range of health indicators. A review of data from more than 300 000 individuals

indicated that social support was associated with a 50 percent reduction in risk of mortality (Holt-Lunstad, Smith & Layton, 2010). This effect was consistent across age, sex, and initial health status, and was strongest among continuous measures of complex social integration. The beneficial effect of social support was comparable in magnitude to the well-known harmful effect of smoking.

Although the effects of social support have been well documented, the reasons for these effects are unclear. Certainly, one possibility is that social support may be associated with material support in times of stress. Social support may also provide a means of discovering or testing coping strategies or a way of altering stress appraisals, as suggested by the transactional model. For example, Shelley Taylor's research (Taylor, 2006; Taylor et al., 2000) suggests that humans evolved affiliative neurocircuitry that activates during times of stress and prompts social-approach behaviour as a coping mechanism. This has been termed the tend-and-befriend response to stress and is more common among females.

PERSONALITY

Personality represents a psychosocial variable associated with the aetiology, development, and progression of medical conditions. **Alexithymia** is a personality characteristic originally introduced to describe a cognitive-affective pattern of behaviour frequently observed in patients with so-called psychosomatic disorders. The salient features of alexithymia include: (1) difficulty identifying and describing subjective feelings, (2) difficulty distinguishing between feelings and bodily sensations of emotional arousal, (3) constricted imaginal capacities, and (4) externally oriented cognitive style (Taylor et al., 2000). Alexithymia has been linked to an increased risk and a worsened prognosis of several medical conditions, including cardiovascular disease, cancer, and gastrointestinal disorders (De Vries et al., 2012; Lumley, Neely, & Burger, 2007; Porcelli et al., 2003; Tolmunen et al., 2010). Type A personality is another psychosocial factor that affects medical conditions. We will return to some of these issues elsewhere in this chapter. For now it is time to turn to some specific disease states.

④ BEFORE MOVING ON

> It is almost impossible to follow health stories in the media without coming upon an article or report of a study that suggests that stress is a causal factor for some disorder or other. Reports of this nature seem to surface almost monthly. This raises the question of whether the role of stress in health and illness may be oversold. When a concept becomes so pervasive and all-encompassing, many scientists become skeptical about whether it has any meaning at all. Do you think the stress concept has been oversold? In what areas do you think it has value, and in what areas might it be useless? What kinds of evidence do you think it is important to be able to see before we conclude that stress plays a role in the onset or development of a disorder?

Age fotostock/Superstock

Employees with high-demand jobs and unpredictable, berating bosses are prone to miss work due to illness.

Disease States and Psychosocial Factors

Psychosocial factors have been considered as possible contributors to many diseases. To illustrate the range of such contributions and the nature of thinking in this field, we will focus on three disease states: infectious disease, gastric ulcers, and cardiovascular disease.

INFECTIOUS DISEASE

Case Notes

Sarah is a student in her first year of medical school. It is her fifth year at university. She is a competitive athlete, in very good health, and careful to watch her diet. She had just finished a gruelling set of exams and was on an airplane flying home for Christmas break when she noticed the first symptoms of what she recognized as the flu. By the start of the next day, she was experiencing full-blown symptoms: high temperature, aches and pains, a deep cough, and a runny nose. Sarah, who is not used to being sick, was amazed by the intensity of her bout with the flu. She totally lacked energy and was barely able to make it out of bed on Christmas morning. Eventually, her symptoms improved, but there were residual effects when she returned to university after the break.

Although we all know that they are caused by infection, many people attribute infectious diseases like colds or the flu to the stresses and strains of daily life. Furthermore, the symptoms of some infectious diseases, like genital herpes, often seem to be exacerbated (made worse or made to flare up) during periods of emotional turmoil. What is the evidence that such casual observations may be valid?

Several studies have examined whether stressful life conditions predict or increase the likelihood of infectious diseases (Cohen & Herbert, 1996). In one of the most intriguing, Cohen, Tyrrell, and Smith (1993) exposed healthy individuals to nasal drops containing respiratory viruses or uninfected saline. Participants were quarantined for seven days after experimental exposure, and during this time indicators of infection were measured, including severity of cold symptoms, immune system markers of infection taken from nasal fluids, and measurements of mucous nasal tissue (using the weight of used facial tissues!). Prior to the study, participants were assessed with respect to the number of stressful life events that had occurred to them in the previous 12 months, the perceived stressfulness of their lives, and current negative emotions. Those with higher perceived stress and negative affect (the tendency to experience unpleasant emotions) were indeed more likely to have clinical evidence of a cold and to show "hard" immune system changes indicative of infection than were subjects with lower stress. The underlying mechanism by which psychological stress might increase susceptibility to infection is unknown, but may reflect the functioning of the HPA axis.

In a more detailed study of the contribution of stress to infectious diseases (Cohen et al., 1998), volunteers were infected with rhinovirus ("common cold") drops and then followed to determine whether they became symptomatic. In addition, they underwent an extensive interview about their experience with life stressors in the last year. Participants who had experienced distinct stressors lasting one month or more had a higher likelihood of developing a cold than those whose stressors lasted less than a month. Long-standing difficulties associated with work (particularly unemployment or underemployment) and with interpersonal relationships (such as marital difficulties or grudges) were the main stressors that predicted cold symptoms.

There have been several studies of psychological influences on diseases mediated by the herpes viruses, such as genital herpes, cold sores, and mononucleosis (Chida & Mao, 2009). Once introduced, herpes infections remain in the body in a latent state, manifesting clinical disease only occasionally. Hoon and colleagues (1991) studied herpes symptoms in college students and reported that symptom recurrence was associated with variations in psychological stress.

It is natural to suspect that such stress effects on infectious diseases must be mediated by influences of stress on the immune system. For example, Glaser and colleagues (1994) measured the presence of antibodies to Epstein-Barr virus during a baseline period and during fall and spring examinations among medical students known to be infected. Both examination periods were associated with increases in antibodies to the virus, indicating its reactivation. However, we still lack clear understanding of the immune mechanisms responsible.

ULCER

Case Notes

One Sunday morning, Jack awakened with a peculiar burning sensation in his stomach. He didn't think much of it and attributed it to having overdone things the night before. He skipped breakfast, as he was inclined to do, and spent a typical Sunday morning watching football. The aching increased to such a point that the normally stoic Jack began complaining to his family. After a late lunch, it got better. Throughout the next two weeks, the burning pain returned periodically, but not every day, so Jack really did not think much was amiss. If he had, it would not have made much difference, because Jack was getting married that month and did not have time to think about it anyway. A few weeks later the wedding took place, and Jack and his wife departed on their honeymoon.

Over the next two weeks, however, the stomach pains grew worse, and Jack promised himself that he would see a doctor as soon as he got home. As it turned out,

Jack did not get that option. The morning before they were due back, Jack and his wife set out to drive home, but had to pull the car over after about an hour because Jack was experiencing extreme pain and vomiting blood. He was taken to the nearest hospital, diagnosed with a perforated ulcer, and told he was lucky to be alive. Although he recovered well following hospitalization and changes to his diet, Jack's marriage did not thrive. He and his wife divorced after a few years. He would later confide that the months and weeks leading up to the wedding were full of conflict for him due to, among other things, his ambivalence about getting married. He directly attributed the cause of his ulcer to his psychological condition at the time.

If you were asked to name a disease-state affected by emotion, there is a good chance that ulcers would come to mind. The association has been long established in the public consciousness, perhaps because we are very aware of the influence of emotional states on the gut. Most of us have experienced discomfort in the stomach during emotionally charged times, so it is not difficult to believe that emotional distress may lead to disease of the gut. Good-quality statistics on ulcers are difficult to obtain. However, a survey of a broadly representative sample of 1036 Canadian adults suggested that approximately 1 percent of the population experienced ulcer-like symptoms in the preceding year (Tougas, Chen, Hwang, Liu, & Eggleston, 1999). Indeed, the ulcer was one of Franz Alexander's "classic" psychosomatic disorders. As we shall see, there is some truth to these preconceptions. However, ulcers also illustrate the complexity of disease processes, because it is now generally accepted that they have a bacteriological cause. We are left with the need to sort out the implications for understanding the role of psychosocial determinants of ulcer disease.

First of all, what is an ulcer? A gastric ulcer is an erosion of the lining of the stomach or duodenum. Ulcers can be life-threatening when they perforate, but even when they do not they can produce excruciating pain. The events leading to an ulcer are thought to involve an interaction between the stomach's own digestive juices and its natural defence mechanisms. The digestive juices, one of which is hydrochloric acid, are produced and secreted in the stomach in order to digest food. They are highly corrosive to living tissue, including the stomach itself, which is normally protected by a mucosal lining. Ulcers occur when the digestive fluids penetrate the lining, thus leaving the stomach, or duodenal wall, defenceless against their corrosive action.

What role might psychosocial factors play in such lesions? Here we are left to piece together lines of information from clinical observations, epidemiological studies, and experiments in animals and humans. Clinicians have long observed that stressful life circumstances are associated with the development of ulcers in their patients. Alexander (1950) argued that a very specific, though unconscious, psychological conflict involving an unsatisfied desire for love was the main cause. This desire, symbolized by food, was thought to produce a state of chronic readiness to eat, which would lead to breakdown of the stomach lining and consequent disease by continually stimulating the physiological accompaniments of digestion. Appropriate treatment involved psychoanalysis geared toward uncovering the underlying conflict. There is little empirical support for this theory, and its influence is mostly of historical interest. However, other observations suggest psychological processes that may be more clearly involved.

Several studies have reported associations between profoundly stressful life conditions and ulcers (Levenstein, 2000). For example, during the German bombardment of London in the Second World War, rates of hospitalization for perforated ulcers were observed to increase significantly (Spicer, Stewart, & Winser, 1944). Prospective epidemiological investigations have shown that there is a significant increase in risk of development of peptic ulcer associated with measures of life stress (Levenstein, 2000; Levenstein, Kaplan, & Smith, 1995). For example, Levenstein and colleagues (Levenstein et al., 2015) evaluated the association between life stress and ulcers in a sample of 3379 Danish adults who were followed for more than 10 years. Individuals who scored in the highest tertile for life stress were more than twice as likely to develop ulcers relative to individuals in the lowest tertile. Further, the risk was independent of *H. pylori* infection, indicating a strong psychosocial mechanism.

There have also been advances in our understanding of psychological aspects of ulcers, which follow from the understanding that the brain is an important regulator of the stomach and gut through autonomic and neuroendocrine mechanisms described earlier. We know, for example, that during stress-induced sympathetic arousal, blood flow is diverted away from the stomach lining to the skeletal muscles. It has been suggested that this may decrease the effectiveness of the mucosal lining of the stomach in protecting it against digestive juices, since blood vessels within that lining are thought to play a role in the deactivation of gastric fluids (Pinel, 1997).

Hypersecretion of digestive acid appears to be an important factor contributing to the development of ulcers. Studies have shown that psychological distress is associated with increased secretion of gastric acids, and that patients with duodenal ulcers respond to laboratory stressors with greater quantities of acid secretion than healthy controls (Levenstein, 2000). Another factor is slow, rhythmic contractions of the stomach that are different from the more frequent rhythmic contractions associated with the feeding cycle (Weiner, 1996). When such contractions occur in rats, gastric erosions develop (Garrick et al., 1989). Although this association has not been observed in humans, the animal observations make the argument for stress as a factor in ulcer disease more plausible (see Focus box 7.2 for a discussion of causal inference).

What is the evidence that stress can cause ulcers in animals? Since Selye's original observations, several methods have been used to demonstrate that manipulations of stress can produce ulcers. One common method is to restrain experimental animals by wrapping them tightly in a tube or some other device. Restrained animals reliably show more gastric ulceration than do controls (Brodie, 1971). Although this procedure does not provide a very realistic model of

human stressors, it has the advantage of reliability and gives investigators the opportunity to investigate some of the mechanisms that are responsible for ulcers.

Such research has indicated that various brain regions involved in the regulation of emotional states are crucial for the development of restraint-induced ulcers. Peter Henke of St. Francis Xavier University, for example, showed that direct manipulation of the central nucleus of the amygdala by electrical stimulation increases gastric ulceration (Henke, 1988, 1992), whereas other manipulations, such as electrical stimulation of areas of the hippocampus that, in turn, affect the amygdala, are associated with reductions in ulceration due to restraint stress (Henke, 1990). Such findings establish the importance of brain regions in determining whether or not ulceration will occur during stress. Moreover, the particular brain regions implicated are known to be key structures involved in emotional states. For example, LeDoux (2000) has shown that the amygdala plays a critical role in the emotion of fear. The amygdala is known to influence bodily responses to stress by activating neurosecretory cells of the hypothalamus, thereby eliciting neuroendocrine and autonomic responses. For these reasons, it seems very unlikely that the association of threat appraisal, gastric ulceration, and the amygdala is coincidental.

Perhaps the most elegant studies implicating psychological factors in the development of ulcers were reported in the late 1960s and early 1970s by Jay Weiss of Rockefeller University. Weiss was interested in separating the physical and psychological aspects of stress. The stressor he employed was electric shock delivered to rats' tails by an electrode. In one study (Weiss, 1970), the shock was predicted by a warning signal (a beeping tone). Another group was exposed to both shocks and tones, but the events occurred at random so that the tones did not reliably predict the shocks. Yet another group was exposed to identical environmental conditions, but no tones or shocks. Examinations of the stomachs of these animals indicated that the unshocked rats had very little stomach ulceration; rats that were exposed to shocks without warning showed extensive stomach ulceration. The interesting finding was that rats that were shocked after a warning tone showed degrees of ulceration only slightly higher than the unshocked rats. Note that rats in the two shock conditions received the *identical* number and intensity of shocks; the only factor that could have explained why one group had more lesions than the other was the *predictability* of the stressor.

For decades, it was commonly accepted that ulcers were often a consequence of stress. But in 1982, Australian physicians Barry Marshall and Robin Warren hypothesized that ulcers were a consequence of a gut infection resulting from hardy, corkscrew-shaped bacterium called helicobacter pylori (see Marshall, 2001). Desperate to prove this theory, Marshal took some *H. pylori* from the gut of a person with ulcers and drank it! As the days passed, he developed gastritis, the precursor to an ulcer, proving that the bacterium was an underlying cause of ulcers. It is now understood that *H. pylori* attacks the lining of the stomach, allowing acid through and leading to ulcers. It might be tempting, therefore, to conclude that stress plays no role in ulcer formation, but the issue is probably more complicated. For example,

FOCUS 7.2

Inferring Causality in Health Psychology

Is there a will to live? Does stress cause cancer? Does a particular kind of personality make one likely to become arthritic? While there is increasing acceptance of the contribution of psychological factors to illness and disease, many people, including health psychologists, continue to be skeptical. How do we begin to sort out reasonable answers to such questions?

As explained in Chapter 4, the gold standard for establishing causality is the experimental study in which an investigator manipulates one possible causal variable while holding all other variables constant, and observes the effects on an outcome. In the health sciences it is often difficult, for practical or ethical reasons, to meet the strictures of the experimental method. The development of a disease such as rheumatoid arthritis, for example, may occur over many years, and this is difficult to study in a laboratory. Similarly, it would obviously be unethical to conduct a study in which people were exposed to severe stress in order to establish the role of stress in disease.

Epidemiological and correlational research (discussed in Chapter 4) can fill in some of the gaps. Hill (1965; see also Young, 1998) has outlined a number of criteria that may be applied to evaluate whether a psychological variable plays a causal role. A basic criterion is *association*; the psychological variable is more likely to be present when the disease is present than when the disease is not present. The case that there is a meaningful relationship is further supported by *consistency* across numerous studies and *strength* of association; that is, the variability in a psychological variable accounts for a great deal of the variability in an outcome. Yet none of these criteria show that the relationship is one of cause and effect. The fourth criterion, *precedence*, requires evidence that the alleged cause existed *before* the outcome developed. A common but expensive means

of establishing precedence is the **longitudinal study**, in which a large group of people are evaluated for psychological or behavioural features and are then followed up, years or decades later, to determine whether they have developed a disease.

Several influential longitudinal studies have helped to establish precedence for psychological variables. For example, in the Harvard Mastery of Stress Study (Funkenstein, King, & Drolette, 1957), students enrolled at Harvard University in 1952, 1953, and 1954 underwent an extensive battery of interviews, questionnaires, and psychological stress tests. Later investigations of the health status of these individuals indicated that participants who experienced high anxiety during psychological stress testing and participants who perceived their parents to be uncaring were at substantially higher risk of a variety of illnesses 35 years later (Russek & Schwartz, 1997).

The final criterion relates to the logic of explanation. There must be both a biologically and a psychologically plausible mechanism linking a characteristic to the disease or illness outcome. Animal models or analogue studies are often used to investigate possible mechanisms (American Psychosomatic Society, 1996). For example, Anisman and his colleagues (Sklar & Anisman, 1979) at Carleton University have conducted studies to clarify the processes by which stress might affect cancer. To do this, they manipulated stressful experiences and observed their effects on growth of malignant tumours that they had experimentally implanted in mice. Of course, the variables manipulated in mice are not much like the stresses that humans experience, and mice are not humans. We must be very careful when generalizing from one species to another. However, it may be possible through such studies to illuminate the forces that affect human disease. ●

---

while it is estimated that most of the world's population are infected with *H. pylori*, most of those infected will never develops ulcers. This suggests the possibility of a more complex association between bacterial infection and stress that contributes to the ultimate expression of ulcers.

While studies of restraint and other forms of stress have helped to map the neural pathways that may be implicated in stress effects, there has been relatively little research in recent years extending these concepts to ulcer disease in humans. So far, our knowledge of stress and its psychosocial determinants has had little effect on the treatment or prevention of ulcers.

Considerable excitement was aroused in the medical community by the discovery of a bacterium, *Helicobacter pylori*, now believed to play the primary role in the genesis of ulcers (Rathbone & Healey, 1989). The bacterium is present in the stomachs of large proportions of individuals with ulcer disease and antibodies to it are present in their serum. Moreover, treatment with drugs to eliminate *H. pylori* produces improvement in affected patients (Graham et al., 1992). Does this discovery mean that stress is no longer relevant to ulcer disease? Not at all. Although *H. pylori* plays an important role in the genesis of ulcer disease, it cannot be

said that that role is exclusive. As Weiner (1996) has pointed out, antibodies to the bacterium have also been found in the serum of healthy controls. According to Levenstein (2000), only 20 percent of people who test positive for the bacterium show evidence of ulcer. Similarly, a review of 25 randomized controlled trials (n=5555) assessing the effect of H. *pylori* eradication on the resolution of ulceration reported equivocal results (Du et al., 2016). Therefore, the mere presence of *H. pylori* is not sufficient to produce disease. The bacterium also appears in association with a number of other diseases, calling into question its specificity of action. Finally, patients have been shown to improve even though the infection has not been eliminated.

The discovery of a bacterial agent is in no way inconsistent with the findings that implicate psychological conditions. As the diathesis-stress model emphasizes, psychological factors, such as stress, may lead a person to be more vulnerable to the influence of a physical agent. Bosch and colleagues (2000) have provided evidence that psychological stress may play an important role in the effects of *H. pylori* itself. Saliva was collected from healthy young men before, during, and after they watched a video depicting bloody dental procedures. The saliva samples were then purified in a laboratory

John Candy

John Candy was a Canadian success story. A member of the famous Second City comedy troupe, he was popular for his characterizations of public and imaginary figures on the television program *SCTV*. He parlayed his early successes into a career in movies, appearing in such successful films as *Stripes*; *Planes, Trains and Automobiles*; and *Uncle Buck*. On March 4, 1994, at 43 years of age, Candy died suddenly from a heart attack caused by a coronary embolism. He was well known for being overweight. A smoker, he also had a strong history of heart disease in his family (his father died in his thirties from heart disease). Candy was aware of his risk and had made attempts both to lower his weight and to quit smoking. We will never know for certain whether other psychological variables may have played a role in his death. What is certain is that he lived a pressured lifestyle, and it is rumoured that, at the time of his death, he was working hard to advance his career after some critical disappointments.

Theo Westenberger/Paramount/Kobal/REX/Shutterstock

dish and exposed to *H. pylori*. In this way, the researchers were able to determine the adhesion of *H. pylori*; that is, the effectiveness with which the bacterium establishes the first stage in the process of infection. Adhesion of *H. pylori* more than doubled in the saliva samples taken during stress exposure, thus suggesting that stressful conditions may play a role in the effectiveness of the microbe. More recently, Guo and colleagues (2009) have shown in mice that the stress of observing another mouse in distress enhances the ability of *H. pylori* to colonize gastric tissue, probably through the influence of glucocorticoid receptors.

Based on the proportion of participants in well-controlled studies who provided no evidence of psychosocial vulnerability factors and evidence of the excess of stressors among ulcer patients relative to controls, Levenstein (2000) has estimated that psychosocial variables are probably involved in 30 to 65 percent of cases. As discussed in this and earlier chapters, interactions between mind and body are complex, and there is rarely one single factor that accounts for any condition. Thus, ulcer disease represents, in Levenstein's (2000, p. 176) terms, "[t]he very model of a modern etiology."

CARDIOVASCULAR DISEASE

Diseases of the vascular system—the heart and the blood vessels—are the leading causes of death and disability in Western societies. The two disease states that account for most of these deaths are **ischemic heart disease**, in which blood supply to the heart becomes compromised, leading to **myocardial infarction** (heart attack), and **stroke**, in which the blood supply to the brain is interrupted, leading to death of neural tissue. The disease processes underlying both end points are sufficiently similar that they are

considered two sides of the same coin. Statistics for 2011 indicate that, in Canada, 60 910 people died of heart disease or stroke, accounting for 25 percent of deaths that year (Statistics Canada, 2014). Raw mortality, however, does not tell the whole story. Cardiovascular diseases are responsible for more **potential years of life lost** (**PYLL**)—a measure calculated by subtracting age of death from an individual's life expectancy—than any other cause except cancer and accidents. Cardiovascular disease also causes significant suffering and disability among survivors. Techniques for early identification and treatment have increased the chances of survival, and advances in rehabilitation have also improved the prospects for recovery. Nevertheless, many people who live with cardiovascular disease face diminished abilities, anxiety, and suffering, and their families must also adjust to the consequences of the disease.

As a result of high rates of morbidity and mortality, cardiovascular disease has been the focus of intensive research, and a great deal has been learned about it. This knowledge has paid off in a dramatic decline in death rates, which have dropped by almost 50 percent since the 1950s. As part of this research, the behavioural and psychological processes related to developing, triggering, and recovering from cardiovascular disease have been well studied.

CARDIOVASCULAR DISEASE PROCESSES To understand how psychosocial variables may contribute to cardiovascular disease, you need a basic understanding of the disease process. The cardiovascular system provides nutrients and oxygen, the basic requirements for life, to all tissues of the body and serves as a highway for the elimination of waste products. To do this, the heart acts as a pump, delivering blood, with its various constituents—platelets, plasma, and so on—through an extensive branching network of arteries, arterioles, capillaries, venules, and veins called the **vasculature**. The blood vessels consist of an opening, or *lumen*, and layers of cells that serve as the "tubing." The control of blood supply within this closed system is intricate. It is helpful to think of a water pumping system, wherein the heart is the pump and the vasculature is a hose. As the heart pumps, the blood constituents are distributed through the tubing in cycles that correspond to the pumping action. The peak of the wave of blood flow corresponds to the contraction of the left ventricle of the heart. This is the main chamber that pumps blood into the major arteries of the body at a point during the cardiac cycle that is called *systole*. However, when the pump is at rest, at a point in the cardiac cycle termed *diastole*, blood will still be flowing, albeit at a much reduced pressure. The pressure of the blood flowing through the vasculature is commonly measured in your doctor's office with the use of a *sphygmomanometer* (blood pressure cuff) and expressed in two numbers: **systolic blood pressure/diastolic blood pressure**, in terms of the number of millimetres of mercury (mm Hg) displaced by the measurement device (e.g., 120/70 mm Hg).

Persisting with the pump and hose analogy, we can see that the pressure within the hose will be influenced by two factors. The first is simply the amount of liquid being pushed into the hose with each beat of the pump; the more liquid, the greater the pressure, everything else being equal. Think of what happens with a garden hose when you turn the faucet up to "full blast." The more you open the faucet, the greater the pressure and the farther the water will spray. The second is the diameter of the tubing. What happens if you squeeze a garden hose (see Figure 7.6)? The pressure of the fluid within increases and the spray will be longer. Much the same thing happens when the diameter of the blood vessels is narrowed. Thus, blood pressure is a consequence of two major variables: **cardiac output** (the amount of blood pumped by the heart) and **total peripheral resistance** (the diameter of the blood vessels). Cardiac output is itself determined by two other variables: the rate at which the heart beats (commonly measured in beats per minute) and the amount of blood ejected on each beat (stroke volume).

This excursion into the physiology of the cardiovascular system is important because it allows us to begin to explain the mechanisms through which psychological factors can affect disease processes. Recall from our discussion

of the autonomic nervous system that one of its targets is the cardiovascular system. Sympathetic and parasympathetic fibres can affect both cardiac output and peripheral resistance. Activation of the sympathetic system affecting beta-adrenergic receptors on the heart will speed up its rate, producing an increase in cardiac output and, consequently, in blood pressure. Activation of other components of the sympathetic system affecting alpha-adrenergic receptors can cause constriction of the blood vessels, again yielding an increase in blood pressure. Activity of the parasympathetic system opposes these effects. Complex feedback mechanisms, involving blood pressure receptors located in the carotid artery, allow the hypothalamus to regulate blood pressure. In this way, the brain is always adjusting output and resistance to maintain blood pressure within certain limits.

Recall, as well, that the neuroendocrine system also influences the cardiovascular system. In particular, release of the catecholamines, epinephrine and norepinephrine, from the adrenal medulla reinforces the changes produced by sympathetic nervous system arousal, producing increased heart rate, peripheral resistance, and blood pressure. In addition to these effects, however, note that the catecholamines are distributed to the heart and vasculature by circulating *through* the bloodstream. Catecholamines can thereby not only affect the ongoing activity of the heart and vasculature, but also interact with blood constituents, such as the blood cells, and the cells lining vessel walls. Thus, these two physiological systems, both of which are regulated by the brain and consequently responsive to psychological influences, are ideally located to exert an ongoing influence on the system in which cardiovascular disease takes place.

CARDIOVASCULAR RISK FACTORS Deaths due to myocardial infarction can result from disturbances in the normal pumping rhythm of the heart (**arrhythmias**) or from compromised supply of blood to the heart itself. These proximal causes of death, as well as stroke, are influenced primarily by an underlying disease state called **atherosclerosis**, a buildup of deposits, known as *plaques*, on the walls of the blood vessels (see Figure 7.7). The growth of atherosclerotic plaques can

FIGURE 7.6   Plumbing Analogy for the Human Cardiovascular System

ATHEROSCLEROSIS

FIGURE 7.7   The Buildup of Atherosclerotic Plaque

ultimately narrow the openings of arteries enough to compromise the blood supply to the heart or the brain, leading to myocardial infarction or stroke.

Atherosclerotic plaques are complex structures built up from matter deposited on arterial linings over the course of a lifetime: primarily lipids (blood fats, especially cholesterol), but also blood platelets and cell fibres. Autopsy studies have shown the development of atherosclerosis (**atherogenesis**) as early as two years of age. Most people show signs of atherosclerosis by their thirties. These observations emphasize the long time frame over which the disease develops. Over decades, subtle influences on the disease process can play an important role. On the other hand, the slow development of the disease process gives plenty of opportunity for prevention.

But what do atherosclerotic plaques have to do with behavioural or psychosocial variables? For one thing, individual health-related behaviours may contribute directly to atherogenesis. Dietary factors, such as frequent consumption of fat and cholesterol, make lipids available for plaque formation. Smoking, too, is thought to play a role in atherogenesis. High blood cholesterol and cigarette smoking are considered major **modifiable risk factors** for cardiovascular disease. Physical activity and exercise are **protective factors** that are thought to reduce risk of cardiovascular disease, at least in part by preventing atherosclerotic buildup. Another potential source of atherogenesis lies in the effects of the ANS and endocrine regulatory mechanisms discussed above.

Blood pressure can vary substantially over the course of a day. Large variations can cause turbulence in the blood vessels, particularly at points where they branch into smaller vessels. This applies *shear stress* powerful enough to damage the cells of the vessel walls. According to one theory of plaque formation, lipids, blood platelets, and other constituents recruited to fix the walls become gathering spots for other atherogenic material. Additionally, circulating catecholamines may contribute to plaque formation by affecting the tendency of blood platelets to "stick" to one another.

Yet another factor that contributes to risk of cardiovascular disease is **hypertension**, a characteristically high level of resting blood pressure (defined as a reading of more than 140/80 in a doctor's office). Hypertension can result from a variety of background causes, but in approximately 90 percent of cases it is "essential," which means that a single cause cannot be identified.

PSYCHOSOCIAL FACTORS IN CARDIOVASCULAR DISEASE The activity of the cardiovascular system is clearly and sometimes profoundly altered by psychosocial stimuli. In one study, healthy young men were exposed to four standardized situations (Prkachin, Mills, Zwaal, & Husted, 2001). In one, they squeezed a hand dynamometer for five minutes. In a second, they simply counted forward from the number "1." In a third, they performed mental arithmetic, and in a fourth, they were interviewed about an event that had made them angry. Systolic and diastolic blood pressure

increased for all four tasks, most dramatically during the anger interview. This study exemplifies a common method for examining how psychological variables affect physiological responses. Physiological functions such as heart rate or blood pressure are measured while people are exposed to an explicit, psychologically stressful provocation. Hundreds of studies using this **stress reactivity paradigm** have shown that many cardiovascular functions are responsive to changing psychological conditions.

In 1984, David Krantz and Stephen Manuck formally hypothesized that the risk of cardiovascular disease increases with individual differences in **cardiovascular reactivity**; that is, how much an individual's cardiovascular function changes in response to a psychologically significant stimulus. The study of cardiovascular reactivity has provided some important insights. Commonly measured cardiovascular functions such as heart rate, blood pressure, and peripheral resistance can be influenced readily by psychological stressors (Turner, 1994), but so, too, can hormones like epinephrine, norepinephrine, and cortisol (Dimsdale & Ziegler, 1991; Kuhn, 1989). More subtle changes in the cardiovascular system, such as the percentage of blood pumped by the left ventricle during each beat (Ironson et al., 1992; Legault, Langer, Armstrong, & Freeman, 1995) and even abnormalities in the motion of the heart's chamber walls, can also be produced by psychological stress (Rozanski et al., 1988). Mills and Prkachin (1993), at the University of Waterloo, even found that exposure to psychological stressors could reverse the reduction in "stickiness" of blood platelets produced by dietary supplements containing essential fatty acids.

Manuck and colleagues (Manuck, Kaplan, Adams, & Clarkson, 1989; Manuck, Kaplan, & Clarkson, 1983) have also provided experimental evidence that cardiovascular reactivity contributes to the development of atherosclerosis in Cynomolgus monkeys raised in an experimental colony. The monkeys were fed a high-cholesterol diet. Heart rate was measured at rest and while the monkeys were threatened by a "monkey glove" that had previously been used to capture them. At the end of each study, the researchers measured atherosclerotic deposits on the arteries supplying the animals' hearts. Monkeys that showed a higher increase in heart rate in reaction to threat also showed significantly more atherosclerosis. In other work, Kaplan, Manuck, and colleagues have shown that socially disrupting primate colonies by repeatedly moving the monkeys between groups can promote the development of atherosclerosis, even if the animals are not fed an atherogenic diet (Kaplan et al., 1983).

David Spence and colleagues at the University of Western Ontario found evidence that these findings generalize to humans. In a large sample of middle-aged men and women studied for several years, ultrasound imaging was used to measure plaque build up in the carotid arteries. The best predictor of worsening atherosclerosis over a two-year period was the magnitude of systolic blood pressure increase during the Stroop colour–word conflict test, in which participants must name the colour of ink in which a colour word is written (Barnett, Spence, Manuck, & Jennings, 1997). Patients highly reactive to this particular psychological stressor showed accelerated development of the disease process underlying heart attack and stroke.

Exaggerated cardiovascular reactivity likely results in long-term erosive effects with the capacity to trigger acute cardiovascular events. Carroll and colleagues (2012) examined the association between blood pressure reactivity in response to acute mental stress task and 16-year cardiovascular disease mortality among a sample of 431 men and women. Individuals scoring in the top quartile of blood pressure reactivity were more likely to die of cardiovascular disease over the subsequent 16 years of follow-up. This association was independent of age, sex, body-mass index (BMI), physical activity, long-standing chronic illness, and resting blood pressure.

The majority of research has investigated the phenomenon of exaggerated cardiovascular reactivity with the presumption that blunted reactivity (i.e., less change in heart rate and blood pressure than would typically be expected during a given stressor) is benign or protective. Recent evidence has challenged this presumption and indicated that blunted physiological reactivity is associated with a range of adverse behavioural and health outcomes, including depression, obesity, addiction, smoking, and impulsivity (refer to Carroll et al., 2017, for a review). It is becoming increasing clear that the association between health and cardiovascular reactivity forms an inverted U with blunted and exaggerated reactivity being particularly problematic.

The intensity of the response of the cardiovascular system to stress is associated with cardiovascular disease, but so is the extent to which elevations in blood pressure or heart rate due to a stressor persists after the stressor is no longer present (i.e., **cardiovascular recovery**). A meta-analysis of 41 studies evaluating cardiovascular responses to stress reported that delayed cardiovascular recovery (defined as sustained cardiovascular activation above baseline levels during the post-stress recovery period) was associated with an increase in risk for hypertension and cardiovascular disease (Chida & Steptoe, 2010). It has been proposed that delayed cardiovascular recovery may be sustained through persistent activation of stress-related thoughts and emotions (Gerin et al., 2006). Research in our laboratory supports this hypothesis, indicating that people who tend to ruminate (i.e., experience repetitive and unwanted thoughts about the causes and consequences of stressful events) do not adapt to a stressor that is repeated across multiple laboratory testing sessions (Johnson et al., 2012).

PSYCHOLOGICAL FACTORS IN CARDIOVASCULAR DISEASE
The Canadian physician Sir William Osler, sometimes referred to as the grandfather of behavioural medicine, was one of the earliest proponents of the modern era to draw attention to the association between styles of behaviour and heart disease. He described the typical patient with atherosclerosis as a " . . . keen and ambitious man, the indicator of whose engine is always at 'full speed ahead'" (Osler, 1910, p. 839).

Osler's idea that the heart attack is associated with a particular type of personality remained dormant until it was taken up in the mid-twentieth century by a pair of American cardiologists. Friedman and Rosenman (1959) hypothesized the existence of a pattern of behaviour that increases risk of myocardial infarction and death. The pattern involved people who appeared to be "aggressively involved in a chronic . . . struggle to achieve more and more in less and less time, and if required to do so, against the opposing efforts of other things or other persons" (Friedman & Rosenman, 1974, p. 67). Friedman and Rosenman developed an interview to identify people with this behaviour pattern, which they termed **Type A**. This was an important advance because it lent itself to systematic epidemiological investigations. In the landmark Western Collaborative Group Study, Friedman, Rosenman, and others assessed the health and health habits of more than 3000 people, who were followed systematically over the next eight and a half years (Rosenman et al., 1975). Mortality statistics revealed two important findings. First, people assessed as Type A were approximately twice as likely to die from heart disease as people assessed as Type B (i.e., those who are more relaxed and calm). Second, the risk associated with Type A behaviour was independent of other risk factors for heart disease, such as smoking. This appeared to be the first clear identification of a psychological characteristic that met conventional criteria for designation as a "risk factor."

Not all studies, however, confirmed an association between Type A behaviour and heart disease. Subsequent evidence indicated that the risk exists in only some of the components of the Type A pattern. Look at the variety of characteristics subsumed under the Type A label: hyperalertness, time urgency, job involvement, competitiveness, and hostility. Do these components always go together? It is possible to imagine someone who is hyperalert but not competitive, or time urgent but not hostile, isn't it? Interest has shifted to identifying which components most directly affect risk of heart disease.

Consistently, measures of hostility have been associated with symptoms of heart disease and death. Hecker, Chesney, Black, and Frautschi (1988) reanalyzed data from the Western Collaborative Group Study, including the Type A interviews, and determined that hostility was the main characteristic accounting for increased risk of heart disease. A number of studies using the Cook-Medley hostility scale (a questionnaire derived from the MMPI; Cook & Medley, 1954) have also documented this association. For example, Barefoot and colleagues (1989) studied the health status of 118 lawyers who had been given the MMPI about 28 years earlier when they were healthy young adults. High hostility scores were associated with a significant increase in the likelihood of death at follow-up.

Although not all studies have confirmed this association, meta-analyses (e.g., Miller, Smith, Turner, Guijarro, & Hallet, 1996) support the conclusion that hostility and related characteristics are a factor in cardiovascular morbidity and mortality (Meta-analysis is a method of examining the findings of many studies as a whole. See Chapter 17 for a fuller discussion).

Just what is this characteristic called hostility? The words we use to describe psychological characteristics or behaviours are imperfect and often fail to capture all their nuances. In the case of hostility, the construct involves several features. Barefoot (1992) emphasized three components: *affective* features involving a tendency to respond to situations with anger and contempt; a *cognitive/attitudinal* dimension involving a tendency to view others with cynicism and to impute bad intentions to them; and a *behavioural* dimension involving direct and subtle aggressiveness and antagonism. Consistent with this analysis, subscales of the Cook-Medley scale measuring cynicism, hostile affect, and aggressive responding predicted likelihood of early death in the study by Barefoot and colleagues (1989).

How would hostility lead to health risk? What mechanism would apply? In a comprehensive analysis, Timothy Smith (1992) outlined five possible models:

Psychophysiological reactivity model: It suggests that hostile people are at higher risk because they experience exaggerated autonomic and neuroendocrine responses during stress.

Psychosocial vulnerability model: It suggests that hostile people experience a more demanding interpersonal life than do others.

Transactional model: A hybrid of the first two models, posits that the behaviour of hostile individuals constructs, by its natural consequences, a social world that is antagonistic and unsupportive. Consequent interpersonal stress and lack of social support increase the vulnerability of these people.

Health behaviour model: It suggests that hostile people may be more likely to engage in unhealthy behaviours (e.g., smoking, drug use, high-fat diets) and less likely to engage in healthy practices, such as exercise.

A final theory: It is the link between hostility and poor health outcomes is the result of a third variable, **constitutional vulnerability**, with which they are both associated.

It is difficult to pick and choose among these alternatives because there is evidence to support each one. For example, several studies have supported the hypothesis that hostile people show enhanced physiological arousal to psychological stress. Interestingly, however, such responses may occur only when the stressful conditions are relevant to the hostility characteristic. For example, in one study hostile participants differed from non-hostile participants in their cardiovascular responses to a word-identification test only when they were also exposed to social harassment (Suarez & Williams, 1989). Prkachin, Mills, Kaufman, and Carew (1991) found that hostile participants showed a "slow burn" effect. Unlike non-hostile people, their blood pressure increased gradually during a difficult computer task when they were led to believe erroneously that their performance

According to recent studies, it is not this man's stressful job and drive to get ahead that put him at risk so much as the hostility he is expressing.

Bruce Ayres/The Image Bank/Getty Images

was poor. Both the psychosocial vulnerability and the transactional model derive support from studies showing that hostile people have fewer social supports and more stressful life events than do non-hostile people (Hardy & Smith, 1988; Smith & Frohm, 1985). Prkachin and Silverman (2002) provided support for the transactional model by showing that hostile people are less likely than non-hostile people to engage in tension-defusing behaviour (e.g., social smiling) during stressful interactions. Finally, several studies have shown that hostile people smoke more, use alcohol more, consume more calories, and engage in less exercise than non-hostile people (Smith, 1992).

One relevant set of observations involves physiological response to anger. Studies have shown that recalled experiences of anger elicit distinct and powerful changes in the cardiovascular system (Prkachin et al., 2001). Ironson and colleagues (1992) asked people to recall and describe an event that had made them angry, while measuring the proportion of blood ejected from the left ventricle by an imaging technique called radionuclide ventriculography. Decreased left ventricular ejection fraction (LVEF) is an indicator of compromised cardiovascular function. LVEF decreased during anger recall in coronary artery disease patients but not in healthy controls.

Evidence has increasingly emerged about the importance of another psychological characteristic—depression—in cardiovascular morbidity and mortality. Frasure-Smith, Lesperance, and Talajic (1993), from McGill University, studied more than 200 patients who had recently survived a heart attack. When they had recovered sufficiently, patients were interviewed and categorized as depressed or not according to modified DSM-III-R criteria. You might wonder, wouldn't anybody who has just had a heart attack be depressed? Indeed, sadness and worry are extremely common in such circumstances, but people do vary in their reactions. In this study, only 16 percent of patients met the DSM criteria for a major depressive disorder. The researchers followed up these patients six months later—an important milestone, because most deaths following a heart attack occur within that time. Depression soon after the heart attack was associated with a greater than fivefold increase in the risk of dying within six months, independent of other predictors such as disease severity and history of previous heart attack. Frasure-Smith and colleagues (1999) repeated this observation with a larger sample and a different method of assessing depression. They showed that the elevated risk of mortality associated with depression was approximately the same in men and women.

In the years since the pioneering work of Frasure-Smith and colleagues, many studies have investigated the relationships among depression, heart disease, and death. Rugulies (2002) and Wulsin and Singal (2003) performed meta-analyses of prospective studies of this relationship; that is, of studies that investigated the risk of developing heart disease among people who showed previous evidence of depression. These studies indicate that depression is associated with an approximate 60 percent increase in risk of developing heart disease. Likewise, Barth, Schumacher, and Herrmann-Lingen (2004) performed a meta-analysis of studies that have investigated outcomes of depression among patients who already have coronary heart disease. They found that depression is associated with a twofold increase in risk of death within approximately two years among people with heart disease (see also Kop & Plumhoff, 2011).

Whooley and Wong (2013) have reviewed potential explanations of the impact of depression on cardiovascular disease. Two possible explanations—that the relationship simply reflects the severity of cardiovascular disease (i.e., the worse the heart condition, the more depressed the patient) or that the relationship is a consequence of toxic effects of antidepressant medication—cannot be supported by the available evidence. Plausible pathways generally fall into two categories: biological and behavioural factors.

Considerable evidence suggests that the association between depression and cardiovascular disease can be explained by behavioural factors, including physical activity, medication non-adherence, and social isolation. The prospective Heart and Soul Study evaluated whether behavioural factors explained the association between symptoms of depression and cardiovascular events in a sample of more than 1000 outpatients with stable coronary heart disease who were followed for nearly five years (Whooley et al., 2008). Patients with baseline depressive symptoms had a 50% greater rate of subsequent cardiovascular events. Importantly, adjustment for physical activity, smoking, and medication non-adherence were associated with 32%, 10%, and 5% reductions in the strength of the association between depressive symptoms and cardiovascular events, respectively. The association between symptoms of depression and cardiovascular disease was eliminated after adjustment of all three health behaviours. Win and colleagues (2011) reported a similarly strong mediating effect of physical activity on the association between symptoms of depression and cardiovascular events in a sample of almost 6000 patients that better generalized to women and minorities.

The association between depression and cardiovascular disease might also be explained by biological factors, such as alterations in autonomic and neuroendocrine regulation of the heart associated with depression. Depression in cardiac patients has been found to be associated with a number of changes in autonomic function, such as increased heart rate and decreased heart-rate *variability* that are themselves predictors of complications of heart disease (Carney et al., 1995; Krittayaphong et al., 1997). Moreover, post-heart-attack patients whose depression responds favourably to drug therapy show increases, whereas patients whose depression does not respond favourably show decreases in heart-rate variability (Khaykin et al., 1998).

Greg Miller has provided evidence that depression may affect the risk of heart disease and death through inflammatory mechanisms, which are increasingly understood as fundamental contributors to atherogenesis (Libby, 2002). In one study (Miller, Stetler, Carney, Freedland, & Banks, 2002), young, otherwise healthy but depressed individuals showed large elevations in C-reactive protein and interleukin 6 compared with controls. C-reactive protein and interleukin 6 are important because they mediate inflammation and have been directly implicated in the development of atherosclerosis. More recently, Miller and his colleagues have shown that, in response to the acute stress of a mock job interview, depressed people show impairments in the ability of their white blood cells to inhibit inflammatory processes (Miller, Rohleder, Stetler, & Kirschbaum, 2005).

As we have seen, research conducted over the last two decades has yielded an abundance of new information about the relationship between psychosocial variables and cardiovascular disease (for a comprehensive review, see Everson-Rose & Lewis, 2005). This section has reviewed some of the psychological characteristics that are currently believed to play a role in the development of heart disease and some of the mechanisms by which psychological variables may exert their effect. Just how important are they? We know, for example, that smoking and a poor diet increase risk for heart disease, and we know that physiological risk factors, such as high blood pressure and diabetes, also play a role. Surely these are much more important and powerful influences, are they not?

In a massive investigation—the INTERHEART study—Salim Yusuf, of McMaster University, and a large team of co-investigators identified more than 15 000 people who had suffered their first heart attack, as well as almost 15 000 controls. Participants were identified in 52 countries on every inhabited continent. For each participant, the investigators performed measurements of a large number of known or suspected treatable risk factors, including smoking, dietary patterns, physical activity, blood constituents, and psychosocial factors. Their measure of psychosocial factors included self-reported stress at home (e.g., irritability, anxiety, sleep loss), work stress, financial stress, major life events, locus of control, and depression. The results of the INTERHEART study (Yusuf et al., 2004) suggested that nine risk factors—smoking, the apolipoprotein A/apolipoprotein B ratio (a measure of blood lipids), high blood pressure, diabetes, abdominal obesity, low consumption of fruits and vegetables, lack of consumption of moderate amounts of alcohol, low physical activity, and psychosocial factors—accounted for more than 90 percent of the risk of heart attack. The pattern of associations was generally comparable around the world and in both men and women. Of the nine risk factors, the three that had the greatest impact were raised blood lipids, smoking, and psychosocial factors, in that order. In other words, the influence on cardiovascular disease of psychosocial variables such as those discussed in this chapter is substantial and important in public health terms. As research in this field has progressed, our ideas about the manner in which such influences operate have become more complex and more refined. We will no doubt learn much more as the twenty-first century progresses.

⑤ BEFORE MOVING ON

Psychophysiological reactivity is a term that can be purely descriptive, in which case it simply refers to physiological reactions to psychological stimuli. On the other hand, it is sometimes used to refer to a variable on which people differ characteristically, with some people being highly reactive, others not reactive at all, and most of us somewhere in between. Describe how psychophysiological reactivity, in either sense of the term, helps to explain the origins of ulcer and cardiovascular diseases.

⑥ BEFORE MOVING ON

It is important to be able to see the connection between empirical findings and the conclusions they support. In this chapter, we have reviewed evidence that psychological factors can contribute to the onset or exacerbation of infections, ulcers, and cardiovascular diseases. For each disease state, pick one empirical study that has been covered and describe how the evidence supports a role for psychological influences. You should also be able to describe some limitations to the conclusions that can be drawn.

Treatment

If psychosocial factors contribute to disease, it seems sensible that psychological approaches would be useful in treatment. A variety of such approaches have been developed, with varied results. Broadly speaking, two classes of intervention characterize work in this field: (1) generic approaches to the management of stress and related problems, and (2) interventions directed toward specific psychosocial variables thought to play a role in the etiology of disease.

Generic stress management programs attempt to address either the physiological arousal response or the behaviours and thought processes believed to play a role in eliciting arousal. Relaxation training is often used to prevent or inhibit stress-induced sympathetic and neuroendocrine responses. Techniques range from teaching the control of specific muscle groups to autogenic training, a multi-faceted procedure that encourages people to invoke images of warmth and heaviness.

Cognitive-behavioural techniques are also commonly used. They focus on helping the individual to identify thinking styles that promote stress, such as negative self-statements, and to devise new ways of thinking and acting to counteract stress (see Chapter 17, and compare with the examples of cognitive-behavioural treatments described in Chapters 5 and 8). Such methods are often informed by Lazarus's transactional model and can be seen as attempts to modify appraisal and coping processes.

Linden and Chambers (1994), of the University of British Columbia, reported a meta-analysis of stress management in the treatment of hypertension. Their results indicated that stress management could be as effective as the standard prescription drugs when the interventions were targeted and individualized to the patients' problems. More recently, Linden and Moseley (2006) reported a meta-analysis of controlled trials investigating the effects of psychological treatments such as biofeedback and stress management for hypertension. Their results indicated that such interventions do, in fact, produce significant reductions in systolic blood pressure. Interestingly, these researchers also concluded that interventions that involve multiple components (e.g., biofeedback and stress management) or that are individualized based on a patient's specific psychological characteristics produce especially marked reductions.

A variety of treatment techniques have been developed to address specific psychosocial variables. Most of this work has been informed by a cognitive-behavioural, transactional perspective. Probably the best-known example is the Recurrent Coronary Prevention Project (Friedman et al., 1986). Patients who had suffered a heart attack were assigned to one of two conditions. One was a standard cardiac counselling intervention involving education about risks and risk factor control. In the other, patients also underwent intensive counselling to change Type A behaviours. The Type A counselling, which took place in group sessions over four and a half years, included education about Type A behaviour; developing self-awareness about triggers of Type A behaviour; reducing time urgency, anger, and hostility; and increasing patience and empathy. After three years, patients who had received the Type A counselling program showed a reduction in measured Type A behaviour. They also had just over half as many recurrences of cardiac events as the control patients.

Larger trials targeting psychosocial variables to reduce morbidity and mortality following cardiovascular disease have not been universally supportive. The ENRICHD (ENhancing Recovery In Coronary Heart Disease) trial evaluated the effect of non-pharmacological treatment of depression on mortality and recurrent myocardial infarction (Berkman et al., 2003). Nearly 2500 patients with myocardial infarction and depression were enrolled and randomized to receive usual care or a median of 11 sessions of individually tailored cognitive behaviour therapy for depression over the course of 6 months. Results were mixed. Although depression improved, there was no difference in morbidity and mortality between the two groups. Follow-up analyses indicated that depression was an independent risk factor for death following myocardial infarction, despite the fact that the treatment of depression was not associated with a decrease in this risk (Carney et al., 2003). On possible confounding factor was the use of antidepressant medication, which reached 20.6 percent in the control group and 28 percent in the intervention group by the end of follow-up. Interestingly, antidepressant medication use was associated with a significant reduction in risk of morbidity or mortality (Berkman et al., 2003). Arguably, it is important to treat depression following myocardial infarction as doing so improves psychological outcomes and makes it easier for the patients to adhere to medical regimens necessary for survival.

Although it is possible that the specific skills targeted in the Recurrent Coronary Prevention Project or in Ornish's intensive lifestyle intervention program (Ornish et al., 1998) may be critically important for therapeutic benefits, it is worth noting that the interventions also address several other relevant psychosocial variables. In particular, the programs emphasize and encourage social support. Indeed, as these types of intervention have evolved, they have begun to place greater emphasis on group interaction

Many people report that meditation or yoga reduces stress, which, in turn, may help to alleviate stress-related medical problems.

and on encouraging emotional communication (Billings et al., 1996). Undoubtedly, such experiences can contribute to the development of new ways of appraising and coping. Emotional communication may also enhance the ability to "process" emotional experiences and promote new ways of interacting with others. There is evidence that all these changes may play a role in promoting health and preventing disease.

CANADIAN RESEARCH CENTRE

Dr. Kim Lavoie

As important as it is to understand how psychosocial factors contribute to disease, it is even more important to discover ways of preventing, treating, or mitigating their negative effects. An exemplary program of research into clinical interventions in health psychology and behavioural medicine has been led by Dr. Kim Lavoie, Professor of Psychology and Chair of Behavioural Medicine at Université du Québec à Montréal, co-director of the Montreal Behavioural Medicine Centre, director of the Chronic Disease research division at Hôpital du Sacré-Coeur de Montreal, and Chair of the Health Psychology and Behavioural Medicine Section at the Canadian Psychological Association. Dr. Lavoie and her colleagues have been involved in research that is focused on reducing chronic disease morbidity and mortality by understanding how psychological (e.g., stress, anxiety, depression, motivation) and behavioural (e.g.,

smoking, diet, physical activity, adherence) factors influence the development and progression of chronic disease, including cardiovascular disease, asthma, and chronic obstructive pulmonary disease (COPD).

In her earlier work, Dr. Lavoie and colleagues investigated the impact of psychiatric disorders on patients with heart and lung disease. This research has highlighted the importance of screening for and treating psychiatric disorders in patients who experience these chronic diseases. For example, her research has highlighted that 34 percent of adults with asthma experience a psychiatric disorder that worsens asthma control and quality of life (Lavoie et al., 2005). Similarly, she has demonstrated that patients treated for COPD in an outpatient setting who have a psychiatric disorder experience greater risk of COPD-exacerbations (Laurin et al., 2009). Finally, Lavoie et al. evaluated the validity and reliability

of exercise stress tests among patients with cardiovascular disease and comorbid depression (Lavoie et al., 2004). Indices of exercise stress test performance were lower among patients with depression, and resulted in more false negative tests, cautioning the validity of exercise stress testing among cardiac patients with depression.

Dr. Lavoie and colleagues have more recently focused on the development and implementation of evidence-based interventions designed to help patients with chronic disease reduce the frequency of behaviours that are problematic to health and increase the frequency of those that are beneficial (i.e., health behaviour change). The development and management of chronic diseases (e.g., cardiovascular, COPD, asthma, cancer) are heavily influenced by behaviours, including smoking, poor diet, alcohol consumption, physical activity levels, and medication non-adherence. Thus, behaviour and lifestyle interventions are often first-line recommendations when it comes to the prevention and management of chronic diseases. Yet, behaviour change is difficult to initiate and even more challenging to maintain. Dr. Lavoie has targeted health behaviour change from the perspective of the patient as well as the health care provider.

Changing one's behaviour is a challenging task. It has been suggested that there is no impending pharmaceutical discovery, surgical innovation, or governmental policy change with greater potential for reducing rates of morbidity and mortality than increasing the percentage of treatment plans that patients carry out as prescribed (Sabaté, 2003). Despite this call to action, there has been little guidance on how to motivate health behaviour change. Dr. Lavoie and colleagues have designed interventions to enhance a patient's self-efficacy and motivation for behaviour change using principles and techniques derived from self-determination theory (Ryan & Deci, 2000) and motivational interviewing (Miller & Rollnick, 2013). In one such intervention, patients with poorly controlled asthma who were not using their inhaled corticosteroids as prescribed were randomized to receive four brief (15 to 30 minute) motivational counselling sessions (i.e., collaborative, person-centred counselling sessions for strengthening a person's motivation and commitment for change by exploring and resolving ambivalence) or usual care (Moullec et al., 2014). Results indicated that brief motivational counselling produced clinically relevant improvements in adherence to inhaled corticosteroids, symptoms of asthma, and increased patients' confidence in their ability to control their asthma.

In her most recent program of research, Dr. Lavoie and colleagues have received funds from the Canadian Institutes for Health Research (CIHR) to train health care providers in the use of motivational communication to improve patient-provider communication and promote health behaviour change. This is a pan-Canadian study that specifically targets specialist physicians whose practices involve treating the highest proportion of patients who could arguably benefit the most from lifestyle counselling about health behaviour change (i.e., cardiologists, respirologists, and internists). If successful, this research will help generate a framework and methodology for training physicians in a critically important yet often neglected clinical skill that seeks to improve physician-patient communication, optimize care, and improve chronic disease outcomes.

Finally, Dr. Lavoie and colleagues have developed a professional practice network of Canadians who specialize in health behaviour change and promotion. She co-founded and chairs *Can-Change: Canadian Network for Health Behaviour Change and Promotion* (http://can-change.ca/). She also regularly conducts workshops to train health care providers in motivational counselling. The work of Dr. Lavoie and her team is representative of research and practice in behavioural medicine. It is multidisciplinary, involving the full spectrum of professionals who deal with cardiac and respiratory patients: cardiologists, respirologists, nurses, psychiatrists, physiatrists, psychologists, and rehabilitation workers. It addresses basic theoretical questions and practical outcomes. Finally, it is oriented to important issues that affect the lives patient with chronic diseases.

SUMMARY

- There is a long history of attempts to explain the origin of illness and disease by psychological processes. Advances in psychological and physiological methods have lent a new credibility to these ideas.

- The widespread influence of psychological factors on physical illness is recognized in DSM 5 by a distinct diagnostic category: Psychological Factors Affecting Other Medical Conditions.

- Biologically plausible mechanisms for the occurrence of certain diseases exist in the physiological changes known to accompany psychological states. Such changes can be mediated in complex ways by the autonomic, neuroendocrine, and immune systems and their interactions.

- Psychological stress, a basic psychological process that stimulates physiological disease mechanisms, is complex and regulated by cognitive, personality, and social variables that can enhance or diminish risk of disease.

- A number of disease states, including the common cold, ulcers, and heart disease, can be understood, at least in part, by examining psychological and psychophysiological variables.

- Theory and findings in this area have contributed to the development of promising psychological treatments for physical disorders.

KEY TERMS

alarm (p. 152)

alexithymia (p. 156)

appraisals (p. 154)

arrhythmias (p. 162)

atherogenesis (p. 163)

atherosclerosis (p. 162)

behavioural medicine (p. 147)

cardiac output (p. 162)

cardiovascular reactivity (p. 163)

cardiovascular recovery (p. 164)

cellular immunity (p. 151)

constitutional vulnerability (p. 165)

dualistic (p. 146)

exhaustion (p. 152)

general adaptation syndrome (GAS) (pp. 152-153)

health behaviour model (p. 165)

health psychology (p. 147)

humoral immunity (p. 151)

hypertension (p. 163)

ischemic heart disease (p. 161)

longitudinal study (p. 160)

modifiable risk factors (p. 163)

myocardial infarction (p. 161)

nonspecific immune responses (p. 151)

potential years of life lost (PYLL) (p. 161)

primary appraisals (p. 154)

protective factor (p. 163)

psychoneuroimmunology (p. 152)

psychophysiological reactivity model (p. 165)

psychosocial vulnerability model (p. 165)

resistance (p. 152)

secondary appraisals (p. 154)

stress reactivity paradigm (p. 163)

stroke (p. 161)

systolic blood pressure/diastolic blood pressure (p. 162)

total peripheral resistance (p. 162)

transactional model (p. 165)

Type A (p. 164)

vasculature (p. 162)

KATE HARKNESS

CHAPTER

8

Aurumarcus/E+/Getty Images

Mood Disorders and Suicide

LEARNING OBJECTIVES

AFTER READING THIS CHAPTER, STUDENTS WILL BE ABLE TO:

1 Describe the symptoms and clinical features of the major unipolar and bipolar mood disorders.

2 Explain how biological, psychological, and environmental factors can work together to cause mood disorders.

3 Identify the major classes of medications used to treat unipolar and bipolar mood disorders.

4 Define cognitive-behavioural therapy and describe its basic techniques in treating major depressive disorder.

5 Compare and contrast the three forms of adjunctive psychotherapies for bipolar disorder.

6 Explain how biological, psychological, and social factors can all contribute to suicide.

Lindsey was an "army brat." She moved almost every year as a child and, as a result, never fit in at school. In fact, she was bullied very badly at one school. However, things turned around for Lindsey when she entered high school. Her father had retired from the military by this time and Lindsey was able to spend all four years of high school in the same city. She excelled at sports and formed a strong group of friends. Lindsey married her high school sweetheart, Tom, the summer after graduation. They both enlisted in the military because they thought it would be a fun adventure and would help pay for their post-secondary education. Lindsey completed basic training, but then became pregnant. She and Tom decided that she would leave the military and raise their children. Soon after baby Molly was born, Tom was stationed in an unfamiliar suburb; one month later, he was deployed to Iraq.

At this point, things began to fall apart for Lindsey. Housebound with an infant, she missed Tom terribly and felt isolated in her new surroundings. An overwhelming sense of loneliness fell over her and she began to have crying spells several times a day. It became a struggle for her to get out of bed in the morning and she rarely showered or changed out of her pyjamas. She felt worthless in her capacity as a mother and began to resent her daughter. After a particularly difficult night with Molly, Lindsey called her mother and confessed to thoughts of killing herself and her baby. Lindsey's mother took the next flight out and took Lindsey to the hospital. After two days of inpatient treatment, during which Lindsey was started on escitalopram, a selective serotonin reuptake inhibitor (SSRI), Lindsey was sent home in the care of her mother and referred for outpatient treatment at a university hospital. There, she was enrolled in a treatment study investigating the combination of escitalopram and interpersonal psychotherapy (IPT) in the treatment of severe major depression.

After four weeks of treatment, Lindsey started sleeping better and saw her energy level improve. In weekly IPT sessions, she explored the difficulty of her role transition to that of wife and mother in the context of her husband's absence. She also worked with her therapist on skills needed to seek support and explored the difficulty of making friends in the context of her early history of bullying. After 20 weeks of treatment, Lindsey felt much better. She had joined a support group for people whose spouses were deployed overseas and had joined a local parenting group in her neighbourhood. Lindsey remains cautiously optimistic about the future. She has finally fallen in love with Molly and is finding new joy in motherhood. Nevertheless, she has decided to put off having another child for a few years and is looking forward to starting university when Tom returns home.

***

Jay's earliest childhood memories are of visiting his mother in the hospital. Jay's mother suffered from bipolar I disorder and was in and out of the hospital for most of his early life. She ended her own life when Jay was 12 years old. Fortunately, Jay had a very strong relationship with his father, and their bond only deepened following his mother's death.

Jay always struggled academically, and in Grade 8 he was given a diagnosis of attention deficit/ hyperactivity disorder (ADHD). In high school, his attention and hyperactivity problems increased, and his mood became labile. He was morose and sullen one day and jumping out of his seat, talking a mile a minute, the next. Jay also became more difficult to handle at home, and his father was reminded of behaviours he had seen in his late wife—for example, staying up all night making plans to "solve the world's problems" and refusing to go to school because "I'm smarter than all of them." Finally, Jay's guidance counsellor set up an appointment with a psychiatrist.

Jay's father was devastated to learn that Jay was suffering from pediatric bipolar disorder. Jay was placed on carbamazepine (Tegretol), an anticonvulsant medication, and he and his father participated in family-focused therapy (FFT). Through the FFT sessions, Jay became educated about the symptoms of bipolar disorder and the importance of staying on his medication. Together, Jay and his father learned skills to improve their communication. Despite several weeks of treatment, Jay's symptoms did not improve and he slipped into a deep depression. As a result, Jay's psychiatrist increased his dose of Tegretol and added an antidepressant medication, buproprion (Wellbutrin). This combination worked for Jay and his mood stabilized. Jay graduated from high school and enrolled in a local community college. Given the stress of a new school and living independently, Jay's chances of relapse are very high. Jay's father and psychiatrist are trying to ease his transition by setting up disability services with his school and reinforcing with Jay the importance of staying on his medication. With continued support and ongoing treatment, everyone hopes Jay will avoid his mother's tragic fate.

Historical Perspective

Depression has existed throughout human history. In ancient times, as discussed in Chapter 1, all mental disorders were explained as possession by supernatural forces. By the classical Greek era, however, attempts were made to explain mental disorders using scientific approaches. Hippocrates (460–377 BCE), for example, lived at the time of Hellenic enlightenment, when great advances were made in all areas of knowledge. He applied Empedocles' (490–430 BCE) humoral theory to mental disorders and proposed that "exaltation" (mania) was caused by an excess of warmth and dampness in the brain and that "melancholia" (depression) was caused by an excess of black bile, which could be seen as a heavy residue in the blood or discolorations on the skin. As late as the seventeenth century, clinicians attempted to cure melancholia by draining blood from patients in an attempt to rebalance the body's humours (i.e., "bloodletting").

Throughout Roman times, philosophers and physicians came to recognize the importance of emotional factors in causing depression. For example, Cicero (106–43 BCE) stated that "perturbations of the mind may proceed from a neglect of reason," and was the first to suggest psychotherapy as a treatment for melancholia.

By the fourth century, the Christian church predominated Western thinking, and supernatural explanations for mental disturbance (e.g., possession by the devil) flourished again for many centuries. Natural theories of mental illness did not re-emerge in any serious way until the seventeenth century. Robert Burton's *Anatomy of Melancholy* was published in 1621 and provided a detailed and scholarly account of the psychological (e.g., fear, solitude) and social (e.g., poverty) causes of depression that is still read today.

The work of Emil Kraepelin (1855–1926) began the modern age of theories about the etiology of depression. Kraepelin coined the term *manic-depression* and described both depressive and manic forms of this disorder. His descriptions formed the basis for the definition of the **mood disorders** contained in the modern diagnostic systems, such as the DSM-5 (American Psychiatric Association [APA], 2013).

The early twentieth century also saw a resurgence of psychological explanations of mental disorders through the work of Sigmund Freud and his student Karl Abraham. Their early psychodynamic model drew a parallel between depression and grief. In a 1917 essay, Freud noted that in mourners who are unable to resolve their grief, the anger they feel toward their lost loved one is turned inward as self-denigration. This leads to symptoms that are similar in both acute grief and depression, including weeping, loss of appetite, difficulty sleeping, loss of pleasure in life, and withdrawal. According to Freud and Abraham, individuals most likely to become depressed following a loss are those whose needs either were not met, or were excessively met, during the oral stage of development. These individuals spend their lives searching for love and approval from others, which then intensifies feelings of loss when a loved one dies (Bemporad, 1992). Freud and Abraham recognized that some individuals develop depression despite the absence of a loss. Therefore, they developed the concept of **imagined loss**, such that the individual unconsciously interprets other types of events as severe loss events (Jackson, 1986). In this formulation, even a failure at work or an argument with a friend could be interpreted as a loss (e.g., loss of esteem, loss of love). Therefore, the impact of these events is more severe for these people than it is for those who do not have this personality tendency to over-interpret events as losses. As such, these events serve as catalysts for the development of depression.

Diagnostic Issues

Have you ever felt sad, depressed, or "down"? Have you felt less interested in the things you usually enjoy doing? What about the opposite: Have you ever felt really good, excited, or "high"? Have you ever been more involved in activities than usual? These are symptoms of depression, on the one hand, and mania, on the other, and it is very likely that most people would answer yes to almost all of these questions. Almost everyone goes through transient periods of feeling down and "depressed" as well as through periods of feeling high and "on top of the world." Indeed, life would be very boring if we always felt the same neutral emotion all the time. What distinguishes these very normal mood fluctuations from the changes seen in clinical mood disorders are their *duration* and their *severity*.

For example, whereas most people can point to hours or days here and there when they have felt down or depressed, the DSM-5 criteria for major depressive disorder state that symptoms must be present for most of the day, more days than not, *for at least two weeks* (duration). Similarly, whereas most people can relate to difficulties falling asleep at night, individuals who meet criteria for this symptom of major depressive disorder require more than an hour to fall asleep nearly every night (severity). Furthermore, to meet DSM-5 criteria for a mood disorder, several symptoms must co-occur. For example, the DSM-5 criteria for major depressive disorder include nine symptoms, of which five must be present to achieve a diagnosis. Therefore, it is only when multiple symptoms co-occur and meet stringent criteria about duration and severity that a mood disorder is present.

It is important to note that the DSM-5 criteria represent arbitrary categorical conventions. There is nothing magical about five symptoms (why not four?) or two weeks (why not three?). Indeed, Dr. Kenneth Kendler (1998) has shown that depression, by its nature, is a continuous phenomenon, and that individuals with only four (or three) symptoms may still suffer considerably. Indeed, several researchers have argued that in future editions of the DSM, depression should be defined dimensionally as on a continuum with normal sad mood (e.g., Andrews et al., 2007; Brown & Barlow, 2009). Nevertheless, the DSM-5 is useful because it provides a common language to enable mental health professionals and patients to talk about symptoms and disorders.

Mood disorders in the DSM-5 are classified into two broad categories: *unipolar* and *bipolar*. **Depressive disorders** involve a change in mood in the direction of *depression*, whereas **bipolar and related disorders** involve periods of *depression* cycling with periods of *mania*. Each is discussed in turn in the text that follows.

Depressive Disorders

Depressive disorders include a set of conditions that share as common features the presence of sad, empty, or irritable mood, along with a number of additional somatic and cognitive symptoms that significantly impact the individual's functioning.

Major Depressive Disorder

Major depressive disorder (MDD) is often referred to as the "common cold" of mental disorders because it is so prevalent. It is also devastating in its impact. According to the World Health Organization (2008), it is the leading cause of disability worldwide and is the second-leading contributor to the global burden of disease. A 2000 paper by Canadian business and medical leaders reported that depression costs the North American economy $60 billion per year, more than half of that in lost productivity, and named depression an "unheralded business crisis" (Wilson, Joffe, & Wilkerson, 2000).

Depression itself is a very normal human emotion that exists on a continuum from very mild and transient feelings of sadness ("down in the dumps") to the severe, persistent, and debilitating feelings that characterize individuals with major depression. When most of us describe feeling "depressed," we are referring to these mild, transient mood states. However, the use of the word *depression* in this context can make it difficult for people to understand what individuals with MDD experience. Friends and family members may wonder why the depressed person cannot just "get over it." People with MDD may be accused of "faking it" to get attention and may be labelled as "weak" or even morally inferior. The fact is that MDD is a very real and serious disorder that involves biological, emotional, cognitive, and behavioural changes; and can impair functioning in all areas of a person's life. The criteria for a major depressive disorder are presented in Table 8.1.

PREVALENCE AND COURSE

MDD affects 1.35 million people in Canada, or 5 percent of the population (Murray & Lopez, 1996). Canadian rates of all mood disorders by age and sex are presented in Figure 8.1. One of the main factors that accounts for the devastating impact of MDD is the disorder's recurrent course. Approximately 50 percent of individuals who experience one episode of depression will have a second, and up to 90 percent of those who experience two or three episodes will have future recurrences (Solomon et al., 2000). The episodes themselves last between six and nine months, on average, although they can last for years (APA, 2013).

The average age of first onset of MDD is early to mid-twenties (APA, 2013). However, MDD is increasingly being recognized as a disorder that affects children and adolescents. According to the 2015 National Survey on Drug Use and Health (NSDUH; Center for Behavioral Health Statistics and Quality, 2016) in the United States, the 12-month prevalence of a major depressive episode in adolescence was 12.5 percent. Adolescence is also the time when sex differences in major depression incidence emerge. Using data from a large-scale study of depression, American psychologist

TABLE 8.1   DSM-5 DIAGNOSTIC CRITERIA FOR MAJOR DEPRESSIVE DISORDER

A. Five (or more) of the following symptoms have been present during the same 2-week period and represent a change from previous functioning; at least one of the symptoms is either (1) depressed mood or (2) loss of interest or pleasure. **Note:** Do not include symptoms that are clearly attributable to another medical condition.
  1. Depressed mood most of the day, nearly every day, as indicated by either subjective report (e.g., feels sad, empty, hopeless) or observation made by others (e.g., appears tearful). (**Note:** In children and adolescents, can be irritable mood.)
  2. Markedly diminished interest or pleasure in all, or almost all, activities most of the day, nearly every day (as indicated by either subjective account or observation).
  3. Significant weight loss when not dieting or weight gain (e.g., a change of more than 5% of body weight in a month), or decrease or increase in appetite nearly every day. (**Note:** In children, consider failure to make expected weight gain.)
  4. Insomnia or hypersomnia nearly every day.
  5. Psychomotor agitation or retardation nearly every day (observable by others, not merely subjective feelings of restlessness or being slowed down).
  6. Fatigue or loss of energy nearly every day.
  7. Feelings of worthlessness or excessive or inappropriate guilt (which may be delusional) nearly every day (not merely self-reproach or guilt about being sick).
  8. Diminished ability to think or concentrate, or indecisiveness, nearly every day (either by subjective account or as observed by others).
  9. Recurrent thoughts of death (not just fear of dying), recurrent suicidal ideation without a specific plan, or a suicide attempt or a specific plan for committing suicide.
B. The symptoms cause clinically significant distress or impairment in social, occupational, or other important areas of functioning.

Dr. Benjamin Hankin reported that rates of depression grow steadily and equally for both sexes throughout childhood, but then begin to diverge at about age 10. Rates of depression then continue to increase dramatically throughout adolescence for girls, whereas they tend to level off for boys (Hankin, Abramson, Moffitt, Silva, McGee, & Angell, 1998).

Finally, it should be noted that individuals with MDD often suffer from one or more additional (i.e., "comorbid")

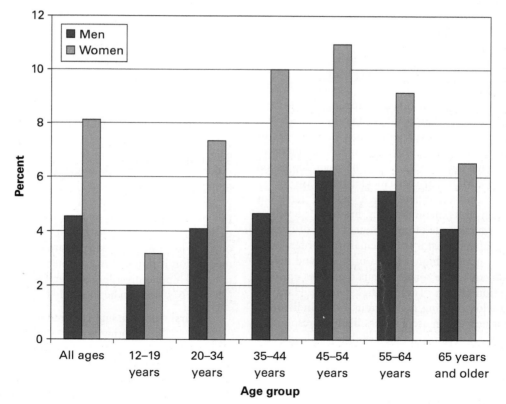

**FIGURE 8.1   **Percentage Reporting Mood Disorders, by Age Group and Sex, Household Population Aged 12 and Older, Canada, 2009

TABLE 8.2   DSM-5 DIAGNOSTIC CRITERIA FOR PERSISTENT DEPRESSIVE DISORDER (DYSTHYMIA)

A. Depressed mood for most of the day, for more days than not, as indicated by either subjective account or observation by others, for at least 2 years. **Note:** In children and adolescents, mood can be irritable and duration must be at least 1 year.

B. Presence, while depressed, of two (or more) of the following:
  1. Poor appetite or overeating.
  2. Insomnia or hypersomnia.
  3. Low energy or fatigue.
  4. Low self-esteem.
  5. Poor concentration or difficulty making decisions.
  6. Feelings of hopelessness.

C. During the 2-year period (1 year for children or adolescents) of the disturbance, the individual has never been without the symptoms in Criteria A and B for more than 2 months at a time.

D. Criteria for a major depressive disorder may be continuously present for 2 years.

E. There has never been a manic episode or a hypomanic episode, and criteria have never been met for cyclothymic disorder.

F. The disturbance is not better explained by a persistent schizoaffective disorder, schizophrenia, delusional disorder, or other specified or unspecified schizophrenia spectrum and other psychotic disorder.

G. The symptoms are not attributable to the physiological effects of a substance (e.g., a drug of abuse, a medication) or another medical condition (e.g. hypothyroidism).

H. The symptoms cause clinically significant distress or impairment in social, occupational, or other important areas of functioning.

Source: Reprinted with permission from the *Diagnostic and Statistical Manual of Mental Disorders, Fifth Edition.* (Copyright © 2013). American Psychiatric Association. All Rights Reserved.

mental disorders. The most common class of comorbid disorders is the anxiety disorders, affecting more than 50 percent of patients with MDD (Hirschfeld, 2001). Depressed individuals with comorbid conditions experience a more severe and chronic depression, and their response to treatment is slower and less complete (Hirschfeld, 2001).

Persistent Depressive Disorder

Persistent depressive disorder is defined as a chronic low mood, lasting for at least two years, along with at least three associated symptoms (see Table 8.2). The prevalence of persistent depression in the population is approximately 3 percent (Weissman, Leaf, Bruce, & Florio, 1988). Many individuals with persistent depression also experience recurrent episodes of MDD superimposed on their chronic low mood. Another presentation of chronic low mood is persistent major depression (i.e., full criteria for MDD have been met for at least two years).

Dr. Daniel Klein and others have found that persistent depression, in all of its manifestations, has higher levels of impairment, a younger age of onset, higher rates of comorbidity, a stronger family history of psychiatric disorder, lower levels of social support, higher levels of stress, and higher levels of dysfunctional personality traits than does episodic major depression (Klein, Taylor, Dickstein, & Harding, 1988; Klein, Taylor, Harding, & Dickstein, 1988). Individuals with persistent depression are also less likely to respond to standard depression treatment than are those with episodic major depression (McCullough, 2005).

Bipolar Mood Disorders

Mania is defined as a distinct period of elevated, expansive, or irritable mood that lasts at least one week and is accompanied by at least three associated symptoms. **Hypomania** is a less

severe form of mania that involves a similar number of symptoms, but those symptoms need to be present for only four days. Symptoms of mania include increased energy, decreased need for sleep, racing thoughts, pressured speech, and problems with attention and concentration. Judgment is also impaired, and these individuals may go on spending sprees, engage in substance abuse or risky sexual behaviour, or may even become aggressive. Individuals in a manic episode may feel that they are special in some way, or that they have been "chosen" to fulfill a special mission. The DSM-5 diagnostic criteria for a manic episode are provided in Table 8.3. Note that some individuals can experience both manic/hypomanic and depressive symptoms at the same time. This is called a "mixed" state. At least three symptoms of the opposing episode state are required to meet criteria for mixed features.

At first, the symptoms of mania may be experienced as enjoyable. Individuals may feel an abundance of energy and report that they are able to get a lot of things done. Their minds may seem clear and sharply focused, allowing them to solve difficult problems and make keen insights. Indeed, this positive side to the manic state may lead some people to deny the negative impact their symptoms may be having on their lives, delay seeking treatment, or stop taking their medication if they are in treatment. As the noted psychiatrist, and bipolar disorder sufferer, Dr. Kay Redfield Jamison (1995, p. 67), states in her book *An Unquiet Mind*,

> At first when I'm high, it's tremendous . . . ideas are fast . . . like shooting stars you follow until brighter ones appear . . . All shyness disappears, the right words and gestures are suddenly there . . . uninteresting people, things become intensely interesting. Sensuality is pervasive, the desire to seduce and be seduced is irresistible. Your marrow is infused with unbelievable feelings of ease, power, well-being, omnipotence, euphoria . . . you can do anything . . . but somewhere this changes.

TABLE 8.3   DSM-5 DIAGNOSTIC CRITERIA FOR MANIC EPISODE

A. A distinct period of abnormally and persistently elevated, expansive, or irritable mood and abnormally and persistently increased goal-directed activity or energy, lasting at least 1 week and present most of the day, nearly every day (or any duration if hospitalization is necessary).

B. During the period of mood disturbance and increased energy or activity, three (or more) of the following symptoms (four if the mood is only irritable) are present to a significant degree and represent a noticeable change from usual behavior:
1. Inflated self-esteem or grandiosity.
2. Decreased need for sleep (e.g., feels rested after only 3 hours of sleep).
3. More talkative than usual or pressure to keep talking.
4. Flight of ideas or subjective experience that thoughts are racing.
5. Distractibility (i.e., attention too easily drawn to unimportant or irrelevant external stimuli), as reported or observed.
6. Increase in goal-directed activity (either socially, at work or school, or sexually) or psychomotor agitation (i.e., purposeless non-goal-directed activity).
7. Excessive involvement in activities that have a high potential for painful consequences (e.g., engaging in unrestrained buying sprees, sexual indiscretions, or foolish business investments).

C. The mood disturbance is sufficiently severe to cause marked impairment in social or occupational functioning or to necessitate hospitalization to prevent harm to self or others, or there are psychotic features.

D. The episode is not attributable to the physiological effects of a substance (e.g., a drug of abuse, a medication, other treatment) or to another medical condition. **Note:** A full manic episode that emerges during antidepressant treatment (e.g., medication, electroconvulsive therapy) but persists at a fully syndromal level beyond the physiological effect of that treatment is sufficient evidence for a manic episode and, therefore, a bipolar I diagnosis.

Note: Criteria A–D constitute a manic episode. At least one lifetime manic episode is required for the diagnosis of bipolar I disorder.

Source: Reprinted with permission from the *Diagnostic and Statistical Manual of Mental Disorders*, Fifth Edition, Text Revision. (Copyright © 2013). American Psychiatric Association. All Rights Reserved.

As the episode progresses, symptoms may become more severe and start to be experienced as disturbing and even frightening: "the fast ideas become too fast, and there are far too many . . . overwhelming confusion replaces clarity . . . you stop keeping up with it—memory goes. Infectious humor ceases to amuse. Your friends become frightened . . . everything is now against the grain . . . you are irritable, angry, frightened, uncontrollable, and trapped" (Jamison, 1995, p. 67). At their most extreme, these individuals can experience a break with reality, or psychosis.

BIPOLAR I AND BIPOLAR II

In **bipolar I disorder**, an individual has a history of one or more manic episodes with or without one or more major depressive episodes. A depressive episode is not required for the diagnosis of bipolar I disorder, but most patients have both manic and depressive episodes. **Bipolar II disorder** is defined as a history of one or more hypomanic episodes with one or more major depressive episodes. Bipolar II disorder can be more difficult to diagnose than bipolar I because hypomanic episodes are not as severe as manic episodes. Hypomanic episodes may be experienced as a period of successful high productivity, and, indeed, many people with bipolar II are reluctant to take mood-stabilizing medication because they experience their hypomania as enjoyable. For both disorders, the hypomanic/manic episodes typically last between two weeks and four months, while the depressive episodes last between six and nine months. Rates of suicide range between 10 and 15 percent.

The lifetime prevalence rate in the population of bipolar I disorder is approximately 0.8 percent and of bipolar II disorder is 0.5 percent (Kessler, Rubinow, Holmes, Abelson, & Zhao, 1997). Rates do not differ between men and women. The mean age of onset of bipolar disorder is 20 years. There is now a growing consensus that bipolar disorder can onset in childhood, and current estimates place the prevalence of bipolar disorder in children at 0.5 percent. Children with bipolar disorder often do not meet the strict DSM-5 definition, and tend to have a rapid-cycling or mixed-cycling pattern. Experts believe that children and adolescents with bipolar disorder are under diagnosed and undertreated due to a lack of understanding about pediatric bipolar disorder. This is a controversial issue, however, as other experts argue that a focus on pediatric bipolar disorder may lead to over diagnosis of this condition and the application of inappropriate treatments (e.g., mood stabilizers, antipsychotic medications) to large groups of children who in fact suffer from disorders other than bipolar disorder (e.g., ADHD). Indeed, one study found that the number of American children and adolescents treated for bipolar disorder increased forty-fold from 1994 to 2003 and has been increasing ever since (Moreno et al., 2007). The investigators suggested from these findings that doctors have been more aggressively applying the diagnosis to children, and not that the incidence of the disorder in children has increased.

CYCLOTHYMIA

Cyclothymia is a chronic, but less severe, form of bipolar disorder. It involves a history of at least two years of alternating hypomanic episodes and episodes of depression that do not meet the full criteria for major depression. The lifetime prevalence of cyclothymic disorder is 0.4 to 1 percent, and the rate is equal in men and women, though women more often seek treatment. Because the mood swings are relatively mild and the episodes of hypomania may be enjoyable, individuals with cyclothymia often do not seek treatment. However, this group is at risk for developing full-blown bipolar disorder. In particular, antidepressant medication should be used with caution in this group as these medications can trigger manic episodes in vulnerable patients.

RAPID CYCLING SPECIFIER

The DSM-5 defines rapid cycling bipolar disorder as the presence of four or more manic and/or major depressive episodes in a 12-month period. The episodes must be separated from each other by at least two months of full or partial remission, *or* by a switch to the opposite mood state (i.e., mania to depression or vice versa). Patients with a rapid cycling presentation have higher rates of disability and lower rates of response to treatment (Sachs & Gardner-Schuster, 2007). Rapid cycling can be induced, or made worse, by antidepressant medications. Therefore, it is important for patients who are receiving antidepressant treatment to also receive a mood stabilizer (e.g., lithium). Some researchers also identify ultrarapid (cycling every few days) and ultradian (cycling that occurs daily) cycling. However, other investigators believe that these patterns reflect the mood lability inherent in the bipolar disorder diagnosis. Therefore, these additional **specifiers** are not present in the DSM-5.

Mood Disorder with Seasonal Pattern

Seasonal affective disorder (SAD) can occur in both unipolar MDD and bipolar disorder and is characterized by recurrent depressive episodes that are tied to the changing seasons. In northern latitudes, episodes generally occur in the winter months, whereas in southern latitudes they tend to occur in what we consider the summer months (which, after all, are the winter months there). Approximately 11 percent of patients with major depression have SAD. In the general Canadian population, its prevalence is 2 to 3 percent, as compared with 1.3 to 3 percent in Europe and less than 0.9 percent in Asia (Levitt, Boyle, Jofee, & Baumal, 2000).

Early research attempting to explain the seasonal pattern of SAD focused on melatonin, a hormone that is secreted at night by the pineal gland. As the sun provides increased light in the morning, melatonin release is normally lowered. This causes body temperature to rise, triggering the body processes to move to their awake state. Individuals with SAD,

---

APPLIED CLINICAL CASE

Demi Lovato

Demi Lovato has never shied away from the spotlight. She got her break early as a child star of the Disney Channel movie *Camp Rock* and then transitioned as a young adult to a successful recording career. Despite her great success, Demi spent much of her life feeling vulnerable, sad, and withdrawn. There were times when she couldn't even get out of bed. These periods of intense depression and self-loathing alternated for Demi with periods of intense productivity. During these periods Demi would stay up all night writing songs. She says, "sometimes I felt invincible, and it was these moments when my mind would go all over the place." As is common for many people with bipolar disorder in the early stages, Demi did not understand what was happening to her and she turned to dangerous behaviours as a way to self-medicate. She made headlines in 2009 for cutting scars, in 2010 for her struggle with the eating disorder bulimia, and again in 2011 for cocaine dependence, which ultimately landed her in an inpatient rehabilitation facility for several months. It was at this point that the then 22-year-old received a diagnosis of bipolar disorder. She states that, "getting a diagnosis was a kind of relief. It helped me start to make sense of the harmful things I was doing to cope with what I was experiencing. Now I had no choice but to move forward and learn how to live with it, so I worked with my healthcare professional and tried different treatment plans until I found what works for me." Demi is healthy now and attributes her success to committing herself to her treatment and seeking the support of her

Jon Kopaloff/FilmMagic/Getty Images

friends and family. Demi is now using her new-found strength, as well as her celebrity status, to be a vocal and passionate advocate for those with mental illness. As the spokesperson for Be Vocal: Speak Up for Mental Health, Demi is encouraging others with mental illness to raise their voices to combat stigma.

however, may need more light to trigger decreased melatonin secretion. Therefore, as the nights grow longer in the winter months, melatonin levels remain high, and, thus, there is nothing to prompt the switch from the sleep state to the wake state. As a result, individuals continue to sleep, or feel drowsy when awake. This dysregulation of the natural biological pattern of sleep and wakefulness is referred to as a "phase-delayed circadian rhythm" (Lam & Levitan, 2000).

To complicate matters, however, research evidence reviewed by Canadian psychiatrists Lam and Levitan (2000) found that medications that suppress melatonin were not effective in relieving symptoms of SAD. Also, the 24-hour winter melatonin rhythm does not differ between individuals with and without SAD. Therefore, there is likely more to the story than melatonin dysregulation alone. Substantial evidence does indeed suggest, however, that patients with SAD have phase-delayed circadian rhythms (see Lam & Levitan, 2000). Therefore, therapies that "reset" the circadian clock, such as exposure to morning light ("phototherapy"), may work for some individuals by inducing a "phase advancement" of temperature, melatonin, and other neurochemicals, such as the stress hormone cortisol (Burgess, Fogg, Young, & Eastman, 2004).

Mood Disorder with Peri- or Postpartum Onset

While the birth of a new baby is often one of the happiest experiences in a woman's life, as many as 70 percent of women experience mood swings and feelings of depression up to two weeks after childbirth. In most new mothers these symptoms resolve themselves over time and do not impair functioning. In approximately 10 to 15 percent of new mothers, however, the mood swings are chronic and severe enough to meet the criteria for a major depressive or manic episode. In very rare cases (0.1 percent of new mothers), postpartum mood episodes can include psychotic symptoms such as command hallucinations to kill the infant. Postpartum psychosis has a 5 percent suicide rate and a 4 percent infanticide rate. In 2013, postpartum depression was implicated in the tragic double murder-suicide of a Winnipeg-area woman who was found drowned in the Red River days after her three-month-old and two-year-old children were found fatally injured in her home. American actress Brooke Shields (2005) documents her struggle with postpartum depression in her book, *Down Came the Rain*.

Mood disorders can occur in the peripartum period, which refers to the last month of gestation or the first few months after delivery, and/or in the postpartum period, which refers to any time after that. Peri- and postpartum depression affect women similarly across cultures and socio-economic levels. Risk factors for postpartum depression include a family history of depression, a history of previous depressive episodes, a poor marital relationship and low social support, and stressful life events concurrent with, or immediately following, childbirth (O'Hara, 1995).

There are also a number of biological models of postpartum depression. In particular, some women appear to be very sensitive to the rapid changes in reproductive hormones (e.g., progesterone and estradiol) that occur at delivery (O'Hara, 1995). These hormones play a major role in regulating the brain systems associated with arousal, cognition, emotion, and motivation. Hormone fluctuations also affect multiple other biological systems, including the immune system and the hypothalamic-pituitary-adrenal (HPA) axis (Schiller, Meltzer-Brody, & Rubinow, 2015).

Mood disorder with peri- and postpartum onset affects not only the mother, but also her current and future children. Results of a four-year follow-up study suggest that a mother's postpartum depression is associated with poorer cognitive test scores in her children (O'Hara, Neunaber, & Zekoski, 1984). Another study reported that 32 percent of women with postpartum depression changed their future child-bearing plans significantly, choosing adoption, abortion, or even sterilization (Peindl, Zolnik, Wisner, & Hanusa, 1995). Despite the devastating consequences of this condition, a study found that only 46 percent of physicians screened new mothers at well-baby checkups for postpartum mood disorder (Seehusen, Baldwin, Runkle, & Clark, 2005). As of 2016 there was still no postpartum depression treatment guideline for Canada, or even by province. In contrast, the United Kingdom in 2014 developed a comprehensive clinical pathway for doctors for assessing and treating mental health conditions in the antenatal and postnatal period.

Premenstrual Dysphoric Disorder (PMDD)

PMDD is characterized by *marked* affective lability, irritability/anger, depressed mood, and/or anxiety, plus the presence of additional symptoms of loss of interest in activities, concentration difficulties, low energy, changes in appetite and/or sleep, feelings of loss of control, and/or physical symptoms. Five symptoms must be present to meet DSM-5 criteria for PMDD, and these symptoms must significantly interfere with the woman's functioning. Further, these symptoms must be present for most menstrual cycles in the past year.

The exact causes of PMDD are not currently known, but given its presentation specifically in the week prior to menstruation, researchers have focused on hormonal mechanisms. For example, cyclical changes in ovarian steroids in women with PMDD have been shown to cause decreases in the neurotransmitter serotonin, which is strongly implicated in mood disorders. As such, medications such as selective serotonin reuptake inhibitors (SSRIs), and birth control medications that suppress ovarian cyclicity or contain novel progestins, have been shown to be effective treatments for the condition (Cunningham, Yonkers, O'Brien, & Eriksson, 2009).

The diagnostic category of PMDD has been controversial, and was only added formally to the DSM in its most recent edition. Some groups have been concerned that the diagnosis pathologizes a normal biological process in women (menstruation), and could lead to the inappropriate, and potentially stigmatizing, treatment of women. On the other side of the argument, the 1.8 percent of women in the population who meet the strict DSM-5 criteria for PMDD report that their symptoms are as severe as those experienced during an episode of major depressive disorder, and that they cause marked impairment in their functioning at work, school, or in their relationships. Formal recognition of their symptoms as a diagnosable medical condition opens the door for further research and treatment development for this condition.

① BEFORE MOVING ON

> In the DSM-5, major depression is defined as a category that is presumed to be qualitatively distinct from normal sadness. However, many researchers have argued that in future editions of the DSM major depression should be defined as a dimensional construct, on a continuum with normal sad mood. What are the advantages and disadvantages of defining depression dimensionally versus categorically?

Etiology

There is no single cause for the mood disorders, and researchers now agree that these disorders are likely caused by an interaction of a number of risk factors at a number of levels of analysis. For example, the mood disorders are highly heritable, but a family history of a mood disorder does not guarantee the presence of disorder. A genetic vulnerability likely needs to be expressed as a vulnerable personality or cognitive trait and triggered by stress in the environment. Similarly, stressful life events are one of the strongest triggers of mood disorders, but again, not everyone who experiences stress becomes depressed. The presence of pre-existing vulnerability factors, such as a family history of depression, a history of poor relationships with early caregivers, or particular personality patterns, may need to be present for individuals to succumb to the effects of stress. Therefore, whereas a number of models of etiology are presented below, it is important to keep in mind that these are not competing models, and that no single model provides a complete account of depression. Instead, they each provide a piece of the puzzle.

Psychological and Environmental Causal Factors

The psychological level of analysis examines how variables such as personality, dysfunctional thinking, and maladaptive interpersonal behaviour contribute to the mood disorders. The environmental level of analysis examines the role of stressful life events.

PSYCHODYNAMIC PERSONALITY THEORIES

A number of aspects of psychodynamic theory continue to strongly influence thinking about depression. For example, research has supported the theory that relationships between parents and children are important in shaping a child's temperament, and that neglectful and/or abusive parenting confers a strong risk for later depression (Harkness & Lumley, 2007). In addition, research has confirmed the theory that individuals with a temperamental vulnerability to depression do interpret life events as having a greater impact, and that these events are more strongly related to depression than they are in individuals who do not have this pre-existing vulnerability (Harkness, 2008).

Indeed, the role of personality in depression is still very relevant. In particular, the late Dr. Sidney Blatt and Canadian psychologist Dr. David Zuroff (McGill University) have discussed two personality patterns that they theorize provide a risk for depression—dependency and self-criticism (Blatt, Quinlan, Chevron, McDonald, & Zuroff, 1982; Kopala-Sibley & Zuroff, 2014). Dependent individuals rely excessively on their interpersonal relationships for their sense of identity. They are described as being excessively needy, fearing abandonment, and feeling helpless in relationships. In contrast, self-critical individuals are prone to fears of failure, self-blame, inferiority, and guilt, particularly in areas of achievement. Blatt theorized that these personality styles, which develop as a function of maladaptive parenting styles and/or traumas early in development, render people vulnerable to depression when they face a stressful life event that triggers the personality theme. For example, Lindsey, whom we met in the case study above, would likely score high on a measure of dependency given her inconsistent attachments to peers early in life. Therefore, it is not too surprising that she developed depression when her current life situation ("abandonment" by her husband in new surroundings with no friends) mirrored that early life experience. A great deal of research supports the role of these personality styles as predictors of depression in the face of stress (e.g., Blatt, 2004; Bulmash, Harkness, Stewart, & Bagby, 2009; Kopala-Sibley et al., 2015).

Cognitive Theories

The most enduring cognitive theory of the mood disorders was developed by American psychiatrist Dr. Aaron T. Beck in the 1960s. Beck's great insight was in proposing that a person's emotional response to a situation is determined by the manner in which that situation is appraised or evaluated (Beck, 1967). For example, imagine that you see an acquaintance on the other side of the street. You wave to her, but she does not wave back. What thoughts are running through your head about this situation? What emotions are you feeling? Different people are likely to appraise this same situation differently. For example, if you thought, "I can't believe she didn't even acknowledge me, how rude of her!"

you may feel annoyance or even anger. However, if you thought, "She must not like me, I'm such a loser," you may feel embarrassment, rejection, or sadness. Or, you may have thought, "I guess she didn't see me. Oh well, I'll catch up with her later." In this case, you might not feel any particular emotion at all and may just forget the experience altogether. According to Beck, people with depression, and people prone to depression, are more likely to appraise situations negatively than those not prone to depression and, hence, will be more likely to experience negative mood in response to such situations. The important thing to note is that these day-to-day situations themselves are not necessarily inherently negative (such as in the example above), but the depression-prone individual interprets them negatively. In particular, according to Beck, depressed individuals apply **cognitive distortions** to situations that lead to negative mood. Examples of common cognitive distortions include:

1. *All-or-nothing thinking*: You see things in black-or-white categories. If your performance falls short of perfect, you see yourself as a total failure. Example: When a student got a C on a math exam, she told herself, "I'm a total failure. I'll never get into med school."

2. *Overgeneralization*: You see a single negative event as a never-ending pattern of defeat by using words such as "always" or "never" when you think about it. Example: You are late for a doctor appointment and you tell yourself, "I'm *always* screwing up."

3. *Magnification (catastrophizing)*: You exaggerate the importance of your errors or problems. Example: You forget someone's name when you are introducing him or her, and you tell yourself, "This is *terrible!*"

4. *Jumping to conclusions*: You interpret things negatively when there are no definite facts to support your conclusion. Example: Your girlfriend/boyfriend does not return your call, so you tell yourself, "She or he probably doesn't care about me anymore." You feel so hurt that you mope all day until you discover that she or he was visiting a grandparent in the hospital and did not even get the message that you had called.

According to Beck's model, the foundation of the depressed person's negative cognitive style is the depressive *schema* (Beck, 1976). **Schemas** are hypothetical structures in the mind that contain core beliefs about the self, the world, and the future—the **cognitive triad**. Schemas develop from our early experiences with the world and represent stored memories, images, and thoughts from these experiences. Schemas then guide the selection, encoding, organization, storage, and retrieval of information. We all have schemas and these are central to our understanding of ourselves and our world. The key feature of the depressed individual's schemas are their rigidly negative quality (e.g., "I'm a failure," "My future is hopeless," "No one loves me"), resulting, according to Beck, from negative experiences early in life, primarily with early attachment figures (note that this is an important way in which Beck's cognitive theory is

complementary to psychodynamic theory described above). It is easy to see that if a person has a rigid, pervasive belief that he or she is fundamentally unlovable, the ambiguous event used as an example above could be interpreted as further evidence of unlovability.

Beck's cognitive model is a **diathesis-stress model** (Beck, 1983). Specifically, Beck proposed that the negative cognitive schemas of the depression-prone person remain inactive in the mind, and thus serve as silent vulnerability factors (diatheses) that do not express themselves until activated, or "primed," by a stressful life event that matches the theme of the schema. For example, someone with the schema "I'm a failure" will be at risk for depression when faced with the stress of, say, getting fired from a job or failing a course. In contrast, someone with the schema "I'm unlovable" will be at risk for depression when faced with an interpersonal stress, such as the breakup of an important relationship. (Note that this is another way in which cognitive theory and psychodynamic theory converge.)

A great deal of evidence has emerged over the past 40 years supporting the cognitive model of depression (see Beck & Dozois, 2014; Dozois & Beck, 2008). Research by Canadian psychologists, including Drs. David Clark (University of New Brunswick), Keith Dobson (University of Calgary), David Dozois (University of Western Ontario), Ian Gotlib (formerly at University of Western Ontario, now at Stanford University), and Zindel Segal (University of Toronto), has provided some of the most compelling and important support for this model, showing that depressed individuals do, indeed, display significantly more negative thinking and engage in negative biases when attending to and remembering information (see Clark & Beck, 1999). Dozois and Dobson (2001b) have also found that the negative schemas of depressed individuals are more tightly organized in the mind than those of non-depressed individuals, whereas their positive schemas have a more diffuse organization than the positive schemas of non-depressed individuals. These findings support Beck's notion that the depressogenic schema structure is rigid and tightly interrelated. Furthermore, American psychologists Drs. Lyn Abramson and Lauren Alloy were the first to show that non-depressed individuals with a negative cognitive vulnerability were significantly more likely to develop a first onset of depression over a subsequent four-year follow-up period than were individuals with a more positive cognitive style (Alloy, Abramson, Whitehouse, Hogan, Panzarella, & Rose, 2006). This study was important in showing that negative cognitive style may be a cause of depression and not just part of the symptom profile once the disorder has started (see Alloy, Abramson, Keyser, Gerstein, & Sylvia, 2008).

Research has also focused on how persistently negative ways of thinking makes depressed individuals more likely than never-depressed individuals to preferentially attend to negative information in their environment (Joormann & Stanton, 2016). In direct contrast, individuals with bipolar disorder have been shown to display preferential attention to *positive* stimuli, and particularly cues of *reward* or incentive, in the environment when they are in the manic or euthymic phases of the illness (Johnson, Ruggero, & Carver, 2005).

In a landmark study, the negative attentional bias seen in depression was even shown to affect young girls who had never themselves been depressed, but whose mothers had a history of depression. Further, the presence of a negative attentional bias predicted these girls' development of depression in adolescence (Joormann, Talbot, & Gotlib, 2007). Research by Canadian psychologist Dr. Joelle LeMoult reported success in training girls with a maternal history of depression to direct their attention away from negative stimuli as a way to repair negative mood (LeMoult et al., 2016).

INTERPERSONAL MODELS

A key feature of depression is problems in interpersonal relationships. People with depression have deficient social skills in relation to non-depressed people (e.g., Dykman, Horowitz, Abramson, & Usher, 1991; Lewinsohn, Mischel, Chaplin, & Barton, 1980). Depressed people engage in less frequent eye contact, have less animated facial expressions, and show less modulation in their tone of voice than do non-depressed people (e.g., Youngren & Lewinsohn, 1980). These are all social signs that indicate low interest and attachment with a person's conversational partner. Therefore, it is no wonder that others might judge depressed people as less socially skilled.

While social skills deficits are certainly an important feature of depression, evidence that these deficits *cause* depression is not as compelling. However, there is emerging evidence that a particular type of impaired social skill—*negative feedback seeking*—may serve as a risk factor for depression. According to Dr. William Swann's (1990) self-verification theory, **negative feedback seeking** is defined as the tendency to actively seek out criticism and other negative interpersonal feedback from others that is consistent with their self-schemas. Studies by Swann and colleagues have found that depressed individuals do indeed seek more negative feedback from others and are more rejected by others than non-depressed individuals (Swann, Wenzlaff, Krull, & Pelham, 1992; Swann, Wenzlaff, & Tafarodi, 1992). Other research has demonstrated that individuals who are high in negative feedback seeking are at risk for developing future depression (Joiner, Katz, & Lew, 1997; Timmons & Joiner, 2008).

There is also evidence that an excessive need for interpersonal attachment, support, and acceptance (i.e., *interpersonal dependency*) leads to behaviours that cause and maintain depression. One behaviour that has received attention in this regard is **excessive reassurance seeking**. This concept is defined as the tendency to repeatedly seek assurance about one's worth and lovability from others, regardless of whether such assurances have already been provided. According to Dr. James Coyne's (1976) *interpersonal model of depression*, the depression-prone person may excessively seek reassurance after a negative event, such as an argument. Although this reassurance may be provided (e.g., "Yes, I love you"), the depressed person doubts its sincerity and continues to demand more reassurance. As you might expect, this elicits frustration and irritation in others, thus setting the stage for more interpersonal conflict (see Evraire & Dozois, 2011, for review).

Indeed, consistent with Dr. Constance Hammen's (1991, 2006) **stress generation hypothesis**, depressed individuals have been found to generate stressful life events in the interpersonal domain, including fights, arguments, and interpersonal rejection; that is, depressed individuals contribute to the occurrence of these events due to their maladaptive interpersonal behaviours (Hammen & Shih, 2008). Research by Canadian psychologist Dr. Jeremy Stewart has found that excessive reassurance seeking, in particular, may be in large part responsible for the generation of interpersonal stressors, which then serve to maintain and perpetuate depression (Stewart & Harkness, 2015, 2017). To understand the toxic role of excessive reassurance seeking, consider the following short telephone exchange between Lindsey and her husband early during his time in Iraq. Think about what effects this cycle of negative feedback seeking and reassurance seeking might have had on Lindsey and Tom's relationship and on Lindsey's worsening depression:

Tom: So, how are things going?

Lindsey: Pretty bad. I just can't seem to get motivated to do anything with Molly. I'm such a terrible mother, don't you think? [negative feedback seeking]

Tom: No, of course you're not a terrible mother. It's just hard right now. I'm sure you'll feel better soon.

Lindsey: You're just saying that to make me feel better. I'm a terrible mother and a rotten person.

Tom: Don't talk like that.

Lindsey: But do you still love me? [reassurance seeking]

Tom: Of course I still love you.

Lindsey: No you don't. Who could love anyone who feels this way?

Tom: I love you, okay? Look, I'm going through a lot, too.

Lindsey: I'm a terrible mother and a terrible wife. You just don't understand.

LIFE STRESS PERSPECTIVE

From the breakup of one's marriage or the loss of a close friend, to getting fired from one's job or losing one's home, to finding out one's partner has terminal cancer, or experiencing the death of a parent, stressful life events tax our psychological and physical resources and can cause significant increases in sadness, anxiety, and irritability. In the long term, most people are resilient in the face of even very severe stress and do not suffer lasting psychological effects. For a significant minority, however, stressful life events can trigger a downward spiral into major depression. As indicated above, personality and cognitive vulnerability characteristics, or "diatheses," make some individuals more likely than others to develop depressive or manic episodes in the face of life events (Monroe & Harkness, 2005; Monroe & Simons, 1991).

A very large number of studies conducted over the last 40 years have consistently demonstrated that individuals with depression are nearly three times more likely than those without depression to have experienced a stressful life event prior to onset (Harkness, 2008). Hearkening back to Freud, researchers have determined that "severe" life events and events involving themes of loss are of prime relevance to depression (Brown & Harris, 1989). Examples of severe loss events include finding that your spouse of 20 years has moved out, or learning that your father has died suddenly of a heart attack. Nearly 75 percent of individuals with major depression have suffered at least one severe loss event in the three to six months prior to onset of their depression (Brown & Harris, 1989).

A much smaller number of studies has investigated the relation of life events to the manic episodes of bipolar disorder. The most consistent results have been reported by Dr. Sheri Johnson and her colleagues, showing that in individuals with bipolar disorder, negative loss events preferentially predict increases in *depressive* symptoms, whereas life events related to reward and goal attainment (e.g., getting into graduate school, recognition for a work success) preferentially predict increases in *manic* symptoms (Johnson, 2005; Johnson et al., 2000, 2008). These latter results are consistent with the findings mentioned above that individuals with bipolar disorder show a preferential sensitivity to rewarding stimuli.

CHILDHOOD STRESSFUL LIFE EVENTS Children and adolescents who are the victims of physical, sexual, and/or emotional abuse are two to five times more likely to develop depression in young adulthood than are those without this history (MacMillan et al., 2001). Why is childhood trauma such a strong predictor of depression? Cognitive theories of depression developed by Drs. Aaron Beck and Jeffrey Young suggest that early maltreatment is internalized by the child in the form of negative cognitive schemas, such as "I'm unlovable," "People are out to hurt me," "The world is a dangerous place" (Young, 1994). Consistent with the earlier section on cognitive theories of depression, studies by Dr. Margaret Lumley (University of Guelph) suggest that childhood trauma is related to the development of negative cognitive schemas about the self that are then related to the development of depression (Lumley & Harkness, 2007, 2009; McCarthy & Lumley, 2012). Biological theories of depression point to the strong and pervasive effects of child abuse on the brain. For example, child abuse is associated with the death of cells in the hippocampus and amygdala, two areas of the brain that are critically involved in the regulation of mood and emotional memory (Bremner et al., 2003). Relatedly, research by Dr. Kate Harkness (Queen's University) has shown that child abuse is associated with dysregulation of the body's biological stress response system—the hypothalamic-pituitary-adrenal (HPA) axis (Harkness, Stewart, & Wynne-Edwards, 2011). Research suggests that child abuse even leaves marks at the genomic level; that is, it affects the way different genes turn on and off over the lifespan (Mehta et al., 2013).

Biological Causal Factors

The biological level of analysis examines how dysfunction in the brain and body contributes to the etiology of mood disorders. Next we explore evidence from studies examining the genetic, neurochemical, neuroendocrine, neurophysiological, and neuroimaging levels of analysis.

GENETICS

Both MDD and bipolar disorder run in families, and it is estimated that first-degree relatives of people with MDD are two to five times more likely to develop depression than are individuals from the general population. For bipolar disorder, the link is even stronger: first-degree relatives of people with bipolar disorder have a 7 to 15 times greater risk of developing any mood disorder than does the general population (Alda, 1997). These studies show a strong family link in the mood disorders, but they do not prove that this link is genetic; after all, family members also share the same environment, and environmental influences are very strong in promoting risk for mood disorders.

One method that has been used to tease apart family environment from genetic contributions to the mood disorders is the adoption study(see Chapter 4). In an early study using this method, Mendlewicz and Rainer (1977) found rates of 32 percent for bipolar disorder in the biological parents of affectively ill adoptees as compared to 12 percent in the adoptive parents. Twin studies have also been used to support a genetic cause for the mood disorders. Identical, or *monozygotic* (MZ), twins share 100 percent of their genetic material, whereas fraternal, or *dizygotic* (DZ), twins share 50 percent of their genetic material, just like regular siblings. Twins who are both diagnosed with the disorder are said to be concordant. Consistent with a genetic contribution to mood disorders, several studies have found higher concordance rates for unipolar major depression in MZ twins (40 to 59 percent) than in DZ twins (20 to 30 percent). Concordance rates for bipolar disorder are 65 percent in MZ twins and 14 percent in DZ twins (Farmer, 1996; McGuffin, Katz, & Rutherford, 1991; McGuffin, Katz, Watkins, & Rutherford, 1996). A large analysis of all twin studies regarding MDD concluded that the heritability estimate for MDD is 0.36 (Sullivan, Neale, & Kendler, 2000). Heritability estimates are an indication of the relative contributions of differences in genetic and non-genetic factors to the total variance in the disorder in a population. In its most simplistic sense, imagine a pie divided into slices representing all the different things that could cause depression. The heritability estimate for depression tells us that the genetics slice accounts for 36 percent of the pie. Heritability estimates for bipolar disorder are even higher, at 0.75. That is a lot of pie!

Jay's case earlier in the text is a good example of the genetic contribution to bipolar disorder. Jay's mother suffered from bipolar disorder, which helps to explain Jay's vulnerability to the disorder. Of course, genes are likely not the only contributor in Jay's case, but studies have shown that individuals with a family history of the disorder tend to develop the disorder earlier (i.e., in childhood or adolescence) than those without (Strober et al., 1988). Clarifying the role of genetics in causing his disorder will likely help Jay to understand his symptoms better and will emphasize the need for treatment.

Now that the human genome has been mapped, investigators are in the exciting position of specifying the actual genes involved in the risk for mood disorders. There is no single "mood disorder gene," but a number of candidate genes have been examined, and many show significant promise. Genes are located on chromosomes. Humans have 23 pairs of chromosomes; half of each pair is inherited from our mother and half is inherited from our father. Each chromosome may carry several genes. Each gene has two alleles (one copy on each chromosome). These alleles can be the same if we inherit the same copy of the gene from our mother and father (homozygous), or they can be different if we inherit different alleles from our mother and our father (heterozygous). People often wonder how we get from a gene to what you see in a person. The answer is that every single gene codes for a protein, and proteins are the neurochemical basis of all cellular functioning. Therefore, these proteins tell cells how to grow and function throughout life.

The region of a gene that regulates the function of a chemical in the brain called serotonin has received a great deal of attention as a candidate gene in depression. This gene is located on chromosome 17 and is called the serotonin transporter gene (HTT). The alleles of this gene can either be "short" ("s") or "long" ("l"). The "l" allele results in greater activity of the gene and, thus, in higher function of serotonin in the brain. Serotonin is important for regulating mood and is the chemical targeted by many antidepressant medications, such as Prozac. What is most exciting about this gene is that it appears to have its effect on MDD by heightening individuals' reactivity to stress. For example, a meta-analysis of 54 studies found that individuals who are homozygous (s/s) or heterozygous (s/l) for the short allele of the HTT gene show higher rates of MDD in response to stressful life events than those who are homozygous for the long allele (l/l) (Karg, Burmeister, Shedden, & Sen, 2011). Similarly, Dr. Elizabeth Hayden (University of Western Ontario) and her colleagues have shown that the "s" allele of the serotonin transporter gene is associated with the sort of negative cognitive style and personality described earlier that indicates a vulnerability to depression (Hayden, Dougherty, Maloney, Olino, et al., 2008; Hayden, Klein, Sheikh, et al., 2010). These findings provide some of the best evidence to date for an interaction between our genes, our psychology, and the environment in causing MDD.

NEUROTRANSMITTERS

Neurotransmitters are chemical substances manufactured at the neuron and released at the *synapse*, or the gap between one neuron and another (see Chapter 2). The synapse is the central point of neural communication; when a neurotransmitter is released, it binds to receptors on the post-synaptic neuron. Neurotransmitters can have excitatory effects on post-synaptic neurons, thus increasing their chances of firing new action potentials, or they can have inhibitory effects, thereby reducing the chances of their firing. In the 1950s, researchers discovered dysfunction in two neurotransmitter systems in depression: the *catecholamine* norepinephrine (NE) and the *indoleamine* serotonin (also known as 5-hydroxytryptamine, or 5-HT). Both of these neurotransmitters were found to be responsible for the functions that are disturbed in depression, such as sleep, appetite, energy, and activity level. Furthermore, the first antidepressant medications (tricyclic antidepressants and monoamine oxidase inhibitors) worked by increasing levels of these two monoamines. Subsequent research in the early 1970s integrated a third monoamine neurotransmitter, dopamine (DA), into this model. Therefore, at that time, the prevailing biological theory of mood disorders stated that depression was caused by a deficit of 5-HT, NE, or DA activity, whereas mania was caused by too much NE or DA activity in the context of too little 5-HT activity (Schildkraut, 1965).

Since the 1970s, researchers have uncovered great complexities in the neurotransmitter systems related to mood disorders and, thus, the simplistic biological models have been disconfirmed (Thase, Jindal, & Howland, 2002). First, most patients with unipolar depression do not show reductions in NE activity. However, low NE activity appears to be a key feature of both bipolar disorder and severe unipolar depression. Second, brain imaging techniques have shown that depressed individuals have fewer 5-HT receptors. Having fewer receptors means that 5-HT released at a synapse has fewer places to bind on the post-synaptic cell, thus leading to fewer subsequent action potentials and lower 5-HT neurotransmission. Finally, studies have shown that DA neurotransmission partly depends on the level of 5-HT. Therefore, if there are low levels of 5-HT, DA levels will also decrease. DA is strongly implicated in the regulation of reward processing and motor behaviour and, thus, low levels of this neurotransmitter are thought to be responsible for depressed individuals' reduction in the capacity to experience pleasure and their symptoms of psychomotor retardation (Martinot et al., 2001).

NE, DA, and 5-HT are also theorized to play a role in the manic episodes of bipolar disorder. In particular, some researchers theorize that abnormal DA levels may trigger the hyperactivity and psychosis seen in severe mania, whereas abnormal NE levels may trigger euphoria and grandiosity. In terms of 5-HT, normal levels of this neurotransmitter act to inhibit the activity of some neurons, leading to inhibition of certain behaviours. Conversely, low levels of 5-HT can lead to activation (or disinhibition) of a variety of behaviours. Therefore, a defect in the inhibitory effects of serotonin could lead to wide swings between depression and mania.

The role of DA in the etiology of MDD and bipolar disorder is receiving a lot of attention currently because of this neurotransmitter's role in mediating responses to reward. Depression has long been associated with a lack of responsiveness to reward (*anhedonia*). Research by Diego

Pizzagalli and Michael Treadway has shown that this is a specific problem with the ability to anticipate reward and to extend effort to obtain rewards. These deficits have been tied directly to reduced activity in mesocorticolimbic dopamine pathways (*hypodopaminergia*). In direct contrast, mania may result from too much dopamine signalling in these same pathways (*hyperdopaminergia*). Specifically, neuroimaging studies have found that individuals with bipolar disorder in the manic phase show abnormally elevated activity in areas of the brain with high DA receptor density during tasks that involve anticipating and consuming a reward such as money (see Whitton, Treadway, & Pizzagalli, 2016).

STRESS AND THE HYPOTHALAMIC-PITUITARY-ADRENAL AXIS

In all mammals, stress is modulated through the **hypothalamic-pituitary-adrenal (HPA) axis** (see Figure 8.2). When one encounters the stress of, say, an oncoming Mack truck (or, in humans' earlier days, an oncoming sabre-toothed tiger), the brain releases a substance called corticotropin-releasing hormone (CRH). This, in turn, leads to the release of adrenocorticotropic hormone (ACTH) from the pituitary gland and, subsequently, release of the hormone cortisol from the adrenal gland. All of this neurochemical activity is crucial to our survival, as it produces the critical physiological changes that are necessary for our "fight" or "flight." These changes include increased heart rate and blood pressure, activation of the immune system, and increased alertness (Sapolsky & Plotsky, 1990). These response systems have evolved over the millennia to be time-limited. Once we have escaped from the Mack truck, the stress response shuts off. Specifically, cortisol release during stress stimulates receptors in an area of the brain called the hippocampus that inhibit the HPA axis by negative feedback.

The HPA axis worked very well in helping us to deal with the acute dangers we faced in prehistoric times (i.e.,

stress of the sabre-toothed tiger variety). However, today's stresses are often more chronic, repeated, or uncontrollable (e.g., ongoing relationship problems or financial worries, ongoing physical or sexual abuse). According to noted neuroscientist Robert Sapolsky, these sorts of chronic stressors result in sustained release of cortisol and a breakdown of the negative feedback inhibition of the HPA axis. Prolonged periods of cortisol hypersecretion have been found to kill brain cells and cause permanent damage to the hippocampus (Sapolsky, 2000).

Research has found that depressed individuals, and those who have been exposed to traumatic stressors, such as childhood abuse or military combat, show elevated levels of cortisol in comparison to control groups (Harkness, Stewart, & Wynne-Edwards, 2011; Heim et al., 2000). Further, studies using magnetic resonance imaging (MRI) have found that depressed and traumatized adults have a smaller hippocampal volume in comparison with control groups (e.g., Bremner et al., 2003; Sheline, Sanghavi, Mintun, & Gado, 1999).

Exciting work has emerged on the link between the HPA axis and the immune system in depression. Activation of the HPA axis results in the release of pro-inflammatory cytokines, which are part of the immune response. The evolutionary purpose of these cytokines is to prepare the body to repair wounds resulting from the stress of, say, being attacked by a predator. However, even today's psychological stressors, such as being rejected by a romantic partner or having a history of emotional abuse from a parent, have been associated with heightened levels of pro-inflammatory cytokines (Slavich & Irwin, 2014). With prolonged exposure, pro-inflammatory cytokines are associated with sickness behaviours, including anhedonia and withdrawal. From an evolutionary standpoint, these behaviours may have been adaptive in encouraging withdrawal from the stressful environment. In the current context, they look a lot like depression (see Slavich, O'Donovan, Epel, & Kemeny, 2010). Indeed, there is strong evidence from meta-analyses that individuals with depression have higher levels of certain pro-inflammatory cytokines than non-depressed individuals, and that high levels of these same cytokines prospectively predict the onset of depression (Dowlati et al., 2010).

SLEEP NEUROPHYSIOLOGY

Human sleep occurs in five recurring stages: stages 1 and 2 are considered "light sleep" and stages 3 and 4 are considered "deep sleep," or *slow-wave sleep*. These first four stages are non-rapid eye movement (NREM) sleep and account for 75 to 80 percent of total sleep time. Rapid eye movement (REM) sleep is the fifth stage, which includes rapid eye movements, low muscle tone, and memorable dreaming. When suffering from depression, people experience a loss of slow-wave sleep and an early onset of the first REM stage, as well as a higher frequency and amplitude of eye movements during REM sleep (Germain & Thase, 2008; Thase & Howland, 1995). These sleep abnormalities appear to be controlled by 5-HT and NE and are genetically mediated,

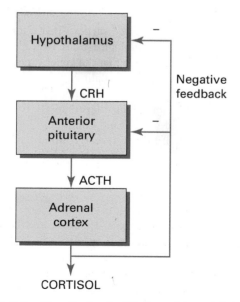

FIGURE 8.2 Hypothalamic-Pituitary-Adrenal Axis

thereby suggesting that they may play a role in causing the disorder (Kupfer & Ehlers, 1989). When patients respond to antidepressant medication, the amount of time spent in REM sleep decreases to normal levels (Wu & Bunney, 1990). Interestingly, the same effect can be achieved by waking a sleeper about to enter the REM phase of the sleep cycle. This delays the onset of REM sleep and also leads to improved mood (Knowles et al., 1979).

Sleep physiology in bipolar disorder has been studied far less. However, a clear connection between the two is evidenced by findings that sleep deprivation triggers the onset of mania in approximately 77 percent of bipolar patients (Jackson, Cavanagh, & Scott, 2003). Frank, Swartz, and Kupfer (2000) suggested that people with bipolar disorder have a genetic vulnerability to sleep–wake cycle disruption. These researchers have found that life events that disrupt a person's sleep–wake cycle, such as working the night shift or having to wake two hours early to take a child to hockey practice, predict the onset of manic episodes among individuals with bipolar disorder (Malkoff-Schwartz et al., 1998, 2000). Interpersonal and social rhythm therapy (IPSRT) is a form of psychotherapy developed for patients with bipolar disorder that teaches them to regulate their social routines to ensure a consistent sleep schedule.

NEUROIMAGING

Over the past 25 years, very sophisticated techniques for examining the brain have been developed. Research using positron emission tomography (PET) has demonstrated that both bipolar and unipolar depression are associated with decreased blood flow and reduced glucose metabolism in the frontal regions of the cerebral cortex, particularly on the left side (Drevets, Price, & Furey, 2008). Interestingly, there is a reversal of this effect when patients shift from depression into mania, with greater right hemisphere reductions seen in mania. *Increased* glucose metabolism has also been observed in several subcortical regions in depression (Drevets et al., 2008). Dr. Helen Mayberg, formerly at the University of Toronto, has found that these deficits normalize following treatment with pharmacotherapy and even psychotherapy (Mayberg et al., 2000).

Research using structural and functional MRI has uncovered the neural circuits involved in the cognitive-emotional deficits of depressed individuals. For example, Pezawas and colleagues (2005) found that individuals with the short allele of the serotonin transporter gene discussed above had smaller volumes of the amygdala and the cingulate cortex (see Figure 8.3). These areas may be particularly important for processing emotional information in depression. In particular, Pezawas and colleagues (2005) have proposed that in depression the cingulate cortex is no longer able to exert its "rational" control over the amygdala. As a result, neurons in the amygdala are activated for longer than they should be in the face of emotional information, thereby increasing the salience of that information. Support for this model comes from a study conducted by Siegle and his colleagues (2002).

FIGURE 8.3 Areas in the cingulate (*right*) and amygdala (*left*) differed in grey matter volume between subjects with the short and long versions of the serotonin transporter gene.

Source: Reprinted by permission from Macmillan Publishers Ltd: *Nature Neuroscience.* Pezawas, L., Meyere-Lindenberg, A., Drabant, E. M., Verchinski, B. A., Munoz, K. E., Kolachana, B. S., et al. 5-HTTLPR polymorphism impacts human cingulate-amygdala interactions: A genetic susceptibility mechanism for depression. *Nature Neuroscience,* 8.6 (June 2005), 828–834. Copyright 2005.

They asked depressed and non-depressed patients to engage in an emotion-processing task (rating whether words were emotionally positive, negative, or neutral) and a non-emotion processing task (a memory test) while inside the MRI scanner. The researchers found that depressed individuals showed elevated activity in the amygdala when they rated the negative words during the emotion-processing task. This elevated brain activity lasted, even throughout the non-emotional memory task. The non-depressed participants showed no such amygdala response. These results indicate that a key feature of depression may be the inability to disengage from negative information. That is, depressed individuals cannot shut off their brains when faced with negative information; as a result, they continue to ruminate about this information even after the stimulus itself is no longer present.

The research just reviewed suggests that the mood disorders have a strong neurobiological basis. However, this text has hopefully also made clear that the genetic, neurochemical, and neurostructural abnormalities seen in depression are not *sufficient* to cause depression, nor does an examination of etiology in the mood disorders that is limited to these abnormalities provide a full and complete picture of the depressed individual. Future research illuminating causal factors in the mood disorders will be guided by a multidisciplinary mandate to integrate biological, psychological, and environmental levels of analysis.

2 **BEFORE MOVING ON**

Research on the role of genes, cognition, and stress in major depression suggests that our biology can change based on input from the environment. Discuss how this is possible using an example of relevance to depression.

Sex Differences in Depression

A consistent finding in research on depression is that women are twice as likely as men to develop depression. This sex difference begins in early adolescence and stabilizes by late adolescence. A World Health Organization study of participants in 15 countries on 4 continents concluded that a female preponderance in depression is seen cross-culturally (Gater, Tansella, Korten, Tiemens, Mavreas, & Olatawura, 1998). The gender disparity in depression is seen across all levels of socio-economic status, ethnicity, and marital status, although women with two or more children at home appear to have the highest rates (Gater et al., 1998). Interestingly, gender differences are not seen in bipolar disorder, where rates are consistently equal in men and women.

Why are women so much more likely to develop depression than men? Are they just more likely to admit to, and seek help for, their symptoms of depression? A number of studies have found no evidence for this explanation. In fact, men are no less willing to disclose symptoms of depression than are women, and men and women with equal levels of symptoms show a similar likelihood of seeking treatment for, and being diagnosed with, depression (Piccinelli & Wilkinson, 2000).

Is there something fundamentally different, then, about women's biology, psychology, and/or social environment that drives this difference? Several complementary explanations have been offered. For example, many studies have found

that young women, especially, are exposed to higher levels of stress in their environment than are young men (e.g., Harkness, et al., 2010), *and* stressful life events are more strongly related to the onset of depression in young women than young men (e.g., Bouma, Ormel, Verhulst, & Oldehinkel, 2008). This heightened sensitivity to stress in women is likely driven by a combination of biological and psychological factors. For example, the gonadal hormones estrogen and progesterone, which come online at puberty, have been found to make the hypothalamic-pituitary-adrenal axis more reactive to stress in females than in males (Piccinelli & Wilkinson, 2000). In addition, women are more likely to ruminate in the face of stress than men, and increased tendencies to ruminate have been found to significantly predict the onset of depression following stress (see Nolen-Hoeksema, Wisco, & Lyubomirsky, 2008). Differences in social roles, and role strain, may also help to account for gender differences in depression. For example, women working outside the home still face economic discrimination, as well as role conflict if they have young children at home. Evidence for the strong effect of social roles is provided by studies revealing that cultural groups in which a high value is placed on the female role (e.g., in Mediterranean countries, among Old Order Amish, or among Orthodox Jews) show the lowest gender difference in rates of depression (Hopcroft & Bradley, 2007). ●

Treatment

PSYCHOTHERAPY FOR UNIPOLAR DEPRESSION

In the early 1980s, the American National Institute of Mental Health (NIMH) funded a large multi-site randomized controlled trial that compared cognitive-behavioural therapy (CBT), interpersonal psychotherapy (IPT), an antidepressant medication called imipramine, and a placebo pill condition. This study was called the Treatment of Depression Collaborative Research Program (TDCRP), and it was very important at the time because it was the first to compare all three of these treatments head-to-head using random assignment to treatment condition, a large sample size, and a placebo comparison. The overall results indicated that there were no differences in efficacy among CBT, IPT, and imipramine, and that all the active treatments were significantly superior to placebo (Elkin et al., 1989).

Based primarily on the results of the TDCRP, CBT and IPT are now recommended by the Canadian Psychological Association Task Force on Empirically Supported Treatments as the psychotherapies with the strongest efficacy in the treatment of unipolar major depression (Hunsley, Dobson, Johnston, & Mikail, 1999).

COGNITIVE-BEHAVIOUR THERAPY Cognitive-behaviour **(or behavioural) therapy (CBT)** is based on the cognitive theory of depression described earlier, which states that one's

emotional reactions to a situation are determined, at least in part, by one's thoughts about that situation (Beck, 1967). Therefore, the goal of CBT is to teach people to become aware of the meanings of and attributions to events in their lives, and to examine how these cognitions contribute to the emotional reactions that follow. CBT is a time-limited treatment that typically involves 16 to 20 sessions. The goal of CBT is for the therapist to use Socratic-type questions and guided discovery to help clients make their own insights into their thought processes (see Dobson & Dobson, 2016). This is believed to be much more powerful than simply telling the client how to think differently.

The following describes some of the more common interventions used in CBT.

Activity Scheduling. One prominent symptom of depression is a loss of interest, and loss of time spent, in activities that used to be pleasurable. As noted, this symptom is likely caused by dysregulated dopamine functioning, which underlies the ability to learn from and seek out rewarding stimuli (Pizzagalli, Iosifescu, Hallett, Ratner, & Fava, 2009). Therefore, an important behavioural technique is to encourage clients to start scheduling these activities back into their lives. The theory is that if depressed people start engaging in these pleasurable activities again, they will correspondingly start to feel pleasure in their lives. Clients start by making a list of all the activities they used to engage in and rating these activities on a score of 0 to 10 in terms of how much pleasure or accomplishment these activities elicited.

1. Situation	2. Moods	3. Automatic Thoughts (Images)	4. Evidence That Supports the Hot Thought	5. Evidence That Does Not Support the Hot Thought	6. Alternative/Balanced Thoughts	7. Rate Moods Now
Who? What? When? Where?	a. What did you feel? b. Rate each mood (0–100%). c. Circle or mark the mood you want to examine.	a. What was going through your mind just before you started to feel this way? Any other thoughts? Images? b. Circle or mark the hot thought.			a. Write an alternative or balanced thought. b. Rate how much you believe each thought (0–100%).	Rerate column 2 moods and any new moods (0–100%).
Thursday, 8:30 P.M. Judy gives me an odd look when I tell her I'm going to AA on Saturday.	Anger 90%	She's upset that I'm going to AA on Saturday. She doesn't see my recovery program as important. She doesn't care about me. She doesn't understand how hard it is not to drink. I can't stand being so angry. A drink will make me feel better.	She's not supportive of AA. She nags me to do things. She doesn't seem to appreciate how hard I work. She's always giving me negative looks, like she did tonight. She yelled at me as I was leaving the house.	She stuck with me during all those years of drinking. She attended Al-Anon meetings for a year. She seemed happy to see me when I came home from work tonight. She tells me she loves me and does nice things for me when we're not fighting. Judy explained that her facial expression was due to remembering her sister's birthday. Judy says she is glad I am in AA, and she wants me to go to meetings.	The look on Judy's face was because she remembered her sister's birthday. 100% She is supportive of my AA attendance and wants me to stay sober. 100% She does care about me. 80%	

FIGURE 8.4 Sample Thought Record

These could range from very mundane activities, such as reading or taking a walk, to activities that involve more time effort, such as visiting friends or signing up for a yoga class. Clients then map out their daily schedules on a calendar and work collaboratively with their therapist to gradually schedule in the activities on their list. This exercise serves an additional purpose of testing and challenging the negative cognitions that likely stopped them from engaging in these once-pleasurable activities in the first place (e.g., "There's no point in going out with my friends; I won't have any fun").

Thought Records. Thought records are used to help clients identify and test their negative thinking patterns (see Figure 8.4). Here, the client is encouraged to focus on a situation that occurred recently and that evoked a strong negative emotion. The client is then encouraged to write down all the thoughts that were running through his or her mind during this situation. Often, these thoughts will include cognitive distortions (e.g., all-or-nothing thinking). The therapist then works collaboratively with the client to evaluate the accuracy of these thoughts by coming up with evidence for and against the thoughts. The client is then encouraged to come up with alternative thoughts that represent a balance of the evidence. Note that these thoughts are not necessarily the opposite of the negative thoughts, and are not necessarily even positive. The point is simply to encourage depressed clients to consider alternative ways of viewing the situations in their lives that are more realistic and in line with the objective evidence. Eventually, through the course of therapy, the client learns to challenge his or her negative thoughts in the moment without needing to fill out a thought record.

BEHAVIOURAL EXPERIMENTS. Another approach that therapists use to help clients challenge their negative beliefs and assumptions about the world is to encourage people to view these thoughts as scientific hypotheses that can be tested in an experiment. For example, the assumption "If I try to talk to new people, I will certainly be rejected" is easy to test empirically. The therapist and client collaboratively design the nature of the experiment and set out clear contingencies. For example, the client might test this thought over the week between sessions by striking up conversations with the people who sit next to him or her in class. The client would then be encouraged to observe and record what takes place. If the client is *not* rejected by these people, this would provide disconfirming evidence for the assumption.

CBT is among the most extensively evaluated of all the psychological treatments for depression, having been studied in more than 80 controlled trials (Beck & Dozois, 2011; Butler, Chapman, Forman, & Beck, 2006; Dobson, 1989). CBT is significantly more effective than minimal or no treatment (Segal & Shaw, 1996). In addition, there is some evidence that CBT may be superior to traditional psychodynamic therapy for depression (Svartberg & Stiles, 1991). A number of randomized clinical trials have also demonstrated that CBT yields comparable results to antidepressant medication for the treatment of depression, with both active treatments producing superior results to placebo control

conditions (see Butler et al., 2006). CBT also appears to be as effective as antidepressant medication even for the treatment of severe depression (DeRubeis et al., 2005; Fournier et al., 2010). Furthermore, when people who responded to CBT were followed for another one or two years, they had significantly lower relapse rates than those who had responded to antidepressant medication (e.g., Hollon, Thase, & Markowitz, 2002; Hollon et al., 2005).

Researchers have found that therapy focusing solely on the behavioural components of CBT (i.e., behavioural activation therapy [BA]) is just as effective as the full treatment including focus on depression cognitions, in terms of both getting people well and keeping them well over the long term (Dimidjian et al., 2006; Dobson et al., 2008; Jacobson et al., 1996). These studies also found that behavioural activation therapy is just as effective as antidepressant medication in the short term, and is more effective than medication at preventing relapse over two years (Dimidjian et al., 2006; Dobson et al., 2008). This is good news because behavioural activation requires fewer resources in time and therapist training than full CBT, and, thus, may be a cost-effective option for many individuals suffering from MDD (Dobson et al., 2008).

An innovative adaptation of CBT incorporates mindfulness meditation as a way of preventing depression relapse. This new treatment, Mindfulness-Based Cognitive Therapy (MBCT), was developed by Canadian psychologist Dr. Zindel Segal and his British colleague Dr. John Teasdale (Segal, Williams, & Teasdale, 2002). It is based on traditional Buddhist mindfulness meditation principles that have been more recently articulated by Dr. Jon Kabat-Zinn (Kabat-Zinn, 2003). The purpose of mindfulness is to promote a non-evaluative awareness of the here and now in an effort to help depressed individuals detach from ruminative thinking and cultivate a decentred, detached perspective to depression-related thoughts and feelings. For example, instead of thinking, "I feel sad; I must be getting depressed again. I'll never be healthy," the patient is taught to think, "This is just a transitory emotion; I'm observing it and letting it pass." There is experimental evidence showing that mindfulness meditation does, indeed, decrease ruminative thinking (Williams, 2008). In the first empirical test of this treatment, 145 patients who had recovered from depression were randomized to continue with treatment as usual (e.g., visit their family doctor) or to receive an eight-week course of MBCT. Patients were then followed for a year. Only 40 percent of patients receiving MBCT relapsed in the follow-up period versus 66 percent of those in the treatment-as-usual group (Teasdale et al., 2000). A second follow-up study compared a group of 123 recovered depressed patients, randomized to receive maintenance antidepressant medication (m-ADM) or medication plus MBCT. The MBCT group experienced a significantly lower rate of relapse over the 15-month follow-up period than did the m-ADM group (47 percent versus 60 percent). MBCT was also significantly more effective than m-ADM in reducing residual depressive symptoms, reducing comorbid conditions, and improving quality of life (Kuyken et al., 2008). The results of this latter study were subsequently replicated by Segal and colleagues (2010).

Interpersonal Psychotherapy. Interpersonal psychotherapy (IPT) was developed in the 1980s by Drs. Gerald Klerman and Myrna Weissman (Klerman, Weissman, Rousanville, & Chevron, 1984). It is based on the early work of psychodynamic theorists that viewed loss and disordered attachment as underlying factors in major depression. In particular, IPT presumes that depression occurs in an interpersonal context and that addressing current problems that depressed clients face in the interpersonal realm is key to relieving symptoms.

IPT is a brief treatment that typically runs from 12 to 16 weekly sessions. Toward the beginning of treatment, the client and therapist work collaboratively to identify the client's source of interpersonal dysfunction with relevance to four areas: (1) interpersonal disputes, (2) role transitions, (3) grief, and (4) interpersonal deficits.

Interpersonal disputes are defined as conflicts in marital, family, or other social relationships. The IPT therapist intervenes by identifying sources of misunderstanding and using communication and problem-solving training to empower the client to change the situation. Role transitions are situations in which the client has difficulty adapting to a life change (e.g., retirement or other job loss, "empty nest," and so on). The IPT therapist intervenes by helping the client to reappraise the old and new roles, identify problems in adapting to the new role, and use cognitive restructuring to alter his or her dysfunctional appraisals of the new role. When the patient's issue is grief, the IPT therapist uses empathic listening to help the client work through the mourning process, and encourages the client to form new relationships. Finally, interpersonal deficits are defined as the main problem for a client who reports either a low number or poor quality of interpersonal relationships. The IPT therapist tries to identify personality issues in the client (e.g., hostility, excessive dependency) that may be interfering with the formation of close relationships, and uses the therapeutic relationship as a model for improving social competence.

The first investigation of this treatment found similar efficacy between IPT and the antidepressant amitriptyline, and both treatments in combination had an additive effect (Weissman et al., 1979). In addition, a study of "maintenance" IPT found that monthly sessions following the remission of depression were effective in preventing depression relapse over three to five years (Frank et al., 2007).

 BEFORE MOVING ON

How does basic research on cognition and behaviour in depression help to inform the techniques used in CBT and its more recent adaptations (BA and MBCT)?

PHARMACOTHERAPY

MEDICATIONS TO TREAT MAJOR DEPRESSION
Medications to treat unipolar depression were discovered serendipitously in the 1950s by physicians looking for effective drugs to treat tuberculosis. **Tricyclic antidepressants (TCAs)** and **monoamine oxidase inhibitors (MAOIs)** were the first antidepressants introduced on the market, and they resulted in a revolution in the treatment of depression. For the first time, patients who had suffered a lifelong pattern of severe, recurrent disorders saw their symptoms remit due to a simple pill. Controlled efficacy trials of these medications emerged through the 1970s and 1980s, further encouraging their use. The first **selective serotonin reuptake inhibitor (SSRI)**, fluoxetine (Prozac), then burst onto the scene in the late 1980s. Prozac was hailed as a "wonder drug" that could make everyone "better than well." However, the wild claims made about Prozac's success were soon dampened by a 1994 analysis of 13 methodologically rigorous trials comparing fluoxetine to placebo (Greenberg, Bornstein, Zborowski, Fisher, & Greenberg, 1994). This study concluded that, "fluoxetine produces modest effects, roughly comparable in magnitude to those of other antidepressants." Nevertheless, several additional SSRIs have entered the marketplace since that time, and newer ones continue to be developed. While none of them works any better than the older antidepressants, patients tolerate them much better. A description of the main classes of antidepressants follows.

Tricyclics. This oldest class of antidepressants is so called because of its three-ringed chemical structure. Common TCAs include Anafranil (clomipramine), Elavil (amtriptyline), Norpramin (desipramine), Pamelor (nortriptyline), Sinequan (doxepin), and Tofranil (imipramine). These medications work by blocking the reuptake from the synapse of NE and/or, less commonly, 5-HT. This means that more of these neurotransmitters are available in the synapse to bind to post-synaptic receptors and trigger new action potentials. No antidepressant that has been developed since the TCAs has been found to have greater efficacy. However, the TCAs are rarely used as a first-line treatment today because of their many side effects, including dry mouth, blurry vision, constipation, urinary hesitation, dizziness upon standing up, sedation, and weight gain. These drugs can also cause or exacerbate cardiac arrhythmias and thus cannot be used in patients with an existing cardiac condition. Finally, the tricyclics are highly lethal in overdose.

Monoamine Oxidase Inhibitors. As their name implies, the MAOIs work by inhibiting an enzyme (monoamine oxidase) that breaks down monoaminergic neurotransmitters (e.g., dopamine, norepinephrine, serotonin) in the presynaptic cell. This means that more monoamines are available to be released into the synapse, to bind with post-synaptic receptors, and to trigger new action potentials. Common MAOIs include Marplan (isocarboxazid), Nardil (phenelzine), and Parnate (tranylcypromine). The MAOIs are rarely used as first-line treatments because of their potentially dangerous side effects. In particular, because MAOIs inhibit the breakdown of amines, patients taking these medications must limit their intake of foods containing amines, especially tyramine (e.g., aged cheese, chocolate, red wine).

Too much tyramine can raise blood pressure to dangerous levels. Patients taking MAOIs also must avoid over-the-counter cold medicines that contain pseudoephedrine (e.g., Sudafed), as well as any drug that works on serotonin, such as another antidepressant.

Selective Serotonin Reuptake Inhibitors. The SSRIs are currently the first-line treatment for unipolar depression because of their relatively mild side effects, their high safety profile (they are not lethal in overdose), and their ease of administration (only one daily dose is required). Common SSRIs include Celexa (citalopram), Paxil (paroxetine), Prozac (fluoxetine), and Zoloft (sertraline). SSRIs work by blocking the reuptake of serotonin into the presynaptic cell. This means that more serotonin is available in the synapse to bind to post-synaptic receptors and trigger new action potentials. Common side effects include nausea, insomnia, sedation, and sexual dysfunction.

Other Classes of Antidepressants. Since the development of the SSRIs, several other classes of antidepressants have emerged. These include (1) serotonin-norepinephrine reuptake inhibitors (SNRIs) such as Wellbutrin (buproprion), Effexor (venlafaxine), Desyrel (trazodone), and Remeron (mirtazapine); (2) medications that work on increasing dopamine transmission, such as Mirapex (pramipexole) and Provigil (mondafinil); and (3) drugs that have other miscellaneous actions on other neurotransmitters such as GABA (e.g., Neurontin [gabapentin]). All of these medications have shown efficacy in comparison with placebo, and they all have slightly different side effect profiles.

A large-scale review of controlled trials of antidepressant medications concluded that approximately 50 to 70 percent of patients who successfully finish a trial of any antidepressant can be expected to respond. This compares to a response rate of 30 percent for placebo (Walsh, Seidman, Sysko, & Gould, 2002). No class of antidepressants has been found to work better than any other, in general, and thus the selection of antidepressant is guided by the drug's side effect profile, its ease of administration, the patient's own history of prior response, any medical issues that might limit use of certain medications, the patient's depressive subtype (e.g., atypical depression), the patient's family history of response, and the drug's cost. Treatment algorithms, such as the Canadian Network for Mood and Anxiety Treatment (CANMAT) guidelines developed by a consensus panel of the Canadian Psychiatric Association, have been developed and updated to try to standardize psychiatrists' approach to choosing an antidepressant and deciding what to do if a patient does not respond (Lam et al., 2016).

It should be noted that an important downside of medications is that they are associated with a high risk of relapse. That is, once people stop taking their medication, and even if they keep taking it, there is a strong chance that their symptoms will return. Therefore, these medications are by no means a "cure" for depression and, as stated above, are significantly less effective in the long run than cognitive-behavioural therapy.

Further, a controversial meta-analysis found that the benefit of antidepressant medication over placebo was found only for patients with severe depression (Fournier et al., 2010). For patients with mildly to moderately severe unipolar depression, antidepressant medication was *no more effective than a placebo*. Based on these results, do you believe that it is ethical to prescribe antidepressant medication to patients with mild to moderate depression severity?

❹ BEFORE MOVING ON

Given what you know about biological treatments for unipolar major depression, what factors might you use to decide which treatment is best for a particular patient?

MEDICATIONS TO TREAT BIPOLAR DISORDER

Similar to major depression, CANMAT has developed empirically supported guidelines for mental health professionals to choose the most appropriate treatment, or combination of treatments, for bipolar disorder (Yatham et al., 2013). Descriptions of the major classes of medications used to treat bipolar disorder follow.

Lithium. A number of chemical salts of the lithium ion (Li+) have been used as mood-stabilizing treatments for more than 100 years. Indeed, in the mid-nineteenth century, lithium was used to treat a range of psychiatric disorders based on theories at the time linking mental illness to an excess in uric acid, which is dissolved by lithium. However, by the turn of the twentieth century, this use of lithium appeared to be forgotten. Lithium was rediscovered in 1949 as a treatment for mania by Australian psychiatrist John Cade. Cade was injecting guinea pigs with lithium in his experiments with uric acid and discovered that the rodents became tranquilized. He soon began successfully using lithium on his own hospitalized manic patients. Researchers still do not know exactly how lithium works in the treatment of bipolar disorder, but there are several theories. For example, lithium deactivates an enzyme called GSK-3B that may be related to the circadian clock. When this enzyme is active, proteins in the body are unable to reset the brain's "master clock," and as a result the body's natural cycles of sleep, metabolism, and activity are disrupted (Yin, Wang, Klein, & Lazar, 2006). In addition, lithium is an antagonist of the neurotransmitter glutamate (Dixon & Hokin, 1998). Glutamate has a general excitatory effect on the brain. Therefore, decreasing the synthesis and/or release of glutamate may account for lithium's stabilizing effect.

The use of lithium requires regular monitoring by a psychiatrist and blood tests because the therapeutic window is very narrow. This means that the dose required to attain a therapeutic effect is only slightly less than the toxic dose. Because lithium interferes with the regulation of sodium and water levels, patients also require regular tests to monitor thyroid and kidney function. Common side effects of lithium include dehydration, weight gain, acne with scarring, thinning of hair, and hand tremor.

Anticonvulsants. Approximately 40 percent of patients with bipolar disorder do not respond to lithium and/or cannot tolerate its side effects. More importantly, lithium often becomes ineffective, resulting in relapse for about 70 percent of people within five years (Gitlin, Swendsen, Heller, & Hammen, 1995). About 25 years ago, doctors discovered that anticonvulsant drugs used in the treatment of epilepsy led to improvements in these patients. Today, they are often prescribed alone, with lithium, or with an antipsychotic drug to control mania. Anticonvulsant drugs include Tegretol (carbamazepine), Depakote (valproate), Lamictal (lamotrigine), Neurontin (gabapentin), Topamax (topiramate), Trileptal (oxcarbazepine), Zonegran (zonisamide), Gabitril (tiagabine), Felbatol (felbamate), Keppra (levatiracetam), Dilantin (phenytoin), and Lyrica (pregabalin).

Many anticonvulsant drugs work by increasing the synthesis and release of the neurotransmitter gamma-aminobutyric acid (GABA), which plays a general inhibitory role in the brain. Others work by *decreasing* the synthesis and release of the neurotransmitter glutamate, which has a general excitatory effect in the brain. Common side effects include dizziness, drowsiness, nausea, tremor, rash, and weight gain. Some anticonvulsants can cause liver or kidney damage or decrease the amount of platelets in the blood. Also, when taken for long periods, anticonvulsants can cause problems with the liver. Finally, pregnant women should not take anticonvulsants because they increase the risk of birth defects.

Antipsychotics. Atypical antipsychotic medications, such as those used to treat schizophrenia, may be used as a short-term treatment during acute manic or severe depressive episodes. These medications may be used to control psychotic symptoms such as hallucinations or delusions and also may be used as sedatives to help with the insomnia and agitation that often accompany manic episodes. Finally, in some people antipsychotic medications have been found to have a mood-stabilizing effect on their own and, thus, can be used for those patients who do not respond to lithium or anticonvulsants.

Antipsychotics used to treat bipolar disorder include Abilify (aripiprazole), Clozaril (clozapine), Geodon (ziprasidone), Risperdal (risperidone), Seroquel (quetiapine), and Zyprexa (olanzapine). These medications are antagonists of multiple neurotransmitter receptors, including serotonin and dopamine. Common side effects include blurred vision, dry mouth, drowsiness, muscle spasms or tremor, facial tics, and weight gain. Antipsychotic medications may also increase the risk of diabetes because they cause rapid weight gain and high cholesterol. Even these newer atypical antipsychotic medications may cause tardive dyskinesia, an irreversible syndrome involving involuntary, dyskinetic movements. The risk of developing tardive dyskinesia increases with the duration and cumulative dose of medication, and it has no treatment. Therefore, antipsychotics should be used only on a very short-term basis, in the smallest dose, and for those patients for whom other mood-stabilizing medications are ineffective.

Antidepressants. The antidepressants discussed in the earlier section on unipolar depression are often used to treat the depressive phase of bipolar disorder. Buproprion appears to be less likely to trigger manic episodes than some of the other antidepressants. In addition, there is some evidence that venlafaxine works more quickly than do other antidepressants. All antidepressants are associated with a risk for triggering mania in bipolar patients, however, so these medications are typically used in conjunction with one of the mood-stabilizing medications discussed above.

Jay was prescribed the anticonvulsant Tegretol to help relieve his symptoms of bipolar disorder. As discussed, though, his initial dose of Tegretol was not effective and he relapsed into an episode of severe depression. It is very common for patients with bipolar disorder to relapse. When this happens, the prescribing physician must decide what else to do to help the patient. In this case, Jay's psychiatrist did two things: (1) increased the dose of Tegretol, and (2) *augmented* Tegretol with another medication—the antidepressant buspirone (Buspar). This strategy worked for Jay. Unfortunately, bipolar disorder is a chronic illness that requires chronic treatment. However, it is often difficult for people with bipolar disorder to take their medication every day for years, especially when they are feeling well. Have you ever stopped taking medicine, such as an antibiotic, when your symptoms went away, even when your doctor told you to keep taking it? Given Jay's young age and inexperience with bipolar disorder, he is at high risk for stopping his medications. If he does, he will very likely suffer another relapse. Next we will discuss how adding psychotherapy to pharmacological treatments can help patients stay on their medication.

COMBINATIONS OF PSYCHOLOGICAL AND PHARMACOLOGICAL TREATMENTS

COMBINATIONS OF PSYCHOTHERAPY AND MEDICATION FOR UNIPOLAR DEPRESSION Since antidepressant medication, IPT, and CBT have all been shown to be efficacious in treating major depression, shouldn't combining them be even more effective? Not necessarily. In fact, randomized controlled trials of CBT, IPT, medication, and their combination have consistently shown that for non-persistent depression of mild to moderate severity, there is no advantage to combining psychotherapy and medication (Segal, Kennedy, & Cohen, 2001). This means that for most cases of depression, treatment choice should be based on the relative risks of pharmacotherapy versus psychotherapy (e.g., side effects, cost, time, availability), responses to past treatments, and patient preference (Segal et al., 2001).

Four caveats to this evidence are worth noting. First, for patients with *severe* depression, there is evidence that the combination of IPT and medication is superior to either alone (Thase et al., 1997). Second, for patients with *persistent* depression, there is evidence that the combination of CBASP (a version of CBT modified for persistent depression) and medication is superior to either alone (Keller et al., 2000). Third, there is evidence that *adding* CBT for patients who fail to respond fully to medication improves remission rates and helps in preventing relapse (Fava, Fabbri, & Sonino, 2002). Fourth, there is evidence that a combination of CBT and medication is superior to either alone in the treatment of adolescents with depression (Treatment for Adolescent Depression Study Team, 2004).

ADJUNCTIVE PSYCHOTHERAPY FOR BIPOLAR DISORDER The most effective treatment for bipolar disorder is medication. Unfortunately, however, even when these patients receive maximum doses of medications, they are at a high risk for relapse. In addition, these patients often continue to show significant impairments in work, family, and social relationships even while medicated. For this reason, researchers have sought to develop psychological treatments that can be added to the pharmacotherapy of these patients.

Family-Focused Therapy. **Family-focused therapy (FFT)** was developed by Dr. David Miklowitz and consists of education for the patient and his or her family members about the disorder and its effect on the patient's functioning, as well as communication and problem-solving training involving all family members. As discussed, Jay and his father participated in FFT. This was important for Jay, particularly because his father was his main source of support during his transition to college. It is possible that Jay and his father had some issues to work out regarding what Jay's bipolar diagnosis now means to their relationship, particularly in the context of Jay's mother's illness and suicide. Working through the thoughts and emotions family members have about bipolar disorder in a structured way with a trained therapist will hopefully help Jay and his father to develop positive ways of interacting that keep their relationship supportive over the long term.

Interpersonal and Social Rhythm Therapy. **Interpersonal and social rhythm therapy (IPSRT)** was developed by Dr. Ellen Frank and is based on the theory that disruptions in daily routines and conflicts in interpersonal relationships can cause relapses of bipolar episodes. Patients are taught to regulate their routines and to cope more effectively with stressful events. A randomized controlled trial comparing IPSRT to clinical management found that the group that received IPSRT experienced significantly fewer relapses during the two-year duration of the study (Frank et al., 2005). Furthermore, the strength of this effect was significantly correlated with the extent to which patients were able to regularize their daily routines.

Cognitive Therapy. Cognitive therapy (CT) for bipolar disorder was developed by Dr. Dominic Lam and is very similar to CBT for unipolar depression, described earlier. Patients are taught strategies that address the unique issues faced in bipolar disorder, including (1) how to regularize their sleep and daily routines, (2) how to regularly monitor their mood to help identify early triggers for manic episode relapses, and (3) the importance of medication compliance. A randomized trial comparing CT to clinical management in the adjunctive treatment of bipolar disorder found that patients in the CT group had significantly fewer relapses of their

bipolar disorder and significantly fewer hospitalizations during the 12-month study period (Lam et al., 2003). The CT group also reported significantly higher levels of psychosocial functioning, fewer symptoms of depression, and less fluctuation in their manic symptoms.

The Systematic Treatment Enhancement Program (STEP) for bipolar disorder was a large-scale, multi-site, randomized, and controlled study developed to test the efficacy of the above three adjunctive psychosocial treatments head-to-head (Miklowitz et al., 2007). Results indicated that patients receiving any one of these psychotherapies were significantly more likely to have recovered after one year of treatment, and they recovered more quickly than patients who received only clinical management with their medication. However, no evidence was found for significant differences among the three psychotherapies. That is, each of these therapies worked equally well when added to medication in the treatment of bipolar disorder.

5 BEFORE MOVING ON

Given what you know about CBT, FFT, and IPSRT for bipolar disorder, what factors might you use to decide which modality to employ for a particular patient?

PHOTOTHERAPY FOR SEASONAL AFFECTIVE DISORDER

As described earlier in this chapter, seasonal affective disorder (SAD) is a mood disorder that affects patients during times of low light (e.g., winter months). Because SAD may be caused by disruptions in individuals' normal circadian rhythms resulting from dysregulations in melatonin production, researchers theorized in the early 1980s that patients with this disorder may be helped by treatments that simulate sunlight. In **phototherapy** (i.e., light therapy), patients sit in front of a small box that contains fluorescent bulbs or tubes. They are exposed to light of a much higher intensity than normal household lighting (2500 to 10 000 lux), thus mimicking sunlight. Patients are instructed to sit in front of the box in the early morning for 30 minutes to 2 hours, depending on the intensity of the light in their box.

While the mechanism by which light therapy works is not entirely understood, it may mimic the natural effects of sunlight on a cascade of neurobiological processes, including gene expression in the adrenal gland, serotonin production in the hypothalamus, and inhibition of melatonin secretion from the pineal gland.

A large analysis of controlled trials involving 332 patients with SAD showed that two hours of daily exposure to a 2500-lux light box resulted in remission in 67 percent of patients with mild depression and in 40 percent of patients with moderate to severe depression (Terman et al., 1989). Based on these results, light therapy is now recommended by the Canadian Psychiatric Association as a first-line treatment for SAD (Lam & Levitt, 1999). A significant advantage of light therapy is that side effects are rare. However, because

Although the mechanism by which it works is still not clearly understood, phototherapy is effective for most people with seasonal affective disorder.

phototherapy may precipitate manic episodes in individuals with bipolar SAD, these patients should be maintained on an effective mood stabilizer before starting phototherapy.

NEUROSTIMULATION AND NEUROSURGICAL TREATMENTS

Despite clear data showing the efficacy of psychotherapy and medication in the treatment of depression, approximately 40 percent of patients remain resistant to treatment.

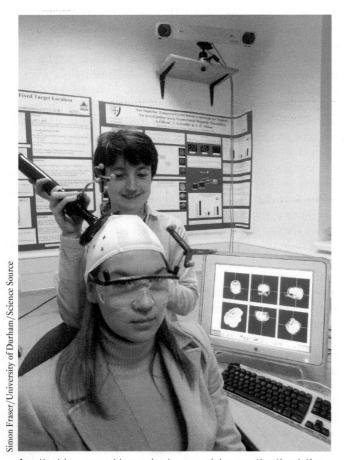

A patient is prepared to receive transcranial magnetic stimulation.

Treatment-resistant depression is defined as a failure to achieve remission following at least two trials of antidepressant medication at an appropriate dose and duration (Thase & Rush, 1997). Many of these patients have failed several treatment trials and have remained persistently depressed for years. Treatment-resistant depression is associated with severe impairments in social, educational, occupational, and health functioning, and these individuals have a significantly lower quality of life than non–treatment-resistant depressed patients (Petersen et al., 2004). Clearly, then, more drastic measures are needed to relieve suffering in treatment-resistant patients. Note that none of the strategies described in the text that follows is recommended as a first-line treatment for depression. They are to be considered only when adequate trials of medication and psychotherapy have failed.

ELECTROCONVULSIVE THERAPY Electroconvulsive therapy **(ECT)** still conjures up very negative images from the previous century of patients strapped to beds convulsing, seemingly in pain. Jack Nicholson's chilling performance in *One Flew over the Cuckoo's Nest* portrays a character transformed into a shell of a man after being punished with repeated bouts of ECT. Unfortunately, these early depictions were often accurate. ECT was used indiscriminately from its discovery in the 1930s to the advent in the 1950s of medications used to treat psychological disorders. Furthermore, in those early years it was administered without the use of anaesthetics, and the electrical current used was much higher than the one used today. Patients suffered seizures so violent that they resulted in broken bones.

The reality of present-day ECT is far from these past horrors. Patients are administered a general anaesthetic and muscle relaxant so that they do not convulse during the seizure. A blood pressure cuff is placed around the patient's ankle, preventing the muscle relaxant from reaching the foot. In this way the physician can ensure that a seizure is occurring by watching the patient's foot move. Patients also wear mouth guards to protect their tongues and teeth from injury. An electrical current is then applied to the patient's brain through electrode pads placed on his or her temples. This induces a seizure that typically lasts for about 25 seconds. After the anaesthetic wears off, patients typically experience a period of confusion that can last up to a few hours. Most patients report persistent memory loss following ECT, involving both retrograde amnesia (forgetting events prior to the seizure) and anterograde amnesia (forgetting events after the seizure). These memory problems usually improve within a couple of months. However, a small percentage of patients complain of continuing memory impairment following ECT. Applying an electrical current to only one side of the brain (unilateral ECT) does appear to be associated with fewer memory problems than is seen with bilateral ECT (Kho, van Vreeswijk, Simpson, & Zwinderman, 2003).

ECT is typically administered 2 to 3 times per week, with a total of between 6 and 12 treatments. An analysis of 73 randomized controlled research trials investigating the efficacy of ECT in treatment-resistant unipolar and bipolar depression concluded that active ECT is significantly more effective than both sham ECT and medication (Carney et al., 2003). In addition, this analysis found that ~~bilateral~~ ECT is more effective than unilateral ECT, and that high-dose electrical stimulus (150 percent above seizure threshold) is more effective than low-dose electrical stimulus (50 percent above seizure threshold). However, these latter two findings need to be considered in light of possible increases in cognitive impairment. ECT is indicated as a first-line treatment only for treatment-resistant depression or depression with severe, life-threatening symptoms where an immediate response is desired (e.g., acute suicidal ideation or psychotic features).

TRANSCRANIAL MAGNETIC STIMULATION Transcranial magnetic stimulation (TMS) uses magnetic fields to alter brain activity and was approved by Health Canada in 2002. During the procedure, a large electromagnetic coil is held against the patient's scalp. An electric current creates a magnetic pulse that travels through the skull and causes small electrical currents in the brain. These currents stimulate nerve cells in the region of the cortex under the coil. The procedure is non-invasive and painless, although patients sometimes report a tapping or knocking sensation in their head, as well as muscle contractions in their jaw or scalp. The procedure lasts about half an hour and is repeated several times per week.

The exact mechanism of action of TMS is still not completely understood. One possibility is that many patients with depression suffer from low levels of brain activity in the left dorsolateral prefrontal cortex (called *left hypofrontality*). Therefore, applying high-frequency magnetic stimulation leads to increased nerve stimulation and consequent blood flow and glucose metabolism in this area (Gershon, Dannon, & Grunhaus, 2003).

A meta-analysis conducted by Health Quality Ontario (2016) of 23 randomized controlled trials comparing active TMS to sham TMS (i.e., the coil is applied, but a magnetic shield against the scalp prevents the magnetic pulse from travelling through the skull) indicate a statistically significant difference in remission rates favouring TMS. However, the magnitude of the difference was small (TMS was only 10 percent better than sham TMS), raising concerns about its *clinical* significance. Further, in the same study, meta-analysis of 6 randomized controlled trials comparing TMS to ECT found that TMS was less effective than ECT, although TMS has fewer adverse effects on cognitive functioning.

VAGUS NERVE STIMULATION The vagus nerve runs from the brain stem through the neck and down to the chest and abdomen. Information travels through this nerve from the brain to the major organs of the body. In **vagus nerve stimulation (VNS)**, a device called a pulse generator is surgically implanted in the patient's chest on the left side. A lead wire attached to the generator runs under the patient's skin up to the neck and is attached to the vagus nerve. The pulse generator delivers electrical signals through the wire to the vagus nerve, which then delivers them to the brain. The implant is permanent and typically delivers stimulation

every 5 minutes for 30 seconds. This stimulation is not felt at all by the patient. VNS has been approved in Canada since 2001 for treatment-resistant unipolar and bipolar depression. Like TMS, the mechanism of action of VNS is still not well understood. VNS leads to increased release of norepinephrine and serotonin, two neurotransmitters known to be important in depression. In addition, VNS leads to increased blood flow in a number of brain regions.

A meta-analysis of six large randomized controlled trials comparing VNS to treatment as usual in patients with treatment-resistant unipolar or bipolar major depression found that VNS was associated with a three times greater likelihood of response, and a five times greater likelihood of sustained remission over five years than treatment as usual (Berry et al., 2013). Interestingly, the time to attain a response in VNS is long, with a median latency of over 10 months in most studies. At the same time, these patients appear to also maintain their remission status, such that at least 50 percent of patients who get better do not relapse over two years of follow-up (Bajbouj & Grimm, 2010).

DEEP BRAIN STIMULATION Deep brain stimulation is an investigational treatment that involves surgically implanting wires directly into the brain that then run from the head, down the side of the neck, and behind the ear to a pulse generator, which is implanted subcutaneously below the clavicle. The pulse generator is calibrated by a neurologist to deliver a particular dose of electrical current into the brain. The precise area of the brain that is associated with the greatest improvement in patients with depression is still under debate. Areas that have been studied include the subgenual cingulate (Mayberg et al., 2005) and the nucleus accumbens (Bewernick et al., 2010). Deep brain stimulation remains the least well studied of the neurostimulation treatments for treatment-resistant depression, likely due to its highly invasive nature and high cost, and the presence of other equally effective options.

Suicide

Suicide is the intentional taking of one's own life. Views on suicide throughout history have been influenced by themes such as religion, honour, and the meaning of life. In Japanese culture, for example, suicide (or *seppuku*) was respected historically as a way to atone for failure. Even today, Japanese suicide rates are among the highest in the world. In contrast, the Judeo-Christian religions, and Islam, Buddhism, and Hinduism all consider suicide to be a dishonourable act. Indeed, in the West it has been viewed as an offence against both God and the sanctity of life. In many historical European societies, people who died by suicide were buried in unmarked plots on the outskirts of cities. A criminal ordinance issued by King Louis XIV of France in 1670 was even more severe: the dead person's body was dragged face down through the streets and then hanged by a noose or thrown on a garbage heap. In Canada, suicide was decriminalized in 1972, the latest among other Western countries except Ireland (Neeleman, 1996).

Attitudes toward suicide in the Western world have changed, and suicide is now viewed as a mental health concern, associated with depression or other psychiatric disorders, inescapable psychological pain, or severe stress. The current focus is on suicide prevention and the treatment of mental disorders associated with suicide. In addition, medical assistance in dying in the case of individuals with a terminal illness became legal in Canada on June 17, 2016.

Worldwide nearly a million people die by suicide annually, and there are an estimated 10 to 20 million attempted suicides every year. In Canada, suicide is among the 10 leading causes of death in the general population, occurring at a rate of 11.3 per 100 000 people (Statistics Canada, 2009). The rate of completed suicide among males (17.3 per 100 000) is more than three times the rate among females (5.4 per 100 000; Statistics Canada, 2009). Among youths aged 15 to 24, suicide is the second-highest cause of death, following traffic accidents; each year, on average, 518 Canadian youths die from suicide. It is important to note that for every completed suicide there are 8 to 10 suicide attempts. Suicide is a devastating problem with huge economic and human costs. Indeed, each suicide costs approximately $850 000 in health care services, autopsies, funerals, police investigations, and indirect costs from lost productivity and earnings (*Ottawa Citizen*, 2003). The impact of these deaths on families, friends, and communities is inestimable. For this reason, it is very important to understand the factors that cause suicide in an effort to better prevent and treat suicidal behaviour.

DEFINITION

A number of behaviours fall under the general category of suicide. *Suicidal ideation* refers to thoughts of death and plans for suicide. Many individuals may express suicidal ideation without ever progressing to a suicide attempt. *Suicidal gestures* (parasuicide) are behaviours that look like a suicide attempt, but are clearly not life-threatening (e.g., taking pills, but not enough to overdose). People who engage in suicidal gestures often do not have an intent to die, but may want to alert others to their suffering. A *suicide attempt* is the carrying out of a suicide plan, which is unsuccessful but for which there was a clear intent to die. A *completed suicide* is a successful suicide attempt. Finally, some individuals engage in deliberate, *self-harm* behaviours, such as cutting or burning. People who self-harm often do so in private as a way of coping with extreme emotional distress. This behaviour often follows an extreme trauma, such as a history of severe abuse, and these individuals sometimes report a feeling of dissociation during the self-harm. We will not consider self-harm further in this section.

EPIDEMIOLOGY AND RISK FACTORS

The strongest risk factor for completed suicide is being male. Men in all age groups are over three times more likely than women to complete suicide, whereas women are three times more likely than men to attempt suicide. Differences in rates of completed suicide between sexes are due to the choice of method, as men choose more lethal methods to end their lives than do women. Suicide rates also differ across age categories, with males aged 19 to 24 and over 70 being at greatest risk (see Figure 8.5).

There is considerable cultural, ethnic, and regional variation in suicide rates. Suicide rates in Canada and the United States appear to fall in the mid-range. The highest rates are found in Germany, Scandinavia, Eastern Europe, and Japan, whereas the lowest rates occur in traditionally Catholic countries such as Italy, Spain, and Ireland (Blumenthal, 1990). There are also regional variations

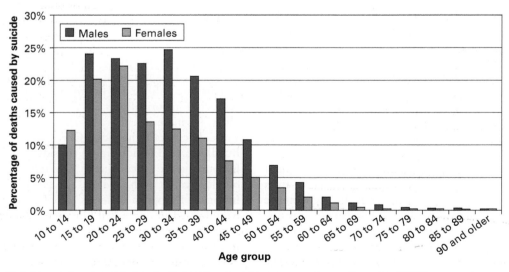

FIGURE 8.5   Suicides as a percentage of all deaths, by age group and sex, Canada, 2009

Source: Created from raw data from Statistics Canada: www40.statcan.gc.ca/l01/cst01/hlth66a-eng.htm within countries. In Canada, Quebec and Alberta have higher-than-average suicide rates for both males and females, while Newfoundland and Ontario have lower-than-average rates (Statistics Canada, 2009). Aboriginal communities in Canada have suicide rates that are two to four times greater than in the rest of the country, and Indigenous men aged 15 to 24 have rates that are five to six times the national average for their age group (Kirmayer, 1994). Indeed, suicide is the leading cause of death for First Nations males between the ages of 10 and 44 (Statistics Canada, 2009). Inuit communities have been particularly strongly affected by suicide. In Nunavut, the suicide rate is 88 per 100 000, which is eight times the national average (Kral, 2003). A devastating number of suicides occurred in the small and isolated community of Moose Factory in Northern Ontario in 2009. In that year alone, 13 teens committed suicide and another 80 made suicide attempts. These disturbing statistics have been related to a loss of cultural identity and hope, as well as to the disorganization of Indigenous communities. Poverty, school failure, family violence, and high rates of substance abuse are also strong contributing factors in these communities (Bagley, 1991; Gotowiec & Beiser, 1994). However, First Nations individuals who do not live on reserves have suicide rates equal to those of the general Canadian population (Cooper, Corrado, Karlberg, & Adams, 1992). Marked differences between Indigenous communities have also been noted. For example, in their study of close to 200 Indigenous communities in British Columbia, Chandler and Lalonde (1998) found that whereas some communities had suicide rates 800 times the national average, other communities had rates much lower than the national average.

WHAT CAUSES SUICIDE?

THE ROLE OF MENTAL DISORDER The number-one cause of suicide is untreated mental disorder. Former Vancouver Canuck Rick Rypien was suffering from depression when he committed suicide at his home in Alberta in August 2011. Wade Belak, a former Maple Leaf enforcer, also suffered from depression prior to his death by suicide later in the same month. The tragic deaths of these professional athletes show that depression does not discriminate. After mood disorders, the most frequently diagnosed mental disorder in victims of suicide is alcohol and substance abuse. Approximately 25 percent of people who commit suicide have alcoholism, and 46 percent have mixed alcohol and substance use disorders. In youth, the rates are even higher, with 67 percent of adolescents and young adults having a substance use disorder at the time of suicide (Reich, Young, & Fowler, 1986). Approximately 10 percent of persons with schizophrenia complete suicide (Miles, 1977).

SOCIAL CONTEXTUAL FACTOR Twentieth-century sociologist Emile Durkheim (1897–1951) believed that suicide is caused by a sense of "anomie," or the feeling that one is rootless and lacks a sense of belonging (Durkheim, 1951).

He believed that the less people feel integrated in their society, the greater the sense of anomie among society members and, hence, the higher the rate of suicide. As such, Durkheim also believed that suicide rates will differ across cultures, as well as within cultures over time as the values of the society change. Durkheim would explain the high rates of suicide among young Indigenous people, therefore, as due to a loss of social and cultural identity, disenfranchisement, and the disintegration of support within Indigenous groups. Durkheim's model could also explain the alarming rise in suicide rates in China. Suicide is now the top cause of death among young adults in China, one of the world's fastest-changing societies (*China Daily*, 2004). The disintegration of traditional collectivist culture has been cited as the main contributor to suicide in China, as young people increasingly leave their rural towns to achieve Western values of individual success in the big cities (China Daily, 2004). Durkheim's theory is very powerful in explaining differences in suicide rates across and within societies. However, it does not explain the root causes of suicide, which account for its existence as a universal human phenomenon.

BIOLOGICAL FACTORS Twin studies have shown that the concordance rates for suicide in monozygotic twins are 5 to 10 times higher than for dizygotic twins (Roy, Nielsen, Rylander, Sarchiapone, & Segal, 1999). In addition, an early adoption study found that the rate of suicide in biological relatives of adoptees was more than six times higher for the group of adoptees who had committed suicide (4.5 percent) than for a control group of adoptees who did not commit suicide (0.7 percent; Schulsinger, Kety, Rosenthal, & Wender, 1979). While suicidal behaviour is likely determined by many genes, the serotonin transporter gene (5-HTT) is one candidate that has received research attention (Currier & Mann, 2008).

Low levels of serotonin have been implicated in suicide using other neurobiological techniques as well, including the post-mortem investigation of brains of suicide victims (e.g., Gross-Isseroff, Blegon, Voet, & Weizman, 2002), the cerebrospinal fluid and blood platelets of suicide attempters (e.g., Åsberg, 1976), and PET imaging. Given that both suicidal behaviour and serotonin function are also associated with aggression and impulsivity, researchers have suggested that there is a problem with the mechanism that inhibits impulsivity and aggression, leading to an increased risk of lethal suicidality (Mann et al., 2000). However, reviews of this literature also state that the relation of the serotonin system to impulsive and aggressive behaviour is complex, and is likely strongly moderated by the environment (e.g., stress) and psychological factors (Glick, 2015).

PSYCHOLOGICAL FACTORS Two psychological theories of suicide predominate in the literature. First, the psychologist Dr. Thomas Joiner and his colleagues have proposed an **interpersonal model** of suicide (van Oren, Witte, Cukrowicz, Braithwaite, Selby, & Joiner, 2010). In this model, high levels of *perceived burdensomeness* (i.e., believing that the person is a burden on others) and *thwarted belongingness* (i.e., feeling alienated and alone), along with feelings of hopelessness about the future, lead to suicidal ideation and intent. This will only progress to the capability for actual suicide attempts through a reduced fear of death and increased tolerance of physical pain. This acquired capability for suicide comes, according to the theory, through repeated experiences of self-harm and suicidal gestures.

Second, Dr. Rory O'Connor (2011) has integrated features of the interpersonal model into a larger **motivational-volitional model of suicide**. This model states that cognitions of defeat, humiliation, and entrapment (i.e., an inability to escape) in response to stressful life events will result in a motivation for suicidal ideation when motivational moderators, such as feelings of thwarted belongingness and perceived burdensomeness, are high. Suicidal ideation will progress to action when volitional moderators, such as acquired capability (habituation/fearlessness about death), impulsivity, and social models of suicide (e.g., family members or friends who have engaged in self-harm or suicide), are high.

The core components of Joiner's and O'Connor's models have received research support. For example, in a large study of 230 suicide attempters, 583 suicide ideators, and 475 individuals with no suicide history, suicide attempters did, indeed, differ from ideators on the volitional factors of fearlessness about death, impulsivity, and exposure to suicidal behaviour in a family member or friend (Dhingra, Boduszek, & O'Connor, 2015). In contrast, and as expected, the two suicide groups did not differ from each other, but did differ from non-suicidal individuals, on the motivational factors.

PREVENTION

The Canadian federal government has passed legislation supporting a national suicide prevention strategy. The nonpartisan bill was strongly endorsed by interim Liberal leader Bob Rae, who himself struggled with depression. In 2004 and again in 2009, the Canadian Association for Suicide Prevention (CASP) released its Blueprint for a Canadian National Suicide Prevention Strategy to provincial governments (CASP, 2004, 2009), which has been used by some provinces in developing their own strategies. It is hoped that a national initiative will enable the development and implementation of standardized, research-based prevention programs that are implemented consistently across the country. Research on suicide prevention has focused on primary preventions that aim to change situations, attitudes, or conditions that predispose individuals toward suicide, and secondary or tertiary interventions that target individuals who have already made suicidal threats or attempts.

Primary preventions include broad public education programs, which seek to teach the signs of mental/emotional distress and to reduce stigma. However, research examining such programs taught in high schools has found that they are not successful. In fact, some researchers have expressed concern that they actually plant the idea of suicide in vulnerable teens, thus increasing their risk (Shaffer & Craft, 1999).

Other primary prevention strategies have focused on restricting access to suicide means. For example, in Britain in the 1950s, 40 percent of all suicides were committed by self-asphyxiation with household cooking gas. In the 1960s, natural gas replaced coal gas, thus reducing the carbon monoxide content. By 1971, suicides by self-asphyxiation had fallen to less than 10 percent of all suicides (Kreitman, 1976), and this method of suicide had disappeared almost completely by 1990 (Williams, 1997). Similarly, a 1998 review of studies examining the relation of suicide and state-implemented gun control legislations from 1982 to 1998 in the United States found that suicide rates typically decreased following implementation of firearm control laws (Lambert & Silva, 1998). Furthermore, suicidal individuals in these studies rarely substituted other means or acquired firearms illegally to commit suicide. Results of these studies strongly suggest that removing the most lethal means of suicide will improve the chances of prevention.

Secondary/tertiary prevention strategies include suicide prevention centres and telephone hotlines. Telephone hotlines have the advantage of being anonymous and offering immediate support. They also are successful in reaching underserved populations, such as those living in rural areas. Most are staffed by volunteers who are supervised by mental health professionals. Research has shown that telephone hotlines are preferred by consumers over mental health centres, and are particularly successful in helping individuals with suicidal ideation. Their use is also related to decreases in suicide rates among white females under age 25, the most frequent users of hotline services (Centers for Disease Control, 1992). However, other research suggests that hotlines have little impact on general suicide rates because they do not reach the people at highest risk for suicide, specifically young males (Shaffer & Craft, 1999).

TREATMENT

The treatment of suicidality depends on the seriousness of the symptoms. The algorithm recommended by the American Association of Family Physicians is displayed in Figure 8.6. Patients who have a clear suicide plan, access to lethal means, and a clear intent to die, and who cannot guarantee their own safety, should be considered a medical emergency and be hospitalized immediately. This is one of the few cases in psychiatric care where an individual's rights may be breached. Specifically, suicidal patients who are a danger to themselves may be hospitalized without their consent, and confidentiality may be breached if, for example, the clinician needs to contact the patient's family or other doctor.

In many cases, the suicidal individual is not in imminent danger and is suitable for outpatient treatment. Meta-analytic evidence has shown that just treating depression with standard anti-depressants or CBT is not enough to reduce suicidal ideation and attempts (Cuijpers et al, 2013). Gregory Brown and A. T. Beck developed a form of CBT specifically to prevent suicide attempts in individuals with significant suicidal ideation (Brown, Henriques, Ratto, & Beck, 2002). The central feature of this form of CBT is to

FIGURE 8.6   Algorithm for the Evaluation of Patients with Suicidal Ideation

identify and modify the thoughts, images, and core beliefs that were activated prior to previous suicide attempts. Therapists also address specific vulnerability factors for suicide, including hopelessness, poor problem solving, poor impulse control, and social isolation. In a study of 120 previous suicide attempters, those randomized to this targeted CBT were 50 percent less likely to reattempt suicide over the subsequent 18 months than were participants in the usual clinical care group. The CBT group also had significantly lower depression severity and hopelessness than the usual clinical care group (Brown et al., 2005).

In addition, the pharmacological agent **ketamine**, a glutamate N-methyl-d-aspartate (NMDA) receptor antagonist, has been explored as an agent that can rapidly reduce suicidal ideation, and thus may be useful in emergency situations of acute suicidality. A small randomized controlled trial showed that a single intravenous infusion of ketamine resulted in a significant drop in suicidal ideation relative to placebo within 48 hours (Murrough et al., 2015). No differences between the two groups were seen at seven days, however, suggesting that adjunctive treatments such as CBT may be required to produce long-lasting changes in suicidality.

6   BEFORE MOVING ON

How can research on the role of biological, psychological, and social factors in suicide help us to understand the alarmingly high rates of suicide among Indigenous teenagers?

Dr. Zindel Segal

Dr. Zindel Segal is the Distinguished Professor of Psychology in Mood Disorders, and the Director of Clinical Training in the Graduate Department of Psychological Clinical Sciences at the University of Toronto. Dr. Segal is providing some of the most important research on cognitive models and treatments for depression. In particular, he is trying to solve the very important problem of depression relapse. Even with today's most effective treatments, the majority of depressed individuals will suffer a return of their symptoms within two years. Indeed, depression is a recurrent condition in at least 50 percent of cases. Segal's research takes a two-pronged approach to this problem. First, he and his colleagues are using innovative methods to identify individuals who are vulnerable to relapse. Second, he is developing innovative treatment methods that specifically aim to prevent relapse in depression.

In his research identifying relapse vulnerability, Segal and his colleagues have been using PET and mood induction techniques to characterize the unique neural and cognitive profile of individuals who relapse. For example, Segal and colleagues (2006) subjected 99 patients who had all recovered from their depression to a sad-mood induction whereby they listened to sad music and thought about a time in their lives when they felt sad.

The researchers then measured patients' cognitive reactivity to the mood induction by having them fill out a measure of dysfunctional thoughts both prior to and following the mood induction. They found that even in this group whose members were *not* currently depressed, those who showed the strongest cognitive reaction to the mood induction were the most likely to suffer a relapse of their depression over the subsequent 18 months (Segal et al., 2006). Segal and his colleagues have theorized that depression relapse vulnerability may be related to the reactivation of negative thinking patterns triggered by transient dysphoric states. That is, in the previously depressed person, mild and transient feelings of sadness may activate negative thinking patterns upon which the patient ruminates (e.g., "I'm sad; my depression must be coming back. I'm never going to get better"), thereby triggering the downward spiral into a full-blown depressive episode. Subsequently, Segal has used neuroimaging methods to show that increased neural activity in the medial prefrontal cortex was associated with rumination in those with a previous depression, but not in health comparison participants. Further, greater activity in the medial prefrontal cortex predicted subsequent depression relapse in the previously depressed group (Farb, Anderson, Bloch, & Segal, 2011).

Photo by Rick Chard. Courtesy of Dr. Zindel V. Segal

Based on these results regarding the *causes* of depression relapse, Segal has helped to develop a treatment specifically geared to preventing relapse: mindfulness-based cognitive therapy (MBCT). This treatment integrates elements of CBT with mindfulness, a meditative practice from Buddhism that was refined by Jon Kabat-Zinn (2003).

Segal's work is an example of translational research at its best. That is, he uses his findings from the basic science of psychopathology mechanisms and *translates* the results of that research into the development of a targeted and cost-effective treatment that prevents the repeated suffering associated with major depression.

SUMMARY

- Depressive disorders involve a change in mood to depression, and include major depressive disorder (MDD) and dysthymia.

- Symptoms of MDD include persistent feelings of sadness, loss of interest in activities, loss of appetite or weight loss, insomnia, low energy, feelings of worthlessness or guilt, difficulty concentrating or making decisions, and suicidality. At least five of these symptoms must be present for at least two weeks, although episodes of MDD typically last for several months.

- Symptoms of persistent depression are chronic feelings of sadness that persist for at least two years, plus at least an additional two depressive symptoms.

- Bipolar disorders involve alternating periods of depression and mania, and include bipolar I disorder (mania alternating with episodes of major depression), bipolar II disorder (hypomania alternating with episodes of major depression), and cyclothymia (hypomania alternating with minor episodes of depression).

- Mood disorders are caused by the interaction of psychological, environmental, and biological variables.

- Early psychodynamic views of depression saw it as stemming from an unresolved regression to the oral stage of development following a real or imagined loss. More recent psychodynamic theories have focused on disruptions of early parent–child attachment and the development of pathological adult relationships.

- Cognitive models stress the role of negative thinking patterns that derive from rigid and tightly connected negative schemas about the self, world, and future.

- Interpersonal models point to specific maladaptive behaviour patterns that depression-prone individuals engage in, ones that heighten risk for interpersonal conflicts and rejections to trigger depression.

- Life stress models propose that depression occurs when a stressful event in the environment triggers an underlying biological or psychological diathesis.

- Biological models of the mood disorders have focused on the role of genetics, neurochemistry, and brain function and structure. Both major depression and bipolar disorder have a strong genetic component, and this may be mediated at least in part by the role of the serotonin transporter gene in heightening sensitivity to stressful life events. Mood disorders are also associated with disruptions in serotonin, norepinephrine, and dopamine neurotransmission. Techniques that look at the function and structure of the brain have found decreased blood flow in certain cortical regions of the brain, as well as increased activity in limbic areas, such as the amygdala, when processing negative information.

- Psychological treatments for major depression include cognitive-behavioural therapy (CBT) and interpersonal psychotherapy (IPT). These emphasize the role of negative thinking patterns and improving interpersonal relationships and functioning through structured, collaborative, and time-limited therapy sessions.

- Biological treatments for major depression involve medications (monoamine oxidase inhibitors, tricyclics, and serotonin reuptake inhibitors) that increase the availability of one or more neurotransmitters. Other biological treatments include electroconvulsive therapy (ECT), transmagnetic stimulation (TMS), vagus nerve stimulation (VNS), and deep brain stimulation (DBS). All of these more invasive techniques have shown promise for severely and chronically depressed patients who do not respond to psychotherapy or medication.

- Biological treatments for bipolar disorder include lithium, anticonvulsant medication, or antipsychotic medication.

- Adjunctive psychological treatments have recently been developed to help improve remission rates and prevent relapse in bipolar disorder. These include family-focused therapy (FFT), interpersonal and social rhythm therapy (IPSRT), and cognitive therapy (CT).

- Suicide is a devastating problem with huge economic and human costs, and it is now the second-leading cause of death in young people. Men in all age groups are over three times more likely than women to complete suicide, while women are three times more likely than men to attempt suicide. Suicide rates also differ across age categories, with males aged 19 to 24 and over 70 being at greatest risk. Indigenous communities in Canada have suicide rates two to four times greater than in the rest of the country.

- Suicide is caused by a variety of social, psychological, and biological variables, including genetic predisposition and low serotonin neurotransmission, a sense of detachment from society, and severe stress.

- Broad primary prevention strategies have not been effective in reducing suicide rates, although strategies that focus on reducing access to lethal means have shown more promise. Treatment of suicide depends on the severity of the behaviour and can range from inpatient hospitalization to outpatient medication and/or psychotherapy.

KEY TERMS

bipolar and related disorders (p. 174)

bipolar I disorder (p. 177)

bipolar II disorder (p. 177)

cognitive-behaviour therapy (CBT) (p. 187)

cognitive distortions (p. 181)

cognitive triad (p. 181)

cyclothymia (p. 177)

depressive disorders (p. 174)

diathesis-stress model (p. 181)

electronconvulsive therapy (ECT) (p. 194)

excessive reassurance seeking (p. 182)

family-focused therapy (FFT) (p. 193)

hypomania (p. 176)

hypothalamic-pituitary-adrenal (HPA) axis (p. 185)

imagined loss (p. 173)

interpersonal and social rhythm therapy (IPSRT) (p. 193)

interpersonal model (p.197)

interpersonal psychotherapy (IPT) (p. 190)

ketamine (p. 199)

lithium (p. 191)

major depressive disorder (MDD) (p. 174)

mania (p. 176)

monoamine oxidase inhibitors (MAOIs) (p. 190)

mood disorders (p. 173)

motivational-volitional model of suicide (p.198)

negative feedback seeking (p. 182)

persistent depressive disorder (p. 176)

phototherapy (p. 193)

schemas (p. 181)

seasonal affective disorder (SAD) (p. 178)

selective serotonin reuptake inhibitor (SSRI) (p. 190)

specifiers (p. 178)

stress generation hypothesis (p. 182)

suicide (p. 195)

transcranial magnetic stimulation (TMS) (p. 195)

tricyclic antidepressants (TCAs) (p. 190)

vagus nerve stimulation (VNS) (p. 195)

R. WALTER HEINRICHS

•

FARENA PINNOCK

•

MELISSA PARLAR

CHAPTER

9

Victor de Schwanberg/Science Source

Schizophrenia Spectrum and Other Psychotic Disorders

LEARNING OBJECTIVES

AFTER READING THIS CHAPTER, STUDENTS WILL BE ABLE TO:

1 Explain why schizophrenia is viewed as one of the most serious, disabling, and complex mental disorders.

2 Identify the steps involved in a DSM-5 diagnosis of schizophrenia and the strengths and weaknesses of this approach.

3 Explain why the concept of diathesis, or vulnerability, is so important in theories of schizophrenia.

4 Describe reasons why genes influence but do not determine who develops schizophrenia.

5 Identify the most common cognitive and neurobiological abnormalities associated with schizophrenia.

6 Identify and explain the effectiveness of antipsychotic medication and psychosocial therapies in the treatment of schizophrenia.

To understand schizophrenia and why it is arguably the most severe and disabling form of mental disorder, try to suspend, at least temporarily, the compelling images, beliefs, and assumptions that tend to crowd in whenever the word *schizophrenia* is mentioned. Concentrate instead on the words of a patient named Ruth as she describes her experience with the disorder:

> Around my neck, and hanging down from each shoulder there is something like a creature. It comes at night. I know it's there because I can feel weight. It coils around me yet remains invisible. An invisible burden. It feels like an enormous leech on my body and it touches me in familiar ways and in intimate places. It reeks of animal smells. It has a strong smell that rises from its sliding body. It is incredibly powerful and irresistible. I can't resist it (Heinrichs, 2001, p. 3).

This woman's name is not really Ruth, but she is a real person and the words are her own, drawn from interview and case notes. Imagine what it must be like to feel and smell something alien and disturbing like this creature and to feel that it has power over you. For Ruth it was not a symptom of an illness, it was an utterly convincing experience. It was her "reality." In fact, the experience was so unpleasant that she thought about suicide as a way of freeing herself. However, instead she went to a local hospital and told the nurses that she was thinking about death. This led to an admission of several weeks during which she was treated for depression—not schizophrenia (see Chapter 8). Ruth never actually told anyone about the creature and only described her thoughts of wanting to die. The antidepressant medication she was given helped with the death feelings, but did not make the "creature" go away. She was eventually given the diagnosis of schizophrenia after reluctantly describing the creature to a psychiatrist.

What could do this to a person? Is such a severe mental illness rooted in Ruth's psychological development and background? Unfortunately, the roots of schizophrenia are difficult to find and trace. Ruth was born in an average-size Canadian city, with parents who also seemed to be average in many ways. There is no record of emotional, physical, or sexual abuse in her past, and neither parent was ever treated for psychiatric problems. Ruth had average marks until the second year of high school, when concentration problems began to emerge. Her marks slipped badly and she stopped doing homework. About this time she suddenly decided to drop out of school and marry her boyfriend. But the marriage lasted only a few months because her new husband left and refused to return. A short time later Ruth began to think about death, and it is unclear exactly when the "creature" experience began.

Did rejection cause her disorder? It certainly did not help, but if emotional pain and rejection were sufficient to cause insanity, wouldn't we all become insane at some time in our lives? In any case, Ruth is just one person with schizophrenia and the disorder has many forms and faces. Consider William, for example, as he describes his experience of schizophrenia:

> The most hilarious aspect of the hospital is the shower. Why would they ask God to have a shower? This makes me laugh. I have heard the voices of great men in history and seen the rainbow of hope. I am willing to take on da Vinci and beat him, but the rhythm of the building is hypnotic and it unbalances me. If only they would do EEG and IQ tests I could prove that I am God. My beard has grown to fulfill the prophecy of a King of Kings, and I know that my powers will be lost on my 33rd birthday. I anticipate my crucifixion. But I will search for the devil and kill him. Perhaps if I kill my brother I will be the only son in the Father's eye. Yes, I must go and look for my brother the devil (Heinrichs, 2001, p. 4).

Unlike Ruth's situation and voluntary admission, it was the police who often brought William to hospital. For example, on one occasion the landlord went to William's apartment looking for unpaid rent. The door was wide open and William was running around the rooms smearing excrement on the walls and furniture. On other occasions he became involved with street drugs and alcohol and was charged with assault. Moreover, a look into William's life and background shows that his mother had schizophrenia and attempted suicide. His father seems to have had normal physical and mental health. William's problems began early with learning difficulties and failures in primary school grades. He left after one year of high school and tried to work, but soon drifted into gang organizations and the use of street drugs and spent a year in jail. Indeed, until his mid-twenties he was more likely to be known to police and spend time incarcerated than to have contact with mental health professionals or hospitals. William subsequently had many psychiatric hospital admissions and was extensively assessed and examined. For example, it was found that he had abnormal reflexes even though his brain scan was normal. In addition, his electroencephalogram (EEG) suggested the possibility of a seizure disorder (epilepsy). Nonetheless, his diagnosis was schizophrenia.

Ruth and William are two very different people who share the same diagnosis. Ruth's family background is largely empty of clues about the causes of mental illness, although she did experience a severe and painful personal rejection. William, in contrast, grew up with familial mental illness and experienced many adjustment difficulties and social adversity long before his psychotic symptoms emerged. He also showed "soft" signs of brain damage. There is no shortage of potential clues in William's case. The two patients with schizophrenia also differed in their symptoms. Ruth was convinced that she could smell and feel a "creature," whereas William tried to live out his "divinity" and "heard" and "spoke" with famous historical figures. Ruth felt weak and controlled and William felt strong and powerful. How can patients be so different and still have the same disorder?

(Based on information presented in Heinrichs, 2001.)

Introduction and Historical Perspective

Across the range of abnormal psychology and psychiatry, is there a disorder as strange and challenging, as poorly portrayed and misunderstood as **schizophrenia**? It is difficult to read about this severe form of mental disorder with an open mind and difficult to resist the popular assumptions and widely held beliefs that spring up whenever the puzzling disorder is mentioned. Images of "raving lunatics," so-called crazy people with danger if not murder in mind, people who are completely irrational and unpredictable—these are the associations of the word *schizophrenia*. And then there is the incorrect idea that the disorder involves

a "split personality," people within people, perhaps in conflict or completely unaware of each other. Of course, not all preconceptions about schizophrenia are negative and sinister. There is also the notion that a person with the disorder is unusually creative or "spiritual," perhaps misunderstood and alienated, but with special insights into the meaning of life and with special access to sources of inspiration and genius denied to "normal" people. Most of these assumptions and ideas are inaccurate or at most partly true. This chapter will explore what is known about schizophrenia—its characteristic features, possible causes, and current treatments.

The two case studies of Ruth and William illustrate an important and basic fact about the disorder: schizophrenia is a complex condition characterized by **heterogeneity**. In other words, there is a tendency for people with the disorder to differ from each other in symptoms, family and personal background, response to treatment, and ability to live outside of hospital. Heterogeneity makes it difficult to predict how a person will be affected by schizophrenia; what their prospects are for the future; and whether their condition will improve, stabilize, or worsen. For example, a significant proportion of patients, perhaps more than two-thirds , improve over time and in response to treatment (Barry, Gaughan, & Hunter, 2012). Indeed, although there is no cure, the outlook for a person with schizophrenia is better than ever before in terms of treatment options and both drug and psychological therapies. Yet not all patients benefit from medication. For example, up to one-third of patients continue to suffer from symptoms such as hallucinations or delusions (Tandon, Nasrallah, & Keshavan, 2010), some endure unpleasant side effects, and many are difficult to assist with counselling or rehabilitation. Also, what does "getting better" really mean? Does it mean that symptoms disappear, or should it also mean that a person is able to resume career and educational plans, reconnect with friends and family, and lead a normal life (Shrivastava, Johnston, Shah, & Burueau, 2010)? Which patients will do relatively well, and who will struggle with partly controlled symptoms and persisting distress for most of their lives? There are only partial answers to these questions. Moreover, many patients and their families have to cope with the stigma and negative image associated with serious mental illness (Corrigan, Morris, Michaels, Rafacz, & Rüsch, 2012). Hence, it is not surprising that a sense of pessimism and uncertainty still surrounds schizophrenia.

PREVALENCE, ONSET, DEMOGRAPHIC AND SOCIO-ECONOMIC FEATURES

In North America and Europe there is less than a 1 percent risk that a person will develop schizophrenia at some point in their lifetime (McGrath, Saha, Chant, & Welham, 2008). However, the **prevalence**, or total number of cases with the disorder at a given point in time, changes depending on how the diagnosis is made (Government of Canada, 2012; Mueser & McGurk, 2004). If the estimated prevalence

Schizophrenia is not
split personality

rate of about 1 percent is accepted, schizophrenia is twice as common as Alzheimer's disease and five times as common as multiple sclerosis. Hence, there may be more than 300 000 people with schizophrenia in Canada.

The development of psychotic symptoms marks the formal onset of the first episode of schizophrenia. While it is possible for the disorder to develop at any age, these symptoms tend to manifest between late adolescence and early adulthood (typically between 15 and 45 years of age). The onset of schizophrenia may be abrupt or gradual, but most often a variety of clinically significant symptoms emerge slowly over time. Men and women are at roughly equal risk and recent evidence suggests the disorder strikes each sex at about the same age (Eranti, McCabe, Bundy, & Murray, 2013). Schizophrenia rarely occurs before adolescence or after 45 years of age. If the disorder develops after the age of 45, it is more common among women and seems to comprise more emotional and mood-related symptoms (Government of Canada, 2012).

Predicting the course and outcome of schizophrenia in individual patients is difficult and in need of further investigation. Overall, poor outcome is more likely among males, individuals who develop the disorder at a younger age, and those who experience a longer delay between the first appearance of symptoms and treatment (Häfner & an der Heiden, 1999). While the course of schizophrenia varies substantially across individuals, it tends to be a chronic and relapsing disorder. The course appears to be favourable in approximately 20 percent, with about one in seven patients experiencing both **remission** (reduction) of symptoms and improved daily life functioning (APA, 2013; Jääskeläinen et al., 2013).

Schizophrenia occurs throughout the world and at all socio-economic levels (Kwok, 2014). Once individuals develop the disorder, they are less likely to complete their education and unemployment rates are as high as 90 percent (Marwaha & Johnson, 2004). People with schizophrenia are more likely to develop additional psychiatric problems, including depression and suicidal behaviour as well as drug and alcohol abuse (Bosanac & Castle, 2013). And then there are the financial and social costs associated with this disabling and often lifelong condition. According to the Canadian Mental Health Association, schizophrenia rivals stroke and heart disease in terms of hospital care, with 1 out of 12 beds occupied by people with the disorder. In addition, costs to the Canadian taxpayer amount to billions of dollars annually in direct and indirect health care, family benefits, social support services, and productivity loss due to morbidity or early mortality (Goeree et al., 2005). More global measures estimate that approximately 3 percent of the total burden of human disease is attributed to schizophrenia. By any measure schizophrenia places a heavy burden on patients, their families, and society.

Over the last three decades, with the rapid growth of knowledge about brain biology and genetics, research on schizophrenia has increased substantially. The number of articles published on the disorder has multiplied since the early 1970s to the current rate of about 5000 articles a year. Similarly, the International Congress on Schizophrenia Research attracted only 175 attendees when it met for the first time in 1987. By 2015 attendance had grown to 1000 researchers, clinicians, and students from over 45 countries and the conference included over 1400 scientific presentations. In Canada, research funding has increased through the Canadian Institutes of Health Research and provincial granting agencies. The National Institute of Mental Health in the United States is directing enormous resources—billions of dollars—to the study of serious mental illness. Yet, despite these efforts, understanding schizophrenia remains a major scientific challenge. It is not even known if the disorder has been part of the human condition for thousands of years or whether it is a latecomer, a "new" disorder that was rare before the year 1800. Could it be that schizophrenia is a "modern" condition and only about 200 years old (see Focus box 9.1)?

❶ BEFORE MOVING ON

> Why is schizophrenia so disabling and in need of so much research funding and study?

HISTORICAL PERSPECTIVE: THE MISSING ILLNESS

It is often assumed that schizophrenia-like illness has always existed because "**madness**" and "insanity" have been documented since the beginnings of civilization, medicine, and writing. Certainly, there are many examples of irrational and bizarre behaviour in the Bible, in other ancient texts, and in the writing of many non-Western cultures (Haldipur, 1984; Hershkowitz, 1998; Jeste, del Carmen, Lohr, & Wyatt, 1985). Yet it is a mistake to assume that a disorder akin to modern schizophrenia has always been part of the human condition. In other words, although "madness" in some form existed in the past, it is uncertain whether these historical disturbances included schizophrenia. For example, descriptions of madness and lunacy before about 1800 suggest that these conditions occurred at any time of life rather than primarily in young people. In addition, experiences like **auditory hallucinations** or "hearing voices" and other sounds occur in up to 70 percent of patients with schizophrenia at some point during their disorder (Andreasen & Flaum, 1991). Yet auditory hallucinations are extremely rare in cases of madness prior to 1700 (Hare, 1988; Torrey & Miller, 2001). Moreover, historically documented madness seldom lasted more than a few days, and was often drug and alcohol–induced or related to other diseases. In fact, the first recognizable descriptions of modern schizophrenia did not appear in English or French until the early years of the nineteenth century (Haslam, 1809/1976; Pinel, 1809).

The historical evidence and lack of case material have encouraged the view that a schizophrenia-like disorder was

An Eighteenth-Century Sculptor with Schizophrenia

Although at least one review (Hare, 1988) has concluded that no clear examples of schizophrenia-like illness can be found in the eighteenth century, one probable case is well known to historians of European art. Franz Messerschmidt (1736–1783) was born and studied in Munich, Germany, and then found employment at the imperial Austrian court in Vienna. There is no doubt that he was an artist of major talent and many contemporaries recognized his outstanding skills as a sculptor and portraitist (see Pötzl-Malikova, 1982). Yet signs of mental disorder were noted soon after he received a teaching appointment in 1769. Although never described as "insane," he was passed over for promotion because of persisting reports of "confusion" and a "not perfectly healthy imagination." Messerschmidt complained that all other teachers were his enemies and he fled from Vienna, eventually living for many years alone on the outskirts of Bratislava.

It seems clear that Messerschmidt had psychological problems, but did he suffer from schizophrenia? There is no evidence that he was ever hospitalized for insanity, although he may have consulted physicians, including, perhaps, Franz Mesmer, the father of hypnosis (see Pötzl-Malikova, 1987). However, it is possible to make a good case for the disorder even in the absence of hospital or physician records. The evidence takes the form of a visitor's account of Messerschmidt's conversations, living situation, and artistic production, written by Friedrich Nicolai in 1785. Nicolai was a travel writer and apparently gained the sculptor's trust to the point where Messerschmidt was willing to talk about his artwork and creative process. Of special interest from the standpoint of abnormal psychology were the artist's descriptions of nightly visits by demons. These demons tortured him "despite having lived a life of chastity." One demon in particular was troublesome, and was referred to as the "demon of proportion." This demon was envious because the artist had almost achieved perfect proportion in his sculpture. Part of the demon's torture involved causing Messerschmidt pain in his lower abdomen and thighs, especially when he was sculpting a part of the face that "is analogous to a certain part of the lower region of the body." In order to control such demons Messerschmidt pinched himself in the right side under the ribs and simultaneously grimaced into a mirror "in the exact required relationship to the pinching of his flesh." According to Nicolai, the sculptor worked on his piece, looked into the mirror at half-minute intervals, and made "with the greatest exactitude,

Franz Xaver Messerschmidt (1736–1783), *Der Gähner* (*The Yawner*). During the years of his illness, Messerschmidt sculpted a series of portrait heads that were given fanciful names after the artist's death. However, it is likely that many were self-portraits and expressed his experience of being tormented by psychotic delusions. Reproduced with permission of the Szépmüvészeti Múzeum, Budapest.

precisely that grimace which he just needed." An example of one of these sculptures is presented in the photograph.

Messerschmidt's experience of being persecuted by envious demons who could be controlled by sculpted facial expressions may represent the kind of **delusional thinking** seen frequently in schizophrenia. In addition, his career decline, increased social isolation, and withdrawal are typical consequences of the modern disorder. Although the biography of Messerschmidt is incomplete, the information on his life and disorder are highly suggestive of a schizophrenia-like condition. And this from a century declared devoid of medical and psychiatric accounts of the condition. ●

very rare, perhaps even absent, until the late eighteenth century. Then, for some reason, cases of insanity surged, with physicians and asylum custodians unable to cope with the rapid increase in numbers. For example, careful record keeping in Canada's Maritime provinces shows that the number of insanity cases per 1000 people in the population increased by more than 2000 percent between 1847 and 1960 (Torrey & Miller, 2001)! It has been speculated that increasing industrialization, the movement of people to cities from towns and countryside, and environmental changes may have been

involved in the sudden and escalating emergence of schizophrenia in modern life.

Of course, the idea that schizophrenia is a recent disorder has many critics. Turner (1992) argued that people in earlier times viewed mental disorder differently and may not have recorded or commented on symptoms and characteristics that help to separate schizophrenia from more generic categories like "lunacy" and insanity. Thus, the disorder existed but was not recognized as a distinct entity until Haslam's (1809/1976) case studies and the later and definitive descriptions of Kraepelin (1896, 1919) and Bleuler (1911/1950). It is important to note, however, that some "modern" psychiatric disorders, including mania and depression (Porter, 1995) as well as mental retardation (Berrios, 1995), are recognizable in historical medical texts and even in ancient writings. Accordingly, there is no easy answer to the question of whether schizophrenia existed in the distant past, and the historical origins of the disorder are likely to remain controversial and uncertain (Heinrichs, 2003).

Typical Characteristics

POSITIVE (PSYCHOTIC) AND NEGATIVE SYMPTOMS

Characteristic symptoms of schizophrenia may be broadly classified as either positive or negative. **Positive symptoms** refer to exaggerated, distorted adaptations of normal behaviour. They include the more obvious signs of **psychosis**, namely, delusions, hallucinations, **thought and speech disorder**, and grossly disorganized or **catatonic behaviour**. **Negative symptoms**, on the other hand, refer to the absence or loss of typical behaviours and experiences. Negative symptoms may take the form of sparse speech and language, social withdrawal, and **avolition** (apathy and loss of motivation). **Anhedonia** (an inability to feel pleasure, as well as lack of emotional responsiveness) and diminished attention and concentration are also considered negative symptoms.

HALLUCINATIONS **Hallucinations** are misinterpretations of sensory perceptions that occur while a person is awake and conscious and in the absence of corresponding external stimuli. In other words, people hear, see, smell, or feel things that are not really present. Alternatively, perhaps they misinterpret normal sensory experiences. Hallucinations occur in all sensory modalities, but auditory hallucinations, in which the person hears voices or noises, are the most common form experienced by patients with schizophrenia. These voices are perceived as distinct from the patient's own thoughts and may include instructions to perform actions that involve self-harm or danger. They may urge the patient to stop fulfilling his or her responsibilities, or the voices may be insulting at one point and complimentary at another. Emil Kraepelin (1919), who first described schizophrenia in detail, mentioned patients who "heard" the roars of Satan, but also whispering children and laughter. One man was told where to stand and when to smile, whereas another heard gossip about his own behaviour.

Research suggests that hallucinations develop from a "misattribution of sensory experience." This involves an inability to discriminate between internal and external sources of information and experience. Patients with schizophrenia who have hallucinations may confuse their own responses and the responses of other people or fail to recognize their own inner speech (Upthegrove et al., 2016). Hence, Ruth, the patient who smelled and felt a creature around her neck, may have failed to recognize her own body and instead experienced its sensations as stemming from somewhere—or something—else. Similarly, hearing voices may result from patients' inability to recognize their own thoughts and a tendency to attribute them to external sources.

DELUSIONS **Delusions** are implausible beliefs that persist despite reliable contradictory evidence. They reflect a disorder of thought content and may include a complex delusional belief "system" or just a single belief relating to one aspect of daily life. Delusions may reflect persecutory, referential, somatic, religious, or grandiose themes and meanings (see Table 9.1). **Persecutory delusions**, or "paranoid" delusions, in which individuals believe that they are being pursued or targeted for sabotage, ridicule, or deception, are the most common form of delusion. Kraepelin (1919) described patients who were convinced that hospital attendants were poisoning the food and water or that the German emperor's spies were tracking them.

Referential delusions involve the belief that common, meaningless occurrences have significant and personal relevance. The advertisement on the back page of a magazine, for example, may be interpreted as a signal to eat a specific cereal for breakfast. In contrast, **somatic delusions** involve beliefs related to the patient's body. Kraepelin (1919) described patients who were convinced that their inner organs had been turned to dust or that they had a special "nerve" of laughter in their stomachs that was the origin of all humour in the world.

A **religious delusion** often involves the belief that biblical or other religious passages or stories offer the way to destroy or to save the world. The case of William, described at the beginning of the chapter, illustrates how someone can believe that he is living out a biblical prophecy. Similarly, **delusions of grandeur** may entail a belief in divine or special powers that can change the course of history or provide

TABLE 9.1 COMMON DELUSIONS EXPERIENCED BY PATIENTS WITH SCHIZOPHRENIA

Type	Content	Examples
Persecutory	A belief that the individual is being conspired against, deceived, or persecuted	"Strangers on the street are undercover agents following me."
Referential	A belief that events, objects, or other individuals have personally relevant meaning	"Each song that a DJ selects for a radio playlist represents a special truth about my life."
Somatic	Perception of a change or disturbance in personal appearance or bodily function	"My body is inhabited by extraterrestrial beings that give me headaches."
Religious	Unusual religious experiences or beliefs	"Satan is leaving messages for me in television programs and emails."
Grandiose	Possession of special or divine powers, abilities, or knowledge	"I have the power to change the course of history."

a communication channel to God. For example, Kraepelin (1919) described a patient who believed that all the world's armies were under his personal command.

One theory proposes that persecutory delusions develop in people who make interpretations of experience too quickly, jump to conclusions based on minimal evidence, and then resist alternative explanations (Freeman, Pugh, & Garety, 2008; Moritz et al., 2017). Another theory proposes a bias in reasoning so that negative events are always perceived as coming from the environment or from other people (Bentall, 1994). Still another theory holds that persecutory delusions reflect an inability to imagine the feelings, perspectives, and experiences of other people (Corcoran, Cahill, & Frith, 1997).

DISORGANIZED SPEECH AND THOUGHT DISORDER

Unusual-sounding, nonsensical speech often signifies the existence of a formal thought disorder, a characteristic given great emphasis by the pioneering Swiss psychiatrist Bleuler (1911/1950) in his early descriptions of schizophrenia. The disorganization of speech in patients with schizophrenia presents itself in several ways. **Loosening of associations** and logical connections between ideas occurs and the thought-disordered patient shifts quickly from one topic to another. In addition, answers to questions are "tangential" or hardly related to the original point or request being made. Bleuler gave many examples of this kind of disturbance, including one by a patient who wrote a letter explaining the nature of the Catholic rosary as "a prayer multiplier, and this in turn is a prayer for multiplying and as such is nothing else but a prayer mill, and is therefore a mill-prayer machine which is again a prayer-mill machine" and continued in this way for several pages (Bleuler, 1911/1950, pp. 19, 28). In current practice, a common way to elicit thought and language disorder is to ask a patient to explain a proverb or saying. For example, one man explained the proverb "Don't change horses when crossing a stream" in the following way: "That's wish-bell. Double vision. It's like walking across a person's eye and reflecting the personality. It works on you, like dying and going to the spiritual world, but landing in the Vella world" (Harrow, Lanin-Kettering, & Miller, 1989, p. 609). Thought disorder reveals itself in the structure of spoken or written language and therefore provides a more objective index of schizophrenic disturbance than symptoms such as hallucinations and delusions. However, it is the least common of the positive symptoms (Andreasen & Flaum, 1991). Thought disorder may reflect the presence of more basic cognitive problems. In particular, a disturbance in speech production and control with abnormal "spread" of activated word meanings seems to be associated with this symptom (Hinzen & Rosselló, 2015; Kreher, Holcomb, Goff, & Kuperberg, 2008).

NEGATIVE AND EMOTIONAL SYMPTOMS

In contrast to the reality distortion of positive symptoms, the negative symptoms of schizophrenia represent deficits and losses in normal functioning. They include avolition and restricted affect. Avolition, or apathy, refers to the inability to initiate and persevere in activities. In addition, many patients have diminished emotional expression—failing to convey any feeling in their face, tone of voice, or body language. The range and intensity of emotional expressiveness is often restricted in schizophrenia. Anhedonia is consistent with the patient's apathy and denotes a lack of pleasure or reward experiences. Negative symptoms of schizophrenia can also be seen in the deterioration of academic or occupational proficiency that is usually observed, perhaps due to a weakening in cognitive efficiency.

Bleuler (1911/1950) was especially impressed with the apparent lack of emotional response in many patients with schizophrenia when crisis situations or emergencies were encountered. For example, he described an emergency evacuation prompted by fire on the hospital ward and noted a striking lack of interest and concern in several patients. Many also neglected their appearance and seemed to lack any drive or motivation, spending long hours in silent and solitary detachment from other people. Negative symptoms are moderately associated with impairment on objective tests of cognitive abilities, including attention, learning and memory, and mental efficiency, and also relate to everyday functioning and community adjustment (Dominguez, Viechtbauer, Simons, van Os, & Krabbendam, 2009; Harvey, Koren, Reichenberg, & Bowie, 2006).

MOTOR SYMPTOMS AND GROSSLY DISORGANIZED OR CATATONIC BEHAVIOUR

These behaviours refer to deficits in movement ranging from agitation to immobility. Grossly disorganized behaviour reflects difficulty with goal-directed behaviour. It thus often manifests itself in unpredictable movements; problems performing everyday activities, such as dressing or preserving personal hygiene and inappropriate sexual behaviour. Catatonic behaviour, in contrast, refers to the other end of the motor spectrum. It involves a significant reduction in responsiveness to the environment wherein patients assume unusual and rigid postures and resist efforts by others to change their position. Alternatively, they may engage in random, undue motor activity, or exhibit **waxy flexibility**, allowing others to move their body and limbs and then maintaining the new position. Catatonic behaviour, especially the rigid maintenance of postures and positions, seems to have been common in the time of Kraepelin (1919) and Bleuler (1911/1950), but is now observed less frequently (Andreasen & Flaum, 1991). Agitated and disorganized or otherwise abnormal movements are seen frequently in patients, but it is unclear whether they represent a distinct group of schizophrenia-related symptoms, medication side effects or the influence of another disorder (Walther, 2015).

Diagnosis and Assessment

DSM-5 DIAGNOSTIC CRITERIA

The diagnosis of schizophrenia is based on six diagnostic criteria identified by the DSM-5 (APA, 2013; see Table 9.2). These criteria encompass a combination of symptoms and clinical features that are considered to define the disorder.

TABLE 9.2   DSM-5 DIAGNOSTIC CRITERIA FOR SCHIZOPHRENIA

A. Two (or more) of the following, each present for a significant portion of time during a 1-month period (or less if successfully treated). At least one of these must be (1), (2), or (3):

1. Delusions.

2. Hallucinations.

3. Disorganized speech (e.g., frequent derailment or incoherence).

4. Grossly disorganized or catatonic behavior.

5. Negative symptoms (i.e., diminished emotional expression or avolition).

B. For a significant portion of the time since the onset of the disturbance, level of functioning in one or more major areas, such as work, interpersonal relations, or self-care, is markedly below the level achieved prior to the onset (or when the onset is in childhood or adolescence, there is failure to achieve expected level of interpersonal, academic, or occupational functioning).

C. Continuous signs of the disturbance persist for at least 6 months. This 6-month period must include at least 1 month of symptoms (or less if successfully treated) that meet Criterion A (i.e., active-phase symptoms) and may include periods of prodromal or residual symptoms. During these prodromal or residual periods, the signs of the disturbance may be manifested by only negative symptoms or by two or more symptoms listed in Criterion A present in an attenuated form (e.g., odd beliefs, unusual perceptual experiences).

D. Schizoaffective disorder and depressive or bipolar disorder with psychotic features have been ruled out because either 1) no major depressive or manic episodes have occurred concurrently with the active-phase symptoms, or 2) if mood episodes have occurred during active-phase symptoms, they have been present for a minority of the total duration of the active and residual periods of the illness.

E. The disturbance is not attributable to the physiological effects of a substance (e.g., a drug of abuse, a medication) or another medical condition.

F. If there is a history of autism spectrum disorder or a communication disorder of childhood onset, the additional diagnosis of schizophrenia is made only if prominent delusions or hallucinations, in addition to the other required symptoms of schizophrenia, are also present for at least 1 month (or less if successfully treated).

They include characteristic symptoms (Criterion A), marked social or occupational dysfunction during the course of the disorder (Criterion B), persistence of the disturbance for at least six months (Criterion C), the exclusion of concurrent schizoaffective or mood disorders during the active phase of schizophrenia symptoms (Criterion D), the exclusion of substance use or medical conditions as a causal influence of the disorder (Criterion E), and consideration of any history of autism spectrum disorder or a communication

disorder of childhood onset (Criterion F). The characteristic symptoms of schizophrenia include delusions (Criterion A1), hallucinations (Criterion A2), disorganized speech (Criterion A3), grossly disorganized or catatonic behaviour (Criterion A4), and negative symptoms (Criterion A5). The first four symptom-related diagnostic criteria for schizophrenia reflect positive symptoms, comprising the more obvious signs of psychosis. The fifth characteristic symptom encompasses negative symptoms. The DSM-5 recognizes two negative symptoms, namely, avolition and diminished emotional expression.

The DSM-5 definition of schizophrenia has been likened to a diagnostic "menu." In other words, the disorder is not defined by any one symptom or cluster of symptoms. Rather, a selection of qualitatively different symptoms is required for a diagnosis and none are unique to schizophrenia. Criterion A specifies that a minimum of two out of the five characteristic symptoms must be present concurrently during the period of acute disturbance referred to as the "active phase" of the disorder. However, the DSM-5 states that the individual must have at least one of three core positive symptoms: delusions, hallucinations, and disorganized speech for a diagnosis.

CASE EXAMPLES Consider Ruth and William and the way their respective clinical profiles fit into the DSM-5 diagnostic criteria for schizophrenia (APA, 2013). Ruth experienced tactile (touch) and olfactory (smell) hallucinations of an animal, which she believed to be hanging around her neck. At least one more characteristic symptom was required for diagnosis. She exhibited withdrawal and diminished emotional expression, which are negative symptoms of schizophrenia. Ruth thus met Criterion A for schizophrenia. William, on the other hand, experienced bizarre religious and grandiose delusions of divinity as well as auditory hallucinations and displayed grossly disorganized behaviour. His symptom picture actually exceeds the number required by the DSM-5 Criterion A.

Both Ruth and William exhibited deterioration in personal, social, and occupation functioning, thus meeting Criterion B for schizophrenia. Ruth neglected her personal hygiene. As well, she was unable to live successfully in supported housing. William was unable to live independently, at times vomiting, defecating, and urinating in his apartment, or engaging in chaotic behaviour. Ruth and William also met Criterion C for schizophrenia, each presenting with more than one month of active symptoms, and experiencing the disturbance for over six months.

It is important and sometimes difficult to distinguish the negative symptoms of schizophrenia from depressive and other mood-related symptoms and also to ensure that positive symptoms do not reflect mood-congruent delusions and hence a mood disorder rather than schizophrenia. Ruth's reduced emotional expression and withdrawal, thoughts of death, suicidal ideas, hopelessness, and self-deprecation suggest the presence of severe depression with psychotic features. However, careful questioning and review of hospital records and interview notes showed that her hallucinations and withdrawal persisted even when

Schizophrenia: Fact and Fiction

Schizophrenia is a complicated disorder surrounded by false beliefs and half-truths. For example, the disorder has nothing to do with "split" or multiple personalities, but this incorrect idea persists in the public mind and entertainment media. Another inaccuracy involves a perceived connection to violence. Many people seem to think that a mental disorder necessarily makes people dangerous and aggressive. However, research shows that schizophrenia is associated with only a slight increase in the risk of violent behaviour (Douglas, Guy, & Hart, 2009; Walsh, Buchanan, & Fahy, 2002). Aggression is most common among younger male patients with a history of violence, a tendency to stop taking medication, impulsivity, and substance abuse (APA, 2013). In fact, drug abuse rather than mental illness by itself seems to substantially increase the risk of violent behaviour (Fazel, Gulati, Linsell, Geddes, & Grann, 2009). The vast majority of people with schizophrenia are not violent and are more likely to be victims of crime than is the general public (Brekke, Prindle, Bae, & Long, 2001).

Instead of aggression against others, schizophrenia brings with it a greater risk for self-harm in the form of suicide (Palmer, Pankratz, & Bostwick, 2005). Approximately 20 percent of individuals with the disorder attempt suicide on one or more occasions and 5 percent succeed (Hor & Taylor, 2010). Suicidal behaviour may be a response to the depressive mood experienced by many patients, but may also reflect the influence of delusions and hallucinations (Hor & Taylor, 2010). Recall the case of Ruth described in the beginning of the chapter. She viewed the idea of taking her own life as a way to escape from very upsetting symptoms.

Another widely held belief is that people with schizophrenia cannot lead productive lives and invariably end up as homeless

"street people." This is certainly not true. Many people with the disorder can work, live independently, and contribute to society. However, deficits in cognition, including social cognition, the stigma of mental illness, and lack of support make it difficult for patients to live autonomously, finish their education, maintain employment, and establish friendships and romantic relationships (Bowie et al., 2008; Penn, Sanna, & Roberts, 2008). Nonetheless, many patients with schizophrenia do well living in the community if they receive appropriate treatment and support.

An unfortunate fact about the disorder is that it significantly increases the likelihood of substance abuse involving alcohol, cannabis (marijuana), and nicotine. It is remarkable that people with schizophrenia seem especially prone to nicotine addiction, with over half smoking cigarettes regularly (APA, 2013). Indeed, smoking is more common in schizophrenia than in other psychiatric disorders, with rates up to 90 percent reported in some studies (Dickerson et al., 2013; Strand & Nybäck, 2005). Furthermore, people with schizophrenia find it extremely hard to quit smoking and tend to start again after completing programs designed to help them stop (Bennett, Wilson, Genderson, & Saperstein, 2013).

The reason why smoking rates remain so high in schizophrenia is puzzling, but research is providing clues. Patients with the disorder may smoke to help them cope with the negative symptoms and cognitive deficits they experience (Šagud et al., 2009). Unlike other forms of substance use, smoking may have benefits for patients because nicotine seems to improve cognitive brain functions, including attention, memory, and sensory processing (Fisher et al., 2012; Freedman, 2014). It follows that cognitive deficits are most severe in non-smoking patients with schizophrenia (Wing, Bacher, Sacco, & George, 2011). No wonder smoking patients find it hard to quit! ●

mood-related symptoms improved. This led to the conclusion that she met Criterion D for schizophrenia.

Additional "exclusionary" criteria include elimination of drug effects or coexisting diseases as causes of psychosis or negative symptoms (Criterion E), as well as the possibility of developmental and childhood disorders as contributing causes (Criterion F). William's history of street drug abuse was excluded as a cause of his psychotic episodes because the episodes occurred independently of his drug intake. Further, although William's childhood history included schooling problems and poor social adjustment, there was no evidence of autism spectrum disorder or communication disorders. Ruth's history was completely clear of both substance abuse and developmental problems.

Other Psychotic Disorders

Schizophrenia is not the only disorder defined by psychotic symptoms. Psychosis can occur following use or abuse of a substance (e.g., a drug) or in combination with a medical

condition. In such a case, an individual may have the characteristic symptoms of schizophrenia, but receive a diagnosis of *substance-induced* or *medication-induced psychotic disorder*. However, there are several other types of psychotic disorders according to the DSM-5 diagnostic criteria. Individuals with *brief psychotic disorder* or *schizophreniform disorder* exhibit key symptoms of schizophrenia (e.g., hallucinations, delusions, disorganized speech), but with durations of less than one month and one to six months, respectively. A diagnosis of *delusional disorder* includes persistent delusions for one month or more without overtly bizarre behaviour or other schizophrenia symptoms. Common delusions include those of persecution, grandeur, and somatic concerns. These are included in the diagnosis as specifiers to provide details as to the type of delusional disorder. Lastly, *schizoaffective disorder* is defined by the same symptoms that describe schizophrenia, but concurrent with a major depressive or manic mood episode. The mood symptoms must be present for approximately half of the illness duration after the onset of psychosis. Schizoaffective disorder, like schizophrenia, is diagnosed if symptoms persist for six months or more.

Schizophrenia differs from other psychotic disorders in that impairment in level of daily life functioning is required for diagnosis. Whether schizoaffective disorder and schizophrenia are truly different disorders is a subject for debate and it is noteworthy that cognitive impairment occurs in both conditions (Heinrichs, Ammari, McDermid Vaz, & Miles, 2008).

CRITIQUE OF DSM-5 AND AREAS FOR FURTHER STUDY

While the DSM-5 diagnosis is currently used as the primary definition of schizophrenia, it is important to be aware of its limitations. The DSM-5 relies on a person's presenting symptoms and history as the main indications of disorder. A significant drawback of this approach to diagnosis is its subjectivity. Symptoms are private experiences that a patient describes to a clinician. There are no instruments that can indicate the presence and intensity of a delusion in the way that a thermometer can indicate a fever. Hence, there is also no independent way to confirm a diagnosis of schizophrenia because the DSM-5 system lacks objective signs or laboratory findings. Although clinicians using structured interviews and explicit diagnostic criteria tend to agree on who has or does not have the disorder, the diagnosis may still be inaccurate. In other words, a reliable diagnosis does not necessarily produce a valid diagnosis. In addition, definitions and diagnostic criteria can change over time. For example, it was once common to apply terms such as *paranoid* (defined by delusions or hallucinations alone) or *catatonic* (defined by abnormal movements or posture) or *undifferentiated* (a mixture of symptoms) to the disorder. However, DSM-5 removed these distinctions on the basis that their reliability is low and their validity uncertain (Tandon et al., 2013). Nevertheless, some symptoms used to define subtypes, such as catatonia, are now used as specifiers to provide further descriptive detail in diagnosis.

The definition of schizophrenia continues to be modified with advances in research, treatment, and diagnostic tools. It is important that the boundaries of any disorder are clearly defined and distinct from related conditions. At the same time, some "grey areas" are recognized. Hence, the DSM-5 includes a new condition called *attenuated psychosis syndrome*. This condition, which requires more study, identifies a person who does not yet have a full-blown psychotic disorder, but who does exhibit mild versions of psychotic symptoms. Identifying individuals with a heightened risk for developing a psychotic disorder is required when attempting prevention or early treatment, but further research is required to determine whether or not this new distinction is useful.

② BEFORE MOVING ON

Why would a person who thinks he hears voices not automatically receive a diagnosis of schizophrenia?

MARKERS AND ENDOPHENOTYPES FOR SCHIZOPHRENIA

What would be required to prove objectively that a person has a disorder like schizophrenia? Objective diagnosis is possible if measurable **disease markers** can be identified, markers that occur in virtually all people with the illness. In principle, a marker is any physical, psychological, or biological characteristic or trait. For example, Alzheimer's disease involves degenerative changes in nerve cells. These changes are observable under a microscope and represent pathological markers that confirm the disease. While symptoms reflect a disturbance in mind and body that is associated with schizophrenia, they are too subjective and private to confirm a diagnosis of the illness. Markers introduce scientific precision into the diagnostic process.

It is possible to further subdivide the marker concept into vulnerability and genetic markers, as well as the closely related concept of **endophenotypes**. A vulnerability marker is a stable and enduring sign or trait of the disorder that occurs before a person actually succumbs to the disorder and experiences symptoms. A vulnerability marker reflects an inherent predisposition to develop the disorder. Such a marker thus allows for the identification of people at risk for becoming ill, even though they may be healthy when the marker is first observed. A genetic marker is a special kind of vulnerability marker. Hence, it is stable and enduring, presents long before onset of the illness, *and* occurs in close relatives of the patient, particularly those who develop schizophrenia. Prevalence among family members implies a genetic component to the marker. Genetic and vulnerability markers may define endophenotypes, which are biological or behavioural predispositions that make the disorder more likely. An endophenotype is "intermediate" between the microscopic world of genes and nerve cells and the experiential and psychological world of symptoms (Braff, Freedman, Schork, & Gottesman, 2007).

Markers and endophenotypes may work in theory, but do they actually exist for schizophrenia? For example, impairment on the Continuous Performance Test (CPT) has been studied as a **cognitive marker** of the disorder. In the CPT, participants observe a string of numbers and are asked to respond (press a button) whenever two identical numbers occur together. On average, patients with schizophrenia consistently score below healthy people on the CPT (Heinrichs & Zakzanis, 1998; Nuechterlein et al., 2015). This impairment reflects deficits in attention and an inability to keep a rule in mind (working memory). The CPT is also an example of a test that taps an ability that is in part inherited (Hill, Harris, Herbener, Pavuluri, & Sweeney, 2008). However, CPT performance is deficient in only 50 to 60 percent of diagnosed patients. This limits its efficacy as a marker, because it is not sensitive enough to detect the hypothetical disease defect in a large majority of schizophrenia patients.

Another potential marker of schizophrenia involves smooth pursuit eye movements. Due to the controlling

FIGURE 9.1   Samples of Eye-Tracking

Source: Based on Iacono, Bassett, and Jones (1988, p. 1140). Copyright 1988, American Medical Association.

influence of attention, our eyes track—or "pursue"—moving stimuli and duplicate the pattern of a continuously moving stimulus in tiny eye movements. Patients with schizophrenia, however, often exhibit irregularities in these eye movements. Their **eye-tracking** records reveal more deviations from the stimulus path, and thus more errors, when compared to a healthy comparison group (Levy, Holzman, Matthyse, & Mendell, 1993; Thibaut et al., 2015; see Figure 9.1). Deficits in eye-tracking may reflect neurological impairments associated with schizophrenia and a predisposition for the disorder. However, once again, even the best eye-tracking indicators are abnormal in only about 50 percent of patients with schizophrenia. Perhaps this task is better suited as a potential marker for a specific variant of schizophrenia or for a broader classification of impairment that includes other psychiatric disorders.

The above examples of potential markers for schizophrenia highlight the difficulty of finding tasks and indicators that are sufficiently sensitive to the disorder. Yet a researcher would not expect 100 percent of the patients in a sample to be abnormal on any given marker task. After all, there may have been errors in diagnosis and some of the patients may not really have schizophrenia. Therefore, some tolerance or allowance for inaccuracy has to be provided. Despite these uncertainties, there is great interest in the discovery of markers and associated endophenotypes that may help to define the disorder more objectively (Owens, Bachman, Glahn, & Bearden, 2016).

Etiology

The psychiatric pioneers who described modern schizophrenia at the turn of the twentieth century did not formulate or test hypotheses about the causes of the disorder.

Kraepelin (1919) noted the hereditary "taint" of dementia praecox and the fact that it "ran" in families. He also thought that the frontal and temporal lobes of the brain must be involved in the disorder, but never developed these notions into a theory or research program. Bleuler (1911/1950) theorized extensively about the mental life and symptoms of people with schizophrenia without ever grappling in detail with what caused the disorder in the first place. He argued, for example, that disconnected or "dissociated" thinking was a fundamental symptom of the disorder, but offered no suggestions about the causes of the symptom. On the other hand, in the first half of the twentieth century, psychoanalysts (see Chapter 2) made a number of suggestions about the causes of schizophrenia. They argued that experiences during infancy, including emotional traumas and inadequate parenting, could lead to a weak and primitive ego that was unable to distinguish wishes and fears from reality (Fromm-Reichmann, 1959; Reichard & Tillman, 1950; Tausk, 1948). It was believed that a severely rejecting mother could be "**schizophrenogenic**," thereby creating the conditions for a weak and primitive ego—the foundation of schizophrenia—in her children (Diamond, 1997).

The Swiss psychiatrist Carl Jung, working with both Bleuler and Freud, gained considerable experience treating people with schizophrenia. Jung (1956) liked to tell the story of how he "discovered" the connection between psychosis and the **collective unconscious**. One of Jung's patients who had schizophrenia maintained that a swinging penis attached to the sun was the source of the wind. This seemed like just another curious delusion to the psychiatrist until he found a strikingly parallel belief in the ancient Persian religion of Mithraism. The belief held that a swinging tube suspended from the sun caused the wind. Jung became convinced that universal symbols existed in the unconscious mind and erupted into waking life in the course of dreams and mental illnesses like schizophrenia.

In contrast with early views that the disorder primarily reflected internal psychological conflicts and processes, sociological research during the 1930s found connections between schizophrenia and poverty. In particular, first admission rates for the disorder were observed to be four times higher in the slums of central Chicago than in its affluent suburbs (Faris & Dunham, 1939). Recent studies support the idea that low socioeconomic status at birth makes development of a psychotic disorder more likely (Kwok, 2014). The relationship between social class and schizophrenia can be seen in Figure 9.2, which incorporates findings from the 1950s.

One view of the social class–illness link was that the cumulative exposure to poverty, crime, and family disturbances led directly to increased cases of schizophrenia (Heinz, Deserno, & Reininghaus, 2013). At the same time, **social drift** explanations held that people with schizophrenia experienced reduced social mobility due to symptoms (e.g., avolition and cognitive impairment) that either limited or prevented the achievement of educational and occupational goals (Goldberg & Morrison, 1963). However, current research evidence suggests that genetic liability influences

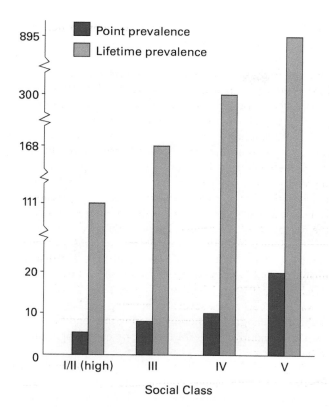

895 —
300 —
168 —
111 —
20 —
10 —
0 —

■ Point prevalence
■ Lifetime prevalence

I/II (high)   III   IV   V

Social Class

FIGURE 9.2   Prevalence of Schizophrenia by Social Class
(rates per 100 000 in New Haven, Connecticut)

Source: Data from Hollingshead & Redlich (1958).

both the risk of schizophrenia and the likelihood of living in impoverished neighbourhoods (Sariaslan et al., 2016). People with the disorder are more likely than healthy controls to live in deprived neighbourhoods, and this increased likelihood extends to patients' brothers and sisters as well. Moreover, identical twins, who have all their genes in common, were more prone than fraternal twins, with 50 percent genes in common, to living in the same poor neighborhoods. Who would have thought that genes could influence where you live?

THEORIES OF SCHIZOPHRENIA

In contemporary research, almost no one believes that a mother can cause schizophrenia by rejecting her child or that delusions reflect an eruption of the collective unconscious or that poverty adequately explains the occurrence of severe mental disorders. Instead, complex psychiatric conditions are seen as the outcome of inherited, biologically based vulnerabilities that interact with maturation and development and with life and environmental stresses and influences to push people over a threshold into psychosis. The assumption is that vulnerability, or **diathesis**, and disorder-promoting events, or **stress,** are both required. In addition, the causal pathway from diathesis-stress to clinical disorder is complex and extends over at least the first decade and a half of a person's life. American psychologist Paul Meehl (1962, 1990) built on

this assumption and proposed the first comprehensive diathesis-stress theory whereby an inherited gene makes a person vulnerable to schizophrenia. However, whether the disorder actually develops depends on the "good" and "bad" effects of other genes, as well as on the social rewards and punishments experienced by vulnerable people as they grow and change from childhood through adolescence to young adulthood.

MEEHL'S THEORY OF SCHIZOTAXIA, SCHIZOTYPY, AND SCHIZOPHRENIA The theory proposes a biological diathesis, termed "**hypokrisia**," that occurs throughout the brain, making nerve cells abnormally reactive to incoming stimulation. A single gene inherited from either parent causes this diathesis. However, the "schizogene" is often expressed weakly in a person and its effects may be compensated by other genes, as well as by experience and environmental influences. Hence, not everyone with the schizogene develops schizophrenia. Moreover, even when the gene is expressed in hypokrisia the defect does not interfere with basic, elementary activities of the nervous system. The brain is still able to regulate bodily processes and register, store, and retrieve information. Hence, hypokrisia does not cause intellectual disability or other gross disorders of brain function. What it does produce is a subtler disturbance that Meehl called "**cognitive slippage.**" Information is disorganized, incoherent, and "scrambled." In Meehl's theory, high intellectual ability can coexist with hypokrisia and cognitive slippage. Yet these defects do distort thinking by causing an exaggerated and persisting tendency to form haphazard connections between ideas, emotions, and events. This "associative loosening" resembles the thought and language disorder described in the section on symptoms. However, in addition, the unselective neuronal firing that causes cognitive slippage gives rise to a gradual increase in punitive, unpleasant social experiences. The brain amplifies feelings of pain and weakens pleasure, making interpersonal relations difficult. This **aversive drift** is related to negative symptoms such as social withdrawal and disinterest. As the brain scrambles and distorts rewarding and punitive emotional associations, the vulnerable person begins to find social contact more and more unpleasant. Increasingly, such a person avoids social interactions and is viewed as strange and subject to disapproval by other people. This negative appraisal in turn accelerates the process of withdrawal and creates a vicious circle.

A person experiencing cognitive slippage and aversive drift is termed a "**schizotype**" in Meehl's theory. But such a person may still be spared the full-blown psychotic disorder of schizophrenia. Schizotypal people suffer from "primary" cognitive slippage, difficulty feeling pleasure, social alienation, and other consequences of aversive drift. However, numerous "moderator" genes that influence everything from intelligence to artistic talent to shyness can prevent or accelerate the development of a person's schizotypy into a schizophrenic disorder. In addition, the environment plays a key role in shaping or limiting the expression of schizotypy. For example, schizophrenia

John Nash's Beautiful Mind: When Schizophrenia and Genius Coexist

John Nash (1928–2015) was born to well-educated parents; his father was an electrical engineer and his mother a teacher. Nash showed impressive intellectual potential early in life, carrying out sophisticated chemistry experiments in his room by the age of 10 and proving complex theorems by famous mathematicians at the age of 15. Yet, while intellectually gifted, Nash struggled in social situations. His peers nicknamed him "bug brains" and he came to prefer a solitary lifestyle to the rejection and discomfort often experienced with other people.

Nash's intellectual gifts were expressed in educational and scientific accomplishments. He was offered a full scholarship to complete undergraduate studies at Carnegie Mellon University, where his performance was described as exceptional and extraordinary. He earned a master's degree along with his bachelor of science after only three years of university and was subsequently offered fellowships at both Harvard and Princeton. It was his Ph.D. research at Princeton that eventually won him the Nobel Prize from the Royal Swedish Academy of Sciences.

In his personal life, the odd and peculiar behaviour noticed by many people became even more apparent as Nash completed postgraduate work and pursued further academic interests. Throughout his time at Princeton, he refused to attend classes on principle, instead pacing the halls or riding a bicycle in tight concentric circles. Rather than read in the library, he would lie atop the tables with his hands behind his head. According to Sylvia Nasar (1998), author of *A Beautiful Mind*, a biography of Nash that was the basis for the 2001 movie starring Russell Crowe, these strange character traits marked the path from simple quirkiness to frank psychosis. By the age of 30, after accepting a faculty position at the Massachusetts Institute of Technology (MIT), Nash began hearing voices and developed a delusional way of thinking. He believed that a front-page story in *The New York Times* contained coded messages from inhabitants of another galaxy—messages that only he could unscramble. Later, he offered one of his graduate students an "inter-galactic driver's license" and a seat on his newly organized world government. He wrote thousands of letters to the government, newspapers, and colleagues. Nash believed that everything had meaning and nothing was random or accidental. He would spend days making odd calculations like converting contemporary politician Nelson Rockefeller's name to a complex numerical representation and then mathematically factoring the resulting number.

Perhaps surprisingly, this brilliant and severely troubled man was married, although the couple later divorced. His wife initially attempted to hide Nash's psychiatric problems, but ultimately brought him to hospital against his will. Like many people suffering from schizophrenia, Nash denied his illness, convinced that he was being persecuted. At the time of his first hospitalization, he was diagnosed with paranoid schizophrenia. During this time, treatments for psychotic illness were primitive and usually ineffective (see "Treatment" later in this chapter). They included

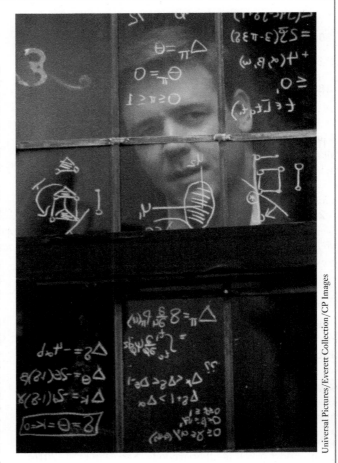

psychodynamic psychotherapy, which has since lost favour as a therapy for psychosis, and insulin shock therapy, long abandoned in favour of medication.

Although his groundbreaking research was probably done before his illness, Nash's case illustrates the possibility that exceptional intellectual ability and achievement can exist in people with schizophrenia. The vast majority of patients with the diagnosis are cognitively impaired, but recent studies reveal that a small number have above-average abilities, especially in verbal skills such as vocabulary (Heinrichs et al., 2008; Vaskinn et al., 2014). Yet, like Nash, these exceptional patients have difficulty functioning normally in the community. It seems that intellectual ability cannot compensate completely for the devastating experience of severe mental illness. Moreover, even the most gifted patients often face social obstacles such as stigma. Indeed, the stigma and negative image of schizophrenia almost prevented Nash from being awarded the Nobel Prize. Many involved with the prize were concerned that giving a prestigious award to a "madman" would embarrass and discredit the Academy of Sciences.

John Nash's experience is unique and atypical compared to most people suffering from schizophrenia, but his amazing story is a testimony to hope, courage, and perseverance in the face of both mental illness and social disapproval.

becomes more probable when a schizotypal person inherits tendencies toward shyness; anxiety; low energy; weak motivation; and low ability, talent, or physical attractiveness. Even so, these "polygenic" characteristics still have to combine with the influence of a social world that punishes undesirable traits before a person crosses the threshold into a diagnosable schizophrenia spectrum disorder. Conversely, different polygenes may combine in such a way that a person becomes a "compensated schizotype." This is someone who is able to function in everyday life, although usually at a cost to him- or herself or to other people. Meehl mentioned Adolf Hitler as an example of compensated schizotype: an intelligent and talented but socially fearful and inadequate person, prone to incoherent and irrational thoughts and impulses.

According to Meehl, the development of schizophrenia is understandable only as the product of all of these complex influences. Primary hypokrisia, cognitive slippage, and aversive drift are modified or intensified by personality, temperament, and cognitive traits, and this takes place within stressful or supportive social environments.

NEURODEVELOPMENTAL DIATHESIS-STRESS THEORIES Meehl's formulation has been criticized for its lack of detail on the nature of hypokrisia and cognitive slippage and for not explaining one of the key features of schizophrenia: its occurrence in late adolescence and early adulthood (Heinrichs, 2001). Hence, a number of theorists have accepted the basic diathesis-stress model as a framework and added ideas and detail regarding the nature of what is wrong in the schizophrenic brain, how it got there, and why the disorder occurs primarily in young people.

For example, psychiatrist Daniel Weinberger (1987, 1995) agreed that a person could inherit a genetic defect that creates vulnerability for the disorder. But he believed it was also possible that subtle brain injuries during fetal development or birth could become a diathesis. In theory, this early damage or lesion may occur in brain regions that normally mature in adolescence, when they are required by the emerging demands of social life and sexuality. It is the stress of maturational demands on the weakened brain that precipitates a psychotic crisis and initial hospitalization. Psychologist Elaine Walker (Walker & Diforio, 1997; Walker, Mittal, & Tessner, 2008) has gone further and specified hormone producing and regulating mechanisms in the brain that are normally "switched" on by stress experiences in late adolescence. However, people with the biological vulnerability for schizophrenia cannot cope with the effects of surging stress hormones on brain chemistry and begin to develop symptoms and clinical illness. This line of reasoning that combines several interacting factors continues to be influential in theories of the disorder (Howes, McCutcheon, Owen, & Murray, 2017).

All of the diathesis-stress theories of schizophrenia hypothesize a biological vulnerability that is either inherited or acquired very early in life. The vulnerability may take the form of neuroanatomical or neurochemical abnormalities, or both. It is the interaction of these abnormalities with maturation, stress, and life events that eventually causes schizophrenia. Yet although the theories explain why the disorder occurs, to what extent are these explanations supported by the facts? We begin with a consideration of genetics and the role of inheritance in the etiology of schizophrenia.

 BEFORE MOVING ON

> How does the concept of diathesis, or vulnerability, differ from the concept of cause?

BIOLOGICAL FACTORS

IS SCHIZOPHRENIA INHERITED? On the basis of shared genes, human characteristics from eye colour and height to illnesses like diabetes and heart disease "run" in families. Indeed, most psychiatric, behavioural, and medical disorders are under at least some genetic influence. This applies to Alzheimer's disease, autism, major mood disorders, and reading disabilities; as well as to epilepsy, peptic ulcer, and rheumatoid arthritis. In addition, within the spectrum of normal behaviour, genes play a role in cognitive abilities such as memory and intelligence and in personality traits such as neuroticism. Genes even play a role in vocational interests and scholastic achievement (McGuffin, Owen, O'Donovan, Thapar, & Gottesman, 1994; Whitman, 2008). Nonetheless, the degree to which these complex illnesses and traits are actually controlled by genes seldom exceeds 50 percent. In many cases, heritability is much lower. Accordingly, nongenetic factors must be of roughly equal importance in determining the emergence of many psychiatric disorders and complex behavioural traits.

A familial **genetic contribution** to the development of schizophrenia has been assumed since the time of Kraepelin (1913, 1919) and Bleuler (1911/1950). Schizophrenia is observed to recur in some families, with a lifetime risk of about 13 percent to the children of a parent with schizophrenia. This compares with a general population risk for the disorder of only about 1 percent (Gottesman, 1991). Hence, having one parent with schizophrenia increases the risk of developing the disorder 13 times. However, even in this relatively "high-risk" situation, about 87 percent of people with a parent who has schizophrenia will remain free of the disorder. This "familiality" effect, summarized in Figure 9.3, shows that the likelihood of a person developing schizophrenia is much higher if a biological relative also has the disorder. The risk is highest for someone with an identical, or monozygotic, twin and then falls off stepwise as the degree of genetic relatedness diminishes.

Yet the genetics of schizophrenia contrast with disorders like Huntington's disease, which has a more straightforward pattern of inheritance. Defects in a single gene cause Huntington's disease, giving rise to a predictable risk: a 50 percent chance of developing the disease if a person has one parent with the disorder, and a 100 percent chance in the unlikely event that both parents are ill. Complex behavioural

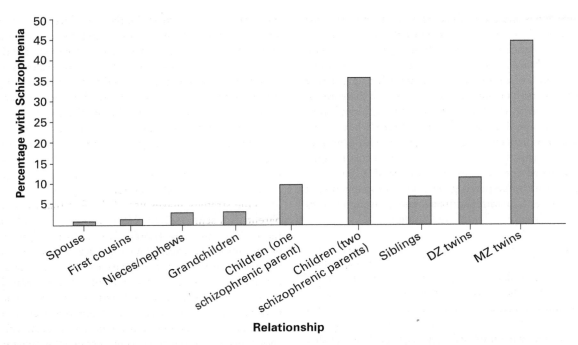

FIGURE 9.3   Prevalence of Schizophrenia Among Relatives of People with Schizophrenia

Source: Data from McGue, M., & Gottesman, I. I. (1989). A single dominant gene still cannot account for the transmission of schizophrenia. *Archives of General Psychiatry, 46,* 478-479; Gottesman, I. I., McGuffin, P., & Farmer, A. E. (1987). Clinical genetics as clues to the "real" genetics of schizophrenia: A decade of modest gains while playing for time. *Schizophrenia Bulletin, 13,* 23-47.

syndromes, including psychiatric disorders such as schizophrenia, do not follow such patterns of inheritance. For example, if a single gene caused schizophrenia, the risk for illness should decrease by a constant factor of 50 percent between different relative classes. This prediction is based on the degree of shared genetic material in relatives, which ranges from 100 percent in the case of identical twins, to 50 percent for parents, to 25 percent for second-degree relatives like aunts and uncles. However, the risk of schizophrenia for someone who has an identical twin with the disorder is only about 48 percent instead of 100 percent. If all genes are in common, including the one that causes schizophrenia, both identical twins should become ill.

Discrepancies between predicted and observed cases of genetic illness can be dealt with through the principle of incomplete **penetrance**. In other words, it is known that a proportion of people with a dominant gene will fail to show the effect of that gene. As suggested by Meehl's theory, the lack of expression may be due to the environment or to other factors in the person's genetic constitution. Hence, the penetrance of the schizophrenia gene may be much less than 100 percent and closer to about 50 percent. This roughly fits the risk of the disorder in identical twins. However, the single gene model still does not work for the other relative classes. First-degree relatives should have a risk for schizophrenia of about 25 percent, but Figure 9.3 shows that the observed risks are much lower. Similarly, second-degree relatives should have a risk of 12.5 percent and not the 3 to 4 percent actually observed.

SEARCH FOR "SCHIZOGENES" Evidence against simple gene models also comes from attempts by molecular biologists to link schizophrenia with single genes and specific chromosomes. These attempts have been consistently unsuccessful (O'Donovan & Owen, 1992, 1996). All in all, the idea that one major gene causes schizophrenia is both contradicted by the facts and rejected by most researchers.

Over the last several decades, research has moved increasingly to complex multiple gene models in accounting for the inheritance of schizophrenia (see Gottesman, 1991; Tiwari, Zai, Müller, & Kennedy, 2010). The field of molecular genetics is considering the likelihood that numerous genes influence the development of schizophrenia. It is possible that as many as 600 "risk" genes may be involved in the disorder (Harrison, 2015)! Unfortunately, the evidence has sometimes been difficult to reproduce (Kendler, 2000). In addition, individual risk genes have extremely small effects, which means that finding them requires the study of very large numbers of patients (Tandon, Keshavan, & Nasrallah, 2008a). For example, any specific gene variant increases the lifetime risk of developing schizophrenia from less than 1 percent to about 1.10 percent. Current approaches compile results from thousands of cases and include the role of environmental influences, while also pursuing new leads such as the concept of endophenotypes discussed earlier (Burmeister, McInnis, & Zöllner, 2008). Recent work is considering the possibility that genes interact with each other in complex ways to influence whether the disorder actually occurs (Mackay, 2014). In addition, the mechanisms that control or influence genes and their effects may be as important for the etiology of schizophrenia as the genes themselves. These **epigenetic** mechanisms may be helpful in explaining why identical twins with the same genes seem to differ in their vulnerability to schizophrenia. For example, Toronto-based researcher Arturas Petronis (2004; Labrie, Pai, & Petronis, 2012) at the Centre for Addiction and Mental Health, in Toronto, has identified processes that "turn" genes "on" or "off," and this regulation may be crucial in determining whether a twin actually develops schizophrenia. Accordingly, although schizophrenia is regarded as a highly heritable disorder, unravelling the biological details of the complex genetics involved will challenge researchers for many years to come.

DO PREGNANCY AND BIRTH COMPLICATIONS PLAY A ROLE IN SCHIZOPHRENIA? The diathesis-stress approach to understanding etiology assumes that a genetic predisposition is only part of the pathway that eventually causes an illness. There must be stressors as well, including other biological or environmental and social events that accumulate and propel the vulnerable person toward schizophrenia. One possible stressor is a mother's exposure to common viruses such as influenza, or "the flu," during pregnancy. Such exposures are linked with increased risk of schizophrenia in the offspring. For example, there is evidence that exposure to the flu virus during the fifth month of pregnancy is associated with an increased risk of schizophrenia in the mother's children later in life (Limosin, Rouillon, Payan, Cohen, & Strub, 2003). However, the incidence of the disorder in people exposed to the virus is still extremely low and some studies have failed to support the relationship (Khandaker, Zimbron, Lewis, & Jones, 2013). Perhaps viral exposure is one of many potential stressors that interact with genetic predisposition and other factors to influence etiology.

Birth-related complications have been proposed as one of these "other" factors. Medical and delivery-related problems at birth may be key environmental and biological events that interact with a genetic diathesis and further predispose a person to schizophrenia. If this idea is true, then high rates of birth complications should occur in children who go on to develop the illness. Birth complications can be studied by interviewing adult patients and their relatives with respect to obstetrical events and by examining birth and health records if these are available. Complications include prolonged labour, preterm delivery, low birth weight, fetal distress, and breathing difficulties. Indeed, it turns out that such complications are more common in the birth records of people with schizophrenia (Cannon, Jones, & Murray, 2002). However, once again, most people with the illness do not have these abnormalities, even though they occur more often than expected by chance or in comparison to healthy people (Heinrichs, 2001; Tandon et al., 2008).

CAN VULNERABILITY TO SCHIZOPHRENIA BE OBSERVED IN CHILDREN AND ADOLESCENTS? Viral exposure during pregnancy and complications during birth are two possible events that may combine with genetic predisposition to increase the risk for schizophrenia. If genes and physical events in the environment combine to cause a vulnerability to the disorder, perhaps this vulnerability can be seen in children and adolescents before they experience symptoms. The question of whether early signs of eventual schizophrenia exist seems a simple one, but there are many difficulties involved in answering it. The most serious difficulty is the absence of a dependable, accurate way of identifying in advance who will go on to have the clinical disorder. Nevertheless, researchers have useful, if imperfect, ways of identifying children who have a greater-than-average likelihood of developing the disorder.

One strategy makes use of the fact that the child of a parent with schizophrenia has at least 10 times the normal risk of developing the disorder. Yet even with a large number of **high-risk children** to maximize the number of eventual patients, a researcher may have to wait for 20 years to discover which children actually develop the disorder. Nevertheless, the available evidence indicates that these high-risk children experience a variety of birth-related complications, motor and cognitive problems, and social difficulties regardless of whether they eventually develop schizophrenia (Hameed & Lewis, 2016). As an alternative strategy, some researchers recruit high-risk adolescents rather than children, especially adolescents beginning to show mild or "attenuated" psychotic symptoms. Attenuated symptoms include suspiciousness (but not intense paranoia) and strange beliefs and experiences (but not actual delusions and hallucinations). Approximately 26 percent of these "clinical" high-risk adolescents go on to develop a psychotic disorder, with schizophrenia the most frequent diagnosis (Fusar-Poli et al. 2013). In addition, there is recent evidence that a significant portion of high-risk adolescents show early signs of having cognitive deficits (Bora, Lin, Wood, Yung, McGorry, & Pantelis, 2014). For example, as early as the age of 13, about a third show lower general intellectual ability (IQ), and motor problems by the age of 16 (Dickson, Laurens, Cullen, & Hodgins, 2012). Interestingly, they do not seem to suffer in terms of academic achievement, including mathematics scores. It must also be that experience in some way shapes the mind and behaviour of those children who later become ill and, as Meehl (1990) acknowledged, this experience is partly psychological and social in nature. There is recent evidence that traumatic experiences in childhood are associated with psychotic experiences later in life, especially in adolescents who also use marijuana (Harley et al., 2010). In addition, it is now clear that a range of adverse experiences, from physical and sexual abuse to bullying, almost triple the likelihood that a psychotic disorder will develop (Varese et al. 2012). Furthermore, although parenting and family experiences do not, by themselves, *cause* the disorder, research shows that family hostility, lack of support, critical attitudes, and over-involvement may make schizophrenia worse, or at least promote relapses and adjustment difficulties (Hooley, 2007). These negative interpersonal communications directed at the family member with the disorder are referred to as **expressed emotion**. However, expressed emotion also occurs in the families of people with mood (Chapter 8) and eating disorders (Chapter 10). This implies that negative family attitudes may make adjusting to psychological problems difficult in general rather than only in relation to schizophrenia.

Overall, the idea of a **cumulative liability** for schizophrenia that shows itself early in behaviour and increases with adverse environmental events and stresses over the course of childhood and adolescence is very appealing. Such a perspective can make up for the apparent weakness of individual stresses and vulnerabilities because it is the accumulation of liability, and not single events, that actually determines whether the disorder occurs. However, the findings do not amount to a very powerful collection of disorder-promoting diatheses and stresses at the present time. Therefore, researchers have looked into the brain to find abnormalities that may contribute to the cause of schizophrenia.

4 **BEFORE MOVING ON**

If genes have a major influence on who develops the disorder, why do most children of a mother or father with the disorder never develop schizophrenia?

IS SCHIZOPHRENIA A BRAIN DISEASE?

Neuropsychological Tests. If schizophrenia is a brain disorder, then part or all of the brain must be abnormal in some way, giving rise to the typical symptoms of the disorder. One of the first regions that interested researchers was the **frontal**, or prefrontal, **lobe** of the brain. This large region includes about a third of the brain and has extensive connections with other structures and regions. The psychiatric pioneers believed that psychological capacities ascribed to the frontal brain were impaired in schizophrenia (e.g., Kraepelin, 1913, 1919). A series of case studies of neurological patients with frontal brain damage showed that personality change, impaired self-awareness, loss of initiative, disorganized thinking, impulsivity, and inappropriate social behaviour were common consequences of damage to this brain area (Ackerly & Benton, 1948; Brickner, 1934, 1936; Harlow, 1848, 1868; Hebb & Penfield, 1940). These features echoed the thought and language disorder, bizarre behaviour, and negative symptoms seen in many patients with schizophrenia. At least on the surface, there were impressive similarities between schizophrenia and frontal brain disease.

FOCUS 9.3

How Different Are Patients with Schizophrenia from Healthy People?

The explosion of research on schizophrenia across many fields from psychology to neurochemistry means that it is often hard, even for researchers, to arrive at a "big picture" of what is known about the disorder. However, the statistical summarizing technique of **meta-analysis** provides a partial solution to this problem. Meta-analysis, also called quantitative research synthesis, compiles all published articles in a field and transforms the individual results into an overall statistic termed the **effect size**. In the case of schizophrenia research, the effect size reflects the degree of difference between patients and healthy people in terms of any selected psychological or biological comparison. Average effect sizes can in turn be used to estimate the proportion or percentage of patients falling outside the healthy range, which is a statistical way of defining "abnormality" (see Chapter 1). A ranked summary of these abnormality estimates is presented in Table 9.3. ●

TABLE 9.3   ASPECTS OF BRAIN AND BEHAVIOUR MOST FREQUENTLY ABNORMAL IN PATIENTS WITH SCHIZOPHRENIA

Rank	Finding	Frequency (%)
1	slowness writing symbols paired with numbers (processing speed)	71–75
2	poor physical coordination and control (neurological soft signs)	68–78
3	impaired ability to filter out redundant information (sensory gating)	63–80
4	impaired learning and recall of words and stories (verbal memory)	62–75
5	increased neurotransmitter receptors in post-mortem brain tissue (dopamine)	47–81
6	blocking of one sensation by the presence of another (backward masking)	46–76
7	impaired ability to attend to one message and ignore another (dichotic listening)	50–71
8	impaired general intellectual ability (IQ)	50–67
9	reduced ability to generate words rapidly (phonemic word fluency)	53–64
10	slow and inaccurate detection of specified letters (Continuous Performance Test)	52–62

Source: Data from Chan, Xu, Heinrichs, Yu, & Wang, 2009; Davidson & Heinrichs, 2003; Dickinson, Ramsey, & Gold, 2007; Fioravanti, Bianchi & Cinti, 2012; Heinrichs, 2001, 2005; Heinrichs & Zakzanis, 1998).

Note: The table shows frequency estimates of different research findings based on meta-analytic findings and average effect sizes.

Although few researchers believe that schizophrenia can be explained completely as a form of frontal brain disorder, the frontal hypothesis remains one of the earliest and most consistent attempts to relate the disorder to a specific brain system. One research strategy is to give patients with schizophrenia cognitive or **neuropsychological tests** that activate and depend on the frontal region (see Chapter 4). Impairment on such a test supports the hypothesis that the frontal brain is defective in the disorder. Some of these tests are relatively simple and others are more complicated and challenging. For example, one common deficit of frontal brain disease is an inability to generate words rapidly and fluently. According to studies with healthy people, the average person can come up with a total of 30 to 35 words that begin with letters like "F," "A," and "S" in three one-minute trials (see Lezak, 1995). Canadian neuropsychologist Brenda Milner (1964), working at the Montreal Neurological Institute, initiated studies showing that patients with surgical removal of frontal brain tissue generated very few words. The "FAS" technique was subsequently applied to patients with schizophrenia and compared to healthy people in 27 separate studies conducted between 1980 and 1997. There was a consistent deficiency in the patient samples, with results suggesting that a clear majority of patients produced fewer words than healthy people (Heinrichs, 2001).

Another neuropsychological test also applied originally by Milner to patients with frontal damage is the **Wisconsin Card Sorting Test** (WCST; Heaton, Chelune, Talley, Kay, & Curtiss, 1993). Most versions involve presenting four "key" cards that depict different shapes, colours, and quantities. The person taking the test is provided with a succession of cards and asked to match each one to a key card. Cards may match on the basis of colour, shape, or number, but only one matching principle is correct at a given time. The examiner controls the matching principle and gives feedback about the correctness of each attempted match without ever disclosing the actual principle. Then, after a succession of correct matches, the examiner changes to a new principle (e.g., shape instead of colour) without telling the test-taker. The object of the test is to discover the new principle each time it changes and to respond with correct matches. The WCST is easy for healthy people with average intelligence, but Milner (1963) showed that patients with prefrontal brain damage achieved abnormally few successively correct matches or "categories." They also tended to repeat or **perseverate** erroneous responses.

The WCST has proven to be the most popular neuropsychological measure in schizophrenia research, used in 43 studies published between 1980 and 1997 (Heinrichs & Zakzanis, 1998). Cumulative results from these studies show that at least half of patients with schizophrenia are consistently impaired relative to healthy people. Moreover, this deficiency is similar in severity to the results of studies conducted with neurological patients who had documented damage to their frontal lobes (Heinrichs, 2001).

Despite this impressive evidence, neuropsychological tests do not provide definitive support for the **frontal brain deficiency** hypothesis in schizophrenia. Most tests are sensitive to more than one brain region, so that poor performance does not necessarily mean that the frontal region, or only the frontal region, is defective. Indeed, many neurological patients without frontal damage also find the WCST hard, and some patients with frontal damage manage to obtain surprisingly good scores (Anderson, Damasio, Jones, & Tranel, 1991; Heaton et al., 1993). Another problem is that poor performance on any single test may be a product of a much more general impairment likely to affect most aspects of cognition and performance. As a group, individuals with schizophrenia have lower IQs than the general population, and this broad intellectual disadvantage may also reveal itself in any individual cognitive test result (Gray, McMahon, & Gold, 2013; Heinrichs & Zakzanis, 1998). Thus, at least some of the time, researchers may be measuring a broad ability factor that depends on the whole brain when they think they are measuring only frontal brain abilities. In addition, neuropsychological research has moved away from the study of separate brain regions, such as the frontal area, to the analysis of coordinated and dynamic combinations of regions that form networks (Menon, 2013). Not surprisingly, several of the most important networks for understanding abnormal psychology include the frontal lobes. Clearly, the question of how the brain produces schizophrenia cannot be resolved with neuropsychological tests alone. Fortunately, the same question can be addressed with biological methods that offer a much more direct picture of brain structure and physiology.

PICTURES OF THE LIVING BRAIN

Description of Structural Techniques. Developments in brain scanning and imaging over the last three decades provide remarkably accurate ways of studying brain biology (see Chapter 4). First, there are imaging techniques that yield a visual or quantitative display of neuroanatomical structure—a picture of the living brain. These techniques include computerized axial tomography (CT) and **structural magnetic resonance imaging** (**MRI**). MRI, in particular, is able to provide clear, detailed images of many brain structures. Since schizophrenia does not involve obvious brain damage as strokes or tumours do, most structural brain imaging research compares the volume and shape of different brain regions in patients and healthy people. The assumption is that abnormally small regions must have sustained some kind of damage, including, for example, nerve cell losses. Alternatively, the brain may not have developed normally in the first place, creating vulnerability for schizophrenia later in life.

Findings from CT and MRI Studies. Using these techniques, researchers have found complex patterns of structural abnormalities in patients with schizophrenia. One of the earliest CT findings was that the third and lateral ventricles, fluid-filled spaces deep in the brain, are abnormally large in patients, suggesting compression or loss of existing nerve tissue (Johnstone, Frith, Crow, Husband, & Kreel, 1976). More recently, other consistent findings from MRI studies include reduced grey matter (tissue containing nerve cell bodies) in the medial and superior temporal, and frontal lobes (Karlsgodt, Sun, & Cannon, 2010; van Erp et al., 2016). These are regions critical for remembering past events, processing sound-based information, and short-term memory/ decision making. Further reported structural differences in patients with schizophrenia include parietal lobe, basal ganglia, corpus callosum, thalamus, and cerebellar abnormalities (Kasai et al., 2002; Niznikiewicz, Kubicki, & Shenton, 2003; Shenton, Dickey, Frumin, & McCarley, 2001).

In addition to measuring grey matter volume, MRI methods can be used to measure the thickness of the cerebral cortex (i.e., the thin outer layer of the brain that covers the hemispheres). Grey matter volume is a product of cortical thickness and surface area. The morphology of cortical thickness also reflects the arrangement, density, and size of nerve cells, fibres, and supportive tissue, making it an especially valuable brain measure. The study of cortical thickness and surface area may therefore help further our understanding of disease-specific neuroanatomical changes in schizophrenia beyond what we have learned from grey matter studies alone. Alterations in development of the nervous system have been reported in schizophrenia and so changes in cortical thickness patterns are expected and have been confirmed by numerous studies (Ehrlich et al., 2012). Figure 9.4 shows multiple areas of cortical thinning in the left and right hemispheres when patients with schizophrenia are compared with healthy controls.

Description of Functional Techniques. Advances in imaging technology extend traditional anatomical imaging to include maps of human brain function. These "functional" imaging techniques include **positron emission tomography (PET)** and **functional magnetic resonance imaging (fMRI)**. PET scanning involves the introduction of a mildly radioactive tracer into the bloodstream of a person and the use of a sensory apparatus, a kind of camera, to detect the tracer's presence and distribution in the brain. Depending on the type of tracer, this method can furnish a display or readout of changes in blood flow, the metabolism or rate at which energy is used, or the location and density of nerve cells containing specific kinds of chemical receptors. Brain regions with higher activity levels use more blood and will have increased levels of the radioactive tracer that will be detected and imaged by the camera.

On the other hand, fMRI works by detecting the changes in blood oxygenation and flow that occur in response to neural activity. When a brain area is more active, it consumes more oxygen, and to meet this increased demand, blood flow increases to the active area. fMRI techniques allow for the production of activation maps showing which parts of the brain are involved in a particular mental process after controlling for brain activity at rest (see Figure 9.5). These most recent technologies are being applied increasingly to schizophrenia (see Huettel, Song, & McCarthy, 2008).

Findings from PET and fMRI Studies. In addition to structural changes, functional activation changes, as measured by both fMRI and PET, have been well documented in patients

FIGURE 9.4   fMRI Images Showing Brain Regions Where Healthy Control Participants Demonstrate Greater Activation than Schizophrenia Patients During Source and Object Memory Tasks

Regions of increased brain activation appear when the person being scanned has to remember an object as well as its location in a previously experienced virtual environment. Together, these "hot spots" of activity may represent parts of a source memory network, which seems to operate less efficiently in people with schizophrenia.

Source: Images generated using FreeSurfer automated image analysis version 5.1.0. (http://surfer.nmr.mgh.harvard.edu/).

FIGURE 9.5 Cortical Thinning in Schizophrenia

Individuals with schizophrenia tend to have widespread thinning of the cerebral cortex in the right and left hemispheres when compared to healthy controls. Cortical thickness reductions are typically observed in the frontal, parietal, and temporal lobes. In this figure, blue areas depict regions in the left cerebral hemisphere where cortical thickness is reduced in patients compared to healthy controls.

Source: Images generated using FreeSurfer automated image analysis version 5.1.0 (http://surfer.nmr.mgh.harvard.edu/).

with schizophrenia. To what extent, then, do these brain imaging techniques support the idea that schizophrenia is a disorder that involves frontal brain regions? Lara Davidson, a former graduate student in clinical psychology at York University in Toronto, compiled the findings of all available studies published between 1980 and 2002 (Davidson & Heinrichs, 2003). The results of this meta-analysis showed that only about 25 percent of patients with schizophrenia have abnormally reduced frontal brain volumes, and less than 50 percent have reduced blood flow or metabolism in the frontal region when engaged in a mental "activation" task. One way of interpreting this outcome is to say that frontal brain impairment probably affects *some* patients with schizophrenia, but the impairment is not a *necessary* part of the syndrome. It is also possible that only the negative symptoms of the disorder reflect an abnormally working frontal brain. In any case, many patients cannot be distinguished from healthy people with structural MRI or functional PET imaging. Of course, as the use of more accurate and informative techniques such as fMRI increases, the evidence in support of the frontal hypothesis may change. Several other brain regions are also of interest in relation to schizophrenia. One of the most researched regions includes the **left temporal lobe** and its many connections with other regions, including the frontal lobes. This is a psychologically vital brain region that controls aspects of attention, the understanding of speech and written language, and interpretation of the visual world. It is in the temporal brain system that sounds are recognized as words, and light patterns as pictures, objects, or human faces. Associated structures such as the **amygdala** and **hippocampus** colour these interpretations with emotion and store them in memory. Kraepelin (1913, 1919) and other psychiatric pioneers knew the psychological importance of the temporal brain region in broad terms and suggested that, along with the frontal

brain, the temporal lobes were the place to look for the causes of schizophrenia.

The evidence compiled and summarized using meta-analysis shows that some psychological abilities associated with the left temporal lobe, especially memory, but also selective attention, are probably deficient in up to 75% of individuals with schizophrenia (see Focus box 9.3 and Table 9.3). Conversely, only a small proportion of patients may have normal attention and memory abilities. However, evidence based on brain imaging (MRI, PET) and more direct measurement of the temporal region tells a somewhat different story. None of these comparisons consistently detect abnormalities in a majority of patients, and hence they were not included in the summary table. Indeed, meta-analysis shows that the volume of the left temporal lobe is reduced in only about 21% of patients, although approximately 38% have an abnormally small hippocampus. The results for altered blood flow and metabolism are complex and inconsistent. Yet here too the evidence in favour of neurobiological abnormalities is not impressive. The average resting activity of the left temporal lobe seems almost the same in patients and healthy people on the basis of PET brain scanning results. Only about 8% of patients have truly abnormal blood flow and metabolism. The proportion rises to about 27% when temporal lobe activity is measured during a cognitive task. In addition, this proportion of patients seems to have an abnormally overactive rather than underactive left temporal lobe. It is noteworthy, however, that many PET findings have poor records in terms of being reproduced by several investigators. In fact, no brain imaging findings make the "top 10" list of findings presented in Table 9.3.

This evidence indicates that, from a biological perspective, the brain regions mediating the perception and storage of meaning and the creation of emotional associations are also the regions involved in schizophrenia. However, research has not yet demonstrated this involvement in a very convincing way. It is cognitive performance and abilities that appear to be most severely compromised by the disorder, whereas biological findings are often abnormal in only a minority of patients. Is it possible that technical limitations, rather than a faulty hypothesis, underpin the weakness of neurobiological findings on both the frontal and temporal brain hypotheses? Perhaps the brain scanners are at fault. They still lack the degree of accuracy needed to detect the kind of microscopic neural abnormalities that underlie the disorder. The near future may hold the answers.

An extension of MRI technology, diffusion tensor imaging (DTI), has allowed for the examination of white matter pathways in the brain. DTI is a critical advancement in neuroimaging, given that brain regions are highly interconnected. The application of DTI to schizophrenia research is fitting because the disorder may involve disturbed communication between and within regions. DTI studies have found that connective tissue or tracts such as the corpus callosum, cingulum bundle, and internal capsule are the areas of the brain most affected in schizophrenia (Kyriakopoulos, Bargiotas, Barker, & Frangou, 2008). More recently, DTI has been used to understand how alterations in white matter pathways are related to symptoms. For example, meta-analytic findings of DTI studies indicate that the left arcuate fasciculus (a band of white matter that acts as a bridge between frontal and posterior parts of the brain) is the most affected white matter tract in patients who experience auditory hallucinations (Geoffroy et al., 2014).

DTI studies provide insight into the *structural* connections (i.e., fibres joining different brain regions), whereas resting-state fMRI studies help us understand the brain's *functional* connections (i.e., activity patterns that suggest communication among brain regions). Resting-state fMRI data are obtained while participants are resting but awake in the MRI scanner. Abnormally functioning brain networks are thought to underlie psychopathology, including psychosis. Evidence suggests that these networks are disrupted in patients with schizophrenia (Menon, 2013). Each network includes the frontal brain regions that are thought to be involved in the frontal brain deficiency hypothesis. Accordingly, frontal brain regions are likely involved in schizophrenia, but they do not tell the whole story. The connections between the frontal regions and other areas of the brain are also important and may help us better understand the abnormalities that underlie schizophrenia.

The next generation of imaging developments may furnish the powerful evidence of fronto-temporal brain involvement in schizophrenia that is currently lacking. Many brain regions and their connections are under study and the field continues to await a succession of strong findings that converge on the same region (see Harrison, 1999). However, it is also possible that part of the schizophrenia puzzle lies in the brain's chemistry.

IS SCHIZOPHRENIA CAUSED BY A NEUROCHEMICAL IMBALANCE? The arrival of the first therapeutic drug treatments for psychotic symptoms during the 1950s inspired researchers to study schizophrenia as a biological disease. If a chemical agent such as a drug was able to reduce symptoms, it might be because brain chemistry was abnormal in the disorder. Perhaps schizophrenia consisted of an abnormality in neurotransmission—the chemical transactions that compose communication between nerve cells at the molecular level. In addition to smaller or malformed brain regions and altered patterns of blood flow and metabolism, the causes of schizophrenia might involve an abnormality or alteration in neurochemistry.

The Dopamine Hypothesis. Researchers in the early 1960s identified a group of brain chemicals involved in the therapeutic effects of antipsychotic drug action. This research showed that **dopamine**, a type of **neurotransmitter**, plays a major role in therapeutic drug effects. The hypothesis that dopamine is central to schizophrenia has been one of the most enduring ideas about the disorder. The strongest support for a connection between abnormal dopamine activity or dysregulation and schizophrenia comes from studies showing that antipsychotic drugs such as chlorpromazine reduce symptoms by blocking dopamine **receptors**, especially the dopamine D2 receptor subtype. Canadian researcher Dr. Phillip Seeman at the University of Toronto carried out the first studies demonstrating the link between dopamine blockade and symptom reduction (Seeman & Lee, 1975). Seeman used postmortem brain tissue samples from patients with schizophrenia to show that the most effective antipsychotic drugs were chemicals that occupied and blocked receptors for dopamine.

Also supporting the dopamine hypothesis of schizophrenia was the observation that several drugs, including cocaine and amphetamine, accentuate or boost dopamine activity rather than blocking it. This enhancement can induce psychotic symptoms that resemble acute schizophrenic episodes. For example, high doses of cocaine taken by people who do not have schizophrenia can result in persecutory fears and paranoia and create a severely distorted sense of reality (Julien, 2007). Cocaine appears to produce these effects in part by boosting the presence of dopamine. Concentrations of dopamine are probably increased in cocaine users, heightening the activity of the neurotransmitter in psychologically important brain regions. Overall, there is a clear tie between increased dopamine activity and psychosis and between blocked dopamine activity and reduced psychotic symptoms.

The evidence on drug effects and dopamine is suggestive, but it does not prove that something is wrong in the dopamine systems of people with schizophrenia or that abnormalities in the neurotransmitter cause the disorder in the first place. However, it is difficult to measure dopamine levels or activity in the brain directly in living people. By the late 1970s, chemical "labels," or **ligands**, that bind selectively with specific receptor sites became available (Seeman, Chau-Wong, Tedesco, & Wong, 1976). This gave rise to a new kind of study, the radioactive binding assay, wherein the density and distribution of various receptors were determined. Initially this could only be done with post-mortem brain tissue obtained from schizophrenia patients, or from healthy people who died of natural causes. Over a 15-year period, researchers looked for evidence that dopamine receptors were abnormally elevated in the brains of people with schizophrenia. Initial findings such as those by Lee and Seeman (1980) were promising, with a majority of patient samples showing increased dopamine receptor densities. However, it was also known that these tissue samples were obtained from patients receiving antipsychotic medication prior to death. There was evidence that dopamine-blocking medication stimulated the brain to make more dopamine receptors. Accordingly, chronic exposure to antipsychotic drugs during life may have caused an artificial increase in receptor numbers and distorted the results of receptor assays of schizophrenic brain tissue samples. Although efforts were made to obtain tissue samples from patients who had been drug free for weeks or months prior to death, it was hard to completely rule out lifetime drug exposure as an artificial influence on receptor-binding studies.

What researchers needed was a way of measuring the density of dopamine receptors in the brains of living patients with schizophrenia.

This possibility was realized with the application of receptor-binding ligands to the field of PET scanning. Instead of injecting tracers that attached to blood cells or glucose, researchers introduced the ligands that attached to dopamine receptors. The innovation not only meant that living people could be studied, but also that individuals who had never been treated with antipsychotic medication could be examined. The PET receptor-binding methods provided the opportunity to determine if schizophrenia involved elevated dopamine receptors without the distorting influence of dopamine-blocking drugs. Initial results (Gjedde & Wong, 1987; Wong et al., 1986) confirmed that a large majority of patients with schizophrenia had dopamine receptor densities exceeding the normal range. However, independent researchers failed to support these findings (Martinot et al., 1990), and the field became mired in controversy. It was unclear whether technical properties of different ligands, the imperfect accuracy of PET scanning equipment, or different samples of patients were responsible for the inconsistent results (Sedvall, 1992).

Since the early 1990s, the original form of the dopamine hypothesis has been modified in light of the available evidence and advances in neurobiology and brain imaging technology. In the most recent revision of the dopamine hypothesis, Howes and Kapur (2009) hypothesize that multiple "hits" (e.g., pregnancy and obstetric complications, stress and trauma, drug use, and genes) interact to result in dopamine dysregulation. The authors claim that this dysregulation is the "final common pathway" to psychosis in schizophrenia. In line with this recent revision of the dopamine hypothesis, it is not surprising that genes known to impact dopamine functioning are not related to the risk of schizophrenia when studied in isolation (Edwards et al., 2016). Genetic vulnerability may be only one of the hits that can lead to psychosis, highlighting the need to study the interaction of multiple hits (Howes et al., 2017). In sum, what was once a fairly simple theory about the role of dopamine in schizophrenia is increasingly complex. It has become progressively more apparent over the past several decades that more than one neurotransmitter may be involved in schizophrenia. For example, another neurotransmitter, serotonin, has been implicated in some of the therapeutic effects of more recent antipsychotic drugs. Moreover, dopamine interacts with other important neurotransmitters, including glutamate, gamma-aminobutyric acid (GABA), and acetylcholine, and some researchers suspect that these substances also contribute to the story of neurochemistry and schizophrenia (González-Maeso et al., 2008; Brisch et al., 2014).

5 BEFORE MOVING ON

Is a single definitive biological abnormality found in all patients with the diagnosis of schizophrenia?

Treatment

For many decades following Kraepelin's (1896, 1913, 1919) pioneering descriptions of schizophrenia, there was no effective medical or psychological treatment for the disorder. In fact, use of the term *treatment* to describe what patients endured is highly questionable. Patients with schizophrenia might be subjected to "great and desperate" methods like prolonged barbiturate-induced sleep therapy, **insulin coma,** or **psychosurgery** (Valenstein, 1986). These were "treatments" to be feared and avoided, but patients' rights were seldom at the forefront during the first half of the twentieth century. There were no therapies with proven effectiveness, and experimental procedures were attempted that lacked scientific or medical justification. For example, insulin coma therapy involved creating a hypoglycemic state (low blood sugar) through administration of high doses of insulin. This resulted in loss of consciousness and frequent convulsions. A few reports suggested that a series of such insulin shocks might reduce a patient's psychotic episodes. However, the technique was never carefully evaluated and brought the risks of heart attacks and strokes to the patient. Some patients with schizophrenia underwent brain surgery—"psychosurgery"—in the form of **frontal lobotomies** or leukotomies, wherein nerve tracts in the frontal brain were cut. As a hospital psychologist, one of the authors (W. H.) once carried out a neuropsychological assessment with a survivor of this sinister era, an elderly woman who had undergone psychosurgery decades before, in a dim past that she could barely remember. This unfortunate woman was left with brain damage and cognitive deficits due to the surgery—and she retained her schizophrenia. Many thousands of patients were operated on with little demonstrable benefit and little concern for ethical requirements like informed consent to treatment.

By the early 1950s, Canada and the United States had hospitalized on an indefinite basis well over half a million patients with schizophrenia and other severe mental disorders. Although the psychiatric pioneers had hoped to bring medical science to bear on the problem of schizophrenia, a patient in 1850 may have been better off in terms of quality of life, if not the disease process itself, than a patient in 1950. Fortunately, within a few years this depressing assessment changed as the first genuine treatments for schizophrenia were discovered and developed.

ANTIPSYCHOTIC MEDICATION

The discovery of drugs to treat the symptoms of schizophrenia is a story of accident, dedication, and insight. A young French naval surgeon named Henri Laborit (see Swazey, 1974) was interested in the syndrome of circulatory shock that occurred during and after surgery. The syndrome included depression and apathy, along with marked physical features like shallow breathing and a bloodless, pale appearance. Shock could sometimes progress to death within hours. Laborit and his colleagues began experimenting with a variety of drugs in an attempt to find a compound that might alleviate the shock syndrome in surgical patients. One relatively new agent called promethazine proved to have a number of intriguing and unexpected properties. The drug made patients drowsy, reduced pain, and created a feeling of "euphoric quietude." Hence, promethazine had psychological effects. It was observed that surgical patients receiving the drug remained conscious without signs of pain or anxiety. Laborit realized that if the drug had psychological effects it must be acting on the brain and not just on the circulatory system.

Laborit's (1950) published observations encouraged researchers to modify the formula of promethazine and enhance its curious, brain-related effects. The upshot of these efforts was **chlorpromazine**, the first genuine antipsychotic medication. It was another 10 years before the new drug's specific value in treating schizophrenia was fully recognized and documented. The initial observations of promethazine and chlorpromazine in psychiatric patients reflected the mood-influencing effects that developed over days and initial weeks. Hence, it was thought that the drugs might be most helpful in patients with mood disorders, mania, and agitation. However, it turned out that antipsychotic effects took several weeks to develop fully. A series of drug effectiveness studies or clinical trials was required to demonstrate the full range of clinical applications for the new medication. Canada played an important part in these drug evaluations through studies by Lehmann and Hanrahan (1954) at McGill University in Montreal. Following the large collaborative National Institute of Mental Health study (1964) in the United States, the evidence was finally conclusive. Chlorpromazine reduced more than agitation, mania, and mood disturbances. It also reduced the symptoms associated with schizophrenia.

A large volume of studies now documents the value of chlorpromazine and its chemical relatives, as well as a "new generation" of medications developed in the 1990s, in alleviating the frequency and severity of hallucinations and delusions, thought disorder, and, to a lesser degree, the negative symptoms of the illness. Patients who receive these medications require less time in hospital, have fewer relapses, and enjoy better life functioning when compared to untreated patients (Julien, 2007; Kane, 1989; Meltzer, 1993). However, these drugs are a way of controlling and managing symptoms and not a cure for schizophrenia. Moreover, a minority of patients does not benefit from antipsychotic drugs, and even responsive patients may have to deal with unpleasant and occasionally disabling side effects. This situation has stimulated the development of improved medications, including **risperidone** and **olanzapine**, that provide symptom control with fewer side effects than the older chlorpromazine family of drugs. Still, many patients experience a return of their symptoms if medication is discontinued or they find prolonged medication use unpleasant. Moreover, drugs may control symptoms, but they cannot provide the occupational and daily living skills or social supports needed to ensure successful adjustment outside of hospital. In fact, the most disabling aspect of schizophrenia may be the cognitive impairment associated with the disorder rather than the positive and negative symptoms. Cognitive impairment plays a major role in limiting skill learning and everyday life functioning. Perhaps not surprisingly, there is intense interest in the development of "cognitive-enhancing" medications that can address these impairments (Harvey & Keefe, 2001). So far, studies on cognitive-enhancing medications have shown disappointing results, even when the studies include medications that are known to be effective in treating cognitive impairments in other disorders (e.g., attention deficit hyperactivity disorder; Harvey & Bowie, 2012). Multiple explanations for these negative results have been proposed. For example, other medications that participants were taking at the time of testing may interfere with the effects of cognitive enhancers. New cognitive-enhancing medications and research studies are being designed and they may provide more promising results in the near future. However, it may be that a combination of cognitive-enhancing medication and cognitive and psychosocial interventions is the best way to improve cognitive impairments.

PSYCHOTHERAPY AND SKILLS TRAINING

The use of psychotherapy in the treatment of schizophrenia has been the subject of considerable controversy. Many pioneers in clinical psychology and psychiatry, including Sigmund Freud, argued that psychoanalysis is ineffective for the treatment of schizophrenia. Several research findings pointing to the poor outcomes of psychotherapy for patients with schizophrenia supported this claim. Further, the established effectiveness of medication as a treatment for schizophrenia in the 1960s contributed to the reluctance to employ psychotherapeutic treatment approaches. At the same time, some researchers and therapists have always insisted on the value and effectiveness of psychoanalytically oriented therapies, leading to lively but inconclusive controversies (Karon & VandenBos, 1981). Adding fuel to the fire, several older literature reviews have noted methodological limitations in previous research, thereby calling into question the value of the studies that rejected psychoanalysis for patients with schizophrenia (Beck, 1978; Mosher & Keith, 1980).

COGNITIVE-BEHAVIOURAL THERAPY More recently, studies of **cognitive-behavioural therapy (CBT)** for patients with schizophrenia have revealed that at least one form of psychotherapy may indeed be helpful in treating this population (Bowie et al., 2012; Beck, Rector, Stolar, & Grant, 2009; Turkington, Dudley, Warman, & Beck, 2004). Indeed, CBT is now recommended as a standard of care by the National Institute for Clinical Excellence, with a particular focus on four principal problems experienced by psychotic patients: (1) emotional disturbance, (2) psychotic symptoms such as delusions and hallucinations, (3) social disabilities, and (4) risk of relapse (Fowler, Garety, & Kuipers, 1995). CBT theory maintains that emotional and behavioural disturbances are influenced by subjective interpretation of life and illness experiences. CBT for schizophrenia integrates analysis and understanding of the patient's symptoms and delusional beliefs through techniques such as psychoeducation, belief modification, and coping strategy enhancement (Kingdon & Turkington, 2005). Normalization is one form of psychoeducation that helps patients understand symptoms by comparing their experiences to those of mentally healthy adults. For example, therapists explain that anomalous experiences can occur in healthy adults who are suffering from sleep or sensory deprivation or from unusually high levels of stress. Moreover, patients are taught how to correctly interpret relevant environmental events and how to respond appropriately to social cues while interacting and communicating with other people. These techniques are thought to help reduce patients' catastrophic interpretations of symptoms and aid in preventing relapse.

Often, therapy develops over a sequence of stages. For example, Canadian psychologist Neil Rector (Beck et al., 2009; Beck & Rector, 2000; Rector, Seeman, & Segal, 2003) focuses initially on engaging the patient with schizophrenia, as a trusting and collaborative therapeutic alliance is critical for success. Establishing this relationship may involve listening, empathic understanding, and gradual exploration of the patient's experiences, combined with gentle questions, which lead to the formulation of a problem list. Next, patients are taught to record and monitor their thoughts and to carry out "homework" assignments. Similar to CBT for depression or anxiety, a thought record or voice diary is often incorporated into treatment to help the patient rationally appraise related symptoms as they occur. For example, recording the intensity and number of voices, affective responses, and self-initiated coping attempts at the time of symptom onset allows the therapist to select novel strategies or improve on existing strategies (i.e., coping strategy enhancement) that will help to reduce symptom severity. Consequently, therapy becomes increasingly focused on the individual's unique clinical presentation. Through careful questioning the patient is encouraged to test the validity of his or her symptoms and to consider their influence on daily life. Alternative explanations are developed for delusions and hallucinations, with belief modification as the final goal of treatment. However, therapists must be careful to maintain a nonconfrontational stance, which often results in therapy progressing at a slow pace. In fact, pushing patients too quickly can result in increases in belief conviction and likelihood of relapse (Nelson, 1997). With respect to negative symptoms, patients are challenged and assisted in identifying the sources of their inactivity or withdrawal, and they participate in "experiments" to create alternative and more rewarding experiences and new interests. The last phase in a CBT program may involve patients learning to direct their own cognitive skill development and progress with an eye toward preventing symptom relapses and severe illness episodes. In fact, because relapse is common among patients with schizophrenia, therapists often create reminder coping cards for common delusions or hallucinations that can be referred to when symptom reoccurrence is imminent or occurring (Chadwick, Birchwood, & Trower, 1996).

A recent review of the evolution of CBT in schizophrenia (Tai & Turkington, 2009) summarized findings from a body of evidence that highlighted the efficacy of this intervention. The authors reported that moderate benefits are shown for both positive and negative symptoms and that these benefits are sustained over time (Malik, Kingdon, Pelton, Mehta, & Turkington, 2009). Most recently, clinicians and researchers have used CBT to target low-functioning, chronically disordered patients with schizophrenia. Results from an 18-month clinical trial by Grant and colleagues (2012) found that patients receiving CBT showed gains in their psychosocial functioning and motivation and experienced reduced positive symptoms (e.g., hallucinations, delusions, disorganization). Furthermore, a meta-analysis of CBT conducted with medication-resistant patients (i.e., patients whose psychotic symptoms remain due to inadequate response to treatment) demonstrated moderate effect sizes for positive and general symptoms maintained at follow-up (Burns, Erickson, & Brenner, 2014). Taken together, the findings from these and other studies are promising. However, research on the predictors of response to treatment (e.g., gender, neurocognitive deficit, insight) is still relatively new and inconclusive (e.g., Brabban, Tai, & Turkington, 2009).

SOCIAL SKILLS TRAINING AND COGNITIVE REMEDIATION
Social skills training is a learning-based intervention model for the treatment of functional disabilities associated with schizophrenia (Chien et al., 2003). Unlike the symptom-focused CBT approaches, social skills training provides rehabilitation for patients with schizophrenia, fostering the development of practical social and living skills. Patients typically receive training in a variety of functional skills, including carrying out appropriate social interaction, coping with common stressors, dealing with household and residential tasks, and developing employment-related abilities. The social skills training approach thus promotes independence and simultaneously reduces stressors.

A meta-analysis of 22 randomized controlled trials, a strict method for evaluating treatments, found that social skills training had moderate effects on social and independent living skills (based on role-play measures), psychosocial functioning, and negative symptoms. Small beneficial effects were observed for relapse rates (Kurtz & Mueser, 2008). These interventions were most effective with younger patients. Continued efforts are needed in developing similarly helpful social skills training for older, more chronic patients who make up a significant proportion of the population with schizophrenia.

Cognitive remediation programs have been used with schizophrenia for the past four decades. These interventions target higher-level thinking skills such as memory, attention, and executive functions to enhance cognitive ability by teaching compensatory strategies, providing practice exercises, and holding group discussions. Remediation training in schizophrenia has significant, but modest benefits for improving cognition and community functioning (e.g., employment, number of hours worked, interpersonal problem-solving skills, social adjustment), with small to medium effect sizes that are maintained at follow-up (Reddy, Horan, Jahshan, & Green, 2014; Wykes, Huddy, Cellard, McGurk, & Czobor, 2011).

Training social cognitive skills, such as recognizing emotions in faces and understanding the mental states of other people not only improves these particular skills, it improves general symptoms and everyday functioning (Kurtz & Richardson, 2012). The combination of these psychosocial approaches to cognitive remediation may enhance rehabilitation (Reddy et al., 2014). Thus, the most effective treatment goes beyond reducing psychotic symptoms and aims to increase patients' quality of life by providing skills that improve cognition and functional independence (Dickerson & Lehman, 2011; Isaac & Januel, 2016).

FAMILY THERAPY Patients with schizophrenia who have the support of family members may benefit from **family therapy**. This psychosocial intervention conceptualizes the patient as a member of a family system (Kazarian & Malla, 1992) and thus tailors treatment to the family as a whole. Accordingly, therapy aims for active involvement of each member of the family in the treatment process. The family system is of particular importance because of the current focus on deinstitutionalization; patients with schizophrenia struggle in adjusting to community life, which may include residing with family members. Patients are thus subject to the influence of daily family interactions and to the emotional communication or miscommunication (e.g., expressed emotion) embodied in these interactions. Therapy for the family of a schizophrenia patient may also entail psychoeducation (McFarlane, Dixon, Lukens, & Lucksted, 2003) about the clinical presentation of the disorder, theories pertaining to its causes, and available treatment options. Furthermore, family members can be informed of the potential impact of schizophrenia on the family unit and trained in problem-solving and stress-related coping skills. Each individual family member is asked to make a commitment to supporting the treatment process.

EARLY INTERVENTION The importance of early intervention in schizophrenia has emerged as a central area of research over the past two decades and has received worldwide attention through international organizations and dedicated peer-reviewed journals. Canadian psychologist Dr. Jean Addington has devoted much of her career to studying people considered at high risk for developing schizophrenia, as well as to those in the prodromal and first episode phases of the disorder. The term *prodrome* refers to the period before the appearance of psychotic symptoms when vulnerable adolescents often become withdrawn and suspicious. Those individuals who progress, or "convert," to psychotic disorder are referred to as "first episode" patients because they are experiencing their first episode of intense and unmistakable symptoms. Results from Addington's work reveal that significant cognitive, social, and functional impairments occur at the beginning stages of the disorder and are not simply a product of many years of hospital admissions or social disadvantage (Addington, 2007). Symptom improvement is probable following early intervention, especially programs that include CBT techniques (Bird et al., 2010; Hutton & Taylor, 2014). Further, the inclusion of family therapy in early intervention programs may reduce the risk of relapse and hospital admission (Bird et al., 2010). Despite these notable benefits of early intervention programs, cognitive impairments persist and social and functional skills, as well as quality of life, remain deficient in patients when compared to healthy peers.

6 BEFORE MOVING ON

Why is it important not to focus exclusively on psychotic symptoms when developing treatments for schizophrenia?

CANADIAN RESEARCH CENTRE

Dr. Sean Kidd

Sean Kidd is a clinical psychologist at the Centre for Addiction and Mental Health in Toronto, Ontario, where he is the Head of Psychological Services in the Schizophrenia Division. He is also an Associate Professor in the University of Toronto's Department of Psychiatry. Dr. Kidd's major research aims comprise understanding and supporting successful transition to community living for marginalized populations with mental health challenges. These populations include individuals with schizophrenia as well as homeless youth.

Dr. Kidd's work typically involves two steps. The first is to carry out an in-depth analysis of the challenges and resources faced by clients in their attempts to participate successfully in community life. This analysis includes reviewing previous studies and considering multiple perspectives on the problem. He then moves on to the second step, which involves developing, applying, and evaluating interventions to improve the success of these clients.

His research with homeless youth in Toronto and Halifax has indicated that many return to being homeless shortly after obtaining housing and many continue to experience poor mental health and difficulties in daily life. Dr. Kidd has built on these findings to develop a program that combines several

Courtesy of Dr. Sean Kidd

interventions. They include reaching out to youth to provide structured guidance and resources as well as mental health interventions (group and individual psychotherapy, family counselling) and peer support. This programmatic intervention is designed to stabilize and connect youth with supports and services during a time of critical need. The approach has proven successful in initial testing and is now being formally evaluated using clinical trials methodology. In addition, Dr. Kidd's approach is being tried in a small northern setting where its relevance for youth in Indigenous communities will be examined.

In the field of schizophrenia, his research highlights the way basic, pragmatic challenges of everyday living can be major roadblocks to improved community functioning. The cognitive difficulties that affect people with schizophrenia are often most noticeable in their own homes. However, this is a setting where mental health workers seldom provide services and evidence-based approaches are rare. Dr. Kidd has worked closely with colleagues to modify and refine an intervention termed Cognitive Adaptation Training so that it can be used more easily in clinical settings. Cognitive Adaptation Training matches supports ranging from the practical (e.g., alarm clocks, signs, how to organize belongings) to the psychological (e.g., behavioural interventions) with an individual's strengths and challenges. The idea is to improve clients' abilities to succeed in the basic tasks of daily life. This is a critical first step in achieving more demanding goals such as employment and a fulfilling social life in the community. His work in this area has progressed from tests of feasibility through to randomized trials. These will determine the effectiveness of Cognitive Adaptation Training as an intervention for early stages of mental illness and as an addition to other approaches including cognitive remediation.

Overall, and in the spirit of moving from research to application, Dr. Kidd seeks to use science to deliver more effective interventions to people facing severe adversity during critical periods of change and challenge.

SUMMARY

- Schizophrenia is a psychotic disorder that may affect both men and women in late adolescence and early adulthood.

- The disorder is complex and heterogeneous in its clinical presentation, course, and outcome.

- Approximately 50 percent of patients with schizophrenia improve over time and in response to treatment, but few achieve their social and occupational potential, and many require lifelong support and remain at risk for suicide.

- Direct and indirect social and health care costs of schizophrenia approach $7 billion a year in Canada.

- Schizophrenia involves characteristic symptoms that must be present for diagnosis, including hallucinations, delusions, thought and language disorder, bizarre behaviour, and withdrawal.

- The diagnosis requires evidence of a decline in social and occupational functioning.

- Having psychotic symptoms for one day does not mean a person has schizophrenia; these symptoms must persist for at least a month unless successfully treated.

- Mood disorders such as depression and other medical and developmental disorders may complicate the diagnosis of schizophrenia and must be ruled out.

- There is no objective test that confirms whether a person has schizophrenia.

- Disorders such as schizophrenia may result from many interacting biological and psychosocial influences rather than from a single cause or event.

- Biological and psychosocial processes may increase or decrease the probability that a vulnerable person develops schizophrenia.

- Most theorists argue that both a vulnerability, or diathesis, and environmental stress are required to cause schizophrenia.

- Having a parent with schizophrenia significantly increases the chances that a young person will develop the disorder.

- The influence of parents on the development of schizophrenia in their children is biological and genetic in nature.

- Many genes are implicated in schizophrenia, but their individual effects are very small.

- Epigenetic processes that turn genes on and off may be as important in causing schizophrenia as the genes themselves.

- Slow processing of information; poor coordination; and deficient attention, perception, and learning are characteristic of most people with schizophrenia.

- Abnormalities of the frontal and temporal lobes of the brain are among the most studied features of schizophrenia, but no single brain abnormality occurs in everyone with the disorder.

- Neuroscience research methods provide increasingly accurate and sophisticated information about the structure and physiology of the brain.

- The most frequently implicated neurochemical abnormality in schizophrenia involves the neurotransmitter dopamine.

- Chlorpromazine was the first effective antipsychotic medication used with schizophrenia patients, reducing the severity of positive and, to a lesser degree, negative symptoms.
- Newer generations of antipsychotic medications claim to provide therapeutic benefits with fewer side effects.
- Antipsychotic medications have little or no effect on the cognitive impairments associated with schizophrenia.
- Significant advances have been made in the application of psychological interventions, such as cognitive-behaviour therapy (CBT), family therapy, and cognitive remediation training.

- Cognitive remediation training has potential value for addressing cognitive impairment and may also reduce some symptoms and improve social functioning in people with schizophrenia.
- Early intervention, whereby medication and psychological therapies are provided before a person develops prolonged psychosis, has become a new and promising focus for clinical researchers.
- Integrated psychosocial and medical therapies offer the most hope for improving the lives of people with schizophrenia.

KEY TERMS

amygdala (p. 221)

anhedonia (p. 207)

auditory hallucinations (p. 205)

aversive drift (p. 213)

avolition (p. 207)

birth-related complications (p. 217)

catatonic behaviour (p. 207)

chlorpromazine (p. 224)

cognitive marker (p. 211)

cognitive slippage (p. 213)

cognitive-behavioural therapy (CBT) (p. 224)

collective unconscious (p. 212)

cumulative liability (p. 218)

delusional thinking (p. 206)

delusions (p. 207)

delusions of grandeur (p. 207)

diathesis (p. 213)

diminished emotional expression (p. 208)

disease markers (p. 211)

dopamine (p. 222)

effect size (p. 218)

endophenotype (p. 211)

epigenetic (p. 217)

expressed emotion (p. 217)

eye-tracking (p. 212)

familiality (p. 215)

family therapy (p. 226)

frontal brain deficiency (p. 219)

frontal lobe (p. 218)

frontal lobotomy (p. 223)

functional magnetic resonance imaging (fMRI) (p. 220)

genetic contribution (p. 215)

hallucinations (p. 207)

heterogeneity (p. 204)

high-risk children (p. 217)

hippocampus (p. 221)

hypokrisia (p. 213)

insulin coma (p. 223)

left temporal lobe (p. 221)

ligands (p. 222)

loosening of associations (p. 208)

lunacy (p. 205)

madness (p. 205)

meta-analysis (p. 218)

negative symptoms (p. 207)

neuropsychological tests (p. 219)

neurotransmitters (p. 222)

olanzapine (p. 224)

penetrance (p. 216)

persecutory delusions (p. 207)

perseverate (p. 219)

positive symptoms (p. 207)

positron emission tomography (PET) (p. 220)

prevalence (p. 204)

psychosis (p. 207)

psychosurgery (p. 223)

receptors (p. 222)

referential delusions (p. 207)

religious delusions (p. 207)

remission (p. 205)

risperidone (p. 224)

schizophrenia (p. 204)

schizophrenogenic (p. 212)

schizotype (p. 213)

social drift (p. 212)

social skills training (p. 225)

somatic delusions (p. 207)

stress (p. 213)

structural magnetic resonance imaging (MRI) (p. 219)

thought and speech disorder (p. 207)

waxy flexibility (p. 208)

Wisconsin Card Sorting Test (p. 219)

DANIELLE MACDONALD

•

KATHRYN TROTTIER

CHAPTER

10

Elena Elisseeva/123RF

Eating Disorders

LEARNING OBJECTIVES

AFTER READING THIS CHAPTER, STUDENTS WILL BE ABLE TO:

1 Describe the symptoms of eating disorders and distinguish among anorexia nervosa, bulimia nervosa, binge-eating disorder, other specified feeding or eating disorders, and an unspecified feeding or eating disorder.

2 Identify the prevalence of eating disorders and illustrate how their prevalence has changed over time.

3 Distinguish between the physical/biological factors that are thought to contribute to the development of eating disorders and those that are thought to be a consequence of eating disorders.

4 Outline the primary etiological factors that are involved in eating disorder symptomatology.

5 Compare and contrast biological treatment (i.e., medication), cognitive-behavioural therapy, and inter-personal therapy in the treatment of bulimia nervosa.

6 Describe a prevention program that has been implemented to decrease the risk of developing an eating disorder, and highlight the main findings of the program.

When Becky was 18 years old, her boyfriend broke up with her. Becky, who is now 19, had been dating her boyfriend for two years. After the breakup she found herself feeling depressed, and her self-esteem suffered greatly. Although she was of average weight, Becky thought she might feel better about herself if she lost a bit of weight, so she began a strict diet. She cut out all added fats such as butter and mayonnaise, desserts, and fried foods. After successfully losing three kilos and receiving positive comments from her friends and family, Becky thought she might feel even better about herself if she lost a bit more weight. In addition to cutting out foods high in fat, Becky decided to restrict herself to eating fruit, vegetables, diet products, and white meat. However, Becky's weight loss did not seem to be improving her self-esteem, and one evening she found herself home alone, feeling particularly down. She decided to allow herself one piece of cake, but after eating it she felt as though she could not stop eating. She ate several pieces of cake, a bag of chips, and half a bag of cookies. After finishing the food, she felt uncomfortably full and anxious about having consumed so many calories and so much fat. She felt that she had no choice but to vomit the food she had eaten.

In the following weeks, Becky found herself engaging in the same pattern of behaviour. Each morning she made a pact with herself to stick to her diet, but in the evenings when she was feeling tired, alone, and bad about herself, she often felt out of control and compelled to eat large amounts of food, which she then felt she had to vomit. Eventually, Becky began to vomit even normal portions of food that she ate during the day. Despite this, she did not lose any more weight and felt worse about herself than before she began to diet.

Introduction and Historical Perspective

Today, many people are familiar with the term *eating disorders*. However, even if you are familiar with the term, you may not be exactly sure what eating disorders are or why they occur. There are many common misperceptions about eating disorders, including that individuals with anorexia nervosa are simply starving themselves on purpose, or that eating disorders are driven by issues of vanity. Many of these misperceptions are rooted in outdated views of what eating disorders are and how they develop. Increasingly in the twenty-first century, mental health movements are focused on increasing accurate awareness and reducing stigma around mental health issues, including eating disorders.

The eating disorder **anorexia nervosa** is characterized by food restriction that leads to a significantly low weight, relative to a person's age, height, and sex, as well as a fear of gaining weight. Anorexia nervosa was first recognized as a mental health disorder in the late-twentieth century (Bruch, 1978), but its symptoms have been described for hundreds, or even thousands of years (Bemporad, 1997). Interestingly, in the Middle Ages, behaviours that would today be described as symptoms of anorexia were seen positively, as evidence of religious asceticism. This demonstrates that the socio-cultural

context of a behaviour can be critical in determining how it is perceived and interpreted (Miller & Pumariega, 2001).

In **bulimia nervosa**, individuals experience episodes of binge eating in which they consume a large amount of food and feel out of control while they eat, often following a period of food restriction. After the binge, they try to compensate for what they have eaten, for example, by engaging in self-induced vomiting, laxative use, fasting, or exercise. Bulimia nervosa was also recognized as a mental health disorder only in the late twentieth century (Striegel-Moore, 1997), although episodes of binge eating and compensatory behaviours have also been described throughout history (Bemporad, 1997).

With the publication of the DSM-5 (APA, 2013), **binge-eating disorder (BED)** has been included as a stand-alone eating disorder. As in bulimia nervosa, recurrent episodes of binge eating occur. However, unlike bulimia, regular, inappropriate compensatory behaviours to try to rid the body of calories are not present. Instead, the binge eating is associated with a variety of eating behaviours (e.g., eating rapidly, eating until uncomfortably full, eating despite not being hungry, eating alone because of embarrassment) and feeling guilt or disgust about the binge eating.

In this chapter, we focus on eating disorders, including anorexia nervosa, bulimia nervosa, binge-eating disorder, and the other specified eating disorders (including purging disorder and night-eating syndrome). In DSM-5, however, eating

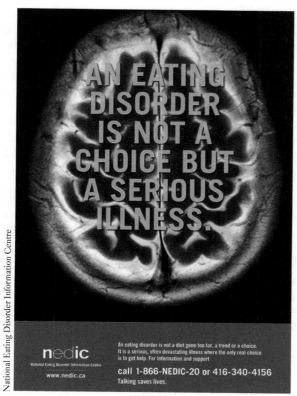

National Eating Disorder Information Centre

This poster from the National Eating Disorder Information Centre in Toronto aims to dispel the myth that eating disorders are a choice.

disorders are classified together with feeding disorders. The feeding disorders include pica (eating non-food substances, such as dirt or paper), rumination disorder (repeatedly regurgitating food), and avoidant/restrictive food intake disorder (ARFID). ARFID resembles anorexia nervosa in some ways: it is characterized by a feeding disturbance that leads to being underweight and/or an inability to eat enough food to meet nutritional/energy needs. However, unlike anorexia nervosa, individuals do not perceive themselves as fat or have a distorted perception of their body weight or shape.

Typical Characteristics

ANOREXIA NERVOSA

Family and friends of individuals with anorexia nervosa may find it difficult to understand why their loved ones are so concerned with weight and shape despite their emaciated appearance. For those who are not familiar with the features of anorexia, and the factors that typically underlie this disorder, it may be difficult to understand the struggle that individuals with anorexia face. Parents are concerned about the serious consequences of their children being so underweight, and often encourage them to eat, as this will seemingly solve their problems. As a result, conflicts with parents about eating are common, and individuals with anorexia may hide or secretly dispose of food, eat alone, or tell others that they have eaten when in fact they have not. To be able to understand and treat this disorder, it is important to recognize that there are a variety of underlying psychological factors associated with anorexia.

Individuals with anorexia have an intense fear of gaining weight, or of becoming fat. This fear is paradoxical, given that they are in fact underweight. To maintain their low weight, they restrict the amount of food they eat. This may begin with a reduction in the total number of calories consumed over the course of a day, and avoidance of foods that are high in calories. However, the number of foods that are avoided often grows to the extent that individuals develop a long list of "forbidden foods" that they refuse to eat. Individuals with anorexia typically believe that eating feared or forbidden foods will result in significant amounts of weight gain—they might even believe that this weight gain will occur immediately after eating the food. A variety of other maladaptive or ritualistic eating behaviours may also develop. For example, individuals may begin eating foods in a set order (e.g., eating vegetables first and leaving certain types of food on their plate, such as high-protein foods, until last), dissecting food into small pieces, and weighing food or fluids before consumption.

Some people with anorexia engage in excessive exercise as a means of achieving weight loss. General restlessness is also common, as well as pacing back and forth and standing rather than sitting. This restlessness may be driven by a desire to burn additional calories; however, it may also be a result of poor nutrition and starvation. Some individuals with anorexia nervosa reach and maintain their low body weight through food restriction and exercise. However, others also engage in **purging** behaviours in order to achieve or maintain weight loss. Purging behaviours include self-induced vomiting, laxative abuse, or abuse of enemas or diuretics. These purging behaviours, which result in the direct evacuation of the stomach, bowels, or bladder, are distinct from other compensatory behaviours that can be used to prevent weight gain, such as fasting or excessive exercise. Although purging behaviours can lead to some weight loss, this is primarily due to dehydration (which itself has serious medical consequences), as a substantial number of calories are still absorbed by the body (Mehler, 2011).

Many individuals who purge also engage in binge eating. From a clinician and researcher's standpoint, it is important to determine whether a patient is engaging in objective binge eating, or whether binges are subjective. Although both types of binge eating are associated with a lack of control over eating, the amounts of food consumed differ. An **objective binge**, as defined by the DSM-5, consists of eating a large amount of food (larger than most individuals would eat under similar circumstances) in a specific time period (e.g., less than two hours). In contrast, if the individual is in fact eating small or normal amounts of food during these episodes (such as one chocolate bar), these would be considered subjective binge episodes.

Anorexia nervosa involves not only a drive for weight loss and a fear of gaining weight, but also a disturbance in body image. This disturbance may be manifested in several ways. Individuals with anorexia may have a disturbance in their view of their body shape. This may be general body dissatisfaction, in which they view their overall weight or shape to be distressingly unacceptable, or may be dissatisfaction with particular body parts, such as their thighs or hips. Individuals with anorexia often perceive their bodies or parts of their bodies to be much larger than they actually are. This disturbance in body image is often linked with low self-esteem, and individuals may use body weight or shape as one of their primary methods of determining self-evaluation. Individuals with anorexia may be hypervigilant in assessing their bodies, and may employ a variety of methods in their assessments, including repeated weighing, measuring body parts (e.g., measuring stomach or leg circumference), or constant checking their body shape in mirrors or other reflective surfaces.

Although the most striking feature of anorexia nervosa is low body weight, other common features of this disorder may be less immediately apparent. These features may concern cognitive, emotional, and physiological functioning; and include social withdrawal, irritability, preoccupation with food, and depression. However, it is important to note that while these features occur frequently in individuals with anorexia, many seem to be linked to the state of semi-starvation that individuals with anorexia are in, as opposed to being a feature of the disorder itself. In other words, during or after recovery, once an individual with anorexia has gained some weight, many of these features may be less severe, or may no longer be present. In the section on physical and psychological consequences of eating disorders, we will further examine this issue, taking into consideration research that shows that individuals who severely restrict their food intake (but do not have an eating disorder) show many of the same features that are present in anorexia nervosa.

BULIMIA NERVOSA

Bulimia nervosa is characterized by episodes of binge eating followed by compensatory behaviours designed to prevent weight gain. As in anorexia nervosa, individuals with bulimia often have low self-esteem, and use weight and shape information as their primary method of self-evaluation. Other features, such as social isolation and depression, are also common in both anorexia and bulimia nervosa. In contrast to anorexia, however, individuals with bulimia are typically within the normal weight range. This, in conjunction with the fact that binge eating and compensatory behaviours are often conducted in private, may make it harder for friends and family to detect the problem.

Individuals with bulimia engage in objective binge eating and, in order to prevent weight gain, engage in a variety of compensatory behaviours. These compensatory behaviours may include fasting and excessive exercise, as well as purging. As mentioned, purging behaviours such as vomiting and laxative abuse are relatively ineffective at producing significant weight loss, and much of the weight loss that occurs as a result of these behaviours is simply due to dehydration. This, in part, accounts for the fact that many individuals with bulimia are within the normal weight range—the purging and compensatory behaviours they engage in may not be sufficient to produce weight loss, relative to the number of calories that are consumed (some of which are digested before purging begins). These purging behaviours also have serious medical consequences, which include, but are not limited to, damage to the teeth from frequent vomiting, impaired renal function, hypokalemia (low potassium), and cardiovascular difficulties such as

arrhythmias. The secretive nature of the binge/purge episodes, in conjunction with the fact that family and friends may not detect a problem, adds to the seriousness of bulimia given the potentially severe medical complications that can arise.

During episodes of binge eating, foods that are high in calories are typically consumed, such as pizza, cake, ice cream, and chips. During these episodes, more calories are derived from fat, and less from protein, compared to caloric intake during non-binge eating episodes (Gendall, Sullivan, Joyce, Carter, & Bulik, 1997). The foods consumed during binge episodes are often considered to be "forbidden foods," and are avoided during periods of dieting and food restriction. This pattern of avoidance may set up a cycle of bingeing and purging. After an episode of binge eating, there is a feeling of physical discomfort (as a result of the large amount of food consumed), in addition to feelings of guilt and worry about weight gain. Many individuals with bulimia engage in self-induced vomiting after binge-eating episodes to relieve this physical discomfort, as well as to compensate for their excessive intake in an attempt to prevent weight gain. After purging, they may begin another period of dieting or restriction, leaving them feeling hungry in addition to feeling guilt and self-hatred about the purging behaviours. This becomes a cyclical pattern of restriction, binge eating, and purging.

In addition to dieting and food restriction, a number of other factors may serve as cues for binge-eating episodes. Heatherton and Baumeister (1991) proposed that episodes of binge eating occur in an attempt to escape from high levels of aversive self-awareness. According to this "escape from self-awareness" model, individuals who binge eat tend to have high expectations of themselves, constantly monitor themselves, and often fail to meet the high standards they set for themselves. Awareness of their failures leads to feelings of anxiety and depression and, as a result, individuals become strongly motivated to escape from this negative state. Heatherton and Baumeister propose that binge eating occurs as a result of a shift in attention. More specifically, binge eating results from individuals shifting focus away from their perceived failure to live up to high standards, and toward the behaviour and positive sensations associated with eating. Additionally, people with bulimia typically experience increased negative emotions directly preceding binge-eating episodes. After binge eating and purging, negative emotions decrease, suggesting that binge eating and purging function to attenuate negative emotions (Smyth et al., 2007).

Upon reviewing the features of anorexia and bulimia nervosa, you might notice that many of them overlap. Individuals with anorexia and those with bulimia both tend to be preoccupied with, and overvalue weight and shape, and have low self-esteem. Furthermore, like individuals with bulimia, some individuals with anorexia nervosa may engage in binge eating as well as purging behaviours. What, then, is the difference between these groups? One of the primary differences between anorexia and bulimia is body weight; whereas individuals with anorexia nervosa are always underweight by definition, individuals with bulimia are typically within their normal weight range. Furthermore, although all individuals with bulimia engage in binge eating and compensatory behaviours, only some individuals with anorexia exhibit these behaviours. Hence, assessing body weight and eating behaviours can allow clinicians to differentiate between anorexia and bulimia nervosa. We will discuss the diagnostic features of both of these disorders and outline assessment techniques for eating disorders later in this text.

BINGE-EATING DISORDER

BED, like bulimia nervosa, is characterized by regular binge eating episodes. Unlike bulimia, however, episodes of inappropriate compensatory behaviours to prevent weight gain do not follow these binge eating episodes. People with BED experience significant distress about their binge eating. Some other characteristics of individuals with BED include eating very rapidly, eating large amounts even when not hungry, eating alone because of embarrassment about the amount that they are eating, or feeling very guilty or disgusted after binge-eating episodes.

One of the first published cases of an individual with BED appeared in the late 1950s (Stunkard, 1959). Stunkard observed a pattern of sporadic binge eating of large amounts of food, in addition to alternating periods of dieting and overeating, in some obese individuals. He presented a case of a man who binged after arguments with his wife. This man would find himself buying large amounts of food at the grocery store and would be unable to control himself (i.e., stop eating) after starting to eat the food. After the binges, this individual felt extremely distressed and experienced self-hatred. His self-hatred was always focused on his eating, rather than on the relationship disputes that often triggered the binge. You may have noticed that there is some overlap with this man's case and the "escape from self-awareness" model that you read about in the previous section on bulimia nervosa. Although Stunkard's original case of BED was an obese male, BED and obesity are distinct but overlapping concepts. Because large quantities of food are consumed during regular binges, with no regular use of inappropriate compensatory behaviours aimed at preventing weight gain, individuals with BED are often overweight and are sometimes obese. However, some individuals with BED are within a normal weight range. Research has shown that individuals with a diagnosis of BED who are not obese have similar concerns about eating, weight and shape, and similar levels of depression as those with BED who are obese (Dingemans & van Furth, 2012). Furthermore, individuals with BED whose weight is not in the obese range tend to be younger, suggesting that over time weight gain may occur if binge eating episodes continue over the months or years. Although overvaluation of weight and shape is not a diagnostic criterion for BED, individuals with BED have weight and shape concerns that are comparable to those with bulimia (Grilo, Masheb, & White, 2010).

Incidence and Prevalence

In a Canadian community sample, Garfinkel and colleagues (1995) found that 1.1 percent of women and 0.1 percent of men had met criteria for bulimia at some point in their

TABLE 10.1 PREVALENCE AND INCIDENCE OF ANOREXIA NERVOSA, BULIMIA NERVOSA, AND BED

	Lifetime Prevalence		Incidence
	Females	Males	
Anorexia Nervosa			
White	0.64%	0.14%	8 per 100 000 population/year
Latino	0.12%	0.03%	
Asian	0.13%	0.07%	
African-American	0.12%	0.18%	
Bulimia Nervosa			
White	0.97%	0.08%	12 per 100 000 population/year
Latino	2.34%	1.73%	
Asian	1.87%	1.14%	
African-American	1.74%	0.90%	
Binge Eating Disorder			
White	1.91%	0.94%	Unknown
Latino	2.71%	1.54%	
Asian	1.66%	0.84%	
African-American	2.22%	0.78%	

Source: Based on Marques, L., Alegria, M., Becker, A. E., Chen, C. N., Fang, A., Chosak, A., & Diniz, J. B. (2011). Comparative prevalence, correlates of impairment, and service utilization for eating disorders across US ethnic groups: Implications for reducing ethnic disparities in health care access for eating disorders. *International Journal of Eating Disorders, 44*, 412-420. doi: 10.1002/eat.20787

lifetime. More recently, Marques and colleagues (2011) examined the lifetime and 12-month prevalence of anorexia nervosa, bulimia nervosa, and BED in more than 8000 participants from four racial/ethnic groups and both genders in the United States (see Table 10.1). The results indicated that White females were no more likely than other racial/ethnic groups to have a lifetime eating disorder. For males, Latino males were significantly more likely than White males to have a lifetime history of bulimia, but otherwise there were no differences in prevalence rates between white men and men of other racial/ethnic groups (Marques et al., 2011). Research has also suggested that other specified feeding or eating disorders (see the section Diagnosis and Assessment) are even more common than either anorexia or bulimia. Prior to the publication of DSM-5, these eating disorders were estimated as having a prevalence rate of 2.37 percent detected in a large community sample of adolescents and young adults (Machado, Machado, Gonçalves, & Hoek, 2007). However, this other specified category included BED prior to DSM-5. Given, that BED is now a distinct eating disorder category and the frequency threshold for a diagnosis of bulimia is now lower, the prevalence of other specified feeding and eating disorders has decreased somewhat (Machado, Goncalves, & Hoek, 2013).

There have been reports of an increase in the incidence of anorexia nervosa during the twentieth century (e.g., Hoek & van Hoeken, 2003; Currin, Schmidt, Treasure, & Jick, 2005).

The incidence of bulimia nervosa also appears to have increased since it was first described in the late 1970s, though rates may have peaked in the mid-1990s (Rosenvinge & Pettersen, 2015). Incidence rates for both disorders in the general population appear to have stabilized and may have even begun to decrease since the early 2000s, although incidence rates in younger age groups—particularly younger women—remain far higher than in the general population (Hoek, 2006; Rosenvinge & Pettersen, 2015). It is unclear to what extent the observed increases in the incidence of anorexia and bulimia throughout the twentieth century are a result of increased awareness and recognition, as opposed to actual increases in incidence (Wakeling, 1996). Regardless of whether the true incidence of anorexia nervosa has increased, there has been an increase in the incidence of registered cases (and, hence, an increased need for treatment facilities; Hoek & van Hoeken, 2003). Despite increased awareness, Hudson and colleagues (2007) indicate that only about half of individuals with bulimia nervosa have ever sought treatment for their eating disorder. Hence, a large proportion of individuals who meet diagnostic criteria for an eating disorder do not receive appropriate mental health care.

Binge eating disorder (BED) has only recently been added to the DSM-5 as a distinct eating disorder. As a result, incidence data from large studies of the general population are not yet available. However, BED has a prevalence that is comparable or slightly higher than that of bulimia nervosa (Marques et al., 2011). Furthermore, less than 40 percent of the individuals who received a lifetime diagnosis of BED had received eating-disorder treatment (Kessler et al., 2013), which fits with the findings already mentioned regarding low levels of treatment received by individuals with anorexia or bulimia nervosa.

PROGNOSIS

Eating disorders have the highest mortality rate of all the psychiatric disorders (Agras et al., 2004). Recent meta-analytic research estimates the mortality rates of eating disorders as between 3.6% and 7.6% for anorexia nervosa, between 1.1% and 2.4% for bulimia nervosa, and between 1.5% and 5.8% for other eating disorders (Arcelus, Mitchell, Wales, & Nielsen, 2011). The most common causes of death among individuals with eating disorders are starvation and nutritional complications (e.g., electrolyte imbalance or dehydration), and suicide (Neumärker, 2000). In fact, as many as one in five deaths in individuals with anorexia are due to suicide (Arcelus et al., 2011). Clearly, eating disorders are serious disorders.

It appears that there is a varied treatment response among individuals with eating disorders. On average, approximately 50% of adults with bulimia nervosa are able to stop binge eating and purging with the current evidence-based individual therapy. Of the other 50%, some show partial improvements and others show no change at all in the frequency of binge/purge episodes (Byrne, Fursland, Allen, & Watson, 2011; Fairburn et al., 2009). In addition, relapse rates are high for eating disorders. One study investigated relapse rates in a group of 240 women who sought treatment for anorexia nervosa or bulimia nervosa, and followed these individuals for up to nine years after their entry into the study (Keel, Dorer, Franko, Jackson, & Herzog, 2005). Relapse occurred in 36% of women with anorexia nervosa who had achieved remission, and 35% of women with bulimia nervosa. Unfortunately, the high mortality rate in eating disorders exists even among individuals who have received treatment. For example, Herzog and colleagues (2000) report that all the participants who died during the course of their study (5.1% of the participants) had received individual psychotherapy and pharmacotherapy.

There is similar variability in course and outcome in samples of individuals with eating disorders who are not seeking treatment. To study the natural course of eating disorders in the community, Keski-Rahkonen and colleagues examined the prevalence and course of eating disorders in the community in a large epidemiological study. In this study, more than half of individuals with lifetime bulimia nervosa and approximately two-thirds of individuals with lifetime anorexia nervosa were able to achieve and sustain remission from their eating disorder within five years of the disorder's onset (Keski-Rahkonen et al., 2007; Keski-Rahkonen et al., 2009). There were no differences in long-term outcomes for either anorexia or bulimia nervosa based on whether or not the individual's eating disorder had been detected by the health care system (although importantly, detection does not necessarily mean that the individual received eating disorder treatment). These findings suggest that over time, many individuals with eating disorders are able to make improvements.

① BEFORE MOVING ON

There remains a persistent stereotype that eating disorders primarily affect white women, despite an increasing recognition that eating disorders affect individuals from all races and genders. Why do you think this stereotype persists? How might this stereotype affect men or people of colour who are experiencing an eating disorder?

Diagnosis and Assessment
DIAGNOSTIC CRITERIA

Case Notes

Rachel is a 34-year-old woman who works full time and lives on her own in an apartment. Rachel has always been quite thin, and her co-workers have commented to her that they wish they could have her figure. In order to maintain her slim figure, Rachel eats small portions, avoids snacking, and always prepares her own food so that she knows what is in it. Although her co-workers are friendly and sometimes go out together after work for dinner and drinks, Rachel has never joined them.

She feels stressed by the idea of ordering at a restaurant and eating in front of other people. She also doesn't want to disrupt her exercise routine, because she is afraid that if she misses one day at the gym, she will fall into a negative spiral and stop exercising completely.

Lately, some of Rachel's friends have noticed that she has been losing weight and looking unwell. Her best friend recently spoke up about her concerns, and Rachel confided to her that it has been difficult to eat normally and maintain her weight since her mother became ill and passed away last year. She started eating even smaller portions than before, and exercising more, during the stressful period of her mother's illness. She feels better emotionally when she exercises, and has gradually increased her exercise routine to one hour a day, five or six days per week. Although she has noticed her weight loss, she still perceives her stomach and thighs as "too big," and she has found it difficult to eat more because she is concerned about gaining "too much" weight. Her friend suggested that she go to her family doctor to discuss some of her issues with weight and exercise. Rachel reluctantly agreed to do so, and was somewhat alarmed when she found out that she had developed low blood pressure, and that her irregular and missed periods were likely connected with her low weight. Her weight was taken at 49 kilograms, at a height of 170 centimetres, giving her a body mass index of 17. Her doctor suggested that he could refer her to a psychiatrist specializing in eating disorders treatment, and she agreed to visit the psychiatrist for further assessment.

ANOREXIA NERVOSA As you have already read, and can observe in the above case example, the central feature of anorexia nervosa is severe food restriction leading to a very low body weight. The DSM-5 defines this as the restriction of energy intake leading to a body weight that is less than

minimally normal/expected (see Table 10.2). The DSM-5 suggests that significantly low weight can be assessed by calculating a **body mass index** (**BMI**)—weight in kilograms divided by height in metres squared. The DSM-5 refers to the guidelines of the World Health Organization, indicating that a BMI of 18.5 is considered to be the lower threshold of a normal weight, and that those with a BMI of less than 17 would be considered to have a significantly low weight. However, the DSM-5 also highlights that those with a BMI between 17.0 and 18.5, and in certain cases even a BMI higher than 18.5 may also be considered to have a significantly low weight, depending on their clinical history. Part of the difficulty in defining a "significantly low weight" is that it is unreasonable to specify a single standard for minimally normal weight that applies to all individuals – particularly because "normal weight" may vary between men and women, and during different age groups within adulthood. Another reason why it is difficult to give a precise definition for low weight is that most people who develop anorexia nervosa do so in adolescence when they are still growing, with the typical onset between ages 14 to 18. For these individuals, an indication of significantly low weight would be a failure to make expected weight *gain* during a period of growth. Clinicians are instructed to consider an individual's body build and weight history when determining whether an individual meets the low weight criterion for anorexia nervosa.

The second criterion is an intense fear of gaining weight or of becoming fat, or persistent behaviour that interferes with weight gain, despite being at a significantly low weight. It is important to note that individuals with anorexia nervosa do not necessarily fear weight gain for aesthetic reasons. Some individuals with anorexia may fear weight gain because they fear losing some of the consequences of their low weights that they view as beneficial. For example, many individuals with anorexia nervosa report that they fear gaining weight because they desire the emotional numbness that is associated with being underweight.

Finally, in order to meet diagnostic criteria for anorexia, an individual must have a distortion in the experience of his

TABLE 10.2   DSM-5 DIAGNOSTIC CRITERIA FOR ANOREXIA NERVOSA

A. Restriction of energy intake relative to requirements, leading to a significantly low body weight in the context of age, sex, developmental trajectory, and physical health. *Significantly low weight* is defined as a weight that is less than minimally normal or, for children and adolescents, less than that minimally expected.
B. Intense fear of gaining weight or of becoming fat, or persistent behavior that interferes with weight gain, even though at a significantly low weight.
C. Disturbance in the way in which one's body weight or shape is experienced, undue influence of body weight or shape on self-evaluation, or persistent lack of recognition of the seriousness of the current low body weight.

Restricting type: During the last 3 months, the individual has not engaged in recurrent episodes of binge eating or purging behavior (i.e., self-induced vomiting or the misuse of laxatives, diuretics, or enemas). This subtype describes presentations in which weight loss is accomplished primarily through dieting, fasting, and/or excessive exercise.

Binge-eating/purging type: During the last 3 months, the individual has engaged in recurrent episodes of binge eating or purging behavior (i.e., self-induced vomiting or the misuse of laxatives, diuretics, or enemas).

or her body and/or undue significance of body weight. Such distortions can include (1) a disturbance in perception of body weight or shape, such that the individual perceives herself as weighing more than she does or being larger than she is; alternatively, she may recognize that she is underweight but may perceive a particular body part as being larger than it actually is; (2) lack of recognition of the seriousness of her current (low) weight; or (3) determining self-worth based primarily on body weight or shape. This last criterion refers to the tendency for individuals with anorexia (and other eating disorders) to evaluate themselves generally based on their typically negative view of their bodies. In order to assess this, Canadian researchers Geller, Johnson, and Madsen (1997) developed the Shape and Weight-Based Self-Esteem Inventory (SAWBS) that measures the importance of weight and shape to self-esteem relative to other factors (e.g., personality, relationships, career/school, and so on). Another Canadian research group has developed a self-report measure of weight-based self-esteem called the Weight-Influenced Self-Esteem Questionnaire (WISE-Q). The WISE-Q measures the influence of weight on how individuals with eating disorders feel about themselves in various domains of self-evaluation (Trottier, McFarlane, Olmsted, & McCabe, 2013). It appears that for individuals with eating disorders, feelings about their weight influence how they feel about other, unrelated domains of self-evaluation (e.g., morality, performance at work or school). Research with the WISE-Q found that when weight influences how individuals feel about themselves in domains that realistically should not be linked to weight/shape (e.g., school performance), relapse following intensive eating disorder treatment is more likely (McFarlane, Olmsted, & Trottier, 2008).

The DSM-5 subtypes anorexia into restricting type and binge-eating/purging type for both research and clinical purposes. **Restricting type** individuals attain their extremely low body weights through strict dieting and, sometimes, excessive exercise. **Binge-eating/purging type** individuals not only engage in strict dieting (and possibly excessive exercise) but also regularly engage in binge eating and/or purging behaviours. The distinction between restricting and binge-eating/purging subtypes is important for research and clinical purposes for several reasons. Binge eating and/or purging behaviours are often directly addressed in treatment and have a variety of physical consequences that may require medical attention. There may also be differences between these groups with respect to their ability to regulate and manage negative emotions and impulsive behaviours (Peat, Mitchell, Hoek, & Wonderlich, 2009). The binge-eating/purging subtype also has a poorer prognosis than the restricting subtype (Peat et al., 2009). When conducting research, it is important to describe exactly what and whom you are studying. The subtypes allow researchers to describe their participants more precisely.

BULIMIA NERVOSA The DSM-5 defines bulimia nervosa as an eating disorder characterized by recurrent episodes of objective binge eating and inappropriate use of compensatory

TABLE 10.3   DSM-5 DIAGNOSTIC CRITERIA FOR BULIMIA NERVOSA

A. Recurrent episodes of binge eating. An episode of binge eating is characterized by both of the following:
   1. Eating, in a discrete period of time (e.g., within any 2-hour period), an amount of food that is definitely larger than what most individuals would eat in a similar period of time under similar circumstances.
   2. A sense of lack of control over eating during the episode (e.g., a feeling that one cannot stop eating or control what or how much one is eating).
B. Recurrent inappropriate compensatory behaviors in order to prevent weight gain, such as self-induced vomiting; misuse of laxatives, diuretics, or other medications; fasting; or excessive exercise.
C. The binge eating and inappropriate compensatory behaviors both occur, on average, at least once a week for 3 months.
D. Self-evaluation is unduly influenced by body shape and weight.
E. The disturbance does not occur exclusively during episodes of anorexia nervosa.

Source: Reprinted with permission from the *Diagnostic and Statistical Manual of Mental Disorders, Fifth Edition.* (Copyright © 2013), American Psychiatric Association. All Rights Reserved.

behaviours. Compensatory behaviours consist of any behaviours meant to "get rid of" or "make up for" the binge, including self-induced vomiting; use of laxatives, diuretics, or other medications; strict dieting; or vigorous exercise to prevent weight gain (see Table 10.3). In addition, the self-evaluation of individuals with bulimia is overly influenced by body shape and/or weight. You might notice that this criterion is the same as one of the three criteria for anorexia nervosa, reflecting the distortion in the experience and significance of body weight in these individuals. Whereas this criterion is a central component of the diagnostic criteria for bulimia nervosa, it is one of three alternative criteria for anorexia nervosa. The third criterion requires that episodes of binge eating and compensatory behaviours occur, on average, at least once a week for three months. Individuals who fail to meet the criteria for frequency or duration, but who are nonetheless regularly having episodes of binge eating and compensatory behaviour, are still considered to have an eating disorder but are not diagnosed with bulimia (see the section on other specified feeding or eating disorders).

BINGE EATING DISORDER Binge-eating disorder (BED) involves recurrent episodes of binge eating, as in bulimia nervosa, but these individuals do not engage in inappropriate compensatory behaviours. In addition to the presence of regular binge eating, individuals must report at least three of the following features associated with binge-eating episodes: eating very rapidly; eating until uncomfortably full; eating large amounts of food even when not hungry; eating alone because of embarrassment about the amount of food consumed; and feeling disgusted, depressed, or guilty after binges. The binge eating episodes must occur, on average,

TABLE 10.4 DSM-5 DIAGNOSTIC CRITERIA FOR BINGE EATING DISORDER

A. Recurrent episodes of binge eating. An episode of binge eating is characterized by both of the following:
  1. Eating, in a discrete period of time (e.g., within any 2-hour period) an amount of food that is definitely larger than what most people would eat, in a similar period of time under similar circumstances.
  2. A sense of lack of control over eating during the episode (e.g., a feeling that on cannot stop eating or control what or how much one is eating).
B. The binge-eating episodes are associated with three (or more) of the following:
  1. Eating much more rapidly than normal.
  2. Eating until feeling uncomfortably full.
  3. Eating large amounts of food when not feeling physically hungry.
  4. Eating alone because of feeling embarrassed by how much one is eating.
  5. Feeling disgusted With oneself, depressed, or very guilty afterward.
C. Marked distress regarding binge eating is present.
D. The binge eating occurs, on average, at least once a week for 3 months.
E. The binge eating is not associated with the recurrent use of inappropriate compensatory behavior as in bulimia nervosa and does not occur exclusively during the course of bulimia nervosa or anorexia nervosa

Source: Reprinted with permission from the *Diagnostic and Statistical Manual of Mental Disorders, Fifth Edition.* (Copyright © 2013), American Psychiatric Association. All Rights Reserved.

at least once per week for three months. Finally, significant distress about binge eating must be present.

The publication of DSM-5 represents the first time that BED has been recognized as a stand-alone, specified eating disorder (as it was previously classified under disorders for further study [see Table 10.4]). There has been some disagreement among researchers as to whether BED is itself a discrete disorder or whether it is a type of bulimia. Some researchers have suggested that BED should be classified as a subtype of bulimia because both disorders have binge eating as a central feature. However, a review of the research on BED has helped to resolve some of the debate about whether this disorder could be considered as a stand-alone eating disorder, by demonstrating that BED appears to be distinct from the other eating disorders, and that there is notable psychopathology and significant impairments in quality of life associated with BED (Wonderlich, Gordon, Mitchell, Crosby, & Engel, 2009). Importantly, although many individuals with BED are obese, this is not a requirement for the diagnosis of BED. Conversely, not all individuals who are obese have regular binge-eating episodes: Approximately 20 to 45 percent of individuals who are obese and attending a weight-loss clinic have symptoms of BED (Brewerton, 1999). Individuals with BED report higher levels of eating disorder psychopathology, and higher levels of depression

and anxiety compared to individuals who are obese but do not have a BED diagnosis (Fandiño et al., 2010).

OTHER SPECIFIED/UNSPECIFIED FEEDING OR EATING DISORDER Although the concept of an eating disorder is typically equated with anorexia, bulimia, and BED, there is another category of eating disorder (other specified/unspecified feeding or eating disorder) that was previously identified as more common than either anorexia or bulimia nervosa in community and outpatient settings (Fairburn & Bohn, 2005). Even in a large Canadian tertiary care centre, which provides specialized intensive treatment, 40 percent of the individuals who received treatment had a diagnosis of an eating disorder that did not meet the criteria for anorexia or bulimia nervosa (Rockert, Kaplan, & Olmsted, 2007).

In the publication of DSM-5, several changes were made to the criteria for eating disorders that were expected to reduce the frequency of individuals who are diagnosed under this "other" category (Keel, Brown, Holm-Denoma, & Bodell, 2011). These changes include the addition of BED as a stand-alone eating disorder, a decrease in the frequency of binge eating needed for a diagnosis of bulimia nervosa, and removing a criterion for amenorrhea for the diagnosis of anorexia nervosa. Indeed, these changes have reduced the proportion of individuals with eating disorders classified in this "other" category (Vo, Accurso, Goldschmidt, & Le Grange, 2016).

The category of "other specified feeding or eating disorder" encompasses eating disorders of clinical severity that do not meet the specific criteria for anorexia, bulimia, or BED (see Table 10.5). In some individuals, the eating disorder resembles the full syndromes of anorexia, bulimia, or BED but does not quite meet full DSM-5 diagnostic criteria (e.g., the case of someone who meets all of the criteria for bulimia nervosa but engages in binge/purge episodes, on average, less than once a week). In other individuals, the psychopathological features of the eating disorder combine in a different way than in one of these three disorders, but are nevertheless clinically significant.

Purging disorder is included in the category of "other specified feeding or eating disorder," (OSFED) and is characterized by the use of inappropriate compensatory behaviours (such as vomiting or laxative use) in the absence of binge eating by individuals who are within the normal weight range. Night-eating syndrome has also been added to this category. Night-eating syndrome is characterized by repeated nocturnal eating (but not binge eating, which would be better accounted for by BED), which causes significant distress and/or impairment in functioning. Both purging disorder and night-eating syndrome lack sufficient research to be classified as distinct eating disorders, although a growing body of evidence suggests that both conditions represent pathological eating behaviour that is associated with significant reductions in quality of life (Keel & Striegel-Moore, 2009; Striegel-Moore, Franko, & Garcia, 2009). Finally, there is the "unspecified feeding or eating disorder" category, which applies to individuals with eating disorder

TABLE 10.5 DSM-5 DIAGNOSTIC CRITERIA FOR OTHER SPECIFIED FEEDING OR EATING DISORDER

This category applies to presentations in which symptoms characteristic of a feeding and eating disorder that cause clinically significant distress or impairment in social, occupational, or other important areas of functioning predominate but do not meet the full criteria for any of the disorders in the feeding and eating disorders diagnostic class. The other specified feeding or eating disorder category is used in situations in which the clinician chooses to communicate the specific reason that the presentation does not meet the criteria for any specific feeding and eating disorder. This is done by recording "other specified feeding or eating disorder" followed by the specific reason (e.g., "bulimia nervosa of low frequency").

Examples of presentations that can be specified using the "other specified" designation include the following:

1. **Atypical anorexia nervosa:** All of the criteria for anorexia nervosa are met, except that despite significant weight loss, the individual's weight is within or above the normal range.

2. **Bulimia nervosa (of low frequency and/or limited duration):** All of the criteria for bulimia nervosa are met, except that the binge eating and inappropriate compensatory behaviors occur, on average, less than once a week and/or for less than 3 months.

3. **Binge-eating disorder (of low frequency and/or limited duration):** All of the criteria for binge-eating disorder are met, except that the binge eating occurs, on average, less than once a week and/or for less than 3 months.

4. **Purging disorder:** Recurrent purging behavior to influence weight or shape (e.g., self-induced vomiting; misuse of laxatives, diuretics, or other medications) in the absence of binge eating.

5. **Night eating syndrome:** Recurrent episodes of night eating, as manifested by eating after awakening from sleep or by excessive food consumption after the evening meal. There is awareness and recall of the eating. The night eating is not better explained by external influences such as changes in the individual's sleep-wake cycle or by local social norms. The night eating causes significant distress and/or impairment in functioning. The disordered pattern of eating is not better explained by binge-eating disorder or another mental disorder, including substance use, and is not attributing to another medical disorder or to an effect of medication.

symptoms that cause distress and/or impairment, but do not meet criteria for any of the specified eating disorders.

DIAGNOSTIC ISSUES

DIFFERENTIAL DIAGNOSIS As is the case with the diagnosis of all mental disorders, when diagnosing an eating disorder, psychiatrists and psychologists must consider and rule out other possible causes for the patient's symptoms. For example, in the case of someone with a probable diagnosis of anorexia or bulimia nervosa, it is important to establish that the symptoms are not due to a medical condition. Several medical conditions cause significant weight loss (e.g., gastrointestinal disease, acquired immune deficiency syndrome), and some even involve disturbed eating behaviour (e.g., Kleine-Levin syndrome, a sleep disorder characterized by excessive sleep alternating with disinhibited behaviour, such as compulsive overeating). It is also important to rule out major depressive disorder, as it may involve either severe weight loss or overeating. However, individuals experiencing these other disorders and conditions will not exhibit the over concern with weight and/or shape that is characteristic of eating disorders and they will not engage in inappropriate compensatory behaviours, as in bulimia nervosa.

Once a psychiatrist or psychologist has determined that an individual has an eating disorder, he or she must then determine which eating disorder the person has. Unlike other disorders, such as anxiety disorders, it is not possible to have more than one eating disorder at the same time. Some of the important distinctions to be made are between bulimia nervosa and the binge-eating/purging type of anorexia, and between bulimia and BED. Someone with the binge-eating/purging type of anorexia may differ from someone with bulimia only with respect to whether his or her weight is significantly below what is expected for his or her height and age. Similarly, it can be difficult to determine whether some individuals engage in inappropriate behaviours to compensate for binges.

For example, imagine the case of an individual who reports regular binge-eating episodes, and who exercises as well. To determine whether a diagnosis of bulimia nervosa would be appropriate, it is critical to determine whether the exercise represents an inappropriate compensatory behaviour. To determine whether exercise is severe enough to be considered "excessive" or inappropriate, the DSM-5 suggests that it should be interfering significantly with important activities or occurring at inappropriate times or in appropriate settings, or the patient should be continuing to exercise despite injury or medical complications. The exercise should also be directly connected to the binge-eating episodes, with the purpose of preventing weight gain, to be considered a compensatory behaviour.

VALIDITY OF DIAGNOSTIC CRITERIA AND CLASSIFICATION Because there can be small distinctions between eating disorder categories, some researchers (e.g., Van der Ham, Meulman, Van Strien, & Van Engeland, 1997) have proposed that eating disorders be conceptualized on a spectrum, rather than as separate diagnostic categories. In other words, they suggest that the eating behaviours and other psychopathology of individuals with eating disorders exist on a spectrum of severity. On a spectrum of binge eating, for example, it has been proposed that BED be the least severe and bulimia with the presence of purging behaviours as the most severe pathology (Hay & Fairburn, 1998).

Support for the spectrum view of eating disorders comes from the fact that many individuals move from one diagnostic category to another (and even back again) across time. As many as three-quarters of individuals with an initial diagnosis of anorexia nervosa cross over into the other subtype of anorexia or into bulimia nervosa. In contrast, few individuals who begin with bulimia cross over into anorexia (Eddy et al., 2008). Fairburn, Cooper, and Shafran (2003) have pointed out that eating disorder diagnoses tend to change in a systematic way over the lifespan. In mid-adolescence, eating disorders most typically resemble anorexia nervosa, whereas the eating disorders of late adolescence and early adulthood tend to resemble bulimia nervosa. Furthermore, in a study of individuals with bulimia nervosa, there was evidence that individuals with a history of anorexia nervosa had lower BMIs and smaller waist and hip circumferences than individuals with bulimia without a history of anorexia (Vaz, Guisado, & Peñas-Lledó, 2003). Individuals who have crossed over from anorexia to bulimia nervosa also remain at risk of relapsing back to anorexia (Eddy et al., 2008). These findings suggest that subclinical features or unique characteristics of anorexia may remain in individuals who cross over from anorexia to bulimia nervosa, supporting the spectrum view of eating disorders.

Many researchers continue to express reservations about the limitations of the classification system used for eating disorders in the DSM-5, and some are looking ahead and considering possible approaches for the DSM-6 that could improve the clinical utility of diagnostic criteria for eating disorders (Fairburn & Cooper, 2011). One approach that is gaining traction is the National Institute of Mental Health's (NIMH) Research Domain Criteria (RDoC) approach (see Chapter 3), which argues that instead of studying mental health disorders based on discrete (and potentially arbitrary) categorical classifications, the best approach may be to examine core underlying features that characterize mental disorders more broadly (e.g., emotion regulation deficits; NIMH, 2016). Nevertheless, despite the emergence of alternative approaches and some of the controversy that has surrounded the changes to the criteria for eating disorders in the DSM-5 (and in particular, the addition of BED as a stand-alone eating disorder), some researchers have found support for the validity of the DSM-5 criteria for eating disorders (e.g., Keel, Brown, Holm-Denoma, & Bodell, 2011).

ASSESSMENT

Assessment for diagnostic purposes and to guide treatment planning is usually conducted using a structured or semistructured interview. Many researchers and clinicians use the **Eating Disorder Examination (EDE)** (Fairburn, Cooper, & O'Connor, 2008) to aid their assessments. The EDE is a structured clinical interview for diagnosing eating disorders that has good reliability and validity. It provides numerical ratings of the frequency and severity of eating disorder symptoms such as binge eating and compensatory behaviours, and also provides normative data on dietary restraint, and eating, weight, and shape concerns. Conducting a diagnostic interview for an eating disorder involves gathering a great deal of information from the individual being assessed. The interviewer must gather information not only about the current and past frequency and severity of dietary restriction, binge eating, purging, and exercise, but also about distorted attitudes and beliefs about weight, shape, and eating; weight history; and current and past menstrual function (for post-menarchal females). The interview should also assess the patient's interpersonal functioning and potential factors that may have contributed to the development and/or maintenance of the eating disorder, as well as the patient's level of available social support.

An additional goal of diagnostic interviews for eating disorders is typically to assess for the presence and absence of other psychological disorders, as other disorders are often present in individuals with eating disorders. Some of the disorders that are often assessed for are substance use disorders, mood disorders, anxiety disorders, obsessive compulsive disorder, post-traumatic stress disorder, and personality disorders.

Another important component of eating disorders assessment is a medical examination that can determine the presence of any physical and/or medical complications associated with eating disorders. These complications will be addressed in greater detail in the following section. It is important to assess for the medical consequences of eating disorders, as they should be addressed and monitored as part of treatment. Furthermore, for some patients, knowledge of the physical and medical complications of their eating disorders can motivate them to pursue recovery.

A final component of many assessments is the administration of self-report questionnaires to complement the information gathered through the clinical interview. One of the most frequently used self-report questionnaires with individuals with eating disorders is the Eating Disorder Inventory, which assesses eating disorder attitudes and behaviours (Garner, Olmsted, & Polivy, 1983). Questionnaires measuring symptoms of depression, general psychopathology, quality of life or impairment, and social support are also often administered.

Physical and Psychological Complications

There are numerous serious medical, psychological, and behavioural effects of eating disorders. In a review of the literature, Agras (2001) indicated that across all the eating disorder subtypes, individuals experience reduced quality of life and their social relationships are negatively affected. In individuals with anorexia, some of the physical and medical complications that may develop include osteoporosis, cardiovascular problems (including lowered heart rate and low blood pressure), decreased fertility, lethargy, dry skin, dry hair and hair loss, and heightened sensitivity to cold. **Lanugo**, a fine downy hair, may grow on the body in order to maintain body warmth. **Amenorrhea**, the absence of at least three consecutive menstrual periods, often occurs in women of childbearing age with anorexia nervosa. Both cognitive and emotional functioning can also be affected, such as difficulties concentrating and increases in irritability. Severe, potentially fatal medical conditions can arise in anorexia, which are typically attributed to semi-starvation, as well as to the purging behaviours that are sometimes present. These include impaired renal function and cardiac arrhythmia.

In individuals with bulimia, as well as the binge/purge subtype of anorexia nervosa, dental problems (such as erosion of tooth enamel) often develop due to the presence of stomach acid during self-induced vomiting. Similarly, individuals who self-induce vomiting may exhibit **Russell's sign** (scrapes or calluses on the backs of hands or knuckles). Electrolyte imbalance, particularly hypokalemia (low potassium), can occur in individuals with bulimia due to frequent vomiting or laxative use. This imbalance can lead to problems with cardiovascular and renal functioning (including gastric rupture and cardiac arrhythmias), which can be fatal. As in anorexia, emotional functioning may also be affected. Furthermore, research indicates that individuals who binge eat are more likely to exhibit comorbid substance abuse (e.g., Root et al., 2010). Additional medical problems and complications can arise from drug and alcohol abuse, posing further difficulties for individuals with eating disorders who already have an elevated risk of mortality (Conason, Klomek, & Sher, 2006). The physical consequences of BED are similar to those associated with obesity, and include an elevated risk of type 2 diabetes, cardiovascular disease, and sleep apnea (pauses in breathing, or very shallow breathing, during sleep).

One complication involved in studying the physical and psychological symptoms of eating disorders is distinguishing between whether a factor is a *cause* or a *consequence* of the eating disorder. For example, malnutrition may exaggerate certain symptoms of personality disorders, so it can be difficult to determine whether, in the absence of malnutrition, apparent personality disturbances are in fact present in an individual who has been diagnosed with an eating disorder. To investigate whether personality disorders endure after recovery from an eating disorder, or are mainly present during the course of an eating disorder, Matsunaga and colleagues (2000) assessed a group of patients who had recovered from their eating disorders for at least a year. These researchers demonstrated that although treatment for eating disorders seems to attenuate the symptoms of personality disorders, there does indeed seem to be a link between eating disorders and personality disorders, even after recovery. This suggests that personality disorders are not merely a consequence of the disorder.

Without conducting prospective longitudinal studies, it can be difficult to distinguish between the causes and consequences of eating disorders. However, a seminal early study conducted by Franklin, Schiele, Brozek, and Keys (1948) has allowed insight into the physical and emotional consequences of semi-starvation and weight loss, both of which may be present in eating disorders. A group of American conscientious objectors during the Second World War agreed to participate in a study on semi-starvation in lieu of military service. This study was initially conducted to gain insight into how to best renourish civilians in Europe who had starved during the war; however, it has also provided critical insights in the field of eating disorders. The participants were healthy, normal-weight males who restricted their eating and engaged in regular physical activity over the course of 24 weeks in order to lose approximately 25 percent of their initial body weight. This food restriction and weight loss had both psychological and physiological consequences for the participants. The semi-starvation led to decreases in heart rate, increases in emotional instability (including depression and irritability), difficulty concentrating, decreased sex drive, and lethargy. Many participants also exhibited dry skin and hair and increases in hair loss. Almost all of the participants demonstrated an increased focus on food, with food becoming the primary topic of conversation. This increased focus on food continued even after the period of food restriction ended, during the rehabilitation period for weight restoration. However, at the end of the 12-week rehabilitation period, there was improvement in many of the symptoms, and the values for the symptoms had returned to near-normal levels 20 weeks after ending the semi-starvation period. The similarity between these symptoms and those present in the eating disorders is striking. This suggests that malnutrition may lead to several of the symptoms present in eating disorders, and that some of these symptoms may be alleviated with improved eating and weight restoration.

2 BEFORE MOVING ON

> Which conceptualization of eating disorders do you prefer—the categorical view (i.e., the current diagnostic categories) or the spectrum view? What are some of the advantages and disadvantages of the current method of classification?

Etiology

GENETIC AND BIOLOGICAL THEORIES

Despite strong social pressures to be thin and widespread body dissatisfaction among young women, eating disorders remain relatively rare. This, in conjunction with the fact that there appears to be a heritable component to eating disorders, highlights the possibility that biological factors play a role in the etiology of eating disorders (Kaye, 2008). The rate of eating disorders in relatives of individuals with anorexia nervosa is four-and-a-half times higher than in relatives of a healthy comparison group (Strober, Freeman, Lampert, Diamond, & Kaye, 2000). Reviews of twin studies, family studies, and molecular genetic studies have suggested that genetics play a significant role in the development of eating disorders. A review of high-quality twin studies indicated that 48 to 76% of the variance in anorexia nervosa, 50 to 83% of the variance in bulimia nervosa, and 41% of the variance in BED is accounted for by genetic factors (Striegel-Moore & Bulik, 2007). Although in recent years numerous genetic studies on eating disorders have emerged, many different genes have been investigated with few replications, which limits our knowledge about the specific influence of genes on eating disorders (Klump & Gobrogge, 2005).

Dysfunctional neurotransmitter activity has also been investigated as another possible contributor to the development of an eating disorder. In particular, a link between serotonin levels and feeding/satiety has been established, and researchers have suggested that a dysregulation of the serotonin system is involved in the pathophysiology of eating disorders (e.g., Brewerton, 1995). Indeed, individuals with anorexia and bulimia demonstrate signs of serotonin dysregulation (e.g., Kaye, Gendall, & Strober, 1998). For example, it appears that anorexia nervosa is associated with reduced serotonin activity (specifically, reduced density of serotonin transporters in women with anorexia nervosa as compared to healthy controls; Bruce, Steiger, Ng Yin Kin, & Israel, 2006).

Further support for the role of serotonin functioning in eating disorders comes from research conducted by Robert Levitan and colleagues (2001) at the University of Toronto. To extend the research demonstrating that individuals with eating disorders have disturbances in their serotonin system, Levitan and colleagues studied polymorphism of the serotonin 1B receptor gene in individuals with bulimia to determine if any association existed between this measure and BMI. They demonstrated that this association does exist—polymorphism of the serotonin 1B receptor gene was associated with a lower minimum lifetime BMI (minimum lifetime BMI was assessed by determining patients' lowest weight since age 17, along with patients' height, to calculate BMI). Hence, individuals with bulimia who exhibited a particular expression of the serotonin 1B receptor gene reported having a lower minimum BMI than individuals with bulimia with different expressions of this gene. These findings support the possible role of genetic factors (in particular, serotonin receptor genes) in bulimia. However, as Klein and Walsh (2004) point out, it is unlikely that eating disorders stem from polymorphism of one gene in particular. It is more likely that sets of genes, interacting with particular environmental factors, are implicated in the development of eating disorders.

Clearly, the development of eating disorders is a complex process that is not the result of the presence of merely one biological factor. These genetic or biological factors, however, may interact with other factors to precipitate the development of eating disorders. Although it seems that gender differences in eating disorders are in part attributable to socio-cultural factors (which are addressed in the next section), it is also possible that gender differences in biological factors, such as serotonergic functioning and hormonal levels, may also account, in part, for the observed gender differences in the prevalence of eating disorders. Researchers at McMaster University suggest that gender differences in the serotonergic system may make women more susceptible to the development of an eating disorder, as females are more susceptible to dysregulation in the serotonin system than are males (Steiner, Lepage, & Dunn, 1997). For example, it appears that dieting alters brain serotonin function in women, but not in men (Walsh, Oldman, Franklin, Fairburn, & Cowen, 1995). Biological changes occurring at puberty may also contribute to the development of eating disorders through secondary mechanisms (rather than directly influencing the development of eating disorders). Eating disorders typically develop during late puberty, or shortly thereafter. Some researchers have postulated that the hormonal changes associated with puberty in females may activate the development of disordered eating, either directly or indirectly (e.g., hormone levels influence body fat composition or eating behaviour, which in turn increases the risk for disordered eating; Klump et al., 2006). However, until more research is conducted, it is premature to draw conclusions about the causal role of gender differences in biological functioning in the development of eating disorders.

It is important to note that the association that has been established between serotonin functioning and eating disorders should be interpreted with caution. As you read earlier in the chapter, it can be difficult to distinguish between factors that may cause eating disorders and factors that are a consequence of the eating disorder. Part of the difficulty in establishing the role of serotonin in the development of eating disorders is the correlational nature of the studies investigating serotonin function in individuals with eating disorders. It is possible that alterations of serotonergic systems in individuals with eating disorders may simply be a function of low weight (in anorexia) or malnutrition associated with the eating disorder (Wolfe, Metzger, & Jimerson, 1997). However, researchers studying serotonin functioning in individuals who had a history of bulimia nervosa and were no longer symptomatic, compared with individuals with current bulimia nervosa and healthy controls, found that serotonin transporter densities were lower than controls in both individuals with active and remitted bulimia nervosa (Steiger et al., 2005). Steiger and colleagues suggest that serotonergic dysregulation may be a trait that increases the risk of developing bulimia. Further research is necessary in order to conclude that serotonin dysregulation is a contributor to the development of eating disorders, as opposed to a lasting consequence of these disorders.

③ BEFORE MOVING ON

Earlier in the chapter, you read about some of the physical consequences of eating disorders. Compare and contrast these physical symptoms, which are thought to be a consequence of malnutrition associated with eating disorders, with the genetic/biological factors that are thought to contribute to the development of eating disorders.

FOCUS 10.1

Thin Ideal Media Images Make Women Feel Bad, Right?

A great deal of research has sought to demonstrate a relation between thin ideal media images and disordered eating behaviours and/or attitudes. A recent meta-analysis showed that exposure to media images promoting the thin ideal is correlated with higher body dissatisfaction, restrictive eating behaviours, and symptoms of anorexia and bulimia nervosa in women (Ferguson, 2013). The effects for women overall were small but statistically significant. However, when samples of women were subdivided into high versus low pre-existing body dissatisfaction, the relationship between media images and body dissatisfaction was much stronger for those women who already had body image concerns (Ferguson, 2013). Additionally the relation between different types of media consumption (e.g., television, magazines, music videos) appears to relate to degree of body dissatisfaction in similar ways (Ferguson, 2013). However, correlational studies cannot demonstrate that exposure to thin body images *causes* body dissatisfaction and other eating disorder–related symptoms. It seems just as likely that individuals who are already dissatisfied with their bodies seek out these images. In response to this problem, a number of experimental studies have manipulated exposure to thin ideal media figures and measured the corresponding effects on body dissatisfaction and other self-perception measures.

The literature suggests that thin media images do have an adverse effect on the body dissatisfaction of some young women. Indeed, a meta-analysis of the literature (Grabe, Ward, & Shibley Hyde, 2008) found that exposure to thin ideal images was associated with higher levels of body dissatisfaction and thin ideal internalization among women compared with exposure to control images. Negative effects were even found on eating beliefs and behaviours. The authors pointed out that it is very concerning that brief experimental exposures to thin ideal images can affect beliefs about eating, dieting, and purging. Additionally, women with pre-existing body image issues were more adversely affected by thin media stimuli presented in research studies than were women who were relatively satisfied with their bodies (Groesz, Levine, & Murnen, 2002).

These frequently observed negative effects of exposure to idealized media images are typically explained using social comparison theory. Studies finding negative effects of idealized media images generally assume that participants are using the thin models as standards of comparison for determining self-evaluations. In line with this hypothesis, studies have shown that when young women engage in upward social comparisons with fashion models on the dimension of attractiveness, decreased appearance satisfaction and increased thin ideal internalization result (e.g., Tiggeman & Polivy, 2010).

Although the majority of studies have found negative effects of thin ideal media exposure, some studies have failed to find any significant effects (e.g., Champion & Furnham, 1999) or have found positive effects on self-perceptions (e.g., Joshi, Herman, & Polivy, 2004). Furthermore, the recent meta-analysis described earlier showed that although there were small effects for women, there were few effects for men or for the general population (Ferguson, 2013), suggesting that gender is likely an important factor to consider in understanding the relationship between thin media images and body dissatisfaction. It is likely that a number of studies finding no significant effects have gone unpublished due to the fact that it can be difficult to publish a study with null results. One potential reason why so many studies have found negative effects of thin media exposure is that women may believe that they *should* feel worse about themselves after viewing these stimuli. In a qualitative interview study, adolescent girls reported that the portrayal of thin models in the media was the major force in creating body dissatisfaction (Wertheim, Paxton, Schutx, & Muir, 1997). If participants believe that viewing idealized media images should make them feel worse about themselves, then they are likely to respond in a negative way to such images when simply asked how the images make them feel.

One Canadian study directly addressed the issue of these demand characteristics in this area of research. Mills, Polivy, Herman, and Tiggeman (2002) demonstrated that when demand characteristics are present (in that participants were aware that their responses to the media images were the topic of interest to the experimenters), dieters report feeling more depressed following exposure to idealized images. However, when demand characteristics were minimized, chronic dieters rated their current body sizes as thinner following exposure to idealized images. The results of this study suggest that rather than using models as standards of comparison, dieters identified with these thin ideal images and were inspired by them or engaged in a positive fantasy in response to them. These findings may help to explain why many women not only voluntarily expose themselves to thin ideal media images but also seem to enjoy looking at them. Even in the cases where thin ideal media images have immediate positive effects, they may have adverse effects in the long term because positive inspirational effects may encourage dieting, which may worsen self-esteem and body satisfaction in the long run. ●

PSYCHOLOGICAL THEORIES

SOCIO-CULTURAL FACTORS According to the socio-cultural model of eating disorders, these disorders are (to at least some extent) a product of the increasing pressures for women in Western society to achieve an ultra-slim body. The mass media are a ubiquitous source of thin ideal images (see Focus box 10.1). Research has shown that in the last half of the twentieth century, there was a steady decrease in the body size of the "ideal" woman. From 1959 to 1988, Miss America contestants and *Playboy* centrefolds became progressively thinner (Garner, Garfinkel, Schwartz, & Thompson, 1980; Wiseman, Gray, Mosimann, & Athrens, 1992; see Figure 10.1). Wiseman and colleagues found that most of these models weighed less than 85 percent of what would have been considered normal for their age and height—meaning that they met the criteria of low body weight for anorexia nervosa.

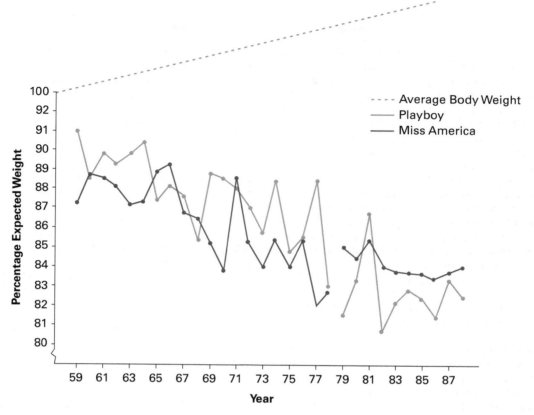

FIGURE 10.1 Average Percentage of Expected Weight of *Playboy* Centrefolds (1959–1978) and Miss America Contestants (1979–1988)

Source: Republished with permission of John Wiley & Sons, from Cultural Expectations of Thinness in Women: An Update, *International Journal of Eating Disorders*, Vol. 11, No. 1, pp. 85–89. 1992; permission conveyed through Copyright Clearance Center, Inc.

Another study examined *Playboy* centrefolds up to 1999 (Sypeck et al., 2006). The results suggest that although the *Playboy* models remained underweight, their weights appear to have stabilized during the last two decades of the twentieth century. The most recent of these studies looked at both American and German *Playboy* centrefolds between 1980 and 2011 (Hergovich & Sussenbach, 2015). Although the models' weights stayed stable, on average their bust sizes decreased and their bodies became more androgynous (i.e., less curvaceous) overall. This change was more pronounced in the American sample. Thus, in addition to an overall thin ideal body weight, the ideal body shape for women has become increasingly less curvaceous over time, particularly in the United States (Hergovich & Sussenbach, 2015).

Internalization of these thin media images is believed to be a causal risk factor for the development of an eating disorder (Thompson & Stice, 2001). Internalization of the thin ideal involves affirming the desirability of socially sanctioned ideals and engaging in behaviours to achieve the ideals (Heinberg, Thompson, & Stormer, 1995). Thin ideal internalization is believed to lead directly to body dissatisfaction (because the cultural ideal is unattainable for most women) and dieting. Both of these variables, in

turn, increase the risk for eating disorder psychopathology. Recently, there has been a shift in the ideal female body presented by the media, such that the women are now presented as both extremely thin *and* extremely toned (Grogan, 2008). Homan (2010) investigated the longitudinal impact of idealization of these athletic ideal images and found that it predicted change in compulsive exercise over the seven-month study period but not body dissatisfaction or dieting. In contrast, thin ideal internalization predicted change in all three outcomes. Importantly, there may also be important racial/ethnic differences in ideal body preferences. In particular, although European-American women tend to prefer thin, athletic body types, African American women may endorse more curvy ideal body sizes (Overstreet, Quinn, & Agocha, 2010). Latina women may simultaneously endorse both the dominant thin ideal, as well as a more curvy ideal body type (Viladrich, Yeh, Bruning, & Weiss, 2009).

It is interesting that while the ideal body size for women has been getting thinner, women are actually becoming heavier. According to the Women's Health Surveillance Report commissioned by Health Canada, the prevalence of being overweight among women increased from 19% in

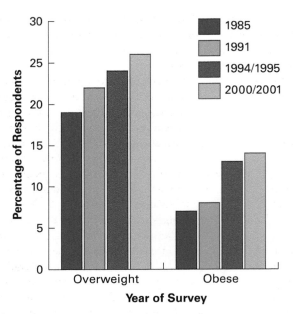

FIGURE 10.2 Percentage of Female Canadians Aged 20 to 64 Considered Overweight and Obese

Source: Physical activity and obesity in Canadian women. In Canadian Institute for Health Information, Women's Health Surveillance Report. 2003.

1985 to 26% in 2000/2001, and the prevalence of obesity among women increased from 7% to 14% during the same time period (Bryan & Walsh, 2004; see Figure 10.2). More recently, the Canadian Community Health Survey found that the prevalence among women of being overweight or obese was 30% and 23%, respectively, in 2004. The prevalence of being overweight or obese among men has similarly increased.

There also appears to be an increasing discrepancy between the average man and the "ideal" man as depicted in the media, such that the ideal man is becoming more muscular, whereas the average man is developing more body fat (Spitzer, Henderson, & Zivian, 1999). However, pressure to obtain the ideal body appears to be greater for women than for men. According to the socio-cultural model of eating disorders, the greater prevalence of eating disorders among women than among men is a result of the greater pressure on women to obtain the "ideal" body. Nonetheless, research suggests that men are indeed susceptible to the potential effects of exposure to idealized male media images (Pritchard & Cramblitt, 2014). A meta-analysis of published experimental literature suggests that exposure to muscular male fashion models leads men to feel worse about their bodies (Bartlett, Vowels, & Saucier, 2008). There is also evidence that exposure to these images is related to negative psychological (e.g., depression) and behavioural (e.g., excessive exercise) outcomes. We further address some of the factors that may play a role in gender differences in eating disorders later in this chapter.

Our society's obsession with thinness for women is so widespread that a moderate degree of body dissatisfaction has been normative among women for some time (Cash,

Morrow, Hrabosky, & Perry, 2004), and is also prevalent among adolescent girls (Lawler & Nixon, 2011). For example, in a sample of 129 adolescent girls between the ages of 12 and 19, 80 percent reported a desire to change their body size (Lawler & Nixon, 2011). This body dissatisfaction encourages many girls and women to diet in an effort to change their weight or shape. In fact, dieting has become so prevalent that it, too, has been described as "normal" for young women (Polivy & Herman, 1987). The question remains, however, why given that almost all women are exposed to socio-cultural pressures to be thin, and many develop body dissatisfaction and engage in dieting behaviours, far fewer go on to develop eating disorders (Polivy & Herman, 2004).

4 BEFORE MOVING ON

Under what conditions do you think thin ideal media images are more likely to have negative effects on young women? How do you think these images might affect older women or men?

FAMILY FACTORS The family has been identified as an important influence in the development of eating disorders. It can provide cultural transmission of pathological values or be a stressor on its own (by being a source of miscommunication or conflict, or through lack of emotional support). It can also be a protective factor by providing support, identity, and comfort. The way in which families communicate cultural ideas about thinness can potentially contribute to the development of eating disorders (e.g., Haworth-Hoeppner, 2000; Strober et al., 2000). When the family environment is critical or coercive, or weight/shape and appearance are prominent themes in the household, the risk of eating disorders increases (Haworth-Hoeppner, 2000).

Family factors such as parental attitudes about weight and shape, and unhealthy eating behaviours in the home may also have a role in increasing eating disorder risk. For example, mothers who make comments about weight and shape, or who engage in dieting behaviours may inadvertently communicate these feelings and behaviours to their daughters, who often emulate them (Coffman, Balantekin, & Savage, 2016; Smolak, Levine, & Schermer, 1999). Additionally, children in families that focus on physical attractiveness and weight may be more likely to develop an eating disorder, especially children who are particularly sensitive to family expectations and values (Davis, Shuster, Blackmore, & Fox, 2004).

Children of mothers who themselves have eating disorders may be at particular risk for developing eating problems. Some of this risk may be genetically inherited, and some of the risk may be transmitted via modelling. For example, the children of mothers who have eating disorders report greater weight and shape concerns and more dietary restraint than children whose mothers do not have eating disorders (Stein et al., 2006). A mother's own eating disorder may also affect her ability to determine how to best feed her child, which may result in feeding her child in a more restrictive manner than women without eating disorders (Reba-Harrelson et al., 2010). Shared vulnerability to negative affect may also help to explain the increased risk of eating disorders in the children of mothers with eating disorders. For example, the children of mothers with eating disorders may be more likely to experience symptoms of depression and anxiety (Reba-Harrelson et al., 2010), which suggests a shared vulnerability towards negative emotions.

PERSONALITY/INDIVIDUAL FACTORS A number of personality traits appear to characterize patients with eating disorders, both before and during their eating disorder, and some individual difference variables may be influential in the development of the pathology. Personality research is, of necessity, correlational in nature, so it is not possible to conclude that these differences are what cause the development of an eating disorder, but the distinctions are nonetheless suggestive.

Personality traits such as perfectionism, obsessiveness, neuroticism, negative emotionality, avoidance of harm, and general avoidance characterize both patients with anorexia nervosa and those with bulimia nervosa (Cassin & von Ranson, 2005). In addition, individuals with anorexia nervosa are often characterized by high levels of constraint, perseveration and rigidity, and low levels of novelty seeking, whereas individuals with bulimia nervosa often exhibit high impulsivity, novelty and sensation seeking, and characteristics overlapping with borderline personality disorder (Cassin & von Ranson, 2005). These traits tend to be present both during the disorder and after recovery (Fairburn et al., 1999; Kaye et al., 1998; Lilenfeld et al., 2000). Some personality characteristics common to eating disorders, such as perfectionism, are found in family members of individuals with eating disorders who do not themselves have any symptoms of eating disorders (Lilenfeld et al., 2000). A review that included prospective studies suggested that the presence of these personality factors increases the risk of developing an eating disorder (Lilenfeld, Wonderlich, Riso, Crosby, & Mitchell, 2006).

Other individual differences have been studied as possible risk factors contributing to the development of eating disorders. These include characteristics such as low self-esteem, identity problems, depressive affect, and poor body image, as well as behaviours undertaken in connection with some of these, including dieting and participation in exercising or sports that emphasize the body (Polivy, Herman, Mills, & Wheeler, 2003).

Low self-esteem is present in many mental disorders, not only eating disorders. For example, low self-esteem is often linked to depression. Low self-esteem and identity diffusion may result from traumatic experiences such as sexual, physical, or emotional abuse, although such negative life experiences are not necessary precursors to the development of an eating disorder. In general, having a negative body image, being a chronic dieter, and having low self-esteem, depression, and identity problems all seem to be risk factors associated with the development of eating disorders (Polivy & Herman, 2002). Longitudinal studies have indicated that these sorts of factors may predict the development of eating disorders before they appear in a given individual (Thompson & Stice, 2001).

Individuals may try to compensate for these problems by trying to construct an identity focused on weight, shape, and excessive control of one's body, to help create a sense of self. This reliance on one's weight and shape, however, can make one more vulnerable to eating problems in the face of threats to this identity. For example, experiences that appear to be unrelated to weight and shape (e.g., feelings of ineffectiveness in other areas) may be mislabelled or misinterpreted as "feeling fat" (McFarlane, Urbszat, & Olmsted, 2011). Clinical observations suggest the extent to which an individual's identity can be influenced by an eating disorder, and how difficulties in treatment can arise as a result of this identification with the disorder (e.g., Bulik & Kendler, 2000). There is evidence that individuals with anorexia or bulimia have more negative (and fewer positive) self-schemas than do control individuals without a history of mental disorders (Stein & Corte, 2007). Self-schemas, in turn, are associated with body dissatisfaction, as individuals who have fewer positive self-schemas are more likely to report higher body dissatisfaction. This research supports the notion that identity impairments are associated with eating-disordered symptomatology (Stein & Corte, 2007).

Dieting, and the embracing of society's idealization of thinness for women that dieting reflects, has itself been implicated as a precipitating factor in eating disorders, especially binge eating (Polivy & Herman, 2002). Despite this, it is clear that very few of the millions of people who are chronic dieters will go on to develop an eating disorder. Similarly, some sports and activities that place extreme emphasis on appearance, body shape, or leanness (such as gymnastics or ballet dancing) are associated with increased risk for eating disorders (Bratland-Sanda & Sundgot-Borgen, 2013). Thus, certain personality and behavioural patterns appear to be contributors to the development of eating disorders, though none of these is a perfect predictor.

MATURATIONAL ISSUES As children develop into adolescence, physical maturation causes increasing sex differences such that males begin to become more muscular, and females become more curvaceous. This pushes males toward the masculine ideal body shape, but for females, pubertal development involves adding body fat, which takes girls further away from the thin ideal female figure (Striegel-Moore, 1993). It may not be a coincidence, then, that eating disorders are most likely to appear around the time of puberty, at the same time that girls develop feelings of body dissatisfaction and start to diet to lose weight because their level of body fat is increasing. The idealization of a thin body shape by the surrounding culture may push adolescent girls toward dangerous dieting practices and a rejection of one's own body shape that contribute, in susceptible individuals, to the development of eating disorders (Polivy & Herman, 2002; Stice, 2002).

In addition, puberty is a time of increasing sex role demands. For girls, this means pursuing the "superwoman ideal" of success in all spheres of life—social, appearance, academic, career, and family. This may require them to attempt to fulfill incompatible role demands, which may be particularly difficult for young girls who have not learned how to prioritize these roles and the demands they make, and which can have negative effects on identity formation (Polivy et al., 2003). Furthermore, girls must cope with the onset of dating and sexuality, which appears to be more stressful for females than for males (Striegel-Moore, 1993).

ADVERSE EVENTS Traumatic events can certainly have negative effects on an individual's self-esteem, body image, and sense of control. It is therefore not surprising that some researchers have suggested that abuse—in particular, childhood sexual abuse—could contribute to an individual developing an eating disorder (Madowitz, Matheson, & Liang, 2015). Studies have found a high incidence of victims of sexual abuse among individuals with eating disorders. For instance, a study of anorexia patients in Toronto found that 40 percent reported being sexually abused in childhood, prior to the onset of the eating disorder, and a total of 59 percent of eating disorder patients in this study reported sexual trauma at some point in their lifetime (Carter, Bewell, Blackmore, & Woodside, 2006). A recent meta-analysis on this topic examined the relationships between different types of childhood maltreatment (i.e., physical, emotional, and sexual abuse, and neglect) and eating disorders (Molendijk et al., in press). All types of childhood maltreatment were significantly associated with all types of eating disorders. Importantly, the prevalence of childhood maltreatment was higher in individuals with eating disorders than in both individuals without mental disorders, and in individuals with other psychiatric disorders.

Additionally, research evidence suggests that having experienced a traumatic event is more strongly associated with development of an eating disorder characterized by binge eating and purging (i.e., bulimia nervosa, anorexia nervosa—binge-eating/purging type, BED, or OSFED with symptoms of bingeing or purging) than with eating disorder symptoms characterized by restriction only. For example, in the previously described study conducted at Toronto General Hospital, patients with the binge/purge type of anorexia were more likely to report a history of childhood sexual abuse than were patients with the restricting type of anorexia (Carter et al., 2006).

A particularly important point is that an elevated incidence of sexual abuse and other trauma has been found in individuals with other psychological disorders such as obsessive-compulsive disorder (e.g., Lochner et al., 2002), suggesting that trauma may elevate the risk of psychological disturbance in general and that the risk may not be specific to eating disorders. Furthermore, although only a minority of individuals who have experienced traumatic events go on to meet criteria for post-traumatic stress disorder (PTSD), rates of PTSD are elevated in those with eating disorders (Hudson et al., 2007). For individuals with both disorders, eating disorder symptoms such as binge eating, purging, or food restriction may function as a way to cope with PTSD (Trottier, Wonderlich, Monson, Crosby, & Olmsted, 2016).

INTEGRATIVE MODELS

The etiology of eating disorders is multifactorial; no single etiological factor alone can account for the development of an eating disorder. Eating disorders are very complex, and it would be simplistic to suggest that one factor could alone produce an eating disorder in any given individual. Consequently, some researchers have proposed integrative models to describe the development and maintenance of eating disorders. For example, Stice (2002) suggests that bulimia nervosa develops and is maintained due to an interaction of risk and maintenance factors. **Risk factors** refer to variables that occur prior to the onset of the disorder, and which prospectively predict the disorder's onset. A **maintenance factor** is a variable that leads the symptoms to persist after their onset. There are a number of important risk and maintenance factors identified by Stice's review of the literature (and that have garnered empirical support). One risk factor is increased body mass, which is believed to put individuals at risk for body dissatisfaction via increased pressure to be thin. Other factors include the sociocultural pressure to be thin and internalization of the thin ideal, which may increase the risk of body dissatisfaction, negative emotions, and likelihood of dieting. These factors are believed to then further increase the risk for eating disorder behaviours. Once binge eating and purging are initiated, negative affect may serve as a maintenance factor because binge eating may temporarily relieve negative emotions. Body dissatisfaction may maintain bulimia nervosa through the persistence of dieting, which further increases vulnerability to binge eating. Perfectionism may also interact with the other discussed factors to increase risk for bulimia, and maintain eating disorder behaviours once they have been initiated (Stice, 2002). Although these integrative models and theories attempt to address the complexity of eating disorders and the many identified etiological factors, they have not yet provided predictive power sufficient to prospectively identify individuals most likely to develop eating disorders.

Eating Disorders in Males

The main features of anorexia and bulimia are similar in males and females. Likewise, the DSM-5 diagnostic criteria for the different subtypes of eating disorders are identical for both males and females. However, individuals who are diagnosed with an eating disorder are predominantly female. Reports estimate that for every male who is diagnosed with anorexia or bulimia, there are 10 to 15 females with these disorders (Bramon-Bosch, Troop, & Treasure, 2000; Braun, Sunday, Huang, & Halmi, 1999). One exception to the disproportionately higher prevalence of eating disorders in females is for the diagnosis of binge eating disorder. Despite these gender differences in the prevalence of anorexia and

Sheena Carpenter

Sheena Carpenter was a young woman who struggled with anorexia nervosa up until the time of her death due to starvation at the age of 22. After learning about Sheena's eating disorder, Sheena's mother, Lynn, sought treatment for her daughter but ran into a number of roadblocks: few available treatment resources were available, and her daughter's motivation to recover was low and transient.

At age 14, Sheena went to a modelling agency where she was told that she would be more photogenic if she had a thinner face. In the years that followed, the first signs of her eating disorder emerged—she wore baggy clothes to hide her dropping weight, and she became obsessed with food. By the age of 18, Sheena's weight had dropped to less than 35 kilos, and her mother discovered that Sheena was inducing vomiting. Over the course of her disorder Sheena was, at times, able to make progress—on two occasions she was able to gain 9 kilos. However, for the most part,

her eating disorder increased in severity over time and she developed many complications, including depressed mood, erosion of her tooth enamel, low electrolytes, and seizures. Her heart, liver, and brain were all damaged. At the time of her death, Sheena weighed only 22.67 kilos.

Sheena's eating disorder was not just about pursuing thinness. Sheena revealed that she had been sexually abused as a child and she experienced intrusive memories related to this. She also had a very close but difficult relationship with her mother. After Sheena's death, Lynn and two of her friends began work on establishing a not-for-profit support centre for people with eating disorders in Toronto called Sheena's Place. Sheena's Place offers group therapy to people in the community with eating disorders, with the goal of providing hope and support. Sheena's Place has grown tremendously since its inception, offering more than 45 support groups to people with eating disorders. Other similar support centres can be found in Canada—including Danielle's Place, also in Ontario, and Jessie's Hope Society in British Columbia.

bulimia nervosa, however, research indicates that the treatment response does not appear to differ for male and female patients (Shingleton, Thompson-Brenner, Thompson, Pratt, & Franko, 2015). Furthermore, it appears that male patients can be treated effectively in a setting that is composed primarily of females (Woodside & Kaplan, 1994).

A recent review of the literature on eating disorders in males (Jones & Morgan, 2010) suggests that similar factors influence the risk of developing eating disorders in men and women, and that the main factors that could explain the gender discrepancy are unresolved. Eating disorders may occur more frequently in women because the strength, or prevalence, of certain risk factors (such as socio-cultural factors) is higher than for men. For example, Andersen and DiDomenico (1992) found that for every diet-related article or advertisement in men's magazines, there were 10.5 in women's magazines. Of course, the fact that women are exposed to more diet-related material than men cannot solely account for why more women develop eating disorders. After all, if this were the case, we would expect to see a higher prevalence of eating disorders in women, given that the majority of women in Western societies are exposed to this type of material.

Within non-clinical populations, there is also evidence that women are disproportionately affected by weight and shape concerns. For example, non–eating-disordered males have less appearance investment and less body image preoccupation compared to non–eating-disordered females (Cash, Morrow, Hrabosky, & Perry, 2004). Nevertheless, body dissatisfaction in non-clinical men is receiving increasing research attention. Research suggests that both heterosexual and gay men prefer a lean but muscular body type (Tiggemann, Martins, & Kirkbride, 2007), whereas women tend to prefer a thin body type (Tiggemann & Lynch, 2001). Similarly, the reported body images of college males tended to be distorted toward perceptions of underweight, whereas females' body

images were distorted toward perceptions of overweight (Betz, Mintz, & Speakmon, 1994). Hence, it is possible that males are more protected than females against the development of eating disorders, given their different types of weight and shape concerns and less frequent dieting behaviours. However, this factor alone cannot account for the development of eating disorders, given that eating disorders are so rare despite the fact that body dissatisfaction is so widespread.

There seem to be some protective factors operating for males; yet, there are still cases of eating disorders in males. Are there certain groups of males that may be more susceptible to developing eating disorders? Some evidence suggests that gay males may have a greater risk than heterosexual males for developing eating disorders. Men who identify as gay are more likely than heterosexual males to be preoccupied with their body size and shape (Strong, Williamson, Netemeyer, & Geer, 2000) and appear to have a higher prevalence of eating disorder symptoms than heterosexual males (Feldman & Meyer, 2007). Furthermore, researchers have indicated that men seeking treatment for an eating disorder are disproportionately likely to identify as gay. For example, Carlat and colleagues (1997) indicated that 41% of the male eating disorder patients they treated identified as heterosexual, whereas 27% identified as gay or bisexual, and 32% identified as asexual. In contrast, there do not appear to be any differences between heterosexual and lesbian or bisexual women with regard to the prevalence of eating disorders (Feldman & Meyer, 2007; Strong et al., 2000).

However, the increased risk of eating disorders within gay males is not ubiquitous. In two studies on eating-disordered populations that included control groups (Mangweth et al., 1997; Olivardia, Pope, Mangweth, & Hudson, 1995), men with eating disorders were not more likely to identify as gay, compared to men without eating disorders. Hence, given the inconsistent findings, it is premature to conclude that there is a strong association between sexual orientation and eating disorders in males. In fact, research investigating disordered eating in both heterosexual-identified and gay-identified males demonstrated that when males' levels of body dissatisfaction and self-esteem were statistically controlled for, there was no significant association between sexual orientation and eating disorder symptomatology (Hospers & Jansen, 2005). This suggests that body dissatisfaction (as opposed to sexual orientation) plays a more central role in the development of eating disorders in males.

Treatment

BIOLOGICAL TREATMENTS

Bulimia nervosa has been treated with antidepressant medication, namely tricyclic antidepressants and selective serotonin reuptake inhibitors. The rationale for treating bulimia with these drugs is that depressive symptoms are common in these patients, and, in addition, serotonin is believed to play a role in binge eating. Meta-analyses, which systematically and quantitatively review available research evidence, suggest that, overall, fluoxetine (Prozac) leads to a moderate initial improvement in binge eating and purging symptoms in non-underweight individuals with eating disorders. However, only a small minority of patients remit from their eating disorder using these drugs, and most patients continue to meet diagnostic criteria (Narash-Eisikovits, Dierberger, & Westen, 2002). Furthermore, meta-analyses have revealed that treatment with antidepressants is inferior to cognitive-behaviour therapy (CBT; described in the next section) at reducing frequency of bingeing and purging, depression, and distorted eating-related attitudes (Whittal, Agras, & Gould, 1999). When CBT is added to antidepressant treatment, antidepressant medication is better than when it is used alone (Narash-Eisikovits et al., 2002), but not better than CBT on its own (Wilson, 1993). Preliminary evidence exists for other second-generation antidepressants (trazodone and fluvoxamine), an anticonvulsant (topiramate), and a tricyclic antidepressant (desipramine). However, replication for all of these medications is required.

Unfortunately, attempts to treat anorexia nervosa with pharmacological agents have not been successful. Neither antidepressants, antipsychotics, nor any other class of drugs has been found to lead to significant weight gain, improve distorted attitudes or beliefs, or supplement inpatient programs (Bulik, Berkman, Brownley, Sedway, & Lohr, 2007).

PSYCHOLOGICAL TREATMENTS

COGNITIVE-BEHAVIOUR THERAPY (CBT) More than 60 randomized controlled trials of treatments for bulimia nervosa have been conducted. On the basis of this research, CBT is considered the leading evidence-based treatment for bulimia and is widely accepted as the treatment of choice among clinicians (Fairburn, 2008; Whittal et al., 1999). According to the cognitive-behavioural model of the maintenance of bulimia, overvaluation of body weight and

shape leads to excessive dietary restriction, which leaves the individual both psychologically and physiologically susceptible to episodes of binge eating. Purging and other excessive means of controlling body weight or shape serve to compensate for binge eating but also maintain binge eating by reducing the individual's anxiety about weight gain and by disrupting learned hunger and satiety cues. Episodes of binge eating and inappropriate compensatory behaviours worsen self-esteem, thereby leading to more dietary restraint and thus more binge eating (Fairburn, 2002).

Individual CBT for bulimia nervosa typically involves three stages that span approximately 20 weeks. In the first stage, the focus is on establishing a regular pattern of eating. This is accomplished through psychoeducation about the connection between restricting food intake and binge eating, and teaching patients to use behavioural strategies (e.g., meal planning, distraction, stimulus control) to eat three meals and two snacks daily without compensating. Self-monitoring is also used to help patients normalize their eating and identify triggers for symptoms. The second stage involves a continued focus on normalized eating, especially with respect to eliminating dieting. This stage also focuses on teaching problem-solving skills and identifying and modifying dysfunctional thoughts and beliefs (especially about body weight and shape). The third stage focuses on strategies for maintaining change and preventing relapse (Fairburn, 2008; Fairburn, Marcus, & Wilson, 1993).

Fairburn and his colleagues have also proposed a cognitive-behavioural theory of the maintenance of anorexia (Fairburn, Shafran, & Cooper, 1998). They suggest that the central feature of anorexia nervosa is an extreme need to control eating and that, in Western society, a tendency to determine self-worth based on body weight and shape is superimposed on the need for control. However, relatively few studies have examined the efficacy of CBT for anorexia nervosa using randomized controlled trial methodology. Research in this area is limited by small sample sizes and relatively high dropout rates (Bulik et al., 2007), as well as by a sizeable proportion of non-randomized studies (Galsworthy-Francis & Allen, 2014). A recent systematic review of the literature indicated that CBT appears to be helpful in reducing treatment drop-out, improving treatment adherence, increasing weight, improving eating disorder symptoms, and reducing relapse (Galsworthy-Francis & Allen, 2014). However, overall, CBT did not consistently outperform the comparison treatments (Galsworthy-Francis & Allen, 2014), indicating that CBT may not work as well for anorexia compared to bulimia nervosa.

Fairburn and colleagues have also proposed a transdiagnostic theory and treatment of eating disorders (Fairburn, 2008; Fairburn et al., 2003; see Figure 10.3). This theory argues that anorexia, bulimia, BED, and OSFED have similar underlying psychopathological processes and maintaining factors and therefore can be treated using similar CBT interventions. Consequently, CBT for eating disorders has been adapted so that it is relevant and can be applied to all individuals with eating disorders, regardless of their specific diagnosis. This adapted form of CBT has been called "CBT enhanced

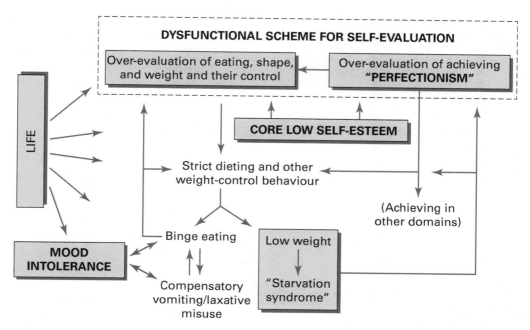

FIGURE 10.3 A Schematic Representation of the "Transdiagnostic" Theory of the Maintenance of Eating Disorders.

Source: Republished with permission of Elsevier Inc., from Cognitive behaviour therapy for eating disorders: A transdiagnostic theory and treatment. *Behaviour Research and Therapy,* 41, 509-528 and 2003; permission conveyed through Copyright Clearance Center, Inc.

for eating disorders (CBT-E)" (Cooper & Fairburn, 2011; Fairburn, 2008). Preliminary research shows that this enhanced CBT is an effective treatment for a variety of eating disorder diagnoses (e.g., Byrne et al., 2011; Fairburn et al., 2009, 2013, 2015).

This is one of several public service announcements sponsored by the National Eating Disorder Information Centre in Toronto.

INTERPERSONAL THERAPY To date, only one other treatment has shown effects on symptoms of bulimia that are comparable to those of CBT. In interpersonal therapy (IPT), the focus is on maladaptive personal relationships and ways of relating to others, because difficulties in these areas are thought to contribute to the development and maintenance of eating disorders (Birchall, 1999). In IPT, the major job of the therapist is to identify which problem area is relevant to the patient—grief, role transitions, interpersonal role disputes, or interpersonal deficits—and to work to improve the client's functioning in that area. IPT differs from CBT in that it does not directly target eating-disordered attitudes and behaviours.

Fairburn and his colleagues developed interpersonal therapy for bulimia nervosa to serve as a comparison treatment to CBT for the purpose of a research trial (Fairburn, Jones, Peveler, Hope, & O'Connor, 1993). In a well-conducted study, Fairburn and his colleagues found that patients with bulimia who received CBT experienced more than a 90% reduction in bingeing and purging one year after treatment. Nearly 40% of the patients had ceased binge eating and compensatory symptoms altogether. What was surprising was the finding that IPT produced effects equivalent to CBT at one-year follow-up, although CBT was somewhat better at the conclusion of treatment. In another study, 220 patients with bulimia nervosa were randomly assigned to receive either CBT or IPT (Agras, Walsh, Fairburn, Wilson, & Kraemer, 2000). These researchers found that 45% in the CBT group and 8% in the IPT group abstained from binge-eating and purging symptoms at the end of treatment. Similarly, CBT led to larger reductions in dietary restraint than did IPT (see Figure 10.4). However, at one-year follow-up there were no significant differences between CBT and IPT,

FIGURE 10.4 CBT versus IPT in the Treatment of Bulimia Nervosa

Source: Based on Agras, Walsh, Fairburn, Wilson & Kraemer (2000). A Multicenter Comparison of Cognitive-Behavioral Therapy and Interpersonal Psychotherapy for Bulimia Nervosa, *Archives of General Psychiatry*, Vol. 57, pp. 459–466.

with individuals who received IPT continuing to improve after the end of treatment. Most recently, enhanced CBT and IPT were compared in another well-designed study that supported the prior findings that CBT outperformed IPT at post-treatment. Like the previous studies, the IPT patients continued to improve after the end of treatment, although in this study, CBT continued to outperform IPT at the end of the follow-up period (Fairburn et al., 2015). Although CBT is still considered the preferred treatment for bulimia nervosa because it reduces symptoms relatively quickly, IPT also appears to be an efficacious option.

NUTRITIONAL THERAPY AND MEAL SUPPORT When a patient has anorexia nervosa, the first priority should be to restore body weight to a minimal healthy level. This is primarily important for medical stability. However, many of the symptoms of anorexia nervosa are due to the effects of starvation. Weight restoration can alleviate many of these symptoms, including cognitive impairments. Relatedly, some degree of weight restoration may be required to facilitate participation in psychotherapy. Both nutritional counselling and meal support are important components of treatment programs for eating disorders. Meal support is common in intensive treatment programs and involves providing emotional support and coaching during or after meals and helping individuals to decrease eating-related rituals (e.g., Leichner, Hall, & Calderon, 2005). Researchers at the British Columbia Children's Hospital have developed meal support training materials for parents of children and adolescents with eating disorders. These materials have been well received by the families, and are being used by clinicians to help involve families in the treatment process (Cairns, Styles, & Leichner, 2007). Nutritional counselling involves learning about what constitutes a normal meal, appropriate portion sizes, and nutritional requirements and the regulation of weight (American Dietetic Association, 2006).

Some individuals with eating disorders seek nutritional counselling as a stand-alone intervention. For example, in a community sample of women with bulimia nervosa, 37 percent of the women who had sought some treatment for their eating disorder had visited a dietitian (Mond, Hay, Rodgers, & Owen, 2007).

FAMILY THERAPY Various forms of family therapy have been employed in the treatment of eating disorders, particularly anorexia nervosa. The specific interventions used vary depending on the specific model of family therapy; however, in general, family therapy focuses on stresses within the family as a whole rather than on individuals, and places responsibility for recovery on both the client and her relatives. The Maudsley approach is a specific, evidence-based family therapy for adolescents with eating disorders. This approach involves an initial focus on recruiting parents to engage actively in managing the patient's weight gain (where relevant) and eating. No attention is paid to the cause of the disorder or to factors that do not directly affect the task of normalized eating. As eating improves and weight approaches normal levels, the therapist helps the family to return control of eating to the adolescent. Only when eating and weight are no longer central to family concerns does the therapist turn to more general adolescent issues independent of the eating disorder (Lock & le Grange, 2005). The available evidence supports the use of family-based therapy for the treatment of adolescents with eating disorders. A recent meta-analysis found that overall, although family-based therapy and individual therapy appear to perform similarly at the end of treatment for adolescents with eating disorders, those who received family therapy did better during the follow-up period (Couturier, Kimber, & Szatmari, 2013). In contrast, family therapy has not been shown to be an effective stand-alone treatment for adults.

SELF-HELP Self-help manuals that seek to disseminate information about eating disorders and strategies for overcoming bulimia and BED have been developed in response to the fact that therapists who specialize in eating disorders are in short supply and that large numbers of individuals with eating disorders do not seek treatment. The majority of these manuals are based on cognitive-behavioural principles. Self-help manuals can be used in several ways, including (1) for provision of an accessible form of information for individuals who might not otherwise have access to expert help, or who may feel too embarrassed to seek treatment; (2) in conjunction with guidance by a non-specialist professional such as a nurse or family doctor; (3) as the first step in a stepped-care approach to treatment delivery, with only those who require further treatment going on to more intensive (and thus more costly) treatments; (4) for administration to patients who are on waiting lists for intensive treatment; and (5) for facilitation of therapist-administered CBT (Carter, 2002).

Published studies of self-help interventions for bulimia nervosa and BED indicate that they are efficacious. In a randomized controlled trial conducted at Toronto General Hospital, Carter and colleagues (2003) examined the efficacy of two unguided self-help treatments for bulimia nervosa: a CBT manual and a nonspecific interpersonal treatment manual. They found equivalent significant reductions in frequency of bingeing and vomiting in both of the self-help groups (these reductions did not occur in the control group). Carter and Fairburn (1998) compared the relative effectiveness of guided and unguided self-help for BED in a randomized controlled trial. Participants assigned to the unguided self-help group followed a CBT manual for a period of 12 weeks. Those in the guided self-help group followed the same treatment manual for the same period of time but also received six to eight brief support sessions with a non-specialist facilitator. Both self-help treatments resulted in statistically significant and equivalent reductions in binge eating. There was a similar pattern of results for eating-disordered attitudes.

Self-help treatments are just beginning to be applied to anorexia. One study examined the efficacy of cognitive-behavioural guided self-help compared to a waiting list control group before admission to an inpatient unit. Results showed that duration of inpatient treatment was significantly shorter among participants who received guided self-help (Fichter, Cebulla, Quadflieg, & Naab, 2008). It is unlikely that self-help will turn out to be an efficacious stand-alone treatment for anorexia given that individuals typically require high levels of support and guidance to make the behavioural and attitudinal changes necessary for recovery.

5 BEFORE MOVING ON

What are the main differences between the different psychological treatment approaches (i.e., CBT, IPT, and family therapy)? What approach would you recommend to an 18-year-old woman diagnosed with bulimia, and why?

PREVENTION

Interventions for eating disorders are predominantly therapeutic. In other words, researchers and clinicians have focused on developing and providing therapies for individuals who have already developed eating disorders. However, some researchers have investigated whether providing preventive intervention programs can decrease the presence of risk factors for the development of eating disorders, and ultimately prevent disordered eating behaviours. One such program, Healthy Schools–Healthy Kids, was applied universally to all Grade 6 and 7 students who participated in the study. This program, developed in Toronto by Gail McVey and her colleagues (McVey, Tweed, & Blackmore, 2007), randomly assigned four schools to either an intervention condition or a control (no intervention) group for comparison. The intervention lasted throughout the school year and incorporated a variety of approaches, including in-class curriculum, a "Girl Talk" peer support group, parent education, and posters, video, and play presentations relating to teasing, peer pressure, size acceptance, and healthy eating. Participants who received the intervention experienced decreases in internalization of the thin ideal between baseline and post-intervention, which were maintained at the six-month follow-up, and a decrease in disordered eating from baseline to post-intervention. In contrast, those in the control condition experienced decreases in thin ideal internalization during the study period, but their scores returned to baseline values at the six-month follow-up. These findings suggest that the intervention was successful, particularly in reducing internalization of the socio-cultural ideal.

Other programs have focused their preventive interventions on individuals who have been identified as high risk for the development of eating disorders. In one study, 480 women between the ages of 18 and 30 who reported having high levels of concern about their weight were randomly assigned to either a waitlist control group or an internet-based prevention program that used cognitive-behavioural strategies aimed at decreasing body dissatisfaction and weight concerns (Taylor et al., 2006). The eight-week-long structured program involved participants logging in once a week to the program, reading new material, and participating in online discussion groups. Participants in the intervention condition reported larger decreases in weight concerns, eating pathology, and drive for thinness after the eight-week program compared to those in the control group, and these effects remained one year after the end of the program. The success of internet-based prevention programs is promising, as this type of program may make it easier for individuals who are at risk for developing an eating disorder to access support.

To further investigate the effectiveness of prevention programs and to determine whether certain factors improve the success of an intervention, a meta-analysis evaluated the effectiveness of 38 eating disorder prevention programs,

Eating Disorder Program, University Health Network (Toronto, Ontario)

Established in 1983, the University Health Network's Eating Disorder Program (EDP) is the largest intensive treatment centre in Canada for adults with anorexia nervosa, bulimia nervosa, and other specified feeding and eating disorders. Individuals from across the province of Ontario can utilize intensive eating disorder treatment through the program. In addition to providing high quality treatment, the EDP conducts clinical research aimed at evaluating the effectiveness of and improving treatments, as well as developing new innovative treatments for individuals with eating disorders.

A multidisciplinary team provides clinical care for individuals in the program. This team is co-led by Dr. Marion Olmsted, a clinical psychologist, and Dr. Patricia Colton, a psychiatrist. Other members of the clinical team include psychologists, psychiatrists, occupational therapists, dietitians, social workers, mental health clinicians, nurse practitioners, and nurses. Each discipline and individual brings specialized experience and expertise to the team (e.g., dietitians offer knowledge about nutrition, whereas the psychologists have extensive training in psychological assessment and research). Moreover, team members across disciplines also share similar roles, such as facilitating therapy groups. The psychotherapy provided in the program includes behavioural interventions (e.g., skills for normalizing eating patterns, interrupting bingeing and purging, and emotion regulation), psychoeducation, cognitive strategies, and cognitive-behavioural interventions targeting interpersonal problems (Olmsted et al., 2010).

In 2015, the Mental Health Commission of Canada published guidelines for *recovery-oriented practice*. This orientation differentiates the traditional approach of "clinical recovery," which focuses on the remission of symptoms, from "personal recovery," which recognizes that individuals can improve their quality of life and reach valued goals, even if they continue to experience symptoms of their clinical disorder (Roberts & Boardman, 2013). Recovery-oriented treatments recognize that each person is a unique individual, and helps patients work toward personal goals and build more meaningful lives as an integral part of their mental health care (Roberts & Boardman, 2013). Consistent with this approach, in 2017 the University Health Network EDP redesigned their treatment services in line with three core patient-care principles: (1) providing flexible, individualized care, (2) providing continuity of care and seamless transition among all three levels of care (inpatient, day treatment, and outpatient), and (3) helping patients make improvements that they can maintain in the long-term. The redesigned program not only focuses on reducing and eliminating eating disorder symptoms but also focuses on helping patients build a life outside of treatment that will support their recovery.

As a training site within a teaching hospital that is fully affiliated with the University of Toronto, the EDP also provides specialized training across disciplines as one of its mandates. Practicum students from various disciplines, psychology and psychiatry residents, and postdoctoral fellows, often complete specialized clinical and/or research training at the EDP.

The EDP aims to provide the best clinical care possible. To maintain this "best practice" culture, it is necessary to conduct research on the effectiveness of the different treatments offered, and on how to improve treatment outcomes. A core theme underlying the research at the EDP is a focus on improving treatments so that they better meet the needs of the patients. One innovative current project, funded by the Ontario Mental Health Foundation, is examining the efficacy of an integrated treatment combining CBT for eating disorders and CBT for post-traumatic stress disorder, for patients who are experiencing both of these problems simultaneously. Eating disorder symptoms and PTSD symptoms may interact with and maintain one another (Trottier et al., 2016), and this project is investigating whether the needs of patients with this symptom profile are better met when both disorders are addressed concurrently. The result of a pilot study of this intervention are promising (Trottier, Monson, Wonderlich, & Olmsted, 2017), and a randomized controlled trial examining the efficacy of this integrated treatment compared to standard eating disorder treatment is currently underway. Another current project aims to deliver an adjunctive substance-use intervention prior to intensive eating disorder treatment in order to better meet the needs of patients with co-occurring substance use disorders. Other research in this centre has focused on examining the effectiveness of intensive treatment (Olmsted, McFarlane, Trottier, & Rockert, 2013) and elucidating predictors of relapse after intensive treatment (Olmsted, MacDonald, McFarlane, Trottier, & Colton, 2015).

all of which included a control comparison group (Stice & Shaw, 2004). More than 50 percent of the interventions resulted in significant decreases in at least one risk factor for eating pathology (such as body dissatisfaction). Furthermore, programs that selected high-risk participants produced larger decreases in body dissatisfaction, dieting, and eating pathology than did universally applied programs. One possible explanation for this is that high-risk participants may be more motivated by the intervention programs because they experience more weight/shape-related distress, and therefore they may engage more in these programs than do those individuals with fewer concerns (Stice & Shaw, 2004).

 BEFORE MOVING ON

> What are some of the advantages and disadvantages of prevention programs that are targeted toward high-risk groups (as opposed to universally applied)? Do you think more schools should implement eating disorder prevention programs? Why or why not?

SUMMARY

- Eating disorders have been described throughout history, and were not always seen as evidence of maladjustment. Although eating disorders have become relatively common in modern Western societies, reports of food restriction and periods of binge eating and purging are not new.

- According to the DSM-5, the central feature of anorexia nervosa is the restriction of food intake, leading to a significantly low weight (i.e., a weight that is less than minimally normal, or expected, for age and height). Individuals with anorexia have an intense fear of gaining weight or becoming fat, or exhibit behaviour that interferes with weight gain. They often believe that eating feared or forbidden foods will result in significant amounts of weight gain. Individuals with anorexia nervosa typically achieve and maintain their low body weight through food restriction and exercising (and are classified as "restricting type"). However, some individuals with anorexia also engage in binge eating and/or purging behaviours. These individuals are classified as "binge-eating/purging type." Anorexia nervosa also typically involves disturbed attitudes and beliefs related to body weight and shape, or a lack of recognition of the seriousness of the low body weight.

- Bulimia nervosa is characterized by episodes of binge eating and engaging in compensatory behaviours to prevent weight gain. Individuals with bulimia nervosa often have low self-esteem and use weight and shape as a primary method of self-evaluation. Other features, such as social isolation and depression, are also common in both anorexia and bulimia nervosa. However, in contrast to anorexia nervosa, individuals with bulimia are typically within the normal weight range. According to the DSM-5, episodes of binge eating and compensatory behaviours must occur, on average, at least once a week for three months for a diagnosis of bulimia nervosa.

- Binge-eating disorder, like bulimia nervosa, involves regular binge-eating episodes that occur at least once a week for three months. However, there are no inappropriate compensatory behaviours to prevent weight gains that occur after the binges. Although individuals with BED are often overweight or obese, it is possible to be within the normal-weight range. Individuals with BED experience significant distress about their binge eating, and there are disturbed eating behaviours and thoughts that are associated with the binge eating.

- The DSM-5 also acknowledges eating disorders of clinical severity that do not meet current diagnostic criteria. These eating disorders are classified as "other specified feeding or eating disorders." In some individuals, these eating disorders resemble the full syndromes of anorexia, bulimia nervosa or binge-eating disorder, and in other individuals the psychopathological features of the eating disorder combine in a somewhat different way. Purging disorder and night-eating syndrome are two examples of an "other specified feeding or eating disorder."

- There appears to have been an increase in the prevalence of eating disorders over the last several decades of the twentieth century, although it is unclear to what extent the increase is due to an enhanced awareness about eating disorders. The prevalence of eating disorders in Canada is similar to the prevalence in other Western countries.

- Assessment for diagnostic purposes and to guide treatment planning is usually conducted using a structured or semi-structured interview. Conducting a diagnostic interview for an eating disorder involves gathering information about current and past frequency and severity of dietary restriction, bingeing, purging, and exercise, as well as distorted attitudes and beliefs about weight, shape, and eating, weight history, and current and past menstrual function (where relevant). Clinicians and researchers often use the Eating Disorder Examination to gather this information.

- Eating disorders are multi-determined. They are very complex disorders, and one factor alone does not produce an eating disorder in any given individual. Our society's preference for thinness may lead to body dissatisfaction and dieting. In vulnerable individuals, these factors may precipitate an eating disorder. Factors such as low self-esteem, family dynamics, trauma, and early maturation may leave an individual susceptible to developing an eating disorder. Genetic and biological predispositions may also contribute to developing an eating disorder. Although integrative models and theories attempt to address the complexity of eating disorders and the many identified etiological factors, they have not yet provided predictive power sufficient to identify the individuals most likely to develop eating disorders.

- There have been few controlled studies of treatments for anorexia nervosa. Weight restoration to a minimal healthy level is of primary importance. There is some evidence that CBT can be beneficial in producing weight gain, improving eating disorder psychopathology, and preventing relapse in adults, and that family therapy is a good option for adolescents. Although antidepressant medication has not been shown to be effective in the treatment of anorexia nervosa, it is helpful in the treatment of bulimia nervosa. However, research suggests that antidepressants such as Prozac are inferior to CBT in the treatment of bulimia nervosa. CBT is considered the treatment of choice for bulimia nervosa and BED. Nevertheless, IPT produces equivalent effects over the longer term.

- Research on the prevention of eating disorders is emerging, with some promising results. Prevention programs that target "high-risk" participants (such as women with high levels of body dissatisfaction) produced larger decreases in body dissatisfaction, dieting, and eating pathology than did universally applied programs.

KEY TERMS

amenorrhea (p. 240)

anorexia nervosa (p. 230)

binge eating/purging type (p. 236)

binge eating disorder (BED) (p. 230)

body mass index (BMI) (p. 235)

bulimia nervosa (p. 230)

Eating Disorder Examination (EDE) (p. 239)

lanugo (p. 240)

maintenance factors (p. 246)

objective binge (p. 231)

purging (p. 231)

restricting type (p. 236)

risk factors (p. 246)

Russell's sign (p. 240)

DAVID C. HODGINS

•

MAGDALEN SCHLUTER

CHAPTER

11

Wragg/E+/Getty Images

Substance-Related and Addictive Disorders

LEARNING OBJECTIVES

AFTER READING THIS CHAPTER, STUDENTS WILL BE ABLE TO:

1 Explain how substance-related disorders are defined and diagnosed.

2 Understand and describe the effects, etiology, and treatment approaches related to alcohol use disorders.

3 Comprehend trends in the prevalence of substance use in Canada.

4 Identify the psychological and physiological effects of various substances of abuse.

5 Describe similarities between substance use disorders and disordered gambling.

6 Describe the most common treatment approaches for various substance use disorders and disordered gambling.

At age 39, Gareth found himself in group therapy describing how he had lost his job and almost lost his life. When he thought back to how it had all begun, he found it difficult to pinpoint when using drugs and alcohol ceased to be fun and a social activity and began to be necessary to maintain day-to-day functioning. Somehow, he had gone from having the world by the tail as an executive at a software company to living in a treatment facility, wondering if he would ever be able to stay off drugs and rebuild his life.

At first, Gareth drank to keep up with his co-workers and business clients, many of whom regularly had "liquid lunches." Although he didn't really like the way alcohol made him feel in the afternoon, he soon found that a little of "the hair of the dog that bit you" at the bar after work helped him to feel better for the drive home. He also found alcohol more pleasing at parties and was able to drink more without getting drunk.

At a party held by a business associate, Gareth was introduced to cocaine, which gave him the energy for extended parties and alleviated the hangovers he often experienced after a night of drinking. He was also amazed by the way that cocaine improved his concentration, energy, and creativity. When high on cocaine he could work longer hours without taking a break, and he began to feel as if he could accomplish anything he set his mind to. The only drawback was the cost of the cocaine, but he could handle even that because he was doing so well in his job.

As he began to use cocaine more frequently, Gareth found that he often needed alcohol or "downers" to help him relax and fall asleep in the evenings. His physician was willing to prescribe benzodiazepines when Gareth explained that he was in a high-pressure job and had trouble sleeping because he worked odd hours and travelled to different time zones. Of course, the benzodiazepine and alcohol use at night meant he was often groggy in the morning and needed cocaine to help him function. His co-workers began to notice changes in Gareth's personality and decreased productivity. Gareth was in danger of losing his job.

One night, this cycle of abuse caught up with Gareth. He had been drinking with some customers right after work and came home at about 7:00 p.m. Tired, he decided to skip dinner and have a nap but could not sleep, so he took a couple of sleeping pills and had another stiff drink. The combination of benzodiazepines and a considerable amount of alcohol on an empty stomach resulted in a loss of consciousness. When his wife got home around 8:00 p.m., she found him asleep on the sofa and could not awaken him. She immediately phoned 911, and help arrived in time. The interview in the emergency room later that evening revealed the drug roller coaster that Gareth was on. His physician and wife insisted that he go directly to a treatment facility and he agreed.

Historically, virtually every culture has employed some legally or socially sanctioned drugs to alter moods or states of consciousness. In our culture, the most widely used substances are alcohol, tobacco, and caffeine, all of which are legal and (at least to some extent) socially acceptable. Many people begin their day with a cup of tea or coffee. Other people include a cigarette. Parties and other social events for adults almost always include alcohol. Although the immediate effects of these substances are usually pleasant, history is full of accounts of the devastating long-term impact of addictive substances.

The latest version of the DSM (APA, 2013) reintroduced as a formal diagnostic concept the term "addiction," which was not used in DSM-III or IV. Substance use disorders are now contained in a section titled Substance-related and Addictive Disorders. Part of this decision was related to the recognition that behaviours other than substances are associated with similar effects for affected individuals, including impairment of control, and continued drive to use despite clear negative consequences. As part of the planning for the DSM-5, the research on a number of behaviours such as sex, work, shopping, and gaming was reviewed. Ultimately, gambling disorder was the only behaviour that had sufficient depth of research to be included at this time. This chapter ends with a description of the current understanding of gambling and gambling disorder.

Historical Perspective

Alcohol and drug use have been around longer than recorded history. Mead, an alcoholic beverage naturally formed by the fermentation of honey, was probably the first alcohol that humans consumed. The ancient Egyptians were known for their drinking, and wine was extensively used by the Hebrews.

Opium derivatives were once widely used in Asian cultures, as well as in ancient Greece and Rome. Therapeutically, they were taken to relieve pain or induce sleep; however, the euphoria that these drugs produced resulted in their widespread use to enhance pleasure. In the Andes, for thousands of years, native populations occasionally chewed the leaf of the coca plant to relieve fatigue and increase endurance. The flower of the peyote cactus has long been used by Indigenous people in South and Central America as part of religious ceremonies. The chemical contained in this flower was valued for its ability to alter consciousness and results in hallucinations similar to those caused by LSD.

The effects of substance abuse were particularly grim as the Europeans colonized North and South America. Alcohol, in the form of beer, was widely consumed, in part because of the poor quality of drinking water. The tavern became the hub of social activity in the colonies and alcohol was an integral part of all social and festive occasions. Consumption levels were extremely high by current standards, even among children. When North American Indigenous people were introduced to European brandy, they discovered a means of being transported into a strange new world of experience. In an inebriated state, people committed crimes and acts of self-destruction previously unheard of (Douville & Casanova, 1967). A hunter might trade his entire winter's catch of furs for a jug or two of whisky, leading to misery and starvation. As a final insult, liquor reduced resistance to many imported diseases (Eccles, 1959).

South American cultures suffered similar effects. Prior to the arrival of the Spanish, alcohol was consumed only collectively, as part of religious ceremonies. A few years after the conquest, Indigenous people commonly used alcohol to escape from the confusion of their disrupted world (Bethell, 1984). There was also a striking increase in the use of coca leaf in the Andes. Formerly used only with the permission of the Inca king or his governor, coca became indispensable for Quechua mine workers because it enabled them to work almost without eating (Bethell, 1984).

Diagnosis and Assessment
DIAGNOSING SUBSTANCE USE DISORDERS

What the general public commonly refers to as alcoholism and drug addiction are formally termed **substance use disorders** in the DSM-5. Substances of abuse are divided into 10 classes: alcohol; caffeine; cannabis; hallucinogens; inhalants; opioids; sedatives, hypnotics, and anxiolytics; stimulants; tobacco; and other or unknown substances. An individual can receive a diagnosis for one or more of these classes (e.g., *alcohol use disorder*, *opioid use disorder*). In general, *substance use disorder* refers to recurrent use of one of these specific substances that leads to adverse consequences. The disorder ranges in severity from mild to moderate to severe, depending on the number of problem indicators. The 11 indicators apply to most classes of substances, with a few minor exceptions (e.g., withdrawal symptoms are not part of inhalant use disorder; there is no caffeine use disorder). Table 11.1 describes the indicators for alcohol use disorder as an example.

TABLE 11.1 DSM-5 DIAGNOSTIC CRITERIA FOR ALCOHOL USE DISORDER

A. A problematic pattern of alcohol use leading to clinically significant impairment or distress, as manifested by at least two of the following, occurring within a 12-month period
   1. Alcohol is often taken in larger amounts or over a longer period than was intended.
   2. There is a persistent desire or unsuccessful efforts to cut down or control alcohol use.
   3. A great deal of time is spent in activities necessary to obtain alcohol, use alcohol, or recover from its effects.
   4. Craving, or a strong desire or urge to use alcohol.
   5. Recurrent alcohol use resulting in a failure to fulfill major role obligations at work, school, or home.
   6. Continued alcohol use despite having persistent or recurrent social or interpersonal problems caused or exacerbated by the effects of alcohol.
   7. Important social, occupational, or recreational activities are given up or reduced because of alcohol use.
   8. Recurrent alcohol use in situations in which it is physically hazardous.
   9. Alcohol use is continued despite knowledge of having a persistent or recurrent physical or psychological problem that is likely to have been caused or exacerbated by alcohol.
   10. Tolerance, as defined by either of the following:
       a. A need for markedly increased amounts of alcohol to achieve intoxication or desired effect.
       b. A markedly diminished effect with continued use of the same amount of alcohol.
   11. Withdrawal, as manifested by either of the following:
       a. The characteristic withdrawal syndrome for alcohol (refer to Criteria A and B of the criteria set for alcohol withdrawal, pp. 499–500).
       b. Alcohol (or a closely related substance, such as a benzodiazepine) is taken to relieve or avoid withdrawal symptoms.

Source: Reprinted with permission from the *Diagnostic and Statistical Manual of Mental Disorders, Fifth Edition.* (Copyright © 2013). American Psychiatric Association. All Rights Reserved.

There are four general groupings of indicators: impairment of control over use, social impairment, risky use, and pharmacological criteria. **Impairment of control** includes taking the substance in greater amounts or for longer than intended. For example, a man may plan to stop for a quick drink at the neighbourhood pub on his way home for dinner but end up spending a few hours drinking. In the traditional concept of alcoholism, impairment of control was referred to as loss of control. Behavioural psychologists have demonstrated that contingencies, rewards, and punishments can influence the use of a substance even in the most affected individuals, which suggests that control is impaired but not entirely lost. Other indicators of impairment of control (see indicators 2, 3, and 4 in Table 11.1) are multiple unsuccessful attempts to cut down or stop, spending a great deal of time obtaining the substance or recovering from its effects, and experiencing a strong craving for the substance. The **social impairment** indicators (indicators 5, 6, and 7) refer to a failure to fulfill major role obligations at work, home, or school; continued use despite clear negative consequences on relationships; and the reduction of other involvements to give priority to using the substance. For example, a person might stay away from an otherwise desirable party if smoking is not allowed. Others may eat only in restaurants where alcohol is served. A woman may have previously been active in a hiking club but have shifted to spending weekend afternoons with friends at a local pub.

The **risky use** indicators (8 and 9) are used in situations in which it might be hazardous, such as driving or operating machinery, and in which there is continued use despite the clear indication that use is causing or exacerbating physical or psychological problems (e.g., headaches, depression).

The **pharmacological dependence** indicators (10 and 11) are tolerance and withdrawal. **Tolerance** means that the person needs increased amounts of the substance to achieve the same effect. Individuals suffering from **withdrawal** experience unpleasant and sometimes dangerous symptoms, such as nausea, headache, or tremors when the addictive substance is removed from the body. These physiological events are a result of the changes that the body has undergone in order to adapt to the continued presence of the drug. Specific drugs have predictable groups of symptoms typically characterized by overactivity of the physiological functions that were suppressed by the substance and/or depression of the functions that were stimulated by the substance. Additional ingestion of the specific drug, or one that is closely related, will alleviate these symptoms. Of course, this is part of the vicious circle that maintains dependence.

In addition to the substance use disorders, a number of **substance-induced disorders** are associated with each of the 10 drug classes, including intoxication, withdrawal, and other substance- or medication-induced mental disorders (e.g., psychotic, bipolar, depressive, anxiety, and sleep disorders). As the name implies, these disorders are sets of symptoms that are caused by the heavy use of specific substances and they generally resolve when the person stops using the substance.

POLYSUBSTANCE USE DISORDER

Research into the short-term and long-term effects of substance use and abuse is plagued by the issue of **polysubstance abuse**, the simultaneous misuse or dependence upon two or more substances. In fact, concurrent dependence appears to be the rule rather than the exception. For example, 80 percent of individuals with alcohol use disorders also smoke cigarettes, and many are likely addicted to both (Weinberger, Funk, & Goodwin, 2016). Research has shown that more than half of cocaine users are dependent on alcohol (Higgins, Budney, Bickel, Foerg, & Badger, 1994), and

---

FOCUS 11.1

Back to the Future: Addiction in the DSM-5

A number of significant changes in how we conceptualize substance use disorders are contained in the DSM-5 (APA, 2013). One major change is in terminology. Since the third edition, the term *substance dependence* has been used to avoid more pejorative terms like *alcoholic* and *addict*. In the DSM-IV-TR, *dependence* referred to both psychological and physiological aspects of reliance on substances. However, the term was confusing—as in other arenas, tolerance refers to a physiological dependence, which may or may not be related to addiction. For example, an individual prescribed pain medications after surgery quickly develops physical tolerance and typically will experience physiological withdrawal when the medication is discontinued. However, the individual does not show any signs of addiction, such as use of the drug to manage feelings or compulsive use. In the DSM-5 we revert to the use of the term *addiction* and drop the use of *dependence*. The name for the section of the DSM that includes alcohol and other drugs is "Substance-related and Addictive Disorders." However, the term addiction is not used in either labelling or describing the disorders. Instead, the more neutral "substance use disorder" has been adopted.

Another change is related to the broadening of the section to include non-substance-related addictions, often referred to as *behavioural addictions*. At this point, only one behavioural addiction is sufficiently well studied and understood to be included in the DSM-5: gambling disorder.

Close consideration was given to including internet gaming addiction as a formal diagnosis as well. However, because research support is limited, a set of tentative diagnostic criteria are included in the DSM-5 appendix as a way of encouraging further study. It is expected that other behavioural addictions, such as sex addiction and work addiction, will also be candidates for future DSM editions. ●

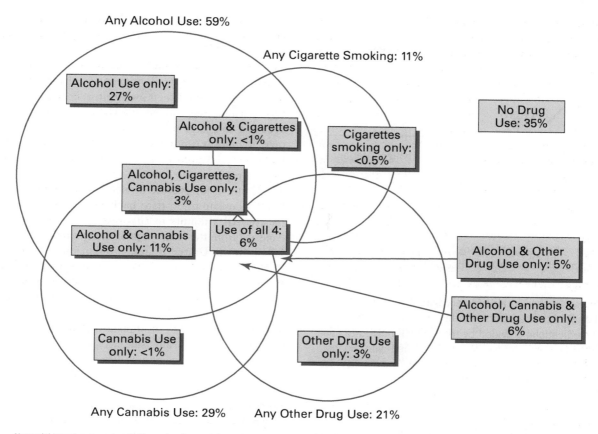

FIGURE 11.1 The Overlap of Alcohol, Cannabis, and Other Drug Use in the Past Year, Ontario Student Drug Use Survey 2015 (Grades 7 to 12)

Source: Adapted from Drug use among Ontario students, 1977-2011: Detailed OSDUHS findings (CAMH Research Document Series No. 32). Toronto, ON: Center for Addiction and Mental Health

more than half of all amphetamine users also abuse benzodiazepines (Darke, Ross, & Cohen, 1994). Opioid addicts often abuse alcohol, cocaine, and benzodiazepines, and illicit use of opioids such as heroin are augmented with legal prescription opioids such as oxycodone (Oxycontin), codeine, morphine, and hydrocodone (Vicodin; Fischer, Cruz, & Rehm, 2006). Sometimes the pattern is that of concurrent, alternating use. To prevent the excessive excitement, irritability, and insomnia associated with chronic amphetamine use, addicts will often consume barbiturates when they want to "come down" or sleep. Later, amphetamines will be used to reduce the sedative effects or morning drowsiness caused by the barbiturates. Polysubstance abuse appears to be on the rise and is more common in young people (Newcomb, 1994). In a study of Ontario high school students (Boak, Hamilton, Adlaf, & Mann, 2015), more than six in ten reported using alcohol, tobacco, cannabis, or another illicit drug in the past year. Figure 11.1 depicts the overlap of substance use. It appears that alcohol is the most common element of involvement in other substance use. A very small proportion of students use cannabis exclusively (less than 1 percent), almost

no students smoke cigarettes exclusively, and 3 percent use any other drug exclusively.

There are a number of health and treatment concerns related to polysubstance abuse. Combining drugs is physically dangerous because they are often synergistic. That is, the combined effects of the drugs exceed or are significantly different from the sum of their individual effects. For example, mixing alcohol and barbiturates or opioids can depress central nervous system (CNS) functioning to a much greater degree than any of these substances alone. Amphetamines and other stimulants, when combined with alcohol, cause physical damage greater than the damage that would be caused by the drugs if they were taken separately (Comer, 1997). To complicate matters, individuals with a history of polysubstance abuse are likely to have more diagnosable mental problems than individuals who abuse only one substance (Moss, Goldstein, Chen, & Yi, 2015). In DSM-5, abuse of each substance is diagnosed separately so that each person is likely to have multiple diagnoses. When treatment is considered, the drug that presents the more immediate threat to health (e.g., opioids, cocaine, alcohol) tends to overshadow others (e.g., smoking, marijuana). However, it is not clear which substance use disorder or other mental disorder should be treated first, or whether all should be treated at the same time.

Case Notes

"When did things start to fall apart?" thought Marianne. Certainly, the car accident had a lot to do with it. She could still vividly remember that evening five years ago. She was to have gone to Florida with Luc that week, but he told her he wanted to end their relationship. So instead she drove the five hours to Toronto to take a computer graphics course. Driving home after three gruelling days, she fell asleep at the wheel and crashed into a wall of rock. She awoke in the hospital with a fractured spine.

Fortunately, she was able to walk again. Three weeks later, she went back to an empty home and a long recuperation. The medications provided by the hospital helped to control the pain and let her sleep. Combined with alcohol, she discovered, they worked even better. The alcohol also dulled her nagging worries about the future.

Eventually, her injuries healed and she again found employment. She managed to stop taking the pain medication, but kept on drinking. Alcohol dulled her back pain, and it made her feel good. She fell into the habit of having a few drinks alone at home each night, often falling asleep in front of the television. She often resolved not to drink that night, but the loneliness and back pain were too much to bear without alcohol. She convinced herself she was not really an alcoholic because she never drank during the day and was never really drunk. Nevertheless, her concentration was off, her work began to suffer, and her social life dwindled. She finally realized that she had a problem and made inquiries about professional services but, as yet, was too ashamed and frightened to admit that she needed help.

 BEFORE MOVING ON

How does the conceptualization of substance use disorders in DSM-5 differ from that of previous conceptualizations?

Alcohol
HISTORY OF USE

Alcohol has been called the "world's number one psychoactive substance" (Ray & Ksir, 1990). By 6400 BCE, people had discovered how to make alcohol in the form of beer and berry wine. The distillation process, in which the fermented solution containing alcohol is heated and the vapours are collected and condensed in liquid form again to create what

were first called "spirits," is believed to have been discovered in Arabia. In addition to the Egyptians and the Hebrews, there is ample evidence that the Greeks enjoyed wine, and later Roman emperors were notorious for their insobriety. It is reported that the people who met Christopher Columbus in the Caribbean had their own form of beer, and the distillation of whisky was commonplace in Ireland by CE 1500, and occurred on a large scale in America by the eighteenth century. Alcohol was not used by Indigenous Canadians until the French brought brandy and the British brought rum from Europe.

Concern for overuse of alcohol and attempts to regulate its consumption date back to earliest recordings of its use. All attempts to suppress alcohol in Europe and America from the fourteenth to the twentieth century have failed. In the United States, Prohibition came into effect in 1920, and did effectively reduce overall alcohol intake. Partial or complete prohibition was also introduced into the majority of Canadian provinces around the same time. However, there was widespread disrespect for the laws, leading to the growth of organized crime and bootlegging (illegal production and sale). Much of the bootlegging originated in Canada and was directed to the United States. Concern about this lawlessness, as well as an appreciation of the revenues to be gained by taxing liquor sales, led to the repeal of Prohibition soon after the Great Depression began. As might be expected, there was a gradual increase in alcohol consumption; per capita consumption equalled pre-Prohibition levels by the end of the Second World War, and continued to rise until it peaked in 1980–1981. Consumption dropped between 1981 and the late 1990s but has again begun to rise. Generally, the greater the economic wealth of a country, the greater the proportion of the population that drinks and the greater the average consumption is (World Health Organization, 2014a).

CANADIAN CONSUMPTION PATTERNS

In 2015, 15 154 Canadians aged 15 and older were interviewed about their alcohol use by telephone using a random-digit dialing survey method (Health Canada, 2016). This bi-yearly survey was launched in 2013 and is similar to earlier surveys. In the recent survey, approximately four out of every five Canadians (77%) reported drinking alcohol in the past 12 months, and 10% had never imbibed alcohol. These figures are slightly lower than those in a 2004 survey, which found that 79% had consumed alcohol in the past 12 months. The rate of past-year drinking is higher for men than for women (81% versus 73%).

People who drank alcohol in the past year can be divided into four categories according to the frequency of drinking and the number of drinks consumed (see Table 11.2 for a definition of a standard drink). The largest groups of drinkers are classified as light infrequent drinkers (less than weekly and fewer than five drinks per occasion) at 36%, and light frequent drinkers (more than weekly and fewer than five drinks per occasion) at 32%.

Canada's Indigenous People

Issues related to substance misuse in Canada's Indigenous people are a significant social concern and are perceived by their leadership to be the top challenge for community wellness (First Nations Information Governance Committee, 2012). Substance effects are complicated by high unemployment, inadequate housing, poor access to health services, and education and economic marginalization. Among First Nation adults, rates of heavy drinking were reported by two-thirds of individuals aged 30 to 49. In contrast to the general population, heavy drinking did not decline after young-adulthood; significant declines were only observed after age 60. Adolescent suicide rates are much higher than the national adolescent rate. It appears that fetal alcohol spectrum disorders (FASD) are much more prevalent and tobacco and injection drug use are also particular concerns among First Nations populations (Shields, 2000).

Over the last 30 years, an increasingly organized network of residential and community treatment centres, which provide culturally based services and support, have been developed as part of a National Native Alcohol and Drug Abuse Program. Originally they were based upon the Alcoholics Anonymous model but over time they have incorporated cognitive-behavioural interventions and sprit-centred approaches that include ceremony, traditions, and indigenous languages (Health Canada, 2011b). The goal is to provide individually based treatments in the context of overall community healing. An excellent example is Alkali Lake in British Columbia:

In reaction to high rates of alcohol addiction, with nearly all of the community seen as dependent, the community engaged in an ongoing healing process to transform health and social conditions, promote individual and community wellness, and revitalize traditional teachings and practices. Guided by continued leadership, commitment and support, this process started with one sober person and expanded to 95 percent of community members indicating that they were clean and sober. Throughout the process, sober community members worked to eliminate the bootlegging of alcohol through collaboration with the RCMP. As well, a voucher system was established with stores in Williams Lake for food and other necessities, where some of the community's heaviest drinkers received these in place of social assistance funds. (Health Canada, 2011b, p 21) ●

About 5% are heavy infrequent drinkers (less than weekly and five or more drinks per occasion) and 4% are heavy frequent drinkers (more than weekly and five or more drinks per occasion).

Young adults are more likely to drink and to drink heavily; consumption peaks in the mid-twenties, then decreases. About 83 percent of young adults aged 20 to 24 drink during the course of a year, compared to 59 percent of youth aged 15 to 19. Single people are more likely to be both casual and heavy drinkers; high-income earners and those with a post-secondary education are also more likely to be current drinkers. However, those with the least education and those out of work reported the heaviest drinking (Canadian Centre on Substance Abuse, 2004a).

Low-risk drinking guidelines have been established by the Canadian Centre on Substance Abuse and endorsed by many professional organizations (e.g., the Canadian Medical Association, the Canadian Paediatric Society, and the Council of Chief Medical Officers of Health) to provide an indication of the *upper limits* on drinking so that drinking is not likely

TABLE 11.2 CONVERTING ALCOHOLIC BEVERAGES INTO STANDARD DRINKS

Beverage (% alcohol)	Usual Bottle Size	Standard Drinks	Usual Serving	Number of Standard Drinks in a Usual Serving
Beer (5%)	340 mL (12 oz)	1.0	340 mL (12 oz)	1.0
Wine (12%)	750 mL (26.4 oz)	5.3	140 mL (5 oz)	1.0
	1000 mL (35.2 oz)	7.0		
	1500 mL (52.8 oz)	10.6		
Fortified wine (18%)	750 mL (26.4 oz)	7.5	85 mL (3 oz)	1.0
Spirits (40%)	340 mL (12 oz)	8.0	43 mL (1.5 oz)	1.0
	710 mL (25 oz)	16.6		
	1135 mL (40 oz)	26.6		
Wine coolers (5–7%)	340 mL (12 oz) variable sizes from 750 mL to 2 L	1.0–1.4	340 mL (12 oz)	1.0–1.4
Pre-mixed liquor beverages (5–7%)	340 mL (12 oz)	1.0–1.4	340 mL (12 oz)	1.0–1.4

Source: Hodgins, D. C., & Diskin, K. M. (2003). Alcohol Problems. In M. Nerson & S. M. Turner (Eds.), *Diagnostic Interviewing* (3rd ed.). New York: Springer.

TABLE 11.3   CANADA'S LOW-RISK DRINKING GUIDELINES

Drinking is a personal choice. If you choose to drink, these guidelines can help you decide when, where, why, and how.
Guideline 1 Reduce your long-term health risks by drinking no more than: 10 drinks a week for women, with no more than 2 drinks a day most days. 15 drinks a week for men, with no more than 3 drinks a day most days. Set aside non-drinking days each week, so you do not develop the habit of drinking.
Guideline 2 Reduce your risk of injury and harm by drinking no more than 3 drinks (for women) and 4 drinks (for men) at any one time. Plan to drink in a safe environment. Stay within the weekly limits outlined in Guideline 1.
Guideline 3 Do not drink when you are driving a vehicle or using machinery and tools; taking medicine or other drugs that interact with alcohol; doing any kind of dangerous (extreme) physical activity; living with mental or physical health problems; living with alcohol dependence; pregnant or planning to be pregnant; responsible for the safety of others; making important decisions
Guideline 4 If you are pregnant, planning to become pregnant, or will soon begin breastfeeding, the safest choice is to drink no alcohol at all.
Guideline 5 If you are a child or youth, you should delay drinking until your late teens. Alcohol can harm the way your brain and body develop. Ask your parents for guidance and follow the local alcohol laws. If you are drinking, plan ahead and stay in control.

Source: Based on Butt, P., Beirness, D., Cesa, F., Gliksman, L., Paradis, C., & Stockwell, T. (2011). *Alcohol and Health in Canada: A Summary of Evidence and Guidelines for Low-Risk Drinking*. Ottawa, ON: Canadian Centre on Substance Abuse.

to lead to physical impairment (see Table 11.3). According to low-risk drinking guidelines, daily alcohol intake should not exceed two drinks for women and three drinks for men, and weekly intake should not exceed 10 drinks for women and 15 drinks for men (Butt et al., 2011).

Surveys have also been conducted of university students across Canada (Adlaf, Demers, & Gliksman, 2005). Overall 90% of all university students had consumed alcohol at some point in their lives. Eighty-six percent reported drinking in the past 12 months. The rates of drinking were highest in Quebec and the Atlantic provinces (89.7% and 85.6%, respectively), and were lowest in British Columbia (78.5%). Although they represented the highest number of drinkers, students from Quebec universities reported the lowest average weekly intake.

University students are also more likely to consume larger quantities on a single occasion, known as "binge drinking." In the survey of university students, 18.5 percent reported drinking five or more drinks twice per month or more. Male students reported drinking more often and more heavily than female students, and students living on their own or in residence drank more than those living at home.

HIGH-RISK DRINKING Alcohol researchers suggest that there is a direct relationship between the overall level of consumption within a population and the number of people suffering alcohol use disorder. Moreover, there is a relationship between an individual's consumption and that person's risk. The Alcohol Use Disorders Identification Test (AUDIT; Babor, de la Fuente, Saunders, & Grant, 1992), a 10-question screening tool, is often administered to estimate risk level (see Table 11.4). The AUDIT was originally developed by the World Health Organization for use in a cross-cultural comparison of brief treatments for alcohol problems. The items were developed to minimize cultural differences in alcohol use and attitudes. The AUDIT has become widely used in surveys of prevalence in different populations, such as medical patients, students, employees, and the general population.

Validation studies of the AUDIT indicate that different cut-off scores are needed for different populations. For the general population, a cut-off of 8 is typically used to indicate high-risk drinking. The AUDIT was used in a 2004 Canadian national study. Among past-year–drinking Canadians, 17% of adults were identified as high risk. The proportion of men was 25% and of women was 9%. More than 30% of those under age 25 were high-risk drinkers compared with only 5% of people aged 65 and older (Canadian Centre on Substance Abuse, 2004a). The AUDIT was also used in the most recent survey of Ontario high school students (Boak et al., 2015). High-risk drinking was reported by 20% of students in Grades 7 to 12.

The devastation wrought by alcohol addiction is not a new thing. This woodcut captures the misery suffered by the addicted in eighteenth-century London.

Lebrecht Music and Arts Photo Library/Alamy Stock Photo

TABLE 11.4   ALCOHOL USE DISORDERS IDENTIFICATION TEST (AUDIT)

Circle the number that comes closest to your actions during the past year.

1. How often do you have a drink containing alcohol?

Never	(0)	2 to 3 times a week	(3)
Monthly or less	(1)	4 or more times a week	(4)
2 to 4 times a month	(2)		

2. How many drinks containing alcohol do you have on a typical day when you are drinking?

1 or 2	(0)	7 to 9	(3)
3 or 4	(1)	10 or more	(4)
5 or 6	(2)		

3. How often do you have five or more drinks on one occasion?

Never	(0)	Weekly	(3)
Less than monthly	(1)	Daily or almost daily	(4)
Monthly	(2)		

4. How often during the past year have you found that you were not able to stop drinking once you had started?

Never	(0)	Weekly	(3)
Less than monthly	(1)	Daily or almost daily	(4)
Monthly	(2)		

5. How often during the last year have you failed to do what was normally expected from you because of drinking?

Never	(0)	Weekly	(3)
Less than monthly	(1)	Daily or almost daily	(4)
Monthly	(2)		

6. How often during the last year have you needed a first drink in the morning to get yourself going after a heavy drinking session?

Never	(0)	Weekly	(3)
Less than monthly	(1)	Daily or almost daily	(4)
Monthly	(2)		

7. How often during the last year have you had a feeling of guilt or remorse after drinking?

Never	(0)	Weekly	(3)
Less than monthly	(1)	Daily or almost daily	(4)
Monthly	(2)		

8. How often during the last year have you been unable to remember what happened the night before because you had been drinking?

Never	(0)	Weekly	(3)
Less than monthly	(1)	Daily or almost daily	(4)
Monthly	(2)		

9. Have you or someone else been injured as a result of your drinking?

No	(0)
Yes, but not in last year	(2)
Yes, during the last year	(4)

10. Has a relative or friend or a doctor or other health worker been concerned about your drinking or suggested you cut down?

No	(0)
Yes, but not in last year	(2)
Yes, during the last year	(4)

Scoring: Each answer is weighted from 0 to 4 as indicated in the brackets. Please note that questions 9 and 10 are scored 0, 2, or 4. A score of 8 or more indicates that a harmful level of alcohol consumption is likely.

Source: Reprinted from *The Alcohol Use Disorders Identification Test: Guidelines for Use in Primary Care* (2nd ed.). © World Health Organization, Babor, T. F., & Higgins Biddle, J. Copyright (2002).

EFFECTS

Ethyl alcohol is the effective chemical compound in alcoholic beverages. It reduces anxiety, produces euphoria, and creates a sense of well-being. It also reduces inhibitions, which adds to the perception that alcohol enhances social and physical pleasure, sexual performance, power, and social assertiveness.

Yet it appears that some of the short-term effects of ingesting small amounts of alcohol are as strongly related to the expectations of the effects of alcohol as they are to its chemical action on the body. In an interesting body of research, participants were told falsely that their drink contained alcohol. These individuals were found to behave more aggressively (Lang, Goeckner, Adessor, & Marlatt, 1975), report greater sexual arousal (Wilson & Lawson, 1976), and report less performance-related anxiety (Abrams, Kushner, Medina, & Voight, 2001) than participants who were not led to believe they were consuming alcohol. Environmental cues and personality can also mediate this effect (Quigley & Leonard, 2006). One study found that individuals with high dispositional aggressivity were more likely to behave aggressively when administered the placebo drink compared to individuals with low aggressivity (Giancola, 2002). It would appear that in some individuals, expectations regarding alcohol's effects are more potent than the actual physical responses.

Unlike most orally ingested psychoactive substances, alcohol does not require digestion to enter the bloodstream. Since ethanol is water-soluble, it can pass directly into the blood from the stomach, although most of it is absorbed from the small intestine. The bloodstream quickly carries it to the CNS. The rate and peak level of absorption depend on how quickly the alcohol gets through the stomach and into the intestine. If alcohol is consumed on a full stomach, such as with a meal, passage to the intestine is more gradual than when consumed on an empty stomach.

Once the alcohol reaches the blood supply, it travels throughout the body and enters most tissues. Alcohol level is usually expressed as a percentage of blood. For example, if there are 80 millilitres of alcohol in 100 000 millilitres of blood, **blood alcohol level (BAL)** is 0.08%. Approximately 95% of alcohol is removed by the liver at essentially a constant rate of 7 to 8 millilitres of ethanol per hour. The remaining 5% of alcohol is excreted by the lungs, which is what Breathalyzers measure to estimate BAL. Thirty millilitres of liquor, 150 millilitres of wine, and one beer have equivalent absolute alcohol content of 15 millilitres. If rate of intake equals rate of metabolism, then BAL will remain stable. If more than a single standard drink is consumed every two hours, then BAL will climb. Because alcohol does not distribute much into fatty tissues, an 80-kilogram leaner person will have a lower BAL than an 80-kilogram less lean person who drinks the same amount of alcohol. The leaner person has more fluid volume in which to distribute the alcohol. Alcohol is further broken down in the stomach by the enzyme **alcohol dehydrogenase**, and women have significantly less of this enzyme. The lower levels of alcohol dehydrogenase in women and the fact that men tend to have a lower proportion of body fat mean that a woman will usually have a higher BAL (and therefore be more intoxicated) than a man of the same body weight consuming the same quantity of alcohol (Frezza et al., 1990; National Institute on Drug Abuse, 1992).

SHORT-TERM EFFECTS The effects of alcohol vary with the level of concentration of the drug (yes, it is a drug) in the bloodstream. In addition, alcohol has what is termed a *biphasic effect*. At lower doses, the effect of alcohol is stimulating, resulting in pleasant feelings. At higher doses, alcohol acts as a depressant, and many may experience dysphoria. High doses can also produce unconsciousness and death. Because alcohol depresses CNS function, rapid ingestion of a large amount of alcohol can inhibit respiration and cause death. Fortunately, alcohol usually causes vomiting or unconsciousness before most people reach this level of intoxication.

Alcohol causes deficits in eye–hand coordination, which can be seen at BALs as low as 0.01 (alcohol only makes you *think* you are the best pool player), and drowsiness shows up on vigilance tasks at levels of 0.06. A 40% decrease in steadiness, as measured by the amount of swaying, is evident at a BAL of 0.06. Decreased visual acuity and decreased sensitivity to taste, smell, and pain are evident at BALs as low as 0.08. Furthermore, at BALs of 0.08 to 0.1, reaction time slows by about 10%, performance on standard intelligence tests falls, memory is poorer, and perception of time is altered. (Five minutes seems like eight—an interesting challenge to the adage "Time flies when you're having fun.") Alcohol begins to affect driving performance at about 0.05, and the curve starts to rise sharply at about 0.08, the legal limit of impairment in many jurisdictions. At the same time that objective measures show poorer performance, the loss of inhibition often gives people increased confidence in their abilities (Tiplady, Franklin, & Scholey, 2004).

Not surprisingly, this increased confidence and impaired performance can easily result in accidents. According to the Traffic Injury Research Foundation (2014), approximately 17% of Canadians reported that they had driven after consuming alcohol in the past 30 days. This number has decreased from the 25% who reported this behaviour in 2010. More than 5% of drivers reported having driven at some point in the year before the survey when they were likely over the legal limit, and 38% of these drivers admitted to driving with passengers in the vehicle.

Drinking large amounts of alcohol quickly, particularly on an empty stomach, can cause memory **blackouts**, an interval of time for which the person cannot recall key details or entire events. Blackouts are much more common among social drinkers than previously thought. Among university students, the reported prevalence of blackouts is typically around 50 percent (Wetherill & Fromme, 2016). Types of events forgotten include participation in a wide range of potentially dangerous events, including driving, unprotected sex, and vandalism (White, Jamieson-Drake, & Swartzwelder, 2002). Women and men were equally likely to report blackouts in this survey, despite the fact that women drank less often and less heavily, which is likely related to the gender differences in the metabolism of alcohol just described. Alcohol is often considered a good way to get a good night's sleep. Although alcohol may cause mild sedation and help a person fall asleep, it suppresses the rapid eye movement (REM) phase of the sleep cycle. Lighter drinking suppresses REM for the first part of the night, but REM will rebound, or increase, in the latter part of the night to compensate. With heavier drinking, REM is suppressed throughout the night. This irregular sleep pattern impedes the restorative effect of sleep, leading to significant daytime sleepiness.

The adverse symptoms of "the morning after the night before" are familiar to many, but not well understood. The symptoms of hangovers range from nausea, fatigue, headache, thirst, depression, and anxiety to general malaise, and it is possible that these symptoms are a result of withdrawal from the short-term or long-term addiction to alcohol. This notion is supported by the popularly recommended cure of "the hair of the dog that bit you." This remedy of taking an alcoholic drink to cure a hangover may appear to minimize the symptoms, but it really only spreads them out. An analgesic for the headache, and rest and time, are probably the wisest "cures."

The extreme thirst that accompanies a hangover is related to alcohol's ability to cause the fluid inside the body's cells to move outside the cells, causing cellular dehydration. In addition, the diuretic effect that causes the body to excrete more fluid than is taken in (an effect that can be quite inconvenient in certain circumstances) contributes to the increase in thirst. Finally, the nausea and stomach upset result because alcohol is a gastric irritant. In addition, the accumulation of acetaldehyde, a by-product of the metabolism of alcohol, is quite toxic, which contributes to the nausea and headache. The fatigue experienced the next day can often be attributed to alcohol's interference with normal sleep patterns and the increased level of activity during the revelry of the evening before.

LONG-TERM EFFECTS Alcohol is ubiquitous in our society and is therefore rarely considered a dangerous drug. In fact, it is a favourite part of many social activities. However, chronic alcohol consumption is related to many diseases. Because alcohol travels though the body in the bloodstream, it comes in contact with every organ, directly or indirectly affecting every part of the body. Factors related to the severity of damage include an individual's genetic vulnerability, the frequency and duration of drinking, and the severity and spacing of binges (Gutjahr, Gmel, & Rehm, 2001). Alcohol is high in calories and, therefore, heavy drinkers often reduce their food intake or, alternatively, experience increased body fat and weight gain (the "beer belly"). Not only are these calories of little nutritional value, but alcohol also interferes with the absorption of nutrients in food that is eaten. Consequently, severe malnutrition and related tissue damage can result. Prolonged alcohol use, with concomitant reduced protein intake, is damaging to the endocrine glands, the pancreas, and especially the liver. Alcohol has also been associated with cancers of the mouth, tongue, pharynx, larynx,

esophagus, stomach, liver, lung, pancreas, colon, and rectum. Finally, the effects of alcohol and nicotine are compounded to increase cancers of the oral region (Gunzerath, Faden, Zakhari, & Warren, 2004; Longnecker, 1994).

Heavy alcohol use has been associated with damage to the heart muscle (cardiomyopathy), high blood pressure, and strokes. On the other hand, there is consistent evidence that moderate alcohol consumption is related to a lower incidence of coronary heart disease. This finding has prompted discussions of a possible protective factor. The suggestion is that consuming one to two drinks of alcohol per day may raise HDL cholesterol ("good cholesterol"), which in turn increases blood flow through the coronary vessels (Di Castelnuovo et al., 2006).

It has been a popular belief that consumption of alcohol permanently kills brain cells, and research has demonstrated that the brains of individuals who abuse alcohol demonstrate tissue reduction, particularly in the hypothalamus and thalamus. One result of this is **Wernicke-Korsakoff syndrome,** a chronic disease characterized by an inability to form new memories and a loss of contact with reality. However, research is conflicting and there is some evidence of brain axon regrowth in the cortex following an extended period of abstinence (Bates, Bowden, & Barry, 2002).

FETAL ALCOHOL SPECTRUM DISORDER The relationship between maternal drinking and birth defects was first called **fetal alcohol syndrome (FAS)** in 1973, and described a pattern of facial dysmorphology, growth retardation, and CNS dysfunction (Jones & Smith, 1973). More broadly, the varieties of impact resulting from exposure to prenatal alcohol fall under the umbrella term *fetal alcohol spectrum disorder* (FASD) and include FAS, partial FAS, alcohol-related neurodevelopmental disorder, and alcohol-related birth defects (see Chapter 14).

SOCIAL EFFECTS OF ALCOHOL MISUSE In a general survey conducted by Statistics Canada (Health Canada, 2010a), respondents (ages 15+) were asked whether their drinking had adversely affected their friendships and social life, physical health, happiness, financial situation, home life or marriage, work or studies, legal situation, learning abilities, or housing in the previous 12 months. About 5.7 percent of individuals reported at least one of these harms in the past year, with men being more than twice as likely as women to report harm. These data illustrate some of the direct social consequences of alcohol abuse.

According to a Canadian Centre for Substance Abuse study (Rehm, Baliunas, Brochu, Sarnocinska-Hart, & Taylor, 2006), alcohol use costs Canadians a staggering $14.6 billion a year in increased health care, law enforcement, and reduced productivity (see Table 11.5 for a breakdown of the ways in which alcohol, tobacco, and illicit drugs impose costs on the Canadian economy). This cost has likely increased since 2002; For instance, the cost of hospitalizations alone for substance use disorders in 2011 was an estimated $267 million, over half of which was from alcohol (Young, & Jesseman, 2014).

TABLE 11.5   THE SOCIAL COSTS OF TOBACCO, ALCOHOL, AND ILLEGAL DRUGS IN CANADA, 2002

	(in millions of dollars)			
	Tobacco	Alcohol	Illegal drugs	Total TAD
1. Direct health care costs: total	**4360.2**	**3306.2**	**1134.6**	**8800.9**
1.1 Morbidity:				
acute care hospitalization	2551.2	1458.6	426.37	4436.2
psychiatric hospitals	—	19.6	11.5	31.2
1.2 inpatient specialized treatment	—	754.9	352.1	1107.1
1.3 outpatient specialized treatment	—	52.4	56.3	108.7
1.4 ambulatory care: physician fees	142.2	80.2	22.6	245.0
1.5 family physician visit	306.3	172.8	48.8	527.9
1.6 prescription drugs	1360.5	767.6	216.8	2344.9
2. Direct law enforcement costs	**—**	**3072.2**	**2335.5**	**5407.8**
2.1 police	—	1,898.8	1432.0	3330.7
2.2 courts	—	513.1	330.6	843.7
2.3 corrections (including probation)	—	660.4	573.0	1233.4
3. Direct costs for prevention and research	**78.1**	**53.0**	**16.5**	**147.6**
3.1 research	9.0	17.3	8.6	34.9
3.2 prevention programs	69.1	33.9	7.9	110.9
3.3 salaries and operating funds	—	1.8	—	1.8
4. Other direct costs	**87.0**	**996.1**	**79.1**	**1162.2**
4.1 fire damage	86.5	156.5	—	243.0
4.2 traffic accident damage	—	756.9	67.0	823.9
4.3 losses associated with the workplace	0.5	17.0	6.6	24.1
4.3.1 EAP & health promotion programs	0.5	17.0	4.2	21.7
4.3.2. drug testing in the workplace	N/A	—	2.4	2.4
4.4 administrative costs for transfer payments	0.0	65.8	5.4	71.3
4.4.1 social welfare and other programs	—	4.3	—	4.3
4.4.2. workers' compensation	—	61.5	5.4	66.9
5. Indirect costs: productivity losses	**12 470.9**	**7126.4**	**4678.6**	**24 275.9**
5.1 due to long-term disability	10 536.8	6,163.9	4408.4	21 109.1
5.2 due to short-term disability (days in bed)	24.4	15.9	21.8	62.0
5.3 due to short-term disability (days with reduced activity)	36.2	23.6	0.1	59.8
5.4 due to premature mortality	1873.5	923.0	248.5	3045.0
Total	**16 996.2**	**14 554.0**	**8244.3**	**39 794.4**
Total per capita (in $)	**541**	**463**	**262**	**1267**
Total as % of all substance-related costs	**42.7**	**36.6**	**20.7**	**100.0**

TAD: Tobacco, Alcohol, and Illegal Drugs; N/A: not applicable "–": not available; EAP: Employee Assistance Programs

Categories in italics are sub-categories of immediate prior category.

Source: Reproduced with permission from the Canadian Centre on Substance Use and Addiction.

In particular, drinking and driving has been recognized as a major social problem. It is estimated that in 2002, 8100 Canadians lost their lives as a result of alcohol consumption. The largest alcohol-related cause of death was liver cirrhosis, followed by motor vehicle accidents and suicide. In addition, there were an estimated 196 000 hospital admissions related to alcohol, the largest number being caused by accidental falls, followed by alcohol dependence and motor vehicle accidents.

ETIOLOGY

The average age at which Canadians start drinking is 14.8 years and has gradually increased over the past two decades (Boak et al., 2015). Alcohol is advertised on television and radio, and in magazines. It is available in every community, and we are encouraged to imbibe at most social gatherings. There is no stigma attached to drinking alcohol; in fact, people are often pressed to explain why they are abstaining. With such extensive social influence, why do only some people become dependent on alcohol, while others do not? There has been extensive research into the etiology and maintenance of alcohol use disorder, and many of these theories have been adopted for other types of substance use disorders, so some generalization is possible.

GENETIC FACTORS It is an accepted fact that alcohol use disorders run in families but, as we have seen in other chapters (see Chapter 4), this does not disentangle the genetic and environmental influences. Twin studies have confirmed that male monozygotic twins are more similar than dizygotic twins in their tendencies to develop problems with alcohol abuse and dependence (Agrawal & Lynskey, 2008). The concordance rate for male monozygotic twins has been found to range from 26 to 77% across studies, compared to a range of 12 to 54% for male dizygotic twins (McGue, 1999). The results for studies of females are more variable, with about half of the available studies showing a significant genetic effect. The concordance rate for female monozygotic twins has been found to range from 25 to 32%, compared to a range of 5 to 24% for female dizygotic twins (McGue, 1999). However, these studies fall prey to the criticisms mentioned in Chapter 4. Adoption studies (also explained in Chapter 4) show a similar pattern of consistent results for men but variable results for women (Gelernter & Kranzler, 2009).

Twin and adoption studies provide evidence for a genetic contribution to the development of alcohol disorders, particularly for men, but what exactly is inherited? Given the complexity of alcohol problems, it is unlikely that only one or two of the up to 100 000 genes composing humans are responsible. Instead, it is likely that multiple genes and patterns of genes are important. Research has focused on genes involved in the sensitivity of receptor sites for a number of neurotransmitters that form part of the reward system of the brain. Genes associated with the GABAergic, dopaminergic, glutamatergic, serotonergic, opioid, and cholinergic systems have been implicated in the susceptibility to alcohol dependence (Gilpin & Koob, 2008). However, the relationship between these systems and alcohol use is complex, and precisely how environmental factors moderate these genetic susceptibilities still needs to be understood.

Another genetic factor that may be involved in alcohol use disorders is the ability to metabolize alcohol. Alcohol is broken down in the liver into a by-product called acetaldehyde, which is further broken down by the enzyme aldehyde dehydrogenase. If acetaldehyde builds up, it causes serious illness. In certain individuals—particularly those of Asian descent—aldehyde dehydrogenase seems to be absent, resulting in unpleasant physiological responses including cutaneous flushing (i.e., facial flushing) and palpitations, perspiration, and headache. These effects provide a biological upper limit on alcohol consumption, which reduces the risk for development of alcohol abuse (Iyer-Eimerbrink & Nurnberger, 2014).

It is important to note that being a son or daughter of someone with an alcohol use disorder does not predetermine

having the disorder personally. Although vulnerable, many such offspring do not develop alcohol problems and many people with alcohol use disorders do not have affected parents. Undoubtedly, environmental factors and personal choice play significant roles in the development or avoidance of problems with alcohol.

NEUROBIOLOGICAL INFLUENCES Biological marker studies attempt to show that alcohol use disorder is inherited by establishing an association between it and other inherited characteristics (see also discussions of linkage analysis in Chapters 8 and 9). Biological processes of individuals with alcohol use disorder, of non-problem drinkers, and of children of both are compared to determine markers of vulnerability to alcohol. One such marker is brain wave activity that can be measured by electroencephalographic (EEG) techniques. Sons and daughters of alcohol dependent fathers have more elevation of resting-state beta wave activity than do children of non-affected fathers (Rangaswamy et al., 2004). Evoked potentials have also been implicated. These are brief changes in EEG responses to external stimuli, such as flashes of light or loud sounds. The P300 response occurs about 300 milliseconds after the presentation of a stimulus and is believed to indicate an individual's attentional abilities. Sons and daughters of parents with alcohol use disorder consistently show smaller P300 amplitudes elicited in a variety of tasks than do offspring of non-alcoholic parents (Hill & Steinhauer, 1993; Iacono, Malone, & McGue, 2003). A similar pattern was found in individuals with alcohol use disorder who were no longer drinking (Porjesz & Begleiter, 1997). Importantly, longitudinal studies show that a reduced P300 response predicts the early onset of alcohol problems (Hill, Shen, Lowers, & Locke, 2000). Taken together, these findings suggest that beta activity and P300 amplitude reflect heritable components for risk of alcohol abuse and are appropriate vulnerability markers.

Neurotransmitters such as GABA (gamma-aminobutyric acid), beta-endorphin, and serotonin are other potential markers for alcohol use disorders. For example, low levels of serotonin have been associated with alcohol-related characteristics such as impulsivity, aggression, antisocial behaviour, reward processing, and alcohol craving in both animals and humans (Hayes & Grenshaw, 2011). However, serotonin operates in a complex manner, with more processes involved than simply serotonin level; these include sensitivity and density of receptors, variation in rate of metabolism and reuptake of serotonin in the synaptic cleft, dietary intake of amino acids, and the cell's recent firing history (Neumeister et al., 2006). Serotonin is not yet a practical marker for alcohol use disorder, in part because serotonin levels are difficult to measure (Tabakoff & Hoffman, 1991), and its precise role in addiction is still being determined.

In addition to neurological influences, heart rate related to the consumption of alcohol has also been studied. Men with relatives who have alcohol use disorder show larger increases in heart rate (Finn, Zeitouni, & Pihl, 1990). In addition, those with the greatest increases in heart rate were more inclined to drink alcohol regularly (Pihl & Peterson, 1991). It has been suggested that heart rate increase is a measure of sensitivity to the stimulating properties of alcohol, and may be viewed as an index of reward (Brunelle et al., 2004).

Although each of the aforementioned biological markers has shown interesting relationships to alcohol use disorder, none has so far been found clinically useful in diagnosing substance abuse or in predicting which individuals will grow up to have alcohol problems. Like the genetic factors discussed earlier, at the present time, these biological markers might be considered indications of a vulnerability and merit further investigation.

PSYCHOLOGICAL FACTORS While one clear profile of an addictive personality has not been established, certain personality characteristics seem to be associated with alcohol use disorder. The strongest association is with the trait of **behavioural disinhibition**. People with alcohol-use problems tend to have greater difficulty inhibiting behavioural impulses (McGue, 1999; Lawrence, Luty, Bogdan, Sahakian, & Clark, 2009); They tend to be more rebellious, more impulsive, more aggressive, and more willing to take risks than individuals without alcohol problems. The severity of the alcohol abuse also appears to be positively associated with the level of impaired inhibitory control over behaviour (Lawrence et al., 2009). These differences predate the onset of the alcohol problems and have been observed as early as age three (Caspi, Moffit, Newman, & Silva, 1996). Interestingly, behavioural disinhibition may be related to serotonin deficiency (Sachs et al., 2013), which, as we mentioned earlier, might be a vulnerability marker for alcohol-use problems.

A second trait that has been shown to be associated with alcoholism is **negative emotionality** or neuroticism. Negative emotionality is the tendency to experience psychological distress, anxiety, and depression. Research shows that affected individuals are more likely to have this tendency than are non-affected individuals (McGue, Slutske, & Iacono, 1999). However, longitudinal data do not provide evidence that this tendency predates the onset of alcohol use and subsequent alcohol problems (Chassin, Flora, & King, 2004). One study found that negative emotionality was associated with a more rapid escalation to alcohol-use problems among adolescents following the onset of drinking (Colder, Campbell, Ruel, Richardson, & Flay, 2002). Negative emotionality appears more likely to be a consequence of alcohol use disorder (Sher, Trull, Bartholow, & Vieth, 1999) than a risk factor.

Several theories have been proposed to explain alcohol misuse. The **tension-reduction**, or anxiety-relief, hypothesis suggests that drinking is reinforced by its ability to reduce tension, anxiety, anger, depression, and other unpleasant emotions. However, support for this hypothesis is inconsistent, probably because alcohol has variable effects on tension, depending on how much is consumed, and only certain individuals experience stress reduction after ingesting alcohol. It also appears that the subjective effects of alcohol depend largely on the expectancies of the drinker.

These expectancies begin to develop in childhood by observing adult drinking behaviours and media portrayals of positive alcohol-related experiences. While tension reduction is a factor in problem drinking for many people, it does not explain all problem drinking behaviour (Young, Oei, & Knight, 1990). The **alcohol expectancy theory** proposes that drinking behaviour is largely determined by the reinforcement that an individual expects to receive from it. Among the expectancies identified by a group of social drinkers were that alcohol positively transforms experiences, enhances both social and physical pleasure and sexual performance and experience, increases power and aggression, alters personal characteristics and improves social skill, and reduces tension (Goldman, Del Boca, & Darkes, 1999). Nevertheless, most of these subjective experiences are a function of expectation and attitude and not a drug effect. In fact, alcohol's pharmacological effects can have the opposite effect of expectation in regard to tension reduction, mood, sexual performance, and social skills.

In support of the expectancy theory, priming positive alcohol expectancies has been found to increase subsequent alcohol consumption in heavy drinkers (Stein, Goldman, & Del Boca, 2000). Additionally, individuals with alcohol-use disorder and heavy social drinkers are more likely than non-problem drinkers to believe that alcohol use will result in positive outcomes (Leeman, Kulesza, Stewart, & Copeland, 2012). Longitudinal research with adolescents also supports the impact of alcohol expectancy on future drinking behaviour; Positive expectancies of alcohol effects predict higher levels of subsequent alcohol use (Smith, Goldman, Greenbaum, & Christiansen, 1995).

Learning and experience also play a role in the development of tolerance for alcohol and other drugs. Dr. Shep Siegel from McMaster University originated a line of research that demonstrated that drug tolerance is partially conditioned to the environment in which the substance is used. Traditionally, tolerance was considered to be related entirely to biological process, a cellular adaptation to the substance. Using animal models, Siegel and others demonstrated that through the principles of classical conditioning, cues in the environment can become conditioned stimuli to the effects of drug use. These cues cause the individual to anticipate the drug effects so that when the drug is actually administered the effects are diminished. Over time, as conditioning continues, the drug effects diminish to a greater extent. Tolerance, or the need for a greater amount of drug for the same effect, is greatest when the conditioned environmental cues are present. This **behavioural tolerance** effect accounts for the observation that heroin addicts can use a larger amount of heroin in their typical environment (where tolerance is greatest) but can fatally overdose when they use the same amount in a novel environment (Siegel, 2016).

SOCIO-CULTURAL FACTORS Alcohol use is influenced by social and cultural factors such as family values, attitudes, and expectations that have been passed on from generation to generation. It seems that people who are introduced to drinking as a rite of passage in an environment in which excessive drinking is socially accepted (and, indeed, encouraged by peer pressure) face an increased risk of developing alcohol problems. In some subcultures, an individual's use of chemicals is seen as a sign of maturity, and this adolescent peer subculture may encourage repeated episodes of substance abuse. Social learning also influences expectancies and, as we have seen, individuals with positive expectancies are most likely to be the heaviest drinkers. Cultural and familial traditions and attitudes toward alcohol use combine to influence the individuals' expectations of the effects of alcohol and their drinking patterns.

Evidence for cultural influence on drinking patterns can be found in comparisons of alcohol problems in different countries. While the consumption of alcohol is worldwide, the patterns of alcohol abuse differ from country to country. In France, where daily drinking is common, individuals with alcohol use disorder are usually steady drinkers who rarely show a loss of control and are prone to physical disorders rather than social disruptions. Although daily drinking is also acceptable in Italy, drinking is usually restricted to mealtime and consumption is limited, and there is a much lower rate of disorder there than in France. In England, Ireland, and North America, problems are often manifested by bouts of extremely heavy drinking and often associated with loss of control and disastrous social consequences. In Muslim countries, where consumption of alcohol is discouraged on religious grounds, alcohol misuse may be limited (Karam, Maalouf, & Ghandour, 2004).

Drinking patterns in the home also influence an individual's use of alcohol. Adolescents' drinking tends to mirror that of their parents. If parents use alcohol to cope with stressful situations or associate heavy drinking with celebration, children will likely adopt the same attitudes. In general,

episodic heavy drinking in parents predicts earlier and heavier adolescent drinking (Vermeulen-Smit et al., 2012). A longitudinal study of alcohol experiences among Canadian adolescents found that the perceived intensity of parental drinking predicted adolescent alcohol use one year later (Van Der Vorst et al., 2013). However, one longitudinal study found no clear link between parental drinking during childhood and drinking behaviour nine years later (Van Damme et al., 2015). Children of parents who drink no alcohol also tend to the extremes of drinking behaviour, either drinking heavily or not at all (Lawson, Peterson, & Lawson, 1983).

The exact etiology of alcohol use disorder has yet to be resolved, but many researchers agree that it is a multidetermined disorder influenced by biological, psychological, and sociological factors. Evidence for a genetic contribution to the development of alcohol use disorder is strong, but it cannot explain why some people with family histories of alcohol problems do not develop drinking problems. Nor does it account for the fact that most of the people who develop these disorders do not have family histories of these problems. Individuals develop expectations about alcohol, must choose to use alcohol, and decide on the way it will be used. The individual with biological and/or psychological vulnerabilities may respond to social influences and personal stressors in a manner that promotes the development of drinking problems. Different combinations of risk factors and environmental liabilities create multiple paths to the development of alcohol use disorders.

TREATMENT

Alcohol and other drug abuse have probably been around for as long as the drugs themselves. Early admonitions against the overuse of alcohol were of a moral nature, and those who

---

Robert Downey Jr.

Robert John Downey Jr. is a Golden Globe Award–winning and Academy Award–nominated actor who also became infamous for a period of alcohol and other drug abuse during the 1990s. Although he continued his acting career during that time, he was frequently in the news for drug-related incidents that led to arrest, incarceration, and mandated substance abuse treatment. Downey relapsed often and dramatically. In 1999 he explained to a judge: "It's like I have a loaded gun in my mouth and my finger's on the trigger, and I like the taste of the gunmetal" (Reaves, 2001). Over the years, Downey has appeared in more than 70 movies and on various television shows, including *Saturday Night Live*. He has also been arrested on numerous occasions, spent a year in state prison, and is well known for falling asleep in his neighbour's bed while under the influence. In 2001, he was fired from the popular television show *Ally McBeal* after being arrested while on parole for suspicion of being under the influence of drugs. A newly established drug court mandated treatment and

Junji Kurokawa/AP Photo/CP Images

probation for Downey, instead of incarceration. Since then, he says he is drug-free and has garnered acclaim for his leading role in the popular *Iron Man* movies. He attributes his recovery to family therapy, 12-step programs, meditation, yoga, and kung fu (Wilde, 2003).

lacked the fortitude to resist temptation were punished. A more liberal view of alcohol and other drug use arose during the Second World War, when many soldiers engaged in substance abuse. A number of treatment approaches have been developed for alcohol use disorder, each with its own proponents and some evidence of effectiveness. In Canada, there are just over 1000 treatment programs. The differing patterns of alcohol abuse suggest that there are various contributors to alcohol use disorder, and it may be that some treatments, or combination of treatments, are better suited for some people under some conditions. Over the past

25 years, there has been a move toward the use of outpatient treatments from the routine use of the standardized 28-day inpatient program. However, efforts to identify specifically which type of individual does best in which type of approach have met with limited success. Generally, treatments are focused on abstinence, meaning that they help the person to stop drinking completely (see Focus box 11.3).

RESIDENTIAL TREATMENT: THE MINNESOTA MODEL
The most common residential treatment for alcohol use disorder is a multimodal approach advocating a 12-step

FOCUS 11.3 Non-abstinence Drinking Goals in Treatment

Originally, controlled-drinking research was used to test the critical hypotheses of the popular disease concept of alcoholism (Pattison, Sobell, & Sobell, 1977). Mark and Linda Sobell (researchers who worked for many years at the Centre for Addiction and Mental Health in Toronto) studied a program for teaching alcoholics to drink in moderation in comparison with an abstinence-oriented program similar to Alcoholics Anonymous (Sobell & Sobell, 1973, 1976). Participants in the study were 40 male alcoholics in a treatment program who were thought to have a good prognosis. Overall results over more than two years of follow-up indicated that individuals in the controlled-drinking group were functioning well for 85 percent of the days, as compared to 42 percent of the days for the abstinence group.

These results were challenged in a subsequent paper. Pendery, Maltzman, and West (1982) reported that they had contacted the men in the Sobell study 10 years later and found that only one of the men in the controlled-drinking group continued to maintain a pattern of controlled drinking; four had died from alcohol-induced problems. This re-evaluation made headlines. The Sobells were charged with scientific misconduct and ethical violations. However, these charges were later refuted by several independent investigative committees. Pendery and colleagues (1982) had not provided follow-up data on the abstinence group—who, it turned out, had fared no better than the controlled-drinking group. This controversy has created lasting mistrust between proponents and opponents of controlled-drinking programs.

A number of other lines of evidence point to the viability of non-abstinence treatment goals for some people with alcohol use problems (Hodgins, 2005). First, as early as the 1940s, follow-up studies of alcoholics have revealed that a proportion of patients, albeit a small group, describe successful and sustained non-abstinence outcomes over follow-up periods of one to eight years (Ambrogne, 2002). The most widely cited of these studies is the Rand report from the mid-1980s that provided a follow-up of a large national U.S. sample of patients from abstinence-oriented inpatient alcohol treatment programs. Remarkably, about 18 percent of patients were described as drinking moderately and problem-free after four years (Polich, Armor, & Braiker, 1981).

Second, patient characteristics have been found to predict success with non-abstinence outcomes. These include younger age, relatively better social and psychological stability, employment, being female, having less severe alcohol dependence, and

having a stronger belief in one's ability to moderate drinking (Saladin & Santa Ana, 2004). Individuals who self-select non-abstinence programs also tend to have fewer alcohol-related problems and symptoms of dependence (Humphreys & Klaw, 2001). Humphreys (2003) argues that groups such as Moderation Management, which allow goal choice, extend the traditional treatment system by attracting people who would not attend traditional treatment. Allowing a choice of goals within treatment systems may be one effective way to increase the numbers of people willing to enter alcohol treatment. It is estimated that as few as 10 percent of individuals with alcohol use disorders attend treatment. More flexibility in goals may appeal to a wider range of people with alcohol use disorders.

Most professionals advise that abstinence is the appropriate treatment goal for drinkers who have had a long history of heavy drinking, where drinking has come to be a pervasive and integral part of their lifestyle, or for those who have suffered serious consequences. However, if they are unwilling to accept abstinence as a treatment goal, they may benefit from treatment aimed at harm reduction (Addiction Research Foundation, 1992).

What are the implications of assuming the "wrong" goal for an individual? A small group of treatment studies have randomly assigned individuals to either abstinence or non-abstinence drinking goals (Adamson & Sellman, 2001; Ambrogne, 2002). These studies comparing drinking goals do not find differences in outcome, which suggests that it is not harmful to allow individuals to attempt to moderate their drinking instead of abstaining. Ambrogne (2002) identified 12 studies that consistently found that some patients were able to sustain non–problematic drinking after treatment over follow-up periods of one to eight years. In fact, there may be an advantage to allowing patients to make their own goal choice. Goals change over time, and treatment can provide experiences that will encourage patients to reconsider and revise their initial goals. In one Canadian study that allowed goal choice among people with severe alcohol dependence, participants choosing moderation initially tended to change their goal to abstinence over time, presumably as a result of lack of success with moderation (Hodgins, Leigh, Milne, & Gerrish, 1997). Choice of abstinence with this group of patients ultimately predicted better outcome at one-year follow-up. In short, the appropriateness of a goal will declare itself over time, and usually in short order. ●

Alcoholics Anonymous philosophy. This model views alcohol use disorder as a disease and is termed the **Minnesota model** because it was popularized by the well-known Hazelden treatment program in that state. For people who show signs of withdrawal, treatment begins in a hospital or detoxification clinic under medical supervision, and often includes prescription drugs. Following detoxification treatment for the physical dependence, treatment of the psychological dependence begins. This component includes education about the consequences of alcohol use and abuse, individual counselling for psychological issues, and group therapy to improve interpersonal skills. Abstinence is the goal, since it is assumed that people with the alcoholism "disease" will never be able to drink in a controlled way. Participants are usually required to attend Alcoholics Anonymous meetings and encouraged to keep going after treatment to address the danger of relapse. Despite the popularity of the Minnesota model, the effectiveness of the approach has not been rigorously evaluated.

PHARMACOTHERAPY Medication has been used in the treatment of alcohol use disorder to assist in detoxification, to reduce the pleasurable effects associated with drinking, and to produce nausea when alcohol is consumed. To make detoxification more bearable, benzodiazepines (tranquilizers) have been administered to alcoholics as a first step in treatment. Since these medications mimic some of the effects of alcohol, they minimize the effects of withdrawal. Doses are gradually decreased as withdrawal symptoms abate.

Medication can also be prescribed as a method of reducing the immediate gratification that accompanies drinking. Naltrexone, an opioid **antagonist drug**, targets the neurotransmitters that mediate alcohol's effects on the brain and "blocks" the pleasurable effects of alcohol. In addition, it helps to reduce the sensation of craving. Studies have shown that naltrexone, in combination with psychosocial treatment, does help some alcohol abusers abstain from alcohol use, particularly those who are finding it difficult to initiate abstinence (Killeen et al., 2004; Chick et al., 2000). Acamprosate is another drug that can be used to reduce craving for alcohol and to reduce distress during early abstinence. It is an **agonist drug** that facilitates the inhibitory action of the neurotransmitter GABA at its receptors. Studies conducted in Europe show that use of Acamprosate in combination with psychosocial treatment doubles the number of people who are successfully abstainers (Swift, 2003). A meta-analysis of acamprosate and naltrexone effectiveness suggested that acamprosate may be particularly effective in abstinence treatment while naltrexone may be more effective with controlled drinking (Carmet, Angeles, Ana, & María, 2004). These medications have the potential to play an important adjunctive role in alcohol treatment. However, success depends on the compliance of the individual, which has been a significant concern with these drugs.

Another medication approach is to make the experience of drinking extremely aversive. **Antabuse** (disulfiram) blocks the action of the metabolizing enzyme acetaldehyde dehydrogenase, resulting in a buildup of acetaldehyde in the body. Like people who naturally lack this enzyme, people who drink alcohol after taking Antabuse experience increased heart rate, nausea, vomiting, and other unpleasant effects. Patients are instructed to take the medication each morning, before the desire to drink becomes overwhelming. The goal is to deter the individual from drinking, but once again compliance is a major hurdle. It is common to have a family member administer Antabuse to the affected individual as part of a treatment program. This approach has the added advantage of helping the family member regain trust in the individual's resolve to not drink.

MUTUAL SUPPORT GROUPS

Alcoholics Anonymous. Alcoholics Anonymous (AA) works with more alcoholics worldwide than any other treatment organization. AA does not use professionally trained staff; it is a self-help group, "a fellowship of men and women who share their experience, strength, and hope with each other that they may solve their common problem and help others to recover from alcoholism" (AA Grapevine, Inc., New York, cited in Rivers, 1994, p. 268). AA got its start in 1935 in a popular Protestant religious following, the Oxford Movement. The movement, dedicated to redeeming humankind through striving for absolute good, consisted of small groups that met weekly for prayer, worship, and discussion. Two members, physician Dr. Bob and stockbroker Bill W. had been trying unsuccessfully to quit drinking, and found the fellowship of the group helpful. They invited more and more problematic drinkers into the group, and when the meetings became too large, they broke away and founded Alcoholics Anonymous.

The AA treatment is based on a disease model, and the goal is complete abstinence. AA members believe that there is no cure for alcoholism; there are only alcoholics who drink and alcoholics who do not drink (in recovery). They believe that they are powerless to control their drinking and must rely on a "Higher Power" to help them. Members are encouraged to attend meetings often and regularly, as social support is central to the program, and to follow the "12 steps" of recovery (see Table 11.6). Members who have stayed sober for a period of time serve as sponsors for newcomers. There are more than 65 000 AA groups in the United States and Canada, and more than 100 000 meetings are held each week all over the world. Many of the groups comprise specific types of individuals such as women, LGBTQ, smokers, non-smokers, and so forth. Active members will often attend more than one group in addition to their "home" group.

AA is an effective treatment for some, and many people credit it with saving their lives. Others find it difficult to embrace because of its reliance on spirituality and its adoption of the disease model. Only a few research evaluations of AA's effectiveness exist, mostly observing the effects when attendance is coerced (e.g., legally mandated by the courts or employers). Results have not been favourable, although

TABLE 11.6 THE 12 STEPS OF ALCOHOLICS ANONYMOUS

1. We admitted we were powerless over alcohol—that our lives had become unmanageable.
2. Came to believe that a Power greater than ourselves could restore us to sanity.
3. Made a decision to turn our will and our lives over to the care of God as we understood Him.
4. Made a searching and fearless moral inventory of ourselves.
5. Admitted to God, to ourselves, and to another human being the exact nature of our wrongs.
6. Were entirely ready to have God remove all these defects of character.
7. Humbly asked Him to remove our shortcomings.
8. Made a list of all persons we had harmed, and became willing to make amends to them all.
9. Made direct amends to such people wherever possible, except when to do so would injure them or others.
10. Continued to take personal inventory and when we were wrong promptly admitted it.
11. Sought through prayer and meditation to improve our conscious contact with God as we understood Him, praying only for knowledge of His will for us and the power to carry that out.
12. Having had a spiritual awakening as the result of these steps, we tried to carry this message to alcoholics, and to practice these principles in all our affairs.

Source: The Twelve Steps and Twelve Traditions. Used by permission from Alcoholics Anonymous World Services, Inc.

the intent of AA is that attendance is voluntary (McCrady, Horvath, & Delaney, 2003). Follow-up studies of alcoholics post-treatment show that those who choose to attend AA have better outcomes than those who do not attend. More rigorous evaluation has been conducted on 12-step facilitation, which involves the use of professionals in encouraging AA attendance with positive results (McCrady et al., 2003).

A number of mutual support groups have been developed to support individuals who do not affiliate with the spiritual aspect of the AA groups. These groups emphasize personal responsibility and rationality as important in recovery. Women for Sobriety and SMART Recovery (Self-Management and Recovery Training) support abstinence from alcohol and other drugs. Moderation Management helps individuals to moderate their drinking versus stopping completely.

PSYCHOLOGICAL TREATMENTS

Behavioural Treatment. The behavioural approach treats problem drinking as a learned behaviour. Alcohol, an unconditioned stimulus, elicits unconditioned responses in the form of pleasant physical reactions. Alcohol becomes associated with these pleasant responses (see Chapter 2 for an explanation of conditioning theory). Therefore, some

behavioural interventions attempt to condition an aversive response to alcohol by pairing alcohol with an unpleasant stimulus. For example, the sight, smell, and taste of alcohol may be presented while the alcoholic is nauseated and vomiting as a result of taking an emetic drug. Theoretically, over time the sensation of nausea should be elicited by the presence of alcohol without the emetic drug (a conditioned response), and the previously positive associations with drinking become negative. Even though a number of theoretically sound procedures have been used, aversion therapy alone has had limited success, although it can be combined with other treatments (Costello, 1975; Nietzel, Winett, Macdonald, & Davidson, 1977).

Other behavioural treatments are based on operant conditioning principles (see Chapter 2). *Contingency management* has been used to manipulate reinforcement contingencies for alcohol use. Contracts between patients and treatment programs may be established that specify rewards (or punishments) contingent on small steps toward sobriety. Contingency management appears to help clients maintain abstinence, and thus, may enhance the effectiveness of treatment (Prendergast, Podus, Finney, Greenwell, & Roll, 2006). A more comprehensive operant program is the Community Reinforcement Approach (CRA; Azrin, 1976). A spouse, friend, or relative who is not a substance user is recruited to participate in the program; both participants learn behavioural coping skills and how to develop contingency contracts. They learn to identify antecedents to drinking, the circumstances in which drinking is most likely, social reinforcers, and the consequences of drinking. They are also taught how to arrange reinforcement contingencies to reward sobriety rather than reinforce drinking. Finally, this comprehensive intervention program also helps alcoholics to develop new recreational options that do not involve alcohol and reduce stress through improvements in practical areas of life, such as employment, finances, and education.

Behavioural self-management is a treatment approach that teaches people with alcohol use disorder to manage their own drinking through behavioural contracting, restructuring of thoughts about drinking, and having individuals recognize the patterns in their drinking. This approach has been offered in groups, in individual format, and in the form of self-help workbooks. It has strong research support, particularly for individuals with less severe alcohol problems (Miller, Wilbourne, & Hettema, 2003), and it has been used with the goals of both complete abstinence and moderated drinking.

Relapse Prevention. Whether the goal of treatment for alcohol use disorder is complete abstinence or moderated drinking, the long-term results of most programs are disappointing. Most treated individuals eventually relapse and develop problems with alcohol again. Relapse prevention treatment aims to avoid relapses if possible, and to manage a relapse if and when it occurs (Marlatt & Gordon, 1985). **Relapse** is seen as a failure of a person's cognitive and behavioural coping skills to cope with life's problems. Maladaptive behaviour is seen as a result of self-defeating thoughts and self-deception that can bring about "inadvertent" slips. Apparently innocent decisions based on distorted beliefs can chain together to create circumstances that increase the risk of drinking. The relapse prevention techniques attempt to help individuals identify these distorted beliefs and replace them with adaptive ones. High-risk situations are identified for each individual and strategies are developed to deal with them. For example, if a person has a history of drinking in response to interpersonal conflict, that person can be taught to recognize the early stages of an argument and talk issues over more calmly, or to leave and go for a walk before tensions mount too high. People are taught to view lapses not as overwhelming failures that will inevitably lead to more drinking, but as temporary occurrences brought on by a specific situation, from which a person can recover. Evaluations have shown relapse prevention to be useful in treating alcohol use disorder (Miller et al., 2003; Witkiewitz & Marlatt, 2004).

Marital and Family Therapy. An individual's pattern of substance abuse is unavoidably linked to close social relationships, though not necessarily caused by these relationships. In family and marital therapy, the relationship, rather than the problem drinker, is seen as the patient. Family therapy focuses on issues of interaction and the notion that a family unit attempts to maintain equilibrium. Established patterns of interaction and resistance to change can inadvertently support alcohol abuse by one member of the family. Family members may have established roles for themselves that are defined by the substance abuse and have become so enmeshed in the drinking problem that they actually prevent changes in the abuse pattern. Such people are described as *codependents*. Even if there is no codependency, marital conflict, such as spousal nagging about drinking, can stimulate bouts of heavy drinking.

In a family with someone with an alcohol use disorder, the alcohol abuse often overshadows other existing or potential problems. In a sense, the abuser becomes a scapegoat. When the individual stops drinking, other troubling issues might develop or become evident. For example, a potentially depressed spouse may manage the depression by dealing with the problem of an alcoholic spouse. When this diversion is no longer available, the depression may unfold. Children in such families often try to be "extra good" and supportive during the drinking phase, and may react to a parent's quitting by acting out. Family members may have reduced their communication because of fear of causing the alcoholic to become violent or drink more, and the communication may remain subdued after cessation of drinking. Each of these areas provides potential targets of therapeutic interventions in the families of alcoholics.

Behavioural marital therapies adapted for treatment of couples in which one partner has an alcohol problem are among the approaches with the strongest empirical support. This approach is focused on teaching communication skills and increasing the levels of positive reinforcement in the relationship. As with the CRA approach, the non-alcoholic partner is trained to reward sobriety rather than reinforce drinking.

BRIEF INTERVENTIONS Brief interventions are one to three sessions in length, offering time-limited and specific advice regarding the need to reduce or eliminate alcohol consumption. These interventions can be offered opportunistically in settings where the individual is seeking help for a related problem. For example, a family physician might raise the issue of alcohol use in patients with gastrointestinal problems or abnormal liver functioning tests, or an emergency room nurse may approach victims of motor vehicle accidents involving alcohol. Alternatively, brief interventions can be offered to individuals with "concerns" about their alcohol use but who are reluctant to seek more formal treatment. One such program, called the Drinker's Check-up, allows individuals to get feedback on their drinking behaviours. Of the treatment approaches for alcohol problems that have been empirically evaluated, brief interventions are among those that have the largest and strongest support.

Particularly effective are brief approaches that focus on the individual's motivation to make changes in his or her drinking (Miller et al., 2003). **Motivational interviewing** is an approach that can be used with clients who present with varying levels of readiness to change their behaviour. In a non-confrontational, accepting manner, the therapist helps the client to identify and freely discuss both the pros and cons of his or her alcohol use. Motivational interviewing is considered to be a client-centred, semi-directive technique wherein the therapist works to increase the client's awareness of the problems and create a discrepancy between behaviours and goals. The therapist supports the client's self-efficacy and autonomy to move toward change. Motivational interviewing can be used as part of brief interventions or as an adjunct for more comprehensive treatments.

 BEFORE MOVING ON

> What causes one person to develop an alcohol problem, while another does not?

Barbiturates and Benzodiazepines

There are a number of drugs considered to be **depressants** because they inhibit neurotransmitter activity in the CNS. We have seen that alcohol is one of these substances, although it was not developed for this purpose. In the DSM-5, the depressant drugs other than alcohol are grouped together as sedative, hypnotic, or anxiolytic drugs, based upon their typical prescribed use as sedatives, sleeping medications, and anti-anxiety medications. Barbituric acid, produced in 1903, was one of the first drugs developed as a treatment for anxiety and tension and later for sleep. Since then, there have been many derivatives of this sedative-hypnotic drug, including those with the brand names Seconal, Tuinal, Nembutal, and Fiorinal. Barbiturates were widely prescribed until the 1940s, when their addictive potential became known. Barbiturates are commonly known as "downers," or according to the colour of their brand name versions (e.g., "blues," "yellow jackets," and "red birds"). Now, another group of drugs belonging to the sedative-hypnotic class called benzodiazepines (e.g., Valium, Librium, Xanax, Ativan) are more frequently prescribed for sleep and anxiety problems. Although these are generally thought of as safer alternatives to barbiturates, they too can be addicting if misused. Barbiturates and benzodiazepines are odourless, white, crystalline compounds, usually taken as tablets or capsules. Long-acting forms are available for prolonged sedation. Shorter-acting versions, used to treat insomnia, are thought to be more addicting.

PREVALENCE

The prevalence of prescription tranquilizer use in Canada has remained stable since 2008, with approximately 10% of the general population, aged 15 years and older, reporting use of prescription sedatives. In 2015, 13.5% of women and 7.3% of men reported using sedatives in the preceding 12 months. Abuse of tranquilizers is also fairly low in Canada. In the same national survey, only 0.3% of Canadians reported abusing sedatives in the preceding 12 months. In a survey of Ontario high school students (Boak et al., 2015), non-medical use of tranquilizers (including benzodiazepines) was 1.3% for males and 3.0% for females.

EFFECTS

The effects of barbiturates and benzodiazepines are similar except that the anxiolytic effects of the benzodiazepines emerge at lower doses, making them the safer alternative. In small doses, these drugs cause mild euphoria. With larger doses, slurred speech, poor motor coordination, and impairment of judgment and concentration occur. Initially, users may be combative and argumentative, but the larger dosages eventually induce sleep. The behaviour observed at this dosage is similar to that seen in alcohol intoxication. In fact, DSM-5 criteria for sedative, hypnotic, or anxiolytic intoxication are very similar to those of alcohol intoxication. Because they depress CNS function, very large doses of barbiturates lower respiration, blood pressure, and heart rate to dangerous levels. The diaphragm muscles may relax excessively, causing suffocation. Coma is also a common outcome. Many people taking barbiturates and benzodiazepines are unaware that their effects are amplified when mixed with other drugs. As an example, the combination of barbiturates with alcohol causes a synergistic effect: the effect of the two drugs is greater than the effects of the sum of the two drugs taken separately. Alcohol greatly increases the sedative and toxic effects of the barbiturate—the effect that nearly killed Gareth in the chapter-opening case. This combination has led to many deaths, both accidental and suicidal.

Chronic use of barbiturates or benzodiazepines can cause what appears to be a constant state of alcohol intoxication. Long-term use causes depression, chronic fatigue, mood swings, and paranoia. It may also result in dramatic personality changes and serious impairments of memory and judgment.

DEPENDENCY

Tolerance to barbiturates develops rapidly. With regular use, increasingly higher doses are needed to achieve sedative effects. Tolerance to the benzodiazepines typically develops much more slowly than tolerance to barbiturates. A user with high tolerance to barbiturates or benzodiazepines attempting to abstain abruptly may experience extreme withdrawal reactions including delirium, convulsions, sleep disruptions, and other symptoms similar to those experienced with alcohol withdrawal.

TREATMENT

Treatment for sedative, hypnotic, or anxiolytic use disorders can be very complicated and may require prolonged hospitalization. Treatment usually involves administering progressively smaller doses of the abused drug to minimize withdrawal symptoms. Many individuals experience **abstinence syndrome**, which is characterized by insomnia, headaches, aching all over the body, anxiety, and depression; and which can last for months (Cambor & Millman, 1991). In addition to the pharmacological interventions, psychological and educational programs are usually advised to treat barbiturate dependency. Narcotics Anonymous mutual support groups, based on the same model as AA, have been set up in most large Canadian cities.

Stimulants

Stimulants are a class of drugs that have a stimulating or arousing effect on the CNS and create their effects by influencing the rate of uptake of the neurotransmitters dopamine, norepinephrine, and serotonin at receptor sites in the brain. The increased availability of these neurotransmitters affects the nucleus accumbens, which is a primary reward centre in the brain. As a group, stimulants are the most commonly used and abused drugs. They include tobacco, amphetamines, cocaine, and caffeine. Medications such as Ritalin and Adderal that are used to treat attention deficit disorder fall into this drug class. In the DSM-5, tobacco and caffeine are classed separately from the stimulants because their effects differ.

TOBACCO

Tobacco use (in the form of cigarettes, snuff, chewing tobacco, cigars, and pipes) constitutes one of the leading public health concerns in Canada. The number of Canadian deaths directly attributable to tobacco use is estimated to be approximately 21 percent of all deaths in the past decade (Statistics Canada, 2012b). This number includes adult smoking-related diseases (e.g., lung cancer and emphysema), childhood illness linked to maternal smoking (e.g., respiratory illness), and deaths due to smoking-related fires.

Smoking prevention and cessation programs have become a priority for national health campaigns. Moreover, society bears major costs related to tobacco use. As shown in Table 11.5, the costs to society related to tobacco are higher than the costs related to alcohol, and much higher than all costs related to illicit drugs.

Nicotine comes from the tobacco plant *Nicotiniana tabacum*, which is a member of the nightshade family. Indigenous to South America, it is now grown in many places throughout the world. In Canada, it was originally grown by the Petun, Neutral, and Huron tribes of southwestern Ontario, who introduced it to French settlers. These colonists began cultivating and trading tobacco as early as 1652. Commercial cultivation began in the 1800s, and Canada now ranks among the top 10 tobacco-producing countries.

PREVALENCE Smoking rates in Canada rose steadily in the 1900s, peaking in the mid-1960s. It is estimated that in 2015, 13% of Canadians over the age of 12 currently smoked cigarettes (Statistics Canada, 2012a). This represents a decline from 1965, when approximately 50% of Canadians smoked regularly, and from 2007, when 19% smoked. In 2010, 13% reported smoking daily, whereas 4% reported smoking occasionally. More males (20%) reported smoking than females (14%). Daily smokers smoked an average of 15.1 cigarettes per day. There are at present more Canadians who have quit smoking than there are current smokers. The decline in smoking over time is likely due to increasing tobacco prices, antismoking media campaigns, and smoking bans in public places such as restaurants, shopping malls, and buses (Wilson et al., 2012).

Of particular concern to public health officials are the rates of smoking among people under age 20, and efforts have been made to restrict cigarette ads that specifically target young people. The number of teen smokers rose in the 1990s but has been steadily declining since 1997. However, tobacco use is still common among Canadian youth. Data collected from the 2008 Canadian Youth Smoking Survey estimated that 18.1% of males and 12.8% of females in Grade 12 were tobacco users (Leatherdale & Burkhalter, 2011). Other high-risk groups for smoking include people with a lower formal education, blue-collar workers, and Indigenous Canadians. An estimated 59% of the First Nations population (Assembly of First Nations and First Nations Information Governance Committee, 2007) and 71% of the Inuit population smoke (First Nations and Inuit Health Branch, 2004).

EFFECTS Nicotine is a CNS stimulant related to the amphetamines. It is an extremely potent chemical and the ingestion of only a few drops, in its pure form, can cause respiratory failure. Lower dosages can interfere with thinking and problem solving, and can cause extreme agitation and irritability along with mood changes. However, the very small amount of nicotine present in a cigarette is not lethal and can increase alertness and improve mood. When inhaled, nicotine enters the lungs and reaches the brain in seconds. Similar to other addictive substances, it stimulates the release of dopamine in the nucleus accumbens. This is thought to contribute to its rewarding and addictive properties (Benowitz, 1990).

Although the short-term consequences of smoking are minimal, the long-term health risks associated with smoking are significant. Smoking has been implicated in the development of lung, esophagus, larynx, and other cancers; emphysema; respiratory illness; heart disease; and other chronic conditions. Most of these illnesses are caused by the carbon monoxide and other chemicals found in tobacco. Although many of the health risks associated with smoking can be minimized 5 to 10 years after a person quits, lung damage is often irreversible (Jaffe, 1995). The health hazards of second-hand (or passive) smoke can be even more dangerous. Because there is no filter for these substances, second-hand smoke contains greater concentrations of ammonia, carbon monoxide, nicotine, and tar than the smoke inhaled by the smoker. As a result, passive smoking is associated with significant health risks in non-smokers, including heart disease, lung cancer, and childhood asthma.

Smoking during pregnancy is associated with problems such as low birth weight, spontaneous abortion, stillbirth, and infant illness and disability. Women who smoke during pregnancy have double to triple the risk of having an underweight baby and 12 times the risk of delivering prematurely. An estimated 23 percent of women smoked during their last pregnancy (Cui, Shooshtari, Forget, Clara, & Cheung, 2014).

DEPENDENCY Dependence produced by nicotine is thought to be even greater than that produced by other addictive substances, including alcohol, cocaine, and caffeine (see Table 11.7; West, 2006). Nicotine dependence develops quickly, and although extremely large doses are required to produce intoxication, its behavioural effects are severe enough to classify many tobacco users as having a substance abuse disorder according to DSM-5 criteria. Smokers become addicted not only because of nicotine's mood-enhancing abilities, but to prevent the effects of withdrawal, which can be quite severe.

So, with smoking, we have a situation that is extremely conducive to dependence: heavy nicotine use does not cause intoxication or behavioural impairment, and it is legally available and relatively inexpensive. A person can smoke all day and avoid the severe withdrawal symptoms—a perfect recipe for addiction. People addicted to nicotine display behaviours much like those of other substance abusers: they often need a cigarette to start their day, they frequently smoke more than they anticipate, and they often spend a great deal of time looking for more cigarettes. Some smokers change their social plans to have continuous access to cigarettes. Furthermore, almost all smokers continue to smoke despite the knowledge that they are seriously damaging their health. There has been some suggestion that some people are more sensitive to the effects of nicotine on dopaminergic neurons, and thus become dependent more quickly (Morel et al., 2014). Certainly, people who begin to smoke when they are teenagers tend to be more dependent than those who start smoking in their twenties.

TABLE 11.7 RELATIVE ADDICTIVENESS OF COMMONLY USED SUBSTANCES AND ACTIVITIES

This table represents experts' assessment of how easy it is to get hooked on various commonly used substances and activities (both legal and illegal) and how difficult it is to stop using them. The estimates represent the proportion of users who develop an addictive pattern at some point in their lives.

Drug/Activity	Plausible Estimate of "Addictive Potential"
Those with at least some usable data	
Heroin	High
Methadone	High
Nicotine	High
Amphetamines	Moderate
Ecstasy	Moderate
Cocaine	Moderate
Alcohol	Moderate
Marijuana	Moderate
Benzodiazepines	Moderate
Gambling	Low
Those with little usable data	
Inactivity	Moderate
Tasty food	Moderate
Barbiturates	Low
Inhalants	Low
Gammahydroxybutyrate (GHB)	Low
Steroids	Low
Stealing	Low
Violence	Low
Diving	Low
Surfing	Low
Fast driving	Low
Exercise	Very low
Sexual behaviours	Very low
Playing computer games	Very low
Chocolate	Very low
Self-harm	Very low
Caffeine	Very low
Watching TV	Very low
Work	Very low
Shopping	Very low

Source: Republished with permission of John Wiley & Sons, from *Theories of Addiction*, Robert West, 2002; permission conveyed through Copyright Clearance Center, Inc.

TREATMENT Despite greater restrictions on smoking in public places and ever-increasing knowledge about the health risks associated with smoking, it can be a difficult habit to break. Research in the United States shows that most smokers want to quit and over half have tried to quit in the past year (Centers for Disease Control, 2011). Most smokers make three or four quit attempts before

achieving lasting success. The majority quit smoking without professional help. Others seek help in the form of widely available self-help materials or through psychological and/or pharmacological treatments.

Psychological Treatments. Psychological interventions have increasingly become conceptualized and organized as an integrated system that includes a range of interventions varying in terms of intensity. Examples include formal face-to-face psychological interventions, brief counselling provided by health care professionals, telephone counselling, online support groups for quitting, and provision of self-help materials for quitting. A review of the research on effectiveness of psychological treatments concluded that there is consistent evidence that counselling is associated with modest smoking cessation success (Schlam & Baker, 2013). The use of self-help materials without counselling or medication is not effective at improving quit rates (Ranney et al., 2006).

The psychological interventions designed to help people stop smoking are usually behavioural or cognitive in nature. As such, they typically help individuals develop skills such as self-monitoring, goal setting, and reinforcement. Some interventions attempt to reduce the pleasure experienced by smokers by forcing them to smoke far more cigarettes than they would normally. The adverse nature of these programs has probably contributed to their lack of success (Sobell, Toneatto, & Sobell, 1990). Other smoking cessation programs involve abrupt abstinence ("cold turkey") or include a period of reduction before the individual quits for good.

Pharmacological Treatments. Smoking cessation medications fall under two main categories: over-the-counter nicotine replacements and medications that are available only by prescription. Nicotine replacement in the form of gum, lozenges, inhalers, or skin patches helps to reduce cravings and other physiological withdrawal symptoms by maintaining a steady level of nicotine in the system. The idea is to break the behavioural habits associated with smoking while simultaneously reducing craving.

Prescription-only medications include bupropion hydrochloride and varenicline tartrate. Both drugs work by targeting receptors in the brain and do not deliver any nicotine to the body. Bupropion hydrochloride (Wellbutrin, Zyban) was originally prescribed as an antidepressant but was subsequently found to be effective in aiding smoking cessation. It works by reducing the severity of nicotine cravings and withdrawal symptoms. Varenicline tartrate (Chantix, Champix) is a prescription drug that works by reducing cravings and decreasing the pleasurable effects of nicotine. There has been some evidence to suggest an association between varenicline and suicidal ideation. It is recommended that health care professionals and patients be very attentive to mood and behavioural changes when taking varenicline. Success rates of pharmacological treatments are greatly enhanced when used in conjunction with psychological therapies (Alberta Alcohol and Drug Abuse Commission, 2004).

3 **BEFORE MOVING ON**

> Despite the relative addictiveness of tobacco, the prevalence of smoking has decreased in recent years. What are some explanations for this trend?

AMPHETAMINES AND DESIGNER DRUGS

Amphetamines and related drugs have effects on the body similar to those of the naturally occurring hormone adrenalin. The two most commonly abused forms of amphetamine are methamphetamine (with street names such as "speed" when injected, and "ice" or "crystal" when smoked in a purified form) and dextroamphetamine (a legally prescribed medication sold under the name Dexedrine). Other street names for these drugs are "bennies," "uppers," "glass," "crank," and "pep pills." Methylphenidate (Ritalin) is used to treat ADHD but can also be abused. Methylated amphetamines, referred to as designer drugs, have both stimulant and hallucinogenic properties. Methylene-dioxymethamphetamine (MDMA), known as "ecstasy" (or simply "E"), has had recent popularity, particularly among young people at raves. Methylene-dioxyamphetamine (MDA) and para-methoxyamphetamine (PMA) are other examples of designer drugs.

Amphetamines were originally developed as a nasal decongestant and asthma treatment in the 1930s. It was discovered that, in addition to shrinking mucous membranes and constricting blood vessels, they also increased alertness and concentration. Consequently, they were used to treat narcolepsy (a sleeping disorder) and later ADHD. Later, the appetite-suppressant qualities of amphetamines also led to their use as a treatment for obesity. Currently, only dextroamphetamine (or Dexedrine, used in the treatment of ADHD) is legally manufactured in Canada. Other amphetamines and related drugs, referred to as "designer drugs," are manufactured illegally in home laboratories.

PREVALENCE The rate of amphetamine and other illicit drug use in Canada is difficult to determine for several reasons. First, unlike alcohol and tobacco (which can be measured by the standard drink or the cigarette), most drugs have no accepted units of measurement. Moreover, because most sales of such drugs are illegal, there are no consumer records or indexes of availability. Consumers may not even know what they are using. Because many are manufactured in illegal laboratories, the contents vary considerably. For example, the RCMP conducted an analysis of ecstasy tablets seized at Vancouver raves (Royal Canadian Mounted Police, 2000). Only 24 percent of the tablets were pure MDMA; the other tablets were mixtures of other substances with or without MDMA. More than one-third contained no MDMA. Thus, it is difficult to define and monitor addiction, or to gauge the social impact of illicit drug use.

Between 1950 and 1970, stimulants were widely consumed by truckers, athletes, students, and others wishing to increase alertness and enhance performance. Since then, amphetamine use in Canada has declined markedly. In the Canadian Centre on Substance Abuse (2004a) national survey, 6% of respondents (aged 15+) reported using amphetamines at some time in their life; Ecstasy use was reported by 4%. Among high school students (Grades 9 to 12), 5.6% of males and 5.1% of females reported ecstasy use in the past year and 1.1% of both males and females reported methamphetapine use, including crystal meth. Among students in Grades 7 to 12, 2.1% reported using an ADHD drug for nonmedical purposes (Boak et al., 2015).

EFFECTS At low doses, amphetamines increase alertness and allow the user to focus attention effectively, offering improved performance on cognitive tasks. Amphetamines also suppress appetite. At higher doses, they induce feelings of exhilaration, extroversion, and confidence, and at very high doses, restlessness and anxiety can occur.

Chronic amphetamine use is associated with feelings of fatigue and sadness, as well as periods of social withdrawal and intense anger. Repeated high doses can cause hallucinations, delirium, and paranoia, a condition known as **toxic psychosis**. To combat undesirable effects such as sleeplessness, many amphetamine users also become dependent upon depressant drugs such as tranquilizers, barbiturates, and alcohol to induce sleep. This can lead to a roller coaster–like vicious circle of drug use (Stein & Ellinwood, 1993).

The physical effects of amphetamines include increased or irregular heartbeat, fluctuations in blood pressure, hot or cold flashes, nausea, weakness, and dilation of pupils. Prolonged use usually leads to weight loss. At very high doses, amphetamines can induce seizures, confusion, and coma. The periods of intense anger associated with prolonged amphetamine use might also contribute to the prevalence of violent death in Canada such as suicides, homicides, and violent accidents (Gourlay, 2000).

The long-term effects of ecstasy have received considerable attention. Based on animal studies, there is a concern that moderate or greater use can lead to permanent depletion

Crack, a fast-acting and highly addictive form of cocaine, is smoked with a special pipe.

of serotonin. There have been reports of long-term neuro-psychiatric problems in users, although the specific role of ecstasy in producing these effects is unclear.

DEPENDENCY Amphetamine tolerance and dependence develops very quickly. The effects of amphetamines do not last long, and users often experience a post-high "crash" marked by feelings of fatigue, irritability, sadness, and craving. Withdrawal from amphetamines also often causes periods of apathy and prolonged sleeping.

COCAINE

Cocaine comes from the *Erythroxylon coca* bush, indigenous to various areas in South America. Its stimulating effects have long been known to the people of these regions, who chew on the leaves to reduce fatigue and induce euphoria. Throughout the 1800s, cocaine was viewed as harmless; it was sold in cocaine-laced cigarettes, cigars, inhalants, and crystals, and was the principal ingredient in a variety of commercial products, including Coca-Cola (Musto, 1992). In 1911 cocaine use was restricted in Canada, and it is now only occasionally used legally as a local anaesthetic for minor surgeries.

In the 1960s and 1970s, cocaine became a popular recreational drug. Due to the high cost, its use was generally limited to those in middle- and upper-income groups. Recently, however, cocaine has fallen in price as cheaper forms such as crack have been introduced.

Cocaine is usually sold on the street in powder form. This powder is often snorted, but can also be rubbed into the skin or mixed with water and injected. Another method of cocaine ingestion is called "freebasing" and involves purifying cocaine by heating it and smoking the residue. (See Table 11.8 for a comparison of methods of taking substances.) Crack is made by dissolving powdered cocaine in a solvent, combining it with baking soda, and heating it until

it forms a crystallized substance (a "rock"), which is then smoked. The process itself is potentially dangerous, because the solvents are highly flammable. It is popular, however, because of its cheapness, since the cocaine used need not be as refined as cocaine for snorting. This method of ingestion also increases the rate of metabolizing the drug and makes it more addictive.

The short-term effects of cocaine appear soon after its ingestion and dissipate very quickly. Crack is especially fast-acting, and may wear off in a few minutes. In small amounts, cocaine use in any form produces feelings of euphoria, well-being, and confidence. Users become more alert and talkative, and experience reduced appetite and increased excitement and energy, due to the stimulation of the higher centres of the CNS. It appears that these effects are primarily achieved by increasing the availability of dopamine at important neuronal sites in the brain. With high doses, the CNS is overstimulated, leading to poor muscle control, confusion, anxiety, anger, and aggression. Continuous use may result in mood swings, loss of interest in sex, weight loss, and insomnia. As with amphetamines, chronic use of cocaine can also lead to toxic psychosis experienced as delusions and hallucinations.

Physical symptoms of cocaine use include increased blood pressure and body temperature, as well as irregular heartbeat. Users may also experience chest pain, nausea, blurred vision, fever, muscle spasms, convulsions, and coma. Death can occur because of cocaine's impact on the brain centres that control respiration.

PREVALENCE The restriction on cocaine use by the Canadian government in the early 1900s led to a decline in its use throughout the first half of the century. This decline coincided with an increase in amphetamine use. When amphetamine use waned in the 1950s and 1960s, cocaine's popularity again increased (Addiction Research Foundation, 1997).

In a 2015 survey, approximately 1 percent of Canadians reported having used cocaine or crack in the past year

TABLE 11.8   METHODS OF TAKING SUBSTANCES

Method	Route	Time to Reach Brain
Inhaling	Drug in vapour form is inhaled through mouth and lungs into circulatory system.	7 seconds
Snorting	Drug in powdered form is snorted into the nose. Some of the drug lands on the nasal mucous membranes, is absorbed by blood vessels, and enters the bloodstream.	4 minutes
Injection	Drug in liquid form directly enters the body through a needle.	20 seconds (intravenous)
	Injection may be intravenous or intramuscular (subcutaneous).	4 minutes (intramuscular)
Oral ingestion	Drug in solid or liquid form passes through esophagus and stomach and finally to the small intestines. It is absorbed by blood vessels in the intestines.	30 minutes
Other routes	Drugs can be absorbed through areas that contain mucous membranes. Drugs can be placed under the tongue, inserted anally and vaginally, and administered as eyedrops.	Variable

(Health Canada, 2017). Among high school students, past year use of cocaine was 2.5 percent, with males and females equally likely to report use (Boak et al., 2015).

DEPENDENCY Cocaine produces intense psychological dependence and results in severe withdrawal symptoms. Cocaine users often feel a crash as the drug begins to wear off, which results in intense craving, depression, and paranoia, followed by fatigue. The craving for cocaine experienced during withdrawal gradually diminishes in intensity, but can take more than a month to disappear completely (Gawin & Kleber, 1986; Weddington et al., 1990).

TREATMENT FOR AMPHETAMINE AND COCAINE ABUSE
Treatment for stimulant abuse is complicated by several factors. Stimulant users are likely to use other drugs to counteract some of the effects of the stimulants. As a result, many are dependent on alcohol or other depressants, making it difficult to decide which dependency to treat first. In addition, people who abuse more than one drug often have comorbid mental disorders, and it is often difficult to determine whether one of these conditions predates the other.

Psychological Treatments. Psychological treatments for stimulant abuse developed in the 1980s were often modelled after the 12-step programs for alcohol. Intervention programs, which normally have abstinence as a goal, have also focused on group therapy, individual counselling, and developing relapse prevention skills (McClellan, Arndt, Metzger, Woody, & O'Brien, 1993). Cognitive-behavioural interventions examine the thoughts and behaviours that precede and maintain stimulant abuse (Joe, Dansereau, & Simpson, 1994). Recently, community outpatient contingency management programs have become popular, in which individuals are rewarded with money and social outings if they remain drug-free. There is some evidence that these programs are superior to 12-step programs (Higgins et al., 1993). Among individuals with mental disorders, contingency management is associated with significant reductions in drug use both during and following treatment, and reductions in psychiatric symptoms (McDonell et al., 2013). Treatment programs have also been developed that integrate the treatment of the drug and comorbid mental health disorders. This integrated approach is considered superior to sequential treatment of the various concerns. Cocaine Anonymous and Narcotics Anonymous mutual support groups are also often recommended to complement the formal treatment program.

Biological Treatments. Biological treatments are usually used as adjuncts to psychological interventions for stimulant abuse. Antidepressants may be prescribed to combat the depression that frequently occurs during withdrawal. In addition, drugs such as methylphenidate may be given to reduce cravings. So far, studies have not found that these medications alone improve outcomes (Gourlay, 2000; Miles et al., 2013). Again, they are probably most beneficial when used in conjunction with a good psychological treatment program.

OPIOIDS

Opioids (also known as narcotics) are a class of CNS depressants—drugs whose main effects are the reduction of pain and sleep inducement. Opium, the alkaloid from which opioids are derived, comes from the seeds of the opium poppy, which is indigenous to Asia and the Middle East. Natural opiates (e.g., morphine, codeine) are refined directly from opium, whereas semi-synthetic opiates (e.g., heroin, oxycodone) are derived from natural opiates. Synthetic opiates (e.g., methadone, Demerol, Percocet) are drugs manufactured to have similar effects to those of the other opiates.

Opioids can be taken as tablets, capsules, suppositories, syrups, or in the form of an injection. In pure form, heroin appears as a white, odourless, bitter-tasting powder that can also be snorted. Most heroin users, however, prefer to mix heroin with water and inject it to produce a more intense high. This is known as "mainlining."

Heroin, the most commonly abused opioid, was originally introduced in 1898 as a replacement for morphine and was viewed as relatively harmless. Not until the early 1900s was it discovered that heroin is even more addictive than morphine. Morphine and codeine are the only naturally derived opioids in common clinical use in North America. Morphine remains a mainstay of analgesia for severe pain, such as that experienced by terminally ill cancer patients, and codeine is present in many common medications, such as cough syrups and painkillers. Although synthetic opiates are used frequently today as analgesics, they can also produce dependence.

PREVALENCE

In 2015 less than 1% of Canadians reported ever having tried heroin (Health Canada, 2016). Among high school students in Ontario, 0.8% reported using it sometime in their life and 0.7% reported using it in the past year. Rates have been generally low but have dropped in the past decade (Boak et al., 2015).

Although the street use of heroin is not a major Canadian problem, the use of prescription forms of opioids by Canadians is of considerable concern. Thirteen percent of Canadians aged 15 years and older reported using opioids in the past year (Health Canada, 2016). Prevalence was not significantly different between males and females. Students are also reporting high levels of use, with 10.0 percent of Ontario students in Grades 7 to 12 reporting past-year use (Boak et al., 2015).

EFFECTS

Opioids mimic the effects of **endogenous opiates**, or the body's natural painkillers. Known as **exogenous opiates**, narcotics affect receptor sites located throughout the body, including the brain, spinal cord, and bloodstream. The narcotics bind to receptor sites at these locations and, in turn, reduce the body's production of endogenous opiates. Thus, someone who stops using exogenous opiates may experience increased pain sensitivity (Cambor & Millman, 1991).

Heroin is perhaps the most addicting of all opiates, in part due to the sensations associated with using the drug. About one minute after injecting heroin, the user experiences an intense pleasurable rush. After this subsides, a euphoria characterized by dulled sensations and dream-like sedation is produced, and the user may appear drunk. Heroin also acts as an appetite suppressant, and even small doses can cause restlessness, nausea, and vomiting (Addiction Research Foundation, 1997).

At higher doses, heroin has extremely dangerous effects: pupils constrict, the skin may turn blue and feel cold and clammy, breathing slows, and coma and respiratory depression

causing death can occur. A major problem is that the impact of any dose can be difficult to determine. In fact, heroin addicts sometimes die from a dosage level that they had previously tolerated. It appears that this is more likely to occur when the drug is taken in an environment that is different from the one in which the drug is usually taken, although it is not clear why this is so (Szabo, Tabakoff, & Hoffman, 1994). In addition, because heroin is produced in an uncontrolled manner and sold on the street, it is often cut with other drugs and its purity is difficult to determine. Many deaths have resulted when, for some unknown reason, the heroin that is sold at a street level is purer than usual, so that the user unwittingly injects too high a dose.

FOCUS 11.4

The Fentanyl Crisis

Canada has seen a marked increase in the number of fatal overdoses due to illicit fentanyl use. Fentanyl is a synthetic opioid that is up to 100 times more potent than morphine. Alberta and British Columbia have been the most affected in this crisis but availability appears to be moving east across the country. Between 2009 and 2014, the rates of fentanyl-related deaths increased sevenfold overall and twenty-fold in Alberta (Canadian Centre on Substance Abuse, 2015). Exposure to fentanyl can occur from several sources. Heroin users may acquire fentanyl-laced Heroin, "fake oxy" tablets that are manufactured to resemble oxycodone, or purposefully seek out fentanyl (Jafari, Buxton, & Joe, 2015).

In an attempt to address this crisis, governments are making naloxone much more easily available to frontline workers such as fire fighters and paramedics and through pharamacies. For example, British Columbia initiated a Take Home Naloxone Program in 2012. Naloxone (Narcan) is a drug that blocks the effects of opioids, including depressed respiration and loss of consciousness, and is used to treat narcotic overdoses in emergency situations. The Take Home program educates opioid users and service providers in overdose prevention, recognition, and response. In addition, sites involved in this program provide prescriptions for naloxone to opioid users. This program appears effective in reducing harms, including deaths, from opioid overdoses (Canadian Medical Association, 2014). Over 581 estimated opioid overdoses have been successfully reversed (Deonarine, Amlani, Ambrose, & Buxton, 2016).

The Harm Reduction Approach

Whereas treatment for drug abuse focuses on reducing or eliminating the use of the drug, **harm reduction approaches** focus on reducing the consequences of the use. Injection is often the preferred method of drug taking and many harm reduction approaches have focused on reducing consequences of this route of administration. Among the other health risks of drug abuse, injection drug use puts the user at risk of contracting HIV or hepatitis C through the use of contaminated needles or other injection equipment such as spoons or containers. Users inject many times per day, so the risk to the individual over time is high. In Vancouver, a study of users found that 28 percent were HIV positive and 86 percent were hepatitis C positive (Spittal et al., 1998).

In the 1980s, the Public Health Department in Rotterdam began to distribute clean needles to a semi-organized group of

heroin addicts. Since then, several countries, including Canada, have established increasingly organized needle exchange services. Canada has 30 needle exchange programs operating across the country (Riley, 1994). These programs are often implemented along with counselling, education, and outreach efforts attempting to encourage addicts to participate more fully in treatment programs. Often the service is mobile, with a van travelling to convenient meeting points with the addicts.

Research demonstrates that needle exchange programs accomplish their harm reduction goals. Users who attend programs compared to those who do not attend reduce their risk behaviours and infection rates (Hurley, 1997) and are more likely to attend treatment programs (United States Department of Health and Human Services, 2000).

Despite these positive effects, concerns about needle exchange programs continue to be voiced. Many are concerned about the risk to the public of providing extra needles to addicts. However, no large public health risks have emerged. For example, the rate at which needles are turned in exceeds the rate at which they are handed out in Vancouver (Vancouver Coastal Health, 2003). There is no evidence of an increase in needle stick accidents in public places such as playgrounds and parks. There is also no evidence that drug dealers are drawn to areas with programs because of a perceived availability of clientele, or that crime rates increase (Videnieks, 2003).

Perhaps the largest objections are to the harm reduction philosophy itself. The harm reduction policy is sometimes seen as supporting illicit drug use by providing drug use paraphernalia. Due to these concerns, the U.S. federal government has a constitutional ban on the use of federal funds to support needle exchange programs and research on their effectiveness (Vernick, Burris, & Strathdee, 2003). In Canada, the police community has expressed concerns at times, although generally a positive working relationship between the police and programs has developed (Canadian Centre on Substance Abuse, 2004b). The establishment of needle exchange programs in Canadian prisons, where injection drug use rates and rates of HIV and hepatitis C infection are far higher than those in the general population, has been more controversial. Despite their successful introduction in prisons in many other countries, there are currently no programs in Canadian correctional institutions (Canadian Centre on Substance Abuse, 2004b). ●

Chronic users may develop a number of physical conditions. Chronic respiratory and pulmonary problems may develop as a result of the effects of heroin on the respiratory system.

Endocarditis, an infection of the lining of the heart, occurs as a result of the use of unsterilized needles. The use of unsterilized injection equipment can also cause abscesses, cellulitis, liver disease, and brain damage. The risk of HIV infection among intravenous drug users is significant, although the introduction of needle exchange programs seems to have been successful at reducing the spread of HIV through needles (Gibson, Flynn, & Perales, 2001).

DEPENDENCY

The withdrawal symptoms associated with heroin and other opioids are extremely severe and begin about eight hours after the last dose. Along with increased pain sensitivity, the user may experience dysphoria, a dulling of the senses, anxiety, increased bodily secretions (runny eyes and nose), pupil dilation, fever, sweating, and muscle pain. Thirty-six hours after a dose, muscle-twitching, cramps, hot flashes, and changes in heart rate and blood pressure can occur, in addition to sleeplessness, vomiting, and diarrhea. These symptoms gradually diminish over a five to 10-day period. Partly because of the intensity of these symptoms, relapse of opioid abuse is extremely common (Addiction Research Foundation, 1997).

TREATMENT

The treatment for opioid abuse typically involves the use of medications. Drugs such as naltrexone act as opioid antagonists and help to alleviate initial symptoms of withdrawal. **Methadone**, a heroin replacement, or a newer medication, **buprenorphine/naloxone,** are often used to reduce the craving after initial withdrawal symptoms have abated. Higher doses of these opioid antagonists are given in the early stages of treatment and are then gradually decreased. The medication is either tapered out completely or is maintained at a steady dose to allow individuals to improve their functioning in other areas of their lives, such as employment and social relationships. Opioid replacement therapy is associated with reduced criminal activity (Rastegar, Kawasaki, King, Harris, & Brooner, 2016) and reduced risk of HIV infection among intravenous drug users (MacArthur et al., 2012). Most experts agree that medication therapy works best in conjunction with good individual and group psychological programs, as well as ongoing peer support.

4 BEFORE MOVING ON

> Why do opioids such as heroin and oxycodone have a high addictive potential?

Cannabis

Case Notes

When Derek was 16 years old and in Grade 11, his older brother turned him on to grass, and he liked it. Derek began to smoke occasionally with his brother during the week. He could get marijuana for other kids from his brother, which made him very popular.

Although Derek's parents and brother had dropped out of school early, Derek seemed academically gifted. However, as his smoking became more frequent, his work habits deteriorated and his attendance dropped. Within a few months, he met suppliers who could provide him with cheaper marijuana and other drugs as well. Derek was now spending more time dealing than doing schoolwork, and he failed his year. But he was earning as much in a day or two as his father did in a week of casual labour.

By the end of the next school year, word of his services reached the ears of the principal. Derek's apartment was raided and a sizable cache of drugs was seized. Derek was sentenced to 18 months in prison.

Upon release six months later, Derek was adamant about going straight. He returned to school and got a job waiting tables. But Grades did not come as easily as before, the other students were all much younger, and the double workload was tiring. He slowly slipped into seeing some of his old acquaintances and smoking the odd joint. When other students asked for drugs, he found it hard to refuse. Derek soon gave up his job and started selling, and using, a variety of drugs.

Derek was referred to one of the authors for a pre-sentencing report after being found guilty of possession of a variety of drugs for the purpose of trafficking. This time, he was also charged with possession of a large number of stolen goods, including a very expensive stereo system. Derek claimed he had received the goods as payment for drugs and did not know that they had been stolen.

Marijuana and hashish come from the hemp plant *Cannabis sativa*, indigenous to Asia but now grown in many parts of the world. The hemp plant was originally (and still is) cultivated for its strong fibres, which can be processed into cloth and rope. However, its psychotropic and medicinal properties soon became known, and it was used for pleasure as well as to treat rheumatism, gout, depression, and cholera. Marijuana consists of the leaves and flowers of this plant, which are dried and crushed. Hashish, made from the resin produced by the plant, is a much stronger form of **cannabis**. Although both forms are most often smoked in cigarette form (called a "joint") or in a pipe, they can also be chewed, added to baked goods, or prepared in a tea. Other names for marijuana and hashish are "pot," "weed," "grass," "dope," "reefer," and "bud." Cannabis does not fit into the usual classification of drug groups. It generally has depressant effects, yet it increases the user's heart rate like a stimulant. It can also produce hallucinations when consumed in large doses, but this is not a usual effect.

PREVALENCE

Marijuana is the most commonly used and most widely available illicit drug in Canada. In 2015, 37.5% of Canadians aged 15 and over reported using cannabis at least once in their lives and 12.3% reported using it in the year before the survey (Health Canada, 2016). Rates were higher among males and for younger adults, although prevalence of cannabis use among females has increased. Rates of lifetime and past-year use are lower than those reported in 2004, when the lifetime and past-year rates were 44.5% and 14.1% respectively.

Among Canadian high school students in Grades 7 to 12, 21.3% reported use in the past year, with males and females equally likely to use. Daily use was reported by 2.1%. Use increases with each Grade from 7 to 12, with 37.2% of people in Grade 12 reporting past-year use (Boak et al., 2015).

Although rates of cannabis use among adults appear to be rising, use among high school students have reduced slightly since 1999 (Boak et al., 2015). Use among university students is similar to that of Grade 12 students. A survey by researchers at the CAMH (Adlaf et al., 2005) found that more than half (51%) of university students across Canada reported using cannabis at some point in their lives. About a third (32%) had used it during the past 12 months, and this varied by region. Students in Quebec reported the highest rates of cannabis use in the previous 12 months (39%), followed by the Atlantic provinces (37%), Ontario (33%), and British Columbia (30%). University students in the Prairie provinces reported the lowest rates of cannabis use (19%).

EFFECTS

The psychoactive effects of cannabis are caused primarily by the chemical delta-9-tetrahydrocannabinol (**THC**). Although the exact mechanisms by which THC exerts its influence are not fully understood, it appears that it acts upon specific cannabinoid receptors in the body and mimics the effects of naturally occurring substances, including the endogenous opiates (Bouaboula et al., 1993). The concentration of THC in marijuana and hashish has increased about fivefold since the 1960s and 1970s, making it difficult to measure accurately the effect of specific doses.

Cannabis involves mild changes in perception along with enhancement of physical experiences. With relatively small doses, most users report feeling mildly euphoric and sociable. A sense of well-being and relaxation usually begins within minutes of ingesting the drug and lasts for two to three hours. Some people, however, find the drug stimulating, and occasionally panic or anxiety is also experienced. At high doses, cannabis has been known to cause hallucinations,

although it seems that this most often occurs when the user has a pre-existing mental disorder. Individuals under the influence of marijuana show deficits in complex motor skills, short-term memory, reaction time, and attention. Physical effects include itchy, red eyes, and both increased blood pressure and appetite (Wilson, Ellinwood, Mathew, & Johnson, 1994). Cannabis has clear effects on ability to drive. Although detection of impairment is considerably more complex than alcohol impairment, a standardized roadside assessment called the Drug Evaluation and Classification (DEC) program has been used throughout Canada since 2008. DEC, which detects use of other psychoactive drugs in addition to cannabis, involves a series of coordination tests, an eye examination, behavioural observations, and toxicology analysis. Drug Recognition Experts (DREs) are individuals trained and certified in conducting DEC evaluations. Certification is essential because of the large number and complexity of factors that need to be considered in each appraisal. A review of DEC evaluation studies found the overall accuracy of DEC evaluations of suspected impaired drivers to be greater than 80 percent (Beirness, LeCavalier, & Singhal, 2007). An analysis of 1400 DEC evaluations conducted in Canada revealed that DREs are extremely accurate (95 percent) in detecting drivers who are impaired by drugs (Beirness, Beasley, & LeCavalier, 2009).

Long-term users often suffer greater lung problems than tobacco smokers, including deterioration in the linings of the trachea and bronchial tubes, which may be a result of holding unfiltered smoke in their lungs for long periods of time. In addition, marijuana and hashish contain much greater concentrations of some known carcinogens (e.g., benzopyrene) than does tobacco, and there is also some evidence that chronic marijuana use can result in fertility problems for both men and women.

Some long-term users develop **amotivational syndrome**, a continuing pattern of apathy, profound self-absorption, detachment from friends and family, and abandonment of career and educational goals. Reduced motivation for goal-directed behaviour in cannabis users appears to be related to repeated doses of THC, supporting the hypothesis that THC can disrupt reward-based learning (Lane & Cherek, 2002). However, it is not yet clear whether cannabis use is a cause, consequence, or correlate of amotivation. Although the amotivational syndrome is thought to be related to the alteration of brain function caused by chronic cannabis use (Musty & Kabak, 1995), it may also be related to depression in long-term users. There is evidence that about 30 percent of regular cannabis users also have symptoms of depression (American Psychiatric Association, 2000; Cambor & Millman, 1991). It is unclear whether depression leads to increased cannabis consumption, or whether it is a result of prolonged use. Among chronic users, cannabis itself may be a significant motivator, causing other behaviours to be seen as less rewarding (Volkow et al., 2016).

Regular use of cannabis has also been linked to increased onset of psychosis (see Chapter 9) in numerous longitudinal studies conducted over the past 30 years. More recent attention has been given to whether this association is causal (i.e., the use of cannabis specifically causes the psychotic symptoms), whether it reflects an underlying shared vulnerability (i.e., people with a vulnerability to psychotic disorder also have a vulnerability to the use of cannabis), or whether people with emerging psychotic disorder self-medicate these symptoms with cannabis. A recent review concluded that the bulk of the research evidence suggests that the link is causal but that a better understanding of who is most at risk is required (Gage, Hickman, & Zammit, 2016).

THERAPEUTIC EFFECTS OF CANNABIS Cannabis has been used in the treatment of several diseases, including cancer, AIDS, and glaucoma. It has been shown that THC can help to alleviate nausea and encourage eating in cancer and AIDS patients. THC has been used to relieve pressure within the eyes in the treatment of glaucoma. Because it is both illicit and thought to be "bad for one's health," most jurisdictions do not currently allow marijuana consumption for therapeutic use, even in extreme cases. However, as of 2001, the Canadian government changed regulations on the possession and production of marijuana for medical purposes so that those with a terminal illness, and those with severe pain from medical conditions (including severe pain associated with multiple sclerosis, spinal cord injury, AIDS/HIV, severe arthritis, and epilepsy), can apply to the Office of Cannabis Medical Access to possess the drug legally. All applications must be supported by declarations from medical practitioners. Patients can also apply for a license to grow their own marijuana for the above purposes (Munroe, 2002).

As of August 2016, the Canadian government changed regulations on the possession and production of cannabis for medical purposes. Individuals with a medical need such as those with a terminal illness and those with severe pain from medical conditions can obtain authorization from a health care practitioner to access quality-controlled cannabis through a licensed producer, or register with Health Canada to grow a small amount of their own for medical purposes (Health Canada, 2016). Legislation is pending to legalize use generally as of July 2018, including the purchasing and cultivation of small amounts.

DEPENDENCY

It has long been believed that cannabis is not addictive, but there is recent recognition that regular use results in both tolerance and withdrawal symptoms, although withdrawal is milder than with other addictive substances. Symptoms include irritability, nervousness and anxiety, loss of appetite, restlessness, sleep disturbances, and anger/aggression (Budney, Moore, Vandrey, & Hughes, 2003). Additionally, about one in 20 Canadians report a cannabis-related concern, the most common of which are impaired control over use, and strong cravings for the drug (Canadian Centre on Substance Abuse, 2004a). According to a recent survey, lifetime prevalence of cannabis use disorder (CUD) among Canadians aged 15 and older is 6.8 percent (Statistics Canada, 2012a). In the 12 months before the survey, 1.3 percent had a cannabis use disorder.

TREATMENT

Several factors complicate treatment of cannabis use disorders. Marijuana abuse often co-occurs with other mental disorders, including use of other substances, and cannabis users rarely seek treatment for marijuana abuse (Copeland, Clement, & Swift 2014). Individuals who do seek treatment have typically been using cannabis for over 10 years. Most individuals who abuse marijuana in Canada are placed in generalized treatment programs, although there are also efforts to develop cannabis-specific treatment approaches. A combination of motivational enhancement and cognitive-behavioural therapy has the greatest evidence of success for individuals with marijuana dependence (Copeland et al., 2014; Stephens, Roffman, & Curtin, 2000). The high rate of relapse following treatment suggests a possible need for adjunctive pharmacotherapy. However, are no currently accepted pharmacological interventions available (Balter, Cooper, & Haney, 2014) and more research is needed on these medications.

Hallucinogens

Hallucinogens are drugs that change a person's mental state by inducing perceptual and sensory distortions or hallucinations. They are also called *psychedelics*, which comes from the Greek words for "soul" and "to make manifest." Hallucinogens have been used in religious or spiritual ceremonies for thousands of years. Many of these drugs are derived from plants, but others are produced in the laboratory. There are many kinds of hallucinogens, but the most well-known are lysergic acid diethylamide (LSD or "acid"), mescaline, and psilocybin (magic mushrooms). Methylene-dioxymethamphetamine (MDMA) or ecstasy (described under "Amphetamines and Designer Drugs" earlier in this chapter) is sometimes included in this category as well.

LSD was first discovered in 1938 by Swiss chemist Albert Hoffman, who was investigating ergot—a fungus that affects cereal plants such as wheat and rye. In 1943 he

Timothy Leary was one of the leaders of a movement that extolled hallucinogens as part of a quasi-spiritual quest to expand consciousness and live life on a higher plane.

accidentally ingested some of the compound he had isolated from this fungus, and subsequently had the first recorded "acid trip." Later, he also extracted psilocybin from a mushroom called *Psilocybe mexicana*.

Hallucinogens can be ingested in capsule or tablet form, or as a liquid applied to small pieces of paper (e.g., stamps or stickers) and then placed on the tongue. The effects of hallucinogens usually begin within an hour of ingestion or sooner and last between six and 12 hours. Mescaline is found in the head of the peyote cactus and is chewed or mixed with food or water. Psilocybin is also chewed or swallowed with water. Phencyclidine (PCP or "angel dust") is a dissociative anaesthetic that is typically smoked for its hallucinogenic properties. Ketamine (K or Special K), a close analogue to PCP, is used as a veterinary anaesthetic. Recreationally, ketamine is injected, snorted, or taken orally. Salvia (*Salvia divinorum*) is a plant native to southern Mexico containing powerful psychoactive chemical properties that lead to hallucinations. Salvia was traditionally ingested by chewing the plant leaves but is more commonly smoked.

PREVALENCE

In Canada, the use of hallucinogens peaked in the 1960s. According to the latest adult survey (Health Canada, 2016), 13.1% reported using hallucinogens (including salvia) sometime in their life, although use in the year before the survey was rare (less than 1%). Use is slightly higher among high school students in Ontario than among Canadian adults, but is also dropping. Past-year use of LSD was 1.5% and of salvia was 2.2% (Boak et al., 2015).

EFFECTS

The subjective effects of hallucinogens depend on a number of variables, including the personality of the user and the amount of drug ingested. People's expectations regarding the effects of hallucinogens appear to play a large role in determining their reaction. In addition, the setting in which the hallucinogens are taken appears to be very important. Users who feel uncomfortable or unsafe in their environment may experience anxiety and fear, which can sometimes escalate into panic or psychotic-like episodes. A very small number of individuals are left with a prolonged psychotic disorder long after the drug has worn off.

People taking hallucinogens report a number of sensory experiences, including vivid visual hallucinations. Objects may waver, shimmer, or become distorted (e.g., limbs may appear very long). People commonly see colourful "halos" around objects; moving objects leave visible trails. Users may also experience *synesthesia*, a transference of stimuli from one sense to another, such as "hearing" colours or "feeling" sounds.

Hallucinogens have an excitatory effect on the CNS and mimic the effects of serotonin by acting upon serotonin receptors in the brain stem and cerebral cortex. LSD, for example, affects the sympathetic nervous system and causes dilated pupils, increased heart rate, elevated blood pressure, and increased alertness. Most hallucinogens are not physiologically dangerous even in high doses. However, hallucinations may lead to a risk of injury if there are extreme distortions in sense of distance, depth, or speed. PCP has effects that are more variable, and larger doses have been linked to convulsions, coma, and death. Individuals often purchase PCP unknowingly under the guise of other drugs such as mescaline.

One of the most frightening and inexplicable consequences of hallucinogen use can be the occurrence of "**flashbacks**," unpredictable recurrences of some of the physical or perceptual distortions experienced during a previous trip. DSM-5 includes a diagnosis called *hallucinogen persisting perception disorder*, which is applied if flashbacks cause significant distress or interfere with social or occupational functioning.

DEPENDENCY

It is widely thought that hallucinogens have little addictive potential, although they may induce psychological dependence. Even heavy users of hallucinogens rarely consume the drug more than once every few weeks, partly due to the fact that tolerance develops within a few days of continuous use. When this occurs, a user no longer experiences the hallucinogenic effects of the drug, although the physiological effects are still manifested. Abstinence from the drug for a few days to a week lowers tolerance to normal levels. Hallucinogens do not appear to cause noticeable withdrawal effects, even after long-term use.

Because hallucinogens do not appear to be addictive, few programs have been developed specifically to treat hallucinogen dependence. Those that have been developed generally focus on addressing the user's psychological dependence on the drug.

Gambling

Social gambling has been part of many societies; it can be recreational and provide exciting and exhilarating entertainment. Gambling shares many characteristics with substance use. Both generate short-lived pleasurable feelings and provide relief from negative feelings, and both ultimately create cravings to repeat the behaviour. Both have the ability to alter mood and level of arousal and, arguably, to induce an altered state of perception. Most Canadians are social gamblers. They limit the frequency of their gambling, and the time and money spent on gambling, and suffer no repercussions from their gambling. However, there is another group of gamblers who will "risk their reputation, their family's security, their life's savings, their work, their freedom, or their safety on the turn of a card, a roll of the dice, or the legs of a horse" (Custer, 1982). They are preoccupied with gambling and unable to resist despite staggeringly negative consequences.

PREVALENCE

In Canada, a large expansion in gambling opportunities occurred in the 1990s when provincial governments began legalizing video lottery terminals (VLTs) and permanent casinos to supplement lottery, bingo, and horse racing gambling. Participation varies from province to province according to availability, but overall about 80% of adults gamble. (Canadian Partnership for Responsible Gambling, 2016).

Lottery games appear to be the most popular form of gambling, followed by instant win tickets and gambling at a casino. Despite restrictions on gambling, a significant proportion of adolescents engage in gambling behaviour. The 2012–2013 Youth Gambling Survey found that 41.6 percent of adolescents had gambled in the previous three months (Elton-Marshall, Leatherdale, & Turner, 2016). Lifetime prevalence was approximately 80 percent.

DEPENDENCY

The issue of whether addiction can occur without the ingestion of a substance is a topic of lively debate. Some researchers argue in favour of a physiological definition of dependence that requires neurophysiological changes in response to the presence of a foreign substance, whereas others adhere to the psychological aspect of dependence. Certain individuals are unable to control the frequency or amount of the behaviour, much like individuals with substance use disorders. Some pathological gamblers have such great difficulty quitting that they even experience withdrawal-like symptoms when attempting to stop. In fact, DSM-5 diagnostic criteria for **gambling disorder** were intentionally patterned after those for substance dependence, and the DSM-5 includes gambling disorder in the Substance-related and Addictive Disorders section of the manual. It has been suggested that gambling and other addictive disorders are functionally equivalent forms of behaviour that satisfy similar needs and that these behaviours may be regarded as cross-addictions. As a result, an addiction model of pathological gambling has gained increasing acceptance among clinicians.

The Canadian Community Health Survey (Marshall & Wynne, 2003) provided a national perspective on gambling problems, including gambling disorder. Gambling was identified as a problem or a potential problem for about 5 percent of the population. Risk factors for problem gambling included being male, being Indigenous, and having a low level of education. Daily gamblers and VLT players were at particularly high risk for problems. In contrast, lottery tickets were associated with the smallest risk for problem gambling (Marshall & Wynne, 2003).

TREATMENT

Canadian psychologists are widely recognized for their contribution to the development of empirically based treatments for problem gambling. Only a few years ago, little was known about how to best treat such individuals. Often, substance abuse treatment programs were slightly modified for use with problem gamblers. Today, research groups across the country are tackling the issue of developing gambling-specific treatment approaches. Robert Ladouceur and his group at Laval University have developed cognitive treatment programs. At McGill University, Jeffery Derevensky and Rina Gupta are working on adolescent treatment approaches; Tony Toneatto and colleagues at the University of Toronto are looking at the effectiveness of treatment for co-occurring mental disorders and gambling problems; At the University of Calgary, the authors of this text and colleagues have developed brief treatment approaches using a motivational approach.

Our brief treatment development work has three underlying assumptions. First, many people recover from substance abuse and other addictions without the help of formal treatment. For example, it is clear that the most common pathway out for Canadians with an alcohol problem is "self-recovery" (Cunningham & Breslin, 2004). We assume that this is also true for people with gambling problems, and we know that people will often not initiate the process of changing until they have suffered significant problems for an extended period of time (Hodgins & el-Guebaly, 2000). Second, as few as 10 percent of problem gamblers, will attend formal treatment (Hodgins, Currie, & el-Guebaly, 2001). Third, the change strategies that problem gamblers use (e.g., avoiding cues to gamble, self-instruction) are similar to those used by individuals attending treatment (Hodgins & el-Guebaly, 2000).

Brief treatments that focus on motivational issues are effective for other addictive disorders (Miller & Rollnick, 2003), can reach individuals not seeking treatment and foster the early use of recovery strategies without requiring that an individual attend a program. Our strategy has been twofold: we have incorporated practical information about recovery strategies into a brief self-help workbook and we have provided individuals interested in using a self-help approach with brief telephone support that focuses on their motivation to implement the change strategies. The workbook focuses on self-assessment of gambling behaviour, goal setting, strategies for not gambling, and recovery maintenance (Hodgins & Makarchuk, 2002).

We have conducted a number of clinical trials of this brief intervention (Hodgins, Currie, Currie, & Fick, 2009; Diskin & Hodgins, 2009). In one trial, we followed participants for 24 months and found that those who received the workbook–motivational intervention had better outcomes than those who received the workbook only. About 37 percent were abstinent from gambling, and an additional 40 percent had significantly reduced their expenditures on gambling (Hodgins, Currie, el-Guebaly, & Peden, 2004).

Web-based interventions also show promise in the treatment of disordered gambling. The wide availability of the internet makes it a potentially useful tool for improving the accessibility of treatment services (Swan & Hodgins, 2015). Promising results have been found with cognitive-behavioural and brief treatment methods. For example, Carlbring and colleagues (2012) found that internet-based CBT with additional minimal therapist contact significantly reduced problem gambling; these gains were maintained at a three-year follow-up.

5 BEFORE MOVING ON

What are the benefits of brief treatment, self-recovery, and harm reduction approaches? What are some characteristics that gambling shares with substance use?

SUMMARY

- DSM-5 sets out the criteria for substance intoxication and substance use disorders in the section called Substance-related and Addictive Disorders, which also includes gambling disorder.

- Alcohol is the world's number one psychoactive substance, with almost 80 percent of Canadians reporting drinking in the past year. Alcohol may result in positive feelings in the short term, but over time it acts as a depressant. Alcohol causes deficits in coordination, vigilance, and reaction time. These physical and psychological effects can result in negative consequences economically, socially, and medically. Treatment for alcohol use disorders includes abstinence-based treatments (AA, Minnesota model), pharmacotherapy medication (benzodiazepines, Naltrexone, Acamprosate, Antabuse), and psychological treatments (behavioural interventions, relapse prevention, marital and family therapy, brief interventions).

- One of the major problems in treating substance abusers is the phenomenon of polysubstance abuse. Research has demonstrated that concurrent dependence may be the rule rather than the exception. In the DSM-5, an individual can receive a diagnosis for each separate drug that is being abused.

- The use of tranquilizers (including barbiturates and benzodiazepines) is fairly low in Canada. Barbiturates and benzodiazepines are considered depressants because they inhibit neurotransmitter activity in the CNS. The euphoria produced by small doses turns to poor motor coordination at higher doses, and can prove fatal in too large a dose. Treatment usually involves pharmacological treatment (progressively smaller doses of the abused drug) in combination with psychological and educational programs.

- In 2015 it was estimated that 13 percent of Canadians over the age of 14 smoked cigarettes. Nicotine is a CNS stimulant. Lower dosages can interfere with thinking and problem solving, and can cause extreme agitation and irritability along with mood changes. The small amount of nicotine present in a cigarette is not lethal and can increase alertness and improve mood. Treatments for smoking cessation include psychological (behavioural or cognitive) and pharmacological (nicotine replacement and prescription medication) interventions.

- Six percent of Canadians report having used amphetamines at least once in their life. Short-term effects of low dosages of amphetamines include increased alertness and ability to focus attention. This may lead to enhanced cognitive performance. Higher dosages, preferred by drug addicts, may produce feelings of exhilaration, but restlessness and anxiety may also be present. Prolonged use may lead to paranoia, toxic psychosis, periods of chronic fatigue, or a "crash" when the drugs wear off.

- In 2015 about 1.2 percent of Canadians reported having used cocaine or crack in the past year. The short-term effects of cocaine appear soon after its ingestion and wear off very quickly. Crack is especially fast-acting, and its effects may wear off in a few minutes. In small amounts, cocaine use in any form produces feelings of euphoria, well-being, and confidence. Continual use may result in mood swings, loss of interest in sex, weight loss, and insomnia.

- Treatments for stimulant abuse developed in the 1980s were often modelled after the 12-step programs for alcohol. They include psychological (cognitive behavioural) and pharmacological (e.g., antidepressants) interventions.

- Opioids are a class of CNS depressant drugs whose main effects are the reduction of pain and sleep inducement. Opioids mimic the effects of endogenous opiates, or the body's natural painkillers. The illicit use of prescription opioids is a significant concern in Canada. Since 2009, the number of opioid-related overdoses has increased exponentially. The treatment for opioid abuse typically involves the use of medications (naltrexone, methadone).

- In 2015, 37.5 percent of Canadians aged 15 and over reported using cannabis at least once in their lives and 12.3 percent reported using it in the year before the survey. Cannabis involves mild changes in perception along with enhancement of physical experiences. With relatively small doses, most users report feeling mildly euphoric and sociable. At high doses, cannabis has been known to cause hallucinations, although it seems that this most often occurs when the user has a pre-existing mental disorder. Most marijuana abusers in Canada are placed in generalized treatment programs, although there are also efforts to develop cannabis-specific treatment approaches using a cognitive-behavioural treatment model.

- In 2015 approximately 13 percent of Canadian adults reported using hallucinogens sometime in their life, although use in the year before the survey was less than 1 percent. People taking hallucinogens report a number of sensory experiences, including vivid visual hallucinations. Hallucinogens have an excitatory effect on the CNS and mimic the effects of serotonin by acting upon serotonin receptors in the brain stem and cerebral cortex. Because hallucinogens do not appear to be addictive, few programs have been developed specifically to treat hallucinogen dependence.

- It is clear that alcohol, tobacco, and illicit drugs are a major health hazard and cost our country billions of dollars annually, in direct and indirect expenses. There is evidence that educating communities has had some positive effects with alcohol and tobacco use, but there is a disturbing trend toward increased use of several illicit drugs, particularly by teenagers and young adults.

- Social gambling is increasingly popular in Canada. Approximately 75 percent of Canadians engage in some form of gambling. Gambling shares many characteristics with substance use including short-term pleasurable feelings, relief from negative feelings, and cravings to

repeat the behaviour. The DSM-5 diagnostic criteria for gambling disorder were patterned after those for substance dependence. Current treatment approaches for disordered gambling include cognitive-behavioural and brief treatments that focus on motivational issues.

KEY TERMS

abstinence syndrome (p. 274)

agonist drug (p. 271)

alcohol dehydrogenase (p. 264)

alcohol expectancy theory (p. 268)

amotivational syndrome (p. 282)

amphetamines (p. 277)

Antabuse (p. 271)

antagonist drug (p. 271)

behavioural disinhibition (p. 268)

behavioural tolerance (p. 268)

blackouts (p. 264)

blood alcohol level (BAL) (p. 264)

brief intervention (p. 273)

buprenophrine / naloxone (p. 281)

cannabis (p. 281)

depressants (p. 273)

endogenous opiates (p. 279)

ethyl alcohol (p. 264)

exogenous opiates (p. 279)

fetal alcohol syndrome (FAS) (p. 265)

flashbacks (p. 284)

gambling disorder (p. 285)

hallucinogens (p. 283)

harm reduction approaches (p. 280)

impairment of control (p. 258)

low-risk drinking guidelines (p. 261)

methadone (p. 281)

Minnesota model (p. 271)

motivational interviewing (p. 273)

negative emotionality (p. 268)

nicotine (p. 275)

opioids (p. 279)

pharmacological dependence (p. 258)

polysubstance abuse (p. 258)

relapse (p. 272)

risky use (p. 258)

social impairment (p. 258)

stimulants (p. 274)

substance-induced disorder (p. 258)

substance use disorders (p. 257)

tension-reduction (p. 268)

THC (p. 282)

tobacco (p. 274)

tolerance (p. 258)

toxic psychosis (p. 277)

Wernicke-Korsakoff syndrome (p. 265)

withdrawal (p. 258)

STEPHEN P. LEWIS

•

STEPHEN PORTER

CHAPTER

12

Marekuliasz/Shutterstock

The Personality Disorders

LEARNING OBJECTIVES

BY THE END OF THIS CHAPTER, STUDENTS WILL BE ABLE TO:

1 Differentiate between personality traits and disorders in accordance with the *Diagnostic and Statistical Manual* (DSM-5).

2 Understand how personality disorders differ from other disorders that may have overlapping symptoms.

3 Identify the three clusters of personality disorders, and define each disorder.

4 Define and differentiate egosyntonic and egodystonic.

5 Differentiate between antisocial personality disorder and psychopathy.

6 Understand how obsessive-compulsive personality disorder (OCPD) differs from obsessive-compulsive disorder (OCD).

7 Identify and summarize the four main etiological perspectives of personality disorders.

Bikram is 26 years old. He lives alone in Calgary but is supported by his parents after recently losing his job. He spends most of his days alone on his computer or reading books about ghosts and urban legends. His parents describe him as always being "different" and an "odd child." They say Bikram has an intense belief in paranormal activity; he says that he believes in the existence of ghosts and claims to have seen them in the past. Bikram has difficulty forming relationships and is very anxious in social settings. His anxiety does not wane when interacting with others, even in situations in which he has familiarity (e.g., gatherings with family friends). Bikram is highly suspiciousness of others and is very superstitious. He avoids walking under ladders and believes he is cursed with "negative energy" for having broken a mirror when he was younger.

***

Amelie is 22 and was hospitalized in St. John's following an episode of self-injury that warranted medical attention. During her intake interview, it was found that she cut herself deeply in response to intense and what she perceived as intolerable emotional pain that followed a break-up. During the time she is hospitalized, Amelie shares with her doctors that she has cut herself since she was a teenager and that she did this to "deal with" past childhood trauma. Specifically, she was abused by an uncle when she was seven. She also indicates that she engages in a number of other high-risk behaviours, including heavy drinking, binge-eating, and promiscuity. In her relationships, Amelie describes a pattern of falling in love quickly with others but that this does not last long; she reports that none of her relationships end well and she does not speak to any of her ex-partners, some of whom she despises for the way they "abandoned me." When asked about her emotional life, she described herself as warm and caring; however, she also said that she has difficulty regulating her mood and has intense mood swings. Sometimes she has angry outbursts in which she feels threatened and then lashes out at others. She said this has resulted in getting fired from several jobs and losing friendships. When she's alone she describes a sense of not knowing who she is and feeling empty inside. She sometimes feels as though she is "not there" and that she is watching herself from the outside.

***

James enjoyed a good upbringing in a well-to-do family in British Columbia. His family reports that he was a likeable child, but that he lied frequently from a young age and was "like Jekyll and Hyde," changing from being friendly to aggressive in an instant. As he got older, he was seen as charming and engaging, and was very popular with women. He became a musician in a rock band. James has a long history of violence against both men and women. His pattern of violence is diverse such that some of his violent acts were highly premeditated (including sexual assaults, an attempted murder, and a robbery), while many others seemed spontaneous. In fact, he once put his "friend" in a wheelchair over a poker hand. He is now an incarcerated serial rapist.

There are aspects of their personal style (or personality) that contribute to a range of difficulties for Bikram, Amelie, and James. In some cases (e.g., Amelie), the impact is personal distress. Interestingly, however, the personality of all of these individuals negatively affects their social interactions, or in the case of James, can cause serious harm to others. None of these individuals has any one of the other conditions identified in Section II of the DSM-5 (e.g., a mood or anxiety disorder). Yet, each is unable to function in a manner that is adaptive and flexible. Indeed, each seems to be dominated by a single main negative feature (eccentricity in Bikram's case, instability in Amelie's case, and utter selfishness in the case of James) that dominates his or her behaviour and thinking. All three people would very likely meet the diagnostic criteria for a personality disorder.

The Concept of Personality Disorder

How would you describe your best friend? Your answer will likely focus on his or her personality characteristics, or on the manner in which he or she consistently behaves, feels, and thinks. Perhaps your friend is friendly, outgoing, confident, and charismatic. Or maybe your friend is shy, quiet, and passive. All people display some consistency in their behaviour, emotions, and thinking, and this consistency is the basis for describing people's "personality." For instance, we readily describe people we know as being meek or aggressive, friendly or hostile, kind or cruel, shy or outgoing, or sensitive or easygoing. There are countless adjectives used to describe people. And, many people will exhibit variability in these characteristics. For example, you may usually be an outgoing, talkative person, but you may feel great distress or even "clam up" during a public presentation. When we describe someone as having a personality characteristic we are referring to a feature that is typically displayed over time and in various (but not necessarily all) situations. These cross-situationally consistent and persistent features are described by personality theorists as **traits**. People have different levels of various personality traits, the combination of which describes his or her overall personality. The focus of this chapter is on patterns of highly maladaptive personality traits known as **personality disorders**.

According to the DSM-5 "a *personality disorder* is an enduring pattern of inner experience and behavior that deviates markedly from the expectations of the individual's culture, is pervasive and inflexible, has an onset in adolescence or early adulthood, is stable over time, and leads to distress or impairment" (APA, 2013, p. 645). While this definition is similar to those found in most textbooks on personality, it ignores the fact that most people's behaviour is also modified by context. One feature of people with personality disorders, however, is that their personality is more rigid and inflexible. It is displayed, to a large extent, independently of context. In a given situation, their behaviour often seems highly inappropriate to most others. In some cases, they may initially display appropriate behaviour but cannot typically sustain it for long periods or when under stress. In fact, according to the DSM-5, personality traits constitute a personality disorder only when they are *inflexible* and *lead to distress or impairment*. People with personality disorders also show a far more restricted range of traits than do most people. Whereas we would describe most people we know well as having a variety of key traits (e.g., generous, friendly, ambitious), individuals with personality disorders are more likely to be characterized by a single dominant, albeit dysfunctional, trait.

Other mental disorders, such as depression, schizophrenia, or anxiety disorders, are associated with subjective distress. That is, distress that primarily affects the person with the condition. Interestingly, however, while personality disorders can certainly impact the individual afflicted with the disorder (e.g., in borderline personality disorder, avoidant personality disorder), they tend to also cause distress for other people. For example, people with antisocial personality disorder (ASPD) or narcissistic personality disorder may see nothing wrong with themselves, or even believe that other people have the problem. People with ASPD, in particular, can wreak havoc on the lives of those around them through persistent violence, lying, and manipulation.

As a reader, you justifiably may ask why (and perhaps whether) we need to "pathologize" or diagnose a condition that causes the affected person little distress. This is actually a highly controversial issue. On the one hand, the field of abnormal psychology does not wish to cause harm to a person through the stigma of a diagnostic label such as "personality disorder." Further, we run the risk of circular logic with such labels by implying that they have some explanatory power. For example, if we explain the destructive behaviour of someone with ASPD as resulting from his or her condition or "illness," we are using circular reasoning (because we diagnose the condition based on such behaviour). On the other hand, abnormal psychology seeks to classify these conditions in order to aid in the prediction, diagnosis, and treatment of behaviour. Psychopathy is a good example of a construct that helps to predict behaviour. Knowing that criminal offenders meet criteria for psychopathy allows us to predict that they are far more likely to perpetrate predatory violence than are their non-psychopathic counterparts. Moreover, three large-scale prospective longitudinal studies, known as the Children in the Community Study of Developmental Course of Personality Disorder (Cohen, Crawford, Johnson, & Kasen, 2005), the Collaborative Longitudinal Personality Disorders Study (Skodol et al., 2005), and the McLean Study of Adult Development (Zanarini, Frankenburg, Hennen, Reich, & Silk, 2005), have been consistent in their conclusions that personality disorders represent a significant health problem for those with the condition (e.g., interpersonal conflicts, suicide attempts, violent/criminal behaviour) and in their association with extensive treatment use.

1 BEFORE MOVING ON

> How does the DSM-5 define personality traits and personality disorders? When do personality traits constitute a personality disorder? How do personality disorders differ from other major mental disorders?

This chapter reflects the current model for personality disorders advocated by the DSM-5 in Section II. The DSM-5 provides six formal criteria in defining personality disorders:

- Criterion A states that the pattern of behaviour must be manifested in at least two of the following areas: cognition, emotions, interpersonal functioning, or impulse control.

- Criterion B requires that the enduring pattern of behaviour be rigid and consistent across a broad range of personal and social situations.

- Criterion C states that this behaviour should lead to clinically significant distress in social, occupational, or other important areas of functioning.

- Criterion D requires stability and long duration of symptoms, with onset in adolescence or earlier.

- Criterion E states that the behaviour cannot be accounted for by another mental disorder.

- Criterion F requires that the behavioural patterns are not the result of substance use (e.g., drugs or alcohol) or of another medical condition.

DSM-5 lists the specific personality disorders according to three broad **clusters**:

- **Cluster A** *odd and eccentric disorders* (paranoid, schizoid, and schizotypal);

- **Cluster B** *dramatic, emotional, or erratic disorders* (antisocial, borderline, histrionic, and narcissistic); and

- **Cluster C** *anxious and fearful disorders* (avoidant, dependent, and obsessive-compulsive).

In addition to these three clusters, the DSM addresses (a) *personality change due to another medical condition* and (b) *other specified personality disorder and unspecified personality disorder*. Personality *change due to another medical condition* is a persistent disturbance in personality that is the direct result of a medical condition, such as a frontal lobe lesion. The *other specified personality disorder and unspecified personality disorder* is a category provided to address two situations. In the first, the individual meets criteria for a general personality disorder and exhibits symptoms of a number of personality disorders, but the criteria for any single personality disorder are not met. In the second, the individual might meet criteria for a general personality disorder but the key symptoms are not reflected in the existing personality disorders.

 BEFORE MOVING ON

> What are the six criteria that define personality disorders? Do the names of the three clusters of personality disorders meaningfully depict the disorders they encompass? Which disorders fall into which category? Should we group personality disorders together? Why or why not? What are the two additional personality disorders that do not belong to a cluster? Why do they exist?

Table 12.1 presents the clusters with characteristic features. While Clusters A and C appear to have enough features in common to make reasonably cohesive groups, Cluster B seems somewhat heterogeneous and even confusing (Frances, 1985). Perhaps this is one reason that personality disorders are a somewhat neglected diagnostic category.

Although definitional problems concerning personality disorders should be acknowledged, the assessment of these conditions represents an important issue in clinical and forensic settings. For one thing, when someone has a personality disorder it can greatly complicate the treatment of other mental disorders. Part of the difficulty is that personality disorders can disrupt the alliance between a therapist and a client. In addition, personality disorders can sometimes be mistaken for another mental disorder. For example, schizotypal personality disorder shares features (although less severe) with schizophrenia. Indeed, schizotypal personality disorder is also listed under "schizophrenia spectrum and other psychotic disorders" to aid with differential diagnosis.

TABLE 12.1 PERSONALITY DISORDERS LISTED IN DSM-5

Paranoid personality disorder is a pattern of distrust and suspiciousness such that others' motives are interpreted as malevolent.

Schizoid personality disorder is a pattern of detachment from social relationships and a restricted range of emotional expression.

Schizotypal personality disorder is a pattern of acute discomfort in close relationships, cognitive or perceptual distortions, and eccentricities of behavior.

Antisocial personality disorder is a pattern of disregard for, and violation of, the rights of others.

Borderline personality disorder is a pattern of instability in interpersonal relationships, self-image, and affects, and marked impulsivity.

Histrionic personality disorder is a pattern of excessive emotionality and attention seeking.

Narcissistic personality disorder is a pattern of grandiosity, need for admiration, and lack of empathy.

Avoidant personality disorder is a pattern of social inhibition, feelings of inadequacy, and hypersensitivity to negative evaluation.

Dependent personality disorder is a pattern of submissive and clinging behavior related to an excessive need to be taken care of.

Obsessive-compulsive personality disorder is a pattern of preoccupation with orderliness, perfectionism, and control

Personality change due to another medical condition is a persistent personality disturbance that is judged to be due to the direct physiological effects of a medical condition (e.g., frontal lobe lesion).

Other specified personality disorder and unspecified personality disorder is a category provided for two situations: 1) the individual's personality pattern meets the general criteria for a personality disorder, and traits of several different personality disorders are present, but the criteria for any specific personality disorder are not met; or 2) the individual's personality pattern meets the general criteria *for* a personality disorder, but the individual is considered to have a personality disorder that is not included in the DSM-5 classification (e.g., passive-aggressive personality disorder).

A wrong diagnosis could lead to the wrong treatment plan, or possibly a mistaken drug prescription. In addition, while the treatment of personality disorders has been traditionally viewed as difficult and the prognosis poor, the situation is improving with the development of more effective therapeutic approaches.

Studies investigating the **prevalence** of personality disorders have examined rates among inpatient, outpatient, and community populations. Depending on the sample and method of diagnosis, prevalence rates vary considerably. For instance, relative to structured interviews, self-report measures will likely yield underestimates of ASPD because individuals are reluctant to admit that they engage in antisocial behaviours. Accordingly, the use of multi-method assessment is relevant to broader diagnostic issues as well as to treatment and prediction issues. For example, Klein (2003) evaluated patients' and informants' (e.g., intimate partners, relatives, friends) reports of personality disorders in predicting outcomes in a seven-and-a-half-year follow-up of 85 outpatients with major depression. Both patients' and informants' reports uniquely predicted depressive symptoms and global functioning at follow-up. Interestingly, only informants' reports made an independent contribution to predicting social adjustment. This suggests that at least some patients with personality disorders may not be cognizant of the negative impact they have on those close to them.

Unfortunately, little research has examined the prevalence of personality disorders among the general Canadian population. While the Public Health Agency of Canada (2002), has examined personality disorders among individuals in institutional settings, these data have major limitations because most people with personality disorders who are hospitalized are a risk to themselves or to others. In contrast, most others go untreated or are treated in their community rather than in hospitals. Among both women and men, the highest rates of hospitalization for personality disorders in 1999 were among people between 15 and 44 years of age. More than three-quarters (78 percent) of all admissions were between these ages, and rates were higher among women than men. In all age groups, personality disorders were more likely to be a contributing rather than the main factor determining length of stay in hospital. This is because personality disorders are associated with other conditions, such as suicidal behaviour, that lead to hospitalization. The average length of stay in hospitals due to personality disorders was 9.5 days.

In another study, Séguin and colleagues (2006) conducted **psychological autopsies** of 102 individuals who died by suicide in New Brunswick. A psychological autopsy is a research method used after someone dies by suicide and involves comprehensive (often structured) interviews with others in the life of the deceased (e.g., partners, family, friends) as well as those involved in their health care to obtain detailed information about the deceased individual and what might have contributed to the individual's suicide. Findings from this study found that 52 percent of the cases involved personality disorders, half of which were from Cluster B.

Again though, these findings only provide a partial picture of the range of personality disorders in Canada given the narrow focus of the sample. It is clear that data concerning the prevalence of these disorders in community samples in Canada are greatly needed!

Given the above, we often have to look to research from other countries to get a sense of personality disorder rates. For example, a study conducted in the United States examined the lifelong prevalence of personality disorders in a community sample, with findings indicating that the overall (lifetime) rate of personality disorders was 6.7% (Zimmerman & Coryell, 1990). More specifically, rates across the three clusters were 3.6% for Cluster A (with schizotypal being the most common), 2.7% for Cluster B (with antisocial and histrionic being the most common), and 2.7% for Cluster C (with dependent and obsessive-compulsive being the most common). Studies in Europe tend to reveal somewhat lower rates (Maier, Lichtermann, Klingler, Heun, & Hallmayer, 1992). Comparisons of these and other findings suggest that about 6 to 9 percent of the entire population, including community, hospitalized, and outpatient samples, will have one or more personality disorders during their life (Merikangas & Weissman, 1986). Samuels and colleagues (2002) had clinical psychologists assess personality disorders in 742 adult participants living in Maryland. They found that the overall prevalence of all personality disorders was 9 percent. The authors also examined various demographic characteristics associated with personality disorders. Cluster A disorders were most prevalent in men who had never married. Cluster B disorders were most prevalent in poorly educated men, and Cluster C disorders were most common among those who had graduated from high school but who had never married (for a critique of this study see Lenzenweger, Lane, Loranger, & Kessler, 2007).

Studies published in the *Journal of Clinical Psychiatry* and the *Journal of Personality Disorders* provide some of the highest estimates of personality disorders to date. Conducted by the National Institute on Alcohol Abuse and Alcoholism and the National Institutes of Health, the first study focused on a representative community survey of 43 000 American adults. The authors (Grant et al., 2004) estimated that from 2001 to 2002, 14.8 percent of American adults (30.8 million) met the diagnostic criteria for at least one DSM-IV-TR personality disorder. Overall, the risk of having avoidant, dependent, and paranoid personality disorders was greater for females than for males, whereas the risk of having ASPD was greater for males than for females. The authors found no gender differences in risk for obsessive-compulsive, schizoid, or histrionic personality disorders. The authors of this study also identified the following factors associating with having a diagnosed personality disorder: being Native American or Black; being a young adult; having low socio-economic status; and being divorced, separated, widowed, or never married. This study must be considered with caution, as it has been criticized for relying on a new diagnostic interview administered by laypersons instead of a well-validated interview by trained clinicians (Lenzenweger et al., 2007).

Moreover, it is important to remember that viewing gender, ethnicity, or marital status as risk factors in themselves is problematic as it simplifies the nature of risk and provides little (if any) explanation or context to account for *why* these factors associate with personality disorder risk. In the second study, based on a community sample of 644 children tracked from early childhood through adolescence and into early adulthood, Crawford and colleagues (2005) estimated the prevalence of any personality disorder to be 15.7 percent. As with the Samuels and colleagues (2002) study, however, the Crawford and colleagues (2005) sample has been criticized for not being representative of the greater U.S. population (Lenzenweger et al., 2007).

In an effort to address some of these methodological limitations and present nationally representative estimates of clinician-diagnosed personality disorders in the general U.S. population, Lenzenweger and colleagues (2007) examined the responses to questions from the International Personality Disorder Examination administered to 5692 participants. According to results from a sub-sample of more than 200 participants who were administered the complete measure 5.7% met criteria for Cluster A disorders, 1.5% for Cluster B disorders, 6.0% for Cluster C disorders, and 9.1% for any personality disorder. Gender, race/ethnicity, family income, and marital status were not significantly related to any of the personality disorder measures.

Generally speaking, prevalence rates are higher among those in inpatient versus outpatient settings. For example, borderline personality disorder, the most commonly diagnosed personality disorder among patients in treatment, has been reported in 11% of outpatients and 19% of inpatients (Widiger & Frances, 1989). Rates of ASPD vary depending on whether psychiatric patients or criminal offenders are surveyed. In psychiatric outpatients, the prevalence rates are near 5%, but jump to 12 to 37% for psychiatric inpatients. In prison populations, the rates range from 30 to 70% (Widiger & Rogers, 1989).

Traditionally, personality disorders have been viewed as distinct from other mental problems (e.g., major depression, schizophrenia). This is reflected in previous iterations of the DSM (e.g., DSM-IV), where personality disorders were located in a distinct section from mood disorders, eating disorders, psychotic disorders, and most other conditions. This may, at least in part, explain why personality disorders appear toward the end of Section II in the DSM-5 (despite their early onset considering the organization of Section II to temporally reflect development). Relative to personality disorders, the so-called *clinical disorders* (e.g., schizophrenia, bipolar disorder) have more pronounced symptomatology and have a greater likelihood of referral to mental health professionals. This may also account for why the main clinical disorders in DSM-5 tend to be referred to as "mental illnesses" when compared to personality disorders. Technically, however, they would all be mental illnesses by virtue of their inclusion in the DSM.

Whereas older research indicated that 80% or more of people with personality disorders never seek treatment (Drake & Vaillant, 1985), results from the National Comorbidity Survey Replication (Lenzenweger et al., 2007) suggested that 39% of people with a personality disorder receive treatment for their mental health or substance abuse difficulties. Those with Cluster B disorders sought treatment the most (49.1%), followed by those with Cluster C disorders (29%) and Cluster A disorders (25%). Most of the respondents sought treatment from general medical providers (19%), followed by psychiatrists (14%) or other mental health professionals (17%).

An important distinction between personality disorders and other DSM-5 disorders is that most individuals suffering from major mental health difficulties (e.g., schizophrenia, bipolar disorder) have far more impaired functioning than do most patients with personality disorders. An objective evaluation of people with personality disorders indicates impaired life circumstances, but their actual abilities appear relatively intact compared to those with major mental disorders (Millon, 1996). Also, as mentioned earlier, for many people with personality disorder, their functioning is **egosyntonic**. That is, they do not view it as problematic. In contrast, most other mental disorders are generally considered **egodystonic** as they cause distress and are viewed as problematic by the individual. Intervention for those with personality disorders, then, must initially address the issue of motivation for treatment and treatment readiness.

Diagnostic Issues

Personality disorders have traditionally presented more diagnostic problems than most other mental disorders because of the lower reliability of their diagnosis (Rogers, Duncan, Lynett, & Sewell, 1994), their poorly understood etiology (Marshall & Barbaree, 1984), and weaker treatment efficacy (Kelly et al., 1992). With respect to diagnosis, two indices of reliability are important. Inter-rater reliability—that is, the agreement between two raters—ranges from 0.86 to 0.97 for the personality disorders (Maffei et al., 1997). Test-retest reliability—that is, agreement in diagnosis over time—has traditionally been much weaker, ranging from 0.11 to 0.57 (Zimmerman, 1994), although this seems to have been improving in recent years (see below).

There are, however, other challenges to the DSM's definitions of personality disorder and questions of whether a "diagnosis" is even warranted. For example, Canadian researcher John Livesley and his colleagues (Livesley, 1986; Livesley, Schroeder, Jackson, & Jang, 1994) have argued that personality disorders are better viewed as constellations of traits, each of which lie along a continuum, rather than as disorders that people simply have or do not have. For example, one could view extreme levels of conscientiousness (e.g., being very rigid, highly perfectionistic, miserly), as involved in obsessive-compulsive personality disorder. This conceptualization of personality disorders as traits along a continuum is acknowledged in the DSM-5. It also aligns with the manner by which personality traits tend to be conceived (i.e., viewed on a dimension). We discuss these issues in more detail toward the end of this text. In addition, as explained in the next section, others have suggested that the diagnostic criteria for some personality disorders are gender biased (Kaplan, 1983), or that their application permits the gender biases of the diagnostician to influence diagnosis (Ford & Widiger, 1989).

There are, in fact, many problems with the notion of personality disorder that have not been resolved, and it is clear that further research is needed before a clearly defined set of criteria is developed. Nonetheless, most clinicians agree that some people consistently show maladaptive, inflexible, and restricted ways of behaving, feeling, and thinking that are best described as relating to personality. In the end, it is not so much whether personality disorders exist, but rather how they can be defined in a way that is unbiased, reliable, and leads to effective treatment or prediction. Among the various diagnostic issues, researchers have identified gender and cultural bias in the diagnostic criteria as subjects of concern. These biases, it is suggested, contribute to the broader problem of unsatisfactory reliability.

GENDER AND CULTURAL ISSUES

An important consideration when making a DSM-5 diagnosis is to ensure that the client's functioning does not simply reflect normative responding in the client's culture. As our populations become increasingly culturally diverse, clinicians might misdiagnose if they do not take adequate precautions to determine whether certain attitudes and behaviours are appropriate for distinct cultures or societal subgroups. For example, economically disadvantaged children living in inner cities may learn self-interested strategies in order to survive. These strategies may, in the eyes of a more privileged clinician, appear to reveal psychopathology, whereas in reality they are adaptive given the environmental context.

Similar concerns exist for gender biases in the diagnosis of personality disorders. Sex role stereotypes may influence the clinician's determination of the presence of personality disorders (Pantony & Caplan, 1991). For example, clinicians have been shown to be reluctant to diagnose males with histrionic personality disorder and are unlikely to consider females as having ASPD (Samuel & Widiger, 2009; Widiger & Spitzer, 1991). The emphasis on aggression in the criteria for ASPD may result in underdiagnosing in females because of gender differences in the prevalence and expression of aggression. In addition, Henry and Cohen (1983) have suggested that clinicians typically overdiagnose borderline personality disorder (BPD) in women. For example, in one study an average of 80 percent of people diagnosed with BPD were women (Widiger & Trull, 1993). It is difficult to know whether these results reflect a true gender difference in the occurrence of the disorder, or whether they reflect inappropriately gender-biased criteria or application of the criteria. A more recent study conducted by Boggs and colleagues (2005) discovered that the diagnosis of BPD in females (versus males) may be due to the criteria themselves.

Specifically, there was a gender bias in the criteria for BPD and in the view that BPD manifests differently in men than in women. Finally, this study concluded that this gender difference in the symptoms of BPD was not reflected in the DSM-IV criteria (the most recent version of the DSM at the time that the study was conducted); the DSM-5 criteria also do not address the symptoms characteristic of BPD in men.

As another example, histrionic personality disorder has long been diagnosed more commonly in females than in males (Reich, 1987), and studies asking participants to rate the diagnostic criteria indicate that most people view the features of the disorder as decidedly feminine (Sprock, Blashfield, & Smith, 1990). In an interesting examination of gender bias, Warner (1978) had 175 mental health professionals make a diagnosis after reading a case history. The patient was described as a woman in half of the cases and as a man in the other half, but the case description remained the same. Of those clinicians who were given the "female" case, 76 percent diagnosed the patient as suffering from a hysterical personality disorder (the earlier name for histrionic personality disorder), while only 49 percent applied that diagnosis when the patient was described as a man.

Ford and Widiger (1989) also examined these issues, but looked at gender bias both in the diagnostic criteria *and* in the diagnosis of histrionic personality disorder. They found that, while the specific diagnostic criteria for histrionic personality disorder were found with equal frequency among men and women, women were more likely to be diagnosed with the disorder. In another study of histrionic personality disorder, women were more commonly diagnosed, whereas an epidemiological survey of more than 3000 community adults revealed the same prevalence in males and females (2.2 percent) (Nestadt et al., 1990). This finding suggests either bias in referrals to psychiatric clinics for people with histrionic features or gender bias in the application of the diagnosis among those who are referred.

The gender biases witnessed in diagnosing personality disorders have sometimes become "systemic," such that large numbers of males or females are virtually excluded from a diagnosis category because of their gender. For example, psychopathy—one of the most harmful personality disorders, although not yet formally listed in DSM-5—is diagnosed in approximately 15 to 25 percent of male federal inmates in Canada (translating into thousands of men). However, very few female federal inmates ever receive this classification because the Correctional Service of Canada apparently views being female as largely incompatible with being psychopathic, a belief that is not in accordance with research. For example, Rutherford, Cacciola, and Alterman (1999) examined the prevalence of psychopathy in a group of 137 women seeking treatment for cocaine dependency. The findings showed that 19 percent of the women scored in the moderate to high range on the Psychopathy Checklist–Revised, 12 of whom were diagnosed with APD according to the DSM-IV. Clearly, psychopathy can occur in women, despite the reluctance—perhaps politically driven—of some agencies to concur with the research.

It is difficult to know whether differences in the prevalence of personality disorders across genders and ethnic groups represent biases in diagnosis or reflect *true differences*. One study looked at this issue by examining ratings of both diagnosticians and the patients themselves. Grilo and colleagues (2003) compared the distribution of borderline (BPD), schizotypal (STPD), avoidant (APD), and obsessive-compulsive (OCPD) disorders across three groups: Caucasians, African-Americans, and Hispanics. The researchers used both a clinician-administered diagnostic interview and a self-report instrument. The results indicated higher rates of BPD in Hispanic than in Caucasian and African-American participants, and higher rates of STPD among African-Americans than Caucasians. Self-report data reflected the same patterns, suggesting that there may be true cultural differences in the risk for certain disorders.

RELIABILITY OF DIAGNOSIS

Concerns regarding cultural and gender insensitivity in diagnostic strategies underscore larger issues related to the reliability and validity of diagnosing personality disorders. These are not new concerns and they have governed revisions to the DSM since 1980. For instance, the early field trials with DSM-III (APA, 1980) revealed rather poor reliability for the personality disorders, suggesting that clinicians often fail to agree on a particular diagnosis for a specific patient. However, the manner by which diagnoses are made, and the time spent collating relevant diagnostic information (e.g., presence of symptoms, impact on functioning) may contribute to better reliability. Indeed, it is likely that most personality disorders can be reliably diagnosed given enough information and effort. Imagine if oncologists or cardiologists did not "have time" to diagnose cancer or heart disease reliably! Sometimes, the consequences of a missed personality disorder can be as devastating.

Notwithstanding issues regarding the reliability of personality disorder diagnoses, the situation appears to be improving. Adding support for this are recent studies suggesting that personality disorder diagnoses may be becoming more reliable. For example, Zanarini and colleagues (2000) examined both the inter-rater and the test-retest reliability of Axis I and II disorders using structured DSM-IV-based interviews. The results indicated at least "fair to good" inter-rater reliability for *all* personality disorders diagnosed by experienced clinicians. In addition, all personality disorders, except for narcissistic personality disorder and paranoid personality disorder, showed "fair to good" test-retest reliability.

A major goal of research examining the reliability of personality disorders has been to determine their stability over time. Interestingly, it is possible that these conditions may not be as chronic as once believed (Bornovalova, Hicks, Iacono, & McGue, 2009; Ericson, Tuvbald, Raine, Young-Wolff, & Baker, 2011). For example, Skodol and colleagues (2005) reported that fewer than one half of patients with a personality disorder remained at or above the diagnostic criteria for their initial diagnosis every month for a follow-up period lasting two years. These findings are consistent with those of two other large-scale longitudinal studies, the Children in the Community Study of Developmental Course of Personality Disorder (Cohen et al., 2005) and the McLean Study of Adult Development (Zanarini et al., 2005), which found that personality disorders were not as enduring as was once thought.

COMORBIDITY AND DIAGNOSTIC OVERLAP

One further problem with the diagnosis of personality disorders concerns their independence from each other as well as other mental disorders. The terms *comorbidity* and *overlap* are often used synonymously in the literature when, in fact, they refer to two conceptually distinct features of diagnosis. **Comorbidity** should be used to describe the co-occurrence of two or more different diagnoses for one person. **Overlap**, on the other hand, refers to the similarity of symptoms in two or more different disorders (i.e., some of the same criteria apply to different diagnoses). Diagnostic criteria for different conditions should be distinct, but for some personality disorders the criteria remain sufficiently vague or require such significant inference by the clinician that overlap seems likely. For example, narcissistic personality disorder (NPD) and antisocial personality disorder (ASPD) are both associated with a lack of empathy or concern for others.

Researchers have highlighted problems with overlap between specific disorders. For example, in one study, 47 percent of those diagnosed with borderline personality disorder (BPD) met the criteria for ASPD and 57 percent met the criteria for histrionic disorder (Widiger, Frances, & Trull, 1987). A recent study found that schizotypal personality disorder was associated with both borderline personality disorder and narcissistic personality disorder (Lentz, Robinson, & Bolton, 2010). Another example is a study that revealed that psychopathic individuals with antisocial personality disorder often show overlapping symptoms with both schizoid personality disorder and narcissistic personality disorder (Coid & Ullrich, 2010). While some degree of co-occurrence is expected with any condition, these rates are quite high and raise questions about the nature of overlapping symptoms across different personality disorders.

Comorbidity also exists between personality disorders and other mental disorders. A recent World Health Organization study estimated that worldwide, over half (51.2 percent) of individuals diagnosed with personality disorders meet the criteria for at least one other mental disorder (Huang et al., 2009). A specific example is the comorbidity between borderline personality disorder and mood disorders. This comorbidity has led to suggestions that borderline disorder might better be classified as a mood disorder (Nakdimen, 1986), an issue which continues to be debated (Tryer, 2009; Parker, 2014). Despite these issues, the Collaborative Longitudinal Personality Disorders Study (Skodol et al., 2005) established that diagnostic criteria for the individual personality disorders related better with each other than with criteria from other personality disorders. This led these researchers to conclude that the diagnostic criteria of each of the personality disorders show some discriminant validity.

Historical Perspective

Historically, most attention on personality disorders has focused on what we now call antisocial personality disorder, or the related condition psychopathy. The well-known writings of Niccolò Machiavelli (1469–1527) advocated for the use of unscrupulous, manipulative, amoral, and deceptive behaviour in achieving power in politics and society (Campbell, 2003). Based on his writings, the term *machiavellianism* has become synonymous with callous, manipulative, and deceptive personality characteristics (see Campbell, 2003; Fehr, Samson, & Paulhus, 1992; Wilson, Near, & Miller, 1996). Machiavellianism, in addition to subclinical narcissism and subclinical psychopathy, comprise the "Dark Triad"—a constellation of personality traits that are deemed to be socially aversive (Paulhus & Williams, 2002).

One of the first written descriptions of the psychopathy was by Pinel (1809), whose work was discussed in Chapter 1. Pinel described a psychiatric condition associated primarily with amorality rather than psychosis. He referred to this condition as *manie sans délire*, or madness without delirium. In such patients, he observed profound deficits in emotion but no apparent reasoning/intellectual dysfunction. Such patients were prone to stealing, violence, and lying, but seemed to have no other mental health difficulties.

Similar to Pinel's notion, British psychiatrist James Pritchard (1835) coined the term *moral insanity* to delineate a mental condition characterized by an absence of morality, rather than the "madness" seen in other psychiatric patients. Like Pinel, Pritchard observed that while there clearly was emotional dysfunction in such patients, their cognitive abilities were intact. Pritchard (1835) further discussed how individuals suffering from moral insanity seemed to completely disregard the moral, ethical, and cultural norms of society. He thought that the "moral principles of the mind" were "perverted or depraved" in these men. Koch (1891, as cited in Millon, Simonsen, & Birket-Smith, 1998) objected to the term *moral insanity* and gave the opinion that a more appropriate term would be *psychopathic inferiority*. In his view, the condition of psychopathy stemmed from a type of biological abnormality that resulted in personality anomalies such as extreme selfishness. This conceptualization of psychopathy, with its focus on personality pathology, was more closely aligned to the modern conceptualization of psychopathy than were earlier views.

Sociologists also took interest in the early part of the twentieth century. Not surprisingly, they saw social conditions as critical. Accordingly, they replaced the term *psychopath* with the descriptor *sociopath* (Birnbaum, 1914). Partridge (1930) argued that individuals with this psychopathic inferiority were exhibiting a "social" disorder and coined the term *sociopath*, reflecting the idea that the condition involved an "anti-society" view of life. Such views were eventually incorporated into the APA's first edition of the DSM in 1952, which described a "sociopathic personality disturbance, antisocial reaction."

The current conceptualization of psychopathy is founded largely in the clinical observations of psychiatrist Hervey Cleckley. With a series of clinical case vignettes presented in his classic text *The Mask of Sanity* (1941), Cleckley proposed that there are a number of defining characteristics of the disorder, including emotional, interpersonal, and behavioural elements. Cleckley observed that psychopaths were unresponsive to social control and behaved in a socially inappropriate manner. Further, he described a profound emotional deficit, such that deep emotion and anxiety were missing in the psychopath. In fact, he theorized that a lack of emotion was at the core of the disorder, with other symptoms following from this emotional shallowness. For the past four decades, Dr. Robert Hare and colleagues at the University of British Columbia have worked toward operationalizing Cleckley's criteria for psychopathy, aimed at the generation of a highly reliable diagnostic tool for researchers: the Psychopathy Checklist (Hare, 1980), revised in 1991 and 2003 (Psychopathy Checklist–Revised; Hare, 1991, 2003).

Etiology

Aside from mentions of "hereditary taint" in prominent psychiatric texts (e.g., Krafft-Ebing, 1886/1939), little consideration was given to potential causes of personality disorders in the nineteenth century (e.g., Porter, 1996). This trend began to change with the development of the psychodynamic school and the publication of the first etiological theories of psychopathy in the 1920s (e.g., Partridge, 1928, 1929). Theories related to the etiology of psychopathy continued during and after the 1940s, with contributions from learning theorists (e.g., Schachter & Latane, 1964), psychoanalysts (e.g., Arieti, 1963), and psychophysiologists (e.g., Hare, 1970). In fact, in a 1967 bibliography (Hare & Hare, 1967), 218 studies fell under the category of etiology—more than any other topic on psychopathy. Unfortunately, however, fewer efforts have focused on other personality disorders. Consequently, there are still no firm conclusions about the factors that *cause* personality disorders. In what follows, we briefly cover the main current theories about the etiology of personality disorders. More detail is covered in the section on specific disorders where there is more empirical evidence (i.e., antisocial and borderline disorders).

PSYCHODYNAMIC VIEWS

Psychoanalysts see personality disorders as resulting from disturbances in the parent–child relationship, particularly in problems related to separation-individuation (Mahler, Pine, & Bergman, 1975). This refers to the process by which the child learns that he or she is an individual separate from the mother and other people and, as a result, acquires a sense of him- or herself as an independent person. Thus, according to psychodynamic theorists, difficulties in this process result in either an inadequate sense of self (e.g., borderline, narcissistic, or histrionic personality disorders) or problems in dealing with other people (e.g., avoidant or antisocial personality disorders). There is clear evidence that adults with personality disorders are far more likely than other people to have had difficult childhoods, including the loss of a parent through death, divorce, or abandonment (Pert, Ferriter, & Saul, 2004; Robins, 1966) or parental rejection (McCord & McCord, 1964; Russ, Heim, & Westen, 2003). This evidence has also served to bolster other environmental theories of personality disorders, particularly attachment theory (Ainsworth & Bowlby, 1991) and learning-based theories (Turkat & Levin, 1984).

ATTACHMENT THEORY

As with many mental disorders, dominant thinking on the nature/nurture debate has undergone dramatic shifts over time. During the 1990s, it became somewhat unfashionable to explain personality pathology as being rooted in childhood (Porter, 1996), with biology being seen by many as the primary cause, especially for APSD and psychopathy (e.g., Hare, 1993; Livesley, Jang, & Vernon, 2003). More recently, the Children in the Community Study of Developmental Course of Personality Disorder established that "PD symptom constellations identified in adulthood have their origins in childhood" (Cohen et al., 2005, p. 481).

Many theorists are again turning to the role of early relationships in contributing to personality pathology in adulthood. Attachment theory asserts that children learn how to relate to others, particularly in affectionate ways, by the way in which their parents relate to them. When the attachment bond between parents and the child is positive (i.e., the parents are loving, encouraging, and supportive), the child will develop the skills and confidence necessary to relate effectively to others. The parent–child bond serves as a template for all later relationships (Bowlby, 1977). When this bond is poor, children will lack confidence in relationships with others (i.e., they will be afraid of rejection, and they will not have the skills necessary for intimate relationships). This analysis has been applied to various personality disorders (Links, 1992; Patrick, Hobson, Castle, & Howard, 1994), and empirical evidence appears to support the role of disrupted attachments in the etiology of these disorders (Coons, 1994; Torgersen & Alnaes, 1992; West, Keller, Links, & Patrick, 1993).

Researchers at the University of British Columbia (Bartholomew, 1990; Dutton, Saunders, Starzomski, & Bartholomew, 1994) have shown that if parent–child attachments are poor, the child will typically develop adult relationship styles that are characterized by ambivalence, fear, or avoidance. Poor attachments typically lead to deficits in developing intimacy (Marshall, Hudson, & Hodkinson, 1993), such that various maladaptive ways of dealing with interpersonal relationships are likely (Marshall & Barbaree, 1984).

Levy (2000) has argued that poor attachment bonds are an antecedent to violence and antisocial patterns in children. The fact that personality disorders usually become obvious during late adolescence when the demands for social interaction become pre-eminent lends some support to the importance of attachment deficits in the origin of these disorders. Consistent with these claims, Goldberg, Mann, Wise, and Segall (1985) found that patients with personality disorders typically described their parents as either uncaring or overprotective, or both.

Finally, in a multi-site study, Battle and colleagues (2004) examined the childhood histories of 600 patients diagnosed with a personality disorder or major depressive disorder. The study confirmed that rates of childhood maltreatment among individuals with personality disorders are generally high (73 percent reporting abuse; 82 percent reporting neglect). As expected, borderline personality disorder was more consistently associated with childhood abuse and neglect than were other disorders. Of course, it is not possible to establish causation (only correlation) using this approach. Nonetheless, these findings show the very high prevalence of negative childhood experiences in those with a personality disorder.

COGNITIVE-BEHAVIOURAL PERSPECTIVES

Cognitive-behavioural theorists have suggested a variety of factors that may contribute to the emergence of personality disorders. Cognitive strategies or schemas (e.g., beliefs, assumptions, and attitudes) are said to develop early in life, and in individuals with personality disorders these schemas become rigid and inflexible (Beck, Freeman, & Davis, 2004; Shapiro, 1981; Young, 1999; Young, Klosko, & Weishaar, 2003). Young defined negative schemas as broad and pervasively maladaptive themes that people hold about themselves and their relationships with others. Because they form early in life as a result of damaging experiences (e.g., abandonment), Young believed that negative schemas are familiar. The views of new events become distorted to maintain the validity of the schemas. People cope with their negative schemas in ways that may have been adaptive when they were children trying to survive in a damaging environment (e.g., by surrendering or overcompensating), but they continue coping in this same manner into adulthood.

Linehan (1987, 1993; Linehan, Cochran, Kehrer, & Barlow, 2001) argued that people who develop borderline personality disorder come from families who consistently invalidate their childhood emotional experiences and oversimplify the ease with which life's problems can be solved. Accordingly, they learn that the way to communicate and get the attention of their parents (and, as a consequence, to communicate with others) is through a display of major emotional outbursts. Linehan's theory has been applied primarily to those with borderline personality disorder, but it could apply to other personality disorders, particularly those in Cluster B (i.e., dramatic, emotional, or erratic disorders).

Of course, parents may also model inappropriate personal styles themselves, and there is considerable evidence that modelling is a powerful influence on children's behaviour (Bandura, 1976). In addition, parents may inappropriately reward or punish behaviour and the expression of attitudes. Parents of children who engage in antisocial behaviour, for example, have been shown to reward or punish their children non-contingently (Bauer & Webster-Stratton, 2007; Snyder, 1977); that is, their responses are not related to the child's behaviour.

BIOLOGICAL FACTORS

Biological accounts of personality disorders have been most thoroughly explored with ASPD, and we will discuss them in more depth when we describe that disorder later in this chapter. Basically, however, biological theorists have claimed that there is either brain dysfunction or a genetic or hormonal basis for these conditions. Cloninger, Svrakic, and Przybeck (1993), for example, proposed that specific disturbances in neurotransmitter systems in the brain characterize particular types of personality disorders. Similarly, Siever and Davis (1991) suggest that different biological processes are associated with four dimensions (i.e., cognitive-perceptual organization, impulsivity-aggression, affective stability, and anxiety-inhibition) that together determine personality. In this regard, disruptions in the biological underpinnings of these four factors might be expected to produce unique personality disorders.

Although the evidence showing the value of these general theories is limited, there has been some support for biological factors in personality disorders (Depue, Luciana, Arbisi, Collins, & Leon, 1994). The strongest support, as we will see, comes from research with antisocial personality theories. But more recent work also suggests the likelihood of biological influences on other disorders, such as schizotypal personality disorder. Hans, Auerbach, Styr, and Marcus (2004) examined lifetime major mental disorder and personality disorder diagnoses among 116 young people (aged 12 to 22). Forty-one participants had a parent with schizophrenia, 39 had a parent with a mental disorder other than schizophrenia, and 36 had parents with no mental disorder. One central finding was that both schizophrenia and schizotypal personality disorder occurred exclusively in children of parents with schizophrenia. Children of parents with schizophrenia also were at increased risk for avoidant personality disorder but not paranoid personality disorder. These relationships were particularly strong for males. These findings strongly suggest that there is a familial vulnerability to schizophrenia spectrum disorders (especially schizotypal personality disorder) that is observable before adulthood.

Raine and colleagues (2002) took a different approach to examining biological correlates of personality disorders. Specifically, these researchers focused on a brain region known as the prefrontal cortex. It was already known that structural prefrontal deficits existed in some patients with schizophrenia. The authors examined whether such deficits would also be found in patients with schizophrenia spectrum personality disorders. They assessed prefrontal grey and white volumes using magnetic resonance imaging (MRI) in a community sample of 16 individuals with schizotypal/paranoid personality disorder, 27 healthy control individuals, and 26 psychiatric controls. The personality disorder group showed reduced prefrontal volume and poorer frontal functioning compared to both other groups. More recently, functional MRI (fMRI) studies on patients with borderline personality disorder have begun to appear. These studies have mapped both the structure and the functioning of the brains of people with borderline personality disorder while they engage in emotion-inducing tasks, such as recalling emotional autobiographical events or viewing various emotional expressions on faces. The studies have implicated dysregulated responding of the prefrontal areas of the brain as well as fronto-limbic dysfunction in the form of overactivation of the amygdala (Beblo et al., 2006; Minzenberg, Fan, New, Tang, & Siever, 2007; Schnell, Dietrich, Schnitker, Daumann, & Herpertz, 2007; Schnell & Herpertz, 2007; Silbersweig et al., 2007).

Examining concordance rates among twins provides another approach to test the role of biology in personality disorders. Coolidge, Thede, and Jang (2001) investigated the heritability of personality disorder features in 112 pairs of 4- to 15-year-old twins, including 70 monozygotic and 42 dizygotic twin pairs. The children's parents provided information about the children's features using a tool measuring 12 personality disorders according to the criteria in DSM-IV-TR. The analyses showed that the median "heritability coefficient" for the 12 scales was .75 (ranging from a high of .81 for the dependent and schizotypal personality disorder scales to .50 for the paranoid personality disorder scales). The results suggested that childhood personality disorders may have a substantial genetic component.

SUMMARY OF ETIOLOGY

There are various theories regarding the causes of personality disorders. In keeping with most other disorders, some synthesis of these theories seems to make the most sense. There is clear correlational evidence of biological, family, and learning processes, and there is some (limited) support for psychodynamic accounts. With respect to Cluster A disorders, the most prominent observations are genetic links with both schizophrenia and mood disorders. Biological variables such as impaired eye-tracking, as measured by smooth-pursuit eye movements, have also been investigated as signs of biological bases for Cluster A disorders (Zemishlany, Siever, & Coccaro, 1988). For Cluster B disorders, the two etiological factors that have received the best support are biological factors and attachment problems. Investigations of causal factors specifically with Cluster C disorders have been very limited, despite the prevalence of the disorders (Morey, 1988). In general, causes of the personality disorders remain murky; longitudinal (lifespan) approaches are essential to resolve the lingering mysteries and are currently being conducted (see Cohen et al., 2005; Skodol et al., 2005; Zanarini et al., 2005).

❸ BEFORE MOVING ON

> What are the four main perspectives used to explain the etiology of personality disorders? Are there any definite causes of personality disorders? After reviewing each theory, which perspective appears to be the most legitimate? Do certain theories seem more fitting for some personality disorders than others? Why or why not?

The Specific Disorders

Two personality disorders have received the bulk of research attention over the past several years: antisocial personality disorder and borderline personality disorder. Accordingly, our primary focus will be on these, with briefer descriptions of the remaining disorders.

Cluster A: Odd and Eccentric Disorders

PARANOID PERSONALITY DISORDER

Pervasive **suspiciousness** concerning the motives of other people and a tendency to interpret what others say and do as personally meaningful in a negative way are the primary features of someone with paranoid personality disorder. These individuals consistently misread the innocent actions or comments of others as being threatening or critical, and they expect other people to exploit them. Consequently, individuals with this disorder tend to be hypervigilant, and they take extreme precautions against potential threats from others. They believe that other people intend to hurt them, and they are reluctant to share anything personal for fear it might be used against them. In addition, they are typically humourless and eccentric, and are seen by others as hostile, jealous, and preoccupied with power and control. Not surprisingly, they have numerous problems in relationships; most people cannot tolerate their need to control and particularly their jealous and suspicious nature. Frequently, patients who are paranoid become socially isolated, and this seems only to add to their persecutory ideas.

These features, identified both in the diagnostic criteria and in clinical reports, have been confirmed in research. For example, compared with participants with no diagnosis, individuals with paranoid PD experience far more paranoid thoughts throughout their life (Turkat & Banks, 1987), have greater difficulty dealing with ambiguity and are more suspicious (Thompson-Pope & Turkat, 1988), and are more likely to misread social cues as evidence of hostility by others (Turkat, Keane, & Thompson-Pope, 1990).

Since paranoid personality disorder occurs commonly among relatives of individuals with schizophrenia, a genetic link with schizophrenia has been proposed. Some researchers have even suggested that paranoid personality disorder may be a subtype of schizophrenia (Kendler, Masterson, & Davis, 1985). A more common view is that paranoid PD is a related disorder, or a "cousin" of schizophrenia. The main difference in paranoid PD and paranoid schizophrenia is the severity (e.g., in terms of bizarreness, extension) of people's paranoid beliefs. In schizophrenia, paranoid beliefs are sufficiently bizarre and ingrained that they are considered "psychotic"— that is, a **delusion**. In paranoid PD, the individual's paranoid beliefs are non-bizarre, within the realm of possibility, and pertain to general suspiciousness, even though they are mistaken.

In a large-scale study among adolescents in New York, paranoid PD was one of the four most persistent types of personality disorder identified (Bernstein et al., 1993). Recent data also suggest that paranoid personality disorder is one of the most commonly diagnosed personality disorders in community samples (Edens, Marcus, & Morey, 2009). You might imagine that attempting to provide treatment to someone who distrusts everyone, including the clinician, is very difficult. In fact, it is likely that only a very small proportion of individuals with this disorder would seek or accept treatment.

SCHIZOID PERSONALITY DISORDER

Individuals with this condition seem completely uninterested in having any sort of intimate involvement with others, and they display little in the way of **emotional responsiveness**. They come across as being detached, aloof, or self-absorbed. Individuals with schizoid PD rarely experience intense emotions and may be puzzled by the passions of others. These individuals typically spend significant time alone and can appear cold and indifferent toward others. In fact, they seem not to enjoy relationships of any type, apparently preferring to be alone. Unlike most of us, they avoid social activities and do not seek or seem to desire sexual relations. There seems to be little doubt that most do not have the skills necessary for effective social interaction, but they also appear uninterested in acquiring such skills.

There are several diagnostic concerns related to schizoid PD. For example, in some ways, this condition's presentation may mirror some of the negative symptoms (e.g., flat affect) observed in schizophrenia. Other issues have also been documented. Morey's (1988) examination of the impact on diagnostic practices of the changes from DSM-III to DSM-III-R revealed that the frequency of schizoid diagnoses increased significantly (from 1.4 percent of patients to 11 percent). This was apparently due to a reduction in the frequency of the diagnosis of schizotypal PD and a corresponding increase in diagnosing schizoid PD. Unfortunately, this makes it difficult to compare research on schizoid PD conducted before and after the publication of the DSM-III-R. One of the main problems with this diagnostic category is that it has been the focus of little methodologically sound research. As a consequence, little knowledge has since been offered about this disorder. Perhaps as a result of the changes in previous diagnostic criteria, published studies frequently confound schizoid and schizotypal features, and do not, therefore, permit any definitive conclusions. More recently, data from the Children in the Community Study of Developmental Course of Personality Disorder led Cohen and colleagues (2005) to conclude that schizoid PD appeared to be distinct from paranoid and schizotypal PD. They suggested that schizoid PD may be more related to asocial disorders such as Autism Spectrum Disorder.

SCHIZOTYPAL PERSONALITY DISORDER

The major presenting features of individuals with schizotypal personality disorder are **eccentricity** of thought and behaviour. Much like Bikram from earlier in this chapter, many are extremely superstitious and have thoughts that are permeated by odd beliefs. For instance, individuals with this condition may engage in magical thinking and believe in paranormal phenomena (e.g., telepathy, clairvoyance); it is not uncommon for these individuals to see such skills in themselves. The nature of their odd beliefs can turn others away, which results in them being socially isolated. Such isolation may increase the likelihood for unusual thoughts and perceptions, as there is little opportunity to check the accuracy of their cognitions.

Like paranoid PD, and to a lesser extent schizoid PD, this condition has some similarities with schizophrenia. However, the difference lies in the severity and quality of the symptoms. Although their beliefs, perceptual experiences, speech, and behaviours are odd and they tend to isolate them from others, they are not usually considered to be so eccentric as to meet the criteria for delusional or hallucinatory psychotic experiences. There is, however, considerable disagreement on this issue. For example, McGlashan (1994) claimed that transient psychoses characterize these patients, and Kendler (1985) concluded that schizotypal PD is simply a subtle form of schizophrenia. Research examining biological features has found strong similarities between patients with schizotypal PD and those with schizophrenia (Siever, 1985). In addition, many family members of patients with schizophrenia exhibit schizotypal symptoms (Kendler, 1985). More recent research has revealed that, while the symptoms of schizotypal PD remain the same, the severity of the symptoms varies depending on sex and age (Fonseca-Pedrero, Lemos-Giráldez, Muñiz, García-Cueto, & Campillo-Álvarez, 2008; Paíno-Piñeiro, Fonseca-Pedrero, Lemos-Giráldez, & Muñiz, 2008). These issues are addressed in the DSM-5 in the *Schizophrenia Spectrum and other Psychotic Disorders and Personality* Disorders sections.

The literature regarding treatment of schizotypal personality disorder mirrors the approach taken with etiology; that is, the emphasis is on the schizophrenic-like features. Low doses of antipsychotic drugs may relieve the cognitive problems and social anxiety experienced by these individuals (Goldberg et al., 1986); antidepressant medication has also yielded positive effects (Markovitz, Calabrese, Schulz,

& Meltzer, 1991). Overall, medication has positive, although modest, effects (Gitlin, 1993). Controlled studies of psychological forms of treatment have not been reported. Unfortunately, the long-term prognosis for schizotypal PD is generally poor.

Cluster B: Dramatic, Emotional, or Erratic Disorders

As noted earlier, the four disorders in Cluster B do not seem to have as much in common with each other as is implied by their collective grouping. Whereas histrionic and borderline disorders may be perceived as dramatic, it is hard to see what this descriptor has to do with antisocial personality disorder. Indeed, except for a limited range of emotional expression among these individuals, none of the Custer B descriptors seem to fit those with ASPD. Hence, some suggest that those with ASPD belong to a separate category of personality disorders (Lykken, 1995).

ANTISOCIAL PERSONALITY DISORDER AND PSYCHOPATHY: A CONFUSION OF DIAGNOSES

You were introduced to James at the beginning of this chapter. People like James are among the most dangerous individuals in society, as reflected by a consistently higher rate of criminal behaviour than other offenders throughout adulthood (e.g., Harpur & Hare, 1994; Porter, Birt, & Boer, 2001). James's personal style occurs often in individuals who are diagnosed as having APD. On the surface, he is charming and persuasive, but this masks a self-centred and, in his case, criminal lifestyle. Not all patients with antisocial personalities commit crimes, although most of them who are so diagnosed by clinicians have a criminal record. This may simply reflect the fact that it is their criminal behaviour that brings them to the attention of psychiatrists or psychologists. However, the behavioural features of ASPD do predispose these patients to crime, and unlawfulness is one of the examples that DSM-5 provides of the disregard that those with antisocial personalities display toward others.

DESCRIPTION OF THE DISORDER Individuals thus identified have been referred to as **psychopaths**, **sociopaths**, or dyssocial personalities, with these terms sometimes being used interchangeably. In fact, in correctional settings, the terms *psychopathy* and *ASPD* have been confused for decades. Many researchers and clinicians continue to use the concept of psychopathy rather than following DSM-5 criteria, or vice versa.

However, it is important to recognize that ASPD and psychopathy are *not* the same (e.g., Hart & Hare, 1997). Psychopathy incorporates a richer set of emotional, interpersonal, and behavioural features than the DSM-5 definition of ASPD, which chiefly focuses on observable behaviour. The relatively few criteria reflecting emotional and interpersonal processes in the diagnostic manual, as well as the results of studies (Rogers et al., 1994) comparing the DSM and other measures of ASPD (e.g., PCL-R and the ICD-10 of the World Health Organization, 1992), underscore this concern. However, there is some overlap between ASPD and psychopathy, such that only a small proportion of individuals who qualify for a diagnosis of ASPD are psychopathic, whereas most individuals who are psychopathic would qualify for an ASPD diagnosis (Hare, 2003; Hart & Hare, 1997). According to Coid and Ullrich (2010) ASPD and psychopathy are in fact related, but that psychopathy is more severe than ASPD. In other words, ASPD and psychopathy have an asymmetric relationship. As such, we will consider ASPD and psychopathy to be related but separate entities in the following sections.

The debate regarding the utility of differentiating concepts of ASPD and psychopathy has led to some confusion. Central to this issue is whether the DSM criteria sufficiently reflect the personality domain of the disorder. Employing essentially behavioural criteria may increase diagnostic reliability, but may also yield a group of individuals who are markedly variable in terms of personality traits (Blackburn, 1992). The advantage of using the most widely accepted measure of psychopathy—the Psychopathy Checklist–Revised (PCL-R; Hare, 1991, 2003)—is that it considers

both behaviour and personality. Studies of the PCL-R have revealed that two factors, personality traits and lifestyle instability, are *necessary and sufficient* for a diagnosis (Hare, Hart, & Harpur, 1991). Furthermore, the PCL-R emotional/affective criteria (such as shallow affect) are highly reliable if the rater has the appropriate training (e.g., Hare, 2003).

Unlike the other personality disorders, the essential feature of ASPD is a pervasive pattern of disregard for and violation of the rights of others that begins in childhood or early adolescence and continues into adulthood. The increasing reliance on behavioural indices of the disorder introduced since DSM-II has raised concerns regarding the relation of the diagnostic criteria to clinical conceptions of the related construct of psychopathy (Hare et al., 1991). The notion of psychopathy as a destructive constellation of personality characteristics has a long history (as discussed earlier). Indeed, it was this clinical concept that originally led to the definition of ASPD. Again, it is important to highlight that the DSM-5 criteria for ASPD are a highly reliable set of indicators of a socially deviant lifestyle; however, they are not the best criteria for tapping the core features of psychopathy (e.g., shallow affect, lack of empathy), which are best measured by the Psychopathy Checklist–Revised.

FOCUS 12.1 | ## Paul Bernardo and Karla Homolka

Serial offenders who commit sexual assaults and/or homicides continue to be a major concern to the public. Paul Bernardo, known as the "Scarborough Rapist" and a diagnosed psychopath, sexually assaulted numerous Ontario women over the course of several years in the early 1990s. Although he was a suspect in the investigation of the rapes, he was not arrested and his violence escalated until he—along with his wife, Karla Homolka—raped and murdered three young women, including Homolka's own sister. Bernardo and Homolka abducted two teenage girls separately and held them captive for several days and videotaped their actions while they repeatedly and brutally sexually assaulted them. After several days of torture, the girls were murdered and their bodies were disposed of. When these callous crimes were revealed, the public was outraged—all the more so because a woman was involved. In one of the most notorious plea bargains in Canadian legal history, Homolka entered into a deal with the Ontario Crown Attorney's office on May 14, 1993, in which she agreed to plead guilty to two counts of manslaughter in return for a 12-year sentence (see Galligan, 1996). During the sentencing hearing, evidence was presented that she had played a direct role in the drugging, sexual assault, and death of her 15-year-old sister. Prior to the plea bargain, Homolka had been assessed by several mental health professionals. In March 1993, she had been admitted into a hospital where she underwent lengthy evaluations by two psychiatrists and two psychologists. The clinical reports include numerous diagnoses and clinical descriptions, from stress, anxiety, and depression to learned helplessness, post-traumatic stress disorder, lack of affect, and other indicators of "battered woman syndrome," whereas little evidence was found for psychosis or sexual deviance. The domestic violence she had experienced at the hands of Bernardo had reportedly left her like a "concentration camp survivor," and had contributed to her involvement in the murders (Galligan, 1996).

However, the true extent of Homolka's culpability in the murders was revealed in the videotapes that were later recovered. Her claims of being under her husband's control—central to the plea bargain—appeared to be blatantly false (see Wrightsman & Porter, 2005). On the videotapes they had made of their violence, these predatory offenders clearly derived enjoyment from the suffering of the victims. It was reported that Homolka spoke with and sexually assaulted the victims with a smile on her face. As a student of psychology, how helpful do you think the descriptions provided by the mental health professionals were in helping the court make the right decisions? Did Homolka successfully deceive the court? How does this case inform your opinion of the reliability and validity of DSM disorders and the diagnostic process? ●

Frank Gunn/CP Images   Phil Snel/CP Images

ANTISOCIAL PERSONALITY DISORDER (APD) The DSM-5 criteria for the diagnosis of APD include seven exemplars reflecting the violation of the rights of others: nonconformity, callousness, deceitfulness, irresponsibility, impulsivity, aggressiveness, and recklessness. Sean Penn gave a remarkably accurate portrayal of ASPD in the movie *Dead Man Walking*. Reflecting a **polythetic** approach (meaning only a subset of symptoms or behaviours is required for a diagnosis, unlike most medical diagnoses), three or more of the above symptoms must be met for the diagnosis to be applied.

Prevalence. The DSM-5 reports lifetime prevalence rates for ASPD between 0.2% and 3.3% for both males and females. These results are comparable to the United States National Comorbidity Survey Replication (Lenzenweger et al., 2007), which reported a prevalence rate of 0.6% in males and females combined. The incidence in forensic settings, as expected, is likely higher since criminal behaviour is a dominant feature of ASPD.

Estimates in Great Britain (Chiswick, 1992) indicate a prevalence rate of approximately 25 to 33% of patients in Special Hospitals. This high number presumably occurs because criminals who are considered to have a psychiatric disorder are diverted to these Special Hospitals, whereas those who do not are simply imprisoned. Hare (1983, 1985) reported higher estimates in Canadian prisons using DSM-III-R, where approximately 40% of offenders were diagnosed as having APD. Similar data from another correctional sample were provided by Hart and Hare (1989), reflecting the relative overdiagnosis using DSM-III criteria (50% incidence of APD) compared with an early version of the Personality Checklist (12.5% incidence of psychopathy). These rates are slightly lower than estimates provided by Quebec researchers Côté and Hodgins (1990), who used yet another assessment strategy, the Diagnostic Interview Schedule (Robins, Helzer, Croughan, & Ratcliff, 1981). In a random sample of 495 male inmates, Côté and Hodgins diagnosed 61.5% as having APD using the diagnostic interview criteria.

Etiology of APD. Several lines of investigation have been pursued in an attempt to explain the following major characteristics of persons with ASPD: callous disregard for others, impulsivity and poor self-regulation, rule breaking and criminality, and exploitation of others. Initially, social and family factors were highlighted (Robins, 1966); here, the view was that parental behaviours can influence the development of antisocial functioning. This led to the application of family systems approaches to treatment, in which empirically determined risk factors are targeted within a family-centred model of service delivery (Henggeler & Schoenwald, 1993). This multi-systemic therapy approach has produced some promising outcome data (Borduin et al., 1995) and this has further encouraged the idea that disruptive families are causal factors in the disorder. Moffitt's (1993) work on developmental trajectories indicates that a minority of youth become involved in rule breaking and delinquent behaviour at an early age and that this is sus-

tained throughout their lifespan in one form or another. This research also suggests the importance of familial/parental factors and genetic features as risk factors for developing ASPD. There have been two major systematic literature reviews (Miles & Carey, 1997; Rhee & Waldman, 2002) that collectively analyzed a relatively large body of empirical studies on the genetic influences on antisocial and aggressive behaviour. Both of these reviews incorporated twin and adoption studies in their analyses and both converged on the importance of genetics in the development of aggressive and antisocial behaviour. This literature has yielded heritability estimates for measures of antisocial behaviour/aggression ranging from 44 to 72 percent (Blair, Peschardt, Budhani, Mitchell, & Pine, 2006).

However, while a strictly biological explanation has been found to be insufficient to account for the etiology of antisocial behaviour (Raine, 1993), such factors appear to interact with childhood experiences to produce criminality. There appear to be neuropsychological markers that, in combination with specific environmental circumstances (e.g., criminogenic environment, poor parenting, neglect, and physical abuse), interact to make children vulnerable to developing an antisocial lifestyle and personality (Mealey, 1995).

Finally, there are psychological explanations for ASPD that focus on inadequate self-regulation. Lykken (1957), for example, suggested that such individuals are essentially fearless. This **fearlessness hypothesis** claims that those with ASPD have a higher threshold for feeling fear than do other people. Events that make most people anxious (e.g., the expectation of being punished) are thought to have little or no effect on those with ASPD. A recent study provided support for this hypothesis by confirming that there appears to be an attentional mechanism that reduces the fear response in individuals with ASPD (Dvorak-Bertsch, Curtin, Rubinstein, & Newman, 2009).

Despite this line of research, some social learning theorists have questioned the validity of the fearlessness hypothesis. For instance, Schmauk (1970) suggested that, since Lykken's research (see Figure 12.1) and other studies

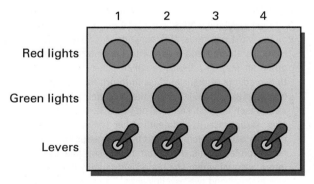

FIGURE 12.1 Lykken's Lever Apparatus to Test Avoidance Learning

Lykken (1957) devised this apparatus for his study of avoidance learning in individuals with APD. The participants had to learn a sequence of 20 correct lever presses.

Source: Based on Lykken, David T (1957). A study of anxiety in the sociopathic personality, *The Journal of Abnormal and Social Psychology*, Vol. 55(1), Jul 1957, 6-10.

used an electric shock as a form of punishment, the findings might only be relevant to shocks and other forms of physical punishment. Schmauk pointed out that, as children, individuals with ASPD appear to have been exposed to severe physical punishment from their parents or guardians that was frequently not contingent upon their behaviour. As a result, Schmauk suggested that these individuals might have learned to be either indifferent to physical punishment or oppositional to such attempts at controlling them. **Oppositional behaviour** has been thoroughly examined in children (Campbell, 1990) and refers to a tendency to do the opposite of what is being asked of the person. In the present case, oppositional behaviour would result in the punished behaviour showing an increase rather than the expected decrease.

To test this idea, Schmauk repeated Lykken's study but employed three different kinds of punishments: physical (electric shocks), tangible (participants lost money for errors), and social (reprimands by the experimenter for errors). With electric shocks as punishments, Schmauk replicated Lykken's findings, and he obtained similar results with the social punishments. That is, in response to both types of punishments, individuals with APD performed poorly relative to their counterparts. However, when the APD group lost money for pressing the wrong lever, they quickly learned to avoid the shocked levers and, in fact, did so more successfully than had their counterparts under any of the punishment conditions (see Figure 12.2). Schmauk concluded that individuals with APD were differentially responsive to different kinds of punishment as a result of early learning experiences, rather than completely fearless or unresponsive to all punishment.

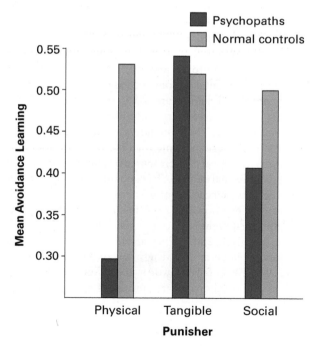

FIGURE 12.2 Effects of Different Types of Punishment on Psychopaths

Source: Based on Schmauk, F. J. (1970) Punishment, arousal, and avoidance learning in sociopaths. *Journal of Abnormal Psychology*, 76, 325–335.

Newman and his colleagues have described the pathology of psychopaths (as measured by the PCL-R) as due primarily to information processing deficiencies (Wallace, Schmitt, Vitale, & Newman, 2000). Through a series of laboratory and process-based investigations, they concluded that psychopaths suffer from a generalized information processing deficiency involving the *automatic* directing of attention to stimuli that are peripheral to ongoing directed behaviour. That is, once engaged in reward-based behaviour, the psychopath is less likely to attend to other cues to modulate his or her ongoing response. In contrast, the antisocial and criminal behaviour exhibited by those with ASPD involves schema-based deficits. These deficits comprise antisocial schemas and cognitive distortions not requiring automatic attentional cueing. Such research supports the idea that psychopathy and ASPD are different diagnoses implying different etiology, intervention, and prognosis.

Course and Prognosis of APD. Robins and Regier (1991) reported that the average duration of ASPD, from the onset of the first symptom to the end of the last, was 19 years. This remittance over time of symptoms has been described as the *burnout factor*, with the expectation being that symptoms will disappear by the fourth decade of life. However, Arboleda-Florez and Holley (1991) have presented data refuting the view that there is burn out among individuals with ASPD. These conflicting data are confusing and it is hard to make sense of them. Correctional Service Canada researchers Porporino and Motiuk (1995) found that in the context of comorbid ASPD and substance, the post-release performance is poorer than in those offenders who have only one of these disorders.

Treatment for APD. Reviews of treatment efficacy for patients with APD have been generally pessimistic (Reid & Gacono, 2000; Suedfeld & Landon, 1978). Many of the early studies, however, suffered from poor methodology. As pointed out by Paul Gendreau (1996) of the University of New Brunswick, programs delivered in previous decades did not reflect contemporary knowledge of effective treatment programs for resistant clients, so it may be premature to discount the potential for modifying the destructive behaviours of these clients. Attrition from treatment programs is also high, and this has proved to be predictive of subsequent reoffending. Lastly, in substance abuse treatment, individuals with ASPD fare more poorly than do other patients (Alterman & Cacciola, 1991). Surprisingly, therapeutic hope has not vanished. Approximately two-thirds of psychiatrists think that individuals with ASPD are sometimes treatable (Tennent, Tennent, Prins, & Bedford, 1993). Despite a poor response to hospitalization, prognosis is improved for these clients if there is a treatable anxiety or depressive feature to their behaviour (Gabbard & Coyne, 1987) or if they can be convinced to form an effective therapeutic alliance (Gerstley et al., 1989). According to current views, treatment should be aimed at symptom reduction and behaviour management rather than at a cure (Quinsey, Harris, Rice, & Cormier, 2006).

Treatment of other resistant clients suggests a **responsivity factor**. That is, treatment must be responsive (or matched) to a particular patient's needs and interpersonal style. Poor treatment performance may, in part, be caused by an intervention that is of insufficient intensity (Gendreau, 1996), viewed by patients as irrelevant (Miller & Rollnick, 1991), or seen as involuntary (Gabbard & Coyne, 1987). Several of these issues have been specifically considered in the context of the provision of treatment, yet they remain untested hypotheses. Researchers at the Oak Ridge Mental Health Centre in Ontario (Rice, Harris, & Quinsey, 1996) have pointed out that treatment programs vary for these clients according to the extent that either personality or criminality is emphasized, and yet a problems-based approach would appear to enhance compliance and efficacy.

Many of the more recent developments in treatment programs for criminal populations have involved significant contributions from Canadian researchers in forensic hospitals (e.g., Quinsey et al., 2006) and in prisons (e.g., Serin & Kuriychuk, 1994). While treatment targets for these samples have sometimes obscured the distinction between criminality and antisocial personality, they typically include a focus on some combination of aggressive and antisocial attitudes and beliefs, impulsivity or poor self-regulation, social skills, anger, assertiveness, substance abuse, empathy, problem solving, and moral reasoning (Serin & Preston, 2001). For many of these targets, there are structured program materials; however, the technology to measure treatment gains remains relatively unsophisticated. Furthermore, the overreliance on self-report assessment methods is problematic in a population in whom honesty is suspect.

Another strategy for managing antisocial or acting-out behaviour, particularly in closed settings, has been pharmacotherapy. Short-term use of psychopharmocological agents is most often used to manage difficult or threatening behaviour. However, the side effects of long-term drug use and problems of noncompliance have been noted in forensic patients (Harris, 1989). While short-term use of antipsychotic, anti-anxiety, and sedative medications is not uncommon, symptom alleviation is rarely sustained, and patients are typically provided with no new skills to improve their ability to deal with future situations. For some patients, medication may reduce arousal level sufficiently for them to participate more fully in cognitive-behavioural treatment (Rice & Harris, 1993).

Summary of ASPD. While the DSM-5 criteria for ASPD are simplified and reliable, these criteria have not served to bridge the conceptual differences between divergent views regarding the preferred diagnostic criteria or the assessment of these clients. It is important to note that alternatives to the diagnostic criteria, such as the PCL-R and ICD-10, may yield better assessments, in the view of experienced clinicians.

Currently, treatment initiatives can be only partly guided by theory (Rice & Harris, 1997b; Serin & Preston, 2001). Prognosis even after treatment remains relatively poor for patients with ASPD. For example, Hanson and Morton-Bourgon (2005) collectively analyzed the results

of 82 studies examining persistent sexual offending (*n* = 29 450 sexual offenders) and found that the major predictors of future sexual offences by both adolescents and adults were an antisocial orientation and deviant sexual preferences. An antisocial orientation was also a major predictor of future non-sexual violent offences. Interestingly, many of the variables traditionally targeted in sexual offender treatment programs (e.g., psychological distress) showed little or no relation with future sexual offences. Conceptualizing treatment as a management strategy rather than as a cure is perhaps a more helpful framework and likely protects clinicians from undue optimism. Further, targeting responsivity factors (i.e., those factors that are related to the antisocial behaviour) may yield enhanced treatment efficacy, but this remains an empirical question.

PSYCHOPATHY Although psychopathy is not listed in the DSM-5, an enormous amount of research has been devoted to the disorder in the past two decades, probably more than to APD, or all other personality disorders combined. Psychopaths are a distinctive subgroup of offenders best described by their unique interpersonal and affective disposition. They are egocentric, deceptive, callous, manipulative individuals who lack remorse and emotional depth. Readers interested in viewing a film depiction of a psychopath might consider *The Last King of Scotland,* in which Forest Whitaker plays the role of Ugandan dictator Idi Amin. Whitaker effectively conveys the superficially charming, charismatic, and grandiose qualities of the disorder that are often used to mask a selfish, deceitful, callous, and antisocial lifestyle. He received the Best Actor award at the 79th Academy Awards for his portrayal of Amin.

Psychopaths commit a disproportionate amount of antisocial and violent behaviour in society, extending to both nonsexual and sexual violence (Hart & Hare, 1997; Porter et al., 2000). In addition to their aggression and violence, psychopaths are chronic deceivers, often but not always lying for instrumental reasons such as to escape punishment. Häkkänen-Nyholm and Hare (2009) revealed that offenders with high PCL-R scores are more likely to deny charges or claim self-defence. These offenders are also likely to be convicted of a less serious crime than the one they committed, be granted an appeal of their sentence, and be granted undeserved conditional release. Psychopathic non-sex offenders were the most successful at garnering conditional release, but even the psychopathic sex offenders were more successful than non-psychopathic non-sex offenders (Porter, ten Brinke, & Wilson, 2009). They are "users" of others, in their attempts to obtain money, drugs, sex, or power (e.g., Hart & Hare, 1997; Porter & Woodworth, 2007; Woodworth & Porter, 2002). Many psychopaths are con artists with a long history of frauds and scams; some even become cult leaders, corrupt politicians, or successful corporate leaders, before their frequent downfall (e.g., Babiak & Hare, 2006).

Not only are psychopaths successful scam artists, they also appear to have a heightened ability to discern vulnerable individuals from non-vulnerable individuals. To successfully dupe someone, it is important to target an individual who is easy to manipulate. There are many characteristics associated with vulnerability, including low self-esteem, low assertiveness, and increased depression and anxiety (Egan & Perry, 1998). Psychopaths have demonstrated a keen ability to detect these signs of vulnerability among others in a number of studies. Book, Quinsey, and Langford (2007) found that psychopathic individuals were better able than are non-psychopaths to sense a lack of assertiveness after simply viewing a two-minute video of a vulnerable target. In another study, researchers found that psychopaths were able to detect vulnerability based on gait and non-verbal cues alone (Wheeler, Book, & Costello, 2009). Finally, in another investigation, it was found that men who possessed a high number of psychopathic traits had nearly perfect recall of sad and unsuccessful females who are likely to be highly vulnerable (Wilson, Demetrioff, & Porter, 2008). It is unknown at this time how psychopaths detect vulnerability in others, but the authors of this chapter are currently investigating this phenomenon.

It is important to note that diagnostic strategies other than those outlined in DSM-5 are gaining prominence in the forensic literature. For example, the PCL-R (Hare, 1991) enjoys international popularity as both a research instrument and a clinical tool (e.g., Hemphill & Hare, 2004). Psychopathy, as measured by the PCL-R, is characterized by 20 criteria scored from 0 to 2 for a maximum score of 40. As recommended in the manual, a minimum score of 30 is the cut-off for classifying psychopathy. The PCL-R score is highly reliable over time and has a high level of validity according to much research (e.g., Fulero, 1995; Stone, 1995). Increasingly, the PCL-R is used in assessments to inform judicial decisions, principally because of its predictive validity in terms of recidivism (i.e., the commission of new criminal offences following some previous involvement in the criminal justice system) (Douglas, Vincent, & Edens, 2007; Serin & Brown, 2000).

Despite the definitional differences between ASPD and psychopathy, little distinction has been made between ASPD and psychopathy in the legal system (Lyon & Ogloff, 2000). Some authors (e.g., Harding, 1992) suggest that the reluctance to use the term *psychopathic* stems from its pejorative connotations. Psychopathy, however, is a resilient term that has enjoyed a relative resurgence in use in correctional and forensic settings (Hare, 2003). In the media, psychopathy has been prominent in descriptions of infamous offenders such as Clifford Olson and Paul Bernardo. Such sensationalism, however, does little to inform the public or clinicians regarding the disorder, as many or most psychopaths are not serial rapists or murderers. Many "white-collar psychopaths" are successful in business or politics (e.g., Babiak & Hare, 2006).

Psychopathy and Aggression. As outlined by Porter and Porter (2007), researchers have established a strong link between psychopathic traits and aggression or violence in both adult offenders and psychiatric patients. Porter, Birt, and Boer (2001) found that psychopaths incarcerated in Canadian correctional institutions had perpetrated an average of more than seven violent crimes, nearly twice the average of their counterparts. This link helps us predict whether an offender is likely to commit future violent behaviour (e.g., Harris, Rice, & Quinsey, 1993; Hemphill, Hare, & Wong, 1998; Rice & Harris, 1997a; Salekin, Rogers, & Sewell, 1996). For example, Canadian researchers Serin and Amos (1995) found that psychopaths were about five times more likely than their counterparts to engage in violent reoffending within five years of their release from prison. Although the prevalence of psychopathy in civil psychiatric patients is low compared to that among criminal offenders (e.g., Douglas, Ogloff, Nicholls, & Grant, 1999), a consideration of psychopathy still helps to predict future aggression in this population. Skeem and Mulvey (2001) examined future violence in 1136 psychiatric patients from the MacArthur Violence Risk Assessment project, and found that PCL-R scores predicted future serious violence, despite a low base rate (8 percent).

Not only do psychopaths commit more violence, they commit particularly heinous violence. Williamson, Hare, and Wong (1987) found that psychopaths' violent crimes were more likely to have a motive of material gain (45.2%) than were non-psychopaths' (14.6%). Further, non-psychopaths (31.7%) were more likely to display high levels of emotion in their offences than were psychopaths (2.4%). Cornell and colleagues (1996) found that offenders who had committed at least one previous act of instrumental (planned with an external goal) violence had higher PCL-R scores than offenders who had only committed acts of reactive violence. In addition, psychopaths adhere to the selective impulsivity theory (Juodis, Starzomski, Porter, & Woodworth, 2012). That is, they are not out of control, but are able to quickly weigh the pros and cons of their actions. They will act impulsively only if the consequences are worth the risk. Woodworth and Porter (2002) examined the relationship between psychopathy and homicide. In a sample of 125 incarcerated homicide offenders from two Canadian federal institutions, psychopaths were more likely to have engaged in "cold-blooded" predatory homicides (93.3%) than were non-psychopathic offenders (48.4%). Research has revealed that psychopaths are likely to commit a number of other violent crimes including spousal abuse (Shaw & Porter, 2012) and rape (Porter et al., 2001).

In addition to committing more cold-blooded violence, psychopaths may even enjoy inflicting the violence. Research has addressed the possible link between psychopathy and sadistic interests. Holt, Meloy, and Stack (1999) found that sadistic traits were more common in violent psychopaths than in violent non-psychopaths. Further, there is a modest correlation (.21 to .28) between PCL-R scores and deviant sexual arousal (e.g., Barbaree, Seto, Serin, Amos, & Preston, 1994). A team of Canadian researchers (Porter, Woodworth, Earle, Drugge, & Boer, 2003) examined the relation between PCL-R scores and the types of aggression evidenced during the crime in a sample of 38 Canadian sexual murderers. Homicides committed by psychopaths showed a higher level of both gratuitous and sadistic violence than did homicides perpetrated by non-psychopathic offenders. In fact, most psychopaths (82.4 percent) had committed sadistic acts on their victims, compared to 52.6 percent of the non-psychopaths.

Prevalence of Psychopathy. Hare (1996, 2003) estimates that 1 percent of the population is psychopathic (meaning that we have more than 300 000 psychopaths in Canada). However, it is very difficult, if not impossible, to conclusively determine the prevalence of psychopathy in the community. Imagine psychopaths receiving a survey questionnaire in which they are asked whether they lack remorse, lie frequently, are callous individuals, and so on. The researcher is unlikely to receive many honest responses!

However, there is a wealth of research to allow conclusions about the prevalence of psychopathy in forensic populations. In federal correctional settings, approximately 15 to 25 percent of inmates are psychopaths, according to the PCL-R (e.g., see Hare, 2003). Rates of psychopathy among Canadian offenders also appear to vary according to security level, with psychopaths being overrepresented in maximum-security prisons (Wong, 1984).

Research with female inmate samples (outside Canada) indicates a base rate of psychopathy of 9 to 31 percent (e.g., Kennedy, Hicks, & Patrick, 2007; Vitale, Smith, Brinkley, & Newman, 2002; Warren et al., 2003).

Etiology of Psychopathy. There has been an abundance of etiological theories concerning psychopathy, ranging from evolutionary (Lalumière, Harris, & Rice, 2001; Mealey, 1995; Quinsey, 1995) and neurobiological (Raine, Lencz, Bihrle, LaCasse, & Colletti, 2000) explanations to environmental models involving early childhood trauma or maltreatment (McCord & McCord, 1964; Porter, 1996). However, at present, the data are primarily correlational in nature and it is not possible to offer a definitive causal account.

Biological theorists have observed that psychopaths tend to differ from non-psychopaths in terms of their underlying biological functioning and neurological processing. Psychopaths are insensitive to the emotional content of information, especially language (Hancock, Woodworth, & Porter, 2011; Willamson, Harpur, & Hare, 1991) and emotional pictorial information (Christianson et al., 1996). The limited existing neuroimaging studies implicate brain abnormalities in psychopaths. Such abnormalities have been identified in the prefrontal cortex, hippocampus, angular gyrus, basal ganglia, and amygdala (e.g., Abbott, 2001; Blair, 2001, 2003; Brower & Price, 2001; Deeley et al., 2006; De Oliveira-Souza et al., 2008; Kiehl et al., 2004; Mitchell, Colledge, Leonard, & Blair, 2002; Stevens, Charman, & Blair, 2001; Yang et al., 2005). For example, because of an apparent dysfunction of the amygdala, psychopathic individuals appear to use alternative (primarily cognitive) means of processing emotional material to compensate for the absence of appropriate limbic input (which normally provides prompt information about the affective characteristics of stimuli).

Neurotransmitters have also been implicated in psychopathic behaviour. Soderstrom, Blennow, Manhem, and Forsman (2001) found that PCL-R scores were predicted by lower 5-HIAA concentrations (a metabolite of serotonin) and high catecholaminergic activity (HVA) in the cerebral spinal fluid of violent forensic inpatients. The authors concluded that the impulsive aggression of psychopaths may be linked to serotonergic hypofunctioning in combination with a high dopamine activity. Despite these compelling findings, the data are correlational, and much more research is required to establish whether such biological correlates are causal factors.

Three relatively recent studies have reported important data on the genetic contributions to psychopathy. Blonigen, Carlson, Krueger, and Patrick (2003) had 353 male adult twins complete a self-report measure of psychopathic traits and found moderate levels of heritability for the subscales measuring affect-related traits of the disorder. Blonigen, Hicks, Krueger, Patrick, and Iacono (2005) examined 626 pairs of 17-year-old male and female twins and found significant heritability on measures of fearless dominance and impulsive antisocial behaviour. Viding, Blair, Moffitt, and Plomin (2005) published data on 3500 twin pairs of children from the Twins Early Development Study. These researchers indexed the callous and unemotional component of psychopathy at age seven and found significant group heritability and no environmental influence on this component of psychopathy. Such findings have led some researchers to argue that there is a stronger genetic cause as opposed to social cause of psychopathy (Blair et al., 2006).

As with most mental disorders, it is unlikely that biology tells the whole story of how psychopathy develops. Almost certainly, environmental factors play a role. More than 40 years ago, McCord and McCord (1964) argued that there is an association between early emotional deprivation (i.e., parental neglect, erratic punishment) and psychopathic characteristics in adulthood. There are some data to speak to their claim. Weiler and Widom (1996) found that children who were abused or neglected went on to have higher PCL-R scores than matched controls who had not been maltreated. Using a retrospective design, Marshall and Cooke (1995, 1999) found that psychopaths had experienced a more negative upbringing (e.g., poor discipline, emotional abuse/neglect) and negative school experience than had non-psychopaths. More recently, Campbell, Porter, and Santor (2004) examined the criminal, clinical, and psychosocial correlates of psychopathy in a sample of 226 incarcerated adolescents. Only 9.4 percent of the sample showed a high level of psychopathic traits. Thirty-three percent of the sample had a history of experiencing physical abuse and 50 percent had a history of non-parental living arrangements such as foster care. High psychopathy scores in these adolescents were associated with both the experience of physical abuse and disrupted living arrangements.

Porter (1996) has suggested that there are in fact two pathways that can lead to the development of psychopathy. In the case of *fundamental psychopathy*, the disorder is the inevitable result of a biological (probably polygenic) predisposition within the individual that hinders the development of affective bonds. In the case of *secondary psychopathy*, the development of the disorder is heavily dependent on and the result of negative environmental experiences during the formative years of childhood, such as extreme neglect or abuse. With secondary psychopathy, the profound affective deficit may be the result of the individual's ability to detach him- or herself from his or her emotions, as opposed to an inability to actually experience emotions, as is the case with fundamental psychopathy. More recent research has generated some evidence in support of this existence of, and distinction between, primary and secondary psychopaths (Skeem, Johansson, Andershed, Kerr, & Louden, 2007). Further, another recent study that used a large sample of inmates found support for dissociation as a mediator between childhood maltreatment and higher PCL-R scores measuring an impulsive and antisocial lifestyle (Poythress, Skeem, & Lilienfeld, 2006). Thus, it is possible that psychopathy may have its roots in biological predispositions and/or environmental experiences, depending on the individual.

Course and Prognosis of Psychopathy. Like all personality disorders, psychopathy is typically a lifelong condition. Precursors to psychopathy emerge early in childhood as "callous/unemotional" traits (Frick, 2006; Frick, Bodin, & Barry, 2000; Frick & Ellis, 1999; Lynam, 2002), which map closely onto adult psychopathic traits (Frick, 2002; Munoz & Frick, 2007; Salekin & Frick, 2005). As outlined by Campbell and colleagues (2004; Hare & Neumann, 2009), although the existence of psychopathy in adults is generally accepted, the appropriateness of diagnosing psychopathy in children and youths is much more controversial, with a host of ethical concerns. Nonetheless, it is important to focus on the presence of psychopathic traits in this group, given their associations with specific patterns of future antisocial behaviour (Forth, Kosson, & Hare, 2003).

Campbell and colleagues (2004) note that adolescents with a high level of psychopathic traits are more likely to have an earlier onset of conduct problems and to present with a greater variety and severity of delinquent behaviours (e.g., Smith, Gacono, & Kaufman, 1997). Such adolescents are also more likely to have symptoms and diagnoses of conduct disorder, narcissistic personality disorder, and oppositional defiant disorder (e.g., Murrie & Cornell, 2000). In addition, such adolescents have been found to score high on measures of impulsivity (Stanford, Ebner, Patton, & Williams, 1994) and sensation seeking (Vitacco, Rogers, Neumann, Durrant, & Collins, 2000). Research conducted in Canada revealed that psychopathy has a moderate to high level of stability, with behavioural and interpersonal factors having the greatest stability (Lee, Klaver, Hart, Moretti, & Douglas, 2009).

Treatment of Psychopaths. One of the key requirements for successful psychological treatment is motivation on the part of the client. Not surprisingly, observations on the effectiveness of treatment with psychopaths have not been encouraging (Hare, 1998; Lösel, 1998; Rice, 1997; Rice, Harris, & Cormier, 1992). For example, Richards and colleagues (2003) evaluated the role of psychopathy in treatment outcome in a large sample of adult female offenders. Psychopaths showed poorer response to substance abuse treatment in terms of noncompliance, violent and disruptive rule violations, avoidance of urinalysis testing, poor treatment attendance, and low therapist progress ratings. Using a sample of adult male offenders, Hobson, Shine, and Roberts (2000) found that higher PCL-R scores were associated with a higher incidence of misbehaviours (e.g., lying, verbal outbursts) in a treatment group.

Despite the huge obstacles, some researchers remain optimistic that an effective intervention strategy with psychopathic individuals can be devised with further research. Skeem, Monahan, and Mulvey (2002), for example, found that longer involvement in outpatient treatment (at least seven sessions) reduced the risk of violence among psychopathic individuals discharged from a non-forensic inpatient setting when compared to those who received less than seven sessions of treatment.

APPLIED CLINICAL CASE

Sophie's Experience

Sophie, now 25 years-old, was admitted to a hospital inpatient unit following an overdose that occurred following a heated argument with her boyfriend who she thought was leaving her. She has significant difficulty being alone and fears being abandoned. Sophie has a history of emergency room visits due to self-injury; she has been frequently brought to the hospital by her boyfriend or friends. Sophie reports cutting or burning herself fairly regularly to cope with anxiety and traumatic flashbacks since she was 12 years old. She also reports feeling chronically empty and unsure of who she is as a person. Sophie reports being sexually abused as a child by a neighbour and then bullied as an adolescent. Following a comprehensive diagnostic assessment, Sophie was diagnosed with borderline personality disorder. Upon release from hospital, she began taking part in outpatient dialectical behaviour therapy (DBT). While in treatment Sophie learned how to identify different emotions and cognitions, especially those that follow stressful events such as arguments with others. In addition to this, she learned how to better tolerate distress, self-soothe when upset and feeling alone, and to mindfully meditate. Due to her difficulties communicating her feelings with others and her tendency for angry outbursts, she has also learned how to more effectively communicate her feelings with others. After a year of DBT, Sophie reports only cutting herself on a few occasions and not at all in the past several months. This represents a significant decrease from the time before her hospitalization. She also reports getting along better with friends and family and has not overdosed or attempted suicide at all since starting treatment. Although her relationship with her boyfriend ended soon after her hospitalization, Sophie has managed to come to terms with this loss; she was able to use cognitive restructuring techniques to challenge her initial view that he abandoned her. While she still struggles with feelings of emptiness she has learned to better tolerate these experiences.

Any way you look at it, adult psychopaths represent a unique group of offenders who can be expected to be resistant to treatment. According to leading researchers, programs should focus on changing and managing behaviour rather than on changing the core personality traits of the psychopath (Quinsey et al., 2006; Wong & Hare, 2005). Behaviourist techniques (e.g., token economies) that are strictly defined and implemented by institutional staff have shown some success within institutions; however, the gains observed within institutions may not generalize to the community for many of those who are eventually released (Quinsey et al., 2006). Intense supervision in the form of probation or parole is often necessary, and in some extreme cases preventive detention is warranted (i.e., long-term/indeterminate incarceration) (Quinsey et al., 2006). Treatment providers must be especially careful not to be deceived into perceiving progress when they are really observing a performance worthy of an Academy Award.

4 BEFORE MOVING ON

> What are the key differences between psychopathy and antisocial personality disorder? If you were to see a client in a forensic setting, what symptoms or behaviours would you look for to differentiate between the two? What tools would you use to aid in your diagnosis?

BORDERLINE PERSONALITY DISORDER

Borderline personality disorder (BPD) may be one of the most poorly named personality disorders. Historically, the diagnostic label was meant to describe a person on the border between neurosis and psychosis. Many laypersons assume that the term refers to someone on the "border" of psychosis or "going crazy," which is not typically the case. Most people with BPD do not experience psychotic symptoms and such views are arguably pejorative and contribute to stigma. Indeed, there is a significant stigma associated with BPD; we discuss this further in the text that follows.

DESCRIPTION OF BORDERLINE PERSONALITY DISORDER Borderline personality disorder (BPD) can generally be characterized by **instability** across various domains of personality functioning. Specifically, the hallmark features of BPD are: (a) fluctuations in and difficulty regulating emotions, (b) an unstable sense of one's identity, (c) instability in social relationships, and (d) impulsive behaviour. For example, in response to intense negative emotions (e.g., anxiety, sadness, anger), which are perceived as intolerable, individuals who have BPD may engage in a range of impulsive and potentially harmful acts, such as excessive spending, reckless driving, promiscuity, and binge-eating. Unsurprisingly, this can have significant consequences for those with BPD and those in their lives (e.g., romantic partners, family). For an excellent overview of BPD and its treatment, you might wish to watch *Back From the Edge* a documentary developed by the New York Presbyterian Hospital. It includes several stories from those with lived BPD experience and interviews from experts in the field, including Marsha Linehan and Otto Kernberg. The video can be watched on YouTube: www.youtube.com/watch?v=967Ckat7f98.

In addition to the aforementioned risky behaviours, is not uncommon for individuals with BPD to engage in non-suicidal self-injury (NSSI; APA, 2013)—the purposeful damaging of a person's own body without lethal intent (Klonsky, Muehlenkamp, Lewis, & Walsh, 2011). Indeed, one BPD diagnostic criterion involves engagement in NSSI (e.g., self-cutting, burning), suicidal ideation, or suicidal behaviour, including suicide attempts. Rates of NSSI among those meeting criteria for BPD can be as high as 70 percent (APA, 2013), and are especially high in adolescent populations (for a recent review, see Kaess, Brunner, & Chanen, 2014). In addition to NSSI, most who have BPD report suicidal ideation and many have attempted suicide. Tragically, about 8 to 10 percent of individuals with BPD die by suicide (APA, 2013). For these reasons, it is critical that treatment of BPD incorporate ongoing comprehensive risk assessment and safety planning.

Individuals diagnosed with BPD commonly experience emotional instability. They tend to be more emotionally reactive to stressors and have difficulty regulating emotions (e.g., sadness, anger) when they occur. Understandably, emotional instability can translate into major relationship difficulties. For example, individuals with BPD can be emotionally volatile and argumentative with others (e.g., romantic partners, family). This can result in frequent conflicts and tumultuous, short-lived relationships. The relationships of individuals with BPD can be further impacted by the manner by which they alternate between idealizing and devaluing their partners.

At the same time, individuals with BPD also seem unable to tolerate being alone and can become desperate about relationships. For example, they may go to extreme lengths (e.g., making suicidal threats) to avoid being alone. It is important to avoid jumping to conclusions about what this may connote. While these actions may be viewed as attention-seeking and manipulative, which may make sense on the surface, it is important to consider these responses in the proper context. For example, such extreme reactions often stem from difficulty knowing how to effectively regulate intense feelings, fears of abandonment (which may be rooted in childhood experiences), and how to appropriately communicate with others.

In addition to the typical symptoms of BPD, there are also several associated features that may or may not be present in all patients with the disorder. For example, individuals with BPD may blame their relationship problems on others instead of accepting any personal responsibility, and they may also attempt to undermine their achievements when they have nearly succeeded in reaching their goals (such as dropping out of university shortly before graduation). In addition, some people with BPD experience psychotic-like symptoms or even dissociation during times of stress. These symptoms are not usually sufficiently severe to require an additional diagnosis but nevertheless affect these individuals' functioning (APA, 2013).

BPD AND SELF-INJURY: AN IMPORTANT DISTINCTION
Historically, NSSI has been viewed as a prominent feature, and at times, even an indicator of BPD. On the one hand, this is perhaps unsurprising. As noted, rates of NSSI among those with BPD are high (APA, 2013), particularly among adolescents with BPD (Kaess et al., 2014). However, it is important to note that NSSI is neither sufficient nor necessary for a BPD diagnosis (APA, 2013; Glenn & Klonsky, 2013; Lewis & Heath, 2015). Not all who meet BPD criteria will self-injure. Moreover, most who self-injure do not have BPD (for reviews see Lewis & Heath, 2015; Klonsky et al. 2011).

According to a growing line of research, including studies by researchers at the University of British Columbia, NSSI can be meaningfully distinguished from BPD (Glenn & Klonsky, 2013) and BPD symptoms (Klonsky & Olino, 2008). Interestingly, there is also a growing body of literature suggesting that NSSI may constitute its own diagnostic category within the DSM—namely, NSSI disorder (APA, 2013). Part of the rationale behind this effort is to avoid conflating NSSI and BPD. Moreover, there is growing evidence indicating that NSSI disorder is not only distinct from other conditions but that many of its proposed diagnostic features can be reliably and validly assessed (for a review see Selby, Kranzler, Fehling, & Panza, 2015).

Another key issue warranting discussion is how others may view NSSI and those who enact it. It is not uncommon for NSSI and many other BPD behaviours to be viewed as attention-seeking. In fact, as pointed out by Canadian researchers, such views about NSSI specifically are common in across lay and clinical contexts (e.g., Lewis, Mahdy, Michal, & Arbuthnott, 2014; Muehlenkamp, Claes, Quigley et al., 2013). These views are unhelpful in several ways. Not only do they fuel an unhelpful and often stigmatizing discourse about why people self-injure but these views are also inconsistent with the voluminous body of scholarly work on NSSI. Indeed, NSSI is rarely—if ever—an attention-seeking act. In a review of the literature by Klonsky from the University of British Columbia, the most commonly cited reason for NSSI is to obtain relief from negative emotions that are perceived as painful and intolerable (see Klonsky, 2007). As discussed above, context when understanding behaviour is important. If we take into account the intense and at times volatile emotional experiences of those who BPD, and their inability to know how to effectively channel or cope with these feelings, it is perhaps unsurprising that NSSI is used to obtain momentary relief from these experiences. It makes sense, then, that emotion regulation constitutes a central focus of treating BPD, and NSSI (see Linehan, 1993; Klonsky et al., 2011).

PREVALENCE, STABILITY, AND DIAGNOSTIC ISSUES
BPD has a lifetime occurrence in approximately 2% of the population (but may be as high as 5.9%). As noted earlier, BPD may be more common in women than in men, with

women being diagnosed with BPD 75% of the time (APA, 2013). Recall, however, there are a number of considerations (e.g., biases in gender expectations) that may account for this.

Another issue that has generated a fair bit of debate concerns the utility of a BPD diagnosis among adolescents. While some suggest that BPD is reasonably stable over time (Barasch, Frances, Hurt, Clarkin, & Cohen, 1985), Stone (1993) reported that, of patients diagnosed with BPD as emerging adults, only one quarter still meet diagnostic criteria by middle age. This begs the question of when a BPD diagnosis should be made. Adding to this debate is whether we can reliably make a diagnostic decision about individuals whose personality is arguably still developing. Other major reasons against BPD being diagnosed in adolescents pertain to some of its key features, including affective instability or identity, both of which are normative experiences for many young people. Others have expressed concern that rendering a diagnosis so early may have longer-term stigmatizing effects thereby shaping how others view and ultimately, how clinicians treat these individuals (see Chanen & McCutheon, 2008; Kaess et al., 2014).

Despite these concerns, a number of recent empirical studies have indicated that a BPD diagnosis in adolescence can be reliability and validly made (Chanen, Jovev, McCutcheon, Jackson, & McGorry, 2008; Miller, Muehlenkamp, & Jacobson, 2008). According to a Canadian study, this can occur among youth as young as 12 to 14 years of age (Glenn & Klonsky, 2013). Furthermore, some evidence suggests that both adolescent and adult BPD have a similar stability in course—at least after two years (Chanen, Jackson, McGorry, Allot, Clarkson, & Yuen, 2004). In addition, there may be incremental validity in the provision of a BPD diagnosis in adolescents over and above other forms of mental disorder (Kaess, von Ceumern-Lindenstjerna, Parzer, Chanen et al., 2012; Chanen, Jovev, & Jackson, 2007). Perhaps the most compelling argument, however, stems from the disorder-specific treatment of BPD and that early intervention in adolescents is beneficial (e.g., Chanen & McCutheon, 2013; Kaess et al., 2014). That is, when identified early enough with BPD, individuals tend to respond well to BPD-specific treatments that may have prophylactic (i.e., preventative) effects over the long-term.

ETIOLOGY OF BPD
The etiology of BPD has been debated for many years, with the different views emphasizing childhood experiences, biological factors, psychodynamic processes, and social learning. Certainly, the evidence strongly implicates disruptions in the family of origin and childhood abuse and neglect as very significant factors in the development of borderline personality disorder (Links, 1992; Marziali, 1992). Patients with BPD typically recall their parents as either neglectful (Paris & Frank, 1989) or abusive (Bryer, Nelson, Miller, & Krol, 1987). Briere and Zaidi (1989), in a study of 100 females seen at an emergency service, found that females who had been sexually abused during their childhood were five times more likely to be given

a diagnosis of BPD than were female patients who had not been sexually abused. Caution should be exercised here, however, to not assume causality; past abuse is a non-specific risk factor for myriad mental health difficulties (e.g., PTSD, depression)—not just BPD.

Despite problems with determining the accuracy of traumatic childhood recollections (e.g., Loftus, 2003; Porter, Yuille, & Lehman, 1999), the findings to date suggest that attachment problems with parents may be an etiological factor in BPD. Patients with BPD have significant difficulties with adult relationships, and this may be understood to result from a fear of, or ambivalence about, intimacy. People who have problems with adult intimacy are considered to have developed these difficulties as a result of poor parent–child attachments (Berman & Sperling, 1994), which fail to instill the self-confidence and skills necessary for effective intimacy (Bartholomew, 1989) and fail to provide an adequate template for adult intimate relationships (Bowlby, 1988). For example, many adults who as children had poor relationships with their parents have an interpersonal style that is described as **anxious ambivalent**. These adults often harbour intense fears of abandonment but they strongly desire intimacy with others and, consequently, persistently seek out romantic partners. However, once they begin to get close to their partner, they become anxious and begin to back away from the relationship. While they desire closeness, they appear to be afraid of it. This is precisely the relationship style that characterizes borderline patients. The features of BPD may then be seen as attempts to adjust to their desire for, but distrust of, intimacy.

Murray (1979) has suggested an association between minimal brain dysfunction and the development of BPD. He proposed that the distorting effects of minimal brain dysfunction on perceptual processes may interfere with effective parent–child relationships and that these effects may continue to disrupt relationships throughout the lifespan. According to Murray, confused perceptions, emotional instability, and poor impulse control typical of minimal brain dysfunction may lead to BPD behaviour. A recent study that examined the brains of individuals with BPD revealed that these individuals have significantly reduced right hippocampal volumes compared to healthy participants (Sala et al., 2011). A similar study found that individuals with BPD also have reduced volumes of grey matter in the dorsolateral prefrontal cortex (DLPFC) (Brunner et al., 2010). The hippocampus and the DLPFC both play a pivotal role in the sustaining and controlling (or lack thereof) of impulsive and aggressive behaviour (Bellani et al., 2010; Sala et al., 2011). Research investigating this claim has generally supported the idea that a subset of individuals with BPD have soft neurological signs (Marziali, 1992), but the evidence is far from convincing at this time.

Available evidence suggests a relatively high incidence of BPD features in the first-degree relatives of patients with BPD (Links, 1992); this has been taken by some to suggest familial transmission of the disorder (Baron, Risch, Levitt, & Gruen, 1985). Of course, familial transmission of a disorder

may be the result of environmental rather than genetic factors. Torgersen (1984) found no support for a genetic contribution to the development of either BPD or schizotypal PD in a study of Norwegian twins, but the number of participants was very small.

Linehan's (1987, 1993) biosocial theory describes BPD primarily as dysfunction of the emotion regulation system. According to the theory, people with BPD have a biologically predisposed difficulty in regulating their own emotions. Individuals who are biologically vulnerable may include those who experience emotional reactions more intensely, those who are more sensitive to various emotional stimuli, or those who take longer to return to a baseline level of emotional arousal after an emotional reaction. This vulnerability interacts with exposure to a pervasively invalidating environment (i.e., one that minimizes, rejects, blames, or attributes pejorative characteristics to an individual's responses) to result in an emotionally dysregulated system that is believed to underlie the aforementioned symptoms. Treatment for BPD is often challenging because the etiology of the disorder is still largely unclear (Paris, 2009).

TREATMENT OF BPD Dialectical behaviour therapy (DBT), developed by Marsha Linehan (Linehan & Heard, 1992), has attracted major international attention in the treatment of BPD. Originally developed as a treatment for women who engaged in self-injury and suicidal behaviours (Robins & Chapman, 2004), the approach has been tailored to patients with BPD, although its application has been expanding. One of the main features of this approach is the acceptance by the therapist of the patient's maladaptive and at times self-destructive behaviours (Linehan, et al., 2001). In addition, several standard behavioural procedures are used, such as exposure treatment for the external and internal cues that evoke distress, skills training (e.g., distress tolerance, mindfulness, interpersonal effectiveness), contingency management (i.e., use of positive reinforcement for desired behaviour), and cognitive restructuring. The dialectical process describes "both the coexisting multiple tensions and the thought processes and styles used and targeted in the treatment strategies" (Linehan & Heard, 1992, p. 249).

According to Robins and Chapman (2004), DBT is the only outpatient psychotherapy that has been shown to be effective with patients with BPD. Linehan and colleagues (1991) compared the treatment outcome of 22 female patients with BPD assigned to DBT with 22 patients who were provided with "treatment as usual." At the end of one year of treatment, those assigned to DBT had made fewer suicide attempts and had spent less time in hospital than those allocated to the other treatment program. An important additional observation was that while only 17 percent of the patients treated with DBT dropped out, almost 60 percent of the other group withdrew prior to treatment termination. Although both groups displayed less depression and hopelessness after treatment, there were no group differences on these measures.

Linehan and colleagues (2006) reported the results of a two-year randomized controlled trial (101 women) for suicidal behaviours and BPD comparing DBT to therapy provided by experts. Compared to the therapy provided by the experts not using DBT, patients who received DBT were half as likely to make a suicide attempt, made fewer visits to psychiatric emergency departments, required less hospitalization for suicidal thoughts, and were less likely to drop out of treatment. A more recent study with a Canadian sample compared the effectiveness of DBT to general psychiatric management among individuals with BPD (McMain et al., 2009). The results of this study demonstrate that both DBT and general psychiatric management significantly reduced common symptoms of BPD, including psychological distress, degree of suicidal ideation and behaviour, and health care utilization (Linehan et al., 2001).

 BEFORE MOVING ON

> What are the four main areas of instability in BPD? What are the most common reasons for non-suicidal self-injury? Do you think that BPD should be diagnosed in adolescent populations? Why or why not? What do you think is the strongest theory to explain the development of BPD?

HISTRIONIC PERSONALITY DISORDER

People with histrionic personality disorder (HPD) can sometimes be "the life of the party." Indeed, attention-seeking behaviours tend to characterize people with this disorder. In fact, there seems to be little that someone with HPD will not do to solicit attention. They are overly dramatic in their emotional displays, self-centred, and constantly attempting to be the centre of attention. They may dress provocatively and be overly sexual in inappropriate contexts such as a job interview. The flamboyant displays of individuals with HPD are apparently intended to make others focus on them, as they seem unable to tolerate being ignored. Indeed, they may become quite annoyed if another person in a group setting receives more attention than they do. These individuals may also over-react to what others would normally consider insignificant events. Their insincerity and shallowness, however, make it difficult for them to hold other people's attention for long. As a consequence, they typically have few friends. Because of their strong need for attention, they tend to be very demanding and inconsiderate, and not surprisingly, their relationships are often short-lived and tumultuous. Again, as a result of their need to be the centre of attention, these individuals are often flirtatious, and seem unable to develop any degree of deep intimacy in relationships. Their behaviour causes considerable distress to themselves and to others with whom they become involved.

NARCISSISTIC PERSONALITY DISORDER

Patients who are narcissistic are grandiose and consider themselves to have unique and outstanding abilities. They have an exaggerated sense of self-importance; indeed, egocentricity

According to Greek myth, the beautiful youth Narkissos fell in love with his own reflection in a spring; to punish him for his excessive self-love, the gods transformed him into the flower called the narcissus.

is the staple characteristic of these individuals. If you were to have a conversation with someone who has NPD, you would quickly get the impression of "me me me," with every topic somehow being turned to the person's own greatness. They are so preoccupied with their own interests and desires that they typically have difficulty feeling any concern for others; this can mirror the empathy deficit seen in ASPD or psychopathy. However, unlike these latter conditions, individuals with NPD are easily hurt by any perception that their greatness is not being recognized. Similarly, their self-esteem is readily shattered by negative feedback from others, presumably because they desire only admiration and approval. This is commonly referred to as the narcissistic paradox. The self-absorption of these patients frequently leads to an obsession with unrealistic fantasies of success. They expect, and demand, to be treated as "special." This, coupled with a lack of empathy, leads them to exploit others to serve their own needs. Like those with HPD, the actions of those with NPD alienate others. Thus, these individuals are frequently lonely and unhappy. When frustrated or slighted, they can become vengeful and verbally or physically aggressive.

Ronningstam and Gunderson (1990) claim that research has validated these features as characteristic of NPD. However, while Morey (1988) reported a remarkable increase (from 6.2 percent of patients to 22 percent) in the application of the diagnosis from DSM-III to DSM-III-R, others found no cases of NPD in a sample of 800 community participants (Zimmerman & Coryell, 1990). When NPD is diagnosed, there is considerable overlap with BPD (Morey, 1988).

Although encountering an individual with NPD is rare, one of the authors of this chapter recently experienced the behaviour of a narcissist while completing a practicum in a forensic setting. During the brief consultation, the individual displayed all the characteristic personality traits associated with narcissistic personality disorder, including grandiosity, egocentricity, and an elevated sense of self-importance. Specifically, the individual paid very little attention to the professional during the interview. While this individual was being questioned about a previous offence and his current progress, he assumed superiority and spoke in a condescending manner to the interviewer. Further, the individual spent the majority of the consultation answering text messages on his phone; when he did acknowledge the professional, he was extremely patronizing. By behaving in this way, the individual revealed his strong feelings of superiority and high levels of egocentricity.

With the increasing popularity of the internet and social media, research has begun to focus on the types of individuals most likely to use these media outlets. One such study revealed that a high degree of narcissism was related to increased overall internet use (Mehdizadeh, 2010). Specifically, narcissistic individuals used social networking sites to promote themselves and were most likely to change their photos, write status updates, and write notes. A similar study discovered that individuals who possess a high number of narcissistic traits displayed more self-promoting and sexy images of themselves on their Facebook profiles (DeWall, Buffardi, Bonser, & Campbell, 2011). Although personality disorders are characterized as egosyntonic, a recent review of narcissism across a wide range of traits revealed that individuals high in narcissism are often aware that others perceive them less favourably than they perceive themselves, that they are able to make positive first impressions that eventually deteriorate, and that they do appear to have some insight into their narcissistic traits (Carlson, Vazire, & Oltmanns, 2011).

⑥ BEFORE MOVING ON

> What are the general themes of each of the three personality disorder clusters? Define each of the DSM-5 personality disorders and explain some of the key symptoms. How are histrionic personality disorder and narcissistic personality disorder different? How are they similar?

Cluster C: Anxious and Fearful Disorders

Although avoidant and dependent personality disorders appear to share anxieties and fears as primary features, obsessive-compulsive personality disorder seems to be characterized more by a preoccupation with orderliness and rules. Again, there seems to be little value in clustering these disorders in the same category. Information regarding etiology and effective intervention specific to these disorders is sparse.

AVOIDANT PERSONALITY DISORDER

Avoidant personality disorder (APD) is characterized by a pervasive pattern of avoiding interpersonal contacts and an extreme sensitivity to criticism and disapproval. Individuals with APD tend to avoid intimacy with others, although they clearly desire affection (unlike schizoid personality disorder). As a result, they frequently experience terrible loneliness. While social discomfort and a fear of negative evaluation are commonly experienced, the fundamental fear of those with APD is social rejection. These individuals restrict social interactions to those they trust not to denigrate them; however, even with these people, they refrain from getting too close for fear of ultimate rejection. Understandably, these

fears cause many problems for individuals with APD, including disrupted interpersonal relationships as well as severely restricted job options, academic pursuits, and leisure activities. Their avoidance of intimacy also distresses other people who may wish to form a close relationship with them.

People with more avoidant personality styles have been documented in the literature well before their inclusion in the context of APD. For instance Karen Horney (1945) noted that there were people who found interpersonal relationships of any kind to be such an intolerable strain that "solitude becomes primarily a means of avoiding it" (p. 73). Millon (1969) was the first to use the term *avoidant personality* to describe people who actively avoided social interactions. He suggested that children rejected by their parents would lack self-confidence and would, as a consequence, avoid others for fear of further rejection (Millon, 1981). This notion fits with the extensive literature on parent–child attachments and the consequences of parental rejection for adult relationships. While some children with poor parental bonds develop an anxious/avoidant relationship style, others grow up to be so afraid of intimate relationships that they become avoidant of any depth in whatever relationships they form. These are just the characteristics that identify avoidant personality clients.

Some researchers found considerable overlap between avoidant personality disorder and dependent disorder (e.g., Trull, Widiger, & Frances, 1987) while others have reported overlap with BPD (Morey, 1988), previously described. There is also a problem differentiating avoidant disorder and social phobia. Indeed, there is considerable overlap between these conditions (Turner, Beidel, Dancu, & Keys, 1991) with some researchers indicating they only differ in symptom severity (Cox, Pagura, Stein, & Sareen, 2009; Holt, Heimberg, & Hope, 1992).

DEPENDENT PERSONALITY DISORDER

People with this condition appear to be afraid to rely on themselves to make decisions. They seek advice and direction from others, need constant reassurance, and seek out relationships in which they can adopt a submissive role. Not only do they allow other people to assume responsibility for important aspects of their lives, but also seem to desperately need to do so. They seem unable to function independently, and typically ask their spouse or partner to decide what job they should seek or what clothes they should purchase; they tend to defer to others for most, if not all, of the decisions in their lives. Individuals with dependent personality disorder (DPD) subordinate their needs to those of other people, even people they hardly know. This may lead to involvement in abusive relationships or destroy relationships with partners who could be beneficial to them.

Reich (1990) observed that the relatives of male patients with this disorder were likely to experience depression, whereas the relatives of female dependents were more likely to have panic disorder. Relatedly, individuals with panic disorder have been found to have comorbidity with various personality disorders, including DPD (Johnson, Weissman,

& Klerman, 1990). As discussed earlier, it is critical to consider cultural context when diagnosing personality disorders. This is especially true with DPD, which is arguably the most culture-laden of the personality disorders. Specifically, DPD is rooted in the individualistic culture of North America, but is not as prevalent in collectivist cultures (Chen, Nettles, & Chen, 2009).

OBSESSIVE-COMPULSIVE PERSONALITY DISORDER

Major features of obsessive-compulsive personality disorder (OCPD) include inflexibility and a desire for perfection. It is the centrality of these two features, and the absence of obsessional thoughts and compulsive behaviours, that distinguish this personality disorder from obsessive-compulsive disorder (discussed in Chapter 5). Preoccupation with rules and order makes these patients rigid and inefficient as a result of focusing too much on the details of a problem. Individuals with OCPD also attempt to ignore feelings, since they consider emotions to be unpredictable. They tend to be moralistic and judgmental, which can contribute to difficulty when dealing with other individuals.

Knock, knock, knock, Penny? A popular example of a television character with many features of OCPD is Dr. Sheldon Cooper, played by Emmy winner Jim Parsons, on *The Big Bang Theory.* Sheldon demonstrates many of the traits associated with OCPD, including a preoccupation with details, lists, rules, and order (i.e., his strict adherence to eating specific take-out meals depending on the day of the week), rigidity and stubbornness (i.e., his insistence that he is the only individual who is allowed to sit on the left side of the couch), and his unreasonable insistence that others submit exactly to his way of doing things (i.e., the roommate agreement). Although Sheldon has never been officially diagnosed with OCPD, and often claims on the show "I'm not crazy. My mother had me tested," he does provide an excellent example of several of the behaviours that would often characterize OCPD.

Since the DSM-III-R, very little research has been published on OCPD. The exception to this is the research alluded to above that distinguishes OCPD and OCD. Studies using objective measures have found a clear independence between these two conditions. However, when using projective techniques or clinical interviews, co-occurrence of the two disorders has been reported (Cawley, 1974; Slade, 1974). In fact, in one study found that other personality disorders (e.g., avoidant, dependent, schizotypal PDs) were more likely to co-occur with OCD than was OCPD (Joffe, Swinson, & Regan, 1988). More recently, researchers have revealed that OCPD is not phenomenologically different from OCD, and that OCPD is simply a marker of obsessive-compulsive severity (Lochner et al., 2011). Furthermore, Garyfallos and colleagues (2010) discovered a high rate of comorbidity between OCD and OCPD and suggested that individuals with both of these disorders should constitute a subtype of OCD.

 BEFORE MOVING ON

> How does obsessive-compulsive personality disorder differ from obsessive-compulsive disorder? What differences would you expect to see in the symptoms of clients with each of these disorders, and how would their treatment plans differ?

Treatment

There are numerous obstacles to providing effective treatment to clients with personality disorders. As Gorton and Akhtar (1990) observed, two important factors make it difficult to evaluate treatment with the personality disorders: (1) many of these patients are not themselves upset by their characteristic personality style and so do not seek treatment, and (2) the dropout rates from treatment among these patients is extremely high. Because individuals with personality disorders have difficulties in their relationships, this understandably translates into difficulties forming and maintaining a strong therapeutic alliance in therapy. For some clients, the treatment context itself is a barrier to treatment. For example, treatment provided to an individual with ASPD or psychopathy tends to be court-ordered or provided in prison. This is likely not the best environment for developing a trusting therapeutic alliance. In addition, many individuals with personality disorders have problems maintaining focus on the therapeutic process between sessions. Even when the focus in treatment is on another condition, those patients who also have a personality disorder do more poorly (Reich & Green, 1991). In recent years, however, far more effort has been devoted to developing treatment programs specifically for these patients, although to date outcome data are limited.

According to Sperry (2003), five basic premises are essential to achieving effective treatment outcomes with patients diagnosed with a personality disorder: (1) these disorders are best conceptualized in a way that considers both biological and psychological factors, and the more effective treatment will reflect this approach, (2) before treatment, it is important to assess the individual's amenability to treatment, (3) effective treatment is flexible and tailored to the individual client, (4) the lower the level of treatability in the client, the more the therapist must combine multiple treatment approaches, and (5) the basic goal of treatment should be to help the client improve in his or her overall level of functioning. Now, we discuss some of the major approaches used in the treatment of personality disorders. These are consistent with Sperry's recommendations, and include (1) object-relations therapy, (2) cognitive-behavioural approaches, and (3) medication.

OBJECT-RELATIONS THERAPY

Leading proponents of an object-relations approach have been Kernberg (1975) and Kohut (1977). In their view, treatment should be aimed at correcting the flaws in the self that have resulted from unfortunate formative experiences (e.g., childhood abuse or neglect). The relationship between patient and therapist serves as a vehicle for confronting, in a supportive way, the patient's defences and distortions. This process is slow and, if successful, produces gradual changes. Thus, treatment is seen as necessarily long term. In the only controlled evaluation of this approach, Stevenson and Meares (1992) treated 30 patients with BPD, and followed them up for one year. At follow-up, 30 percent of the patients no longer met DSM criteria for BPD. Single-case reports of similar treatment programs for NPD have also yielded encouraging results (Kinston, 1980), but more extensive and more rigorous evaluations are required to determine the true value of this approach.

COGNITIVE-BEHAVIOURAL APPROACHES

Dr. Aaron Beck and his colleagues have extended his cognitive analyses to the personality disorders and suggested that treatment must correct the cognitive distortions of these patients in order to be successful (Beck Davis, & Freeman, 2015). Beck's treatment is directed at challenging the core beliefs that are thought to underlie the difficulties that people with personality disorders experience. This approach is referred to as **cognitive restructuring**, and is the basis for change, along with skills training and behavioural practices (see Chapter 17). To date, however, adherents of this promising approach have not produced controlled evaluations. This appears to be at least partly explained by the relatively recent development of this approach and the claim by Beck and colleagues (1990) that, unlike the application of cognitive therapy to other difficulties (e.g., major depression), treatment of personality disorders will take far longer.

Schema therapy, developed by Jeffrey Young (Young, 1999; Young et al., 2003), involves a cognitive-behavioural approach to the treatment of personality disorders; however, it also incorporates gestalt, object-relations, and psychodynamic treatment techniques while placing a heavy emphasis on clients' early difficult life experiences and on their current therapeutic relationship. A review of treatment efficacy for personality disorders suggests that CBT significantly reduces symptoms and enhances outcomes for all the personality disorders (Matusiewicz, Hopwood, Banducci, & Lejeuz, 2010). A randomized trial of schema-focused therapy (SFT) versus transference-focused therapy (TFT) for 88 patients with severe BPD symptomatology demonstrated that SFT patients had a significantly lower dropout rate compared to TFT patients over three years (27 percent versus 50 percent) and that SFT patients showed greater improvements on all clinical and quality-of-life measures administered compared to TFT patients (Giesen-Bloo et al., 2006).

Dialectical Behaviour Therapy (DBT), described above and also rooted in CBT, has been adapted for use with a variety of conditions beyond BPD (e.g., eating disorders, attention deficit/hyperactivity disorder, depression). However, little is known about its efficacy with these conditions (Robins & Chapman, 2004). Similarly, even though its use has been expanded, to date no work on the application of DBT to other personality disorders has been published despite reason to believe it may have utility for other personality disorders.

Canadian therapist Ariel Stravynski and his colleagues (Stravynski, Lesage, Marcouiller, & Elie, 1989) have applied behavioural approaches employing social skills training and desensitization to the problems of patients with avoidant personality disorder. However, the benefits of these programs have not been evaluated at long-term follow-up, and Alden (1989) observed that most of the treated patients remained socially uncomfortable.

PHARMACOLOGICAL INTERVENTIONS

Patients with BPD have been treated using a variety of pharmacotherapy treatments, including antidepressants (e.g., SSRIs, tricyclics, MAOIs), mood stabilizers (e.g., lithium carbonate), anxiolytics (e.g., anti-anxiety medications), opiate antagonists, and neuroleptics. These pharmacological agents have varying degrees of effectiveness (APA, 2001). Overall, patients with BPD have been successfully treated with some level of success when using medications such as amitriptyline (an antidepressant), thiothixene and olanzapine (both antipsychotics), and carbamazepine and lamotrigine (both anticonvulsants). Depending on symptom presentations, some people with BPD may be differentially responsive to either antipsychotic or antidepressant medications. For instance, in one study, researchers found that antipsychotics were most effective among individuals with BPD who also displayed psychotic-like features (Goldberg & colleagues, 1986). In another study, antidepressants were found to yield significant improvements for those with BPD and major depression (Cole et al., 1984). Finally, Reich and colleagues (2009) found that anticonvulsants were effective at reducing affective instability and impulsivity in individuals with BPD.

As for other personality disorders, Goldberg and colleagues (1986) found low doses of thiothixene to be beneficial for those with schizotypal PD. These individuals also seem to respond to antidepressants (Markovitz et al., 1991); however, the benefits of any medications with this personality disorder are modest at best (Gitlin, 1993). Medication has been used with those with ASPD for short-term management of problematic and threatening behaviour. However, long-term side effects, lack of symptom alleviation, and noncompliance indicate that this approach has, at best, a modest impact. In combination with other intervention strategies, however, it may prove helpful.

8 **BEFORE MOVING ON**

Many patients who have a personality disorder do not believe that there is anything wrong with them. Do these patients exhibit egosyntonic or egodystonic symptoms? Considering the various forms of treatments that are available, which would be most effective for dealing with this type of patient, and how would you attempt to deal with his or her resistance? How might this method differ from treatment of other major mental illnesses (e.g., schizophrenia, bipolar disorder)

Dr. Robert Hare

Photo by Scott McCall. Courtesy of Dr. Robert Hare

Dr. Robert Hare is emeritus professor of psychology, University of British Columbia, where he has taught and conducted research for some 35 years, and president of Darkstone Research Group Ltd., a forensic research and consulting firm. He has devoted most of his academic career to the investigation of psychopathy, examining its nature, assessment, and implications for mental health and criminal justice. He is the author of several books, including *Without Conscience: The Disturbing World of the Psychopaths Among Us*, and more than 100 scientific articles on psychopathy. He developed the Psychopathy Checklist–Revised (PCL-R) and co-authored its derivatives, the Psychopathy Checklist: Screening Version, the Psychopathy Checklist: Youth Version, the Antisocial Process Screening Device, and the P-Scan (for use in law enforcement). Dr. Hare's assessment tools are used in every developed country. In addition to his extensive research activities, he consults with many law enforcement agencies, including the FBI and the RCMP, sits on the Research Advisory Board of the FBI Child Abduction and Serial Murder Investigative Resources

Center (CASMIRC), and is a member of the FBI Serial Murder Working Group. He was also a member of the advisory panel established by Her Majesty's Prison Service to develop new programs for the treatment of psychopathic offenders. His current research on psychopathy includes assessment issues, developmental factors, neurobiological correlates, risk for recidivism and violence, and the development of new treatment and management strategies for psychopathic offenders. More recently, Dr. Hare has extended the theory and research on psychopathy to the business and corporate world with the development of the B-Scan-360, an instrument used to screen for psychopathic traits and behaviours.

Dr. Hare continues to lecture widely on psychopathy and on the use and misuse of the PCL-R in the mental health and criminal justice systems. Among his most recent awards are the Silver Medal of the Queen Sophia Centre in Spain; the Canadian Psychological Association Award for Distinguished Applications of Psychology; the American Academy of Forensic Psychology Award for Distinguished Applications to the Field of Forensic

Psychology; the Isaac Ray Award, presented by the American Psychiatric Association and the American Academy of Psychiatry and Law for Outstanding Contributions to Forensic Psychiatry and Psychiatric Jurisprudence; and the B. Jaye Anno Award for Excellence in Communication, presented by the National Commission on Correctional Health Care. He was also made an affiliate member of the International Criminal Investigative Analysis Fellowship.

The Future of Personality Disorders in the DSM. Although the DSM-5 was published in 2013, the APA already is considering changes to the personality disorders section for future versions. Specifically, the DSM-5 includes a proposal for a new method of assessing personality disorders in Section III, Emerging Measures and Models. There are a number of reasons for the personality disorders to be revised, including the excessive co-occurrence of personality disorders and comorbidity among various clinical disorders, the poor temporal stability of diagnoses, and the use of arbitrary thresholds for diagnosis (Bornstein, 2011). After a thorough review of the personality disorder literature, the workgroup responsible for suggesting amendments to the diagnosis of personality disorders decided that four of the current personality disorders should be removed from the DSM completely: schizoid personality disorder, histrionic personality disorder, paranoid personality disorder, and dependent personality disorder. To account for the personality disorders that will be removed, a "Personality Disorder Trait Specified" (PDTS) category has been proposed.

In addition to the removal of four of the personality disorders, a change to the way in which clinicians diagnose personality disorders also has been proposed. Since the first version of the DSM, the diagnosis of personality disorders, much like all conditions, has been categorical; individuals have to meet a certain number of the criteria to reach the cut-off to be diagnosed with a personality disorder. The proposed change is to shift to a hybrid dimensional-categorical model for personality disorders and personality disorder assessment. This shift will involve a completely new method for diagnosis, replacing the categorical method with a measure of self- and interpersonal functioning, as well as a continuum of personality traits. Clinicians will have to assess a client's overall personality functioning by assessing self-functioning, characterized by impairments in identity and self-direction, and interpersonal functioning, characterized by impairments in empathy and intimacy. Similar to the current model, clinicians must also assess whether the client possesses the pathological personality traits associated with the personality disorder in question.

It is expected that this shift to a dimensional-categorical model will reduce the amount of concurrent personality disorders and comorbidity with other major mental illnesses (Samuel, Lynam, Widiger, & Ball, 2011). While the proposed revisions to the model of personality disorders were not accepted for the first version of the DSM-5, this model is currently being tested and will likely be implemented in future versions of the DSM.

> Considering what you now know about personality disorders, what do you think of the hybrid model proposed for future versions of the DSM? Do you agree with the proposed deletions of four of the current personality disorders? Why or why not? Do you think personality disorders should be conceptualized using a more dimensional approach? Why or why not?

SUMMARY

- Personality disorders comprise maladaptive personality traits. All people have relatively consistent characteristics that make up their personality. Personality disorders are distinguished from normal personality traits by being rigid, maladaptive, and monolithic. People with personality disorders typically have many intact abilities but have impaired functioning (especially socially) because of their disorder. Personality disorders (i.e., psychopathy or APD) were first clearly described in the early nineteenth century. The present set of personality disorders first appeared in DSM-III as Axis II, separate from the Axis I "clinical" disorders. While the same set of personality disorders is included in the DSM-5, the multi-axial system is no longer used in the current version of the DSM, and the personality disorders are now included in Section II of the manual.

- Personality disorders are more rigid and often more difficult to treat than are other major mental disorders. Other mental disorders (e.g., schizophrenia, bipolar disorder) are primarily considered to be egodystonic because they cause distress and are viewed as problematic by the individual sufferer. Personality disorders are often considered to be egosyntonic. In fact, most individuals diagnosed with personality disorders do not report experiencing any distress in interpersonal relations or daily functioning (with exceptions, of course, e.g., borderline personality disorder, avoidant personality disorder). It is often the family and friends of an individual with a personality disorder who seek help for the individual, because those closest to the individual most often feel the effects of personality disorders.

- The DSM-5 lists 10 disorders, grouped into three clusters: odd and eccentric disorders (paranoid, schizoid, schizotypal); dramatic, emotional, or erratic disorders (antisocial, borderline, histrionic, narcissistic); and anxious and fearful disorders (avoidant, dependent, obsessive-compulsive). It also lists two other disorders: "Personality change due to another medical condition" and "other specified personality disorder and unspecified personality disorder." Personality disorder diagnoses tend to have lower reliability than those of other major mental disorders, and there is considerable comorbidity as well as overlap among these disorders. Further, many have argued that the diagnostic criteria reflect cultural and gender bias, although this is not conclusive.

- The essential feature of ASPD is a pervasive, ongoing disregard for the rights of others. Special diagnostic issues and confusion over prevalence and research outcomes arise because ASPD is similar in some respects to the related construct of psychopathy. The latter, as measured by PCL-R, focuses on core emotional and interpersonal processes as well as behaviour, whereas the DSM-5 criteria for ASPD are largely behavioural. Social and family factors have been cited as etiological factors for ASPD; there is some support for genetic factors as well. Studies have shown that psychopaths are at high risk for future violence and that treatment outcomes are generally poor. BPD is characterized by fluctuations in mood (emotional instability), an unstable sense of identity, instability in relationships, and behavioural instability (impulsivity). Diagnostic criteria are still debated for several disorders. Disruptions in the family of origin are the most common etiological explanation. Treatment for personality disorders in general is difficult to evaluate, because many patients never seek treatment. Among the main approaches used those rooted in cognitive-behavioural theory, though medications are also used. There are few well-controlled studies of any treatments for most of these disorders.

- Obsessive-compulsive personality disorder and the more commonly known obsessive-compulsive disorder are distinct constructs. OCD can be found in the Obsessive-Compulsive and Related Disorders section, whereas OCPD is listed under the Personality Disorders. These disorders can be distinguished by the symptoms displayed; due to these differences, OCD and OCPD require different interventions.

- Etiological explanations have focused on psychodynamics, attachment theory, cognitive-behavioural perspectives, and, most recently, biological factors such as genetics, neurotransmitters, or brain dysfunction. Unfortunately, the majority of the data are correlational. Of the 10 DSM-5 disorders, APD has received the bulk of research attention due to the harm caused by those with the disorder.

- The DSM-5 includes two chapters on the personality disorders, the first in Section II and the second in Section III. The criteria set forth in Section II are those that are currently being implemented. The chapter in Section III proposes drastic revisions to the personality disorders chapter, including abolishing four of the existing personality disorders (schizoid personality disorder, histrionic personality disorder, paranoid personality disorder, and dependent personality disorder), as well as adding a new diagnosis of personality disorder trait specified. The DSM-5 authors have also proposed to change the model used to diagnose personality disorders from categorical to a hybrid dimensional-categorical model. This shift will involve a completely new method for diagnosis, replacing the categorical method with a measure of self and interpersonal functioning, as well as a continuum of personality traits. It is unknown when this new model of assessing personality traits will be implemented but it will likely be included in revisions of the DSM-5.

KEY TERMS

anxious ambivalent (p. 310)

attachment theory (p. 297)

clusters (p. 291)

cognitive restructuring (p. 314)

comorbidity (p. 295)

delusions (p. 299)

dialectical behaviour therapy (p. 310)

eccentricity (p. 300)

egodystonic (p. 293)

egosyntonic (p. 293)

emotional responsiveness (p. 299)

fearlessness hypothesis (p. 302)

instability (p. 308)

oppositional behaviour (p. 303)

overlap (p. 295)

personality disorders (p. 290)

polythetic (p. 302)

prevalence (p. 292)

psychological autopsy (p. 292)

psychopaths (p. 300)

responsivity factor (p. 304)

sociopaths (p. 300)

suspiciousness (p. 299)

traits (p. 290)

CAROLINE F. PUKALL

•

KATE S. SUTTON

CHAPTER

13

Sexual and Gender Identity Disorders

LEARNING OBJECTIVES

AFTER READING THIS CHAPTER, STUDENTS WILL BE ABLE TO:

1 List and provide examples of each phase of the sexual response cycle as developed by Masters and Johnson.

2 Compare and contrast lifelong versus acquired sexual dysfunction, and generalized versus situational sexual dysfunction. Provide one example of each of the following: a lifelong generalized male sexual dysfunction, a lifelong situational female sexual dysfunction, an acquired generalized male sexual dysfunction, and an acquired situational female sexual dysfunction.

3 Describe the rationale for sensate focus, and describe the stages of this treatment tool for a couple in which the male partner has been diagnosed with erectile dysfunction.

4 Identify the different dimensions of gender and explain how inconsistencies among them can result in sexes other than male or female.

5 Compare and contrast the following: paraphilias and paraphilic disorders. Provide an example of each.

6 Explain how a clinician currently makes a diagnosis of "rapist" using the DSM-5.

When David phoned for an appointment, he asked whether he could arrange to arrive at the office unseen by other clients to avoid recognition. He said that he was married and his problem was "impotence," so the therapist encouraged him to bring his partner to the initial interview. The therapist understood that "impotence" can cause a lot of shame for many clients, but she informed him that the waiting area was a safe space and others would not be made aware of why he was coming to therapy.

During the history taking, David reported that he had always doubted the adequacy of his sexual responsiveness. Although he could develop an erection and have an orgasm during masturbation, he believed that he wasn't "highly sexed like most guys" because he did not share his classmates' fascination with pornography and vulgar jokes. He became upset by his continued masturbation, believing that it was an "abnormal" sexual outlet, and he worried about whether he could engage in penile-vaginal intercourse in the future.

He reported having little sexual experience with others. He first tried to have intercourse on his 18th birthday, when his father hired a sex worker to teach his son how to "be a man." David was not able to perform with the sex worker. He was so ashamed that he begged her not to tell anyone, but later he boasted about his prowess. The episode with the sex worker confirmed David's worst fears of not being able to perform. To avoid facing such embarrassment again, he broke off relations with women as soon as they made any sexual overtures. Eventually, he stopped dating entirely.

David graduated from college and was working as a firefighter when he began to develop a strong friendship with Alicia, a colleague at work. Eventually, she made it clear that she was interested in more than friendship. Before he knew it, David had agreed to marriage. He felt that he had led her on by allowing such a close bond to develop and hoped that in the security of a caring rela-tionship, his capacity for a sexual relationship with a woman would grow.

Alicia did not seem to expect sex before marriage and, to his relief, when he finally admitted his problem to her the week before their marriage, she understood and was calm, stating that they would work it out together. David was nevertheless panicked by the thought of meeting his wife's sexual demands; however, on their honeymoon, David found that he was able to have intercourse on several occasions. Many more times, however, Alicia was interested but David could not get an erection and quickly backed out of the encounter; he began to avoid situations in which sex might occur.

As the years passed, Alicia remained the sexual initiator, and David grew more and more anxious. He began to avoid kissing Alicia for fear that the physical intimacy might lead to sex. Gradually, conflict between them increased. Alicia, who was thinking about having children, began to press David "to do something about [his] impotence." David became more anxious about failure with each unsuccessful attempt. He would sometimes try to satisfy Alicia with oral sex, but his "failure to perform" always left him feeling inadequate, and he withdrew emotionally, leaving her upset.

By the time they sought therapy, David and Alicia felt quite hopeless about the future of their relationship. They saw therapy as a "last-ditch effort" to save their marriage, but they were also motivated by the joint desire to have children.

This case illustrates a particular type of sexual dysfunction (i.e., erectile disorder) that represents a persistent failure to achieve satisfaction in sexual relations. Other sexual dysfunctions will be described, as will specific paraphilias (i.e., intense and persistent atypical sexual interests). This chapter will also describe *gender dysphoria:* the condition of people whose gender identity (i.e., perception of oneself as male or female) is not in line with their biological sex.

Historical Perspective

Conceptions of the appropriateness or deviance of human sexual behaviours have varied considerably throughout history (Bullough, 1976). Sex is one of the most discussed human behaviours, although these discussions are often superficial and skirt substantive issues. For example, sex education often takes the form of a recitation of knowledge about physiological functioning and anatomical facts rather than a discussion of actual behaviours and their associated thoughts and feelings.

Brown (1985) suggests that the Judeo-Christian tradition has had a significant influence on notions about appropriate and inappropriate sexual behaviours within our society. He contends that the prevailing attitudes at the time the Bible and the Talmud were written condoned "sex between men and very young girls in marriage, concubinage, and slavery" (p. 23). Not surprisingly, some of the remarks in these historical documents are in conflict with today's values. Christian notions of acceptable sexual behaviour evolved in the West primarily through the teachings of St. Augustine, who declared that sexual intercourse was permissible only for purposes of procreation, only when the male was on top, and only when the penis and vagina were involved. Thus, oral-genital sex, masturbation, anal sex, and presumably all forms of precoital activities were considered sinful, as were sexual activities with someone who could not conceive, such as a child or a same-sex partner.

Science in the sixteenth and seventeenth centuries offered support for these Christian teachings by attributing all manner of dire consequences to so-called excessive sexual activity. These views were popularized in 1766 by Tissot in his treatise on the ills of onanism (solitary masturbation). Tissot attributed a whole variety of ills to masturbation and recommended that the state establish controls on sexuality, although just how these controls were to be enacted was not made clear. Popular writers on sex in the nineteenth century took up Tissot's claims with gusto. The Reverend Sylvester Graham and Dr. John Harvey Kellogg published treatises declaring that masturbation caused numerous problems, including lassitude, dullness, defective development, untrustworthiness, and even ill health and rounded shoulders. Parents were warned to watch for these signs and prevent the destructive behaviour at all costs. Excessive sexuality could be counteracted by healthy activities and a diet of bland foods.

Graham developed Graham Crackers and Kellogg developed Corn Flakes to meet this need.

Krafft-Ebing (1901) published the first strictly medical textbook on atypical sexual behaviours, called *Psychopathia Sexualis.* Again, masturbation was blamed for numerous illnesses. The range of sexual behaviours considered to be deviant was initially extremely broad, including whatever was thought to differ from prevailing beliefs about acceptable practices. Accordingly, up to the early part of the twentieth century, the list of atypical activities included a variety of sexual practices that are no longer officially listed as "abnormal."

Research on sexuality has not progressed at the same rate as has research on other human issues, apparently as a result of notions concerning the privacy of sex. Such notions have encouraged the general public to view sex researchers with suspicion. The publication of Alfred Kinsey's research (Kinsey, Pomeroy, & Martin, 1948; Kinsey, Pomeroy, Martin, & Gebhard, 1953) investigating human sexual practices was greeted with animosity by the general public, the media, and many of his scientific colleagues because his findings upset established beliefs about sexuality. His data revealed that masturbation, oral sex, and same-sex sexual behaviour, for example, were engaged in by far more people and with far greater frequency than was previously believed. Masters and Johnson's (1966) study of human sexual response was greeted with much the same animosity. Starting in the 1990s and continuing today, several sexuality studies in the United States were stopped as a result of political pressure, despite the fact that they had already been carefully screened and approved by scientific communities (Udry, 1993). Although less of an issue in Canada, some studies have come under scrutiny by the government, resulting in loss of research funds and less funding available to researchers. However, in general, the lay public and governmental agencies in Canada demonstrate greater tolerance of sex research.

Diagnostic Issues

As in all other areas of human functioning, it is necessary to have at least an approximate idea of what is typical (including some indication of the frequency of behaviours) in order to define atypical functioning. Simple frequency of a problem, however, will not always do. Premature ejaculation, for example, is subject to both parties' perception of the act, and can therefore cause problems based on this perception (Byers & Grenier, 2003). Even if most men ejaculated rapidly upon being sexually aroused, would this be considered typical? It certainly would be from a statistical point of view, but if the person and his partner were dissatisfied and sought help, the diagnosis of a problem would nevertheless be likely from a clinical standpoint.

Satisfaction with present functioning is an important criterion, reflected in DSM-5's definition of sexual dysfunctions. A problem for reliable diagnosis is that DSM-5's criteria require diagnosticians to make somewhat subjective judgments: to decide, for example, whether a client's experiences are "persistent," "recurrent," or "delayed." There are no perfectly objective standards for these qualities, which will vary within the same individual from one time and setting to another.

In the DSM-5, the question of distress of the person suffering from, or being affected by, a paraphilic disorder versus a paraphilia is more straightforward than in the previous DSM. Paraphilias—intense and persistent atypical sexual interests—cannot be diagnosed as a disorder unless the individual experiences distress or impairment because of the paraphilia, or harms others. For example, a person who engages in sexual sadism with consenting, adult partners as part of a kinky lifestyle and is not distressed by this behaviour would simply have a paraphilia called sexual sadism, but one who engages in this behaviour and harms others would be diagnosed with sexual sadistic disorder. So, a paraphilia is a necessary, but not sufficient, condition for having a **paraphilic disorder**, and a paraphilia does not justify or require clinical intervention.

Although same-sex sexual attraction will not be discussed as a topic in this chapter, the history of "homosexuality" as a disorder is relevant in terms of the role of the prevailing mindset of society in determining what "problems" are considered mental disorders. "Homosexuality" is no longer considered to be a disorder; however, in the time up to and including the publication of the DSM-II (APA, 1968), "homosexuality" was listed as a disorder, and people (mostly males) with this sexual orientation were subjected to treatment aimed at changing their attraction from same-sex to other-sex partners. Same-sex sexual behaviour was also illegal, and all too often those engaging in such behaviour were imprisoned. In 1973, the APA's Nomenclature Committee recommended that "homosexuality" be removed from the list of disorders. However, the committee also suggested the addition of "sexual orientation disturbance" to refer to those who were attracted to members of the same sex and experienced conflict with their sexual orientation or who wished to change their orientation. Accordingly, the DSM-III (APA, 1980) included **egodystonic homosexuality** and, although this category was dropped from the DSM-III-R (APA, 1987) and DSM-IV (APA, 1994), both included, as one possible form of a sexual disorder not otherwise specified, "persistent and marked distress about sexual orientation" (APA, 1994, p. 538). These remarks about sexual orientation are not included in the DSM-IV-TR or DSM-5.

Sexual Response

It is difficult to gain an understanding of what most people "do" sexually and how often people engage in various kinds of sexual activity. There are wide ranges in types and frequency of sexual behaviour, and differences can be seen

TABLE 13.1 RESPONSE TO THE QUESTION: "HOW OFTEN DO YOU THINK ABOUT SEX?"

	"Several times per day"	"A few times per week"	"A few times per month"
Men	46.1%	25.0%	4.6%
Women	10.6%	42.3%	18.3%

Source: Based on How Much Does Gender Explain in Sexual Attitudes and Behaviors? A Survey of Canadian Adults, Archives of Sexual Behavior June 2007, 36(3), pp. 451–461.

within an individual depending on age, sexual experience, partner status, length of relationship, and many other factors. Also, sex is a private topic for most people, so simply asking the people we know may not give us accurate information (or any information at all!). Research can sometimes shed light on questions related to sexuality (e.g., how does sexuality differ between men and women?), but we also have to keep in mind that people who participate in sexuality studies likely differ from those who do not. Regardless, research has shown some interesting differences in frequency of fantasies and sexual behaviour patterns between men and women. In an investigation into the sexual activity of Canadians (Fischtein, Herold, & Desmarais, 2007), results indicated that adult men fantasized about sex much more frequently than did women (see Table 13.1). Another survey reported that 61 percent of men compared to 38 percent of women reported masturbating during a specified one-year period (Das, 2007). Furthermore, of those who do report masturbating, men do so over three times more frequently than women (Laumann, Gagnon, Michael, & Michaels, 1994). In addition, men report an earlier age at first intercourse and a greater number of sexual partners (Fischtein, Herold, & Desmarais, 2007). All of this makes intuitive sense; these patterns fall right into the sex stereotypes we all have, that men are more sexually permissive and less discriminating and women are more sexually cautious. But if men are consistently reporting a higher number of sexual partners than women, who exactly are these men having sex with?

In an ingenious experiment devised to investigate this issue, Alexander and Fisher (2003) used the bogus pipeline to examine sex differences in self-reported sexuality domains. Male and female participants were randomly assigned to one of three conditions: the bogus pipeline condition, in which participants were given a false polygraph test while they answered questionnaires after being told that the polygraph would detect dishonest responding; the anonymous condition, in which participants were asked to fill out the questionnaires privately and leave them in a locked box; and the exposure-threat condition, in which participants were asked to give their names to the experimenter and complete the questionnaires while the experimenter was in the room. Results indicated that the smallest sex differences in behaviour were found in the bogus pipeline condition; the authors suggest that the participants were motivated to answer honestly given the

Sex therapists Virginia Johnson and William Masters.

belief that false responding would be detected. Slightly larger sex differences were found in the anonymous condition, and the largest differences were found in the exposure-threat condition. Interestingly, although women underreported sexual behaviours in the anonymous and exposure-threat conditions as compared to the bogus pipeline condition, men's responses were consistent across conditions. Specifically, women underreported frequency of masturbation and pornography use; in the bogus pipeline condition, however, the results for these behaviours were similar for men and women. It appears as though sex differences in reported sexual behaviours may at least be partly explained by sex differences in reported as opposed to actual sex differences. So it is important to keep a critical eye when drawing conclusions about sex differences in the domain of sexuality.

To emphasize this point, a recently published meta-analytic study demonstrated that sex differences were typically small in such behaviours as intercourse incidence, younger age at first intercourse, and number of sexual partners (Petersen & Hyde, 2010), indicating that men and women are more similar than different for most behaviours reported.

The issue of sex differences aside, research has revealed considerable cultural differences in sexuality. For example, Canadians tend to have more permissive sexual attitudes than do Americans; 29 percent of Americans as compared to 12 percent of Canadians feel that premarital sex is morally wrong (Widmer, Tread, & Newcomb, 1998). Furthermore, certain countries have sexual norms that differ considerably from those of Canadians. On the island of Inis Beag off the coast of Ireland, for example, the citizens have no knowledge of sexual practices; in fact, during sexual intercourse both parties keep their underwear on, and a female orgasm is unheard of (Messenger, 1993). However, there are some common sexual trends across cultures. Kissing is the most common sexual technique in nearly all cultures, whereas incest is considered universally taboo (Firestone, Dixon, Nunes, & Bradford, 2005).

Some norms for sexual behaviour also change with time. Beginning in the mid-1960s, liberalization of attitudes toward sexuality appeared to be accompanied by greater sexual experience (there are few earlier statistics available). A study of Canadian university students reported that, from 1968 to 1978, the percentage of female students who had had intercourse increased from 32 to 58%, and of male students from 40 to 62% (Barrett, 1980). More current estimates suggest that the trend is continuing for both genders: 10 to 13% of 14-year-olds, 20 to 25% of 15-year-olds, 40% of 16-year-olds, and 50% of 17-year-olds have engaged in penile–vaginal intercourse (Maticka-Tyndale, 2001).

Interestingly, people have different views of what constitutes sex. Canadian sex researcher Sandra Byers (University of New Brunswick) and her colleagues surveyed students' definitions of "having sex" (Byers, Henderson, & Hobson, 2009). Not surprisingly, less than 5% of students defined behaviours that did not include genital touching as "having sex." Only 12 to 15% included manual genital touching in their definition of having sex, and 24 to 25% included oral-genital stimulation. Ninety percent of students agreed that vaginal–penile intercourse was having sex, but only 83% agreed that anal–penile intercourse was sex.

William Masters and Virginia Johnson (1966) were the first investigators to study and document the physiological stages that take place in human sexual response. They noted the changes that occur in the body during sexual arousal, orgasm, and the return to the unaroused state, and referred to this sequence as the **sexual response cycle**. Masters and Johnson divided the sexual response cycle into four stages: excitement, plateau, orgasm, and resolution.

During the *excitement* stage, the genital tissues of both males and females swell as they fill with blood (vasocongestion). This causes erection of the penis in men and engorgement of the clitoris and vaginal lubrication in women. Furthermore, the testes and nipples become engorged, muscular tension and heart rate increase, and breathing becomes more rapid and shallow. See Focus box 13.1 for the role of thermal imaging in measuring sexual response in current studies in males and females.

The *plateau* stage consolidates this arousal, with additional swelling of the penis and vaginal tissues. In men, the testes become elevated and may reach one and a half times their unaroused size. In women, the clitoris retracts underneath the clitoral hood and the inner part of the vagina expands. During *orgasm*, both sexes experience rhythmic, muscular contractions at about eight-second intervals. In men, orgasm comprises two stages, which quickly follow one another. First, seminal fluid collects in the urethral bulb, at the base of the penis. As this happens, there is a sense of orgasmic inevitability and nothing can prevent ejaculation from following. Within two or three seconds, contractions lead to expulsion of the ejaculate from the penis. Women experience contractions of the uterus and of the muscles surrounding the vagina during orgasm. Blood pressure and heart rate reach a peak during

Bettmann/Getty Images

**FOCUS
13.1**

A Hot Topic: Measuring Sexual Arousal in Men and Women

To date, the psychophysiological measurement of sexual arousal, and by extension, our understanding and treatment of sexual arousal problems, has differed between men and women. While the measurement of male erectile functioning in a laboratory setting has led to clinical guidelines and pharmaceutical treatment options for erectile dysfunction (Connoly, Boriakchanyavat, & Lue, 1996; Goldstein et al., 1998), similar studies in women have not been successful (Graham, 2010a, 2010b). Part of the issue is that different instruments have been used to measure physical sexual response in men and women, making it impossible to directly compare male and female sexual arousal. Furthermore, the numerous practical and quantitative limitations with widely used instruments for the measurement of female physiological sexual arousal have limited the use of these devices in clinical settings and have not made it possible to quantify physical parameters for arousal disorders (Prause & Janssen, 2006).

Researchers in Canada, however, may be close to solving these problems through the use of thermographic imaging to assess physiological sexual response (Kukkonen, Binik, Amsel, & Carrier, 2007). Thermography cameras, similar to night vision goggles, pick up infrared emissions from the human body through remote sensing and provide temperature readings of the target in focus. As temperature is directly related to blood flow, and genital blood flow is a physical marker of sexual response, thermography offers a unique way to examine sexual arousal in men and women through the measurement of genital temperature. Because the camera does not require any physical contact with participants, the same methodology can be used for both sexes, allowing for a direct comparison of sexual arousal between men and women.

Dr. Kukkonen, an assistant professor at the University of Guelph, published the first direct comparison of male and female sexual arousal using modern thermographic cameras. By recording genital and thigh temperature while participants watched sexually arousing, neutral, anxiety-provoking, or humorous film clips, Kukkonen and colleagues found that temperature increases were specific to the genitals during the sexual arousal condition only (Kukkonen et al., 2007, 2010). Of interest is that both men and women had significant correlations between their self-reported sexual arousal and genital temperature, indicating that this physical measure matched how participants were feeling, a finding contrary to most previous research on women. In addition, a comparison of male and female sexual response demonstrated that there were no differences in the time to peak sexual arousal, although a subsequent study found significant differences between men and women in the resolution of sexual arousal following orgasm (Paterson, Shuo Jin, Amsel, & Binik, 2014).

Thermography has been used to assess genital temperature differences in men and women with sexual dysfunction (Cherner & Reissing, 2013; Sarin, Amsel, & Binik, 2014; 2016) as well as to examine the impact of mood and age on sexual response (Hodgson, Kukkonen, Binik, & Carrier, 2016; Kukkonen, Binik, Amsel, & Carrier, 2009). These studies indicate that thermography holds great potential as a tool to measure physiological sexual response. The ability to directly compare sexes, in particular, allows researchers to address issues of sex differences and similarities in sexual arousal, which may answer the age-old question of whether men and women are really that different. ●

Source: Dr. Tuuli Kukkonen, PhD, Assistant Professor of the University of Guelph.

orgasm, and there are involuntary muscular contractions. Following orgasm, the body gradually returns to its pre-aroused state, in the stage that Masters and Johnson called *resolution.* Shortly after ejaculation, men experience what is called a *refractory period* during which they are unresponsive to sexual stimulation. Women, however, may be able to experience multiple orgasms without any refractory period. Although Masters and Johnson did not include same-sex oriented individuals in their sample, it is likely that the physiological responses of same-sex partners follow similar patterns as just described. Or do they? See Focus box 13.2 for research examining sexual arousal in same-sex partners

FOCUS 13.2

Nonspecificity of Sexual Response in Androphilic Women

Research by Dr. Meredith Chivers at Queen's University in Kingston, Ontario, suggests that the patterns of sexual response in women and men are not opposite sides of the same coin. By studying the relationship between people's sexual attractions (to women, men, or both) and sexual responses in the laboratory to stimuli depicting women or men, Chivers has discovered a compelling gender and sexual-orientation difference: whereas men's physiological and psychological sexual responses are strongly related to their sexual attractions to women or men, a pattern of response described as *category specific*, heterosexual women's are not—they are *nonspecific* (Chivers, Reiger, Latty, & Bailey, 2004). Women who report sexual attractions exclusively to men (called androphilia) show physiological sexual responses to stimuli depicting women and men; their self-reported arousal (that is, how sexually aroused they report that they feel) is, however, more strongly related to their sexual attractions. Women who are sexually attracted to women (called gynephilia), on the other hand, do show greater arousal to sexual stimuli depicting women than men, suggesting that their arousal patterns are more category specific than those of heterosexual women (Chivers, Bouchard, & Timmers, 2015). These results may relate to the greater fluidity and flexibility in women's same- and other-gender attractions; with a capacity to be sexually responsive to both genders, women's sexuality may not be as restricted as men's.

The reasons for these differences in the *specificity* of sexual arousal are not currently known, but other research by Chivers and colleagues suggests that, for women, physiological sexual response may be triggered by a number of sexual cues such as sexual activities or contexts. Chivers showed women and men films of bonobos mating, along with films of human couples engaged in sex, while measuring physiological and psychological sexual responses. Only women showed significant increases in physiological responses to the bonobo film, though both women and men reported not feeling aroused by this unusual stimulus (Chivers & Bailey, 2005). These results suggest that, despite being an unarousing film psychologically, something about watching bonobos have sex was sufficient to cause women to experience an increase in genital vasocongestion. In another study, Chivers' research team presented images of core sexual stimuli—just images of genitals, without sexual activities or other sexual cues—and showed that androphilic women had significantly greater genital responses to images of penises, a gender-specific pattern of sexual response to sexual cues from their preferred gender (Spape et al., 2014). These results indirectly suggest that the sexual activities or contexts shown in typical laboratory sexual films may provoke a nonspecific sexual response in women.

Chivers and colleagues provided a number of possible explanations for androphilic women's nonspecific sexual response (Chivers, 2017). For example, women's genital responding to a broader range of sexual cues may have very little relationship to a woman's sexual desires or attractions and is, instead, an automatic, protective response. Vaginal lubrication, necessary to reduce the likelihood of genital injury and to make sexual penetration more comfortable, is thought to result from a process called *transudation*—fluid passing into the vaginal canal caused by genital vasocongestion. So even though a woman might not feel sexually aroused, her body is prepared for the possibility of sex, similar to how even vegetarians might find themselves salivating to the smell of a cooking steak: they may not actually want to eat the steak, but the smell is a powerful cue that leads to an automatic reflex that aids in chewing and swallowing food.

The potential for disconnect between physiological and psychological states of sexual responding is not exclusive to women; men can show this too, and, conversely, some women show strong agreement between these two states. On average, however, the concordance between genital and psychological sexual responses in the laboratory is significantly greater for men. Chivers and her colleagues quantified *sexual concordance* in a recent meta-analysis and reported that the average agreement for women is a correlation of about 0.26, whereas the correlation is about 0.66 for men (Chivers, Seto, Lalumière, Laan, & Grimbos, 2010). The reasons for this difference are still under investigation by several laboratories. ●

Source: Contributed by Dr. Meredith Chivers of Queen's University.

---

and heterosexual men and women. Figure 13.1 depicts the sexual response cycles of men and women derived from Masters and Johnson's research.

Helen Singer Kaplan (1979) proposed an alternative model of sexual stages, consisting of desire, excitement, and orgasm. An important contribution of her work was the distinction of desire as primarily a psychological component to sexual response. She also treated the stages as independent components, and noted that many sexual experiences do not necessarily follow the full sequence described by Masters and Johnson. Thus, a couple's sexual encounter may sometimes involve excitement followed by diminished arousal without orgasm. This information is valuable in that it suggests that many sequences of sexual response exist.

Many older individuals engage in sexual intercourse well into their eighties and nineties, although the frequency of sex decreases with age (Kessel, 2001). It is also evident that as women experience menopause, interest in sexual activity and sexual intercourse usually decreases (Palacios, Menendez, Jurado, Castano, & Vargas, 1995), which is associated with a more general reduction in sexual interest (Dennerstein, Smith, Morse, & Burger, 1994). These effects were demonstrated to be attributable to menopause independently of the effects of aging (Dennerstein, Dudley, Lehert, & Burger, 2000). However, Dennerstein and colleagues also showed lowered levels of sexual responsivity with age in women who were not menopausal.

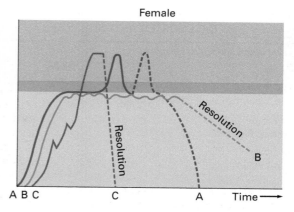

FIGURE 13.1 Levels of Sexual Arousal During the Phases of the Sexual Response Cycle

Masters and Johnson divided the sexual response cycle into four phases: excitement, plateau, orgasm, and resolution. During the resolution phase, the level of sexual arousal returns to the pre-aroused state. For men there is a refractory period following orgasm. As shown by the broken line, however, men can become re-aroused to orgasm once past the refractory period and their levels of sexual arousal have returned to pre-plateau levels. Pattern A for women shows a typical response cycle; the broken line indicates multiple orgasms, should they occur. Pattern B shows the cycle of a woman who reaches the plateau phase but for whom arousal is "resolved" without orgasm. Pattern C shows the sexual response of a highly aroused woman who passes quickly through phases.

---

1 BEFORE MOVING ON

> It is important to note that people's sexual response cycles vary immensely; for example, men can experience multiple orgasms, although this feature was not captured in the Masters and Johnson model. What are some of the advantages and disadvantages of models that combine hundreds of responses into a general representation?

Sexual Dysfunctions

As the following case illustrates, multiple factors (for example, shame and ignorance about sex, anxiety about sex, lack of experience with physical affection, and low self-confidence) may contribute to the development of sexual dysfunctions. Joan's problem developed over time, becoming worse the more she worried about it. By the time someone like Joan consults a therapist, the problem has typically become more complex and involves secondary difficulties, such as relationship problems and low self-esteem.

Case Notes

Joan sought help at the insistence of her best friend, in whom she had confided. Recently, Joan had become interested in a man. Ron, she believed, was gentle and caring, and she wanted to return his affection. Joan had never had an orgasm, and she thought that this had contributed to the breakdown of her only previous relationship and was afraid it would impair matters with Ron.

Joan had been raised in a strict religious family in which the word *sex* had never been spoken. Anything to do with the body was held to be shameful and disgusting. Joan had never touched her own body except while washing, and felt uncomfortable even seeing herself undressed in a mirror. Her parents never showed open affection, and, although her mother hugged her, her father merely shook her hand when she left home for university.

Joan was sexually inexperienced and tolerated Ron's advances because she was too embarrassed to protest. She grew very fond of him and enjoyed the tenderness he showed her, although she found the intensity of his sexuality frightening and completely foreign to her own experience.

Joan felt constricted by Ron's sexual needs, which she felt obliged to satisfy but resented. She was completely unable to express her own wishes but expected him to know what she wanted. Finally, in frustration, she broke off her relationship with him, refusing to return his phone calls or open his letters.

Joan had read some popular materials about sexuality in the last several years and had begun to think that there was something wrong with her. The books suggested that she should not be afraid or ashamed of her own sexuality, but she could not shake these negative feelings.

The DSM-5 (APA, 2013) uses an amalgamation of Masters and Johnson's (1966) and Kaplan's (1979) components of the sexual response in classifying sexual dysfunctions. It categorizes them according to which of the three

TABLE 13.2 SEXUAL DYSFUNCTIONS: CATEGORIES AND SUBTYPES

Sexual Desire and Arousal Disorders
Subtypes
Female sexual interest/arousal disorder
Male hypoactive sexual desire disorder
Erectile disorder
Orgasmic Disorders
Subtypes
Delayed ejaculation
Female orgasmic disorder
Premature (early) orgasm
Genito-pelvic Pain/Penetration Disorder

Source: Based on Diagnostic and Statistical Manual of Mental Disorders, 5th Edition, American Psychiatric Association, 2013.

stages is affected: desire, arousal, or orgasm. A separate category deals with instances in which pain during intercourse (dyspareunia) and/or difficulty with vaginal penetration (vaginismus) is the primary complaint (see Table 13.2).

Each of the sexual dysfunctions can be further classified into several subtypes. For example, if the person has always experienced the problem, the disorder is called **lifelong sexual dysfunction**; if it is of fairly recent onset, it is said to be an **acquired sexual dysfunction**. In addition, sexual dysfunctions may be apparent with all partners and even during solitary sexual activity, in which case they would be termed **generalized sexual dysfunctions**; when the problems are apparent in only one situation (for example, with the client's partner, or only during masturbation), they are known as **situational sexual dysfunctions**.

Data reveal lifetime prevalence rates for sexual complaints of 43% for females and 31% for males (Laumann, Paik, & Rosen, 1999) and incidence rates (i.e., currently has a disorder) of 23% among women (Bancroft, 2000). The most frequent sexual dysfunctions for women are those involving desire and arousal issues, whereas the most frequent dysfunctions for men are premature ejaculation and erectile disorder; in this analysis, women reported more sexual dysfunction comorbidities than men (McCabe et al., 2016a).

It certainly seems as if some degree of sexual dysfunction is common: "The lifetime prevalence of sexual dysfunctions may be so high that almost every man or woman who lives a long life can be expected to qualify for a diagnosis at some time" (Levine, 1989, pp. 215–216). However, it is important to keep in mind that individuals may experience sexual difficulties without necessarily being dissatisfied with their sexual relationships or function (Laumann et al., 1994).

② BEFORE MOVING ON

> Think about the specifiers of lifelong versus acquired sexual dysfunction, and generalized versus situational. Which combination do you think would be most difficult to treat? Most easy? Which would most likely have a biological or psychological basis?

SEXUAL DESIRE AND AROUSAL DISORDERS

Both Kinsey and Masters and Johnson found that the frequency of masturbation among men varied from less than once per month to several times per day. However, all of these men regarded their own frequency as "normal"; they thought that those with higher frequencies were "abnormal," and they considered lower frequencies to be indicative of "low sex drive." These two examples illustrate both the differences among individuals in sexual behaviours and associated desire and the subjective nature of people's definition of the "normal" frequency of sexual desires.

In the DSM-5, a diagnosis of **male hypoactive sexual desire disorder** is made when a client describes persistently or recurrently deficient (or absent) sexual/erotic thoughts or fantasies and desire for sexual activity. These symptoms must be distressing and present for a minimum of six months. Although the DSM-5 treats desire problems as separate from arousal problems for men, a combination of "lack of sexual interest" and "arousal disorder" has resulted in the diagnosis of **female sexual interest/arousal disorder** in women. The rationale for this amalgamation is based on findings from several studies indicating that the processes of desire and arousal overlap for many women (Brotto, 2010a; Graham, 2010b). Unfortunately, similar data do not yet exist for men.

Hypoactive desire is among the most difficult dysfunctions to define, because of the importance of context. Desire may occur in some situations but not in others, and sexual activity may occur without desire, in both males and females. The discrepancy between partners' desire levels can create a circular problem, affecting the quantity and quality of both the sexual and the emotionally intimate relationship (Clement, 2002). Furthermore, social pressure for high levels of sexual interest may play a role in elevating performance pressure and creating unrealistic expectations.

In fact, some have criticized the existence of such a diagnosis as a reflection of culturally imposed standards that are typically male-centred and hypersexual. The very term *hypoactive* implies an established standard—but whose? A population average? A clinical consensus? However it is defined, a standard of desire is value-laden and many question its appropriateness.

Sexual arousal disorders involve difficulty becoming physically aroused when the person desires such arousal. In males, sexual arousal, or lack thereof, is usually gauged by penile erection, not the only physiological response but certainly the most obvious. Female sexual arousal, however, is less directly evident, and women can engage in penetrative sexual activity without arousal. Approximately 20 percent of women report difficulty with arousal and lubrication during sexual activities (Laumann et al., 1999). As mentioned, arousal disorder as a separate entity in women is no longer a distinct diagnosis in the DSM-5 (APA, 2013).

Erectile disorder characterizes difficulties with obtaining an erection during sexual activity, maintaining an erection until the completion of sexual activity, and/or a marked decrease in erectile rigidity in about 75 to 100 percent of sexual occasions. These symptoms must be distressing and be present for a minimum of six months. Erectile disorder is a commonly reported male sexual dysfunction (McCabe et al., 2016a). Several factors can influence the rates of erectile disorder, including smoking, heart disease, and age, the last factor being particularly important given that the prevalence of erectile disorder increases with age (Mulhall, Luo, Zou, Stecher, & Galaznik, 2016).

Erectile problems, while certainly not new, have gained increased public attention, partly because of current expectations for lifelong sexuality, women's increased expectations of sexual satisfaction, and media attention (Wincze & Carey, 2001). Erectile problems can be psychologically devastating for men and can contribute to significant relationship problems. Difficulty attaining or maintaining an erection often leads to embarrassment, depression, and even suicidal inclinations. Not surprisingly, erectile disorder has a high comorbidity with depression (McCabe et al., 2016b). Because the problem carries such connotations about masculinity, some men with erectile difficulty are likely to delay seeking help and to avoid confronting the problem, and may try home remedies before approaching a professional. The relationship with a sexual partner is likely to be affected, not only by the erectile problem; but also by the avoidance, depression, and other secondary problems that follow. As a result, by the time a man and his partner seek help, the problem is likely to seem overwhelming and to be much more complex and intractable than it might have been had he sought help earlier.

ORGASMIC DISORDERS

Both males and females may experience difficulty in reaching orgasm. Prevalence rates of orgasmic issues in females is estimated to be 16 to 25 percent, and in males, 10 to 20 percent (McCabe et al., 2016a).

The DSM-5 diagnostic criteria for **female orgasmic disorder** require the presence of either a marked delay in, marked infrequency of, or absence of orgasm; or markedly reduced intensity of orgasmic sensations in about 75 to 100 percent of sexual occasions. The symptoms must cause distress and be present for a minimum of six months.

Kinsey was the first researcher to pay attention to female orgasms, counting them for women as he did for men (Kinsey et al., 1953). In his work, Kinsey noted that women were more likely to experience orgasm through masturbation than with a partner, a finding that has since been replicated (Spector & Carey, 1990). These observations led to marked changes in the way women's sexual functioning was viewed.

Delayed ejaculation is diagnosed when there is a marked delay in ejaculation or a marked infrequency or absence of ejaculation, which is present in about 75 to 100 percent of sexual occasions and for a minimum duration of six months. These symptoms must be distressing to warrant the diagnosis. In men with this condition, orgasm may be possible only with oral or manual stimulation or only during erotic dreams, but not during intercourse. Rates for complaints of delayed ejaculation range from 1 to 10 percent (McCabe et al., 2016a).

Premature (early) ejaculation is defined as a persistent or recurrent pattern of ejaculation occurring during partnered sexual activity within approximately one minute following vaginal penetration and before the individual wishes it. Although the diagnosis can be applied to individuals engaging in nonvaginal penetrative sexual activities, specific duration criteria have not been established yet for these activities. The symptoms must be distressing and present for six months minimum, and they must occur in all, or almost all (75 to 100%), sexual occasions. It affects 8 to 30% of men (McCabe et al., 2016a), and instances of premature ejaculation occur in 75% of men during at least one point in their lifetime (Wang, Kumar, Minhas, & Ralph, 2005).

The one-minute criterion is based on studies conducted by several investigators who objectively measured the average duration of sexual intercourse. Specifically, duration was measured using the time interval between penetration and ejaculation, known as intravaginal ejaculatory latency time (IELT; Waldinger, 2005). Normative IELT data have been obtained and results generally indicate that the average duration is between five and six minutes (Waldinger, 2005; Waldinger, Hengeveld, Zwinderman, & Olivier, 1998). In an attempt to operationally define this criterion, Waldinger and colleagues (1998) interviewed 110 individuals diagnosed with premature ejaculation and found that 90% of men ejaculated within one minute of penetration, and 60% ejaculated within 15 seconds; therefore, it was suggested that premature ejaculation should be defined as ejaculating in less than one minute in greater than 90% of episodes of sexual intercourse (Wang et al., 2005).

Undoubtedly, IELT provides a simple and objective method to assist in the diagnosis of premature ejaculation (Jannini, Lombardo, & Lenzi, 2005). However, some suggest that solely focusing on latency is one-dimensional and ignores several essential features of this disorder (Wang et al., 2005). Indeed, an adequate assessment should be multi-dimensional and, as such, include objective data (i.e., IELT) in addition to other features, such as voluntary control over ejaculation, sexual satisfaction in both partners, and the presence of distress.

GENITO-PELVIC PAIN/PENETRATION DISORDER

The DSM-5 replaced the formerly termed category of "sexual pain disorders" that contained two disorders—*dyspareunia* and *vaginismus*—with the overarching category of **genito-pelvic pain/penetration disorder**. This diagnosis involves persistent or recurrent difficulties with one or more of the following: vaginal penetration during intercourse; marked vulvovaginal or pelvic pain during vaginal intercourse or penetration attempts (a core feature of dyspareunia); marked fear or anxiety about vulvovaginal or pelvic pain in anticipation of, during, or as a result of vaginal penetration; and marked tensing or tightening of the pelvic floor muscles during attempted vaginal penetration (a core feature of vaginismus). These symptoms must be present for at least six months and cause distress to the individual.

The main rationale for including one category combining the previously separate conditions of dyspareunia and vaginismus was that it was difficult to reliably differentiate the two on measures of pain and pelvic muscle tension (Binik, Bergeron, & Khalifé, 2007; Reissing, Binik, Khalifé, Cohen, & Amsel, 2004). Although women with vaginismus tend to display more distress related to penetration and avoidance-based behaviours than women with dyspareunia (Reissing et al., 2004), these characteristics are not sufficient to justify separate diagnoses. Dr. Irv Binik, at McGill University's Department of Psychology, has been one of the leading researchers on dyspareunia and vaginismus for many years, and he played a key role in the revised DSM-5 definition.

Studies have indicated that prevalence rates of dyspareunia range from 8 to 22 percent (Latthe, Latthe, Say, Gulmezoglu, & Khan, 2006). Interestingly, different subtypes of dyspareunia exist, based on pain location and pattern (Meana, Binik, Khalifé, & Cohen, 1997; Boardman & Stockdale, 2009). Provoked vestibulodynia is likely the most common form of dyspareunia in young women, affecting 8% between the ages of 18 and 40 (Harlow et al., 2014). It is characterized by a severe, sharp/burning pain at the entrance of the vagina in response to vaginal penetration. It affects many aspects of women's lives other than sexuality (e.g., relationship adjustment, mood) (Pukall et al., 2016). Prevalence rates of vaginismus in clinical settings generally range from 5 to 17 percent (Lahaie, Boyer, Amsel, Khalife, & Binik, 2010). The true incidence and prevalence of genito-pelvic pain/penetration disorder is difficult to determine, given significant methodological problems, and the recent definition change.

HYPERSEXUALITY

The concept of **hypersexuality**, or sexual addiction, is not new. In his eighteenth-century *Mémoires écrits par lui-même*, Giovanni Jacopo Casanova De Seingalt (known simply as Casanova) provided clear illustrations of an intense preoccupation with pursuing sex with women. Later, in *Psychopathia Sexualis*, Richard von Krafft-Ebing (1901), described what he called "hyperaesthesia" (i.e., excessively increased sexual desire). Krafft-Ebing labelled this disorder as either "nymphomania" (excessive desire in women) or "satyriasis" (excessive desire in men). However, the modern conceptualization of hypersexuality is most often credited to Patrick Carnes, an American psychologist, who described a series of patients who he believed to be suffering from an "addiction" to sex (Carnes, 1983, 1989).

The behavioural component of hypersexuality has received increasing attention and has been suggested as an essential feature of this disorder. To quantify sexual frequency, some researchers rely on an index, termed *total sexual outlet* (TSO), initially described by Kinsey and colleagues (1948). TSO was based on the number of orgasms achieved through any combination of methods (e.g., intercourse, masturbation) during a specific week. Research has suggested that few males (5 to 10 percent) report a sexual outlet of seven or more times per week and that this level of sexual activity is rarely maintained over time (e.g., Janus & Janus, 1993; Kinsey et al., 1948). Based on such evidence, Kafka (1997) proposed that those with hypersexuality would have TSOs of seven or more per week, over a period of at least six months. While this definition is useful, it is clearly not sufficient. For example, the applicability of this criterion to women is problematic, given research suggesting that a significant proportion of women have difficulty reaching orgasm (Laumann et al., 1994). Additionally, there is some dissension as to whether excessive levels of sexual behaviour are, in fact, pathological. For example, higher sexual frequency within a stable relationship correlates with higher psychological functioning (Längström & Hanson, 2006).

The notion of hypersexuality as a sexual addiction has been widely criticized (for a summary of these criticisms, see Ley, 2012). There is strong disagreement regarding the theoretical underpinnings of the problem, from addiction (Carnes, 1983; Goodman, 1997), to compulsivity (Quadland, 1983; Coleman, 2003), to the dual control model (Bancroft & Janssen, 2000; Bancroft, Graham, Janssen, & Sanders, 2009), and to desire dysregulation (Kafka, 2007). Brain imaging studies have further muddied the arguments on all sides, though most of the participants have been those with problematic pornography use rather than those with multiple sexual partners and infidelity. A recent study suggested that problematic pornography use may represent a behavioural addiction based on increased activations in a brain area linked with reward (ventral striatum) when participants were presented with cues predicting erotic pictures, but not for cues predicting monetary gains. Activation in the ventral striatum was correlated with the frequency of pornography use and masturbation (Gola et al., 2016). Similar conclusions were reported by Brand and colleagues (2016). Kühn and Gallinat (2016) noted that that hypersexuality is associated with numerous brain alterations. In contrast, a study by Steele and colleagues (2013) examined brain responses of people with hypersexuality using electroencephalography (EEG) during the presentation of visual cues. Results suggested that hypersexuality is related to desire dysregulation, rather than to addiction. Other studies also show inconsistencies with the addiction model (e.g., Prause et al., 2016).

Despite the strong opinions on all sides regarding etiology and theory, there is a fair amount of consistency with regard to the essential features of the problem. Those with hypersexuality typically report experiencing a loss of control over sexual urges, fantasies, and behaviours, and they often engage in sexual activity to regulate negative emotional states (e.g., anxiety, depression). Atheoretical treatment-focused models have been recently proposed with aims of treating the presenting symptoms, rather than viewing those with hypersexuality as a homogenous group. For example, it is important to examine those with hypsersexuality who are, or are not, paraphilic. Other subtypes include: (1) those who present with problems with pornography and masturbation, (2) those with infidelity and multiple partner issues, and (3) those "designated" as patients by their partners or their own imposed (religious) norms around "normal" sexuality (Cantor et al., 2013; Sutton et al., 2015).

Although hypersexuality has never been included as an official diagnostic category in any of the DSM versions, it is included as a diagnosis (excessive sexual drive) in the International Classification of Diseases (ICD-10) of the World Health Organization (1992). There is also a diagnosis for excessive masturbation in the ICD-10, classified under "Other specified behavioural and emotional disorders with onset usually occurring in childhood and adolescence."

Hypersexuality has been identified in approximately 3 to 6 percent of the general population (Black, 2000), affecting more men than women. It is associated with a variety of emotional and physical problems, including depression, relationship instability, sexual dysfunction, and sexually transmitted infections (Kafka, 2007; Raymond et al., 2003).

ETIOLOGY OF SEXUAL DYSFUNCTIONS

Most of the research conducted on the causes of sexual dysfunctions has focused on specific disorders, although all of these disorders possess common factors to some degree. Early reports in the literature expressed the belief that most female sexual dysfunctions were the result of some interference with psychological functioning (Berman, Berman, Chhabra, & Goldstein, 2001). A recent paper indicated similar risk factors for sexual dyfunction for men and women. Risk factors include diabetes, heart disease, urinary tract disorders, chronic illness, depression and anxiety (as well as the medications used to treat these disorders), substance abuse, and psychosocial factors (e.g., poor relationship quality) (McCabe et al., 2016b). Clearly, both physical and psychosocial factors are involved in the development of most, if not all, sexual dysfunctions, although one factor or another may be more important in a given case.

Almost everyone experiences some sort of sexual performance difficulty at some point. Excessive alcohol, for example, may cause a temporary lessening of desire or interfere with feelings of arousal, erection, or orgasm. After a long period without sex, or during the first time with a new partner, premature ejaculation may occur. Usually the problem disappears with the situation that caused it. However, a person who is very upset by such an experience may carefully monitor his or her responses during the next sexual encounter. This second perceived failure, of course, only leads to greater anxiety, and a chronic dysfunction may emerge.

Research findings are consistent with the idea that the person's perspective plays a part in the development or maintenance of sexual dysfunction. For example, men with erectile disorder typically do not pay attention to the arousing properties of sex but rather focus on the threatening consequences of their likely failure to produce an erection (Bach, Brown, & Barlow, 1999). Whether these psychological factors in erectile disorder precede or follow the development of clients' problems is irrelevant for treatment purposes, since it is the maintenance factors that are important for change. Let us now consider etiological factors associated with some of the specific sexual dysfunctions.

SEXUAL DESIRE AND AROUSAL DISORDERS People with sexual desire disorders are generally not interested in sexual activity, a pattern sometimes evident in depressed patients. This similarity has led to speculation that hypoactive sexual desire may result from depression. Cyranowski and colleagues (2004), for example, found a correlation between high levels of depressive symptoms and reduced levels of sexual desire. In another investigation, Hartmann, Heiser, Ruffer-Hesse, and Kloth (2002) found that a significant number of women with sexual difficulties also satisfied the diagnostic criteria for a mood disorder. With the widespread use of SSRI antidepressants, there is evidence that hypoactive sexual desire may result from depression or from the medication used to treat it (Renshaw, 1998).

Kaplan (1979) emphasized other psychological factors in sexual desire disorders, such as dysfunctional attitudes about sex, relationship problems, and a strict upbringing that associated sexual pleasure with guilt. Indeed, these appear to be factors in all sexual dysfunctions (also see Wincze, Bach, & Barlow, 2008).

In addition to psychological difficulties that may precipitate sexual dysfunctions, hormonal imbalances may be associated with problems. Certainly, hormones such as **estrogen** (the "female" sex hormone), **testosterone** (the "male" sex hormone), and **prolactin** are involved in sexual activity and desire, and variations in the levels of these hormones can lower or increase sex drive (Rosen & Leiblum, 1995). However, the evidence suggests that low hormonal levels contribute to only a few cases of hypoactive sexual desire disorder (Kresin, 1993).

Perhaps the most commonly reported factor associated with arousal disorders, and to some extent all sexual dysfunctions, is what Masters and Johnson (1970) originally called performance anxiety. **Performance anxiety** is the response of individuals who feel that they are expected to perform sexually. Worried that their performance will not be up to the expectations of their partner, they become *spectators* of their own behaviour, monitoring their own sexual performance and the perceived responses of their partner. When this happens, the person's focus is on the performance rather than on enjoyment of the sexual experience. Like the watched pot that never boils, the spontaneous sensory response of sexual arousal is blocked or limited. However, anxiety can affect sexual functioning simply as a result of increased activity in the sympathetic branch of the autonomic nervous system. When sympathetic activity occurs, as happens when someone is anxious, its activity inhibits the parasympathetic branch. Since sexual arousal is associated with activation of the parasympathetic branch, inhibition of this branch by sympathetic activity will interfere with sexual arousal and may, as a result, cause sexual dysfunction.

Weisberg and his colleagues (Weisberg, Brown, Wincze, & Barlow, 2001) examined this idea in a laboratory study. Fifty-two sexually functioning men were instructed to watch two erotic films. Following the viewing of these films, the men were given bogus feedback indicating that they had a low erectile response. The men were divided into two groups.

Group I was given an external fluctuating attribution (i.e., the films were poorly made), while Group II was given an internal, stable attribution (i.e., problematic thoughts about sex). The participants were then instructed to watch a third erotic film. Individuals in Group II, who were given the problematic sexual thoughts feedback, experienced lower erectile responses than Group I, who attributed their reported sexual malfunctioning during the first films to external factors (i.e., poor videos). This study suggested that the attributions we make regarding our sexual performance may affect our future ability to perform.

Erectile disorder involves a complex interplay between physiological and psychological factors. Physiological factors include cardiovascular disease, neurological diseases, or various medications, whereas psychological factors include performance anxiety (described above), depression, problems in the relationship, and psychological traumas. Other risk factors for **erectile disorder** include age, diabetes, hypertension, cigarette smoking, and alcoholism (Russell & Nehra, 2003). Hormonal factors have also been proposed, where a loss of **androgens** may contribute to erectile dysfunction. Overall, both psychological and organic causes are important and should be considered in a comprehensive assessment.

ORGASMIC DISORDERS Orgasmic disorders are generally thought to involve primarily psychological factors, but certain medical conditions (for example, heart or circulatory problems) and some medications can cause anorgasmia in women. Again, relationship difficulties are common, although it is often hard to know whether these difficulties preceded or were caused by the sexual dysfunction. Limited sexual techniques, a lack of understanding of their own response, and partners who do not understand their needs may all play a role, as does an inability to "let go" and allow the natural response to sexual stimulation to occur. As shown in the case of Joan, these barriers are more difficult to overcome if a person feels constrained in discussing sex with his or her partner or in exploring techniques.

Premature (Early) Ejaculation. Two types of premature (early) ejaculation have been identified: primary and secondary. Secondary premature ejaculation occurs in men who previously had ejaculatory control. In such cases, Metz, Pryor, and Nesvacil (1997) found that premature (early) ejaculation could be caused by trauma to the sympathetic nervous system, abdominal or pelvic injuries, prostatitis, urethritis, or, as Althof (1995) found, withdrawal from narcotics. Primary premature (early) ejaculation could be caused by various problems. It may be a conditioned response to rapid ejaculation from the age when boys masturbated and ejaculated rapidly out of convenience (as cited in Carver, 1998), or when young men attempt sexual intercourse under pressure or once again in situations where they had to ejaculate fairly rapidly. With repeated experiences, the conditioning effect becomes stronger. Men may also avoid sex due to feelings of guilt and shame, and thus in clinical situations may be more

likely to be diagnosed with low sexual desire when they are simply trying to avoid premature ejaculation. Thus, it is evident that premature (early) ejaculation is largely thought to be psychological in nature, based around men's sensations and perceptions (Byer, Shainberg, & Galliano, 2002).

GENITO-PELVIC PAIN/PENETRATION DISORDER Many studies have investigated psychogenic mechanisms and have reported several potential causal factors for genito-pelvic pain/penetration disorder such as negative sexual attitudes, unpleasant or traumatic sexual experiences such as sexual violence or childhood sexual abuse, and various cognitive styles associated with anxiety. In addition, physical factors such pelvic floor muscle dysfunction and other genital and non-genital factors have been implicated (Lahaie et al., 2010; Pukall et al., 2016).

TREATMENT OF SEXUAL DYSFUNCTIONS

PSYCHOLOGICAL INTERVENTIONS Until the publication of Masters and Johnson's (1970) book describing their treatment approach, there was very little literature on therapy for sexual dysfunctions. Masters and Johnson described a comprehensive and intensive approach that required couples to live in their clinic for two weeks. Many aspects of Masters and Johnson's approach have been retained or modified at other clinics, so that most programs now share a number of common elements. Most programs see sexual dysfunctions as involving two people and, as a consequence, they typically suggest that both partners attend treatment.

Communication and Exploration. The majority of programs begin with an extensive assessment of the couple, including a detailed sexual history (see Wincze et al., 2008). This is typically followed by sex education, where information is provided and maladaptive ideas about sex are challenged. Procedures are provided for enhancing communication between the partners, not only about sexual matters, but about all issues that may cause disharmony. Effective sexual communication first requires each partner to develop an understanding of his or her own sensations and bodily response. Acceptance of their own bodies may be limited because of embarrassment or guilt. Accordingly, sex therapists often suggest exercises in which clients privately explore their own bodies and use masturbation to become aware of their own arousal response. Clients also learn to communicate their specific sexual preferences to one another so that they can please each other sexually.

Sensate Focus. An important component in sex therapy programs is what Masters and Johnson (1970) called **sensate focus,** essentially a form of desensitization applied to sexual fears. It is assumed that once the sexual dysfunction has emerged, the person develops performance anxiety or fear, which serves to worsen and entrench the problem.

Given that many sexual dysfunctions are associated with anxiety or fear and performance anxiety, sensate focus is often employed to redirect attention away from the specific sexual response and toward the sexual interaction (Linschoten, Weiner, & Avery-Clark, 2016). Sensate focus involves a series of exercises where partners engage in pre-determined stages of sexual interaction (Weiner & Avery-Clark, 2014). In the first step, they undress together with the light on to desensitize any embarrassment they may have about being naked together. They next take turns at massaging or touching one another all over, except for the genital or breast areas. They are learning to enjoy touching and being touched without any fear of imminent demands for sex. After several sessions of this, each person begins to tell the partner during the touching exercises what he or she enjoys. All of these sessions are interspersed with discussions with their therapist, which is meant to enhance communication skills and to identify and deal with any problems that arise during the touching sessions. As the couple becomes comfortable and they begin to expand their enjoyment of the associated physical pleasures, they progress to the next stage: genital and breast touching. There is still, however, a moratorium on sexual intercourse to allow the couple to enjoy sexual sensations and arousal without the fear of having to perform. The aim is to eliminate "spectatoring," allowing each partner to relax and focus on his or her own pleasure. Once the couple can maintain their pleasure without fear, they are advised to enter the last stage of sensate focus, which is designed specifically for the problem that brought them to the clinic. In this final stage, the ban on sexual intercourse is lifted. However, the couple is instructed to progress slowly and they follow a particular gradual program aimed at overcoming the specific dysfunction.

In addition to sensate focus, there are several behavioural exercises aimed at particular sexual dysfunctions. The stop-start and squeeze techniques, for example, are behavioural approaches used to treat premature ejaculation, and can be used either with or without a partner (Cooper et al., 2015). With the stop-start technique, manual stimulation of the penis occurs until the earliest signs of approaching orgasm are perceived, at which point stimulation is stopped. After a period of time (approximately 40 seconds to 1 minute), stimulation recommences. This procedure is repeated so that the entire process lasts approximately 15 minutes (employing as many stops as is necessary). Sometimes, just stopping is not enough to prevent ejaculation. In those cases, the squeeze technique is employed by squeezing around the coronal ridge of the penis. Although it is not painful, the squeeze technique diminishes arousal and prevents ejaculation. When the individual can last approximately 15 minutes with only one or two "stops," the couple can proceed to more arousing stimulation methods (e.g., oral sex). Another commonly used behavioural exercise, vaginal dilatation (i.e., the use of dilators to aid in relaxing the vaginal opening), is recommended for those who have genito-pelvic pain/penetration disorder. Vaginal dilatation involves the gradual insertion of dilators of increasing diameter during general body (e.g., deep breathing) and pelvic floor muscle relaxation exercises to normalize muscle tone (Goldstein et al., 2016).

EVALUATION OF PSYCHOLOGICAL INTERVENTIONS Masters and Johnson (1970) claimed that more than 80 percent of their clients were successfully treated for their various dysfunctions. However, they used a rather loose criterion of success and did not follow up with their clients for long enough to properly evaluate the maintenance of their gains.

More careful evaluations have shown that the main symptoms of vaginismus and premature (early) ejaculation can be quite successfully treated with the type of therapy just outlined (Beck, 1993). High success rates for vaginismus have been reported when the main outcome measure is vaginal penetration; however, it appears that sexual pleasure and pain reduction may need more specific clinical attention given that outcome measures assessing these variables have not shown concomitant changes at post-treatment (Lahaie et al., 2010). Treatment for premature ejaculation through psychological (e.g., addressing sexual skills, self-esteem, performance anxiety) and behavioural approaches (e.g., stop start technique) is promising (Althof, 2016), as is psychological treatment for erectile dysfunction (Althof & Needle, 2011). For problems such as low desire or orgasmic dysfunction in women, masturbation exercises appear to enhance the effects of comprehensive therapy (LoPiccolo, 1990). Psychological approaches to genito-pelvic pain/penetration disorder (e.g., sex therapy, mindfulness) have also yielded positive outcomes in pain reduction and sexual function (Goldstein et al., 2016).

Overall, psychologically based interventions have been quite successful in treating sexual dysfunctions. Some cases in which they are not successful might be attributable to undetected physical problems.

PHYSICAL TREATMENTS Physical treatments are best used in conjunction with psychological approaches, even in cases where there is a clear organic cause. In erectile disorder that has a physical basis, for example, there are nevertheless psychological features once the disorder is established. In these cases, the man will very likely become afraid of failing and develop performance anxiety, which may remain a problem even after the physical cause has been corrected.

Medications have been shown to be helpful in some cases of sexual dysfunction. With regard to erectile dysfunction, several muscle relaxants, including phentolamine (e.g., Regitine), papaverine (e.g., Pavabid), and alprostadil (e.g., Caverject), can be self-injected into the corpus cavernosum of the penis, which facilitates an erection by relaxing isolated human penile erectile tissue and cavernous arteries (El-Sakka, 2016). Alprostadil, in particular, represents the most common form of **intracavernous treatment** for erectile dysfunction and, upon administration, erections may last for an hour or longer, irrespective of whether there is direct sexual stimulation. Intracavernous treatment using Alprostadil is extremely efficacious, particularly for men who experience problems with the transmission of nerve signals that regulate their erections.

Efficacy rates for intracavernous therapy are extremely high, such that up to 94 percent of individuals undergoing this treatment have reported subsequent sexual activity (Hatzimouratidis & Hatzichristou, 2005; Mohr & Beutler, 1990). However, complications include penile pain, the development of scar tissue, prolonged erections (i.e., priapism), and fibrosis. Despite the positive results of this treatment, the fact that many men find this procedure painful, or at least unpleasant, has led to high discontinuation rates and limited treatment compliance (Althof & Turner, 1992).

Antidepressants have also been used, typically in the treatment of premature (early) ejaculation, as they have demonstrated the ability to delay the ejaculatory response and have led to improved sexual satisfaction in some men (Althof & Seftel, 1995). Aphrodisiacs have also been historically implicated in sexual arousal. The first kind of aphrodisiac is psychophysiological, affecting one's five senses—the idea being that one's senses can be stimulated to heighten sexual awareness. The second kind of aphrodisiac is internal and based on the old belief that certain products have sexually stimulating qualities. Examples include various foods, herbal remedies (e.g., Ginkgo biloba), alcohol, and "love potions" (Slovenko, 2001). However, the positive effects of these aphrodisiacs have not been supported by research.

Considerable publicity has accompanied the announcement of the phosphodiesterase inhibitors (PDE5 inhibitors) designed to treat erectile disorders. The three most common agents within this class are sildenafil (marketed under the trade name Viagra), tadalafil (Cialis), and vardenafil (Levitra), and all restrict the breakdown of cyclic guanine monophosphate, which leads to increased blood flow and stronger erections. Each medication has been approved by Health Canada, although some adverse side effects have been noted (e.g., problems with vision). Some patients prefer one type over another, given differences with regard to duration of action (Viagra has the shortest duration at four to six hours and Cialis has the longest duration, up to 36 hours) and interactions with fatty foods (Hatzimouratidis et al., 2016).

PDE5 inhibitors are generally safe, and side effects are typically mild (e.g., headache, flushing, visual disturbances); however, these medications are contraindicated in men who use nitrates to manage cardiovascular disease. Given the encouraging results and typically mild side effects, these drugs have become the first-line treatment option for erectile disorder, with intracavernous treatment being recommended as second-line. Other physical treatments that are recommended for erectile disorder include topically applied or urethrally administered Alprostadil (Hatzimouratidis et al., 2016).

Pelvic floor physiotherapy has emerged as a potential treatment for men with erectile dysfunction (primarily in the UK; Dorey et al., 2004)—although the use of vacuum erection devices is more common—and for women with a common form of dyspareunia, provoked vestibulodynia. Both retrospective (Bergeron et al., 2002) and prospective studies (Goldfinger, Pukall, Gentilcore-Saulnier, McLean, & Chamberlain, 2009) have documented positive outcomes in terms of pain reduction and improvements in sexual function after treatment.

FIGURE 13.2 Penile Implant

Nucleus Medical Media Inc/Alamy Stock Photo

Surgical interventions are also recommended for some individuals with sexual dysfunctions. For example, vestibulectomy (surgical removal of the superficial vestibule) for women with provoked vestibulodynia is the most commonly reported treatment and has positive outcomes (Bergeron, Pukall, & Mailloux, 2008). Penile implants for those with erectile disorder are typically recommended as an option after other treatments (drugs, injections) have yielded unsatisfactory results. While a number of different implants were used in the past, the most popular approach is to implant inflatable silicone cylinders in the penis (see Figure 13.2). These cylinders are joined to a reservoir of fluid that has been inserted into the patient's abdomen along with a tiny pump in the scrotum. To produce an erection, the pump is pressed, which pushes fluid from the reservoir into the cylinders. As the cylinders fill, they cause the penis to become erect. These implants have been associated with positive outcomes for the patient and their partners (Bertero & Antunes, 2015).

③ BEFORE MOVING ON

Imagine a heterosexual couple presenting to a sex therapy clinic in which the male has severe erectile dysfunction. Intercourse is impossible and their main goal is to be able to have intercourse again. Their therapist assigns them the first two steps of sensate focus. The couple is baffled. Why is their therapist asking them to not have sex when their goal is exactly that? How would you explain this apparent paradox to this couple?

Gender Identity

Boys are expected to act like boys, and they are allowed little latitude before they are labelled "sissies." Girls who play hockey and prefer trucks to dolls are tolerated much better, but are still labelled as "tomboys" and often encouraged to also pursue more "feminine" activities. Indeed, Western society presents a very rigid view of what is considered "male" or "female" and offers very little room for expressions outside of these two extremes, especially for males. In many non-Western cultures, however, the existence of individuals who are neither traditionally masculine nor traditionally feminine has long been recognized and accepted; in fact, such gender-variant individuals may be given a specific name and accorded a distinct role in society. In several Indigenous cultures, rituals conducted at or before puberty give a boy the option to choose between the status of a conventional male or that of a transgendered male—a "two-spirit" (male–female) person, or *berdache*. Berdaches wear special clothing fashioned from male and female attire, practise mostly female occupations, and engage in sexual relationships with conventional men. They are often shamans (healers who derived their curative powers from their knowledge of the spirit world), chanters, dancers, or mediators. Such latitude in creating room for a third sex is lacking in Western society; although some individuals resist categorization by "gender-bending" (i.e., actively transgressing expected gender roles), some transpeople may feel forced to "fit" into either the male or female category, and others may choose to "switch" their sex through the lengthy, painful, and difficult process of sex reassignment (also called gender affirming, or gender confirming) surgery.

Despite the greater latitude offered to women in expressing male behaviours, when butch lesbian and trans-activist Leslie Feinberg (1949–2014) was growing up, Feinberg was such a tomboy that social rejection was common (Gilbert, 1996). As Feinberg matured, the female role chafed so much that eventually Feinberg moved to New York and began to pass as a man. Feinberg dressed like a man, acted like a man, and self-described as a "masculine-feminine."

In making this transition, Feinberg self-identified as "transgendered," or simply "trans." Feinberg rejected their categorization as female and insisted on having the right to live as they pleased without harassment. Feinberg's transformation dealt with more than gender: Feinberg became a spokesperson for a new movement of those in society who have been marginalized. These are the women and men who feel that they are the victims of cruel accidents of biology—that they were born the wrong sex.

Despite many people's assumption that gender is a clear-cut concept, there are many different dimensions of gender, including the following: chromosomal gender (XY in males and XX in females), gonadal gender (testes in the male and ovaries in the female), prenatal hormonal gender (testosterone and anti-Mullerian hormone in the male but not in the female), internal accessory organs (e.g., prostate in the male and Fallopian tubes in the female), external genital appearance (e.g., penis in the male and vulva in the female), assigned gender (based on the external genital appearance at birth, resulting in the "it's a boy" or "it's a girl" announcement that then affects society's labelling of that child and the gender in which the child is raised), and **gender identity** (a person's basic sense of self as male or female, the first signs of which appear between 18 and 36 months of age) (Money, 1987). **Gender role** is the collection of those characteristics that a society defines as masculine or feminine. Because roles relate to social standards, ideas about gender role change over time and from culture to culture. In some instances, these "variables of gender" do not all coincide. In rare cases where the actual biological variables are discordant, an **intersex** condition may occur, with the reproductive structures or sexual anatomy presenting as a variation of what is typically considered to be "male" or "female." When biological variables are consistent, but are discordant with the person's sense of self, **gender dysphoria** (previously labelled as gender identity disorder, or GID) occurs.

GENDER DYSPHORIA

A trans activist, such as Leslie Feinberg, might appear to fulfill the DSM-5 criteria for gender dysphoria (see Table 13.3). Feinberg experienced a strong desire to be, and to be treated as, the other gender. The incongruence between a person's experienced/expressed gender and assigned gender is key to this diagnosis; however, also necessary for the diagnosis is clinically significant distress or impairment in social, occupational, or other important areas of functioning (APA, 2013, p. 453). Feinberg argued that these individuals were perfectly well adjusted to their transgendered life, although society may have had difficulty with it. Such individuals may fulfill some of the cross-gender requirements for the diagnosis, but they do not completely fit the criteria because their gender dysphoria appears not to result in severe distress.

In the DSM-5, two separate diagnoses of gender dysphoria exist, based on the age of the individual presenting with the complaint: gender dysphoria in children and gender dysphoria in adolescents and adults. Both have two possible subtypes (with or without a disorder of sex development, e.g., Turner syndrome), and the diagnosis pertaining to older individuals has an additional specifier of whether the individual is post-transition (i.e., has undergone at least one form of cross-sex treatment and is living full time as the desired gender).

Because they feel as if they are physically the wrong sex, people with gender dysphoria may cross-dress or attempt to rid themselves of secondary sex characteristics in other ways. They may request hormonal treatment or other physical alterations, such as electrolysis to remove facial hair, in attempts to assume the role of the other sex. In some instances, they undertake genital and/or non-genital surgeries (e.g., breast reduction/augmentation, chest contouring) to change their anatomy.

Green and Blanchard (1995) reported that GID (gender identity disorder; the former label for gender dysphoria)

TABLE 13.3 DSM-5 DIAGNOSTIC CRITERIA FOR GENDER DYSPHORIA

Gender Dysphoria in Children

A. A marked incongruence between one's experienced/expressed gender and assigned gender, of at least 6 months' duration, as manifested by at least six of the following (one of which must be Criterion AI):

1. A strong desire to be of the other gender or an insistence that one is the other gender (or some alternative gender different from one's assigned gender).

2. In boys (assigned gender), a strong preference for cross-dressing or simulating female attire; or in girls (assigned gender), a strong preference for wearing only typical masculine clothing and a strong resistance to the wearing of typical feminine clothing.

3. A strong preference for cross-gender roles in make-believe play or fantasy play.

4. A strong preference for the toys, games, or activities stereotypically used or engaged in by the other gender.

5. A strong preference for playmates of the other gender.

6. In boys (assigned gender), a strong rejection of typically masculine toys, games, and activities and a strong avoidance of rough-and-tumble play; or in girls (assigned gender), a strong rejection of typically feminine toys, games, and activities.

7. A strong dislike of one's sexual anatomy.

8. A strong desire for the primary and/or secondary sex characteristics that match one's experienced gender.

B. The condition is associated with clinically-significant distress or impairment in social, school, or other important areas of functioning.

Gender Dysphoria in Adolescents and Adults

A. A marked incongruence between one's experienced/expressed gender and assigned gender, of at least 6 months' duration, as manifested by at least two of the following:

1. A marked incongruence between one's experienced/expressed gender and primary and/or secondary sex characteristics (or in young adolescents, the anticipated secondary sex characteristics).

2. A strong desire to be rid of one's primary and/or secondary sex characteristics because of a marked incongruence with one's experienced/expressed gender (or in young adolescents, a desire to prevent the development of the anticipated secondary sex characteristics).

3. A strong desire for the primary and/or secondary sex characteristics of the other gender.

4. A strong desire to be of the other gender (or some alternative gender different from one's assigned gender).

5. A strong desire to be treated as the other gender (or some alternative gender different from one's assigned gender).

6. A strong conviction that one has the typical feelings and reactions of the other gender (or some alternative gender different from one's assigned gender).

B. The condition is associated with clinically significant distress or impairment in social, occupational, or other important areas of functioning.

occurs more commonly in children than in adults, with 3% of boys and 1% of girls identified as having the disorder. In fact, the gender dysphoria associated with a disorder most commonly begins in childhood (Tsoi, 1990). However, in adults the prevalence of gender dysphoria disorder is quite low: for males, prevalence ranges from 0.005 to 0.014%, and for natal females, from 0.002 to 0.003% (APA, 2013).

ETIOLOGY OF GENDER DYSPHORIA

Very little is known about the origins of gender dysphoria. Unfortunately, what data are available present a rather confusing picture, although most authorities in the field consider gender dysphoria to result from some as yet unspecified combination of biological and psychological factors.

A tragic Canadian "test case" that offers some insight into the nature/nurture debate emerged accidentally when one of a pair of male monozygotic twins had his penis cut off during a botched circumcision (Colapinto, 2000). Instead of undertaking the repeated, difficult, and possibly unsatisfactory surgeries necessary to reconstruct a penis, sexologist John Money persuaded the parents to have the boy surgically "reassigned" as a girl. Thus, nature (that is, the hereditary component) was held constant between the twins because of their identical genetic makeup. Only the nurture component varied for the two: one twin was subsequently reared as a girl, the other as a boy. The reports indicated that the reassigned twin became feminine in behaviour and interests. At puberty, she was given hormonal replacement therapy in order to develop breasts and other female secondary sex characteristics. This case is still cited by many writers as evidence that "gender identity is something one *learns* at a very young age" (Barlow & Durand, 1995, p. 419). Such conclusions overlook follow-up information on the reassigned twin (Colapinto, 2000). The professionals who studied this case maintained that, as a young adolescent, the child was extremely masculine (Diamond, 1982). It was clear that this child had not adjusted well to being a female. When the child was told at age 14 of the botched circumcision, it devastated him. He adopted the male role, changed his name to David, and later married. Tragically, he committed suicide in 2004, just two years after his twin brother overdosed on antidepressant medication and as his own marriage was dissolving. The many years he suffered attempting to adapt to the role of a female apparently had no effect on his gender identity, and although this is only a single case, it supports the idea that gender identity is minimally influenced by environmental experiences.

Some theorists have suggested that gender dysphoria may be caused by either genetically influenced hormonal disturbances or exposure during fetal development to inappropriate hormones. Evidence has come from heritability studies. Several studies have reported evidence indicating a significant heritable pattern for children with GID (Coolidge, Thede, & Young, 2002; Zucker, 2005; Zucker & Bradley, 1995). In one study, Coolidge et al. (2002) examined the heritability and prevalence of GID in a non-retrospective study of 314 child and adolescent twins. Results indicated that GID within this sample was highly heritable. It has also been proposed that an excess or absence of testosterone during a critical point in fetal development may affect the individual's gender identity. One of the most predominant neurobiological theories for the development of gender dysphoria has focused on the role of prenatal hormones. In particular, prenatal exposure to male-typical levels of androgens masculinizes postnatal behaviour, whereas underexposure to male-typical levels of androgens has the opposite effect (Zucker, 1990). Although theoretically complex and not frequently studied, some investigators have pointed to the overrepresentation of left-handed individuals presenting with gender dysphoria (GID as it was called then) compared to individuals without gender dysphoria as evidence for instability in neurodevelopment and a general biological marker (see Zucker, Bealieu, Bradley, Grimshaw, & Wilcox, 2001). It is important to note that research in this field is controversial at times, and there is no one agreed upon theory regarding the development of gender dysphoria. Although the evidence presented above appears compelling, some reviews have also cautioned against the hormonal hypothesis (Bancroft, 1989; Bradley & Zucker, 1997; Carroll, 2007).

Psychodynamic and social learning theories of human behaviour emphasize the importance of early childhood experiences and the family environment. In psychoanalytic theory, the basic conflict resulting from a boy's failure to separate from the mother and develop an independent identity creates a gender identity problem (Meyers & Keith, 1991). Behavioural theory (Bernstein, Steiner, Glaiser, & Muir, 1981) suggests that the basis of gender dysphoria lies in encouragement by parents of gender-inappropriate behaviours, combined with the lack of a same-sex adult model and overprotection by the opposite-sex parent. Some believe that parental characteristics might give children insufficient means to identify with the same-sex parent or to interact in cross-gender reinforcement situations. However, it is important to consider that child-related factors may be evoking certain parental responses as well (Cohen-Kettenis & Gooren, 1999). Cohen-Kettinis and Arrindell (1990) conducted retrospective studies on the child-rearing practices of the parents of adults with and without gender dysphoria. Those males who identified as, and transitioned to, females reported their fathers as less emotionally warm, more rejecting, and more overly controlling. Females who identified as, and transitioned to, males reported that both parents were less emotionally warm, but stated that only their mothers were more overprotective, as compared to the controls. Studies of the importance of the influence of parental behaviours during this developmental period have so far been somewhat supportive of a relationship between parental child-rearing behaviour and adulthood gender dysphoria, although there is also disagreement in the field as to the validity of these theories.

TREATMENT OF GENDER DYSPHORIA

Dr. Kenneth Zucker worked extensively with children with gender dysphoria at the Centre for Addiction and Mental Health in Toronto. When parents present cross-gender–identified children for treatment, the clinician faces a difficult issue. Some feel it is inappropriate to try to change gender identity, but increasing evidence has indicated that these individuals experience significant distress (Zucker, 1990; Zucker, 2005). The most systematic information on associated problems in these children has come from parent-report data using the Child Behaviour Checklist (Achenbach & Edelbrock, 1983). Several studies have shown that boys and girls diagnosed with gender dysphoria display more behavioural problems and experience more social ostracism than do same-sex siblings and age-matched controls (Cohen-Kettenis, Owen, Kaijser, Bradley, & Zucker, 2003; Zucker, 2005). Consequently, attempts have been made to encourage gender-appropriate behaviour and to discourage cross-gender behaviour among these children through various psychotherapeutic techniques. In the short term, these interventions may affect cross-gender behaviour, but little is known about their long-term impact on gender disorders of children.

Some, but not all, people with gender dysphoria eventually request hormonal treatment or surgery to "reassign" them to the opposite sex (Lawrence, 2003). The most recent edition of the World Professional Association for Transgender Health (WPATH) Standards of Care, Version 7 (www.wpath.org; WPATH, Standards of Care V7, 2011) notes that sex reassignment surgery is effective and medically necessary—meaning that it is not conducted simply for the patient's convenience, but that there is scientifically accepted evidence of favourable outcomes for those with gender dysphoria. The Standards of Care include the

Dr. Richard Raskin

Dr. Richard Raskin was born in New York City in 1934. Richard was the captain of Yale University's tennis team and went on to become an ophthalmologist and professional tennis player. Richard had been dressing as a woman since he was a child. He married in the early 1970s and had one child. After 10 years of psychoanalysis and the marriage ending in divorce, Richard underwent sex reassignment surgery and became Dr. Renée Richards.

Renée is noted for her impact on the "courts." When a number of female professional tennis players complained that her participation in the U.S. Open would result in unfair competition, the U.S. Tennis Association denied her entry. When they told her that she could not play, she suddenly became "the world's activist for the sexually disenfranchised" (Giltz, 2007). In 1977 the New York Supreme Court overturned this policy and ruled in favour of transsexual rights. Renée went on to reach the women's double finals, continued to play tennis until 1981, and ranked twentieth overall. She has published two autobiographies, one in 1986 (*Second Serve*) and another in 2007 (*No Way Renée: The Second Half of My Notorious Life*).

Portrayals of transpeople in the media can be seen in movies such as *The Crying Game, Breakfast on Pluto, Boys Don't Cry, Normal, Transamerica, The Danish Girl*, and *Hedwig and the Angry Inch*, and in television shows such as *Bones, Dirty Sexy Money, Transparent, The L Word, Nip/Tuck*, and *Ugly Betty*.

Dr. Richard Raskin/Dr. Renée Richards before (left) and after (right) sex-reassignment surgery.

following minimum eligibility criteria for sex-reassignment surgery: (1) Persistent, well documented gender dysphoria, (2) Capacity to make a fully informed decision and to consent for treatment, (3) Age of majority in a given country, (4) If significant medical or mental health concerns are present, they must be well controlled; and (5) 12 continuous months of hormone therapy (unless medical issues preclude the use of hormones); and for some genital surgeries, the individual must also have 12 continuous months of living in a gender role that is congruent with their gender identity. This "real-life test" helps to ensure that patients are able to function fully in the desired gender role before potentially irreversible measures are undertaken. This requirement is no longer needed to obtain hormones, for non-genital surgeries (e.g., breast augmentation), or for hysterectomy (surgical removal of all or parts of the uterus), overiectomy (surgical removal of one or both ovaries), or orchiectomy (surgical removal of one or both testicles).

Toronto researchers have found that hormonal therapy assists in developing the desired secondary sex characteristics (Dickey & Steiner, 1990), and is a crucial aspect in mental health outcomes (Costa & Colizzi, 2016). Males treated with feminizing hormones show breast enlargement, increased fat deposits, and decreased muscle mass, as well as decreased facial and body hair. Their capacity to have erections and to ejaculate diminishes. Treatment of females with testosterone leads to an increase in muscle bulk and facial hair, deepening of the voice, enlargement of the clitoris, and suppression of ovarian function.

There are numerous empirical studies and reviews reporting outcome data on sex reassignment surgery and, while methodological concerns are evident, these procedures have resulted in satisfactory outcomes in the majority of patients (Colebunders, Brondeel, D'Arpa, Hoebeke, & Monstrey, 2017). More specifically, patients usually experience satisfaction with interpersonal functioning and general psychological health but have reported negative effects on cosmetic results and sexual functioning. One study conducted by Lawrence (2003) examined factors associated with satisfaction and regret following sex-reassignment surgery in 232 male-to-female patients where the surgeon and his surgical technique are the same across all participants. One year after the operation, patients were asked to complete a questionnaire evaluating their attitudes and experiences. Most patients were very satisfied, claiming that it improved their quality of life. Only a few patients experienced regret, and that was only on an occasional basis. Dissatisfaction was usually associated with unsatisfactory physical or functional results of the surgery. Yet, psychological issues can still occur and, as such, most clinics now offer psychotherapy and counselling both before and after surgery for their trans clients. Clients who receive such counselling appear to do better than clients who do not receive assistance with the transition from one gender to another (Green & Fleming, 1990).

④ BEFORE MOVING ON

Consider just one of the unique challenges that a person with gender dysphoria may experience. Although this individual's experience of maleness or femaleness is in his or her head and part of a constant inner reality, society sees only the physical body of this person and treats him or her accordingly. The larger society is only acting on what is observable without any regard for that person's inner experience. Understandably, the person with gender dysphoria considers this treatment unwanted, ignorant, and offensive as it is not part of his or her reality. What do you think would be best for all involved—to change the inner experience of the person with gender dysphoria, to change the physical appearance of the person with gender dysphoria, or to change society's perception?

The Paraphilias
Case Notes

Shortly after his fiftieth birthday, Joseph Fredericks was sent to prison for life for the murder of an 11-year-old boy. Fredericks had kidnapped the boy from a shopping mall in Brampton, Ontario, and then repeatedly raped him before stabbing him to death.

Fredericks's history revealed that in his second year at school, he had been assessed by a school psychologist who concluded that his intelligence was extremely low. Fredericks was taken from his poverty-stricken parents and placed in an institution for the intellectually disabled, where he knew no one and lost all contact with the parents he loved. Many years later, it was discovered that Fredericks's intelligence was within the normal range.

Fredericks was introduced to sexual activities by older residents of the institution. Frightened at first, he soon sought out other boys for sex. There was little else to do in the institution and sex became his only pleasure.

At age 17, Fredericks was considered too old for the institution and sent out into the world with some money in his pocket but no idea what to do with it. He did

not know how to find a room or a job. Because he was assumed to be incapable of learning, he had not been taught any job skills. He went on welfare until he found casual work. Since he had no friends or relatives that he knew of, Fredericks soon began to seek out the company of young boys, the only people he had ever learned to relate to. He was arrested for sexual molestation soon after leaving the institution and repeated this behaviour over the next 30 years. In 1985, he was sent to Kingston Penitentiary for five years, but was released after serving two-thirds of his sentence because he was considered to pose no great risk to the community.

Evidently, this conclusion was disastrously mistaken, for within a few weeks he had murdered the young boy. Fredricks' case influenced a shift in Canadian public policy for sex offenders toward the greater emphasis on community protection. Risk to the community is assessed through actuarial tools, many of which were created in Canada, such as the Static-99R (Phenix, Helmus, & Hanson, 2015) and the Sexual Offender Risk Appraisal Guide (SORAG) (Quinsey et al., 2006).

DSM-5 describes unusual sexual interests as **paraphilias**, which means "beyond the usual" (*para*) form of love (*philia*). According to the diagnostic manual, paraphilias are characterized by "intense and persistent sexual interest other than sexual interest in genital stimulation or preparatory fondling with phenotypically normal, physically mature, consenting human partners" (APA, 2013, p. 685; see Tables 13.4 to 13.11). The DSM-5 defines a **paraphilic disorder** as a paraphilia that is currently causing distress or impairment to the individual, or a paraphilia that causes personal harm, or risk of harm, to others when acted upon. According to this perspective, which has taken decades for the DSM to adopt, if a clinician ascertained the presence of a paraphilia, it would not necessarily require psychiatric diagnosis or intervention. Only in the case that

TABLE 13.4 DSM-5 DIAGNOSTIC CRITERIA FOR FETISHISTIC DISORDER

A. Over a period of at least 6 months, recurrent and intense sexual arousal from either the use of nonliving objects or a highly specific focus on nongenital body part(s), as manifested by fantasies, urges, or behaviors.
B. The fantasies, sexual urges, or behaviors cause clinically significant distress or impairment in social, occupational, or other important areas of functioning.
C. The fetish objects are not limited to articles of clothing used in cross-dressing (as in transvestic disorder) or devices specifically designed for the purpose of tactile genital stimulation (e.g., vibrator).

Source: Reprinted with permission from the *Diagnostic and Statistical Manual of Mental Disorders, Fifth Edition.* (Copyright © 2013). American Psychiatric Association. All Rights Reserved.

this paraphilia caused distress to the individual experiencing it or harm to others would it then be diagnosed as a paraphilic disorder. In addition, the criterion for the paraphilic disorders that involves nonconsenting persons is more specific in terms of the number of nonconsenting persons involved, and this number varies depending on the **paraphilic disorder**. Note that all disorders specify a period of at least six months' duration and need to be manifested by fantasies, urges, or behaviours in order for the diagnosis to be made.

PARAPHILIC DISORDERS

FETISHISTIC DISORDER The DSM-5 describes **fetishistic disorder** as recurrent and intense sexual arousal from either the use of nonliving objects or a highly specific focus on a nongenital body part, or parts.

Since it is mostly men who appear at clinics for treatment of fetishisms, it is often presumed that these fixations are primarily found in males, indeed, a recent study on paraphilias in a non-clinical sample found that significantly more men (28 percent) than women (11 percent) reported arousal to fetishes (Dawson, Bannerman, & Lalumiere, 2016). Of the fetishistic objects that have been reported in the literature, women's underwear or women's shoes appear to be among the most common, but there are reports of fetishisms for leather, rubber, plastic, babies' diapers (clean or dirty), furs, and purses. Indeed, almost any object, or even a behaviour, can become a fetish. For example, apotemnophilia is the fetish for amputation and genital mutilation. One case was even documented where a man cut off his own penis due to a genital mutilation fetish (Lowenstein, 2002). Many individuals have more than one fetish (Scorolli et al., 2007).

Those with object fetishes typically like to smell or rub the object against their bodies or, in some cases, wear the article or have their partner wear it. When the articles worn by the person with the fetish are clothes of the opposite sex and this behaviour is considered distressing, it is called *transvestic disorder*, which we will describe in more detail in a moment. Some people with fetishes are driven to steal their desired objects. It is often this theft rather than their actual sexual behaviour that gets them into trouble with the law.

Very little is known about the psychological adjustment of fetishists, but many of those who enter treatment appear in all other aspects to be quite well adjusted. Fetishists who accept their own feelings, odd though they may seem to others, and who have found ways of meeting their desires in ways that do not harm others and do not interfere with their social functioning, do not seem to pose a problem. And indeed, since they would not meet the criterion of distress, they would not be diagnosed by DSM-5 standards as having a disorder.

We know very little about the origin of fetishes, although many fetishists report that their unusual sexual attraction began in childhood. Early etiological hypotheses were based on a psychoanalytic perspective, but it is not clear how such theories can be empirically tested (Lowenstein, 2002). More recently, classical conditioning and social learning

Many transvestites are aroused by cross-dressing, although not all cross-dressers have transvestic fetishism. As with this man, it is impossible to tell just from looking at someone what their motivations are for cross-dressing.

Paul Cox/Alamy Stock Photo

perspectives were advanced, highlighting the importance of early childhood events and social interaction. Finally, a number of authors have considered biological factors and their association with fetishism, with most focusing on temporal lobe abnormalities. El-Badri and Robertshaw (1998), for example, conducted a study in which they found that temporal lobe epilepsy or a disturbance in the temporal area was associated with fetishism. It is likely that none of these explanations accounts for all cases of fetishism.

TRANSVESTIC DISORDER A person who cross-dresses—wears the clothing associated with the opposite sex—to produce or enhance sexual excitement is said to be a **transvestite** (or to have transvestism) in the DSM-5. The diagnosis of transvestic disorder applies to individuals whose cross-dressing or thoughts of cross-dressing are always or often accompanied by sexual excitement, and who are emotionally distressed by this pattern, or who feel that it impairs social or interpersonal functioning. Transvestic disorder is rare in males and is extremely rare in females (APA, 2013). Evidence from the first population-based study (Långström & Zucker, 2005) of 2450 randomly selected men and women indicated that 2.8 percent of men and only 0.4 percent of women reported episodes of transvestic fetishism, suggesting that this is primarily a male disorder. Most individuals with transvestic fetishism begin cross-dressing in childhood (Dzelme & Jones, 2001).

TABLE 13.5   DSM-5 DIAGNOSTIC CRITERIA FOR TRANSVESTIC DISORDER

> A. Over a period of at least 6 months, recurrent and intense sexual arousal from cross-dressing, as manifested by fantasies, urges, or behaviors.
> B. The fantasies, sexual urges, or behaviors cause clinically significant distress or impairment in social, occupational, or other important areas of functioning.
>
> *Source:* Reprinted with permission from the *Diagnostic and Statistical Manual of Mental Disorders, Fifth Edition.* (Copyright © 2013). American Psychiatric Association. All Rights Reserved.

People cross-dress for various reasons. Performers who earn their living impersonating people of the opposite sex, known as "drag queens," are not transvestites unless they are sexually excited by their work, which few seem to be. Dressing in drag is most commonly associated with the gay community; however, most transvestites are heterosexual. Docter and Prince (1997) conducted a study of 1032 male transvestites and found that 87% identified themselves as heterosexual, 83% were married or had married at some point during the survey, and 69% had fathered children. Similarly, Långström & Zucker (2005), in their large sample, indicated that no man reported a primary same-sex sexual orientation.

In general, most transvestites state that cross-dressing allows them to express themselves, although significant proportions of these men seek therapy or counselling to help them with the effects of cross-dressing—for example, anxiety and depression (Docter & Prince, 1997), which, it should be noted, may not result from transvestism directly but from being social outcasts.

SEXUAL SADISM AND MASOCHISM AND THEIR ASSOCIATED DISORDERS
Sexual sadism describes a sexual preference toward inflicting pain or psychological suffering on others. **Sexual masochism**, on the other hand, describes individuals who enjoy experiencing pain or humiliation from another individual. Sexual sadism disorder and sexual masochism disorder are diagnosed when the individual has acted upon these sexual urges with a nonconsenting person,

TABLE 13.6   DSM-5 DIAGNOSTIC CRITERIA FOR SEXUAL SADISM DISORDER

> A. Over a period of at least 6 months, recurrent and intense sexual arousal from the physical or psychological suffering of another person, as manifested by fantasies, urges, or behaviors.
> B. The individual has acted on these sexual urges with a nonconsenting person, or the sexual urges or fantasies cause clinically significant distress or impairment in social, occupational, or other important areas of functioning.
>
> *Source:* Reprinted with permission from the *Diagnostic and Statistical Manual of Mental Disorders, Fifth Edition.* (Copyright © 2013). American Psychiatric Association. All Rights Reserved.

or the sexual urges or fantasies cause clinically significant distress or impairment in social, occupational, or other important areas of functioning (APA, 2013). There is some dissension as to whether these disorders are, in fact, mutually exclusive, with some researchers suggesting that sadistic and masochistic partners routinely switch roles (Reinisch & Beasley, 1990), whereas others (e.g., Kingston & Yates, 2008) report that individuals typically adopt one specific role.

When sexual sadism and masochism are discussed in a consenting context, they are often referred to in the context of BDSM, or "kink." Both of these terms can overlap in their meaning, but BDSM refers specifically to bondage and discipline, domination and submission, and sadism and masochism. Many sadists and masochists are generally well-adjusted individuals with otherwise conventional lifestyles. Sadistic and masochistic fantasies are also common in the general population. For example, in a study conducted at the University of New Brunswick, Renaud and Byers (1999) indicated that 65% of students reported fantasies of being tied up, while 62% had fantasies of tying up someone else. Kinsey reported that approximately 50% of males and females experienced an erotic response as a result of being bitten while engaging in sexual activity. When listening to a story depicting sadomasochistic activity, 12% of females and 24% of males reported an erotic response (Kinsey, Pomeroy, Martin, & Gebhard, 1953).

So what exactly are sexual sadism and sexual masochism? Sexual sadism is when a person experiences sexual pleasure from inflicting physical pain or psychological suffering on another person, often to gain power or to humiliate the other person. For most, sadistic elements are ritualized and symbolic rather than actual painful experiences, and extreme forms of pain and torture are rare. However, some sadists find ritualized sadism with a willing partner to be unsatisfying and seek out nonconsenting partners, thus satisfying the definition of a sexual offence. These sadists will be considered in more detail in the later section dealing with rape.

Sexual masochism can range from harmless behaviour, such as being restrained, to potentially dangerous activity, such as **hypoxyphilia** (also known as **autoerotic asphyxia** or **asphyxiophilia**). This particular behaviour involves the deliberate induction of unconsciousness by oxygen deprivation,

TABLE 13.7   DSM-5 DIAGNOSTIC CRITERIA FOR SEXUAL MASOCHISM DISORDER

> A. Over a period of at least 6 months, recurrent and intense sexual arousal from the act of being humiliated, beaten, bound, or otherwise made to suffer, as manifested by fantasies, urges, or behaviors.
> B. The fantasies, sexual urges, or behaviors cause clinically significant distress or impairment in social, occupational, or other important areas of functioning.
>
> *Source:* Reprinted with permission from the *Diagnostic and Statistical Manual of Mental Disorders, Fifth Edition.* (Copyright © 2013). American Psychiatric Association. All Rights Reserved.

chest compression, strangulation, enclosing the head in a plastic bag, or various other techniques. Oxygen deprivation is usually self-induced and follows a ritualistic pattern, terminating just prior to losing consciousness. Unfortunately, when miscalculations occur, they sometimes result in death. Death from this practice is most common in those who practise their rituals alone, as opposed to with a partner. Most deaths involve males, likely reflecting the fact that, as far as we can tell, this practice, like most other paraphilias, is most common in males.

In addition to the characteristics of pain and humiliation, several other features have been associated with sadism and masochism, such as fantasy and ritualization (Santtila, Sandnabba, Alison, & Nordling, 2002). Participants in sadomasochistic behaviour also often engage in elaborate rituals and use a variety of equipment (e.g., handcuffs, masks). Ritualistic patterns of sexual behaviour involve the assignment of roles to partners and require them to engage in specific sequences of behaviours. Among the variety of role plays enacted, the "master and slave" game, wherein the sadist leads the masochist around by a leash and requires him or her to perform degrading activities, seems to be the most commonly performed (Sandnabba, Santtila, Alison, & Nordling, 2002). While some individuals contain this behaviour to the context of specifics clubs or events, others adopt this as a lifestyle, seeking a long-term relationship in which each partner plays the dominant or submissive role.

The causes of sadism and masochism are unclear, although several theories have been advanced, including psychodynamic, behavioural, social learning, and physiological perspectives. While some have highlighted the importance of early negative childhood experiences (Blum, 1991), others have suggested that this conclusion is premature (Sandnabba et al., 2002) and needs further investigation. Other evidence has pointed to biological mechanisms and highlights the release of endorphins (which produce feelings of euphoria) in the brain in response to pain.

There are four specific paraphilic disorders involving sexual desires that, if enacted, constitute criminal offences. **Exhibitionistic disorder** in the DSM-5 involves exposure of the genitals to an unsuspecting person, **voyeuristic disorder** entails secretly looking at naked people, and **frotteuristic disorder** is touching or rubbing against a nonconsenting person for the purpose of sexual pleasure. **Pedophilic disorder** describes recurrent fantasies or behaviours involving sexual activity with prepubescent children.

EXHIBITIONISTIC DISORDER Exhibitionism is the most frequently occurring sexual offence in Western countries. According to one survey, 33% of university women have been the victims of an exhibitionist (Cox, 1988). Yet Byers and colleagues (1997) found that only 6% of arrested sex offenders in New Brunswick were exhibitionists. Abel and colleagues (1987) found that exhibitionists committed in excess of 70 000 acts of exposure, for an average of 514 acts per offender. Furthermore, exhibitionists have the highest rate of reoffending, with up to 57% being reported again within four years of the original conviction (Marshall, Eccles, & Barbaree, 1991). Freund (1990) found that many exhibitionists also peep into windows to watch women undressing or having sex (voyeurism), and as many as 12% had also committed rape. Dr. Philip Firestone and his research group at the University of Ottawa (Firestone, Kingston, Wexler, & Bradford, 2006; Rabinowitz Greenberg, Firestone, Bradford, & Greenberg, 2002) have investigated the characteristics of various types of sexual offenders, including exhibitionists. They found that a substantial number of exhibitionists go on to commit more serious "hands-on" sexual offences and that such individuals are at greater risk for committing another offence when compared to other types of sexual offenders. In addition, standardized psychological tests have indicated that these men score in the lowest fifth percentile of general sexual functioning and demonstrate significant levels of deviant sexual arousal, as indicated by phallometric assessments. The DSM-5 specifies exhibitionistic disorder according to preferred developmental stage of the victim: prepubertal children, physically mature individuals, or both (APA, 2013).

TABLE 13.8 DSM-5 DIAGNOSTIC CRITERIA FOR EXHIBITIONISTIC DISORDER

A. Over a period of at least 6 months, recurrent and intense sexual arousal from the exposure of one's genitals to an unsuspecting person, as manifested by fantasies, urges, or behaviors.
B. The individual has acted on these sexual urges with a non-consenting person, or the sexual urges or fantasies cause clinically significant distress or impairment in social, occupational, or other important areas of functioning.

Source: Reprinted with permission from the *Diagnostic and Statistical Manual of Mental Disorders, Fifth Edition.* (Copyright © 2013). American Psychiatric Association. All Rights Reserved.

TABLE 13.9 DSM-5 DIAGNOSTIC CRITERIA FOR VOYEURISTIC DISORDER

A. Over a period of at least 6 months, recurrent and intense sexual arousal from observing an unsuspecting person who is naked, in the process of disrobing, or engaging in sexual activity, as manifested by fantasies, urges, or behaviors.
B. The individual has acted on these sexual urges with a non-consenting person, or the sexual urges or fantasies cause clinically significant distress or impairment in social, occupational, or other important areas of functioning.
C. The individual experiencing the arousal and/or acting on the urges is at least 18 years of age.

Source: Reprinted with permission from the *Diagnostic and Statistical Manual of Mental Disorders, Fifth Edition.* (Copyright © 2013). American Psychiatric Association. All Rights Reserved.

BEFORE MOVING ON

> How many people do you know who have been the victim of exhibitionism, for example? How common do you think this is? For females? For males? What reaction is expected from the victims when the exhibitionist "flashes" that person? What is the best way to respond to this kind of situation?

VOYEURISTIC DISORDER Voyeurs or "Peeping Toms" are individuals who experience recurrent and intense sexually arousing urges/fantasies or behaviours involving the observation of unsuspecting individuals who are naked, disrobing, or engaged in sexual activity (APA, 2013). An essential feature of this disorder is that the person of interest must be unaware that he or she is being watched. Usually, voyeurs do not seek sexual relations with the person being watched and will often masturbate while engaged in the voyeuristic activity or later in response to the memory of what the person has witnessed. The DSM-5 specifies that voyeuristic disorder cannot be diagnosed in individuals under the age of 18, in order to avoid pathologizing normative sexual interest and behaviour during puberty.

The available research on voyeurs is quite limited. Most research has identified that voyeuristic activity occurs prior to age 15 (Abel & Rouleau, 1990; APA, 2000). Moreover, while most voyeurs are not dangerous, some do commit "hands-on" sexual offences and many present with comorbid paraphilic disorders. As examples, Abel and Rouleau (1990) found that 37 percent of their sample of voyeurs (*n* 62) had been involved in sexual assault and more than half in child molestation, and Freund (1990; *n* 94) found that 19 percent had engaged in sexual assault.

FROTTEURISTIC DISORDER Almost all detected frotteurs are male. Frotteurism (or *frottage*—from the French *frotter*, "to rub"), according to the DSM-5, refers to touching or rubbing up against a noncompliant person so that the frotteur can become sexually aroused and, in many cases, reach orgasm. These offences typically occur in crowded places such as busy sidewalks, stores, or shopping malls, or on packed public transport. The impersonal nature of this type of sexual contact is considered by some authorities (Money, 1987) as essential to the pleasure of the frotteur. Abel and colleagues (1987) found that while some frotteurs keep the contact brief and furtive to make it appear accidental, others seem unconcerned about being detected and are more intrusive and aggressive, fondling the victim's genitals, buttocks, or breasts, or rubbing the penis vigorously against the victim until orgasm occurs. Observations like these encouraged Langevin (1983) to view frotteurism as a form of sexual aggression belonging to the same category as rape. He pointed out that both are aggressive forms of direct sexual touching without the consent of the victim.

PEDOPHILIC DISORDER Pedophilic disorder is evident most often in males and describes individuals who exhibit a predominant sexual interest in, or preference toward, prepubescent children (Freund, 1981; Marshall, 1997). Specifically, this paraphilia is characteristic of recurrent, intense sexually arousing fantasies, sexual urges, or behaviours involving sexual activity with a prepubescent child (defined as aged 13 years or younger in the DSM-5), although many report that body type, rather than age, is what really defines whether a minor is pre-pubescent or not (e.g., Blanchard, 2013; Lang, Rouget, & van Santen, 1988). Additionally, either the individual must have acted on these sexual urges or the sexual urges/fantasies have caused marked distress or interpersonal difficulty. Lastly, the individual being assessed is at least 16 years old and at least five years older than the victim (APA, 2013).

TABLE 13.10 DSM-5 DIAGNOSTIC CRITERIA FOR FROTTEURISTIC DISORDER

> A. Over a period of at least 6 months, recurrent and intense sexual arousal from touching or rubbing against a nonconsenting person, as manifested by fantasies, urges, or behaviors.
> B. The individual has acted on these sexual urges with a nonconsenting person, or the sexual urges or fantasies cause clinically significant distress or impairment in social, occupational, or other important areas of functioning.

Source: Reprinted with permission from the *Diagnostic and Statistical Manual of Mental Disorders, Fifth Edition.* (Copyright © 2013). American Psychiatric Association. All Rights Reserved.

TABLE 13.11 DSM-5 DIAGNOSTIC CRITERIA FOR PEDOPHILIC DISORDER

> A. Over a period of at least 6 months, recurrent, intense sexually arousing fantasies, sexual urges, or behaviors involving sexual activity with a prepubescent child or children (generally age 13 years or younger).
> B. The individual has acted on these sexual urges, or the sexual urges or fantasies cause marked distress or interpersonal difficulty.
> C. The individual is at least age 16 years and at least 5 years older than the child or children in Criterion A.
>
> **Note:** Do not include an individual in late adolescence involved in an ongoing sexual relationship with a 12- or 13-year-old.
>
> *Specify* whether:
>   **Exclusive type** (attracted only to children)
>   **Nonexclusive type**
> *Specify* if:
>   **Sexually attracted to males**
>   **Sexually attracted to females**
>   **Sexually attracted to both**
> *Specify* if:
>   **Limited to incest**

Source: Reprinted with permission from the *Diagnostic and Statistical Manual of Mental Disorders, Fifth Edition.* (Copyright © 2013). American Psychiatric Association. All Rights Reserved.

It is important to note that the terms *pedophile* and *child molester* are often used interchangeably, which creates confusion as they are not the same thing (Barbaree & Seto, 1997; Kingston, Firestone, Moulden, & Bradford, 2007). A **child molester** is an individual who has engaged in a sexually motivated act against a prepubescent child, without an indication of preference, whereas a **pedophile** is an individual who has displayed a preference for sexual behaviour with a child (O'Donohue, Regev, & Hagstrom, 2000). This distinction is important, as not all child molesters are pedophiles, and some pedophiles may not have committed a sexual offence against a child (i.e., they may abstain from sexual activity with their preferred age group) (Konopasky & Konopasky, 2000). The prevalence of pedophilia ranges from 40 to 50 percent among males who sexually offend against children (Blanchard et al., 2001).

Several problems associated with the diagnosis of pedophilic disorder have been identified, and researchers have questioned the value added by the use of such a label (Marshall, 1997; O'Donohue et al., 2000). For example, the definition also seems to allow for the disorder to be diagnosed on a history of sexual acts alone, thereby blurring the line between the mental disorder of pedophilia and criminal sexual acts against children, which, as noted above, are not one in the same (First & Frances, 2008). Specific concerns have also included the ambiguous nature of the terms *recurrent* and *intense* within the diagnostic criteria, which possibly contributes to reduced reliability. In fact, one study (Levenson, 2004) evaluated the reliability of various diagnoses in a sample of 295 adult incarcerated sexual offenders, and results indicated that the diagnosis of pedophilia was clearly below acceptable standards (kappa = 0.65). Also, a possible contributor to the lack of reliability is the exclusion of specifiers for whether the individual is sexually attracted to prepubescent children, pubescent children, or both. These specifiers would have been termed *classic type*, *hebephilic type*, and *pedohebephilic type*, respectively (Blanchard, 2013).

On the one hand, the best predictor of recidivism (i.e., the rate at which sexual offenders with adult victims re-offend after serving a period of incarceration) that we have to date is arousal to children as measured by penile plethysmography (ppg) (Hanson & Bussière, 1998), suggesting that, despite some who question the value of providing a diagnosis of pedophilic disorder (e.g., Marshall, 2007; Marshall, Marshall, Serran, & Fernandez, 2006), this diagnosis is still an important one to explore in those who have offended against children. It is important to note that research findings are not unequivocal, as others (see Moulden, Firestone, Kingston, & Bradford, 2009; Wilson, Abracen, Picheca, Malcolm, & Prinzo, 2003) have found a DSM diagnosis of pedophilia was unrelated to long term recidivism.

RAPE The term *rape*, in its traditional sense, refers to forced penetration of an unwilling female's vagina by a male assailant's penis. Not only did this definition exclude the rape of males, it placed quite unnecessary emphasis on penile–vaginal intercourse. In terms of legal processes, this requirement of demonstrated forced vaginal intercourse in order to obtain a conviction of rape caused so many problems that Canadian legislators decided to change the law. Rape, as a criminal offence, and various other sexual crimes were replaced in 1983 in Canadian law by three crimes of *sexual assault*. These three types of sexual assault are defined by varying levels of forcefulness by the offender and incur, upon conviction, increasing lengths of possible sentences. These improvements in the law served to make clear the intrusiveness of these crimes, and to diminish the legal relevance of whether penetration had occurred. This is quite reasonable, since the severity of psychological damage caused by an incident of sexual assault does not depend only on whether the vagina was penetrated, but on many other factors as well. Over and above sexual objectification, many offenders also make a point of degrading and humiliating their victims and may physically hurt them. The current Canadian laws better reflect the reality of sexual assault than did the earlier rape laws.

Because sexual assault laws have not been similarly modified in most jurisdictions of the United States, nor in other countries, most researchers continue to use the terms *rape* and *rapist*. For convenience, we will use these terms, but this should not be taken to imply support for the old laws. The current Canadian laws, we believe, are superior to any in the world in terms of encouraging victims to report and in having the courts focus on the appropriate issues.

Because of these changes, and because there are now restrictions on questioning the victim in court about previous sexual experiences, more victims are coming forward. However, there are still numerous examples of women being re-victimized through the court process by insensitive judges or lawyers or expert witnesses who uphold myths of women being partially responsible for being sexually assaulted (e.g., through the way they dress or "tease" men), and sexual assault remains a markedly underreported crime. Koss (1992), from a thorough analysis of survey data, concluded that the real rate of rape was 6 to 10 times as high as the officially recorded statistics. Relying on estimates such as these, Marshall and Barrett (1990) took the official Canadian figures for 1988 and multiplied them by four (a conservative strategy) to estimate the true frequency of rape in Canada. This calculation suggested that more than 75 000 women are raped in Canada every year, at the frightening rate of one every seven minutes. As Figure 13.3 reveals, strangers actually constitute a very small percentage of rapists. Date rape and rape by acquaintances is a far more prevalent problem, and has certainly received some much needed media attention over the past few years, particularly in the context of college and university campuses. There have been numerous examples of attitudes supportive of rape on campuses throughout North America, for example, the pro-rape chant at one Canadian university in 2013 that sparked nationwide attention (CBC, 2013, December 19). More recently, the Brock Turner case at Stanford University in California highlighted the appalling acceptance of rape in American society when a judge issued a six-month sentence for a conviction

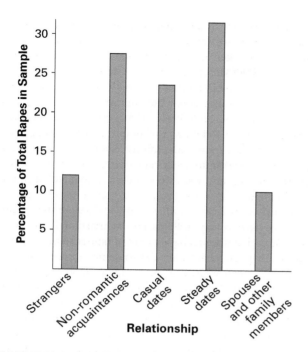

FIGURE 13.3 Relationships of Rapists to Their Victims

Source: Based on Koss, M. P. (1988). Stranger and acquaintance rape: Are there differences in the victim's experience? *Psychology of Women Quarterly, 12*, 1–24.

Note: These data are drawn from a large-scale survey of women attending colleges in the United States.

that held a guideline minimum sentence of six years. The acceptance of rape was further perpetuated by Mr. Turner's father when he referred to the crime as "20 minutes of action" for which his son should not be severely punished (*The Atlantic*, 2016, June 17). Donald Trump's presidential win despite his reference to his comments about sexual assaulting women as being "locker room" talk further speaks to the acceptance of rape culture present in American society today.

Until quite recently, forcible sex by a spouse was not covered by the sexual assault laws of most countries, and it is still excluded from these laws in many places. In addition, several studies have investigated its recidivism rate, demonstrating that after 5 to 10 years in the community, more than 25 percent of rapists will commit another sexual assault; this rate is typically higher than is found among child molesters (Firestone et al., 1998; Harris et al., 2003).

In contrast to pedophilia, there is no formal paraphilic diagnosis in the DSM-5 to identify men who prefer sexual activity with a nonconsenting partner. Some evaluators have diagnosed rapists with sexual sadism, though certainly not all rapists are sadists. Marshall, Kennedy, and Yates (2002) found that they could not distinguish rapists diagnosed as sadists from those who were said not to be sadists on any of the above features nor on any other feature. Furthermore, internationally renowned experts could not agree on the diagnosis of sexual sadism applied to 12 quite violent and brutal rapists (Marshall, Kennedy, Yates, & Serran, 2002).

The primary problem facing diagnosticians in deciding whether a rapist meets the criteria for sexual sadism is that the diagnosis must be based on the offender being sexually aroused by the idea of physically or psychologically hurting another person. Unless the offender tells the diagnostician that he is aroused by these characteristics (or any other feature), there is little alternative for the clinician except to guess what arouses the offender. Phallometric assessment could answer this question, but to date no one has demonstrated that phallometric testing can identify sadists, although some researchers have tried (Seto & Kuban, 1996). These problems with the diagnosis of sexual sadism are also true for other paraphilias (Marshall, 1997).

While most rapists do not exhibit a sexual preference toward nonconsenting sexual activity, clearly some do. An interesting hypothesis has been proposed, which differentiates among three distinct sexual arousal patterns seen in rapists (Lalumière, Quinsey, Harris, Rice, & Trautrimas, 2003). The three profiles include **biastophilia**, a sexual preference toward nonconsenting and resisting but not necessarily physically suffering victims; *sadism*, a preference toward the suffering or humiliation of others; and *antisociality*, a marked sexual indifference to the interests and desires of others. Studies reporting on sexual preferences have indicated some support for the above categories (Lalumière et al., 2003).

⑥ BEFORE MOVING ON

Consider the following legal definition of rape in Canada that was in effect prior to 1983: forced heterosexual intercourse of a woman by a man outside of marriage. In addition, a victim's prior sexual experience could be considered as evidence of her consent. What implications did this definition have for married versus single women, for female versus male victims, and for women with prior sexual experience?

UNUSUAL SEXUAL VARIANTS Psychologist John Money (1984) claims that there are many more paraphilias than are listed in the diagnostic manual. He suggests that there are at least 30 or more different types, although DSM-5 has a category that would accommodate these, if they cause distress or harm to others, called Other Specified Paraphilic Disorder. Sexual satisfaction derived from receiving enemas (klismaphilia), as well as urination (urophilia) or defecation (coprophilia), occurs frequently enough that pornographers cater to such interests. Some less frequent paraphilias, however, involve activities that break the law, such as sex with corpses (necrophilia) or with animals (zoophilia or bestiality), or that take the form of obscene telephone calls (scatologia). All of these unusual sexual variants, although occasionally described in the literature, are far too infrequently seen at clinics to permit adequate descriptive research.

ETIOLOGY OF SEXUAL OFFENDING Over the years, many theorists have speculated about the origins of sexual offending. As noted above, not all sexual offenders have deviant sexual preferences. It is clear that no single explanation can account for all sexual offending. Below are some of the many theories put forth identifying possible explanations for those who are paraphilic and those who are non-paraphilic offenders.

Conditioning Theories. McGuire, Carlisle, and Young (1965) were the first to propose that conditioning was the basis of acquired preferences motivating men to engage in unusual or offensive sexual behaviours. A young male, for example, might be caught in the act of masturbating by an attractive woman, and this association between high sexual arousal and a woman seeing his exposed penis might, according to this conditioning account, serve to entrench an attraction to (or preference for) exposing his penis to women. Similar accidental associations between sexual arousal and seeing younger children were said to be the conditioning bases of future child molestation, while masturbating to pornographic images of, or to thoughts of, sexually assaulting a woman were said to instill a preference for rape.

A similar theory, which assumes that sexual offenders are aroused by their deviant acts, was advanced by Kurt Freund, who began his outstanding career in his native Czechoslovakia but lived and worked in Toronto from the 1960s until he died in 1996. Freund outlined what he called a **courtship disorder theory** of sexual offending. Freund (1990) suggests, by analogy with animal courtship behaviour, that there are four phases in human sexual interactions: (1) looking for and appraising a potential partner, (2) posturing and displaying oneself to the partner, (3) tactile interaction with the partner, and (4) sexual intercourse. Freund's notion of courtship disorder suggests that fixation at any one of these stages produces sexual offending. Fixation at stage 1 would result in voyeurism; at stage 2 in exhibitionism; at stage 3 in frotteurism; and at stage 4 in rape.

These theories have some intuitive appeal as long as we accept that these offensive behaviours are sexually motivated. However, not all sexual crimes are driven exclusively by sexual desires. Marshall and Eccles (1993), in their review of the relevant literature on animal and human sexual behaviour, found little supporting evidence for conditioning theories.

Feminist Theories. Feminist theories of sexual offending are quite diverse, but they do have common threads. Feminist theorists typically see sexual abuse as arising naturally out of the socio-cultural environment of our societies, which they see as essentially patriarchal (Brownmiller, 1975; Clark & Lewis, 1977). In this context, these theorists point to the differential ways in which parents and other influential people (e.g., peers, teachers) respond to boys and girls. According to this analysis, girls are encouraged to be submissive, co-operative, nurturing, and emotional, whereas boys are encouraged to be dominant and competitive and are discouraged from displaying any emotions (other than perhaps anger). Feminists see this difference as setting up women and children to be dominated by, and to be subservient to, adult males. Such a power differential provides few constraints on men's behaviour toward women and children, which may facilitate sexual abuse.

Feminist theorists typically see rape as a non-sexual, or pseudo-sexual, offence. They emphasize instead offenders' apparent anger toward women, as seen in their efforts to humiliate the victims and to exercise power and control. Canadian psychologist Juliet Darke (1990) examined both what rapists said about their own motives and victims' perceptions. Both sources revealed that more than 60 percent of rapes involved some form of intentional humiliation of the victims. Consistent with feminist analyses, Seidman and colleagues (1994) found that rapists attending community clinics were angrier toward women than were matched, non-offending males.

Consistent with the idea that patriarchal structures encourage rape, Sanday (1981), in her examination of data from 156 tribal societies, found higher rates of rape in societies characterized by patriarchal systems. In these rape-prone societies, women were seen as the property of men and were excluded from all positions of power and influence. These societies, where violence was endemic, had far higher rates of sexual assault than did societies where both sexes were treated more equally. Rape was less common in societies in which women were respected and had an equal say in religious, political, and economic matters.

In terms of men's likelihood to rape, there is a fairly extensive body of literature indicating that approximately 30 percent (and even higher in some studies) of non-offending males acknowledge that they would rape a woman if they knew they could get away with it (Malamuth, 1986; Malamuth, Heavey, & Linz, 1993). These figures, taken at face value, are quite startling and appear to strongly support feminist claims. However, it is difficult to determine how to rate a response that amounts to a guess about what the respondent might do in a purely hypothetical situation.

Despite some problems with the evidence taken to support feminist views of sexual assault, the analyses offered by feminists have radically changed and expanded our understanding of these crimes. They have made it clear that these are primarily crimes committed by men (which needs explaining in any theory of sexual assault) and that there are clear socio-cultural bases to sexual offending. Most importantly, lobbying by feminists has changed the way we deal with sexual abuse as a society. The investigation and prosecution processes have been made far easier on victims than they were just a few years ago, and the offenders who are identified are more likely to be convicted and jailed than excused and let go, as so many were in the past.

The feminist perspective is sometimes accused of being anti-male, but it actually credits males as human beings who are able to control their sexual desires. Rather than exclusively teaching women what to wear and how to act in order to avoid being a victim, feminists argue that men need to be taught how to respect women and society needs to change from a complicit "rape culture" to one that focuses on dismantling gender stereotypes of both males and females. There has been much discussion over rape culture on college and university campuses. In 2011, a Toronto, Ontario police officer, Michael Sanguinetti said that "women should avoid dressing likes sluts in order not to be victimized" while addressing concerns about rape on a local university campus. While he later apologized, "SlutWalk" was organized in response to this statement, a march/rally in which individuals protest rape culture through sharing of their own experiences, dressing in "slutty" clothing, and/or marching in support of victims.

Neurodevelopmental Theories. It has been hypothesized that neurodevelopmental problems prenatally or in early childhood maybe be associated with increased risk of pedophilia (it is unknown whether this would also be true for other paraphilias). Non-right-handedness and minor physical anomalies are signs of neurodevelopmental problems in utero, and in support of a neurodevelopmental hypothesis, non-right-handedness was found more frequently in pedophiles (Cantor et al., 2004), as were minor physical anomalies (Dyshniku et al., 2015). Pedophiles were also more likely to have head injuries before, but not after, the age of 13 years (Blanchard et al., 2002). Findings from numerous studies also show that pedophiles have lower IQs than non-pedophile offenders, and they are more likely to have repeated school grades or received special education (Blanchard et al., 2007, Cantor et al., 2004). In comparison to non-pedophiles, pedophiles show deficits in brain activation associated with sexuality when they are viewing sexual pictures of adults (Walter et al., 2007) and have decreased grey matter volume through various areas of the brain (Schiffer et al., 2007; Schiltz et al., 2007), decreased white matter volume in the temporal and parietal lobes (Cantor et al., 2008), as well as a number of deficits in the cortical regions associated with the recognition of sexual stimuli (Cantor et al., 2008). It is important to note that inconsistent findings in this literature appear to be due to differing comparison subject groups (e.g., other criminals versus non-criminals as the control group). These studies suggest that people with certain early neurodevelopmental disruptions may have a susceptibility to pedophilia, though further research is needed.

Childhood/Social Development Theories. Marshall and his colleagues (Marshall & Barbaree, 1990; Marshall, Hudson, & Hodkinson, 1993; Marshall & Marshall, 2000) have integrated a broad range of evidence to suggest that the childhoods of sexual offenders create a predisposition for aggression and a social inadequacy that makes them readily attracted to deviant sexual behaviours. These deviant acts, unlike prosocial sexual behaviours, require few social skill, have no built-in obligations to others, and do not require the offender to be concerned about the other person's needs or rights. Deviant sexual acts, then, might appeal to males who are lacking in social skills and who are self-centred. Also, sexual offences provide the opportunity to exercise power and control over others, and this experience may be particularly satisfying to powerless males who lack self-confidence. Sexual offenders do typically have disrupted childhoods, and there is clear evidence that such experiences leave a child feeling unlovable, lacking in self-confidence, with poor social skills, and with a propensity for antisocial behaviour

(Loeber, 1990). In this theory, however, it is not just poor parenting that produces sexual offending; socio-cultural factors, accidental opportunities, and transitory states all contribute to the complex array of influences that set the stage for sexual offending.

Empirically-Derived Theories. Concern about recidivism in sexual offenders has led to an abundance of research dedicated to assessing the risk of sexual offenders. This knowledge has helped our understanding of possible factors of origin, as well as maintaining factors, in sexual offending. Three main risk factors in sexual offending are: (1) sexual deviance, for example, pedophilic disorder; (2) antisocial traits (i.e., traits associated with antisocial personality disorder); and (3) intimacy deficits, including poor social skills and identification with children (Seto et al., 2011).

TREATMENT OF SEXUAL OFFENDERS Prior to the 1970s, most treatment programs for sexual offenders were derived from some form of psychoanalytic theory. However, the programs were not very effective (Furby, Weinrott, & Blackshaw, 1989), so clinicians turned to other models for direction.

Medical Interventions. The aim of medical interventions is to eliminate or to reduce sexual drive so the person will be uninterested in sex or will easily be able to control the expression of deviant interests. Physical castration: the surgical removal of the testicles, essentially eliminates the body's production of testosterone, the sex steroid that primarily activates sexual drive. The relationship between testosterone and sexual aggression is well established (Bradford, 2000). Castration is associated with lower recidivism rates in offenders (Bradford, 2001). Given the irreversible nature of this approach and the significant side effects, there is considerable controversy surrounding this procedure (it is not permitted in Canada except to save a person's life when it is endangered by disease). Chemical castration (i.e., the reduction in testosterone resulting from the action of pharmacological treatment) has not drawn the same ethical criticisms; the changes it produces are reversible when the drug is withdrawn. Anti-androgens reduce sexual interest, fantasies, and behaviours in sexual offenders (Rösler & Witztum, 2000), though side-effects are considerable. Alternatives include selective serotonin reuptake inhibitors (SSRIs) and luteinizing hormone-releasing hormone agonists (LHRH agonists). Both medications have demonstrated an ability to reduce or alleviate sexual fantasy, urges, and behaviours (Briken, Nika, & Berner, 2001; Fedoroff, 1993; Rösler & Witztum, 1998) without causing significant side effects.

The evidence appears to demonstrate a valuable role for medications in the treatment of sexual offenders. However, these have typically been administered while the offender was involved in psychological treatment making it somewhat difficult at present to identify the contribution of medications to treatment effectiveness.

Behaviour Therapy. In the late 1960s, behaviour therapists were just beginning to extend their treatment theories to sexual offenders. Bond and Evans (1967), for example, developed a simple approach to treatment based on the assumption that these offensive behaviours were driven by deviant sexual preferences. They thought that all that was necessary in treatment was to eliminate these deviant preferences (e.g., a sexual attraction to children, or to forced sex, or to exposing oneself) and the offending behaviour would disappear. Typically, sexual preferences in these early studies were modified by associating the deviant thoughts with a strongly aversive event, such as an electric shock to the calf muscles. Rice, Quinsey, and Harris (1991) examined this treatment program, offered at the Oak Ridge Mental Health Centre in Ontario during the 1970s and early 1980s, and found that it was ineffective. This finding is not surprising given that from what we know to date, we cannot change a person's sexual preference, and many sexual offenders do not have deviant preferences in the first place.

Comprehensive Programs. As a result of the lack of benefits from these early behavioural interventions, more comprehensive approaches began to emerge based primarily on a cognitive-behavioural perspective. American psychiatrist Gene Abel and his colleagues (Abel, Blanchard, & Becker, 1978) were among the first to develop such programs, and similar programs have been developed in Canada (Lang, Pugh, & Langevin, 1988; Marshall, Earls, Segal, & Darke, 1983; Yates et al., 2000). The longstanding "gold standard" approach (Nunes et al., 2007 to treatment is the Risk/Need/Responsivity model (Andrews & Bonata, 2003), which posits that interventions are most effective if they match the level of risk of the offender, as determined through assessment ("risk"). Once risk is determined, treatment should target risk factors specific to that client ("need") in a manner accessible to the client's cognitive abilities and other individual characteristics, such as culture and personality ("responsivity").

In terms of content, comprehensive programs typically address sexual offenders' tendency to deny or minimize their offending, although the emphasis on taking responsibility for offending has lessened in more recent years given that research has demonstrated that whether or not an offender admits to his crime is not related to recidivism (Hanson & Bussiere, 1998; Hanson & Morton-Bourgon, 2004). A more recent study has found that, for some offenders, specifically those who are deemed low-risk and those who are incest offenders, denial is associated with increased recidivism (Nunes et al., 2007). Taking responsibility for offending is only one part of the treatment programs. Sexual offenders are trained to identify factors that might increase their risk of reoffending, and they are taught ways to deal with these problems should they arise. Commonly addressed risk factors include those related to sexuality (e.g., sexualized coping, hypersexuality, and deviant sexual preference), those related to self-regulation (e.g., impulsivity, substance use, anger management), and those related to social skills (e.g., intimacy deficits, loneliness, appropriate social support systems). Many of these risk factors are empirically derived through risk assessment tools (e.g., Stable-2014;

Fernandez et al., 2014) In addition to the above, current programs (e.g., Marshall, Marshall, Serran, & Fernandez, 2006; Yates et al., 2000) emphasize the role of positive psychology in the treatment of sexual offenders, which takes into account the offenders' strengths and helps them to construct a meaningful and prosocial life. This positive psychological approach was introduced to sexual offender treatment with the "Good Lives Model" (Ward & Gannon, 2006; Ward & Stewart, 2003). Some have questioned the added benefit of this approach (Andrews, Bonta, & Wormith, 2011).

Benefits of Treatment. To evaluate the effects of treatment, it is necessary to follow treated offenders for several years after their discharge from treatment or release from prison, and to compare their reoffence rates with a matched group of untreated offenders. The ideal treatment outcome design would require the random allocation of those who volunteered for treatment—to either treatment or no treatment (Quinsey, Harris, Rice, & Lalumière, 1993)—but unfortunately this ideal study cannot easily be implemented for a variety of ethical reasons. As such, treatment evaluators have adopted alternative strategies, such as incidental matching procedures, where treated participants are matched with untreated sexual offenders on demographic features and offence characteristics.

Two large-scale meta-analyses have evaluated the extent to which sexual offender treatment is associated with lowered recidivism rates. First, Hanson and colleagues (2002) reviewed the sexual offender treatment outcome literature and found 42 studies, with a total of 9316 participants. Results indicated that treatment was associated with reductions in both sexual and general recidivism (i.e., the percentage who reoffended). General recidivism includes a re-offence of any type. These beneficial effects were found to be greatest among those programs that employed the broad cognitive-behavioural approach described in the previous subsection. Furthermore, these benefits were evident whether the program was based in the community or in an institutional setting. Second, Lösel and Schmucker (2005) provided the largest and most recent meta-analyses of sexual offender treatment outcome. Specifically, this review included published and unpublished studies that were reported in a variety of languages. The final review consisted of 80 comparisons derived from 69 studies (n 22 181). With regard to sexual, violent, and criminal recidivism, the treatment group displayed reductions of 37, 44, and 31 percent, respectively, compared to the base rates of the control groups. As such, the results indicated a positive treatment effect for all types of recidivism.

Table 13.12 summarizes the data generated by Hanson's analyses. Clearly, treatment can be effective, but this is not to say that all treatment programs reduce sexual offender recidivism. In Hanson and colleagues' study, those programs based on approaches other than cognitive-behavioural ones were ineffective, although Hanson did not evaluate any medically based treatments.

TABLE 13.12 REOFFENCE RATES FROM CURRENT COGNITIVE-BEHAVIOURAL TREATMENT PROGRAMS

	Treated	Untreated
Sexual recidivism	9.9%	17.3%
General recidivism	32.3%	51.3%

Source: Based on Hanson, R. K., Gordon, A., Harris, A. J., Marques, J. K., Murphy, W., Quinsey, V. L., & Seto, M. (2002). "First report of the collaborative outcome data project on the effectiveness of psychological treatment for sex offenders," *Sexual Abuse: A Journal of Research and Treatment,* 14(2), 169–194.

Two other ways to look at the benefits of treatment for sexual offenders is to consider the reduction in the number of innocent victims harmed by these offenders and the financial savings associated with treatment benefits. In a study of the effects of their community-based program, Marshall and Barbaree (1988) found that each recidivist sexually abused at least two further victims. Marshall and Barbaree's results indicated that 13% of the treated offenders re-offended, compared to 34% of the untreated offenders. This is a difference of 21%, which, given that the recidivists abused at least two victims each, means that for every 100 treated offenders more than 42 innocent people were saved from suffering. In addition, Marshall (1992) calculated the costs incurred by police investigations, the prosecution of an offender, and his imprisonment. He found that it costs taxpayers $200 000 to convict and imprison each sexual re-offender. Table 13.13 presents a calculation of the estimated financial benefits of treating sexual offenders by subtracting the costs of treating 100 offenders from the savings resulting from the reductions in recidivism produced by treatment. Obviously, treating sexual offenders can be effective and, when it is, fewer victims suffer and taxpayers are saved considerable money.

TABLE 13.13 COST-BENEFIT ANALYSIS OF TREATING SEXUAL OFFENDERS

		Treated	Rate of Reoffence Untreated	Reduction in Reoffenders
Prison program		24%	52%	28%
Reduction in number of victims per 100 offenders treated (i.e., 28 × 2 victims per reoffender)	=	56		
Cost per reoffender (to convict and imprison)	=	$ 200 000		
Cost to prison service to treat and supervise 100 offenders	=	$1 000 000		
Savings per 100 offenders treated:				
Savings (28 × $200 000)	=	$5 600 000		
Less costs	=	$1 000 000		
TOTAL SAVINGS	=	**$ 4 600 000**		

Source: Reoffence data are from Hanson and colleagues (2002) and cost-benefit analysis is derived from Marshall (1992). Data from Kluwer Academic Publishers, *Sexual Abuse: A Journal of Research and Treatment,* 14(2), 2002, 169–194, "The 2000 ATSA report on the effectiveness of treatment for sex offenders" by Hanson et al.

CANADIAN RESEARCH CENTRE

Dr. Elke Reissing, Human Sexuality Research Laboratory

Dr. Elke Reissing is a full professor in the School of Psychology and director of the Human Sexuality Research Laboratory (HSRL) at the University of Ottawa. She also serves as the Coordinator of Practica and Internships for the clinical psychology program and is the supervisor for sex therapy servces at the Centre for Psychological Services and Research (CPSR).

Originally, Dr. Reissing came to Canada from Germany with a plan to complete one year of undergraduate studies at Concordia University in Montreal, but she stayed for her Ph.D. studies at McGill University and accepted a faculty position at the University of Ottawa. At McGill, she worked with Irv Binik and a close cohort of graduate students, which included Marta Meana, Sophie Bergeron, and Caroline Pukall—all groundbreakers in the study of sexuality who inspired her work with sexual pain disorders in general and vaginismus in particular.

Dr. Reissing joined the University of Ottawa for a pre-doctoral, clinical

Photograph by Stéphanie Houle. Copied with permission of the Faculty of Social Sciences, University of Ottawa.

internship at the Centre for Psychological Services in 2001 and as faculty the following year. She developed the HSRL, which is home to industrious clinical and experimental graduate students in psychology, focusing on sexuality research. Current research programs in the lab address sexuality and aging broadly defined, with a focus on pelvic floor and sexual health. Dr. Reissing also has a private practice where she works mostly with clients who are unable to experience intercourse because of anxiety and pain. In her role as supervisor of sex therapy training at the CPSR, she and her students work with a broad range of sexual health concerns. Services there are provided by senior Ph.D. students in clinical psychology who are supervised session-by-session by Dr. Reissing. Sex therapy is based on the scientist-practitioner model and, because the clinic is a training site,

it is one of the few places offering sex therapy at greatly reduced fees.

Dr. Reissing has also served on the executive committee of the Canadian Sex Research Forum and is a member of editorial boards of scientific journals covering first-rate research topics related to sexuality and psychology.

Dr. Reissing's main research interest lies in the examination of women who have such severe difficulties with vaginal penetration that they cannot experience intercourse, use tampons, or have a gynecological examination. This may be due to pain with attempted penetration or fear of possible pain. Difficulties may also be due to fear and/or disgust related to vaginal penetration. All women seem to share one aspect: a very tense pelvic floor that makes penetration attempts painful and ultimately impossible. In the past, a diagnosis of vaginismus—now

genito-pelvic pain/penetration disorder—focused solely on pelvic floor pathology, but increasingly, psychological factors are being taken into account. This is not to pathologize women but rather to understand the scope of the problem and the severity of their suffering, and to come up with more effective treatment solutions. Pelvic floor muscle function, however, also plays an important role in general sexual function and possibly in sexual enhancement. Dr. Reissing's current projects focus on the role of the pelvic floor in sexual sensations, sexual mindfulness, and orgasm experience. In addition, the role of stress on the pelvic floor (e.g., through physical exercise, pregnancy) and potential consequences for sexual health are examined. Research questions are typically addressed across the lifespan with a focus on older women in particular.

SUMMARY

- Masters and Johnson developed the sexual response cycle based on their research examining the physiological correlates of human sexual response.

- During the excitement stage, the genital tissues of both males and females swell as they fill with blood, causing penile erection and vaginal lubrication, among other changes.

- The plateau stage involves additional swelling of the penis, vaginal tissues, and other areas as the body gets ready for orgasm.

- During orgasm, both sexes experience rhythmic, muscular contractions of the pelvic and genital areas, and males ejaculate.

- Following orgasm, the body returns to its pre-aroused state during the resolution stage. Males experience a refractory period, but some of them may have the capacity to be multiply orgasmic, as some females do.

- Several sexual dysfunctions are listed in the DSM that can affect people in the following areas: desire, arousal, orgasm, and pain.

- Lifelong sexual dysfunctions have always been experienced by the individual, and acquired sexual dysfunctions are those that are of recent onset.

- If sexual dysfunctions are apparent in all sexual situations, they are categorized as generalized, whereas when the problems are apparent in only one situation, they are known as situational.

- Sensate focus is a form of desensitization applied to sexual fears and anxiety.

- Gender can differ on many dimensions, including the following: chromosomal gender, gonadal gender, prenatal hormonal gender, internal accessory organs, external genital appearance, assigned gender, gender identity, and gender role.

- There are several paraphilic disorders that involve nonconsenting persons. Exhibitionistic disorder involves exposure of the genitals to an unsuspecting stranger, voyeuristic disorder entails secretly looking at naked people, and frotteuristic disorder is touching or rubbing against a nonconsenting person for the purpose of sexual pleasure.

- The DSM-5 does not include a formal paraphilic diagnosis to identify men who prefer sexual activity with a nonconsenting partner.

- To diagnose these individuals, clinicians often used the diagnosis of other specified paraphilic disorder and listed the descriptor of rape to explicate the type of mental disorder.

KEY TERMS

acquired sexual dysfunction (p. 326)

androgens (p. 330)

asphyxiophilia (p. 339)

autoerotic asphyxia (p. 339)

biastophilia (p. 343)

child molester (p. 342)

courtship disorder theory (p. 344)

delayed ejaculation (p. 327)

egodystonic homosexuality (p. 321)

erectile disorder (p. 330)

estrogen (p. 329)

exhibitionistic disorder (p. 340)

female orgasmic disorder (p. 327)

female sexual interest/arousal disorder (p. 326)

fetishistic disorder (p. 338)

frotteuristic disorder (p. 340)

gender dysphoria (p. 333)

gender identity (p. 333)

gender role (p. 333)

generalized sexual dysfunctions (p. 326)

genito-pelvic pain/penetration disorder (p. 327)

hypersexuality (p. 328)

hypoxyphilia (p. 339)

intersex (p. 333)

intracavernous treatment (p. 331)

lifelong sexual dysfunction (p. 326)

male hypoactive sexual desire disorder (p. 326)

paraphilias (p. 337)

paraphilic disorders (p. 338)

pedophile (p. 342)

pedophilic disorder (p. 340)

performance anxiety (p. 329)

premature (early) ejaculation (p. 327)

prolactin (p. 329)

sensate focus (p. 330)

sexual masochism (p. 339)

sexual response cycle (p. 322)

sexual sadism (p. 339)

situational sexual dysfunctions (p. 326)

testosterone (p. 329)

transvestite (p. 338)

voyeuristic disorder (p. 340)

JESSICA K. JONES

•

PATRICIA M. MINNES

•

MARJORY L. PHILLIPS

CHAPTER

14

Raysay/Shutterstock

Neurodevelopmental Disorders

LEARNING OBJECTIVES

AFTER READING THIS CHAPTER, STUDENTS WILL BE ABLE TO:

1 Explain the challenges of assessing the abilities of individuals with intellectual/developmental disorders.

2 Identify different ways that intellectual disabilities might be caused.

3 Identify variables that need to be measured when evaluating community integration and inclusion.

4 Explain varying prevalence rates for autism spectrum disorders.

5 Explain the cognitive impairments that are the defining features of specific learning disorders.

Joe proudly points to his baseball cap bearing a picture of Niagara Falls. He eagerly announces that he took a boat ride to the bottom of the Falls, went to the top of a tower in an elevator with windows, and had his own motel room next to Jim and Mary's room. Joe's delight is contagious; one cannot help but smile as he talks about the trip organized to celebrate his 50th birthday.

At age 12, Joe was sent to an institutional facility for individuals with disabilities when his parents could no longer manage his behaviour. His parents were older and lived in the country, a three-hour drive from the institution. Joe saw little of his family, and after a few years he lost contact altogether. He attended the institutional school and later worked in the vocational workshop. A psychological assessment at age 37 found Joe to have a mild developmental handicap. He was able to read, spell, add, and subtract at a primary school level. Joe had well-developed verbal expressive skills and good comprehension; and could manage personal care with limited supervision. Joe's major problem was his impulsivity and temper. Whenever his routine was changed, Joe would start shouting, swearing, and threatening. When Joe became particularly upset, he would bang his head and scratch himself. After taking psychotropic medication for many years to control these outbursts, Joe developed motor coordination problems that were thought to be side effects of the medication.

Joe's institution was scheduled to close in a few years, and his assessment indicated that he would be a good candidate for community living. So, after 25 years in the institution, he was moved to a new group home. He still worked daily in the facility workshop, and he would hang around the institution and hide from group home staff when it was time to go home. He continued to have outbursts of temper, and his shouting disturbed the neighbours. He would "borrow" other residents' things and become upset if they did not want to watch his television programs or listen to his favourite music. Joe would also bully a younger resident and would bother one of the female residents by standing close to her, stroking her arm, and staring at her.

Joe was enrolled in a program called Living with Others, through which he learned the importance of allowing personal space and strategies to manage anger. He practised relaxation exercises and met regularly with a psychologist to talk about his fears and concerns. The psychologist found that change and unexpected events triggered feelings of loss of control related to Joe's long history of abandonment. Joe's outbursts improved to the point where he no longer required regular medication to manage his anger.

Since he was unhappy at the group home, Joe was considered for a new program called Home-share, in which adults with developmental disabilities live with families in the community. On Joe's first weekend visit with Jim and Mary, he was anxious and became agitated on three occasions, but he was able to calm down in their large garden. After three more visits over the next two months, Joe asked if he could move in with Jim and Mary. Finding their house too quiet since their youngest son had left for university, Jim and Mary agreed. They were pleased with Joe's progress over the next few months and came to consider him a member of the family.

Historical Perspective

Throughout history, and particularly since the mid-nineteenth century, changing attitudes toward people with developmental disabilities have been reflected in policies and models of service delivery (Wolfensberger, 1975).

For centuries, such people were regarded as subhuman, a menace, or an object of dread. Even today, people with developmental disabilities may be given lower priority for services than others or excluded from medical and surgical interventions.

Between 1870 and 1890, attitudes shifted toward viewing people with disabilities as objects of pity, burdens

Moron
Mentally 10–12 years old

High Grade Imbecile
Mentally 8–10 years old

Medium Imbecile
Mentally 6–8 years old

Low Grade Imbecile
Mentally 4–5 years old

This illustration, taken from The Survey, displays the places where different grades of Mentally Defective persons "stop and can go no farther." Steps in mental development illustrate where they "stumble"; the limit of a development in each type is presented as a "staircase whose trends were occupied by individuals assigned on the basis of supposed levels of innate intelligence."

Idiot
Mentally 3 years and under

FIGURE 14.1 1914 Classification of Mentally Defective Individuals

Source: Ontario Sessional Papers (1914) 23:72.

of charity, and "holy innocents" (Wolfensberger, 1975). Asylums were built to protect them. However, in the later nineteenth and early twentieth century, genealogical studies by Goddard (1912) and others emphasized that mental retardation was inherited. People with disabilities came to be viewed as a threat to the moral and intellectual fibre of society; the growing **eugenics** movement called for segregation, sterilization, the restriction of marriages, and institutionalization to protect society from this threat. Further, some argued that without segregation they would taint regular society with their criminogenic ways due to the believed association between disabilities and crime (Trent, 1994).

The *medical model* dominated the first half of the twentieth century. Increasing numbers of individuals, then known as the mentally retarded, were viewed as needing continual medical care and were thus institutionalized. However, few institutions were able to provide more than custodial care for the growing numbers of residents. As institutions became more crowded and under resourced, challenging behaviours became increasingly difficult for staff, and medication became the treatment of choice.

The late 1950s and early 1960s represented a time of major change in the field of developmental disabilities. The publication of *Christmas in Purgatory* (Blatt & Kaplan, 1966), including photos of the appalling living conditions in institutions (Blatt & Kaplan, 1966), led to litigation and eventually the closure of institutions. At the same time, interest in environmental influences on behaviour and the rise of

behaviourism led to the application of applied behavioural analysis in educational programs. For the first time, people with mental retardation were viewed as able to learn regardless of the degree of disability.

Gradually, the medical model was replaced by the social philosophy of *normalization,* and changing attitudes were reflected in policies promoting the ethical use of least intrusive practices and minimally restrictive environments.

From the 1960s to the present, deinstitutionalization, educational mainstreaming, and community-based services have been major goals. People with developmental disabilities have gained increasing visibility through media coverage of the Special Olympics, and through television and films that increase public exposure and awareness. In the 1990s self-advocacy movements grew through organizations such as People First and the National Association of Retarded Citizens in the United States (Shogren & Broussard, 2011). Since 2000, people with intellectual disabilities have become increasingly visible in the community, engaging in socially valued roles. Actors with intellectual disabilities have appeared in films and on television (see the Applied Clinical Case). While attitudes toward people with intellectual disabilities seem to be increasingly positive, negative attitudes continue to occur and reflect the need for ongoing education to improve awareness, increase comfort, and reduce stigma (Brown & Percy, 2011). One recent example of positive public education is a British television series called *The Special Needs Hotel.* This program, which premiered on CBC television in 2016, follows young people with developmental disabilities who are attending Foxes Academy to learn hospitality skills needed to work in a large hotel.

A Note About Terminology

Neurodevelopmental disorders are a heterogeneous group of disabilities. There may be unusual physical features; deficits in language, motor ability, and other functional skills; and patterns of behaviour such as impulsivity, hyperactivity, aggressiveness, or **stereotypy** (the repetition of meaningless gestures or movements). The terminology associated with intellectual and developmental disorders varies across jurisdictions and can be confusing. In recent years, the term **intellectual disability** (ID) has been increasingly adopted in Canada, Europe, and Australia. The United States adopted the term *intellectual disability* relatively recently after widespread debate (Schalock, 2002; Smith, 2002). The term *intellectual disability* (*intellectual developmental disorder*) replaced the term *mental retardation* in the DSM-5 under the umbrella category of neurodevelopmental disorders (APA, 2013; see Table 14.1). In Britain, the longstanding term *learning disability* has replaced the previous term *mental handicap*. This term can be confusing, as the term *learning disability* when used in North America refers to a specific learning disorder (e.g., in reading, writing, arithmetic), whereas in Britain it refers to an intellectual or developmental disability. In Canada, the term *developmental disability* is often used interchangeably with *intellectual disability*, but in the United States the term *developmental disability* has a broader definition in that individuals may have mental or a physical impairment or a combination of these. For the ease of reading and purposes of this section, assume that the terms *intellectual disability*, *developmental disability*, and *mental retardation* are synonymous.

TABLE 14.1 DSM-5 DIAGNOSTIC CRITERIA FOR INTELLECTUAL DISABILITY (INTELLECTUAL DEVELOPMENTAL DISORDER)

Intellectual disability (intellectual developmental disorder) is a disorder with onset during the developmental period that includes both intellectual and adaptive functioning deficits in conceptual, social, and practical domains. The following three criteria must be met:

A. Deficits in intellectual functions, such as reasoning, problem solving, planning, abstract thinking, judgment, academic learning, and learning from experience, confirmed by both clinical assessment and individualized, standardized intelligence testing.

B. Deficits in adaptive functioning that result in failure to meet developmental and socio-cultural standards for personal independence and social responsibility. Without ongoing support, the adaptive deficits limit functioning in one or more activities of daily life, such as communication, social participation, and independent living, across multiple environments, such as home, school, work, and community.

C. Onset of intellectual and adaptive deficits during the developmental period.

Source: Reprinted with permission from the *Diagnostic and Statistical Manual of Mental Disorders, Fifth Edition.* (Copyright © 2013). American Psychiatric Association. All Rights Reserved.

Intellectual Disability

PREVALENCE

The prevalence of intellectual disability (ID) is difficult to determine. Many studies report "ascertained" or "administrative" prevalence rates, which refer to the numbers of cases found in official records. However, these numbers are not accurate in that they do not include the total number of persons with developmental disabilities in the population but

---

APPLIED CLINICAL CASE

Actors with Disabilities

Chris Burke was one of the first people with Down syndrome to work as an actor. Burke first acted in the ABC movie *Desperate* and then played the main role of Corky in the television show *Life Goes On*. He also made guest appearances on *Touched by an Angel* as Taylor, an angel who has Down syndrome.

Burke is a frequent inspirational speaker and travels as a goodwill ambassador for the National Down Syndrome Society (NDSS). He is also editor-in-chief of the NDSS quarterly magazine, *Straight Talk*. Burke published his autobiography, *A Special Kind of Hero*, in 1991, as well as a chapter entitled "Believe in Yourself" in the 1999 book *Down Syndrome: A Promising Future, Together*, edited by T. J. Hassold & D. Patterson.

Source: http://en.wikipedia.org/wiki/Chris_Burke_(actor).

Andrew H. Walker/Getty Images Entertainment/ Getty Images

rather those who are known to service agencies. National health studies in the UK have suggested that although individuals with intellectual disabilities are approximately 2 percent of the general population, support services actually know of a substantially smaller proportion of the adult population (Emerson, Hatton, Robertson, et al., 2011). To determine true prevalence, the number of individuals born with developmental disabilities and mortality rates are required (Roeleveld, Zielhuis, & Gabreels, 1997). The data available are also problematic due to the varying definitions used within studies and sample differences as a result of age, gender, and ethnicity (Leonard & Wen, 2002). The majority of statistics are based on U.S. samples, and statistics also vary depending on the classification system and the measures used. The World Health Organization (WHO) cites the true prevalence rate of what is now defined as intellectual disability in industrialized countries as 3%. However, American researchers debate whether the figure should be 1 or 3% (Munro, 1986) and UK researchers utilize 2% as their prevalence rate. The administrative data from Canadian provincial studies (Health and Welfare Canada, 1988) suggest a prevalence of at least 8 per 1000 altogether across all age groups, with approximately half (4 per 1000) falling within the mild range (IQ 50 to 70) and the other half falling within the severe range of intellectual disability (IQ less than 50).

Diagnostic Issues

Although intellectual functioning, or IQ as measured by standardized tests, is the most basic criterion for intellectual disability, there have been important changes in the definition and criteria over the years.

These criteria now comprise the level of IQ required and the inclusion of deficits in adaptive behaviour. In North America, the American Association on Mental Retardation (AAMR), founded in 1876 and now known as the American Association on Intellectual and Developmental Disabilities (AAIDD, Schalock, Luckasson, & Shogren, 2007), has strongly influenced the definition and classification of

intellectual disability through the publication of classification manuals since 1921.

Traditionally, intellectual functioning has been determined on the basis of psychometric testing and IQ scores (see Chapter 4). As shown in Figure 14.2, IQ scores are normally distributed, with a mean of 100 and a standard deviation of 15.

The choice of diagnostic cut-off point, however, has been somewhat arbitrary and has changed several times over the years (Zigler & Hodapp, 1991). For example, for many years, IQ scores falling two standard deviations below the mean were considered to be within the intellectually disabled range. Scores within this range were divided into four subcategories: mild (IQ 50–55 to 70), moderate (IQ 35–40 to 50), severe (IQ 20–25 to 35), and profound (IQ less than 20). Then in 1959 the fifth edition of the AAMR classification manual (Heber, 1959) raised the cut-off to one standard deviation below the mean (IQ less than 85) and created a fifth level called "borderline." These changes raised the prevalence of intellectual disability from approximately 3 to 16 percent of the population, leading to increased demands on services for persons with disabilities. In 1973 the cut-off was returned to 70; in 1992 it was raised slightly to 75 (plus or minus 5 points) to accommodate errors in measurement.

Since the 1980s, the diagnosis of what is now called intellectual disability has required an additional assessment of independent functioning or adaptive behaviour as well as IQ testing. Adaptive behaviour encompasses conceptual, social, and practical abilities, including areas of communication; self-care; domestic, academic, social, or community leisure and work skills.

A number of other descriptive changes have been introduced in recent editions of the AAMR classification system. The approach is more positive, with criteria representing a broader, more ecological perspective. The level of functioning is seen to represent not only the strengths and capabilities of the individual but also the environmental support or services available to that person (Schalock et al., 1994). Thus, rather than diagnosing someone as having "moderate intellectual disability," which gives the impression of a fixed

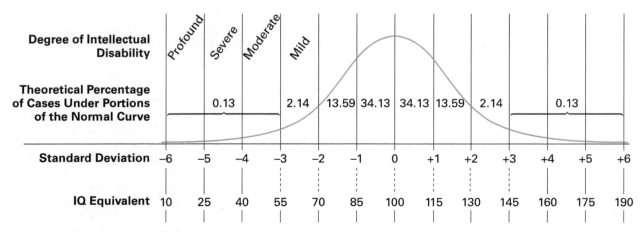

FIGURE 14.2 Distribution of IQ Scores

state, the diagnosis might read, in part, "able to complete activities of daily living with limited support." In 2010 the AAIDD introduced its most recent definition of intellectual disability that highlights the multi-dimensional relationships among individual functioning, support, participation, health, and environment (Schalock et al., 2010). These changes have been incorporated into the DSM-5 in tables addressing severity levels of intellectual disability (see Table 14.2).

TABLE 14.2   SEVERITY LEVELS FOR INTELLECTUAL DISABILITY (INTELLECTUAL DEVELOPMENTAL DISORDER)

Severity Level	Conceptual domain	Social domain	Practical domain
Mild	For preschool children, there may be no obvious conceptual differences. For school-age children and adults, there are difficulties in learning academic skills involving reading, writing, arithmetic, time, or money, with support needed in one or more areas to meet age-related expectations. In adults, abstract thinking, executive function (i.e., planning, strategizing, priority setting, and cognitive flexibility), and short-term memory, as well as functional use of academic skills (e.g., reading, money management), are impaired. There is a somewhat concrete approach to problems and solutions compared with age-mates.	Compared with typically developing agemates, the individual is immature in social interactions. For example, there may be difficulty in accurately perceiving peers' social cues. Communication, conversation, and language are more concrete or immature than expected for age. There may be difficulties regulating emotion and behavior in age-appropriate fashion; these difficulties are noticed by peers in social situations. There is limited understanding of risk in social situations; social judgment is immature for age, and the person is at risk of being manipulated by others (gullibility).	The individual may function age-appropriately in personal care. Individuals need some support with complex daily living tasks in comparison to peers. In adulthood, supports typically involve grocery shopping, transportation, home and child-care organizing, nutritious food preparation, and banking and money management. Recreational skills resemble those of age-mates, although judgment related to well-being and organization around recreation requires support. In adulthood, competitive employment is often seen in jobs that do not emphasize conceptual skills. Individuals generally need support to make health care decisions and legal decisions, and to learn to perform a skilled vocation competently. Support is typically needed to raise a family.
Moderate	All through development, the individual's conceptual skills lag markedly behind those of peers. For preschoolers, language and pre-academic skills develop slowly. For school-age children, progress in reading, writing, mathematics, and understanding of time and money occurs slowly across the school years and is markedly limited compared with that of peers. For adults, academic skill development is typically at an elementary level, and support is required for all use of academic skills in work and personal life. Ongoing assistance on a daily basis is needed to complete conceptual tasks of day-to-day life, and others may take over these responsibilities fully for the individual.	The individual shows marked differences from peers in social and communicative behavior across development. Spoken language is typically a primary tool for social communication but is much less complex than that of peers. Capacity for relationships is evident in ties to family and friends, and the individual may have successful friendships across life and sometimes romantic relations in adulthood. However, individuals may not perceive or interpret social cues accurately. Social judgment and decision-making abilities are limited; and caretakers must assist the person with life decisions. Friendships with typically developing peers are often affected by communication or social limitations. Significant social and communicative support is needed in work settings' for success.	The individual can care for personal needs involving eating, dressing, elimination, and hygiene as an adult, although an extended period of teaching and time is needed for the individual to become independent in these areas, and reminders may be needed. Similarly, participation in all household tasks can be achieved by adulthood, although an extended period of teaching is needed, and ongoing supports will typically occur for adult-level performance. Independent employment in jobs that require limited conceptual and communication skills can be achieved, but considerable support from co-workers, supervisors, and others is needed to manage social expectations, job complexities, and ancillary responsibilities such as scheduling, transportation, health benefits, and money management. A variety of recreational skills can be developed. These typically require additional supports and learning opportunities over an extended period of time. Maladaptive behavior is present in a significant minority and causes social problems.

(Continued)

Severity Level	Conceptual domain	Social domain	Practical domain
Severe	Attainment of conceptual skills is limited. This individual generally has little understanding of written language or of concepts involving numbers, quantity, time, and money. Caretakers provide extensive supports for problem solving throughout life.	Spoken language is quite limited in terms of vocabulary and grammar. Speech may be single words or phrases and may be supplemented through augmentative means. Speech and communication are focused on the here and now within everyday events. Language is used for social communication more than for explication. Individuals understand simple speech and gestural communication. Relationships with family members and familiar others are a source of pleasure and help.	The individual requires support for all activities of daily living, including meals, dressing, bathing, and elimination. The individual requires supervision at all times. The individual cannot make responsible decisions regarding well-being of self or others. In adulthood, participation in tasks at home, recreation, and work requires ongoing support and assistance. Skill acquisition in all domains involves long-term teaching and ongoing support. Maladaptive behavior, including self-injury, is present in a significant minority.
Profound	Conceptual skills generally involve the physical world rather than symbolic processes. The individual may use objects in goal-directed fashion for self-care, work, and recreation. Certain visuospatial skills, such as matching and sorting based on physical characteristics, may be acquired. However, co-occurring motor and sensory impairments may prevent functional use of objects.	The individual has very limited understanding of symbolic communication in speech or gesture. He or she may understand some simple instructions or gestures. The individual expresses his or her own desires and emotions largely through nonverbal, nonsymbolic communication. The individual enjoys relationships with well-known family members, caretakers, and familiar other, and initiates and responds to social interactions through gestural and emotional cues. Co-occurring sensory and physical impairments may prevent many social activities.	The individual is dependent on others for all aspects of daily physical care, health, and safety, although he or she may be able to participate in some of these activities as well. Individuals without severe physical impairments may assist with some daily work tasks at home, like carrying dishes to the table. Simple actions with objects may be the basis of participation in some vocational activities with high levels of ongoing support. Recreational activities may involve, for example, enjoyment in listening to music, watching movies, going out for walks, or participating in water activities, all with the support of others. Co-occurring physical and sensory impairments are frequent barriers to participation (beyond watching) in home, recreational, and vocational activities. Maladaptive behavior is present in a significant minority.

Source: Reprinted with permission from the Diagnostic and Statistical Manual of Mental Disorders, Fifth Edition. (Copyright © 2013). American Psychiatric Association. All Rights Reserved.

THE CHALLENGES OF ASSESSING INTELLIGENCE

Although classification systems such as those adopted by the DSM and AAIDD place heavy emphasis on the level of IQ or intellectual quotient, the use of IQ tests has been the subject of considerable controversy in recent years. First, such tests were not devised to take into account sensory, motor, and language deficits, which can contribute to poor performance. Second, when people have had sheltered or limited experiences because of their disability or when they have lived in isolated institutions, their testing performance may be biased because the test environment is unnatural and unfamiliar, and the examining situation may be overwhelming. They may not be motivated or understand what is expected of them or may not take the initiative to solve problems (Zigler, Hodapp, & Edison, 1990). For these reasons, intellectual quotient scores may not accurately reflect people's overall intellectual functioning or cognitive abilities. Moreover, it is questionable whether scores on the lower end of the scale are valid because the major intelligence tests such as the Wechsler Scales and early editions of the Stanford-Binet were not standardized on people with IQ scores lower than 70. However, a number of changes to the fifth edition of the Stanford-Binet Intelligence Scales (Roid, 2003) have made it a more useful instrument in evaluating older children and adults with disabilities.

MEASURING ADAPTIVE BEHAVIOUR

The assessment of adaptive behaviour or level of independent functioning has added greatly to the utility of psychological assessments. Measures used to assess adaptive behaviour include the Vineland Adaptive Behavior Scales Third Edition 2006 (Sparrow, Cicchetti, & Saulnier, 2016), the Adaptive Behavior Assessment System Third Edition (ABAS-3;

Harrison & Oakland, 2015), and the Scales of Independent Behavior-Revised (Bruininks, Woodcock, Weatherman, & Hill, 1996). Most scales can be completed during interviews with parents, teachers, or caregivers, but some versions can be filled in by survey or used as an informant checklist.

Adaptive behaviours or daily living skills are generally clustered under four domains: communication (i.e., expressive, receptive, and written language), daily living or personal living skills (e.g., eating, dressing, personal hygiene, domestic, and community living skills), socialization or social interaction skills (e.g., interpersonal relationships, coping, leisure skills), and motor skills (e.g., gross movement, fine motor coordination). Other measures of adaptive behaviour are evaluated in assessing activities of daily living (e.g. walking, eating) and instrumental activities of daily living (e.g. cooking, driving). On some measures of adaptive behaviour challenging behaviours or maladaptive behaviours are also identified.

INTERVIEWING STRATEGIES

Gathering information from people with developmental disorders is an important aspect of any clinical assessment. However, the reliability of the information gathered is critical (Finlay & Lyons, 2001). Unfortunately, it is often assumed that people with disabilities cannot give reliable information. On the other hand, some may err by assuming the opposite (Wyngaarden, 1981). When obtaining information from caregivers or family, caution should be applied as they may inevitably also provide biased information influenced by their experiences. Seminal work by Edgerton (1967, 1993), an anthropologist, noted the tendency to overestimate higher functioning individuals with disabilities by their "normal" appearance and verbal abilities. He emphasized the stigma of the disability and the need that disabled persons felt to deny their cognitive handicap and attempt to pass as normal in society; he referred to this phenomenon as the **"cloak of competence."** Another area of concern is **acquiescence**, or the tendency of individuals with developmental disorders to answer affirmatively or agree in interviews (Finlay & Lyons, 2002). Several factors can contribute to acquiescence, including social desirability, particularly to a person in authority, motivational and personality factors, as well as cognitive and linguistic limitations. However, the wording or sentence structure used in questions may also play an important role. To improve the reliability of answers given in interviews, research has indicated that interviewers should use different types of questions, such as yes–no, forced choice, or, on occasion, open-ended, while also giving the person an opportunity to answer "I don't know" (Finlay & Lyons, 2002). Alternative formats such as drawing or picture response cards to supplement an interview can also be helpful. At the same time, it is important to provide comprehension checks and systematically check for response bias (Sigelman et al., 1981). A number of studies have found individuals with disabilities are at greater risk for suggestibility when interviewed due to acquiescence, poor memory, and low self-esteem (Gudjonsson, Murphy, & Clare, 2000).

❶ BEFORE MOVING ON

Intelligence testing and standardized interviews have frequently been criticized as putting individuals with developmental disabilities at a disadvantage compared to their non-disabled peers. Given what you know about the abilities of people with different types of developmental disabilities, what precautions would you suggest that clinicians take when assessing such individuals?

Etiology

Neurodevelopmental disorders have many causes. Some have clear organic causes; some relate to environmental factors; some reflect an interaction between genetics and environment. For example, damage due to an environmental toxin will have different effects on a child, depending on inherited factors such as temperament or birth weight. Conversely, genetically based disorders can have different outcomes depending on the availability of medical and educational services. It is not possible in this chapter to provide comprehensive coverage of all causes of neurodevelopmental disorders. Therefore, a number of disorders have been selected to represent different types of damage occurring at different stages of development. A more detailed list of examples is outlined in Table 14.3.

GENETIC CAUSES

There has been a revolution in the field of genetics for the last decade or so. With developments in technology our understanding of genetic causes of developmental disabilities has grown exponentially. At the same time, we have discovered that the genetic underpinnings of these disorders are much more complex than we initially thought. In addition to major chromosomal abnormalities such as Down syndrome and Fragile X syndrome that were diagnosed through microscopic examination of cells, we now have techniques to identify small pieces of chromosomes that are either missing or duplicated. These pieces are called copy number variations or CNVs and are associated with developmental disabilities. Tests called microarrays used to identify these changes are available clinically and yield 10 to 20% positive results among people with ID. We have technology available now that can examine the full sequence of a person's DNA and as a result tests can be conducted to detect mutations that affect one or a small number of nucleotides in the DNA. All together these techniques can diagnose a genetic cause for approximately 55 to 70% of moderate to severe ID. These mutations can be inherited or spontaneous (Vissers, Gilissen, & Veltman, 2016). The genetics of mild intellectual disability is less well studied and understood. Approximately, 14% of developmental disabilities associated with mild intellectual deficits also have a genetic basis (Percy, Lewkis, & Brown, 2003).

With greater understanding of the genetic causes of developmental disabilities, researchers and clinicians hope to be able to develop improved diagnostic procedures. However,

TABLE 14.3 DISORDERS ASSOCIATED WITH INTELLECTUAL DISABILITY

Prenatal Causes	Perinatal Causes	Postnatal Causes
A. Chromosomal Abnormalities	**A. Intrauterine Disorders**	**A. Head or Brain Injuries**
1. Autosomes	1. Placental insufficiency	1. Cerebral concussion
Trisomy 21 (Down syndrome)	a. Placenta previa/hemorrhage	2. Cerebral contusion or laceration
Translocation 21 (Down syndrome)	b. Toxemia/eclampsia	3. Intracranial hemorrhage
2. X-Linked	2. Abnormal labour/delivery	**B. Infections**
Fragile X syndrome	a. Prematurity	1. Encephalitis
3. Other X chromosome disorders	b. Premature rupture of membranes	a. Herpes simplex
XO syndrome (Turner)	c. Abnormal presentation, for example, breech	b. Measles
XYY syndrome	3. Obstetrical trauma	c. HIV
XXY syndrome (Klinefelter)	4. Multiple birth	2. Meningitis
B. Metabolic Disorders	**B. Neonatal Disorders**	a. Streptococcus pneumonia
1. Amino acid disorders	1. Hypoxia	b. Influenza type B
Phenylketonuria (PKU)	2. Intracranial hemorrhage	**C. Seizure Disorders**
2. Carbohydrate disorders	3. Neonatal seizures	**D. Toxic-Metabolic Poisons**
Galactosemia	4. Respiratory disorders	1. Lead
3. Nucleic acid disorders	5. Infections	2. Mercury
Lesch-Nyhan disease	a. Meningitis	**E. Malnutrition**
C. Neural Tube Defects	b. Encephalitis	**F. Environmental Deprivation**
1. Anencephaly	c. Septicemia	1. Abuse
2. Spina bifida	6. Head trauma at birth	2. Neglect
D. Environmental Factors		
1. Intrauterine malnutrition		
a. Maternal malnutrition		
b. Placental insufficiency		
2. Drugs, toxins, teratogens		
a. Thalidomide		
b. Alcohol		
c. Cocaine		
d. Methylmercury		
e. Radiation		
3. Maternal diseases		
a. Diabetes mellitus		
b. Rubella		
c. Syphilis		
d. Toxoplasmosis		
e. Cytomegalovirus		
f. Hypothyroidism		

Source: Based on American Association on Mental Retardation. (1992). *Mental retardation: Definition, classification and systems of support* (9th ed.). Washington, DC: Author.

such advances also raise complex ethical, legal, and social issues associated with new approaches to prevention and intervention (Percy et al., 2003). Research has highlighted behavioural and neurocognitive patterns as well as different developmental pathways for different genetically related disorders (Dykens, Hodapp, & Finucane, 2000). **Behavioural phenotypes** (the pattern of social, cognitive, and behavioural abnormalities) have been described for a particular number of disabilities. Current research is now focused on neuropathological mechanisms related to specific behavioural characteristics and potential pharmacological treatments (Hagerman,

River, & Hagerman, 2008). Further, the area of epigenetics is expanding genome research with the study of changes caused by modification of gene expression rather than alteration of the genetic code itself.

AN OVERVIEW OF GENETICS Essentially, the traits we inherit from our parents are carried by thousands of genes found in each of our cells. Genes are found in specific positions on chromosomes. Each human cell contains 23 pairs of chromosomes, each pair including one chromosome from each parent. Forty-four of these are matching and called autosomes.

The additional two are called the sex chromosomes. Females have two X chromosomes; males have an X and a Y chromosome. An X chromosome is contributed during conception by the mother, and either an X or a Y is contributed by the father (Patton, Payne, & Beirne-Smith, 1986).

Developmental disorders may be caused by single or multiple genes alone or in association with environmental factors. Single gene disorders are less common than disorders caused by multiple genes (Percy et al., 2007).

There are three types of inheritance: dominant, recessive, and sex-linked or X-linked. In dominant inheritance, if one parent of either sex has a defective gene, that gene "assumes 'control' over or masks its partner gene and therefore will operate whether an individual gene pair is similar or dissimilar" (Patton et al., 1986, p. 164). A child has a 50% chance of inheriting either the defective or the normal gene from the parent with the defective gene. Examples of dominant inheritance that may lead to intellectual disability are tuberous sclerosis and neurofibromatosis. In recessive inheritance, genes "in a sense 'recede' when paired with a dissimilar mate and therefore only are influential when matched with another recessive gene" carrying the same trait (Patton et al., 1986, p. 164). Therefore, both parents need to carry a defective gene for the disorder to occur. There is a 25% chance that two copies of the defective gene will be inherited and the child will be affected, a 50% chance that the child will be a carrier of the disorder (i.e., the child carries one defective gene but may not display signs of the disorder), and a 25% chance that the child will not be affected and not be a carrier (Percy et al., 2007). Disorders associated with recessive inheritance include phenylketonuria, Tay-Sachs disease, and galactosemia.

In X-or sex-linked inheritance, the abnormal gene is carried on the X chromosome. In females, the gene is generally recessive and will operate only when it appears on both X chromosomes. Disorders transmitted in this way therefore primarily affect males, who have only one X chromosome; the Y chromosome is not able to dominate or override the trait. A male child has a 50 percent chance of being affected. There is a 50 percent chance that a female child will carry the defective gene, but the degree to which she is affected is relatively limited. X-linked disorders associated with intellectual disability include Fragile X syndrome (described later in this chapter) and Lesch-Nyhan syndrome.

Inherited disorders can be identified through a blood test. Genetic screening can also determine whether both parents (in the case of recessive disorders) or the mother (in the case of X-linked disorders) carries an abnormal gene and runs the risk of bearing a child with the disorder. For example, since Tay-Sachs disease is found largely among Jews of Eastern European ancestry, some Jewish couples undergo testing before trying to conceive.

CHROMOSOMAL ABNORMALITIES Chromosomal disorders occur as a result of a structural alteration in the chromosome or due to a person having a greater or smaller number of chromosomes. Although chromosomal abnormalities are genetically related, they are not inherited and occur spontaneously at conception. The best-known chromosomal abnormality associated with intellectual disability is **Down syndrome**, first described by Langdon Down in 1866. In 1959 the genetic link was discovered by Jerome Lejeune and his colleagues. There are three types of Down syndrome. The most common is **trisomy 21**, which occurs in 95 percent of cases of Down syndrome. Whereas the normal human cell has 23 pairs of chromosomes, one chromosome in each pair provided by each parent, in Down syndrome there is an extra chromosome on pair 21. Thus, persons with Down syndrome have 47 rather than 46 chromosomes. Trisomy 21 occurs in approximately 1 in 700 live births, with a larger proportion occurring in older mothers. The incidence increases dramatically from approximately 1 in 350 for women between the ages of 35 and 39 to 1 in 100 after age 40 (Baroff, 1986). More recently, research has indicated that the risk of Down syndrome may increase when the father is over 40, regardless of the mother's age (Hook, Cross, & Regal, 1990; see Figure 14.3). Down syndrome is discussed in more detail later in this chapter.

Two other causes of Down syndrome are **translocation** and **mosaicism**. In the former, part of the twenty-first chromosome breaks off and attaches to another. This occurs in approximately 4 percent of cases. This type of anomaly is not associated with maternal age. In mosaicism, cell division occurs unevenly, so that some cells have 45 chromosomes and some have 47. This type occurs in only 1 percent of cases. Whereas individuals with Down syndrome due to translocation have all the features found in trisomy 21, people with mosaic Down syndrome may have fewer physical characteristics, better speech, and higher intellectual functioning, depending on the number of cells affected.

PRENATAL SCREENING Prenatal screening for chromosomal and other abnormalities is possible through a number

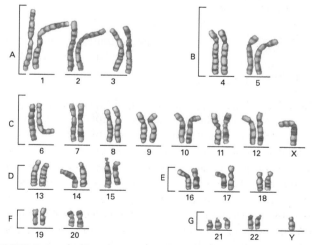

FIGURE 14.3 Chromosomes of a Person with Down Syndrome

Karyotype (a type of diagram developed from photomicrographs of chromosomes) of a person with the most common type of Down syndrome, showing the third chromosome at pair 21.

of methods. Maternal serum screening (MSS) is carried out through a blood test 15 to 20 weeks into the pregnancy. MSS detects alpha-fetoprotein (AFP) as well as two hormones produced by the placenta. The levels of these substances can help identify women at higher risk of having babies with chromosomal abnormalities such as Down syndrome or neural tube defects such as spina bifida (Wald et al., 1992).

The nuchal translucency (NT) test may also be carried out with women who are at risk of having a baby with Down syndrome (e.g., women over 35 years). The test is usually done between 10 and 14 weeks. The test involves measurement of the amount of fluid at the back of the fetus's neck through ultrasound. If increased levels of AFP following MSS or increased fluid levels following NT are detected, indicating greater risk of fetal abnormality, follow-up tests such as amniocentesis are usually recommended (Borruto, Comparetto, Acanfora, Bertini, & Rubaltelli, 2002).

Amniocentesis is a procedure conducted between the eleventh and eighteenth weeks of pregnancy. With the assistance of ultrasound, a needle is inserted into the amniotic sac via the pregnant woman's abdomen. A small amount of amniotic fluid is withdrawn, and cells contained in the fluid are then cultured in the lab. Studies of amniocentesis indicate diagnostic accuracy of up to 99.4 percent, with the estimated risk of complications such as infection or miscarriage being approximately 0.5 percent greater than in pregnancies without amniocentesis (Baroff, 1986).

A test known as **chorionic villus sampling (CVS)** involves obtaining cells from the placenta. Minor complications such as cramping or vaginal bleeding occur more frequently following CVS than amniocentesis and the overall miscarriage rate is somewhat higher (2 to 5 percent) than after amniocentesis. However, figures for transcervical as opposed to transabdominal CVS are quite low at approximately 1 percent (Machalek, Brown, Birkan, Fung, & Percy, 2003). This test can be carried out earlier, between the tenth and twelfth weeks of pregnancy. If a chromosomal abnormality is found, the parents may choose to terminate the pregnancy.

Over the last few years, a new screening technique has been developed. In this approach, circulating fetal DNA in the mother's serum is tested for many conditions including some associated with developmental disabilities (Mackie, Hemming, Allen, Morris, & Kilby, 2017). These techniques can also identify inherited genetic abnormalities. Prenatal screening techniques are advocated by those in favour of preventing developmental disabilities, but opposed by many others who advocate for the basic rights of people with disabilities.

METABOLIC DISORDERS Phenylketonuria (**PKU**) is the best known of several rare metabolic disorders that can cause intellectual disability. PKU has been described as an "inborn error of metabolism." It is caused by an autosomal recessive gene occurring in approximately 1 in 10 000 to 15 000 live births in North America (Harris, 1995). As a result of a recessive gene passed on from each parent, a liver enzyme localized on chromosome 12 is inactive, causing an inability to process or metabolize the amino acid phenylalanine. This substance builds up in the brain to toxic levels, leading to intellectual disability (Cheetham, Gitta, & Morrison, 2003).

PKU is now detected through a blood test shortly after birth. Affected infants are given a low-phenylalanine diet, which includes primarily fruits and vegetables and eliminates most protein-rich foods such as fish, meat, and eggs. Protein required for development is provided through a special dietary supplement. Follow-up studies indicate that children started on the diet before three months of age will function intellectually within the normal range whereas untreated children often have moderate to severe intellectual disability (Dobson, Kushida, Williamson, & Friedman, 1976). Although there is general agreement that a low-phenylalanine diet should be started as soon as possible within the first few weeks of life, there is little agreement regarding when to stop the diet. As many foods contain phenylalanine, it is difficult for school-aged children and adolescents to adhere to the diet, but if the diet has been followed during the preschool years, the most damaging effects of the disorder will have already been prevented. However, research has documented a decrease in abilities following discontinuation of the diet (Koch et al., 1996) and medical researchers have begun to recommend that the diet be maintained across the lifespan (Merrick, Aspler, & Schwartz, 2001). Canadian support groups continue to advocate for government funding for coverage of specialized diets into adulthood (*http://canpku.org*).

Other metabolic disorders include congenital hypothyroidism, hyperammonemia, Gaucher's disease, and Hurler's syndrome. Congenital hypothyroidism occurs in approximately 1 in 4000 newborns and can be detected through a screening test at birth. If not treated through replacement of the hormone thyroxine, children will be small and have poor muscle tone and severe intellectual disability (Cheetham et al., 2003). Hyperammonemia, which occurs in 1 in 30 000 children, involves a deficiency in the enzyme that normally transforms the neurotoxic ammonia (produced when protein is broken down into component amino acids) into urea, which is excreted in the urine. If this process does not take place, ammonia builds up and brain damage or death may occur. Treatment through dietary regulation is less effective than in PKU. Gaucher's disease and Hurler's syndrome also involve deficient enzymes. Both are progressive neurological disorders associated with intellectual disability and early mortality. Treatment through enzyme replacement frequently has only limited success (Cheetham et al., 2003).

ENVIRONMENTAL CAUSES

THE PRENATAL ENVIRONMENT Developmental disability can result if the fetus is exposed to toxins or infections or if the blood supply lacks nutrients or oxygen. Maternal health, therefore, is very important. Inadequate nutrition; the use of alcohol, tobacco, or drugs; infections such as rubella or AIDS; and exposure to radiation can all affect infant development (Durkin, 2002).

Maternal Infections. **Rubella** (also known as German measles) during the first three months of pregnancy can lead to intellectual disability, visual defects, deafness, heart disease, and other problems. Fortunately, the incidence of rubella-related problems has declined with routine vaccination.

HIV. In the past 20 years, the number of children reported to have **HIV** has increased dramatically. Developmental delays or disabilities occur in 75 to 90 percent of children with HIV who do not receive appropriate treatment (Durkin, 2002; Renwick, Goldie, & King, 1999). HIV can be transmitted from mother to infant during pregnancy and delivery, or through breast milk. According to Canadian statistics, HIV was transmitted from mother to child in 78 percent of children with HIV from birth to age 14 (Health Canada, 1998). A child with HIV may display symptoms including poor growth, recurring diarrhea and fevers, feeding problems, respiratory problems, and pain. Other symptoms affecting the brain and spinal cord include delayed growth and development, cognitive delays and memory problems, distractibility, language and motor impairments, social skill deficits, behavioural problems, and loss of earlier attained developmental milestones (Renwick et al., 1999).

Fetal Alcohol Spectrum Disorder (FASD). Alcohol consumption during pregnancy can lead to a number of defects of varying degrees. Prenatal and postnatal growth retardation and central nervous system dysfunction are common. Figure 14.4 shows the typical facial features of a child with **fetal alcohol syndrome disorder (FASD),** including short eye openings, an elongated, flattened area between the mouth and nose, thin upper lip, and flattened cheeks and nasal bridge. Head circumference is frequently below the third percentile. Cleft palate, heart and kidney damage, and vision defects are also found (Chudley et al., 2005).

FASD is one of the most common known causes of intellectual disability, found in 1 to 3 per 1000 live births

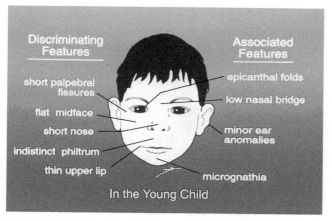

FIGURE 14.4 The Facial Features of a Child with Fetal Alcohol Syndrome

Source: The Facial Features of Fetal Alcohol Syndrome, Ann Pytkowicz Streissguth, © 1994, in Alcohol use and its medical consequences: a comprehensive teaching program for biomedical education. Unit 5, Alcohol: pregnancy and the fetal alcohol syndrome (2nd ed). Milner-Fenwick, Timonium, Md. 1994.

(Streissguth & O'Malley, 2000). FASD is the term recently adopted (CMAJ; Cook et al., 2016) following recognition of the wider spectrum of disabilities and presentations seen with and without the overt physical dysmorphology associated with the disorder. It is believed to affect 1 in 100 Canadians. The fact that infants born to alcoholic mothers do not always exhibit FASD dysmorphology reflects the complex interplay of genetic and environmental factors contributing to these disorders, including socio-economic status, pattern of consumption, nutritional status, and the use of tobacco and drugs such as cocaine and marijuana (Nulman, Ickeowicz, Koren, & Knittel-Keren, 2007). Neurological and behavioural effects are estimated to occur approximately three times as often as FASD (3 to 5 per 1000 live births). The incidence of FASD among alcoholics is estimated to be 25 per 1000 (Abel, 1984). A study in Seattle (Sampson et al., 1997) gives a conservative estimate that the combined rate of FASD and associated effects is at least 9.1 per 1000, which is almost 1 in every 100 live births.

In an effort to address the lack of consensus on prevalence, Canadian diagnostic guidelines have been developed that recommend a multidisciplinary approach to assessment, diagnosis, and intervention as best practice. Early diagnosis is critical to promote early intervention and support, not only for affected children but also for their parents and siblings who may have similar undiagnosed challenges (Chudley et al., 2005). Appropriate supports can also help to reduce the risk of secondary disabilities frequently found in individuals with FASD (Clark, Lutke, Minnes, & Ouellette-Kuntz, 2004).

Binge drinking has been shown to have a particularly significant impact on fetal development (Gladstone, Nulman, & Koren, 1996; Streissguth, Barr, & Sampson, 1990). Children of women who drank five or more drinks on one occasion were more likely to have developmental delays of up to three months in reading and arithmetic and to require special educational support. This study suggests that heavy drinking on even a few occasions may be more damaging than moderate drinking over a longer time. The link between paternal drinking patterns and FASD is not clear, and further research is required to determine its impact on fetal development (Jenkins & Culbertson, 1996).

Children with FASD exhibit a range of problems at varying stages of development. Prenatal exposure to alcohol is associated with deficits in cognitive and executive functioning that last a lifetime (Wass, 2008). Cognitive functioning varies from relatively minor learning problems to severe intellectual disability (Kalberg & Buckley, 2007). Individuals with FASD may have behavioural challenges, including problems with impulse control, attention deficit/hyperactivity disorder, social difficulties (Bishop, Gahagan, & Lord, 2007), enuresis (bedwetting), and eating and sleeping difficulties (Noland et al., 2003).

It is difficult, however, to distinguish such inherited tendencies from the effects of environmental deprivation resulting from ongoing alcoholism in the family. The effects of FASD are not confined to childhood. Secondary disabilities continue into adulthood, with problems such as poor judgment, inappropriate sexual behaviour, drug problems, delinquency, unemployment, and a variety of psychiatric problems (Streissguth, Bookstein, & Barr, 1996).

Other Drugs. Early development of the fetus can also be severely affected by certain drugs. The anticonvulsant Dilantin, chemotherapy, and hormone therapy have all been found to have teratogenic effects, including facial anomalies, malformed limbs, and a risk of later cancer (Batshaw & Perret, 1986). Congenital limb deficiency, although rare, is one of the best-known examples of teratogenic effects. It received a great deal of attention in the 1950s and 1960s when **thalidomide**, a drug prescribed by European and Canadian physicians for nausea (Tausig, 1962), was found to cause limb deficiencies or malformations in infants (McBride, 1961). Alcohol consumption and cigarette smoking have been found to be associated with a higher risk of low birth weight, microcephaly, and hearing deficits (Olsen, Pereira, & Olsen, 1991).

BIRTH-RELATED CAUSES Advances in obstetric and neonatal intensive care in recent years have reduced the risk of brain damage and intellectual disability as a result of birth-related trauma. Nevertheless, extreme prematurity or a lack of oxygen during prolonged or complicated labour and delivery can result in developmental problems including visual deficits, cerebral palsy, and speech and learning difficulties.

POSTNATAL ENVIRONMENTAL FACTORS: PSYCHOSOCIAL DISADVANTAGE

Childhood environment can have an important effect on cognitive as well as physical and emotional development. Psychological and social deprivation due to lack of stimulation and care can impair intellectual development. Poverty, poor nutrition, large family size, lack of structure in the home, and low expectations for academic success may all be contributing factors. Children learn by experience and by modelling adult behaviour; if they are given little opportunity to practise cognitive skills or to watch adults practising them, it seems reasonable that they would not develop as rapidly as children given ample opportunity and encouragement to practise reasoning and communication skills.

Most individuals with disabilities function intellectually within the mild range. They are found more frequently within lower socio-economic groups, and commonly have at least one parent and possibly one or more siblings with developmental delays. More recent research (Emerson & Hatton, 2007) has revealed that children with intellectual disabilities are significantly more likely to come from socially disadvantaged families. The incidence of developmental disabilities in Indigenous groups in Canada is thought to be higher than in the general population (Adelson, 2005). Poverty has been identified as a major risk factor for developmental disabilities among Indigenous families but other factors may also contribute, including high incidence of prenatal trauma due to domestic abuse, FASD, poor housing, malnutrition,

disease, limited access to supports, large families, and high numbers of single-parent families (Fudge Schormans & Mandamin-Cameron, 2007).

As with other disorders (see, for example, the discussion of conduct disorder in Chapter 15), the latter finding can be read in two ways: Do children inherit low intelligence from their parents, or do parents with low intelligence create a deprived environment? Debate continues as to the relative contributions of genetic and environmental factors.

Canadian research conducted with infants and children adopted from Romanian orphanages (Ames, 1992) explored the effects of environmental and social deprivation experienced by children institutionalized in these orphanages. This longitudinal study documented the devastating effects of poor nutrition and limited physical and social stimulation (Ames et al., 1997; Morison, 1997).

PREVENTION AND EARLY INTERVENTION PROGRAMS Research conducted with children living with their natural families has also confirmed the effect of environmental factors on development. Prevention and early intervention programs were first developed in the late 1940s and 1950s with early support for mothers and children, including prenatal care, immunization, and nutritional advice. In the 1960s such programs expanded to include daycare and community mental health centres and stimulating early childhood education programs (the U.S. Head Start program being the best known of the latter; Crocker, 1992).

Currently, the importance of early intervention for infants, toddlers, and preschoolers at risk for developmental delays is recognized internationally (Odom, Teferra, & Kaul, 2004). Evaluative reviews of early intervention and prevention programs (Frankel & Gold, 2007; Ramey & Ramey, 1992) indicate that they can significantly improve intellectual performance and levels of academic achievement as well as developmental outcomes, including greater engagement and social competence, independence, and mastery. Additional outcomes include preparation for inclusive education and prevention of behavioural challenges (Wolery & Bailey, 2002). In a summary of the results of early intervention studies, Ramey and Ramey (1992) outlined a number of "essential daily ingredients" for the development of young children. These include encouragement of curiosity, organizational assistance, positive reinforcement, and skill rehearsal in a supportive and predictable environment void of inappropriate disapproval, teasing, or punishment.

More recent research on best practices also highlights the importance of following principles of inclusion, family-centred practice, and collaborative work across professional disciplines involved with the child and family throughout the intervention process (Frankel & Gold, 2007).

 BEFORE MOVING ON

What are three ways that the impact of intellectual disabilities can be reduced?

Two Specific Disorders

DOWN SYNDROME

Case Notes

Jessica is 14 years old and has Down syndrome. She lives with her parents and a younger brother. Since her birth, Jessica's parents have been determined to give her the best possible opportunities for learning and to integrate her into the community. They were actively involved in an early intervention program focusing on language and motor development. When she was two, they enrolled her in an integrated daycare. Jessica attended regular primary school classes, but received some help from an educational teaching assistant. However, her only real friend was Jan, another girl with Down syndrome. The other children tended to avoid Jessica and Jan unless specifically asked by the teacher to work with them.

Jessica attended Brownies and sang in the church choir, but her favourite activity was swimming with the Special Olympics team. At age 12, a psychological assessment found that Jessica was functioning intellectually in the upper half of the moderate range, but had significantly higher adaptive skills. She could complete most activities of daily living independently or with minimal supervision. She liked to help her mother with the cooking and laundry and liked to watch television or play computer games with her younger brother. Jessica was able to use money and enjoyed shopping for clothes. She could read at a Grade 4 level and do Grade 6 arithmetic.

At age 14, Jessica is preparing to enter high school, but the special education consultant was unsure whether she should be fully integrated. It was decided that she would attend a special class for her weaker subjects (English, history, and geography) but would be integrated for math, music, and physical education. Social isolation continues to be a challenge for Jessica; however, her activities with Special Olympics have provided her with a close circle of friends who also have disabilities.

The physical features of Down syndrome are widely recognized. These include short stature; slanted eyes with an epicanthic fold of skin over the inner corner; a wide and flat bridge of the nose; a short, thick neck; stubby hands and fingers; a large, protruding tongue; and poor muscle tone. Other associated problems include congenital heart disease (Reilly, Huws, Hastings, & Vaughan, 2010), gastrointestinal abnormalities, and congenital cataracts (Lovering, 2003). The degree of intellectual impairment can range from mild to severe, with the largest proportion functioning within the mild to moderate range. Particular difficulties in expressive language are common. Despite a number of methodological challenges, research has begun to provide evidence for a behavioural

A person with Down syndrome.

phenotype for Down syndrome. Characteristics vary according to age. In young children these characteristics include delayed nonverbal cognitive development, and deficits in verbal abilities and auditory short-term memory. Symptoms of dementia occur in approximately half of adults over 50 years with Down syndrome (Chapman & Hesketh, 2000).

Early intervention and education have been shown to contribute to the development and adaptive functioning of people with Down syndrome. While the range of intellectual ability is broad, many individuals with Down syndrome are able to attain basic reading, numeracy, and writing skills, and considerable independence in activities of daily living in the community (Cicchetti & Beeghly, 1990). Some individuals with Down syndrome are able to function at a much higher level. One example is Christopher Burke, an actor with Down syndrome who became well known for his role in the television program *Life Goes On*. Increasingly, individuals with Down syndrome are able to participate in daily living and cope with stressors associated with aging and significant life events.

Life expectancy for people with Down syndrome has increased in the past three decades due to more frequent use of antibiotic medications to reduce infections (e.g., chest, ear, nose, and throat) and surgical treatment of congenital heart disease, both of which are common in individuals with Down syndrome (Pueschel, 2006). However, other health problems occur more frequently in people with Down syndrome than in the general population. These include hypothyroidism, diabetes, obesity, and leukemia (Lovering & Percy, 2007).

Although life expectancy is currently higher for people with Down syndrome than it used to be, adults with Down syndrome are at high risk for developing Alzheimer-type dementia (Dalton & McLachlan, 1986). Research has shown that individuals with Down syndrome over the age of 40 generally show the neuropathological indicators of dementia (Zigman, Schupf, Lubin, & Silverman, 1987). However, the usual behavioural deterioration (e.g., cognitive and visual memory deficits, declines in daily living skills and adaptive behaviour) appears in only 15 to 40 percent of cases (Zigman et al., 1987). The Dementia Scale for Down Syndrome (DSDS) (Gedye, 1995) is an informant-based interview designed to assess dementia among people who are non-verbal and cannot follow instructions.

FRAGILE X SYNDROME

Case Notes

Ryan is a 10-year-old boy with Fragile X syndrome. He lives at home with his parents and older brother Kurt, who also has Fragile X. Ryan's mother has a brother with Fragile X, and her sister has a daughter who is affected. Ryan attends a class for children with disabilities at the local school. He reads at a Grade 3 level and can do simple addition and subtraction. Ryan has a well-developed vocabulary, but he tends to repeat particular phrases from commercials and songs he has heard, and his speech becomes especially repetitive when he is agitated. Ryan enjoys being active. He and his brother like to ride their bikes and to go bowling. They are both on a basketball team organized through the Special Olympics. At home, computer games are a favourite activity.

Ryan and Kurt are able to take care of their personal hygiene with relatively little supervision. They make their own beds and help with chores such as washing the dishes, mowing the lawn, and shovelling snow. They are able to use the microwave to make simple meals and enjoy helping their mother with baking.

Ryan's new teacher was concerned about his limited attention span and frequent outbursts due to frustration intolerance, especially during transitions from one task or setting to another. Ryan's parents were also concerned that he was increasingly irritable; if his routine changed unexpectedly, he would have tantrums, swear repeatedly, and sometimes become physically aggressive.

After consulting with his parents, the school referred Ryan to the school board's psychologist, who observed Ryan at home and at school. She noted that he was distracted in class by other children's activities and by the many pictures and notices on the walls, arts and crafts materials, and books on the shelves, and that he had the most difficulty remaining seated and attentive during class discussions or unstructured time. The teacher rearranged the desks and created some quiet areas set apart by low room dividers. Ryan's desk was placed against the wall, and he was given frequent opportunities to sit in one of the quiet areas. A token program was also devised where Ryan could collect rewards (e.g. stickers) for paying attention and staying in his seat during structured class activities. These could be "cashed in" for computer time during unstructured periods.

The psychologist also suggested that Ryan's parents and his teacher develop a pictorial schedule of daily activities, with a copy kept at Ryan's desk and another posted on the refrigerator at home. Reviewing the schedule for the next day helped to prepare Ryan for changes in routine and reminded his parents and teachers to anticipate changes that might trigger extreme responses by Ryan.

Fragile X syndrome, first described by Martin and Bell (1943), was identified as an X-linked chromosomal abnormality in the late 1960s (Lubs, 1969), and the mutation for the gene causing the disorder (FMR-1 gene) was discovered in 1991 (Oberle et al., 1991; Yu et al., 1991). It is characterized by a weakened or "fragile" site on the X chromosome, as shown in Figure 14.5. Everyone has a copy of the FMR-1 gene on the X chromosome; however, the gene is larger in persons with Fragile X syndrome. DNA molecules are made up of nucleotides, each of which contains a chemical base. The four bases in DNA are adenine (A), cytosine (C), guanine (G), and thymine (T). In Fragile X syndrome, there are extra pairs of cytosine and guanine, called *triplet repeats*. In a normal FMR-1 gene, the range of CGG repeats is between 6 and 50. Individuals with the *full mutation* have more than 200 repeats, whereas individuals with between 60 and 200 repeats are said to have a *premutation*. A person who inherits a Fragile X gene may not be directly affected, but may be a genetic carrier, transmitting the disorder to his or her offspring.

FIGURE 14.5 Schematic Drawing of the Fragile X Syndrome

Source: The Fragile X Syndrome (1983). Dillon, CO: Spectra. Permission granted by Spectra Publishing.

Almost all males who have a full mutation are affected, whereas approximately 50 percent of females will be affected by a full mutation. If a female carrier of a premutation passes this gene to her sons, there is an 80 percent chance that the gene will expand to become a full mutation (Lee, MacKenzie, & Holden, 2003).

Fragile X syndrome is the second-most frequently occurring chromosomal abnormality causing intellectual disability after Down syndrome, and the most common hereditary cause of intellectual disability (Dykens, Hodapp, & Leckman, 1994). Prevalence rates vary but approximately 1 in 400 females is estimated to be an unaffected carrier, and approximately 1 in 2000 is directly affected. Rates for males with the full mutation range from 1 in 700 to 1 in 1000; approximately 1 in 2000 males is an unaffected carrier. Beyond initial identification of clinical features, the diagnosis of Fragile X is made by a blood test. If the person seems to show any of the facial features suggestive of Fragile X, it is worthwhile testing, both for the guidance of relatives considering child-bearing and because the diagnosis may allow access to specialized intervention programs.

Physical features include a high forehead, elongated face, large jaw, large underdeveloped ears, and (in males) enlarged testes. Individuals with Fragile X syndrome display a number of cognitive, behavioural, and physical symptoms, but the degree to which they are affected in any of these varies (Dykens, Leckman, Paul, & Watson, 1988). Moreover, these characteristics are often less pronounced in carrier females. For example, intellectual levels in males vary from moderate intellectual disability to within the normal range, with declines in IQ appearing around puberty.

Males show a particular pattern of cognitive functioning, with weaknesses in sequential processing of information in a particular order (e.g., words in a sentence, a sequence of tasks) but strengths in simultaneous processing of information in a more holistic fashion (e.g., visuo-spatial tasks, recognizing a picture despite missing parts) (Dykens, Hodapp, & Leckman, 1987). In contrast, only approximately one-third of females are mildly mentally retarded, and most display only learning difficulties involving attention, short-term memory, planning, problem solving, and understanding mathematical concepts (Dykens et al., 1994).

Receptive language may be relatively well developed in relation to expressive language in males with Fragile X syndrome. Their speech has been described as "jocular, staccato, perseverative and sing-songy" (Dykens et al., 1994). Vocabulary may be well developed and individuals may be able to express themselves relatively well in certain familiar contexts. Males with Fragile X often have particular problems with communication and socialization, but may show greater strengths in adaptive behaviour, particularly in activities of daily living. Fragile X syndrome is associated with attention deficits, hyperactivity, anxiety, and aggression. Autistic-type behaviours such as hand flapping, hand biting, poor eye contact, and an aversion to being touched

or oversensitivity to certain textures may also occur (Hagerman, 1987). Approximately 25 percent of males with Fragile X syndrome also meet the criteria for a diagnosis of autism (Mazzocco & Holden, 2007).

A national survey focusing on the nature and impact of Fragile X syndrome for individuals and their families (Bailey Jr., Raspa, & Olmstead, 2010) has yielded important new information regarding the occurrence of seizures (Berry-Kravis et al., 2010), self-injurious behaviour, sleep difficulties (Symons, Byiers, Raspa, Bishop, & Bailey Jr., 2010), obesity, and sensitivity to textures and foods (Raspa, Bailey Jr., & Bishop, 2010). In addition, research has documented phenotypical characteristics associated with the Fragile X premutation. These characteristics include the development of motor tremors and ataxia associated with dementia in 4 to 5 percent of older carriers of the FMR-1 premutation (Kogan, Turk, Hagerman, & Kornish, 2008) and premature ovarian failure in women under the age of 40 (Holoch, Stein, Flanagan, & Hansen, 2008). Children with Fragile X, like children with autism, can benefit from structured educational programs that limit distractions, include

A boy with Fragile X syndrome.

regular routines, and provide a good deal of visual information (Braden, 1989).

The Effect of Developmental Disorders on the Family

Over the past three decades, the experiences and needs of families of children with disabilities have been the focus of numerous research studies. Conducting research with families can be complicated due to the use of varied samples and research methods. Until recently, the primary focus of research was on mothers rather than fathers and other family members, and the majority of research used cross sectional as opposed to longitudinal designs. Research has also been criticized for "pathologizing parents" by focusing only on stress and negative outcomes (Helff & Glidden, 1998). Fortunately, newer studies have begun to address some of these limitations giving us a new understanding of the experiences of parents and families. There is little doubt that parents of children, adolescents and adults with disabilities do experience more stress, day-to-day demands, and role restriction than parents of typically developing children (Baker et al., 2003; Minnes, Perry, & Weiss, 2014; Neece & Baker, 2008). However many parents also report positive impacts of raising a child with a developmental disability (Hastings & Taunt, 2002; Williamson & Perkins, 2014). Such outcomes include opportunities for personal growth, improved relations with others, changes in philosophical or spiritual values (Scorgie & Sobsey, 2000), and satisfaction with providing care (Rapanaro, Bartu, & Lee, 2008). The experiences of mothers and fathers have been shown to vary depending on individual and contextual factors. However, a child's challenging behaviour and family poverty have frequently been highlighted as major risk factors for parent well-being (Emerson et al., 2006; Nachshen, Garcin, & Minnes, 2005; Olsson, 2008). The type and degree of disability (Corrice & Glidden, 2009), age of child and parent (Caldwell & Heller, 2007; Esbensen & Seltzer, 2011) and co-morbid psychiatric disorders (Dawson et al., 2016) have also been shown to be important.

Studies of families at different points across the lifespan, such as when a child receives a diagnosis, through the transitions to school, into adolescence, and adulthood have highlighted a changing pattern of parental stress and coping. Heightened stress and upheaval often occur at significant transition points when progress in the child's development might be expected to occur and in association with significant events (e.g., diagnosis of the disability) or ongoing activities (e.g., dealing with health care professionals or teachers, the reactions of family and people in the community (Minnes & Woodford, 2004; Nachshen, Woodford, & Minnes, 2003), and issues arising during the transition out of school (Mackenzie, Ouellette-Kuntz, & Blinkhorn, 2016). Many families, however, are resilient (Grein & Glidden, 2015). The use of coping strategies such as positive reframing or reappraisal of experiences as well as parental empowerment, parent perceived self-efficacy, and parent advocacy have all contributed to positive outcomes (Ewles, Clifford, & Minnes, 2014; Minnes et al., 2015; Weiss et al., 2016). In one of the few longitudinal studies focusing on maternal functioning over a two decade period, maternal personality (emotional stability/instability) and family accord or cohesion were found to be strong predictors of resilience and vulnerability throughout the lifespan (Grein & Glidden, 2015).

Within the broader family system, research has shown that family cohesion, open communication patterns, and patterns of organization and control can help a family cope with the demands of caring for a child with a developmental disability (Perry, Harris, & Minnes, 2004). Marital quality and the co-parenting styles have also been highlighted as contributing to parent well-being (Norlin & Broberg, 2013).

Studies of siblings of children with disabilities have yielded conflicting results (Heller & Arnold, 2010); some report adverse effects (Cuskelly & Dadds, 1992), but others do not (Evans, Jones, & Mansell, 2001; Rossiter & Sharpe, 2001). The nature of sibling relationships can be affected by factors such as disability-related characteristics as well as sibling proximity and the relative involvement of brothers and sisters (Orsmond & Seltzer, 2000). A range of emotions from feelings of guilt and joy, frustration and stress related to caregiving and future planning has been reported (Rossetti & Hall, 2015). However, other studies have found that relationships between adult siblings with and without developmental disabilities are valued by both parties (Burbidge & Minnes, 2014) and are frequently described as "close" (Heller & Arnold, 2010).

While many families report that informal social support from friends, family members, and neighbours can help to reduce the burden on the family, support from social service agencies and professionals has not been consistently shown to contribute to positive outcomes (Jones & Passey, 2004). Families of young children are most likely to report that formal supports are helpful when they are trying to navigate the diagnostic process and service delivery system (McIntyre & Brown, 2016). Positive parental satisfaction with services also has been found to be related to direct work by a professional with their child, understanding issues, and their ability to manage challenging behaviours. Parents' dissatisfaction was found to be related to parents' perceptions of themselves as experts or nonexperts and their views on the services received (Robinson et al., 2016; Weiss, 2002).

There is still much research to be conducted to obtain a clear understanding of the many and varied experiences of families of individuals with developmental disabilities. Multi-site and cross-cultural collaborations using consistent measures and longitudinal designs are needed. The use of theoretical models of family functioning can also help to ensure inclusion of the many relevant constructs and promote consistency to ensure empirically sound results. (IASSIDD, Families Special Interest Research Group, 2014).

Deinstitutionalization and Community Integration or Inclusion

Since the 1970s, services for people with developmental disabilities have been guided by the Normalization principle, a concept introduced in Scandinavia by Bengt Nirje (1969), which suggested that the lives of individuals with disabilities should be as "normal" as possible. Wolfensberger (1972) applied this principle to services for persons with disabilities in North America. In other words, people with disabilities should be given the opportunity to have as normal a lifestyle as possible through participation in activities common to members of society of similar age (Zigler, Hodapp, & Edison, 1990). The United Nations Convention on the Rights and Dignity of Persons with Disabilities, signed by Canada in 2007 and ratified in 2010, highlights the importance of participation and inclusion in society as well as independence of persons with disabilities (McSherry, 2009).

The influence of these changing views has been widespread, contributing to the **deinstitutionalization** of thousands of people with disabilities and the provision of community-based accommodation and services. In Ontario alone, nine institutions were closed between 1974 and 1996, with the number of people with developmental disabilities served in the community increasing from approximately 4600 in 1974 to more than 50 000 in 1996. Closure of the last Ontario institution occurred in 2009. In 2008, legislation governing the care of individuals with disabilities was also changed from the *Developmental Services Act* to the *Services and Supports to Promote the Social Inclusion of Persons with Developmental Disabilities Act* for the purposes of promoting independence and increased choice.

Similar trends are occurring across Canada. Currently, the social and cultural contexts beyond the immediate home, such as family, friends, work, and leisure, are becoming the focus of research and service delivery.

Community integration has been measured in a variety of ways. Cummins and Lau (2003) have summarized several relevant variables in order of frequency of use (see Table 14.4). These researchers see the inclusion of subjective well-being as a positive step forward; however, they note that the majority of studies have measured community integration from an objective perspective rather than from the personal experience perspective of individuals with intellectual disability. They add that the views of parents, staff, or caregivers are frequently measured, but the views of individuals with intellectual disability are frequently overlooked.

MAINSTREAMING AND INCLUSION OF STUDENTS WITH DISABILITIES IN EDUCATIONAL SETTINGS

Social inclusion is a complex, multidimensional concept that refers to an active *process* that can promote development and facilitate participation of individuals with developmental disabilities (Ainscow, 2000). Since the 1980s, inclusion has been accepted in Canada (e.g., *An Act to Amend The Education Act*, 1974, 1980) and the United States as best practice for children with disabilities in the classroom. There have been challenges related to the early identification of developmental disabilities and the limited availability of interventions to address disabilities and associated behaviours, but also related to limited education for teachers on strategies for including students with intellectual/developmental disabilities (Hutchinson et al., 2015; Frankel et al., 2014) and inadequate knowledge transfer among parents, health care providers, and educators in various contexts (Smith, 2007; Villeneuve et al., 2013). The goal of full inclusion in social and recreational as well as educational contexts has not been achieved in many sectors. Children and adolescents with intellectual disabilities have been found to participate in significantly fewer activities and less frequently than typically developing peers. They also have fewer friends with less positive relationships with friends (Taheri et al., 2016; Solish et al., 2010).

PREPARATION FOR COMMUNITY LIVING

As more people with disabilities live in the community, it becomes especially important for them to learn to look after their own needs as much as possible. Many educational programs for people with developmental disabilities have focused on developing social skills and independent living skills and on reducing or managing challenging or maladaptive behaviours. These programs often use systematic observation, task analysis, and various shaping and prompting procedures and reinforcement contingencies.

Audiovisual and computer technologies have facilitated the development of innovative approaches to teaching work-related and social skills, food preparation, and cleaning skills (Wehmeyer et al., 2006). Another study used GPS technology to support independent use of public transportation, which is often necessary for individuals to access social and recreational activities and employment in the community (Davies, Stock, Holloway, & Wehmeyer, 2010).

TABLE 14.4   WHAT IS COMMUNITY INTEGRATION?

Variables Measured in Studies to Date	Variables Needing More Research Attention
Number of activities within the community	How much individuals with intellectual disability value or desire community integration
Number of personal relationships	Satisfaction obtained as a result of community integration
Frequency of access to community resources	Nature of the communities individuals wish to be integrated into
Number of leisure activities outside the home	Subjective well-being

EVALUATING QUALITY OF LIFE

The concept of **quality of life** has been the topic of considerable discussion over the past two decades. (e.g., Brown & Brown, 2004; Schalock, 1996, 1997). In a summary of definitional dimensions of quality of life in the literature, McVilly and Rawlinson (1998) highlight the importance of including both subjective and objective indicators in the measurement of quality of life.

In Canada, an approach developed at the Centre for Health Promotion in Toronto (Renwick, Brown, & Raphael, 1994) divides quality of life into three components: (1) "Being" in physical, psychological, and spiritual domains; (2) "Belonging" in physical, social, and community environments; and (3) "Becoming," focusing on strategies to achieve hopes and goals related to practical issues, leisure, and personal growth.

More recently, the focus of research has expanded to include the quality of life of families and caregivers (Turnbull, Brown, & Turnbull, 2003). Important aspects of individuals' lives for family quality of life include physical well-being, emotional well-being, environmental well-being, and social well-being. Important aspects of quality of life for the whole family include financial well-being, support from others, support from services, and support from society (Brown & Brown, 2004). The concept of family quality of life is currently reflected in changing models of service delivery. These include a shift from deficit-based to strengths-based approaches and interventions that include not only the individual with developmental disabilities but also support for their families (Aldersey et al., 2017; Poston et al., 2003).

3 BEFORE MOVING ON

> Inclusion and integration of individuals with developmental disabilities in schools and other community activities have been supported by legislation in Canada and the United States. However, research has not provided consistent results favouring such approaches. What factors need to be considered when evaluating the success of inclusion and integration programs?

THE ISSUE OF SEX EDUCATION

Since the 1970s, there has been much debate about whether people with developmental disabilities should have the right to enjoy sexual activity, marriage, and children. Historically, individuals with disabilities were seen to be either **asexual** or promiscuous and prohibited from expressing their own sexuality (Murphy, 2003).

Studies in Canada and Scotland have indicated a range of attitudes among residential staff and other professionals working in the field (Jones, Ouellete-Kuntz, Vilela, & Brown, 2008; Murray & Minnes, 1994a, 1994b), Younger and more highly educated staff are generally found to be more accepting, and professionals are frequently more accepting than direct care workers. Parents and staff have been found to express less positive attitudes toward parents with intellectual disability and more cautious views regarding sexual freedom for women with intellectual disabilities than for women without disabilities (Cuskelly & Bryde, 2004; Gilmore & Chambers, 2010). Such differences in attitudes highlight the importance of assessing attitudes to avoid confusion for individuals with intellectual disabilities who may be receiving mixed messages about their behaviour.

With increasing numbers of people with developmental disabilities living in the community, both children and adults with developmental disabilities are at considerable risk for sexual assault and abuse (Lund, & Hammond, 2014; McCarthy & Thompson, 1997; Sobsey, Gray, Wells, Pyper, & Reimer-Heck, 1991). A survey of women with intellectual disabilities living in community residences reported that 75 to 80 percent had been sexually assaulted (Davis, 1989). Such figures may reflect individuals' limited ability to make informed decisions and to give consent to sexual contact (Dukes & McGuire, 2009). Furthermore, inadequate staff screening and environmental factors such as understaffing, staff burnout, limited staff education, and isolation can increase the risk of abuse of individuals with disabilities (White, Holland, Marsland, & Oakes, 2003). There is an urgent need for specialized sex education programs for people with intellectual disabilities, especially as those who are living more independently in the community are at increasing risk of contracting HIV infections and AIDS (Schaafsma, Kok, Stoffelen, Van Doorn, & Curfs, 2014; Whitehouse & McCabe, 1997; Murray & Minnes, 1994b). Individuals with intellectual disabilities, unlike typically developing individuals, often have limited opportunities for education about sexuality and relationships (Bazzo, Nota, Soresi, Ferrari, & Minnes, 2007). Although counselling and psychotherapy have often been seen as ineffective for people with developmental disabilities, recent initiatives have demonstrated that adaptations can be made to accommodate limited expressive and receptive language skills (Lynch, 2004; see the next section on Challenging Behaviours and Dual Diagnosis). Furthermore, programs to help survivors of sexual abuse who have intellectual disabilities (Hickson, Khemka, Golden, & Chatzistyli, 2015; Mansell, Sobsey, & Calder, 1992) are now being introduced through interactive-behavioural group therapy, which involves intensive support and the use of role-playing exercises (Tomasulo, 1994; Tomasulo, Keller, & Pfadt, 1995).

With greater freedom through community living, more adults with ID are having children. Although the issue of whether individuals with ID should become parents continues to be a topic of debate (as in the film *I Am Sam*), research and practice have emphasized the need to focus on developing parenting skills programs, implementing home-based interventions (Wade, Llewellyn, & Matthews, 2008), and providing support rather than constraint to reduce the risk of child abuse and to promote child development (Emerson et al., 2015; Reinders, 2008).

Challenging Behaviours and Dual Diagnosis (i.e. ID and Mental Disorder)

Case Notes

Kevin was a 27-year-old man who had lived in the community since completing a school-to-community life skills program at the local high school six years ago. He lived with his parents until he was 24 and then moved into his own apartment. He continued to have regular, frequent contact with his parents, but was able to manage cooking, cleaning, and other activities of daily living without much supervision. Kevin had two volunteer jobs. Three days a week he helped the cleaners at the local school, and on Fridays he did grocery shopping for an elderly neighbour.

Kevin had been assessed as functioning at the top of the mild range of developmental disability. He could read at a Grade 4 level and understood money fairly well. One of his favourite activities was to take the bus to the mall and hang out at the food court. Kevin had been involved in group social activities organized by the Association for Community Living but had to stop going because of poor frustration tolerance and angry outbursts. These outbursts tended to occur in unstructured situations; when Kevin did not have a clear idea of what to expect, he would become agitated and would shout and sometimes become aggressive.

Kevin longed to have friendships, but his behaviour often alienated others. A recent outburst at the grocery store raised concerns about his ability to keep his volunteer jobs. Without such activities during the day, Kevin would be even more socially isolated.

Kevin had recently become involved with a group of teens, some of whom had been charged with theft. His parents were concerned that his new friends may have been encouraging Kevin to join them on shoplifting sprees and that Kevin might be easily led because he was so eager for acceptance. Whenever they tried to discuss his friends and activities, Kevin became very angry and refused to talk about them stating that it was not their business as he was an adult.

Until the 1980s, it was rare for a person with intellectual disability to be diagnosed with a psychiatric disorder. Emotional and behavioural difficulties were often attributed to an individual's lower intelligence and psychosocial problems rather than a possible mental illness (Borthwick-Duffy, 1994). People with intellectual disability who have limited communication skills and expressive difficulties often exhibit physical or psychological distress through their behaviour (Dykens, 2000). Hence, perceiving mood changes or maladaptive behaviours to be solely a function of the developmental disorder might cause real psychiatric disorders to be missed (Bradley et al., 2007). This phenomenon is called **diagnostic overshadowing.** It is now widely recognized that people with intellectual disabilities are at a three- to fourfold increased risk of developing emotional and behavioural problems associated with psychiatric disorders. Epidemiological studies indicate that they can develop the full range of psychiatric disorders (Dykens, 2000). The symptomology however presents in different ways due to the **pathoplastic** effects of the cognitive impairment on the expression of the psychopathology. Furthermore, individuals with particular syndromes such as Fragile X, as well as individuals with autism spectrum disorders, are at greater risk of co-morbid mental health difficulties (Bradley, Bolton, & Bryson, 2004; Dykens et al., 2000).

In North America, the co-occurrence of serious behavioural or psychiatric disorders in people with intellectual disability has been labelled **dual diagnosis.** Prevalence rates of dual diagnosis, obtained primarily in the United States, vary widely. International estimates of the numbers of children and adults with intellectual disabilities with a psychiatric diagnosis range from 14 to 39 percent (Cooper & Bailey, 2001; Cooper et al., 2006; Emerson & Hatton, 2007). Given the challenges of making diagnoses in this population, adaptations to the mainstream psychiatric diagnostic manual DSM-5 were published in the Diagnostic Manual-Intellectual Disability (DM-ID; Fletcher, Loschen, Stavrakaki, & First, 2007; Fletcher, Barnhill, McCarthy, & Strydom, 2016). In the UK, the Diagnostic Criteria for Psychiatric Disorders for Use with Adults with Learning Disabilities/Mental Retardation (DC-LD; Royal College of Psychiatrists, 2001) was introduced to provide clarity to establishing diagnoses with individuals with intellectual disabilities.

Studies have found that even without a formal psychiatric diagnosis, up to 40% of individuals with intellectual disabilities are receiving medication, counselling, or therapy from a mental health professional for behavioural challenges (Matson & Neal, 2009; Tyrer, Oliver-Africano, Ahmed, et al., 2008; Davidson et al., 1994; Reiss, 1990). A provincial study found that 38% of Ontarians with intellectual disabilities identified mental health difficulties, 43% had undiagnosed health problems, and over half of adults living in the community had been prescribed psychiatric medications (Lunsky et al., 2003).

A combination of psychopharmacology and behavioural approaches is generally the intervention of choice for challenging behaviours such as aggression, destructiveness, and self-injury. The use of intrusive behavioural procedures such as timeout (seclusion), physical or mechanical restraint, and other approaches focusing on punishment has decreased since the 1980s due to ethical concerns regarding the negative impact on the dignity and freedom of persons with intellectual disabilities to make choices and on community attitudes (Condillac, 2007). Positive behavioural support techniques that focus on positive reinforcement, alternative or replacement behaviours, natural consequences, and environmental accommodations have been successfully used in the treatment of aggressive, self-injurious, and disruptive behaviour (Feldman, Condillac, Tough, Hunt, & Griffiths, 2002).

The use of psychotherapeutic interventions with higher-functioning individuals with intellectual disabilities has grown since the 1980s (Beail & Jackson, 2012; Taylor, Lindsay, Hastings, & Hatton, 2012). A British survey (Nagel & Leiper, 1999) indicated that behavioural interventions continue to be used most frequently (81 percent), however; 35 percent of respondents reported using **cognitive-behavioural therapy**, Studies have also shown the benefit of CBT group therapy for individuals with intellectual disabilities and challenging behaviour (Jones, Minnes, Elms, Paret, & Vilela, 2007; Willner, Jones, Tams, & Green, 2002; Willner, Rose, Jahoda, Kroese, et al., 2013).

The lower frequency of psychotherapy use with individuals with ID as compared to the general population may reflect the challenges of using psychotherapeutic approaches with individuals who have comprehension and attention deficits, expressive and receptive language deficits, and other behavioural issues. Nevertheless, strategies to improve and facilitate the process have been developed (Lynch, 2004). These include simplifying the language, presenting information more slowly and in smaller chunks, using nonverbal communication, checking regularly for comprehension, allowing more time for the client to respond, and repeating the information in different ways. In addition, sessions need to be more structured, shorter, and goal-focused for individuals with intellectual disabilities. Therapists may also need to be more directive, using visual aids, role-playing, and real-life situations, and caregivers may need to be involved to facilitate generalization. Assessment and teaching of core skills prior to beginning therapy is recommended (Joyce, Globe, & Moody, 2006). Such prerequisite skills include the ability to identify and differentiate between emotions and beliefs or cognitions and to link emotions and cognitions with an event.

Across jurisdictions, it is well recognized that optimal care includes the **biopsychosocial** approach to assessment and treatment interventions for individuals with dual diagnosis (Bradley & Summers, 2003; Griffiths & Gardner, 2002; McCreary & Jones, 2015). This approach to case formulation accounts for the interactions among biological, psychological, and social contributory factors to problem behaviours. In addition, a range of interventions at several levels is recommended, including behavioural supports, individual therapy, evidence-based medication, environmental modifications, and psycho-education for caregivers and family.

Because of the closure of institutions, community-based crisis intervention services are needed for individuals with dual diagnoses (Davidson et al., 1995). In the absence of such services, families of individuals with dual diagnosis in emotional or behavioural crisis rely upon emergency departments at their local hospital, where practitioners and staff probably have limited training in this field (Bradley & Lofchy, 2005; Lunsky, Lin, Balogh, Klein-Geltink, Wilton, & Kurdyak, 2012). Mainstream clinicians may misinterpret or misdiagnosis

exhibited behaviours however a growing body of research has found that early exposure to disabilities and training for health care professionals can improve attitudes and promote appropriate care (Jones, McQueen, Lowe, Minnes, & Rischke, 2015).

DIGNITY OF RISK AND OFFENDING BEHAVIOUR

Researchers began to study the impact of inclusion and the difficulties that individuals with intellectual disabilities experience when integrating into society after deinstitutionalization. Early on, Perske and Persky (1973) introduced the term **dignity of risk** to refer to right of individuals to choose to take some risk in engaging in life experiences and the consequences that are associated with those risks. Alongside their rights and freedom to access community resources, individuals with intellectual disabilities are also exposed to a number of new and potentially risky situations. It is at this interface between community care and societal consequences that individuals with intellectual disabilities, both as victims and offenders, can interact with the criminal justice system (Jones, 2007).

The study of offenders with intellectual disabilities has grown over the last decade. Prevalence studies of offenders with intellectual disabilities have reported ranges from 15 to 30 percent depending on the definitions used, population samples, settings studied, and methodology utilized (Jones, 2007; Lindsay, Taylor, & Sturmey, 2004). Advances have been made in both assessment and treatment of offenders drawing upon work with the general offender population and evidence-based approaches to reducing offending behaviour and recidivism rates (Lindsay, 2002). More recently, several researchers have begun to explore the application and validity of mainstream risk assessment measures for the population as they relate to both violent and sexual offences. Numerous studies have shown the reliability and validity of such measures, albeit at a lower predictive rate than with the non-ID offending population (Lindsay & Beail, 2004; Quinsey, Book, & Skilling, 2004). This work adds to the growing recognition that there are likely population specific risk factors that need to be addressed in order to reduce recidivism rates and offer empirically based treatments allowing for optimal community rehabilitation (Boer, Tough, & Haaven, 2004).

Autism Spectrum Disorder

Case Notes

Stevie was a four-year-old boy who had been diagnosed with autism. He had been referred to a community behaviour management team because of frequent tantrums, in which he screamed and hit his head and jaw. His parents were concerned that Stevie would seriously injure himself, and were finding it difficult to manage his behaviour. He was on a waiting list for behaviour therapy involving applied behavioural analysis. His day-care has indicated that it may have to reduce his attendance to three days per week because of his disruptive behaviour and risk of self-harm.

From the beginning, Stevie's parents knew that there was something different about their son. Stevie was described as a "good and quiet" baby. He resisted cuddling and seemed to be quite happy to be left alone. As a toddler, Stevie rarely interacted with his older sister and did not show enjoyment when socializing with others around him. He did not show interest in or play with toys like other children. He liked to spin the wheels on his toy cars, tricycle, and wagon. He rarely used these toys in the conventional way and would scream if encouraged to share or play with others. Stevie's parents also noted his lack of communication and use of language. Stevie would make repetitive sounds and imitate what was said to him, but he did not make spontaneous comments or gestures or ask questions.

When Stevie was enrolled in daycare at age four, the director recommended contacting a psychologist. The psychologist observed Stevie at home and at the day-care centre, identifying the behaviours of concern, recording the frequency and duration of Stevie's outbursts, and their antecedents and consequences. A pattern emerged: when Stevie became frustrated for some reason, perhaps because a wheel had fallen off a toy or another child had taken one of his toys, he would scream and hit his jaw; physical restraint or comforting by his parents did not help.

The psychologist concluded that Stevie was frustrated by his inability to communicate his needs and tolerate distress when his needs were not met. She felt that once he was able to communicate and reinforced for doing so appropriately, his tantrums and hitting would gradually decrease. The psychologist referred Stevie to a speech and language pathologist, who assessed his language level and taught him and his parents some basic sign language. In addition, the psychologist wrote a letter requesting that Stevie be enrolled in an intensive behavioural intervention program as soon as possible to promote social development and self-regulation skills.

Autism (from the Greek *autos*, meaning "self") was first identified as a childhood disorder in 1943 by Leo Kanner. He described a sample of children who exhibited a number of distinct characteristics, including a lack of social responsiveness or extreme aloneness and significantly limited or unusual communication patterns. In addition, Kanner noted unusual patterns of behaviour, such as a lack of eye contact; self-stimulation, including rocking, spinning, or flapping; self-injury, including head banging or hand biting; an obsessive interest in particular objects; and an obsessive need

for sameness (see Table 14.6). Early terms for this disorder included "Kanner's syndrome" and "childhood psychosis," the latter reflecting the notion of an association with symptoms of schizophrenia. Childhood schizophrenia, unlike autism, typically involves hallucinations and delusions, average language skills, and normal development until adolescence, and frequent remissions and relapses. In addition, schizophrenia, unlike autism, is equally distributed between males and females (Volkmar, Carter, Grossman, & Klin, 1997). According to the DSM-5 criteria, **autism spectrum disorder (ASD)** is a term encompassing the past DSM-IV diagnostic category of pervasive developmental disorder, including autistic disorder, Asperger's disorder, and pervasive developmental disorder not otherwise specified.

PREVALENCE

Since the 1990s, prevalence estimates of autism have risen steadily (Wing & Potter, 2009). Canadian estimates of the prevalence of autism range from 1 to 3 per 1000 live births (Fombonne, 2003). In the United States, the Autism and Developmental Disabilities Monitoring Network estimated 1 in 68 children have been identified with autism spectrum disorder (CDC; Sui et al., 2016). International epidemiological studies from Canada, the United States, England, France, Scandinavia, and Asia (Troyb, Knoch, & Barton, 2011) indicate that autism is found at similar rates around the world. Higher estimates of 1 in 150 births (Kuehn, 2007) may reflect changes in diagnostic criteria, including a broader range of disorders in the autism spectrum, as well as the use of different diagnostic measures and increasing awareness among the general public and professionals (Wing & Potter, 2002). Autism occurs three to four times as often in males as in females. The sex difference appears to occur among people with higher IQs; no such sex difference is found among individuals functioning at a lower level (Lord & Schopler, 1987). Approximately one-third of individuals with autism do not speak, and up to half exhibit significant psychiatric and/or behavioural problems, including depression, anxiety, and aggression toward themselves or others. Epilepsy and sensory impairments are also common (Bryson, 1996). The strongest single predictor of functional outcome among people with autism has consistently been found to be the development of functional speech by age five (Venter, Lord, & Schopler, 1992).

Description

It is now well known that autism spectrum disorder is a highly heterogeneous disorder characterized by deficits in the main areas of social interaction, verbal and nonverbal communication, and behavioural interests. The plethora of research studies to date support that across the severity levels of autism spectrum disorder social-communication characteristics continue to differentiate between individuals with ASD and other, non-ASD diagnoses (Bishop, Havdahl, Huerta, & Lord, 2016; Carrington et al., 2014).

TABLE 14.5 DSM-5 DIAGNOSTIC CRITERIA FOR AUTISM SPECTRUM DISORDER

A. Persistent deficits in social communication and social interaction across multiple contexts, as manifested by the following, currently or by history (examples are illustrative, not exhaustive, see text):

   1. Deficits in social-emotional reciprocity, ranging, for example, from abnormal social approach and failure of normal back-and-forth conversation; to reduced sharing of interests, emotions, or affect; to failure to initiate or respond to social interactions.

   2. Deficits in nonverbal communicative behaviors used for social interaction, ranging, for example, from poorly integrated verbal and nonverbal communication; to abnormalities in eye contact and body language or deficits in understanding and use of gestures; to a total lack of facial expressions and nonverbal communication.

   3. Deficits in developing, maintaining, and understanding relationships, ranging, for example, from difficulties adjusting behavior to suit various social contexts; to difficulties in sharing imaginative play or in making friends; to absence of interest in peers.

   Specify current severity:

   Severity is based on social communication impairments and restricted repetitive patterns of behavior [see Table 14.6].

B. Restricted, repetitive patterns of behavior, interests, or activities, as manifested by at least two of the following, currently or by history (examples are illustrative, not exhaustive; see text):

   1. Stereotyped or repetitive motor movements, use of objects, or speech (e.g., simple motor stereotypies, lining up toys or flipping objects, echolalia, idiosyncratic phrases).

   2. Insistence on sameness, inflexible adherence to routines, or ritualized patterns or verbal nonverbal behavior (e.g., extreme distress at small changes, difficulties with transitions, rigid thinking patterns, greeting rituals, need to take same route or eat food every day).

   3. Highly restricted, fixated interests that are abnormal in intensity or focus (e.g, strong attachment to or preoccupation with unusual objects, excessively circumscribed or perseverative interest).

   4. Hyper- or hyporeactivity to sensory input or unusual interests in sensory aspects of the environment (e.g., apparent indifference to pain/temperature, adverse response to specific sounds or textures, excessive smelling or touching of objects, visual fascination with lights or movement).

   Specify current severity:

   Severity is based on social communication impairments and restricted, repetitive patterns of behavior [see Table 14.6].

C. Symptoms must be present in the early developmental period (but may not become fully manifest until social demands exceed limited capacities, or may be masked by learned strategies in later life).

D. Symptoms cause clinically significant impairment in social, occupational, or other important areas of current functioning.

E. These disturbances are not better explained by intellectual disability (intellectual developmental disorder) or global developmental delay. Intellectual disability and autism spectrum disorder frequently co-occur; to make comorbid diagnoses of autism spectrum disorder and intellectual disability, social communication should be below that expected for general developmental level.

SOCIAL INTERACTION

Two critical features of autism are social impairment and unusual responses to the environment. Such deficits, while frequently described, are less understood than other aspects of autism (Lord, 1993). From infancy, parents often note the lack of emotional attachment and comfort-seeking behaviours. The child does not anticipate being picked up and may not seek physical contact. Indeed, autistic children may often stiffen their bodies or scream in response to being cuddled or picked up or may seem indifferent to touch. Social interactions are characterized by a lack of reciprocity or spontaneous social overtures.

The nature of the social interactions of autistic individuals differs according to the cognitive and developmental level of the child; however, they continue to be deficient or unusual as compared to peers. For example, young children with autism frequently display relatively little interest in seeking out social interaction and prefer solitary activities. They may also respond with relative indifference to strangers and even to their parents (Volkmar, Carter, et al., 1997).

Abnormal or absent social behaviours are noted in the first two years of life of most children with autism.

Whereas the social environment is of particular interest to normally developing infants and young children, as well as to some children with intellectual disabilities, children with autism are often much more responsive to the non-social environment and curious about inanimate objects or sensory stimuli. Minor changes or unpredictability in the environment (e.g., routines, rearrangement of furniture or objects) can lead to emotional outbursts. Over time, older individuals with autism spectrum disorders may display some attachments to family members and show differential awareness of strangers, but they may continue to have difficulty with social interactions (Sigman & Mundy, 1989).

Autistic individuals without expressive language often do not use the nonverbal signals (e.g., eye contact, gestures, or pointing) that usually guide social interaction. Studies of social orientation indicate that infants with autism show little interest in the human face and often avoid eye contact. In addition, subsequent preverbal social communication skills such as smiling, pointing, and joint attention are frequently absent or significantly delayed. The lack of these skills hampers subsequent symbolic development, including imitation and symbolic play. Whereas normally developing children, and some older children with intellectual disability, readily imitate actions involved in interactive games such as "peekaboo" and "pat-a-cake," children with autism rarely initiate social interaction and prefer solitary activities involving repetitive or stereotyped actions with objects (Stone, Lemanek, Fishel, Fernandez, & Altemeier, 1990).

VERBAL AND NONVERBAL COMMUNICATION

The first three years of a child's life involves rapid development of expressive language. In normally developing children, verbal skills begin with babbling and progress to single words, short but meaningful phrases, and then sentences. However, approximately 50 percent of children with autism are mute. Those who do develop speech often do not communicate meaningfully (Kim, Paul, Tager-Flusberg, & Lord, 2014). Moreover, those who do develop language often have speech that is abnormal in tone and content. As a result, two-way reciprocal conversations are difficult. There is some evidence to suggest that children with fluent speech (i.e., three-word phrases produced spontaneously and regularly in an effort to communicate) by age five are more likely to have higher academic achievement and better-developed adaptive skills by adolescence than are children without such speech by age five (Venter et al.,1992). This measure was found to be as effective in predicting outcome as early IQ or language tests (Lord & Paul, 1997). Nonverbal joint attention and play skills prior to age five have also been found to predict the acquisition of language (Mundy, Sigman, & Kasari, 1990).

Echolalia is a common characteristic of speech in children with autism. In this condition, the child will repeat another person's words or phrases, using the same or similar intonation. **Pronoun reversal** is also common; autistic individuals often refer to themselves as "he" or "she" rather than "I," perhaps because they have trouble shifting reference between speaker and listener or a third party. This aspect of language is thought to be related to deficits in joint attention and to difficulties in understanding the perspectives of others and the distinction between the self and the other (Lord & Paul, 1997; Kim et el., 2014). The latter inability to attribute mental states to oneself and others is thought to be a unique characteristic of individuals with autism spectrum disorder; and early researchers identified this as lacking **theory of mind** (Happé & Frith, 1995).

BEHAVIOUR AND INTERESTS

Children with autism are often recognized by their restricted, repetitive, and unusual behaviours and interests. Hand flapping, rocking, and unusual repetitive movements are often seen as forms of self-stimulation. Individuals with autism also tend to focus on particular aspects of their environment to the exclusion of others and may engage in stereotyped behaviours such as spinning and tapping objects in a repetitive and non-functional way. They may also be preoccupied with sounds, objects, or patterns (e.g., toys organized in a particular way, routines carried out in a particular sequence). Change in such visual or auditory patterns and routines can be particularly stressful (Johnson, Myers, & the Council of Children with Disabilities, 2007). The patterns of sensory stimulation are increasingly studied in children and adults with autism spectrum disorders (Leekam, Nieto, Libby, Wing, & Gould, 2007); as well as the effects of sensory integration interventions (Watling & Dietz, 2007).

The behavioural heterogeneity of ASD is substantially influenced by differences in level of intellectual impairment, language impairment, and co-occurring diagnoses. Approximately 25 to 30 percent of individuals with autism function within the average range of intelligence. These individuals often have meaningful speech and are ultimately able to communicate and function more independently, although social difficulties limit the degree of community integration possible. A small proportion, often called **savants**, display islets of exceptional ability in areas such as mathematics, music, or art, or unusual feats of memory. This combination of extraordinary skills and significant social deficits was well portrayed by Stephen Wiltshire in the film *Beautiful Minds: A Voyage into the Brain* that can be found on Youtube.

Diagnostic Issues

The classification of autism has evolved since it was first included as a diagnostic category in DSM-III in 1980. Autism was first described as a spectrum in the seminal paper by Lorna Wing (1996). Although clinicians are able to reliably differentiate between individuals with autism and individuals who are typically developing, there is often diagnostic confusion between individuals historically called *classically autistic*, those with **Asperger's disorder**, and high-functioning individuals with autism. As a result, the DSM-5 has consolidated symptoms and included a single diagnostic category of Autism Spectrum Disorder, focusing on common behaviours and specific clinical characteristics, such as deficits in social-communication and restricted, repetitive patterns of behaviour (APA, 2013). In addition, information concerning levels of severity is outlined in Table 14.6 to assist diagnostic clarity and support planning.

Case Notes

Matthew was an 18-year-old man with Asperger's disorder, which now is covered by the term Autism Spectrum Disorder. He was relatively high functioning, with fairly well-developed expressive language, and was able to read and write. He was not echolalic in the traditional sense but did exhibit other features of autism,

TABLE 14.6　SEVERITY LEVELS FOR AUTISM SPECTRUM DISORDER

Severity level	Social communication	Restricted, repetitive behaviors
Level 3 "Requiring very substantial support"	Severe deficits in verbal and nonverbal social communication skills cause severe impairments in functioning, very limited initiation of social interactions, and minimal response to social overtures from others. For example, a person with few words of intelligible speech who rarely initiates interaction and, when he or she does, makes unusual approaches to meet needs only and responds to only very direct social approaches.	Inflexibility of behavior, extreme difficulty coping with change, or other restricted/ repetitive behaviors markedly interfere with functioning in all spheres. Great distress/ difficulty changing focus or action.
Level 2 "Requiring substantial support"	Marked deficits in verbal and nonverbal social communication skills; social impairments apparent even with supports in place; limited initiation of social interactions; and reduced or abnormal responses to social overtures from others. For example, a person who speaks simple sentences, whose interaction is limited to narrow special interests, and who has markedly odd nonverbal communication.	Inflexibility of behavior, difficulty coping with change, or other restricted/repetitive behaviors appear frequently enough to be obvious to the casual observer and interfere with functioning in a variety of contexts. Distress and/or difficulty changing focus or action.
Level I "Requiring support"	Without supports in place, deficits in social communication cause noticeable impairments. Difficulty initiating social interactions, and clear examples of atypical or unsuccessful responses to social overtures of others. May appear to have decreased interest in social interactions. For example, a person who is able to speak in full sentences and engages in communication but whose to-and-fro conversation with others fails, and whose attempts to make friends are odd and typically unsuccessful.	Inflexibility of behavior causes significant interference with functioning in one or more contexts. Difficulty switching between activities. Problems of organization and planning hamper independence.

such as occasional hand flapping and obsessive behaviour. He was able to interact socially to some extent but in a rather rigid, stilted fashion. In addition, his way of approaching individuals, especially young women, was often intrusive and inappropriate.

Matthew had always lived at home with his parents. He took the bus to school, where he was integrated into regular classes for computer and physical education and spent the rest of the day in a special class for students who needed one-to-one learning support. Matthew enjoyed sports, especially swimming and playing basketball with his classmates. He also liked to go to the mall, where he could spend his allowance on computer games. In the past year, he had become very involved with the Internet and spent hours online.

Through the school-to-community transition program, Matthew was assigned to a job coach who helped him develop his computer skills to prepare for a work placement at the local library gathering research information from the Web.

ASPERGER'S DISORDER

Some individuals with autism spectrum disorder do not have significantly delayed cognitive or language development. Such individuals are often clinically referred to as having Asperger's disorder. Except for social skills, their adaptive behaviour and interest in the environment are age appropriate, and they may indicate interest in social interaction and establishing friendships or relationships. However, their interactions are frequently observed as socially awkward, odd, or eccentric (Volkmar, et al., 1997).

The symptoms of Asperger's disorder were noted in the literature long before the disorder was recognized. In 1944, a year after Kanner first described autistic children, Hans Asperger described a group of children with similar characteristics. Controversy continues as to whether the disorders described by Kanner and by Asperger are separate conditions or represent different parts of a continuum of autistic spectrum disorders as outlined in DSM-5. Generally, Asperger's disorder has been viewed as a mild version of autism associated with higher intellectual functioning (Gillberg & Gillberg, 1989; Waterhouse et al., 1996).

In recent years, people with Asperger's disorder or with similar traits have been increasingly portrayed in the media. For example, think of Sheldon on *The Big Bang Theory*. Do you think that Sheldon's affected speech patterns, his limited interests, and his difficulties in social interactions meet the criteria for Asperger's disorder? A more extreme example is Jerry Espenson, an attorney on *Boston Legal* who becomes very anxious when dealing with people and exhibits a number of unusual behaviours (e.g., purring, walking with hands on his lap) that are not necessarily typical of Asperger's syndrome. There has also been considerable speculation as to whether a number of famous people had Asperger's disorder (e.g., Canadian pianist Glenn Gould, Albert Einstein).

ASSESSMENT

Due to the heterogeneity and multi-faceted nature of autism spectrum disorders, assessments should be carried out by a multidisciplinary team, including a psychologist, psychiatrist, speech and language specialist, occupational therapist, and teacher. Audiological and neurological assessments may also be conducted. A comprehensive developmental approach to assessment is strongly recommended to obtain or clarify an initial diagnosis, which is necessary before parents can apply for funding or obtain specialized services, and to permit accurate documentation of strengths and deficits in various areas of functioning related to adaptation in day-to-day life (Perry, Condillac, & Freeman, 2002). Among a variety of assessment tools available The Autism Diagnostic Observation Schedule-Second Edition (ADOS-2; Lord et al., 2012) and the Autism Diagnostic Interview–Revised (ADI-R; Lord, Rutter, Le Couteur, & Lord, 2003) are two measures now widely utilized as instruments of choice to evaluate characteristics of autism spectrum disorders. The ADI-R is a structured interview that takes about 90 minutes to complete, whereas the ADOS-2 is a standardized observational measure with different activities according to the age and language abilities of the child.

Etiology

Since Kanner (1943) first presented his 11 cases in the 1940s, the etiology of autism has been a topic of considerable debate and controversy (Glidden, 2001). In the past 30 years, the focus of research has shifted from psychogenic to biological factors.

Genetic factors are now considered to play a dominant role in the development of autism spectrum disorders. The relatively high frequency of autism among siblings of a person with autism; the frequent occurrence of autistic features in individuals with Fragile X syndrome, phenylketonuria (PKU), and tuberous sclerosis; and evidence that the phenotype (the pattern of social, cognitive, and behavioural abnormalities) extends beyond autism support a strong genetic component (Rutter, Bailey, Simonoff, & Pickles, 1997). Overall in about 25 percent of cases of ASD an identifiable genetic cause in the form of copy number variation or mutation is present (Ziats & Rennert, 2016).

For the past two decades, there has been a great deal of media attention concerning a link between the measles/mumps vaccine (MMR) and autism. This concern continues despite the original research being discredited due to a lack of empirical research supporting this link and strong scientific evidence pointing to genetic causes of autism. Parents continue to express considerable concern to the point that they are refusing to have their children vaccinated. The official withdrawal of the original article by the journal publishers and the fact that Wakefield lost his licence to practise in Britain after charges of professional misconduct (Burns, 2010) do not seem to have had much impact on the concerns of parents and the general public regarding the safety of vaccines. Indeed, concerns were raised further when it was suggested that the chemical thimerosol or other preservatives in vaccines were causal agents. Again, concerns continued despite the removal of thimerosol from all vaccines and despite court rulings that denied the links between the MMR vaccine or thimerosol and autism (Fombonne, 2008).

4 **BEFORE MOVING ON**

> Media coverage of the rising rates of autism has fuelled the concerns of parents and the general public. Describe reasons for the varying prevalence rates. How might you address this problem?

Treatment and Intervention

MEDICATIONS AND NUTRITIONAL SUPPLEMENTS

Although biological factors in the etiology of autism have received the most attention in recent years, no medications have been developed specifically to treat the core symptoms of autism (Posey & McDougall, 2001). Nevertheless, the prescription of medications for individuals with autism spectrum disorders has increased significantly in recent years (Filipek, Steinberg-Epstein, & Book, 2006), with a threefold increase in the use of antidepressants, particularly related to prescription of SSRIs for perseverative behaviour (Aman, Lam, & Collier-Crespin, 2003). Anti-psychotic medications are commonly prescribed to address hyperactivity, impulsivity, irritability, and aggression (Posey, Stigler, Erickson, & McDougle, 2008). A survey indicated that 70 percent of children with autism over age eight are receiving some **psychotropic medication** (Oswald & Sonenklar, 2007).

Medications are generally used to regulate levels of neurotransmitters (e.g., serotonin, dopamine, norepinephrine) thought to contribute to maladaptive behaviours frequently associated with autism. Currently, the two best-studied medications in autism include a first-generation agent, haloperidol (Haldol), and a second-generation agent, risperidone (Risperdal). Other second-generation medications, including aripiprazole (Abilify) and olanzapine (Zyprexa), continue to be studied (Malone, 2008; Kwok, 2003). Research evidence summarized by McDougle, Price, and Volkmar (1994) suggested that drugs that increase 5-HT neurotransmission (e.g., clomipramine) may facilitate reduction of repetitive behaviours and aggression and help improve social skills. Dopamine receptor antagonists such as haloperidol are effective in reducing challenging behaviours, but extrapyramidal side effects and tardive dyskinesia (although less with risperidone) can be problematic (Joshi, Percy, & Brown, 2002). Stimulants such as methylphenidate (Ritalin) and clonidine may help to reduce distractibility and hyperactivity. Studies of naltrexone (Neo-Synalar, Nupercainal) have shown some benefit in reducing hyperactivity but little effect on social skills and self-injurious behaviour and aggression. While there was considerable interest in fenfluramine in the treatment of social and sensory functioning, more recent controlled studies have not demonstrated significant effects on the core symptoms of autism. In addition, research data on the six most frequently prescribed medications—methylphenidate (Ritalin), thioridazine (Mellaril), diphenhydramine (Benadryl), phenytoin (Dilantin), haloperidol (Haldol), and carbamazepine (Tegretol)—indicate benefits in less than one-third of cases and adverse reactions in almost half of cases (Rimland & Baker, 1996).

Alternative approaches, including nutritional supplements such as megadoses of vitamin B6 and magnesium, vitamin C, and folic acid, have become popular because they do not have the side effects of prescription drugs (Rimland & Baker, 1996). Well-controlled research on their effectiveness, however, is extremely limited (see Kidd, 2002, for a review). A recent randomized, double-blind, placebo-controlled study, however, provided some support for the effectiveness of omega-3 fatty acid supplements in reducing hyperactivity and stereotyped behaviours (Amminger et al., 2007).

BEHAVIOURAL INTERVENTIONS

Behavioural interventions focusing on cognitive, communication, and behavioural challenges have for many years been demonstrated to be effective with children with autism. In the 1970s, pioneering work by Ivor Lovaas and colleagues began the Young Autism Project at the University of California Los Angeles, which offered behavioural programs designed to alleviate symptoms of autism. Such programs, which were also used with individuals with developmental disorders, focused on developing self-help skills, language, appropriate social interactions, and academic skills and on reducing maladaptive behaviours, including self-stimulation, stereotyped actions, self-injury, and aggression (Lovaas, Koegel, Simmons, & Long, 1973; Lovaas & Smith, 1988).

Reviews of behavioural intervention studies (Horner, Carr, Strain, Todd, & Reed, 2002; Matson, Benavidez, Compton, Paclawskyj, & Baglio, 1996) highlight tantrums, aggression, stereotypy, and self-injurious behaviour as the most frequently addressed challenging behaviours among people with autism. Since the 1990s, the focus has been on stimulus- and instruction-based interventions. Furthermore, evidence is strong for the effectiveness of proactive and positive interventions, with reductions in challenging behaviours occurring in 80 to 90 percent of cases (Horner et al., 2002). Such high success rates depend upon comprehensive functional assessment of reinforcement contingencies and other environmental factors prior to implementation of the intervention (Carr et al., 1999; Tassé, 2006).

Improvements in behavioural approaches over the years have led to increasingly positive results; thus, **applied behavioural analysis** and early intensive behavioural intervention (EIBI) programs, along with targeted government funding, have expanded across North America. Some studies indicate that 75 to 95% of children who participated in EIBI programs developed useful speech by age five (McGee, Morrier, & Daly, 1999). In addition, follow-up studies involving well-controlled, relatively intense (25+ hours per week) programs have reported significant gains (Smith, Groen, & Wynn, 2000). Although some outcome studies have reported that some clients were able to function at a normal level (Green, 1996; Howard, Sparkman, Cohen, Green, & Stanislaw, 2005; Sallows & Graupner, 2005), an evaluation of a large publicly funded and community-based EIBI program in Ontario suggests that outcomes of such programs are variable. In this project, although EIBI was found to lead to successful outcomes for the majority of children, with 75% showing some gains during EIBI and 11% achieving average functioning, many children made no improvements or exhibited more symptoms after receiving the intervention (Perry et al., 2008).

A systematic review of EIBI (Howlin, Magiati, & Charman, 2009) found strong evidence supporting its use; however, the authors note that the greatest treatment gains occur in the first 12 months and that response to intervention varies widely. The continuing need for randomized control trials to clearly demonstrate the efficacy of EIBI was emphasized. It is important to note that non-intensive interventions focusing on communication and social interaction skills are also supported by evidence from randomized control trials (e.g., Howlin, Gordon, Pasco, Wade, & Charman, 2007; Kasari, Freeman, & Paparella, 2006).

Studies have demonstrated that children with autism who begin EIBI before the age of five can develop verbal communication skills (Koegel, 1995). Many programs continue to use traditional operant conditioning principles, shaping and modelling to teach verbal imitation, labelling, asking questions, and appropriate verbal responding (Lovaas, 1977). However, the pragmatics of communication in social situations, including eye contact, appropriate affect, inflection, and conversational skills, also need to be included in such training programs (Koegel, 2000). Communication and social skills are strongly interrelated, and evidence suggests that improved communication skills are often associated with reduced challenging behaviours, such as tantrums, aggression, and self-injury (Donnellan, Mirenda, Mesaros, & Fassbender, 1984). As a result, communication and social skills training are important components of early intervention.

For individuals with autism who do not have functional expressive language, other augmentative communication systems have been developed. Although early studies suggested that manual sign language might be an effective approach, alone or as part of a "total communication" approach (Mirenda & Schuler, 1988), a critical review of the research literature (Schwartz & Nye, 2006) suggests that there is limited evidence that manual sign language training provides significant improvements in some individuals with autism. Alternatively, the use of picture exchange communication systems (PECS) has grown in recent years for children with autism spectrum disorder, especially in the school system. This approach has the advantage of promoting initiated interaction with a variety of communication partners (i.e., the child hands a person a picture to make a request or comment) and motivation due to natural reinforcement. A recent review of empirical research (Preston & Carter, 2009) provides preliminary support indicating that individuals with little or no speech can learn to use PECS; however, to date there is only limited empirical evidence indicating related improvements in associated challenging behaviour, social skills, or speech development.

The fast growing field of computer technology has provided a range of new digital platforms for augmentative or alternative communication strategies. For example, persons with autism have been taught to touch words and pictures on a speech-generating device or computer tablet to make requests or to answer questions. A critical review of the literature highlights initial evidence supporting the use of such devices with individuals with autism (van der Meer & Rispoli, 2010). (See Focus box 14.1 for an example of an approach that did not fulfill its promise.)

Helping people with autism to develop social competence is another important area of intervention. *Social competence* refers to a complex set of skills and competencies needed to navigate social relationships and includes social skills; an ability to regulate one's emotions and behaviours; and an understanding of the social environment, including having theory of mind (Stichter et al., 2010). Group interventions targeting specific social skills and social competence are associated with gains in positive peer interactions, reduced anxiety, and improvements in specific skills such as active listening (Cotugno, 2009). The most frequently addressed social skills behaviours include initiating contact, responding

---

FOCUS 14.1

The Dangers of Hope: Lessons from Facilitated Communication and Other Miracle Cures

For decades, alternative approaches to overcoming various forms of disability have passed in and out of fashion. The success of such movements has been described as a function of "the unhappiness of clients and the vividness of their dreams" (Toch, 1971, p. 44). Parents and caregivers who become strong proponents of alternative approaches frequently ignore concerns raised by professionals and "non-believers." Furthermore, the beliefs of such supporters tend not to change despite strong research evidence disconfirming their views. Families of children with autism seem to be particularly vulnerable to the claims made about unvalidated interventions (Jacobson, Mulick, & Schwartz, 1995).

One of the most controversial techniques to attract such attention is facilitated communication (FC). Claims of dramatic and rapid improvements in behaviour and functioning gave parents great hope. However, research findings have not supported the continued use of this type of communication training.

Facilitated communication (FC) training, developed in Australia in the 1970s, was introduced to Canada and the United States in 1990 by Douglas Biklen from Syracuse University. The technique is described as a "teaching strategy used with people with severe communication impairment requiring aided communication who are not yet able to access a communication aid independently but for whom direct access with their hands is a realistic and desirable goal" (Crossley, 1992). Individuals with communication difficulties are taught to point to pictures, letters, or objects by a facilitator who provides various types of physical support to the hand or forearm. Physical support, it was suggested, can overcome neuromotor problems that limit the

individual's ability to initiate movements, thus interfering with communication. Letterboards, typewriters, or talking computers are often used as part of this process.

The FC technique aroused great hope, excitement and controversy in Canada, Australia, and the United States (Minnes, 1992; Prior & Cummins, 1992). Remarkable success stories emerged of apparently low-functioning children with autism who suddenly demonstrated the ability to read and produce sentences expressing sophisticated ideas and feelings. However, concerns were soon raised about the "ouija board" effect: Were these really the child's own thoughts, or were facilitators unintentionally influencing the child's choice of symbol through subtle body movements (Rimland, 1991).

Over the next few years, dozens of well-controlled studies on FC (see Green, 1994) were conducted to determine reliability and validity of the technique; especially due to numerous reports of FC being used to describe physical and sexual abuse resulting in court cases. The results indicated that, in the majority of cases, messages were not being communicated independently; rather, facilitators were unwittingly influencing the messages being communicated (Rimland, 1993; Wheeler, Jacobson, Paglieri, & Schwartz, 1993). The results of an intensive, multi-method validation study did not provide support for the emergence of hidden literacy skills. Moreover, they noted an "abdication effect," whereby students who could perform basic communication tasks independently became passive when a facilitator was involved (Bebko, Perry, & Bryson, 1996; Perry, Bryson, & Bebko, 1993). ●

appropriately, and engaging in reciprocal interactions. In a majority of studies, the operant conditioning principles have been the foundation for interventions using positive reinforcement (i.e., using praise, tokens, stickers, and so on) for appropriate behaviour (Matson et al., 1996). Through the use of task analysis, target behaviours are broken down into steps, including prerequisite skills. For example, eye contact and joint attention are taught as precursors to asking and responding to questions (Goldstein & Wickstrom, 1986). Skills taught in this way need to be generalized to other individuals and other environments. One successful way of addressing this challenge is the use of typically developing peers as tutors or mediators in school and community settings (McConnell, 2002; Rogers, 2002). In addition parent assisted programs have been found effective for developing appropriate social skills of children and adolescents with autism spectrum disorders (Laugeson, Frankel, Mogil, & Dillon, 2008).

Learning Disorders

Case Notes

Justin is a 13-year-old boy in Grade 8 who was diagnosed with a specific learning disorder at age eight. As a preschooler, Justin received speech and language intervention to address his language delays and difficulties with the articulation of speech sounds. In kindergarten, Justin's teacher noted that he had more trouble than most children in the class in learning his alphabet. By Grade 1, he still could not print his name, nor could he recognize letters or numerals consistently. Justin's parents were perplexed because Justin seemed very bright. For example, he took an interest in the solar system and had memorized the names of the planets. Justin was mechanically inclined and he loved to figure out how to reassemble his family's appliances.

By Grade 3, Justin's struggles with reading and writing affected all areas of school functioning. He read slowly and laboriously, often guessing at a word by using the first letter. The results of a comprehensive psychological assessment revealed that Justin's overall level of intelligence fell in the high-average range, ranking above 86 percent of his peers. He showed specific deficits in phonological processing, which affected his ability to read and to produce written work. Justin began to see himself as stupid and was bullied at school. However, in Grade 8, he was introduced to adaptive technology, including a computer software program that read aloud text as he followed along. He learned keyboarding skills and how to use software effectively to organize his ideas and to check his spelling and grammar. With the aid of a teacher who took a particular interest in him, Justin began to experience greater success at school, although he continued to require more time and effort at homework than did his peers.

HISTORICAL PERSPECTIVE

Learning disorders were first identified in the nineteenth century when physicians observed patients who appeared to be intelligent and physically healthy yet were unable to read and write. The terminology used to reflect this presentation has varied over the years, as have beliefs about the mechanisms underlying the learning impairments. In the early years, most understood reading disorders to reflect a visual/perceptual impairment with difficulties in perceiving and processing letters and words (Snowling, 1996). In 1887, German ophthalmologist Rudolf Berlin coined the term *dyslexia* from the Greek words for "impaired word," while in 1886, British physician W. Pringle Morgan published a case study in the *British Medical Journal* using the term *congenital wordblindness* (Shaywitz, Morris, & Shaywitz, 2008). Popular theories included the belief that individuals with dyslexia perceived letters backwards. However, advances in neuroimaging techniques and in reading research have given support to the understanding that reading disorders stem from a core deficit in **phonological processing** (Kudo, Lussier, & Swanson, 2015; Lonigan, 2006; Snowling & Melby-Lervag, 2016). In 1963, Samuel Kirk introduced the broader term **learning disabilities** to include individuals with difficulties in other arenas, such as mathematics and writing. In Canada, the *Education Act* (1990) included the term *learning disability* to define a subset of students with exceptionalities that required special education programming.

DIAGNOSTIC CRITERIA

In the DSM-5, a specific learning disorder is classified as a neurodevelopmental disorder. There are four essential features of the diagnosis: persistent difficulties learning and using key academic skills despite the provision of interventions that target those difficulties, performance of academic skills that are well below average for chronological age, appearance of the learning difficulties in the school years, and a recognition that learning difficulties are not attributable to other neurological conditions or intellectual disabilities (see Table 14.7).

According to the DSM-5, the specific learning disorder reflects a disruption to the normal pattern of explicit learning of academic skills. In comparison to previous versions of the DSM, the DSM-5 no longer requires a statistical discrepancy between intelligence (IQ) and academic achievement. This reflects research that refutes the validity of using a statistical discrepancy to diagnose a learning disorder (Maehler & Schuchardt, 2011; Mayes & Calhoun, 2005). Intelligence and academic achievement are continuously distributed variables, and selections of a cut-off point for a discrepancy score are arbitrary and inconsistent (Fuchs, Mock, Morgan, & Young, 2003). Moreover, there is no clear evidence that an intelligence/achievement discrepancy is related to learning intervention outcome (Buttner & Hasselhorn, 2011).

Within the diagnostic criteria, the DSM-5 does not require the identification of cognitive processes nor does it address how these processes may contribute to functional impairments in academic learning.

TABLE 14.7   DSM-5 DIAGNOSTIC CRITERIA FOR SPECIFIC LEARNING DISORDER

A. Difficulties learning and using academic skills, as indicated by the presence of at least one of the following symptoms that have persisted for at least 6 months, despite the provision of interventions that target those difficulties:
   1. Inaccurate or slow and effortful word reading (e.g., reads single words aloud incorrectly or slowly and hesitantly, frequently guesses words, has difficulty sounding out words).
   2. Difficulty understanding the meaning of what is read (e.g., may read text accurately but not understand the sequence, relationships, inferences, or deeper meanings of what is read).
   3. Difficulties with spelling (e.g., may add, omit, or substitute vowels or consonants).
   4. Difficulties with written expression (e.g., makes multiple grammatical or punctuation errors within sentences; employs poor paragraph organization; written expression of ideas lacks clarity).
   5. Difficulties mastering number sense, number facts, or calculation (e.g., has poor understanding of numbers, their magnitude, and relationships; counts on fingers to add single-digit numbers instead of recalling the math fact as peers do; gets lost in the midst of arithmetic computation and may switch procedures).
   6. Difficulties with mathematical reasoning (e.g., has severe difficulty applying mathematical concepts, facts, or procedures to solve quantitative problems).
B. The affected academic skills are substantially and quantifiably below those expected for the individual's chronological age, and cause significant interference with academic or occupational performance, or with activities of daily living, as confirmed by individually administered standardized achievement measures and comprehensive clinical assessment. For individuals age 17 years and older, a documented history of impairing learning difficulties may be substituted for the standardized assessment.
C. The learning difficulties begin during school-age years but may not become fully manifest until the demands for those affected academic skills exceed the individual's limited capacities (e.g., as in timed tests, reading or writing lengthy complex reports for a tight deadline, excessively heavy academic loads).
D. The learning difficulties are not better accounted for by intellectual disabilities, uncorrected visual or auditory acuity, other mental or neurological disorders, psychosocial adversity, lack of proficiency in the language of academic instruction, or inadequate educational instruction.

CONTROVERSY IN DIAGNOSIS

According to the DSM-5, assessment of cognitive processing deficits is not required in order to diagnose a specific learning disorder. In contrast, theorists who support the concordance-discordance model (C-DM; Hale & Fiorello, 2004) suggest that specific impairments in cognitive processing are defining features of learning disorders (Backenson et al., 2015; Hale et al., 2010; Menon, 2016; Peng & Fuchs, 2010; Scanlon, 2013). Assessing and understanding the underlying processes that contribute to learning is vital for the development of compensatory strategies, accommodations, and self-advocacy, and for supporting good mental health (Milligan, Phillips, & Morgan, 2015). However, there is a lack of clear evidence to support causal links between cognitive processes and specific academic impairments.

DSM-5 guidelines do not rule out the assessment of cognitive processing, but they also do not provide guidelines for inclusion or interpretation of processing variables (Cavendish, 2013). In Canada, many psychologists in clinical practice utilize the criteria suggested by the Learning Disabilities Association of Ontario (LDAO, 2001) and the Learning Disabilities Association of Canada (LDAC, 2002) as either an alternative or a supplement to the DSM-5. In addition, for the purposes of identification of learning exceptionalities within the Ontario education system, the Ministry of Education Policy/Program Memorandum #8 (2014) is more closely aligned with the LDAO definition than with DSM-5 (www.edu.gov.on.ca/extra/eng/ppm/ppm8.pdf).

Harrison and Holmes (2012) argue for the need for a consensus definition to unite research and clinical practices.

 BEFORE MOVING ON

What are your thoughts on the importance of assessing cognitive processing?

SPECIFIC LEARNING DISORDERS

WITH IMPAIRMENT IN READING   There is general agreement that the core deficit underlying a reading disorder (also known as **dyslexia**) is an impairment in phonological processing (Lonigan, 2006; Shaywitz et al., 2008; Power et al., 2016). Reading requires an understanding that spoken words are composed of the smallest segments of language (phonemes) and that there is a connection between elements of printed words (letters) and phonemes (Sandak, Mencl, Frost, & Pugh, 2004). Children who struggle with reading may have trouble discerning whether words rhyme with each other, may not be able to count syllables in a word, may not detect syllable stress, and/or may struggle to delete individual speech sounds (Power et al., 2016). Individuals with a reading disorder may also have difficulties with reading fluency, resulting in reading skills that are accurate but effortful and slow (Katzir, Youngsuk, Wolf, O'Brien, & Kennedy, 2006).

WITH IMPAIRMENT IN MATHEMATICS   In contrast to the consensus regarding the mechanisms of reading disorders, there are differing theories with respect to core deficits associated with mathematics disorders (also known as developmental **dyscalculia**) (Wong, Ho, & Tang, 2017).

The number sense hypothesis suggests that learning disorder math difficulties reflect an inability to process numerical quantities, including making judgments about quantity and reasoning with symbolic representations of quantity (Ashkenazi et al., 2013; Butterworth, Varma, & Laurillard, 2011). An alternate hypothesis suggests that math disorders reflect core deficits in working memory (Geary, 2011; Menon, 2016; Szucs et al., 2013). However, a number of behavioural factors complicate the identification and diagnosis of math disabilities. For example, low performance in math may reflect factors such as anxiety about performance or a deliberate avoidance of math (Mammarella et al., 2015). Despite a perception that males may be better at math than females, the evidence suggests that there are no sex differences in math performance over time, although females report less motivation and confidence in self-concept regarding math (Royer & Walles, 2007).

WITH IMPAIRMENT IN WRITTEN EXPRESSION Specific learning disorders characterized by difficulties in written expression (including developmental **dysgraphia**) are the least well researched and understood (Beringer, Richards, & Abbott, 2015; Fenwick et al., 2015). Impairments in spelling, writing fluency, and written expression are thought to reflect deficits in multiple neuropsychological processes, including processing speed, working memory, and executive functioning (Fenwick et al., 2015; Semrud-Clikeman & Harder, 2011).

⑥ BEFORE MOVING ON

Why do you think that specific learning disorders with impairment in written expression are the least well understood? What processes are required to produce written work?

PREVALENCE

Specific learning disorders are persistent and continue over the lifespan. The variability in terminology and methodology in specific learning disorder research makes it challenging to identify a general prevalence rate (Fortes et al., 2016; Pham & Riviere, 2015). In the United States, the lifetime prevalence rate of specific learning disorders is 9.7% (Martinez et al., 2016). Rates for reading disorders are estimated to range from 5 to 17% percent among school-aged children (Olzernov-Palchik et al., 2016) and are the most common form of LD, accounting for 80 percent of learning disabilities (Pham & Riviere, 2015; Shaywitz et al., 2008). Mathematics learning disorders have a prevalence rate of 6 to 7 % (Geary, 2011; Wong, Ho & Tang, 2017). More boys than girls are identified with reading disorders (Shaywitz, Shaywitz, Fletcher, & Escobar, 1990), although the issue is complicated by a referral bias for identification and diagnosis in favour of boys whose learning challenges may come to the attention of educators because of disruptive classroom behaviours (Shaywitz et al., 2008).

ETIOLOGY

The etiology of learning disorders is multifactorial. Dyslexia, for example, is both familial and hereditary (Shaywitz, 2008). Snowling and Melby-Lervag's (2016) meta-analysis indicates that familial risk for dyslexia is universal across cultures, reflecting an interaction of genetic, environmental risk, and protective factors. Evidence from twin studies suggests that 50 to 60 percent of the variance in reading is explained by genetics (Olson & Byrne, 2005; Vellutino et al., 2004). Similarly, 50 to 67 percent of the individual differences in mathematics achievement is attributable to genetic variation (Geary, 2011). However, research in the field of response-to-intervention (RTI) approaches to reading disorders (Fuchs & Fuchs, 2006) suggests that environmental changes in the form of specific reading instruction can influence neural systems in the brain (Shaywitz, 2008; Temple, Deutsch, Poldrack, Miller, & Tallal, 2003). Converging neurological evidence suggests that reading activates areas of the left hemisphere, including the tempoparietal cortex and left inferior frontal gyrus (Ashkenazi et al., 2013). Research in the field of mathematics suggests that the right hemisphere is implicated in quantitative processing, including the interior parietal sulcus for tasks such as performing arithmetic calculations (Ashkenazi et al., 2013). The posterior parietal areas of the brain are associated with numerical competence (Simon & Rivera, 2007).

THE RELATIONSHIP BETWEEN LEARNING DISORDERS AND MENTAL HEALTH

Individuals with learning disabilities (LDs) are two to three times more likely to experience mental health challenges (Wilson et al., 2009) and to experience higher rates of stress and mental illness in comparisons with adolescents without learning disabilities (Vedi & Bernard, 2012). For many children and youth with LDs, this may reflect the outcomes of lived experience with learning disabilities; experiencing repeated failure, anxiety about expectations, and a diminished sense of mastery, for example (Milligan, Badali, & Spiriou, 2013). In a seminal meta-analysis of social skills research, Kavale and Forness (1996) found that 75 percent of students with LDs have lower levels of social competence than do comparison children, as assessed by teachers, peers, and themselves. Children and youth who are intelligent but who have specific difficulties in processing information often have difficulty with tasks such as understanding sarcasm, reading body language, recalling information about social situations, or engaging in effective social problem solving (Milligan, Phillips, & Morgan, 2015). Without the protective factors of positive

FOCUS 14.2

Youth at Risk

Approximately 33% of youth in correctional institutions have been identified with learning disabilities (Cruise, Evans, & Pickens, 2011). Why are there so many youth with learning disabilities in the justice system? A number of theories attempt to explain the high correlation between learning difficulties, academic failure, and offences. The *school failure* hypothesis states that having a learning disability places a youth at higher risk for academic failure, lead-ing to negative self-image, increased risk of school dropout, and higher rates of delinquency (Shelton, 2006). Alternatively, the *susceptibility theory* suggests that youth with learning disabilities and problems with mental illness, impulse control, hyperactivity, and behavioural regulation are more vulnerable to opportunities to engage in delinquent behaviour (Chen et al., 2016; Grigorenko, 2006). ●

social relationships, children and youth with LDs experience greater peer victimization and bullying (Baumeister, Storch, & Geffken, 2008; Mishna, 2003), and social rejection (Bryan, Burstein, & Ergul, 2004). Chronic social and academic failures are associated with decreased feelings of self-worth (Vedi & Bernard, 2012). If unrecognized and not remediated, learning disabilities can lead to academic failure, dropping out from high school (Chen et al., 2016), and an increased risk of involvement with the youth justice system (Cruise, Evans, & Pickens, 2011; see Focus box 14.2).

There is emerging evidence to suggest that in addition to the social and emotional sequelae of learning disabilities, a large proportion of individuals with LDs also experience significant mental health challenges. Studies have found 50 percent (Magari et al., 2013) to 82.8 percent (Esmaili et al., 2016) of children diagnosed with a specific learning disorder met criteria for at least one other psychiatric disorder. This subset of individuals with learning disabilities and mental health issues (LDMH) may share common emotion dysregulation and processing difficulties (Milligan et al., 2015).

INTERVENTION

Evidence-based reading interventions target phonemic awareness, phonics, vocabulary development, reading fluency, and reading comprehension strategies, with a focus on explicit instruction, close monitoring of progress, and opportunities for supervised practice (Reschly, 2005). A response-to-intervention approach to reading identification and remediation uses a multi-tiered approach to instruction in which reading strategies are taught to children who are screened to be "at risk" for reading difficulties (Tran, Sanchez, Arellano, & Swanson, 2011). Those who continue to struggle are provided with a more intensive intervention. "Non-responders" to the second tier of intensive reading remediation are likely to be diagnosed with learning disabilities (Buttner & Hasselhorn, 2011).

Mental health intervention reflects a process of learning: Learning new skills, new methods of communication, and new ways of coping. Implementing evidence-based mental health therapies is more effective when the intervention is tailored to the child or youth's individual style of learning and information processing (Milligan et al., 2015).

Outcome research for youth with LD highlights the important role of schools and educators in promoting resiliency and a successful transition to adulthood. Key factors that predict success include providing students with a clear knowledge of LD and compensatory strategies (Skinner & Lindstrom, 2003) in order to promote self-advocacy skills (Test, Fowler, Wood, Brewer, & Eddy, 2005), a supportive school environment (Cruise, Evans, & Pickens, 2011; Malian & Nevin, 2002), positive relationships with effective teachers (Mather & Goldstein, 2001), and emotional support (Panicker & Chelliah, 2016). As Focus box 14.3 shows, with the right support, people with learning disabilities can be successful.

FOCUS 14.3

Famous People with Learning Disabilities

Throughout history, persons of interest and importance have overcome the challenges of suspected or identified learning disabilities to achieve success in their respective fields. These include historical figures such as Hans Christian Anderson (writer), Thomas Edison (inventor), and Woodrow Wilson (American president); business leaders such as Charles Schwab; scientists such as William Hewlett (Hewlett-Packard computers); actors and television personalities such as Tom Cruise, Orlando Bloom, Daniel Radcliffe, Whoopi Goldberg, and Jay Leno; musical artists such as Cher and Joss Stone; and athletes such as Tim Tebow, and Magic Johnson (*www.special-education-degree.net/25-famous-people-with-learning-disorders/*; Aaron, Phillips, & Larsen, 1988). ●

Jean Vanier, Founder of L'Arche

Jean Vanier (1928–) has been described as a social visionary with a keen sense of what makes a compassionate society. He has received many honours for his humanitarian efforts on behalf of individuals with developmental disabilities, including the Order of Canada. Jean Vanier is the son of former Canadian Governor General Georges P. Vanier and Pauline Vanier. He was educated in England and Canada, and after several years serving with the British and later the Canadian Navy he completed a doctorate in philosophy at the Institut Catholique de Paris. In 1964, Jean Vanier founded the first L'Arche community in Trosly, France, northeast of Paris, when he welcomed Raphael Simi and Philippe Seux, two men with disabilities, into his home. The first Canadian L'Arche community was established in 1969, and since that time 130 other L'Arche communities have been established on five continents. Philippe describes his early days with Vanier:

> The first time I met Jean Vanier, it was in a centre where we weren't allowed to leave. I saw him in the chapel, then he gave out soup. He impressed me right away. The table looked really small in front of him because he was so big…. Before, for me, [in the institution] that wasn't a life: all day sitting in a room. We couldn't do anything, we couldn't go outside, it was so boring, nothing to do, nothing. I even cried. I didn't feel good at all. Little by little, things got better at L'Arche. We started off doing things however we could. We cooked meals together, we helped with the food. (*www.larchecanada.ca*)

The L'Arche Mission includes three tenets: (1) to create homes where faithful relationships based on forgiveness and celebration are nurtured; (2) to reveal each person's unique value and the gift that each person has to offer to others; and (3) to change society by choosing to live relationships in community as a sign to the wider society that hope and love are possible. L'Arche recognizes the ability of many people with developmental disabilities to welcome and accept others and to gather a diversity of people together around them in harmony. L'Arche communities are ecumenical and interfaith, encouraging members of their communities to grow in their own faith tradition. L'Arche

David Cooper/Toronto Star/Getty Images

also welcomes people who do not have a religious affiliation.

Vanier, now in his eighties, has passed along his administrative responsibilities within L'Arche to others; however, he continues to live in one of the L'Arche communities in France, where he acts as a mentor to assistants. He is also a frequent speaker at conferences and meetings around the world.

Source: Used with permission of L'arche International.

SUMMARY

- Neurodevelopmental disorders are associated with varying degrees of damage to the brain occurring at different stages of development before, during, or after birth.

- Damage is manifested in a number of ways depending on the condition, including unusual physical features; particular types of cognitive, language, motor, or other deficits; and patterns of behaviour (e.g., hyperactivity, stereotypy, aggressiveness).

- An IQ or intellectual quotient as measured by standardized intelligence tests is the most basic criterion for intellectual/developmental disability; adaptive behaviour is another important component. It is important to address not only individuals' deficits but also their strengths and capabilities, and the supports needed to function well in a given environment.

- The etiology of neurodevelopmental disorders in general and intellectual disability in particular is complex.

In some disorders, the cause is clearly genetic (e.g., chromosomal abnormality). Intellectual disabilities can also be caused by environmental factors at different stages of development (e.g., maternal malnutrition, toxins, or maternal infections; oxygen deprivation; prematurity; or birth-related trauma). The postnatal environment can also significantly affect development. Intervention strategies for people with intellectual disabilities tend to focus on developing social and community living skills and reducing or managing challenging behaviours. Pharmaceutical interventions for severe behavioural problems and mental health difficulties associated with dual diagnosis are recommended. Sex education, while controversial, can increase sexuality awareness and reduce the risk of abuse while promoting more successful integration into the community. Genetic and supportive counselling for family members and parent training can reduce family stress and improve quality of life for individuals with developmental disorders and their families.

- The deinstitutionalization and mainstreaming movements have emphasized the importance of community integration. However they have also highlighted the potential risks of vulnerability and exploitation in community inclusion. Evaluation of community-based care and quality of life has become an important area of work for psychologists.

- Autism spectrum disorder is characterized by deficits in the areas of social communication and behavioural interests exhibited by a lack of social responsiveness or reciprocity, unusual sensory responses to the environment, absent or unusual expressive language and restrictive or repetitive behaviours. Higher-functioning individuals with higher intelligence, more expressive language, and fewer other symptoms are often categorized as having Asperger's disorder.

- Neurobiological and genetic factors are currently considered to play important roles in the development of autism, although the causal processes are still not clearly understood.

- Systematic intensive early intervention programs applying operant conditioning principles have been found effective in developing language and social skills and in managing challenging behaviour. A specific learning disorder according to DMS-5 includes four essential diagnostic features: persistent difficulties learning and using key academic skills despite the provision of interventions that target those difficulties; performance of academic skills that are well below average for chronological age;

appearance of the learning difficulties in the school years; and a recognition that learning difficulties are not attributable to other neurological conditions or intellectual disabilities.

- According to the LDAO definition, learning disabilities are a neurologically based disorder that affects one or more ways in which a person takes in, stores, or uses information. Individuals with learning disorders experience specific impairments in one or more of the cognitive processes related to learning.

- Cognitive processes include phonological processing, working memory, processing speed, language processing, visual-spatial processing, executive functions, and visual-motor processing.

- Learning disorders can impede academic achievement in the areas of reading, writing, or mathematics. They can also impact daily life, such as having difficulty with problem solving, organization, following multi-step instructions, or, sometimes, understanding sarcasm.

- Persons with learning disabilities are two to three times more likely to experience mental health challenges, including anxiety, and difficulties with social competence.

- Early identification by means of a comprehensive psychological assessment, academic remediation and accommodations in the school setting, and support or therapeutic intervention where appropriate, is vital for enabling individuals with LD to accomplish goals and to engage in fulfilling and productive lives.

KEY TERMS

acquiescence (p. 357)

amniocentesis (p. 360)

applied behavioural analysis (p. 376)

asexual (p. 368)

Asperger's disorder (p. 373)

autism (p. 371)

autism spectrum disorder (ASD) (p. 371)

behavioural phenotype (p. 358)

biopsychosocial (p. 370)

chorionic villus sampling (CVS) (p. 360)

cloak of competence (p. 357)

cognitive behavior therapy (p. 370)

deinstitutionalization (p. 367)

diagnostic overshadowing (p. 369)

dignity of risk (p. 370)

Down syndrome (p. 359)

dual diagnosis (p. 369)

dyscalculia (p. 379)

dysgraphia (p. 380)

dyslexia (p. 379)

echolalia (p. 373)

eugenics (p. 352)

facilitated communication (FC) (p. 377)

fetal alcohol syndrome disorder (FASD) (p. 361)

Fragile X syndrome (p. 364)

HIV (p. 361)

intellectual disability (p. 353)

learning disabilities (p. 378)

learning disorders (p. 378)

mosaicism (p. 359)

pathoplastic (p. 369)

phenylketonuria (PKU) (p. 360)

phonological processing (p. 378)

pronoun reversal (p. 373)

psychotropic medication (p. 375)

quality of life (p. 368)

rubella (p. 361)

savants (p. 373)

stereotypy (p. 353)

thalidomide (p. 362)

theory of mind (p. 373)

translocation (p. 359)

trisomy 21 (p. 359)

TRACY VAILLANCOURT

·

KHRISTA BOYLAN

CHAPTER
15

Behaviour and Emotional Disorders of Childhood and Adolescence

LEARNING OBJECTIVES

AFTER READING THIS CHAPTER, STUDENTS WILL BE ABLE TO:

1 Identify the current issues associated with assessing and treating children and adolescents with mental health problems.

2 Describe the prevalence of common childhood mental disorders (ADHD, disruptive behaviour disorders, and anxiety disorders) and their comorbidities.

3 Identify the symptoms and clinical features of common childhood mental disorders.

4 Explain how biological, psychological, and environmental factors can work together to increase the risk of developing these common childhood mental disorders.

5 Identify evidence-based psychological and pharmacological treatments for common childhood mental disorders.

When Sam was four, his mother could not leave him alone with his younger sister, Ellie. It was too dangerous because Sam always hit or pinched her. Reprimanding Sam seemed to do little to discourage his aggressive ways. When Sam entered kindergarten, his teacher raised concerns about his behaviour, indicating that he could not sit still and seemed to enjoy bullying his classmates. When Sam was seven, he started his first fire—a small one—at the park close to his house. By age 10, Sam was sneaking alcohol from his mother's supply. By age 12, he was a habitual glue sniffer, regularly truant from school, and still lighting fires and getting into fights at school and at home. Teachers described Sam as cruel and impulsive. His mother described him as angry and jaded.

Sam was finally seen by a clinician at age 13, after his school insisted he be assessed before he would be allowed to return from his latest suspension. During the assessment, Sam acknowledged that he was angry and irritable most of the time. He also admitted that he liked to drink and that "life was boring." Sam seemed to have little insight into how his behaviour affected those around him. He was not concerned about his poor grades or his family's distress over his behaviour. He just wanted to be "left alone"; he also wanted to find his father so that he could live with him. Under no circumstances was Sam willing to entertain the idea that he had any real problems and he promptly refused to see the clinician again.

Unfortunately, youth like Sam are common in the mental health system. They present to mental health clinics because someone is concerned about them, yet they themselves are unwilling to get help. Youth like Sam are challenging to assess, and they have many signs of current or insidious mental health problems. It is clear that Sam's mental health profile is multi-faceted. He has a smattering of symptoms that are consistent with several disorders, including conduct disorder (early onset), attention deficit/hyperactivity disorder, substance abuse, and perhaps a learning disorder. The complexity of Sam's case seems to be the norm and not the exception in children's mental health. Indeed, in our clinical experience working in child psychology and psychiatry, we most often see children who present with a variety of symptoms. These children, and their families, are often distressed by the way they are feeling and behaving. Their family lives tend to be complicated, and their social and academic lives are compromised. What is especially disconcerting is that the current mental health problems of these children and adolescents represent the beginning of a lifelong trajectory of psychological disturbances. Although this point is daunting and not very encouraging, what is hopeful is that many efficacious treatments are available for behavioural and emotional disorders of childhood and adolescence, and much is being learned about the etiology and developmental course of these disorders.

Historical Perspective of Child and Adolescent Mental Health

As noted by Neve and Turner (2001) in their review of the history of child psychiatry, "History dictates how the child is perceived." With the current means available to study children and families using genetic, neuroimaging, and other scientific methods, scientists and clinicians are helping to expand our knowledge of the complexity of mental disorders in children. Today, most researchers study child psychopathology within a framework that stipulates that mental disorders have some biological basis. However, this has not always been the case, and it is important to appreciate the significant progress that has been made in understanding mental disorders and psychopathology in children over the past centuries.

The recognition of mental disturbance or psychopathology in children has a history that dates to the early nineteenth century; however, the study of children's mental states has evolved most rapidly over the past three decades. Initial accounts of abnormal child behaviour were attributed to inadequate parenting, which meant insufficient moral discipline in upbringing. Because children were thought to be incapable of self-reflection and reason, their behavioural problems were seen as a reflection of their environments, hence they were not seen as having problems with their brain functions. The advent of mandatory schooling for children created the opportunity to identify those who had intellectual delays—the first problems to be identified and studied. Treatment reflected the (then-recognized) importance of providing quality care in early life for children through adequate hygiene, nutrition, exercise, and teaching of moral well-being to parents to improve their children's behaviour.

At the end of the nineteenth century, attention turned to causes of behaviour as related to abnormal brain functioning, based on observations that many disordered children had parents who were unwell or low in intellectual functioning (Still, 1932). A few prominent child psychiatrists advocated for the need for psychiatric assessment and hospitalization for some very dysfunctional or dangerous children. In the twentieth century, Leo Kanner's (1935) first textbook of child psychiatry provided a framework for assessing children and adolescents. This book included sections on (1) personality problems arising from physical illness, (2) psychosomatic problems, (3) problems with behaviour, and (4) practical guidance on how to obtain a mental health history and the use of psychotherapy as a form of treatment. At that time, child guidance clinics were being introduced in schools in the United States and England. These clinics employed child psychiatrists, psychologists, and social workers, reflecting the developing knowledge in the field of educational psychology.

The first forms of research into children's mental disorders were descriptions of children with *infantile autism* and behavioural manifestations of deficient maternal care and overprotection. It was not until the 1960s that epidemiological studies of mental disorders in children began to document the prevalence of common child behavioural problems. The first comprehensive population survey, the Isle of Wight Study (Rutter, Tizard, Yule, Graham, & Whitmore, 1976), included 9- to 11-year-olds, and the Ontario Child Health Study in the 1980s (Cadman, Boyle, Szatmari, & Offord, 1987; Offord et al., 1987; Offord, Boyle, & Racine, 1989) addressed questions that have continued to be of importance to child psychiatry. For example, What are the rates of youth psychiatric disorders? What is the role of intellectual development, physical impairment, and potential social influences on the diagnosis and prevalence of children's disorders? These works were influential because the researchers demonstrated that some childhood disorders persist into adolescence, and do so in characteristic ways.

The main diagnostic text for psychiatric disorders used in North America, the *Diagnostic and Statistical Manual of Mental Disorders* (DSM), has evolved over the years to include child psychiatric disorders (American Psychiatric Association [APA], 1980). Although it has become clear that some disorders have an onset only in childhood (e.g., autism spectrum disorder, intellectual developmental disorder, genetic syndromes; see Chapter 14), other disorders commonly diagnosed in children (e.g., anxiety disorders, mood disorders) may have an onset or occur only in childhood or in adulthood. It remains to be demonstrated whether the manifestations and symptoms of childhood- versus adult-onset mood and anxiety disorders are the same, but most research to date supports the hypothesis that they are.

Treatments in child psychiatry encompassed mostly family therapy and psychoanalytic therapy, influenced by the teachings of Anna Freud and Melanie Klein, prior to the discovery of medications to treat hyperactivity in the 1960s. Since that time, there has been increasing emphasis on the use of medications in children and adolescents, with consideration of not only their efficacy for the disorders in question, but in particular their safety and side effects on behaviour and cognition in the developing person.

CURRENT ISSUES IN ASSESSING AND TREATING CHILDREN AND ADOLESCENTS

Issues that continue to challenge and stimulate research in child psychology and psychiatry include the imperative to study age-specific variation in symptoms and to establish what is normal behaviour or emotion for a child based on his or her age. This is not only because children may present with different symptoms based on their cognitive stage, but also because change and development of new skills or brain maturation may be adaptive to children and reduce their impairments, or symptoms, substantially. This latter feature begs the question: What constitutes disorder in children and how long and how severe must it be to merit treatment? The answer to this question will require complex and challenging longitudinal research studies that examine the persistence and continuity of psychopathology across childhood and adolescence.

More so than adults, youth are influenced by their environments and the lives of others around them because they have less autonomy for their decisions. This reality can also influence the presentation of impairment or symptoms. Furthermore, those who report a child's problems are typically parents or teachers, and not the child per se. What is challenging about the gathering of information from different sources is that those rating child psychological symptoms rarely agree with each other (De Los Reyes & Kazdin, 2005; Offord et al., 1996), a lack of concordance that may be clinically relevant.

Factors particular to child and adolescent mental assessment, including developmental variation in symptoms as well as impairment and informant bias, emphasize the importance of comprehensive diagnostic assessment of the youth. Psychologists and psychiatrists therefore aim to identify mental disorder symptoms in patients, but seek additional information about developmental, medical, social, and educational functioning to obtain a more global picture of the child. Such information is required to direct the development and implementation of treatment plans for the child and his or her family.

In summary, the process of providing a diagnosis for a given clinical presentation and determining whether this diagnosis is valid and reliable is an ongoing effort in the case of adults, and even more so in the case of youth (Jensen, 2003; Wakefield, 1993). Research studies designed to measure continuity and change in children's psychological symptoms are required to support the possibility that some childhood problems do represent severe or long-term impairments and therefore may merit diagnosis. Such research will be more robust when biologically based indicators of impairment (cognitive testing, genetic markers, physiological parameters) are also measured.

① BEFORE MOVING ON

The assessment and treatment of children and youth with mental health issues are associated with many challenges that are specific to this pediatric population. What are some of the current issues associated with child and adolescent mental health assessment and treatment? How are these issues different from those that arise when assessing and treating adults?

Prevalence of Childhood Disorders

Mental disorders in childhood are typically divided into **externalizing problems**, including attention deficit/hyperactivity disorder (ADHD), oppositional defiant disorder (ODD), and conduct disorder (CD); and **internalizing problems**, including separation anxiety disorder (SAD),

selective mutism, reactive attachment disorder (RAD), anxiety disorders, and mood disorders, including the newly added DSM-5 **disruptive mood dysregulation disorder** (DMDD; see Table 15.1). Externalizing problems are also referred to as *disorders of undercontrolled behaviour,* whereas internalizing problems are also referred to as *disorders of overcontrolled behaviour.* Disruptive mood dysregulation disorder although classified as a mood disorder in the DSM-5, represents a perfect intersect between externalizing and internalizing problems, highlighting once again, the complexity of mental problems in childhood and adolescence. Indeed, although a distinction between externalizing and internalizing disorders is made, it is important to note that this distinction does not mean that the two types of disorders cannot coexist in the same person. In fact, **comorbidity** (the co-occurrence of two or more disorders or diseases) is the rule rather than the exception in mental health (see Angold, Costello, & Erkanli, 1999). Results from the National Comorbidity Survey Replication–Adolescent Supplement (NCS-A), a study of 10 123 American youth aged 13 to 18 years, confirm this point. In this nationally representative study, about 40 percent of youth with one psychiatric disorder met the diagnostic criteria for another psychiatric disorder (Merikangas et al., 2010). Moreover, longitudinal studies show that not only do children typically receive more than one diagnosis at a given time, but also that their current diagnosis is often predictive of their receiving the same diagnosis in the future (**homotypic continuity**) or receiving a different psychiatric diagnosis in the future (**heterotypic continuity**).

TABLE 15.1 DIAGNOSTIC CRITERIA FOR DISRUPTIVE MOOD DYSREGULATION DISORDER

A. Severe recurrent temper outbursts manifested verbally (e.g., verbal rages) and/or behaviorally (e.g., physical aggression toward people or property) that are grossly out of proportion in intensity or duration to the situation or provocation.

B. The temper outbursts are inconsistent with developmental level.

C. The temper outbursts occur, on average, three or more times per week.

D. The mood between temper outbursts is persistently irritable or angry most of the day, nearly every day, and is observable by others (e.g., parents, teachers, peers).

E. Criteria A-D have been present for 12 or more months. Throughout that time, the individual has not had a period lasting 3 or more consecutive months without all of the symptoms in Criteria A-D.

F. Criteria A and D are present in at least two of three settings (i.e., at home, at school, with peers) and are severe in at least one of these.

G. The diagnosis should not be made for the first time before age 6 years or after age 18 years.

H. By history or observation, the age at onset of Criteria A-E is before 10 years.

I. There has never been a distinct period lasting more than 1 day during which the full symptom criteria, except duration, for a manic or hypomanic episode have been met.
   Note: Developmentally appropriate mood elevation, such as occurs in the context of a highly positive event or its anticipation, should not be considered as a symptom of mania or hypomania.

J. The behaviors do not occur exclusively during an episode of major depressive disorder and are not better explained by another mental disorder (e.g., autism spectrum disorder, posttraumatic stress disorder, separation anxiety disorder, persistent depressive disorder [dysthymia]).
   Note: This diagnosis cannot coexist with oppositional defiant disorder, intermittent explosive disorder, or bipolar disorder, though it can coexist with others, including major depressive disorder, attention-deficit/hyperactivity disorder, conduct disorder, and substance use disorders. Individuals whose symptoms meet criteria for both disruptive mood dysregulation disorder and oppositional defiant disorder should only be given the diagnosis of disruptive mood dysregulation disorder. If an individual has ever experienced a manic or hypomanic episode, the diagnosis of disruptive mood dysregulation disorder should not be assigned.

K. The symptoms are not attributable to the physiological effects of a substance or to another medical or neurological condition.

For example, Costello et al. (2003) found that children with a history of a psychiatric disorder were three times more likely to have a diagnosis at follow-up compared to those with no previous disorder. They also found that panic disorders, psychosis, verbal tics, encopresis (boys only), and enuresis showed the highest level of homotypic continuity. In terms of heterotypic continuity, they found strong evidence from depression to anxiety and from ADHD to ODD.

The prevalence of child and youth mental disorders has been estimated in several large Canadian (Breton et al., 1999; Meltzer, Gatward, Goodman, & Ford, 2000; Offord et al., 1987) and American (Costello et al., 1996; Shaffer et al., 1996; Simonoff et al., 1997) epidemiological studies. These particular studies have been combined, and disorder-specific prevalence rates have been calculated (Waddell, McEwan, Shepherd, Offord, & Hua, 2005; Waddell, Offord, Shepherd, Hua, & McEwan, 2002). Importantly, only studies that (1) assessed symptoms and impairment using a standardized assessment protocol, (2) included multiple informants such as children, parents, and teachers, and (3) assessed at least 1000 children were included in the summary prevalence rates. As seen in Figure 15.1, anxiety disorders, conduct disorder, and ADHD are the most common psychiatric disorders among children and youth using data from North America. Keeping in mind that many children and youth have comorbid conditions, it is not surprising that the average community

APPLIED CLINICAL CASE

Bullying and Children's Mental Health

Shortly after creating a MySpace account, 13-year-old Megan Meier from Dardenne Prairie, Missouri, received a friendly message from 16-year-old Josh Evans. The two teens quickly hit it off and began an online romance that soon turned ugly. Josh told Megan that he did not want to continue the relationship because he had heard that she was not a good friend to others. Many other hurtful things were said online, including the suggestion that everyone hated Megan and that the world would be a better place without her in it. Megan was so upset by Josh's rejection that she took her own life on October 17, 2006. In the aftermath of her death, a disturbing twist was revealed: Josh Evans was not a real person, but rather had been co-created by Megan's former friend and that friend's mother, Lori Drew, age 47. The two invented Josh with the intention of soliciting information from Megan about her feelings toward Lori's daughter and to "mess with Megan."

Unfortunately, Megan's case is not an isolated incident—far from it. In 1982 three Norwegian boys aged 10 to 14 took their lives in response to bullying. These untimely deaths attracted media and public attention, which led to the initiation of a nationwide campaign against school bullying. Although the suicide of a Japanese 13-year-old in 1986 in response to bullying drew public attention to the issue, it was not until the suicide of another bullied youth in 1994 that Japan's Ministry of Education initiated its own efforts to address bullying in schools (Hymel, Schonert-Reichl, Bonanno, Vaillancourt, & Rocke-Henderson, 2009).

Closer to home, the start of the 2011 school year was rung in with horror as Ontario students Mitchell Wilson (age 11), Jamie Hubley (age 15), and Christopher Howell (age 17) all committed suicide in response to bullying. Despite these tragedies and other youth suicides, Canada's response to "bullycide" has been slow but improvements have started. For example, many provinces now formally addressed bullying in their safe school or education acts. This response is important because bullying represents a formidable threat to children's and youth's mental well-being. In fact, studies have shown that bullied children experience more internalizing disorders than do non-bullied children. They are also at risk for poor educational attainment and report experiencing

Cyberbullying and other forms of bullying are serious threats to mental well-being in youth.

more health-related concerns. Importantly, longitudinal studies of peer-victimized children have shown that while some experience bullying as a consequence of poor adjustment and behaviour, for most, peer abuse *causes* maladjustment (see McDougall & Vaillancourt, 2015). What's more, Vaillancourt and colleagues (2011) showed that being bullied affects the brain. Using a longitudinal design in which Canadian children were assessed four times over a two-year period, these researchers found that peer victimization predicted elevated symptoms of depression, which in turn predicted dysregulation of the hypothalamic-pituitary-adrenal (HPA) axis (stress system). They also found that depression and HPA axis dysregulation predicted memory deficits in a manner that was consistent with published research on depressed adults. These results underscore the aversive nature of bullying that pervasively impacts the individual across multiple domains of functioning.

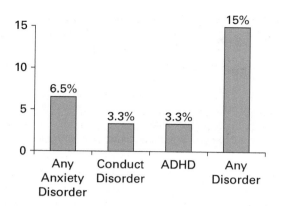

FIGURE 15.1 Prevalence of Selected Mental Disorders in Children and Youth

Source: Based on Waddell, C., & Shepherd, C. (2002). *Prevalence of mental disorders in children and youth.* Vancouver: The University of British Columbia.

prevalence rate is 14.3%. This means that over 800 000 children and youth in Canada have a mental disorder that causes them significant distress and is associated with noteworthy impairment in their social, school, community, and/or family functioning (Waddell et al., 2005). A recent meta-analysis of the worldwide prevalence rates of mental disorders in children and adolescents reported similar prevalence rates (Polanczyk, Salum, Sugaya, Caye, & Rohde, 2015). Forty-one studies from 27 countries, representing every world region were included in the meta-analysis. Results indicated that the worldwide prevalence rate for any mental disorder was 13.4%. Anxiety disorders were the most common mental health disorders affecting youth (6.5%) followed by disruptive disorders (5.7%), ADHD (3.4%), and depressive disorders (2.6%).

The prevalence of mental disorders varies by the sex and age of the child. For example, children under the age of 8 rarely meet diagnostic criteria for conduct disorder, a disorder that is more common in boys than in girls (Loeber, Burke, Lahey, Winters, & Zera, 2000). Results from the NCS-A study showed that the median age of onset for disorders varied considerably by type of disorder (Merikangas et al., 2010). Anxiety disorders emerged by age 6, behavioural problems by age 11, mood disorders by age 13, and substance use disorders by age 15. In this study, girls were more likely than boys to be diagnosed (lifetime prevalence) with a mood disorder (18.3 vs. 10.5%), anxiety disorder (38.0 vs. 26.1%), or eating disorder (3.8 vs. 1.5%), whereas boys were more likely than girls to be diagnosed with a behaviour disorder (23.5 vs. 15.5%) or a substance use disorder (12.5 vs. 10.2%).

② BEFORE MOVING ON

Research about the prevalence and course of childhood psychopathology is burgeoning. Are the rates of psychiatric disorders in childhood increasing, decreasing, or staying the same? Moreover, what are the most common comorbid patterns in children and youth? (Hint: comorbid patterns are described in each disorder subsection.)

Attention Deficit/Hyperactivity Disorder

CLINICAL DESCRIPTION

Attention deficit/hyperactivity disorder (ADHD) is one of the most common psychiatric disorders in childhood and adolescence. In the DSM-5, ADHD is listed in the Neuro-developmental Disorders section, reflective of the fact that ADHD is viewed as a brain-based developmental disorder. Children with ADHD are motorically and often verbally hyperactive, they have problems maintaining their focus in conversations and activities, and they show impulsive or erratic behaviour. These symptoms almost always emerge in early childhood (Greenfield-Spira & Fischel, 2005) and, although some aspects of the disorder improve with age and brain maturation (Halperin & Schulz, 2006), at least one-third of children with ADHD in childhood retain this diagnosis into adulthood (Spencer, Biederman, & Mick, 2007).

CLASSIFICATION OF ADHD Following the current DSM-5 criteria, ADHD is listed in the Neurodevelopmental Disorders section and symptoms are grouped into two categories: *inattention* and *hyperactivity and impulsivity* (see Table 15.2). Based on the main type of symptom that the child presents with, a specifier may be added to the diagnosis: ADHD predominantly inattentive presentation (ADHD-I), ADHD predominantly hyperactive/impulsive presentation (ADHD-H), or ADHD combined presentation (ADHD-HI). In the DSM-IV-TR, children were classified into three subtypes: ADHD inattentive type (ADHD-I), ADHD hyperactive-impulsive type (ADHD-H), or ADHD combined type (ADHD-HI). In the section that follows, this DSM-IV-TR nosology is reflected in the research reviewed, as current research has not incorporated the changes to the DSM-5 (i.e., abandonment of subtypes with the replacement of specifiers).

ADHD-I is more common in girls than in boys and is associated with a greater number of academic problems, especially in the area of mathematical achievement, than are the other two subtypes (Milich, Balentine, & Lynam, 2001). The inattentive symptoms are reflected more in areas such as listening, learning, and remembering. As well, children with ADHD-I subtype tend to have problems with organization and motor control. Accordingly, these children often have messy handwriting and problems eating neatly, for example. Social problems with peers are also common, and seem to increase the risk of development of other types of psychiatric issues not related to ADHD per se (Nijmeijer et al., 2008). ADHD-H and ADHD-HI are three times more common in boys than in girls and are associated with higher rates of comorbid conduct problems than is the ADHD-I subtype (Milich et al., 2001). Children and youth with ADHD-H and ADHD-HI tend to get into trouble, talk to themselves and others, interrupt others, move and fidget, and react more than do children with ADHD-I. Although the motor hyperactivity symptoms associated with ADHD-H and

TABLE 15.2 DSM-5 DIAGNOSTIC CRITERIA FOR ATTENTION DEFICIT/HYPERACTIVITY DISORDER

A. A persistent pattern of inattention and/or hyperactivity-impulsivity that interferes with functioning or development, as characterized by (1) and/or (2):

1. **Inattention:** Six (or more) of the following symptoms have persisted for at least 6 months to a degree that is inconsistent with developmental level and that negatively impacts directly on social and academic/occupational activities:

   Note: The symptoms are not solely a manifestation of oppositional behavior, defiance, hostility, or failure to understand tasks or instructions. For older adolescents and adults (age 17 and older), at least five symptoms are required.

   a. Often fails to give close attention to details or makes careless mistakes in schoolwork, at work, or during other activities (e.g., overlooks or misses details, work is inaccurate).

   b. Often has difficulty sustaining attention in tasks or play activities (e.g., has difficulty remaining focused during lectures, conversations, or lengthy reading).

   c. Often does not seem to listen when spoken to directly (e.g., mind seems elsewhere, even in the absence of any obvious distraction).

   d. Often does not follow through on instructions and fails to finish schoolwork, chores, or duties in the workplace (e.g., starts tasks but quickly loses focus and is easily sidetracked).

   e. Often has difficulty organizing tasks and activities (e.g., difficulty managing sequential tasks; difficulty keeping materials and belongings in order; messy, disorganized work; has poor time management; fails to meet deadlines).

   f. Often avoids, dislikes, or is reluctant to engage in tasks that require sustained mental effort (e.g., schoolwork or homework; for older adolescents and adults, preparing reports, completing forms, reviewing lengthy papers).

   g. Often loses things necessary for tasks or activities (e.g., school materials, pencils, books, tools, wallets, keys, paperwork, eyeglasses, mobile telephones).

   h. Is often easily distracted by extraneous stimuli (for older adolescents and adults, may include unrelated thoughts).

   i. Is often forgetful in daily activities (e.g., doing chores, running errands; for older adolescents and adults, returning calls, paying bills, keeping appointments).

2. **Hyperactivity and impulsivity:** Six (or more) of the following symptoms have persisted for at least 6 months to a degree that is inconsistent with developmental level and that negatively impacts directly on social and academic/occupational activities:

   Note: The symptoms are not solely a manifestation of oppositional behavior, defiance, hostility, or a failure to understand tasks or instructions. For older adolescents and adults (age 17 and older), at least five symptoms are required.

   a. Often fidgets with or taps hands or feet or squirms in seat.

   b. Often leaves seat in situations when remaining seated is expected (e.g., leaves his or her place in the classroom, in the office or other workplace, or in other situations that require remaining in place).

   c. Often runs about or climbs in situations where it is inappropriate. (**Note:** In adolescents or adults, may be limited to feeling restless.)

   d. Often unable to play or engage in leisure activities quietly.

   e. Is often "on the go," acting as if "driven by a motor" (e.g., is unable to be or uncomfortable being still for extended time, as in restaurants, meetings; may be experienced by others as being restless or difficult to keep up with).

   f. Often talks excessively.

   g. Often blurts out an answer before a question has been completed (e.g., completes people's sentences; cannot wait for turn in conversation).

   h. Often has difficulty waiting his or her turn (e.g., while waiting in line).

   i. Often interrupts or intrudes on others (e.g., butts into conversations, games, or activities; may start using other people's things without asking or receiving permission; for adolescents and adults, may intrude into or take over what others are doing).

B. Several inattentive or hyperactive-impulsive symptoms were present prior to age 12 years.

C. Several inattentive or hyperactive-impulsive symptoms are present in two or more settings (e.g., at home, school, or work; with friends or relatives; in other activities).

D. There is clear evidence that the symptoms interfere with, or reduce the quality of, social, academic, or occupational functioning.

E. The symptoms do not occur exclusively during the course of schizophrenia or another psychotic disorder and are not better explained by another mental disorder (e.g., mood disorder, anxiety disorder, dissociative disorder, personality disorder, substance intoxication or withdrawal).

Specify whether:

   314.01 (F90.2) **Combined presentation:** If both Criterion A1 (inattention) and Criterion A2 (hyperactivity-impulsivity) are met for the past 6 months.

314.0 (F90.0) **Predominantly inattentive presentation:** If Criterion A1 (inattention) is met but Criterion A2 (hyperactivity-impulsivity) is not met for the past 6 months.

314.1 (F90.1) **Predominantly hyperactive/impulsive presentation:** If Criterion A2 (hyperactivity-impulsivity) is met and Criterion A1 (inattention) is not met for the past 6 months.

Specify if:

In partial remission: When full criteria were previously met, fewer than the full criteria have been met for the past 6 months, and the symptoms still result in impairment in social, academic, or occupational functioning.

Specify current severity:

Mild: Few, if any, symptoms in excess of those required to make the diagnosis are present, and symptoms result in no more than minor impairments in social or occupational functioning.

Moderate: Symptoms or functional impairment between "mild" and "severe" are present.

Severe: Many symptoms in excess of those required to make the diagnosis, or several symptoms that are particularly severe, are present, or the symptoms result in marked impairment in social or occupational functioning.

ADHD-HI often decrease over time, the fidgeting and restlessness often persist into adulthood (Willoughby, 2003).

COMORBIDITY Children with ADHD, especially those with the hyperactive/impulsive and combined presentations, come to the attention of clinicians because of the impact their behaviour has on others, their parents' or teachers' frustration, and, in later years, their own academic, employment, or relationship struggles. Children with ADHD have higher rates of grade retention, suspension, and dropout, and are less likely to graduate from high school. As well, children with ADHD tend to have other mental health problems. In fact, 50% of children with ADHD have at least one other psychiatric disorder (Spencer et al., 2007). The most common comorbid conditions are oppositional defiant disorder (ODD) or conduct disorder (40 to 60%), learning disorders (25%), anxiety disorders (25%), and, in later years, depression (30%) and substance abuse disorders (40%).

PREVALENCE The prevalence of ADHD in the general population is about 2% among preschool-aged children (Lavigne et al., 1996), 6% among children and adolescents (Polancyzk, de Lima, Horta, Biederman, & Rohde, 2007), and 4% among adults (Polancyzk & Rohde, 2007). The worldwide prevalence rate for ADHD for youth aged between 6 and 18 is estimated at 3.4% (Polanczyk et al., 2015). These rates, however, increased tenfold in psychiatric populations. Overall, more boys than girls are affected by ADHD, but when subtypes are taken into account, more girls than boys are affected with ADHD-I and more boys than girls are affected with ADHD-H and ADHD-HI.

DEVELOPMENTAL TRAJECTORY Most children with ADHD continue to have symptoms that require a chronic approach to management throughout adolescence and into adulthood. The most important long-term issue for youth with ADHD is increased risk for developing another psychiatric disorder (Biederman, Petty, Evans, Small, & Faraone, 2010).

For example, 40 to 50 percent of adults with ADHD have a mood or anxiety disorder at some point in their lives, and one-third of these adults have one or more substance abuse disorders (Gibbins & Weiss, 2007). Research that studies patterns of substance use in youth with ADHD into adulthood has shown that these youth begin substance use earlier than youth who do not have ADHD; the earlier this substance use begins, the worse is the long-term mental health outcome (Molina et al., 2007). Other health and lifestyle challenges are associated with ADHD in adulthood, including a four times greater risk of serious injury, particularly in motor vehicle accidents. Despite comparable education and IQ, adults with ADHD have lower occupational attainment and greater academic problems (Seidman, 2006). Adults with ADHD become parents at an earlier age, have four times as many sexually transmitted diseases in adolescence, and have higher rates of divorce and separation (Flory, Molina, Pelham, Gnagy, & Smith, 2006).

ETIOLOGY

ADHD is the most well-studied child psychiatric condition. Currently, most research focuses on understanding the genetics of ADHD and how brain development in children with ADHD differs from that of children without this disorder (e.g., Halperin & Schulz, 2006). There is a strong biological basis for ADHD in that many of the symptoms are related to delays or abnormalities in the development of the connections between emotional and motor areas of the brain (Halperin & Schulz, 2006). Fortunately, medication and psychosocial treatments are quite effective as they focus on the well-characterized functional and biological deficits of the brain. As such, research on ADHD is a success story with a long history.

The earliest descriptor of the disorder currently known as ADHD was *minimal brain dysfunction*, followed by *hyperkinetic syndrome of childhood*. By the 1970s, it was recognized that hyperactive and disorganized children also had problems sustaining and organizing their attention. As such, in 1970, the syndrome was renamed *attention deficit disorder* (ADD) in the DSM-II. At that time, the diagnosis was made on the basis of three types of symptoms: inattention, impulsivity, and hyperactivity. In the revised edition of DSM-III (APA, 1987), the syndrome was renamed ADHD, and two new diagnostic features were required: *functional impairment* and *symptoms being present before age seven*. The validity of the three subgroups of symptoms began to be tested in the first large prospective treatment study of ADHD in children called the Multimodal Treatment Study of ADHD (Richters et al., 1995). This ongoing study, supported by the National Institutes of Mental Health, involves 579 children and families at seven sites across Canada and the United States.

Over the decades, the literature base on ADHD has expanded substantially. Although we now know more about the long-term course and impairments of ADHD than we do about any other childhood disorder, its effects on the family and child, and some successful treatments, the causes of ADHD are still elusive. This is because heritable and nonheritable factors contribute to the development of ADHD and these factors are interdependent (see Thapar, Cooper, Eyre, & Langley, 2013, for a review). Moreover, ADHD commonly co-occurs with other psychiatric disorders of childhood and involves perhaps the most complicated of brain functions: sustained attention (Barkley, 1997).

Because the causes of ADHD are largely unknown, a discussion of risk factors for ADHD is an important step in finding the true cause(s) of this disorder. The risk factors for ADHD can be categorized accordingly: (1) brain structure and function, (2) genetics, (3) neurotransmitters, and (4) environmental factors. It is well recognized that risk factors interact to cause a given psychiatric condition; thus, the multifactorial causation for ADHD is discussed.

BRAIN STRUCTURE AND FUNCTION Several studies have found that children with ADHD, compared to those without ADHD, generally have reduced brain size (3 to 8 percent reduction), abnormalities in the metabolism of dopamine and noradrenergic neurotransmitters, and abnormalities in the functioning of genes that regulate these neurotransmitter systems (Faraone & Khan, 2006; Halperin & Schulz, 2006). Several magnetic resonance imaging (MRI) studies have shown that ADHD is associated with abnormalities of the prefrontal cortex and basal ganglia (see the review by Rubia, Alegria, & Brinson, 2014). The prefrontal cortex is an area of the brain associated with executive functioning, while the basal ganglia is associated with higher motor control; learning, memory and cognition; and emotional regulation. In a large prospective study of 223 children with ADHD and 223 typically developing controls, Shaw and colleagues (2007) found a marked delay in when children with ADHD attained peak thickness throughout their cerebellum (10.5 years for children with ADHD vs. 7.5 years for typical controls). The cerebellum is responsible for motor control such as coordination and precision but is also involved in cognitive

functions such as attention. Longitudinal structural imaging studies have demonstrated that ADHD is characterized by a "delay in structural brain maturation" (Rubia, Alegría, & Brinson, 2014, p. S3). These findings are consistent with the clinical presentation of ADHD. Individuals with ADHD tend to have poor executive functioning skills, they tend to be clumsy, and they tend to have poor emotional self-regulation. These differences converge on a common problem in ADHD: the regulation of attention by the neurotransmitter dopamine in the prefrontal cortex and basal ganglia.

GENETICS Family and twin studies allow for the examination of differences between genetic and environmental causes of disorders. These studies have shown that more than half of the risk for ADHD in offspring is due to purely genetic factors, with some studies suggesting that the heritability of ADHD is as high as 77 percent (Banerjee, Middleton, & Faraone, 2007; Faraone & Khan, 2006). Genes that have been extensively studied are those responsible for the recycling and transportation of the neurotransmitter dopamine in the synaptic cleft (dopamine receptor 4 and 5; DRD-4, DRD-5), dopamine beta-hydroxylase (DBH), synaptosomal associated protein 5 (SNAP 5), and serotonin receptor 1B (HTR1B). Although much progress has been made in this area of study, a particular gene specific to ADHD has not been identified to date.

PRENATAL RISK FACTORS A number of recent reviews have described the prenatal environmental risk factors associated with ADHD and other disorders of childhood (e.g., Banerjee et al., 2007; Eubig, Aguiar, & Schantz, 2010; Froehlich et al., 2011; Williams & Ross, 2007; Winzer-Serhan, 2008). These reviews point convincingly to the fact that prenatal toxin exposure is related to mental health problems in offspring, in particular to ADHD. The "toxins" include poor diet, exposure to antidepressants, antihypertensives, illicit drugs, alcohol, tobacco, caffeine, mercury, and lead, and pregnancy or delivery complications. More recently, increased risk for ADHD has been linked to exposure to manganese, organophosphates, and phthalates, which may be particularly problematic for boys (Froehlich et al., 2011). However, as Williams and Ross (2007) point out, the prenatal risk factor findings are difficult to interpret because risk factors tend to co-occur and interact together.

PSYCHOSOCIAL RISK FACTORS Psychosocial risk factors include low socio-economic status, large family size, paternal criminality, poor maternal mental health, child maltreatment, foster care placement, and family dysfunction (Banerjee et al., 2007). The role of family dysfunction as a risk factor in ADHD is hard to assess, as the families of many children with ADHD report high levels of distress. However, work by Hechtman (1996) has shown that treatment of ADHD improves family stress and that family stress also decreases as the child grows older or moves out of the home.

GENE–ENVIRONMENTAL INTERACTIONS The current state of knowledge in the field of psychopathology is that psychiatric disorders are not the result of nature *or* nurture, but rather the result of nature via nurture. **Gene–environment interactions** (G × E) describe "any phenotypic event" that is the result of an interaction between genes and the environment (Banerjee et al., 2007, p. 1272). G × E is similar to the **diathesis-stress perspective** of disease, which postulates that environmental stressors should exact their greatest toll on individuals who have an underlying genetic vulnerability (Monroe & Simons, 1991). For example, Martel and colleagues (2011) found that homozygosity for a certain type of dopamine receptor gene that is expressed in the prefrontal cortical regions of the brain was associated with greater risk for ADHD and ODD only when children were also exposed to inconsistent parenting.

An example of a gene–environment interaction in the area of ADHD was uncovered by Khan and colleagues (2003), who found that ADHD symptoms were present in children with the 480-bp DAT 1 risk allele *only when* their mothers smoked during pregnancy. Becker and colleagues (2008) found that for boys but not girls, prenatal smoke exposure was associated with higher hyperactivity-impulsivity in those who were homozygous for the DAT 10r allele. As another example, Neuman and colleagues (2007) found that the odds of being diagnosed with ADHD combined subtype were much higher (2.9 times greater) in twins with a DAT1 440 allele who were exposed prenatally to smoke than among twins without the exposure and risk gene. It is not surprising, then, that Winzer-Serhan (2008), in a review of this literature, concluded that *maternal smoking* during pregnancy is an environmental factor that increases the risk of developing ADHD *in those with a genetic predisposition*, even after controlling for known confounding factors such as maternal age, low birth weight, lower parental education, parental ADHD, and income.

ASSESSMENT AND TREATMENT

Treatments are required to address the different symptom clusters of ADHD and the domains of impairment in both the child and his or her family. Comprehensive assessments of the child's development and academic, social, and family functioning are required to make a diagnosis. Hallmarks of assessment include reports from more than one informant, in ideally two or more contexts, using valid and reliable assessment tools. Clinicians need to identify the severity of impairment and potential worsening factors (e.g., learning disability or anxiety at school may make symptoms worse, or perhaps better) when assessing children. This information is also important to gauge treatment response over time.

Basic assessment requires administering a rating to parents and teachers that covers the symptoms of ADHD and their related impairments. As children approach adolescence, self-report may be helpful (see Snyder, Hall, Cornwell, & Quintana, 2006, for a review of rating scales for ADHD). In addition to symptom surveillance, a clinical interview is required to understand the developmental history of the child, the onset of problems and the degree of impairment from symptoms across multiple settings, differential psychiatric and medical diagnosis (e.g., toxin exposure, head injury), possible psychosocial issues that contribute to the presentation, and family mental health history. Usually, direct communication with teachers is required to understand both classroom behaviour and academic abilities. When the latter is in doubt, psychoeducation testing is necessary to explore the possibility of a learning disability.

PHARMACOLOGICAL TREATMENT The mainstay of treatment for ADHD is the use of stimulant medication (see Table 15.3), which has been shown to be effective in approximately 80 percent of children with ADHD symptoms (Prince, 2006). These medications work by increasing the

TABLE 15.3 SUMMARY OF DRUGS USED TO TREAT CHILDHOOD MENTAL DISORDERS

Disorder	Drug Category	Generic Names	Trade Name
Attention Deficit/Hyperactivity Disorder	Psychostimulant	methylphenidate	Ritalin, Concerta
		amphetamine	Adderall
		dextroamphetamine	Dexedrine
	Norepinephrine reuptake inhibitor	atomoxetine	Strattera
	Alpha2-adrenergic agonist	guanfacine	Intuniv
		clonidine	Catapres
Conduct Disorder			
	Psychostimulant** Alpha2-adrenergic agonist	See above	Risperdal
	Antipsychotic	See above	
		risperidone	
Separation Anxiety Disorder	SSRI* √	fluoxetine	Prozac
Generalized Anxiety Disorder	SSRI	fluoxetine	Prozac

* Serotonin specific reuptake inhibitor. While fluoxetine and citalopram (Celexa) are the only SSRIs indicated for use in children and adolescents in Canada, others commonly used are fluvoxamine (Luvox) and sertraline (Zoloft).

√ Behavioural therapy is the first treatment for SAD and GAD in all cases. However, many highly anxious children with GAD may require medication in combination with behavioural therapy at the beginning of treatment.

** Behavioural therapy is the first treatment for CD in all cases except when there is comorbid ADHD in which treatments for ADHD should be used.

Source: Based on Waddell, C., & Shepherd, C. (2002). *Prevalence of mental disorders in children and youth.* Vancouver: The University of British Columbia.

release of dopamine and norepinephrine from storage sites in nerve terminals and by blocking their reuptake by inhibition of the dopamine transport protein. A newer medication, atomoxetine, alters levels of brain norepinephrine. Several randomized controlled trials covering 8 to 10 years of follow-up demonstrate efficacy and effectiveness of stimulant medications for all subtypes of ADHD (Spencer et al., 2007).

Stimulant medications include short-acting or long-acting **methylphenidate** (**Ritalin**), dextroamphetamine, and amphetamine. Stimulant medications such as atomoxetine act on other neurotransmitters (noradrenaline and serotonin). These medications have been shown to increase vigilance, reaction time, short-term memory, and learning of new material in children with ADHD (Prince, 2006). They also show beneficial effects on other associated problems relating to impulsivity, such as aggressive behaviour, noncompliance, noisiness, and peer relationships. Atomoxetine has been shown to have additional benefits in reducing ODD and anxiety symptoms in ADHD children.

Side effects of stimulant medications are common and include decreased appetite and weight loss, trouble falling asleep, headaches, and increases in pulse and blood pressure. Some children can become more irritable or angry. These side effects are usually short-lived and reverse when the medications are reduced or stopped (Prince, 2006). However, children who take stimulant medications for several years have been shown to have slightly lower height and weight than those who do not take these medications (Swanson et al., 2007). Clinicians recommend that children and adolescents with ADHD remain on stimulant medications throughout childhood and adolescence. Although previously a common practice, drug holidays or periods off medications on weekends or during the summer are not recommended, as they do not help to improve growth and weight gain in children who regularly take stimulant medications (Wilens et al., 2005). Regular follow-up with a clinician to monitor growth, cardiac and developmental milestones, and comorbid conditions is crucial.

Despite the use of stimulants, most children with ADHD will continue to have social, academic, and emotional difficulties. For example, a review of 14 long-term childhood ADHD treatment studies by Schachar and colleagues (2002) found that stimulant medications improved both ADHD symptoms and social behaviour, with one study showing additional benefit in these areas by the addition of other psychosocial treatments. Their review found no benefits of medication on academic functioning and only a minor effect on emotional functioning. As such, emotional and behavioural deficits should be expected to persist following medication treatment alone, and additional treatments that target the acquisition of social and learning strategies are required for the child and his or her parents.

PSYCHOEDUCATIONAL INTERVENTIONS Research supports the benefit of caregiver psychoeducation about ADHD (Cunningham, Bremner, & Boyle, 1995). In this intervention, adults responsible for the child (parents and teachers) are educated about the symptoms, course of the disorder, and deficits associated with ADHD and how they can facilitate the use of the child's strengths to his or her advantage. For example, parents learn about the importance of routines, physical exercise, and supervised or planned activities to occupy the child. They also learn about what to expect in terms of tempers and other intrusive impulsive behaviour so that the parent can identify what is within the child's control. Such information helps parents and teachers to feel that they have a role to play in facilitating the child's development, which is associated with better outcomes in ADHD symptoms (Cunningham, 2007).

ACADEMIC SKILL FACILITATION AND REMEDIATION School-focused interventions for ADHD symptoms are usually required to ensure that the child is achieving the academic and social skills appropriate for his or her age and developmental level. Liaison with teachers or school guidance counsellors helps to identify areas in the child's school day where modifications can occur to accommodate the ADHD symptoms. For example, scheduled breaks from classroom activities, the use of reward systems, appropriate positioning of the child's desk, auditory versus written instructions, and the use of agendas can all help to improve the child's academic performance. Psychoeducational testing to identify learning disorders or attentional and behavioural challenges that may stress children's ability to learn is recommended for most children with ADHD. Such specific interventions around academic organization and remediation have been shown to be most helpful for children with severe ADHD (Chatfield, 2002).

PARENT TRAINING Parent education groups have been shown to help parents develop skills to manage their child's ADHD-related problem behaviour (Cunningham, 2007). Parent training works when parents learn contingency management; specifically, parents learn techniques to help the child modify his or her own behaviour by providing consistent rewards and attention when the child completes a task or ceases a negative behaviour. For example, parents are taught to recognize and then acknowledge when the inattentive child pauses before interrupting a conversation, or asks if he or she can speak prior to doing so. In groups, parents are taught how to identify target behaviour to work on with their child and are given instruction on how to modify the behaviour. Parent training appears to be more useful for younger children, and may need to be repeated for parents as the child grows older to maintain the skills. Examples include the Community Parent Education Program (COPE) developed by Dr. Charles Cunningham and colleagues (1995) at McMaster University in Hamilton, Ontario; Dr. Carolyn Webster-Stratton's (1996) the Incredible Years Parent Program and Drs. Russell Barkley and Christine Benton's (1998) *Your Defiant Child*. A recent meta-analytic review of the effectiveness of various

Parent training is associated with more positive parent–child interactions.

parent training components showed that larger effects were associated with fostering increased positive parent–child interactions and communication skills; teaching parents appropriate use of timeouts and encouraging consistency; and having parents practise new skills with their child during the training sessions (Wyatt Kaminski, Valle, Filene, & Boyle, 2008).

OTHER TREATMENTS There is less convincing evidence for family therapy, cognitive-behavioural therapy, individual psychotherapy, or social skills training in helping a child's ADHD symptoms. This suggests that the most effective treatments are those that help children to enhance their deficient self-motivation and working memory to show what they know as opposed to teaching them something or having them learn a new skill. The current gold standard in the treatment of ADHD is multimodal—a combination of stimulants and some targeted combination of the non-drug interventions just discussed (Daly, Creed, Xanthopoulos, & Brown, 2007). In particular, behavioural parent training and behavioural classroom management are the most well-established non-drug treatments for ADHD (Pelham & Fabiano, 2008).

③ BEFORE MOVING ON

ADHD is a condition associated with specific cognitive deficits and various forms of social, academic, and family impairment. Describe the evidence-based treatment of stimulant medication and what aspects of impairment it is intended to treat. As well, describe the side effects associated with stimulant use.

Oppositional Defiant Disorder and Conduct Disorder

CLINICAL DESCRIPTION

Children with **oppositional defiant disorder** (**ODD**) frequently argue with adults, have many temper tantrums, deliberately annoy others, and are spiteful and vindictive. They do not take responsibility for their actions, blaming others for their outbursts and rude behaviour. Children who display symptoms such as these do not have a developmental disability such as the ones described in Chapter 14; rather, these children meet diagnostic criteria for ODD. ODD is generally diagnosed by the time children are eight years old (see Table 15.4). Children with ODD are very difficult to manage—their negative behaviour and poor attitude are obvious and taxing to parents, teachers, and peers.

Some researchers have argued that ODD is simply an earlier expression of **conduct disorder** (**CD**) (e.g., Loeber, Keenan, Lahey, Green, & Thomas, 1993), which is also characterized by a pattern of hostile behaviour. In fact, one in four boys diagnosed with ODD will eventually be diagnosed with CD (Hinshaw & Anderson, 1996; Loeber et al., 1993), although the majority of children with ODD do not develop CD. Despite this overlap, what differentiates CD from ODD is that the behaviour displayed by the child or youth with CD *violate the basic rights of others or major societal norms or rules* (APA, 2000). The DSM-5 organizes CD behaviour into four major groups: (1) aggression directed toward people and animals; (2) destruction of property; (3) deceitfulness or theft; and (4) serious violations of rules, such as being chronically truant from school before age 13 (see Table 15.5).

ODD symptoms are organized into groupings to distinguish irritable mood from defiant behaviour. Specifically, the irritable mood symptoms are substantially more predictive of later mood and anxiety disorders than is defiant behaviour (Stringaris & Goodman, 2009). As such, the DSM-5 groups symptoms into three types: angry/irritable mood, argumentative/defiant behaviour, and vindictiveness. In DSM-5, ODD is diagnosed even in the presence of conduct disorder, as the research evidence suggests they are sufficiently distinct conditions.

Children and youth who meet diagnostic criteria for CD often display other problems. Like children with ODD, children with CD often have ADHD and learning difficulties (Hinshaw & Lee, 2003; Loeber et al., 2000). Some children with CD display *psychopathic* tendencies (Blair, Peschardt, Budhani, Mitchell, & Pine, 2006; Lynam, 1996). That is, these children show a general disregard for others and are not distressed by their negative behaviour, showing little, if any, remorse for their indiscretions. They are often described as egocentric, manipulative, and cold-hearted and are often extremely violent (Lynam, 1996). For example, one of the authors of this chapter met Jake, a 16-year-old boy who disclosed that on weekends he would drive around town looking for cats for his "experiment." This "experiment" involved calculating how long it took, on average, for a cat's tail to detach from its body

TABLE 15.4 DSM-5 DIAGNOSTIC CRITERIA FOR OPPOSITIONAL DEFIANT DISORDER

A. A pattern of angry/irritable mood, argumentative/defiant behavior, or vindictiveness lasting at least 6 months as evidenced by at least four symptoms from any of the following categories, and exhibited during interaction with at least one individual who is not a sibling.

Angry/Irritable Mood.

1. Often loses temper.

2. Is often touchy or easily annoyed.

3. Is often angry and resentful.

Argumentative/Defiant Behavior

4. Often argues with authority figures or for children and adolescents, with adults.

5. Often actively defies or refuses to comply with requests from authority figures or with rules.

6. Often deliberately annoys others.

7. Often blames others for his or her mistakes or misbehavior.

Vindictiveness

8. Has been spiteful or vindictive at least twice within the past 6 months.

Note: The persistence and frequency of these behaviors should be used to distinguish a behavior that is within normal limits from a behavior that is symptomatic. For children younger than 5 years, the behavior should occur on most days for a period of at least 6 months unless otherwise noted (Criterion A8). For individuals 5 years or older, the behavior should occur at least once per week for at least 6 months, unless otherwise noted (Criterion A8). While these frequency criteria provide guidance on a minimal level of frequency to define symptoms, other factors should also be considered, such as whether the frequency and intensity of the behaviors are outside a range that is normative for the individual's developmental level, gender, and culture.

B. The disturbance in behavior is associated with distress in the individual or others in his or her immediate social context (e.g., family, peer group, work colleagues), or it impacts negatively on social, educational, occupational, or other important areas of functioning.

C. The behaviors do not occur exclusively during the course of a psychotic, substance use, depressive, or bipolar disorder. Also, the criteria are not met for disruptive mood dysregulation disorder.

Specify current severity:

Mild: Symptoms are confined to only one setting (e.g., at home, at school, at work, with peers).

Moderate: Some symptoms are present in at least two settings.

Severe: Some symptoms are present in three or more settings.

TABLE 15.5 DSM-5 DIAGNOSTIC CRITERIA FOR CONDUCT DISORDER

A. A repetitive and persistent pattern of behavior in which the basic rights of others or major age-appropriate societal norms or rules are violated, as manifested by the presence of at least three of the following 15 criteria in the past 12 months from any of the categories below, with at least one criterion present in the past 6 months:

Aggression to People and Animals

1. Often bullies, threatens, or intimidates others.

2. Often initiates physical fights.

3. Has used a weapon that can cause serious physical harm to others (e.g., a bat, brick, broken bottle, knife, gun).

4. Has been physically cruel to people.

5. Has been physically cruel to animals.

6. Has stolen while confronting a victim (e.g., mugging, purse snatching, extortion, armed robbery).

7. Has forced someone into sexual activity.

Destruction of Property

8. Has deliberately engaged in fire setting with the intention of causing serious damage.

9. Has deliberately destroyed others' property (other than by fire setting).

Deceitfulness or Theft

10. Has broken into someone else's house, building, or car.

11. Often lies to obtain goods or favors or to avoid obligations (i.e., "cons" others).

12. Has stolen items of nontrivial value without confronting a victim (e.g., shoplifting, but without breaking and entering; forgery).

Serious Violations of Rules

13. Often stays out at night despite parental prohibitions beginning before age 13 years.

14. Has run away from home overnight at least twice while living in the parental or parental surrogate home, or once without returning for a lengthy period.

15. Is often truant from school, beginning before age 13 years.

B. The disturbance in behavior causes clinically significant impairment in social, academic, or occupational functioning.

C. If the individual is age 18 years or older, criteria are not met for antisocial personality disorder.

Specify whether:

312.81 (F91.1) Childhood-onset type: Individuals show at least one symptom characteristic of conduct disorder prior to age 10 years.
312.82 (F91.2) Adolescent-onset type: Individuals show no symptom characteristic of conduct disorder prior to age 10 years.
312.89 (F91.9) Unspecified onset: Criteria for a diagnosis of conduct disorder are met, but there is not enough information available to determine whether the onset of the first symptom was before or after age 10 years.

Specify if:

With limited prosocial emotions: To qualify for this specifier, an individual must have displayed at least two of the following characteristics persistently over at least 12 months and in multiple relationships and settings. These characteristics reflect the individual's typical pattern of interpersonal and emotional functioning over this period and not just occasional occurrences in some situations. Thus, to assess the criteria for the specifier, multiple information sources are necessary. In addition to the individual's self-report, it is necessary to consider reports by others who have known the individual for extended periods of time (e.g., parents, teachers, co-workers, extended family members, peers).

Lack of remorse or guilt: Does not feel bad or guilty when he or she does something wrong (exclude remorse when expressed only when caught and/or facing punishment). The individual shows a general lack of concern about the negative consequences of his or her actions. For example, the individual is not remorseful after hurting someone or does not care about the consequences of breaking rules.

Callous—lack of empathy: Disregards and is unconcerned about the feelings of others. The individual is described as cold and uncaring. The person appears more concerned about the effects of his or her actions on himself or herself, rather than their effects on others, even when they result in substantial harm to others.

Unconcerned about performance: Does not show concern about poor/problematic performance at school, at work, or in other important activities. The individual does not put forth the effort necessary to perform well, even when expectations are clear, and typically blames others for his or her poor performance.

Shallow or deficient affect: Does not express feelings or show emotions to others, except in ways that seem shallow, insincere, or superficial (e.g., actions contradict the emotions displayed, can turn emotions "on" **or** "off" quickly) or when emotional expressions are used for gain (e.g., emotions displayed to manipulate or intimidate others).

Specify current severity:

Mild: Few if any conduct problems in excess of those required to make the diagnosis are present, and conduct problems cause relatively minor harm to others (e.g., lying, truancy, stay out after dark without permission, other rule breaking).

Moderate: The number of conduct problems and the effect on others are intermediate between those specified in "mild" and those in "severe" (e.g., stealing without confronting a victim, vandalism).

Severe: Many conduct problems in excess of those required to make the diagnosis are present, or conduct problems cause considerable harm to others (e.g., forced sex, physical cruelty, use of a weapon, stealing while confronting a victim, breaking and entering).

when it was slammed repeatedly against the door of his truck. Given the strong evidence that the presence of psychopathic traits in youth with conduct disorder predicts more persistent, severe, and violent conduct behaviour, the addition of a callous and unemotional traits specifier has been added to the DSM-5 (APA, 2013). The specifier asks clinicians to consider if the child or youth shows at least two or more of the following characteristics, which are persistent over 12 months and occur in more than one relationship or setting: (1) lack of remorse or guilt, (2) callous lack of empathy, (3) absence of concern about performance (at school, at work, or in other important activities), and (4) shallow or deficient affect. Clinicians are encouraged to consider multiple sources of information to determine the presence of these traits.

CLASSIFICATION OF SUBTYPES The DSM-5 includes three subtypes of CD: (1) childhood-onset type, (2) adolescent-onset type, and (3) unspecified onset (age of onset is unknown). Individuals diagnosed with childhood-onset CD have at least one core symptom before the age of 10. Severity of CD is also specified in terms of mild, moderate, and severe.

SEX DIFFERENCES Boys are three to four times more likely than girls to meet the diagnostic criteria for CD (Loeber et al., 2000), girls are more likely to be diagnosed with CD at a later age than boys (Burke, Loeber, & Birmaher, 2002), and slightly more boys than girls are diagnosed with ODD (Boylan, Vaillancourt, Boyle, & Szatmari, 2007; Loeber et al., 2000). Although more boys than girls have conduct problems, it is nevertheless important to note the fact that many girls do have disorders of conduct (Zoccolillo, 1993). Conduct problems in girls are strongly associated with problematic outcomes, such as teen pregnancy (Pedersen & Mastekaasa, 2011; Zoccolillo & Rogers, 1991) and suicidal behaviour (Cairns, Cairns, Neckerman, Gest, & Gariepy, 1988), issues that become particularly pronounced if girls with CD become involved with antisocial partners. Unfortunately, studies have shown that females with CD tend to date (and marry) males with CD, termed **assortative mating** (Farrington, Jolliffe, Loeber, Stouthamer-Loeber, & Kalb, 2001). Romantic relationships between two antisocial individuals are associated with more severe negative behaviour, discord in the relationship, and poor parenting of future offspring, who, incidentally, have a higher genetic load for conduct problems (see Genetics).

COMORBIDITY The comorbid conditions associated with ODD and CD tend to be externalizing in nature. For example, in one study, 92.4% of those with lifetime ODD met criteria for another lifetime DSM-IV-TR disorder (45.8% mood, 62.3% anxiety, 68.2% impulse control, 47.2% substance abuse) (Nock, Kazdin, Hiripi, & Kessler, 2007). ODD and CD are highly comorbid with ADHD (Loeber et al., 2000; Offord et al., 1992), with as many as 40% of children with ADHD meeting diagnostic criteria for CD (Szatmari, Boyle, & Offord, 1989). Studies have shown that youth who have conduct problems and ADHD started their trajectory of inappropriate behaviour at a much earlier age than did youth with only CD (Moffitt, 1990a, 1990b). In addition, these children are more likely to exhibit more severe and protracted symptoms than are those with CD alone (Farrington et al., 1990; Magnusson, 1988; Magnusson & Bergman, 1990). This large body of evidence lends strong support to the idea that the combination of CD and ADHD is synergistic and not additive—these children have an earlier onset of CD that is more entrenched, and their symptoms tend to be more aggressive in nature. Perhaps not so surprising, CD is also strongly linked to substance use (Boyle & Offord, 1991), with most studies providing evidence that CD precedes substance use.

Although it may seem illogical, ODD and CD are also linked to internalizing disorders such as anxiety and depression (Angold & Costello, 1996; Blain-Arcaro & Vaillancourt, 2017; Boylan et al., 2007; Loeber et al., 2000), which have been shown to protect children and youth from future antisocial behaviour, but not improvement in psychopathology overall. Longitudinal studies examining the temporal ordering between externalizing problems and internalizing problems suggest three different pathways. The *failure model* (Capaldi, 1991, 1992; Capaldi & Stoolmiller, 1999) posits that engaging in externalizing behaviour increases the probability of experiencing social failure like being rejected by peers, and this in turn, is related to the development of internalizing problems like depression. The *acting out model* (Carlson & Cantwell, 1980) suggests that youth mask their mood problems by behaving aggressively. There is also evidence to support that the associations between externalizing problems and internalizing problems are reciprocal in nature (e.g., Klostermann, Connell, & Stormshak, 2014). In a study of Canadian children assessed yearly from age 10 to age 17, Blain-Arcaro and Vaillancourt (2017) found that symptoms of ODD and CD shared a reciprocal relation with depression. Specifically, although externalizing problems consistently predicted depression over time, there was also evidence that ODD and CD were predicted by depression.

The coupling of externalizing and internalizing problems in childhood and adolescence is consistent with the newly added **Disruptive Mood Dysregulation Disorder** (DMDD) which is found in the Depressive Disorders section of the DSM-5. DMDD is characterized by chronic and severe irritability that is manifested clinically by frequent temper outburst and severe irritability that consists of "persistently irritable or angry mood that is present between the severe temper outbursts" (APA, 2013, p. 156). The prevalence rate for DMDD is 2 to 5 percent and the onset of the disorder is before age 10. Although there is still ongoing research seeking to validate the positioning of DMDD as a mood disorder as opposed to being a disruptive behaviour disorder, at this point in time, DMDD cannot coexist with ODD. In other words, if a child's symptoms meet criteria for both DMDD and ODD, the diagnosis of DMDD is given.

PREVALENCE The worldwide prevalence rate of any disruptive disorder is 5.7% (Polanczyk et al., 2015). The prevalence of ODD in preschool is 9 to 12%; across childhood and adolescence, the rate falls to between 3 and 6% (Boylan et al., 2007). The lifetime prevalence of ODD is estimated at 10.2% (Nock et al., 2007). The prevalence rate for CD has been estimated at 6.6% in children aged 4.5 to 5 with moderate symptoms, and at 2.5% in preschool-aged children with severe symptoms using DSM-IV criteria (Kim-Cohen et al., 2005). Among school-aged children and adolescents, the prevalence of CD ranges from 1 to 10% (Hinshaw & Lee, 2003). DSM-5 notes that the prevalence rates fall to between 2% and 10%, with a median rate of 4% (APA, 2013). Canadian researchers have estimated the prevalence rate to be 8.1% for boys and 2.8% for girls (Offord, Alder, & Boyle, 1986) using DSM-III criteria.

Why is there such a large range in prevalence rates? The establishment of a true prevalence rate for ODD and CD has been hampered by changes in the DSM criteria. In the past decade, there has been a noted drop in the prevalence rates of ODD and CD. This decline is thought to be associated with changes in DSM criteria for these disorders. For example, the DSM-III-R required an additional three symptoms out of a possible 13 for a CD diagnosis, and these symptoms needed to be present for at least six months (Hinshaw & Lee, 2003). Using DSM-IV-TR (and DSM-5) criteria, it is expected that the prevalence rates may begin to increase (Lynam, 1996). This hypothesis is based on the following: (1) that a diagnosis for CD using the DSM-IV-TR criteria now requires that only three of 15 symptoms be present, as opposed to three of 13 using the DSM-III-R criteria; and (2) the two new symptoms (threatening and breaking curfew) that were added to the DSM-IV-TR and retained in the DSM-5 are less severe in nature and hence presumably more common.

DEVELOPMENTAL TRAJECTORY Symptoms associated with externalizing disorders follow a clear developmental sequence. Looking retrospectively (backward), to be diagnosed with antisocial personality disorder (APD; see Chapter 12), there must be evidence of conduct disorder before age 15 (APA, 2000, p. 292). As well, looking backward, most children with CD had ODD (although perhaps not formally diagnosed). However, looking forward, the developmental progression from ODD to CD to APD is less stable. Still, for children with conduct issues that begin early in life and are severe in nature, the aforementioned trajectory from ODD to CD to APD is robust (Loeber et al., 1993; Loeber et al., 2000), especially for boys (Rowe, Costello, Angold, Copeland, & Maughan, 2010). Clinically, this means that psychologists and psychiatrists would be less concerned with a 15-year-old who just started to skip school, shoplift, and break curfew than they would with a 5-year-old who has started a fire in his backyard, told his kindergarten teacher to go to hell, and has seriously injured the family hamster. The latter represents an early extreme, whereas the former is, to some extent, developmentally normative.

Given the developmental progression associated with conduct issues, one might ask whether ODD, CD, and APD are simply the same disorder that manifests differently over time. Although the stability of conduct problems over time is high (Cohen, Cohen, & Brook, 1993; Cote, Vaillancourt, Barker, Nagin, & Tremblay, 2007; Offord et al., 1992), most empirical studies support a distinction between ODD and CD (Biederman et al., 2008; Loeber et al., 2000; Rowe et al., 2010). For example, a recent 10-year prospective longitudinal study showed that ODD and CD predicted different types of future impairment. ODD was linked to major depression and to some extent CD and antisocial personality disorder; however, CD conferred a much higher risk for antisocial personality disorder, substance abuse issues, and bipolar disorder (Biederman et al., 2008). In another longitudinal study, Rowe and colleagues (2010) found that childhood ODD showed stronger predictive associations with emotional disorders in early adulthood, whereas CD in childhood largely predicted behavioural issues in later life.

ETIOLOGY

As is the case with ADHD, the real cause of ODD and CD remains elusive, and these disorders are not likely to be the result of any one factor. Accordingly, a discussion of key risk factors associated with conduct problems is presented and not a discussion of the "causes" of ODD and CD per se.

GENETICS Conduct problems tend to run in families, providing some support for a genetic influence on ODD and CD (Burke et al., 2002; see meta-analysis by Rhee & Waldman, 2002). For example, in one retrospective twin study, the genetic influence on the risk for CD was 71% (Slutske et al., 1997). Other twin studies, including the Quebec Longitudinal Twin Study, have demonstrated that there is a strong genetic basis for antisocial and aggressive behaviour (e.g., Brendgen, Vitaro, Boivin, Dionne, & Perusse, 2006). The heritability estimates for conduct problems that include aggression range from 44 to 72% in adults (Blair et al., 2006), with a higher risk present for male than female offspring (D'Onofrio et al., 2007). Other support for the genetic argument comes from studies demonstrating that children with parents who have a history of antisocial behaviour are more likely to be diagnosed early with CD than are children without an antisocial parent (Burke et al., 2002). Caution must be heeded when interpreting these findings, however, as antisocial parents are not only contributing their genes to their offspring, but also raising them in environments that tend to be less than nurturing. For example, Offord and Bennett (1994) found that among children with CD, 69% of the fathers and 43% of the mothers had a substance abuse problem. Importantly, it is not only antisocial tendencies in parents that confer a risk; other types of psychopathology have been shown to contribute to conduct disturbances. For example, Silberg, Maes, and Eaves (2010) showed that parental depression had both an environmental (the effects of living with a person with a significant mood disorder) and a genetic (inheriting risk genes) impact on the offspring's behaviour. Other studies about the shared heritability of ODD, CD, and depression found that depression was more strongly correlated with ODD irritability symptoms than ODD defiant or CD symptoms (Stringaris et al., 2012). These studies suggest that the shared genetic influences between disruptive behaviour disorders and depression may be mediated by irritability.

NEUROBIOLOGY It is important to recognize that most studies investigating the biological correlates of ODD and CD have, in effect, focused on the biological correlates of *violence* and *aggression*. With this in mind, it has been demonstrated that aggression is associated with decreased glucose metabolism in the frontal lobe (Burke et al., 2002; Moffitt, 1993; Raine et al., 2002) and damage to the orbital and ventrolateral prefrontal cortex (Anderson, Bechara, Damasio, Tranel, & Damasio, 1999; Grafman et al., 1996). This latter finding is interesting because the orbital and ventrolateral prefrontal cortex regulates the neural systems that mediate the basic reaction to threat. Damage to the amygdala, the emotion centre of the brain, has also been linked to impulsive aggressive behaviour (van Elst, Woermann, Lemieux, Thompson, & Trimble, 2000). As well, evidence suggests that aggression is associated with serotonergic abnormalities such as reduction in the turnover of serotonin (Coccaro, 1996). Low norepinephrine has been linked to conduct disorders (Rogeness, Cepeda, Macedo, Fischer, & Harris, 1990), as has low salivary cortisol (McBurnett, Lahey, Rathouz, & Loeber, 2000; van Goozen et al., 1998). Although most people assume that high testosterone is associated with aggressive behaviour, in truth this association is modest at best (Archer, 1991). What has been shown consistently is that aggression is related to the underarousal of the autonomic nervous system (low heart rate and lower skin conductance), especially among psychopaths (see Hinshaw & Lee, 2003).

NEUROLOGICAL FACTORS Several individual factors have been linked to conduct problems. These include early difficult temperament, poor executive functioning, low IQ, reading disorders, lack of empathy, and poor social cognition (Burke et al., 2002; Hinshaw & Lee, 2003; Lovett & Sheffield, 2007). What many studies have failed to consider, however, is the moderating role of ADHD. In other words, it is not clear whether these associations would be as strong (or weaker) if ADHD symptoms were controlled for statistically in the analyses.

PRENATAL RISK FACTORS The in utero environment been has consistently linked to conduct problems. Maternal smoking is predictive of CD (Wakschlag et al., 1997), as is substance abuse (Loukas, Fitzgerald, Zucker, & von Eye, 2001) and pregnancy and birth complications (Arseneault et al., 2002; Raine, Venables, & Mednick, 1997). In a recent large-scale cohort study of 2868 children born in Australia, Robinson and colleagues (2008) found that the most important risk factors for behaviour problems in early childhood were maternal stress and smoking during pregnancy.

PSYCHOSOCIAL RISK FACTORS Psychosocial factors have been studied extensively in relation to conduct problems. These studies have consistently demonstrated that poor parenting, which includes low monitoring, harsh and inconsistent discipline, and child abuse, is strongly linked to externalizing difficulties in children and youth. Other psychosocial correlates include peer rejection, associating with deviant peers (McDougall, Hymel, Vaillancourt, & Mercer, 2001; Poulin, Dishion, & Haas, 1999; Vitaro, Brendgen, & Tremblay, 2000; Vitaro, Trembay, Kerr, Pagani, & Bukowski, 2007), parental psychopathology, lone-parent families, large family size, and teenage parenthood (Hinshaw & Lee, 2003). Children and youth who live in poverty are more likely to display conduct problems than their more affluent peers (Burke et al., 2002; Loeber et al., 2000), but keep in mind that poverty is strongly linked to high-violence neighbourhoods, public housing, lone parenthood, and so on—factors that tend to exacerbate pre-existing negative attitudes and behaviour.

GENE–ENVIRONMENT INTERACTIONS One of the best illustrations of G × E comes from a study conducted by Caspi and colleagues (2002), who found that about 80 percent of

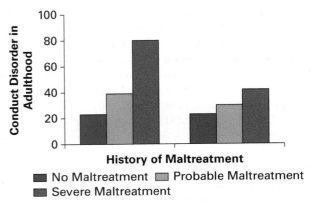

FIGURE 15.2 Conduct Disorder by MAOA Activity Level and Childhood Maltreatment

Source: Based on Caspi, A., McClay, J., Moffitt, T. E., Mill, J., Martin, J., Craig, I. W., et al. (2002). Role of genotype in the cycle of violence in maltreated children. *Science, 297,* 851–854.

individuals who were severely maltreated in childhood *and* had low monoamine oxidase A (MAOA) activity had conduct disorder in adulthood as compared to about 40 percent of individuals maltreated in childhood who had high MAOA activity (see Figure 15.2). MAOA is a gene that produces the enzyme that breaks down neurotransmitters such as serotonin (5-HT), norepinephrine (NE), and dopamine, and, in doing so, renders them inactive. 5-HT plays an important role in the modulation of aggression, NE is implicated in the fight-or-flight response, and dopamine is associated with the pleasure system of the brain. Another example comes from the work of Jaffee and colleagues (2005), who found that physical maltreatment in childhood alone hardly predicted conduct disorder; however, when it was coupled with a high genetic risk for conduct disorder, it did predict conduct disorder. Taken together, these two studies demonstrated that childhood maltreatment alone is a weak predictor of conduct problems, but when combined with a pre-existing genetic vulnerability, the relationship is dauntingly robust.

More recently, researchers have begun to consider *plasticity agents* that are sensitive to the environmental context. Specifically, the **differential susceptibility** theory (Belsky, 1997) and the **biological sensitivity to context** theory (Boyce & Ellis, 2005) suggests that while sources of vulnerability can increase the risk of poorer outcomes, they can also be associated with more *positive* outcomes in the context of more *supportive* environments (see Ellis, Boyce, Belsky, Bakermans-Kranenburg, & van Ijzendoorn, 2011, for review). As one example, in a study of Canadian preschool children, Vaillancourt et al. (in press) found that at high levels of peer victimization, low levels of cortisol were associated with higher physical aggression use. However, at low levels of peer victimization, low levels of cortisol were associated with low use of physical aggression.

TREATMENT

Four diverse treatment methods used for ODD and CD have been examined in controlled trials. These methods include (1) problem-solving skills, (2) pharmacological interventions, (3) parent management training, and (4) school- and community-based treatments. Although many "programs" claim to be effective in the treatment of conduct problems, caution must be heeded as CD in adolescence has been shown to be very resistant to treatment (Kazdin, 1997; Kazdin, Mazurick, & Siegel, 1994), highlighting the need for early intervention.

PROBLEM-SOLVING SKILLS TRAINING Deficits in problem-solving skills, social perception, and social attributions have been consistently found in children with aggressive conduct problems (Crick & Dodge, 1994; Dodge, 1986). These children are more likely to interpret ambiguous situations as being hostile. For example, if pushed, their first interpretation would be that another person did something on purpose, never considering that it may, in reality, have been an accident. These children also have a limited repertoire of behavioural responses, and the strategies they do have tend to be aggressive. Several interventions have been designed with these deficits in mind. Problem-solving skills training typically combines several procedures, which include modelling and practice, role-playing, and reinforcement contingencies (Firestone & Ledingham, 2007). There is evidence to suggest that this type of intervention is effective at reducing problematic behaviour (Kazdin, Esveldt-Dawson, French, & Unis, 1987a, 1987b), although children never really reach normal levels of functioning even after intervention (Kazdin, 1992).

PHARMACOLOGICAL TREATMENT The first consideration in pharmacologic treatment of ODD and CD is to ascertain the presence or absence of comorbid ADHD. If the latter is present, treatments for ADHD, including psychostimulants, alpha2 agonists, or atomoxetine are first line treatments. A recent systematic review of evidence for treatment of ODD and CD suggests that psychostimulants show the largest treatment effect size for disruptive behaviour across all of ADHD treatments, even in the absence of ADHD, but more so in its presence (Pringsheim et al., 2015a). Risperidone, an antipsychotic medication, has been shown to be associated with a moderate treatment effect on disruptive and aggressive behaviour in youth with average IQ and ODD or CD, with or without ADHD (Pringsheim et al., 2015b). Randomized controlled trials comparing lithium, a type of mood stabilizer, to a placebo found that lithium was an effective short-term therapy for *inpatient* aggressive children and adolescents (Campbell et al., 1995; Malone, Delaney, Luebbert, Cater, & Campbell, 2000); however the use of mood stabilizers is not recommended in routine treatment of ODD and CD (Gorman et al., 2015).

PARENT TRAINING Parent training (PT) programs are based on a *social learning causal model* whereby interactions between the parent and the child are considered to maintain and promote conduct problems inadvertently (Firestone & Ledingham, 2007), termed the **coercive process** (Patterson, 1982, 1986). During the coercive process, the child's negative behaviour functions to diminish the negative behaviour of the parent. For example, in the early years, children use aversive strategies such as whining or crying to successfully terminate conflicts with family members (Dishion & Patterson, 1996). The purpose of PT is to develop a new skill set in parents that promotes prosocial behaviour while also applying effective discipline techniques to minimize the negative behaviour. One example, mentioned in the previous section on ADHD, is the Incredible Years Parent Program by Webster-Stratton (1996), a program geared toward children two to eight years of age. To date, several randomized control group evaluations have investigated the effectiveness of this program in treating conduct problems (e.g., Spacarelli, Colter, & Penman, 1992; Taylor, Schmidt, Pepler, & Hodgins, 1998). Results associated with this program have consistently shown a general increase in positive parenting, a decrease in harsh discipline, and, importantly, reductions in conduct problems. Interestingly, the Incredible Years Parent Program has also been used with teachers, with evidence demonstrating positive changes in their disciplinary practices and classroom management skills, as well as decreases in classroom aggression and increases in prosocial behaviour (Webster-Stratton & Reid, 2008).

SCHOOL- AND COMMUNITY-BASED TREATMENT Clinic-based treatment, like that described in the pharmacology section, is limited by the fact that it is available to only a minority of individuals, who often represent the extreme end of the continuum on impairment. Without a doubt, the children and youth we have seen and continue to see in clinical practice tend to receive our care because something extreme—such as a serious violation of the law or a suicide attempt—has happened. When you consider the correlates of ODD and CD, such as poverty, lone-parent families, maternal psychopathology, and so on, it is easy to see why clinical intervention is highly skewed toward the most severe cases. Data on who receives mental health treatment supports our anecdotal observation. For example, according to the Ontario Child Health Study, only one in six children who suffer from a psychiatric disorder receives services (Boyle & Offord, 1990). Complicating matters is the fact that the people who we most want to engage in services such as parent training are the least likely to attend and thus the least likely to benefit from programs (Cunningham et al., 1995; Cunningham et al., 2000; Kazdin, 1993; Kazdin, Siegel, & Bass, 1990). Indeed, the response to parent training programs is often linked to factors that do not relate to the child such as poverty and poor maternal mental health (Reyno & McGrath, 2006).

Complicating matters is the fact that the people who we most want to engage in services such as parent training are the least likely to attend and thus the least likely to benefit from programs (Cunningham et al., 2000; Kazdin, 1993). Indeed, the response to parent training programs is often linked to factors that do not relate to the child such as poverty and poor maternal mental health (Reyno & McGrath, 2006).

TABLE 15.6 COPE: STRUCTURE OF LARGE-GROUP SESSIONS

Phase 1:	Informal social activities.
Phase 2:	Leader outlines session plan.
Phase 3:	Subgroups review homework* successes.
Phase 4:	Large-group discussion of homework projects.
Phase 5:	Subgroups discuss errors made by videotaped coping model.
Phase 6:	Large-group discussion of errors.
Phase 7:	Subgroups formulate alternatives to video-taped errors.
Phase 8:	Large-group discussion of proposed solutions.
Phase 9:	Leader models group's solution.
Phase 10:	Subgroups brainstorm application.
Phase 11:	Dyads rehearse strategies.
Phase 12:	Homework planning.
Phase 13:	Leader closes session.

Source: Cunningham, C. E. (2006). COPE: Large-Group, Community-Based, Family-Centered Parent Training. In R. A. Barkley (Ed.), *Attention-Deficit Hyperactivity Disorder: A Handbook for Diagnosis and Treatment* (p. 487). New York: Guilford Press.

*Homework refers to therapy work. Participants are assigned activities to work through at home with their child.

Recognizing these realities, several programs targeting families through schools and the community have been developed. The Community Education Training Program (COPE), developed by Cunningham (2006), is one example. COPE has been successfully used to reduce symptoms of ADHD and conduct problems in preschoolers, children, and adolescents (e.g., Cunningham et al., 1995). The structure of the training sessions is described in detail in Table 15.6.

An example of a school-based intervention program is one that was developed by Dr. Cunningham and colleagues (1998). In this program, called peer mediation, student volunteers are trained to identify conflict among peers and to intervene (i.e., mediate conflict) quickly and appropriately. The idea is that intervening early in the cycle of conflict should help to reduce the chances of it escalating into something far more serious. Peer mediators monitor the school playground and classroom during times of low surveillance by adults. Results of a randomized controlled trial provide impressive results—a 50 percent reduction in the amount of physical aggression displayed at school (Cunningham et al., 1998).

Programs like COPE and peer mediation are community-based intervention programs that offer important advantages over traditional clinic-based treatment options (Firestone & Ledingham, 2007). Because they are available to all children, these programs increase the likelihood of reaching those who are difficult to engage in children's mental treatment. As well, because they are universal, everyone gets the treatment. These programs also reduce the stigmatization or labelling of children with mental health issues because no one child is singled out for treatment (Offord & Bennett, 1994).

4 BEFORE MOVING ON

It is well recognized that multiple risk factors interact to cause a given psychiatric condition. Describe the multifactoral etiology of the disruptive disorders ODD and CD, paying specific attention to factors that may modify an individual's risk.

Anxiety Disorders

Case Notes

Hannah was eight years old when her parents brought her in for a psychological assessment. Her parents were very concerned because she was refusing to go to school, had no friends, and was "stuck" to her mother at all times.

When asked about her early development, Hannah's parents described a child who was always "clingy" and "fearful." Entry into kindergarten was a disaster because Hannah would not let go of her mother's hand. In fact, her mother had to remove herself forcefully from Hannah's grip every day at school drop-off. At school, Hannah cried the whole day. When her mother asked the kindergarten teacher about Hannah's behaviour and obvious distress, she was told that "many kids do this and within a few weeks she'll stop and start having fun." After several months of intense struggle, Hannah's parents took her out of school. They hoped that by the following year, with increased maturity, Hannah would be ready for school. This did not prove to be the case, however. At the time of her assessment, Hannah was absent from school an average of three days per week. She was so determined to not attend school that she would vomit if forced to go. Hannah also complained more often than not that she had a headache and/or stomach problems.

In addition to her refusal to attend school, Hannah was described by her father as being "worried about everything" and being excessively preoccupied with the idea that something terrible would happen to her mother. She wanted her mother by her side at all times and so she constructed a "rope" made out of towels to connect them. When Hannah was in a different room in the house, she made her mother hold the end of this rope. Her mother called the rope her daughter's "umbilical cord."

Every night, Hannah fought with her parents about where she would sleep. She refused to sleep in her own room. Because her father would not allow her to sleep in the bed with them, Hannah slept on the floor at the foot of their bed.

Needless to say, Hannah's emotional and behavioural issues were taxing to her parents, who worried about their daughter's future and about their marriage. Hannah's dependency on her mother was proving to be a formidable source of stress between Hannah's parents.

After her assessment, Hannah was diagnosed with separation anxiety disorder and generalized anxiety disorder.

Anxious children are often reluctant to separate from their caregivers, especially their mothers.

Having fears and worries in childhood is common. For example, in a large community study, 90 percent of children aged 2 to 14 years old and 3 to 5 percent of adolescents reported at least one specific fear (Lichtenstein & Annas, 2000). The most common fears reported were of animals, mutilation (blood, accidents), and environmental threats (heights, weather).

When fear is age-specific and the intensity is proportional to the perceived threat, it is considered developmentally appropriate. However, many children show excessive levels of fear from their preschool years onward into childhood and, for some, fearfulness can persist throughout their lives. The majority of these excessively fearful children will develop atypical patterns of fears and worries that impair their ability to develop normally. Many of these very fearful children develop anxiety disorders that require clinical intervention.

Although the DSM-IV-TR (APA, 2000) used to list **separation anxiety disorder (SAD)** separately in the childhood disorders section in the DSM-5, it is now classified as an anxiety disorder. Anxiety disorders are among the most common psychiatric disorders affecting children and adolescents. Moreover, children and adolescents can be diagnosed with any of the anxiety disorders listed in the DSM-5 (see Chapter 5). In this section, we focus on the most common anxiety disorder of childhood, SAD, and of adolescence, generalized anxiety disorder (GAD).

CLINICAL DESCRIPTION

The most obvious symptom associated with SAD is *distress* when separated from the attachment figure. It is not uncommon for the distress to culminate into a full-blown panic. Like Hannah, children with SAD constantly worry that something terrible will happen to their parents or other family members. They are fearful of new situations and of meeting new people, as these are unknowns that create a heightened sense of insecurity. Children with SAD also have a difficult time with transitions such as changing activities with the family or going to school on Mondays, after the weekend. Many children with this disorder feel fearful or on edge most of the time, not just in times of transition and stress. They can, however, be calmed when in the presence of their caregiver. Most children with SAD withdraw or appear timid as a means of reducing their exposure to distressing situations, but others can become angry and irritable or throw tantrums when forced to confront situations that heighten their fear.

Specific to SAD are hallmark features of at least three of the following symptoms for a minimum of four weeks: recurrent distress upon separation from a parent, excessive worry about losing a parent, excessive worry that an event will lead to harm to the parent, reluctance to go places without the parent in proximity, reluctance to sleep away from the parent, and nightmares about separation or complaints about physical symptoms when separation is anticipated (APA, 2013; see Table 15.7). In one study, the most frequently occurring symptoms in young children were worries about something happening to their attachment figure; in middle-aged children, excessive distress upon separation from their attachment figure was the most common symptom; and in adolescence it was physical complaints on school days (Last, Strauss, & Francis, 1987).

Children with SAD tend to recover within the first year of its onset; however, a three-year follow-up study found that one-third of children develop other anxiety or mood disorders (Foley, Pickles, Maes, Silberg, & Eaves, 2004). Most children are diagnosed with SAD before puberty (Bowen, Offord, & Boyle, 1990) and the qualifier *early onset* was made if SAD occurs before age six using the DSM-IV-TR. However, in the DSM-5 this specifier was dropped because there was no evidence to support its inclusion.

GAD, previously termed *overanxious disorder of childhood* in the DSM-III (APA, 1980), is diagnosed when (1) the child has many different types of worries or apprehensions, (2) he or she finds it very difficult to control his or her worries, and (3) his or her worries are accompanied by physical symptoms of being tired, restless, easily fatigued, irritable, or tense. For this diagnosis to be made the child must have these problems for a six-month period and, unlike with adults, only one accompanying physiological symptom is required. In adults, three or more physiological symptoms are needed to meet diagnostic criteria. The most common worries expressed by teens with GAD are uncertainties about their grades and school performance and fears about natural disasters, being physically attacked, and being bullied by peers (Weems, Silverman, & LaGreca, 2000).

Jennie Hart/Alamy Stock Photo

TABLE 15.7 DSM-5 DIAGNOSTIC CRITERIA FOR SEPARATION ANXIETY DISORDER

A. Developmentally inappropriate and excessive fear or anxiety concerning separation from those to whom the individual is attached, as evidenced by at least three of the following:

 1. Recurrent excessive distress when anticipating or experiencing separation from home or from major attachment figures.
 2. Persistent and excessive worry about losing major attachment figures or about possible harm to them, such as illness, injury, disasters, or death.
 3. Persistent and excessive worry about experiencing an untoward event (e.g., getting lost, being kidnapped, having an accident, becoming ill) that causes separation from a major attachment figure.
 4. Persistent reluctance or refusal to go out, away from home, to school, to work, or elsewhere because of fear of separation.
 5. Persistent and excessive fear of or reluctance about being alone or without major attachment figures at home or in other settings.
 6. Persistent reluctance or refusal to sleep away from home or to go to sleep without being near a major attachment figure.
 7. Repeated nightmares involving the theme of separation.
 8. Repeated complaints of physical symptoms (e.g., headaches, stomachaches, nausea, vomiting) when separation from major attachment figures occurs or is anticipated.

B. The fear, anxiety, or avoidance is persistent, lasting at least 4 weeks in children and adolescents and typically 6 months or more in adults.

C. The disturbance causes clinically significant distress or impairment in social, academic, occupational, or other important areas of functioning.

D. The disturbance is not better explained by another mental disorder, such as refusing to leave home because of excessive resistance to change in autism spectrum disorder; delusions or hallucinations concerning separation in psychotic disorders; refusal to go outside without a trusted companion in agoraphobia; worries about ill health or other harm befalling significant others in generalized anxiety disorder; or concerns about having an illness in illness anxiety disorder;

Source: Reprinted with permission from the *Diagnostic and Statistical Manual of Mental Disorders, Fifth Edition,* (Copyright © 2013). American Psychiatric Association. All Rights Reserved.

The primary difference between SAD and GAD is that, with GAD, the distress and uncertainty the child feels becomes directed outward to the world around them. They may become concerned about whether others like them, worry about doing badly at school and being uncomfortable, worry that a storm may come and cause damage to their home, or worry that something from outer space will apprehend them. Typically, the physical symptoms become the main source of distress for the child and family, and limit participation in normal activities such as attending school or parties.

When determining the type of anxiety disorder in youth, it is important to note the pervasive, persistent, and impairing nature of the symptoms. Also, the possibility that there are realistic triggers of anxiety (e.g., death, birth, a move, a new school) should be considered. If the stressor persists during the time that the anxiety is experienced, an adjustment disorder should also be considered.

COMORBIDITY Children with anxiety disorders often meet the diagnostic criteria for a mood disorder (Angold et al., 1999; Kovacs & Devlin, 1998). In one epidemiological study that examined comborbidity, 71.4% of 11-year-olds met the diagnostic criteria for depression and anxiety (Anderson, Williams, McGee, & Silva, 1987). In clinical populations, 70% of children with anxiety disorders are clinically depressed and about 80% are reluctant to attend school (Gittelman et al., 1980). Moreover, 70% of children with an anxiety disorder show somatic complaints, and test anxiety is common in these children (Biedel & Turner, 1988). About one-third

of children with SAD present with a concurrent diagnosis of GAD, and another third eventually develop GAD (Last et al., 1987). A recent study on comorbidity among anxiety disorders in a Danish national cohort of psychiatrically referred children and youth revealed that **homotypic comorbidity** (one anxiety disorder with another anxiety disorder) was low, at 2.8%, whereas **heterotypic comorbidity** (e.g., an anxiety with an externalizing problem) was high, at 73.6% (Esbjørn, Hoeyer, Dyrborg, Leth, & Kendall, 2010).

PREVALENCE The worldwide prevalence rate for any anxiety disorder is 6.5% (Polanczyk et al., 2015). The most common types of pathological anxiety are SAD (5%), GAD (3%), social anxiety disorder (1%), and simple phobias (2.5%; Lichtenstein & Annas, 2000). Significantly fewer children experience other common anxiety disorders of adulthood—namely, obsessive-compulsive disorder (OCD), panic disorder, and post-traumatic stress disorder. In childhood and adolescence, anxiety disorders are equally common in both boys and girls. These anxiety disorders have different primary symptoms, but all imply that the child is suffering from impairment in functioning in his or her daily life and that the symptoms have been present for a certain period of time. Studies have shown that many anxious children have multiple types of anxiety. It is generally agreed that these symptoms are similar to those in the adult diagnoses.

DEVELOPMENTAL TRAJECTORY Although most children with anxiety disorders develop normally and achieve age-appropriate academic and social goals, a significant

**FOCUS
15.1**

Suicidal Thoughts and Self-Harm in Youth

Fact: Suicide is the second-leading cause of death among Canadian youth aged 10 to 19 (Health Canada, 1999).

Deliberate self-harm (DSH), a term used to describe purposeful attempts to injure oneself without causing death, and suicide ideation or attempts, meaning that a deliberate plan or attempt to cause an end to one's life has occurred, are unfortunately common events for children and teens. A recent meta-analysis of studies, including more than 500 000 teens reported a suicide attempt rate of 9.7 percent and a 29.9 percent rate for suicidal thoughts. Males are more likely to complete suicide and females are four times more likely to participate in DSH (Hawton & Harriss, 2007). However, does this behaviour and these thoughts indicate risk for mental disorder, and which youth should caregivers be most concerned about?

Although DSH or thoughts of suicide may occur during a short period of distress, recent studies suggest that they are important indicators that mental health problems such as depression, substance abuse, and anxiety disorder are present. In the Great Smokey Mountains Study of more than 1400 youth, almost all youth who reported suicidal thoughts had important psychiatric problems: a diagnosable disorder (61%), a sub-threshold diagnosis (31%), or only significant impaired functioning at home or school (8%; Costello et al., 1996). This large study, consistent with many others, showed that the highest risk for self-injury was associated with having depression and one other psychiatric disorder concurrently.

Youth who self-harm without the intent of suicide may be a different group, and the DSM-5 now includes a diagnosis regarding this behaviour under further consideration called **nonsuicidal self-injury disorder (NSSID)**. Youth who would meet criteria for this disorder have less severe psychosocial impairment and fewer comorbid mental health disorders compared to youth who endorse a suicidal intent associated with self-injury (Zettervquist, 2015). Although further research is required to validate NSSID as a distinct disorder, it is important to recognize that the majority of youth who self-injure even without voiced suicidal intent have made a suicide attempt of have suicidal ideation at other times in their lives (Groschwitz et al., 2015). Therefore, all youth who self-injure must be asked about past suicidal behaviour and ideation to assess their risk of suicide. The most important predictor of future self-harm or suicidal behaviour is having a history of this behaviour; however, abusing drugs and/or access to a firearm increases the risk of completing suicide. Evidence suggests that dialectical behavioural therapy or DBT (Linehan, 2015; Mehlum et al., 2014) is an effective therapeutic intervention for reducing suicidal behaviour in youth by teaching youth specific skills to help regulate their emotions and their urges to self-injure.

Your Life Counts is a registered charitable organization that helps youth aged 13 to 24 to change self-destructive behaviour that can lead to suicide. This organization has an interactive youth-focused website (*www.yourlifecounts.org*) with an email response facility geared toward listening and steadying youth through their moments of crisis and referring them to professional help in their communities when they are often not strong enough to reach out for such help themselves. ●

proportion continue to struggle with anxiety over time. In fact, the homotypic continuity of anxiety disorders is robust, as is heterotypic continuity. For example, in one large longitudinal study, anxiety at age 11 was a very strong predictor of anxiety at age 15 for girls only (McGee, Feehan, Williams, & Anderson, 1992; see also Cohen et al., 1993). In a longitudinal study of children diagnosed with an anxiety disorder before age 13 who were reassessed at age 19, Bittner and colleagues (2007) found that SAD in childhood predicted SAD in adolescence, whereas overanxious disorder (now termed GAD) predicted GAD, panic attacks, depression, and CD in adolescence. Other evidence for the stability of anxiety disorders comes from an 18-month follow-up study of children and adolescents with SAD (Foley et al., 2004). In this study, 80 percent of participants no longer had an anxiety disorder at the end of the study. Those who were still anxious had significantly more depression, oppositional and hyperactive symptoms, and parents with marital distress than those who did not have persisting anxiety. One-third of children with SAD develop GAD, depression, or substance abuse problems, and these particular children appear to have more severe SAD and other mental health problems earlier in their lives (Manassis & Monga, 2001). Youth with anxiety disorders are reported to have increased suicidal ideation and suicide attempts (Brent et al., 1996; see Focus box 15.1). A study of French-Canadian children followed from the time they were in kindergarten until they were young adults found that anxious-disruptive girls (and disruptive boys) were far more likely than their peers to attempt suicide by the time they had reached adulthood (Brezo et al., 2008). These studies suggest that youth with anxiety disorders that persist beyond one year of treatment require monitoring for depression and substance abuse in particular.

⑤ BEFORE MOVING ON

> Many children have fears and phobias in childhood. What are some factors that may influence whether these fears develop into an anxiety disorder?

Research suggests that the developmental chronology of childhood disorders is one that begins with anxiety in early childhood, is followed by behavioural issues in middle childhood, and is then followed by depressive disorders in late childhood (Kovacs & Devlin, 1998). This research suggests that early psychopathology is a strong predictor of later mental health issues. Therefore, although many children grow out of their anxiety disorders, it is nevertheless important to monitor these children, given evidence for both homotypic and heterotypic continuity among a subset of this population.

ETIOLOGY

Compared to externalizing disorders, far less is known about the etiology of anxiety in children and adolescents, despite the fact that they are common to these age groups and are associated with significant distress, impairment, and disability.

TEMPERAMENT Most children with anxiety disorders have a history of anxious temperament in infancy and early childhood. This anxious temperament is described as **behavioural inhibition**, where children display withdrawal or fear behaviour in novel situations (Kagan, 1995; Kagan, Reznick, Clarke, Snidman, & Garcia-Coll, 1984). This temperament style has been shown to persist throughout life in most affected children, and their risk of developing one or more anxiety disorders in later life is two to four times that of children who are not behaviourally inhibited (Chronis-Tuscano et al., 2009; Essex, Klein, Slattery, Goldsmith, & Kalin, 2010; Hisfield-Becker, Micco, Simoes, & Henin, 2008).

BRAIN STRUCTURE AND FUNCTION Brain imaging and physiology research has shown that children and adults with behavioural inhibition or other anxiety disorders have abnormal functioning in a temporal lobe brain structure (the amygdala) that alerts a person to threat and orchestrates the response to it. In addition, they have higher resting heart rates and blood pressure (called physiological hyperarousal) and abnormal stress hormone regulation, which changes in an atypical way with age (see Pine, 2007).

GENETICS As with other mental disorders of childhood, anxiety disorders seem to have a heritable component. Turner, Beidel, and Costello (1987) found that 38 percent of children of parents with an anxiety disorder also had an anxiety disorder. Although anxiety disorders seem to run in families, it is important to bear in mind that this type of familial clustering can also be explained by shared environmental factors such as parenting practices or socio-economic status (Thaper & McGuffin, 1995). Twin studies help disentangle shared environmental influences from the influences of genes. Although many studies have been conducted on adults (e.g., Kendler, Heath, Martin, & Eaves, 1986; Kendler, Neale, Kessler, Heath, & Eaves, 1992), studies examining the heritability estimate in children are few and far between. In one British study, the heritability estimate was 59 percent using parent reports (Thaper & McGuffin, 1995). Interestingly, however, when self-rating of symptoms was used to index anxiety, familial transmission could be accounted for only by shared environmental factors. In a more recent longitudinal twin study, Trzaskowski and colleagues (2011)

found that genetic factors explained most (68%) of the stability in anxiety symptoms, whereas shared and non-shared environmental influences were modest (18% and 28%, respectively). However, using data from eight samples of monozygotic twins, Kendler and colleagues (2011) found that the environment does indeed play an important role in the development of anxiety. In this study, researchers found that as children aged, their environmental experiences contributed to stable and predictable differences in levels of anxiety and depression. In fact, on the basis on their findings, these researchers went as far as to reject the hypothesis that genetic factors alone were responsible for the temporal stability of internalizing disorders. As mentioned above in this paragraph, and in other sections, the current school of thought regarding psychopathology is one that includes G × E interactions.

PRENATAL RISK FACTORS A large body of evidence reviewed by Talge, Neal, Glover, & the Early Stress, Translational Research and Prevention Science Network: Fetal and Neonatal Experience on Child and Adolescent Mental Health (2007) suggest that if a mother experiences considerable enduring stress while pregnant, her child is significantly more likely to have problems with anxiety, and also with learning and attention problems. This is thought to be related to the effect of elevated levels of maternal stress hormone, or cortisol, on the developing brain.

PSYCHOSOCIAL RISK FACTORS Genetic studies of anxiety disorders in children have shown that it is not typical for the same anxiety disorder to be passed from parent to child, suggesting that the genetic risk for anxiety may be channelled by the type of environment in which the child grows up. Seminal research by Dr. Stanley (Jack) Rachman at the University of British Columbia has shown that the child learns what and how to fear from the parent either vicariously (by observing the parent) or through instructions given by the parent (Rachmann, 1977). Children can also learn to fear directly based on experiences in which they have been hurt or frightened (classical conditioning). The effect of the child's anxiety on the parent is not to be ignored, however, as bidirectional effects amplifying the parental experience and distress associated with child anxiety have been noted (Fisak & Grills-Taquechel, 2007).

Although they are likely very relevant, other psychosocial factors such as socio-economic status or parental education have not been studied extensively as risk factors for anxiety disorders. Using data from the U.S. National Comorbidity Survey Replication study, McLaughlin and colleagues (2011) found a strong relationship between child poverty and the onset of child psychopathology, especially anxiety disorders.

GENE–ENVIRONMENT INTERACTIONS Pine (2007) has proposed a model to describe how anxiety disorders develop in susceptible children. Most anxiety can be theorized to result from "fear conditioning." Here, the brain is engaged by threats (aversive stimuli) that the person would naturally want to avoid, and often a neutral stimulus becomes paired—or conditioned—with the threat to induce a similar fear and avoidance response. This pairing, along with its pattern of reinforcement, is largely influenced by the amygdala; hence, people with a genetic predisposition to amygdala dysfunction (i.e., those at risk for anxiety disorders or who have behavioural inhibition) would be more prone to be threatened, or fooled, by non-noxious stimuli. Such stimuli become the focus of childhood fears. Fears diminish over time in most children as the circuitry develops more elaborate connections with the prefrontal (inhibitory) cortex. However, fears persist in those children with behavioural inhibition.

The type of anxiety and the timing of its onset may be related to a combination of genetic susceptibility and environmental exposures. Consistent with this, many anxiety disorders are noted to begin following a period of life stress, and most research on families of anxious children suggests that they are close-knit and that parents are over-involved. It is difficult to disentangle this presentation from the parents' own high levels of anxiety (or of anxiety disorders); thus, additional research in this area is required. Work by Kendler and colleagues (2008) suggests that the genetic or biological component of risk for anxiety may diminish as the child ages, suggesting further the importance of studying the environmental causes of anxiety, particularly in adolescents.

TREATMENT

The primary aim of treatment of anxiety is reduction of children's physical symptoms and their pattern of avoidance of situations or things that provoke their fear symptoms and thoughts. This reduction in physical symptoms of anxiety will help the children think more clearly about their anxieties and, depending on their age, begin to think more probabilistically or neutrally about the fears so that they function more normally. However, modification of the behavioural avoidance is also central. For example, if school avoidance exists, this should be addressed as an urgent issue. Typically, multiple people are involved in any treatment plan for child anxiety disorder.

Treatment of anxiety disorders includes first providing psychoeducation about the causes of anxiety and which of the child's behaviours is most likely related to anxiety. This is provided to the child, parents, and teachers. Behavioural assessment of how the parents and teachers handle the anxiety is required because the way in which adults manage the symptoms often unintentionally reinforces a child's avoidance behaviour. Taking a life history of the child to understand his or her development and its normalcy is important in that a child who has social or language delays will have additional challenges in responding optimally to treatment, and often adults are protective of these children. In most instances of severe child anxiety, ongoing monitoring of how the parents are managing the anxiety is required. Some very anxious parents themselves may require treatment for underlying anxiety disorders.

COGNITIVE-BEHAVIOURAL TREATMENT The most robust evidence for treatment of childhood anxiety disorders exists for cognitive-behavioural therapy (CBT; Cartwright-Hatton, Roberts, Chitsabesan, Fothergill, & Harrington, 2004), with one of the most widely used methods being the Coping CAT program (Kendall & Hedtke, 2006). Components of CBT include extensive education about anxiety and its treatment approach, helping the parents and child learn new ways to cope with anxiety (skills building), and systematic and gradual exposure to anxiety-provoking situations in which they can practise their skills. How children are exposed to anxiety-provoking situations depends on how anxious or functionally impaired they (or the parents) are. For example, children who cannot go to school or want to call their parents every hour would be expected to go to school and remain there until they were less upset prior to calling the parents (or not call the parents at all), or they could call their parents only once a day for a few weeks. In CBT, it is important that all parties agree on what behaviour is acceptable or unacceptable. In addition, after the behavioural intervention, there is an opportunity to debrief with the child about his or her success, or to discuss how to make it more successful next time (mastery).

Many anxious children have a parent who is also anxious. Accordingly, there is evidence to support the inclusion of a parent component when using CBT. For example, Cobham, Dadds, and Spence (1998) found that the efficacy of child-focused CBT was reduced among children whose parents were anxious. However, the provision of a parental anxiety management component enhanced the treatment efficacy among these children.

Some children are so anxious that they cannot succeed with CBT. In these instances, medications can be useful. Indeed, a recent randomized controlled trial of anxious children aged 7 to 17 found that a combination of CBT and the selective serotonin reuptake inhibitor sertraline (Zoloft) produced the best response rates (Walkup et al., 2008).

PHARMACOLOGICAL TREATMENT Similar pharmacological treatments (see Table 15.2) are recommended for SAD and GAD because they probably target similar underlying physiological processes, and because most randomized controlled trials in children include children with both, or more, disorders. Three placebo-controlled studies report significant benefits of the **selective serotonin reuptake inhibitors (SSRIs)** (fluvoxamine, paroxetine, and fluoxetine), emerging by approximately four weeks of treatment (Clark et al., 2005; Rynn, Siqueland, & Rickels, 2001; Wagner et al., 2004). The largest randomized controlled study (128 youth) of longest duration (6 months) found a significant reduction in anxiety symptoms with the drug fluvoxamine after eight weeks (Walkup et al., 2002). At the end of the study, they found that 92 percent of those taking medications stayed well. To date, no studies have been conducted to determine whether youth relapse, or become unwell again, after stopping SSRI medications. These studies, although few in number, suggest that SSRI medications are efficacious at reducing anxiety

FOCUS 15.2

Perfectionism and Mental Health

The role perfectionism plays in the development and maintenance of mental health problems is one that has been embraced primarily by Canadian researchers such as Dr. Gordon Flett from York University, Dr. Paul Hewitt from UBC, and Dr. Simon Sherry from Dalhousie University. Perfectionism is often confused with conscientiousness by the general public and is thus praised and revered. However, research support an opposite view point, demonstrating that perfectionism is in fact a maladaptive personality style (Flett & Hewitt, 2002). Perfectionism is multidimensional and can be characterized by self-imposed high standards that are hard to achieve (i.e., **self-oriented perfectionism**), by the belief that significant others hold high standards and expectations that the person must meet (i.e., **socially prescribed perfectionism**; Hewitt & Flett, 1991), or by a propensity to impose high standards on others and blame them when the standards are not met (i.e., **other-oriented perfectionism**; Hewitt & Flett, 1991). One core feature associated with all the forms of perfectionism is the feeling of failure that is linked to self-criticism and negative self-appraisal (Shafran et al., 2002). Perfectionism is common among youth. In a recent study of Canadian teens assessed yearly from Grade 9 to Grade 12, Vaillancourt and Haltigan (2017) found that close to one in five teens followed a high trajectory of perfectionism.

Perfectionism is an essential feature of obsessive-compulsive personality disorder (APA, 2013; see Chapter 12) and is strongly linked to depression (Vaillancourt & Haltigan, 2017) and suicidal ideology and behaviour (Flett, Hewitt, & Heisel, 2014). Perfectionism is thought to be linked to depression because perfectionists share a lot of the same cognitive attribution biases that people with depression hold (Asseraf & Vaillancourt, 2015). For example, they tend to make polarized assumptions about events ("I failed" or "I passed" with failure equating not being perfect) or form conclusions on the basis of one event ("I am always going to be a failure"); and they tend to assume responsibility for events that are beyond their control ("Everything is my fault").

Perfectionism is a significant barrier to treating many psychological disorders; in particular, treating depression and preventing its relapse. For example, in a longitudinal study of Canadian adults treated for depression, Hawley et al. (2014) found that participants who had high levels of perfectionism were more likely to experience increases in depression symptoms following stressful events post treatment than participants who had lower levels of perfectionism. Considering these links, it is widely suggested that the targeting perfectionism should be a treatment goal when dealing with depressed clients. ●

---

symptoms in children with these types of anxiety disorders (Walkup et al., 2008), but more studies are required to determine whether medications are better than CBT alone.

The most common side effects of SSRIs are gastrointestinal complaints, headaches, and drowsiness. Concerns about increased risk of suicidal ideation in SSRI anxiety trials cannot be answered, as most children with suicidal ideation or depression are excluded and the studies do not include enough participants. For all children or teens taking SSRI medications, close monitoring of suicidal thoughts or feelings of agitation is necessary, as some youth taking such medications may develop these problems (Hetrick, Merry, McKenzie, Sindahl, & Proctor, 2007). Medications with a poor risk–benefit profile include benzodiazepines and tricyclic antidepressants, and these are not recommended for the treatment of anxiety in youth.

SUMMARY

- More so than adults, children and youth are influenced by their environments and the lives of others around them because they have less autonomy for their decisions. This reality can also influence the presentation of impairment or symptoms.

- It is important to consider the impact of life stressors and family context on a child's symptoms. The impact of treatment or cognitive and emotional development on symptom persistence is also important to consider as children continue to grow and mature.

- The opinion of the child's difficulties can differ by the informant. Teachers have been shown to be better respondents than parents about severity of ADHD and social functioning. Parents have been shown to be

the most comprehensive respondents about disruptive behaviour, although they under-report conduct symptoms compared to the child. Adolescents are the most accurate respondents with respect to anxiety.

- These developmental and informant factors specific to children and youth emphasize the importance of comprehensive assessment of symptoms and global functioning from multiple informants in this population.

- One in five youth have a psychiatric disorder. Forty percent of these youth have multiple disorders (comorbidity). Having a childhood disorder substantially increases the risk for developing another disorder (heterotypic continuity) or continuing to have the same disorder (homotypic continuity).

- Some disorders appear to be more common in boys prior to puberty (ADHD) and in girls following puberty (anxiety disorders and mood disorders). Although conduct disorders are more common in boys before puberty, the rates are more similar across sex in adolescence.

- ADHD can be diagnosed in 2% of preschoolers and 6% of children and adolescents. ADHD is 10 times as prevalent in clinical samples. The prevalence of ODD (3 to 6%) and CD (1 to 10%) is similar to ADHD, although more difficult to estimate as many studies do not clearly distinguish the prevalence of ODD from CD (and many do not account for the comorbid condition ADHD). Anxiety disorders are also common, but rates vary by disorder, with the most common presentation being separation anxiety disorder (5% of children) and the least common being social anxiety disorder (1% of children).

- Regardless of the type of disorder, all diagnoses require that the child show evidence of persistent impairment in multiple settings, which can be directly attributed to the symptoms of disorder.

- ADHD is a neuropsychiatric disorder that reflects problems with executive functions, such as the regulation of attention, behaviour, and motivation. The two broad areas of symptom impairment are hyperactivity/impulsivity and inattention. The DSM recognizes ADHD subtypes (now called specifiers) where some children appear more hyperactive or more inattentive and can be classified as such, although most children with ADHD have both hyperactivity/impulsivity and inattention.

- ODD and CD describe youth who have persistent difficulties of reacting negatively toward others with hostility or defiance as a primary problem (ODD) or engaging in behaviour that result in deliberate physical or emotional harm to others (CD). It is clear that these diagnoses describe the behaviour of the youth and not so much their underlying difficulties, such as comorbid disorders (ADHD, anxiety, or learning disabilities) or the difficult social circumstances they live in. For example, recent research suggests there may be a subgroup of ODD youth who struggle with high levels of irritable mood, and a group of CD youth who have psychopathic tendencies.

- Children with anxiety disorders experience all of the following difficulties: mental preoccupations with worries or fears, behavioural or mental actions directed toward avoidance of the perceived source of fear or worry, and physical distress (headaches, tension) because of the worry. What differs across the types of anxiety disorders is the focus of the fear or worry. For example, being worried about a parent's safety is consistent with separation anxiety, being worried about potential embarrassment is consistent with social anxiety, and being worried about unpredictable events is consistent with generalized anxiety.

- Mental disorders present as a result of multiple risk processes that involve components of disturbed biology, environment, and psychological factors. The timing of occurrence of disorder and the severity of the disorder are related to the ways these factors exert their effects for a particular child. It is therefore false to assume that any one factor is causal. When describing a mental disorder and its presentation, it is important to consider how biological, environmental, and psychological factors are of relevance for that child. For example, most children with ADHD have a family history, attesting to its inherited genetic component, and their symptoms typically respond to stimulant medication, suggesting a biological basis for the disorder. Symptoms of ADHD are worse in unstructured environments (such as lunchtime versus in class), attesting to the influence of context in shaping behaviour. Many children with ADHD are difficult to parent or teach and experience difficulties with peers, and their self-esteem is often affected. It is important to intervene in all these areas to help the child with ADHD.

- ADHD: Evidence-based psychological interventions should be provided to all families who have a child with ADHD. These include caregiver psychoeducation, parent-training programs to help parents facilitate more functional behaviour patterns, and school-focused interventions, including psychoeducational testing for learning difficulties and providing classroom modifications to facilitate attention. Pharmacological treatments for ADHD include short- and long-acting derivatives of methylphenidate, dextroamphetamine, and amphetamine. These compounds work by increasing the sensitivity of dopamine receptors in the prefrontal cortex. Children treated with these medications require close medical monitoring. These treatments do not cure ADHD but help reduce symptoms and should be used in concert with psychological interventions.

- ODD and CD: Four diverse treatment methods have been shown to be helpful for ODD and CD: (1) teaching problem-solving skills, (2) pharmacological interventions, (3) parent management training, and (4) school- and community-based treatments. With the exception of pharmacological interventions, these methods help to break the coercive effect of the youth's behaviour on families and peers by teaching others how to respond to the behaviour or increasing the youth's sensitivity to the effects of his or her behaviour on others. Pharmacological interventions are generally focused on the treatment of comorbid conditions (ADHD or anxiety).

- Anxiety disorders: Cognitive-behavioural therapy (CBT) has been shown to be effective for the treatment of childhood anxiety disorders. CBT should include a parent component as many parents have anxiety themselves or reinforce the child's avoidance behaviour. Medications for treatment of anxiety in children and youth include antidepressant medications (serotonin specific reuptake inhibitors), and are used as an adjunct to CBT or as a means of reducing anxiety sufficiently to allow participation in CBT.

- Disruptive mood dysregulation disorder is classified as a mood disorder in the DSM-5 but it represents a perfect intersect between externalizing and internalizing problems. If a child's symptoms meet diagnostic criteria for both DMDD and ODD, the diagnosis of DMDD is given.

- New research suggests that sources of "risk" are not as clear-cut as previously assumed. Specifically, differential susceptibility theory and biological sensitivity to context theory suggest that sources of vulnerability can not only increase the risk of poorer outcomes, but they can also be associated with more positive outcomes in the context of more supportive environments.

- Perfectionism is characterized by self-imposed high standards that are hard to achieve. Perfectionism is common among youth, affecting close to one in five teens. Given perfectionism's strong relation to depression, it is generally suggested that the targeting perfectionism should be a treatment goal when dealing with depressed clients.

KEY TERMS

assortative mating (p. 398)

attention deficit/hyperactivity disorder (ADHD) (p. 389)

behavioural inhibition (p. 406)

biological sensitivity to context (p. 400)

coercive process (p. 401)

comorbidity (p. 387)

conduct disorder (CD) (p. 395)

deliberate self-harm (DSH) (p. 405)

diathesis-stress perspective (p. 393)

differential susceptibility (p. 400)

disruptive mood dysregulation disorder (p. 387)

externalizing problems (p. 387)

gene–environment interactions (p. 393)

heterotypic comorbidity (p. 404)

heterotypic continuity (p. 387)

homotypic comorbidity (p. 404)

homotypic continuity (p. 387)

internalizing problems (p. 387)

methylphenidate (Ritalin) (p. 394)

nonsuicidal self-injury disorder (NSSID) (p. 405)

oppositional defiant disorder (ODD) (p. 395)

other-oriented perfectionism (p. 408)

perfectionism (p. 408)

selective serotonin reuptake inhibitors (p. 407)

self-oriented perfectionism (p. 408)

separation anxiety disorder (SAD) (p. 403)

socially prescribed perfectionism (p. 408)

COREY S. MACKENZIE

•

KRISTIN A. REYNOLDS

CHAPTER

16

Scott Griessel/123RF

Aging and Mental Health

LEARNING OBJECTIVES

AFTER READING THIS CHAPTER, STUDENTS WILL BE ABLE TO:

1 Explain how Canada's population is aging, why it is aging, and what effect our aging population will have on mental health care.

2 Describe the commonly held myths about treating older adults with mental disorders and list reasons for why these myths exist.

3 Describe how the three primary lifespan theoretical models of aging view successful aging.

4 Summarize the various factors that complicate the diagnosis and treatment of sleep disorders in older adults.

5 Briefly summarize what current research tells us about the effectiveness of psychological and pharmacological treatment of mood, anxiety, and sleep disorders for older versus younger adults.

6 Describe the difference between dementia and Alzheimer's disease and list the primary risk factors for developing Alzheimer's disease.

Just after Laura retired at age 65, her only daughter, Stephanie, died in a mountain-climbing accident. Laura and her daughter, a single pediatrician, had always been very close, and people often remarked that they seemed more like sisters than mother and daughter. Immediately after hearing the terrible news, Laura began a whirlwind of activity. First, she arranged single-handedly to have Stephanie's body returned home from Nepal. Next, she planned an elaborate funeral. During these few days, Laura barely slept and never shed a tear. She displayed no sadness, and showed anxiety only about funeral details. Laura wanted everything to be perfect for Stephanie. Her friends praised her strength of character, but her husband, Mark, was silently worried about her frantic pace of activity. For a few weeks after the funeral, Laura's state of agitation persisted. She could not sleep and usually declined food at mealtimes. Migraine headaches, an occasional problem for her before, became almost daily occurrences.

Then, just when Mark had convinced himself that Laura's reactions were normal in the face of such a terrible loss, she began to behave in ways that caused him serious concern. Laura had not cried to this point, but now she began to cry often, sometimes for hours at a time. She still could not sleep well, but now when she was awake she seemed to have little energy for anything that Mark might suggest. Mark was also concerned about how forgetful his wife had suddenly become. She preferred to sit alone in the den doing nothing at all. Laura talked of nothing but Stephanie and of her desire to be reunited with her daughter. Often she said that she, not Stephanie, should have been the one who died.

At other times she would say that Stephanie was with them, that she could see Stephanie sitting in a chair next to hers. When Laura began to speak to Stephanie as though she were really in the room, Mark decided it was time to seek professional help. He did not understand what was happening. He knew that Laura was probably depressed, but he was also afraid that her recent memory problems and hallucinations might be the start of Alzheimer's disease.

Mark made an appointment for Laura to meet with a clinical psychologist, who first conducted a thorough diagnostic workup and then met with the couple. The psychologist reassured them that Laura was not mentally ill. Rather, she was suffering from normal bereavement, particularly because her daughter's death was premature and unexpected. Mark was especially relieved to learn that neither memory problems nor hallucinating the presence of Stephanie was an unusual reaction within the first months after a death. When the psychologist learned that Stephanie's birthday was two weeks away, she pointed out that such anniversaries are commonly times at which symptoms of bereavement worsen. She recommended that Laura begin bereavement counselling right away.

Changing Demography

Although different chronological ages are used to define "older adults" for different purposes, we will use the most conventional dividing line and say that an older adult is anyone over age 65. Around the world, the number of older adults is increasing at an unprecedented rate. The global population reached 7 billion in 2012. At that time 8% of the population (562 million) was aged 65 and older. By 2030,

nearly 1 billion older adults will make up 12% of the global population (He, Goodkind, & Kowal, 2016).

Canada is no exception to this population aging trend. In fact, our population is aging at an even faster rate. As shown in Figure 16.1, Statistics Canada data indicate that 2017 marks the first time in our nation's history when the proportion of adults aged 65 years and older outnumbers the proportion of children aged 14 years and younger. Older adults are expected to comprise approximately one-quarter

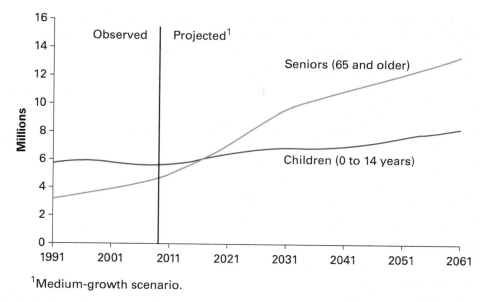

¹Medium-growth scenario.

FIGURE 16.1 Population projections, children and seniors

Source: Statistics Canada, An aging population. Retrieved from: http://www.statcan.gc.ca/pub/11-402-x/2010000/chap/pop/pop02-eng.htm. Reproduced and distributed on an "as is" basis with the permission of Statistics Canada.

of the population by 2036, growing steadily to almost one third by 2061 (Statistics Canada, 2012).

There are two primary reasons for these trends, the most important of which is the aging of the **baby boomers**—people who were born within 20 years following the end of the Second World War in 1945. In 2011 the oldest of the baby boomers started to turn 65. Because this group of individuals spans two decades, we can expected the proportion of older adults to increase the most from about 2020 to 2030 (Statistics Canada, 2006).

The second primary reason for our aging population is that Canadians are living longer than ever. Canadians have one of the longest life expectancies in the world; in 2001 men were expected to live to age 77 and women to age 82 (up from age 69 for men and age 76 for women in 1970; Belanger, Martel, & Caron-Malenfant, 2005). Reductions in mortality among both younger and older adults are due to advances in public health (e.g., immunization, safer drinking water), workplace safety, and newly developed and more effective medications and surgical procedures. In addition, factors such as greater affluence and higher levels of education are thought to contribute to longevity, presumably because more affluent, better-educated people are likely, for example, to have less dangerous jobs that require less physical wear and tear on their bodies, better nutrition, and better health care.

What do these changing demographics mean for the mental health field? As the proportion of older adults in the population increases, so will the number of older adults with mental disorders. This increase will pose a number of challenges for mental health professionals that are addressed in the section Age-Specific Issues of Diagnosis and Treatment. This shift will also result in a number of new opportunities for mental health professionals with interest and expertise in treating older individuals.

❶ BEFORE MOVING ON

As the number of older Canadians increases substantially in the next several decades, some individuals think that this demographic shift will overwhelm our health care system, including mental health care. Others think that this shift will have relatively modest effects on our health care system. What do you think will happen, and why?

An important source of information that will help answer this question is the Canadian Longitudinal Study on Aging (CLSA). This impressive study, which began in 2009, will collect data from over 50 000 men and women between the ages of 45 and 85 and follow them for the next 20 years (Raina et al., 2009). The purpose of the CLSA is to improve our understanding of individual differences in aging, including self-report health variables (e.g., depression), clinical data (e.g., blood pressure), and biomarkers (blood and urine). Data from this study will help improve health services, prevent disease, improve our understanding on how non-medical factors affect aging, and answer questions that can assist health decision-makers (see www.clsa-elcv.ca/about-us).

VULNERABILITY VERSUS RESILIENCE IN OLD AGE

A person is more likely to develop a mental disorder at times of increased vulnerability (Gatz, Kasl-Godley, & Karel, 1996). When people are vulnerable, they may become unable to cope with previously manageable problems or situations. Have you ever found that something as simple as a cold or a headache has reduced your ability to cope with a difficult situation, such as an exam? To take a more dramatic example, a person might be able to cope with being laid off from work, or having a spouse diagnosed with a terminal illness; however, if both happened close together, the person might be overwhelmed and might begin to show signs of clinically significant depression or anxiety. The first challenging life event may be said to have increased the person's emotional vulnerability to the point that he or she is unable to cope with the second significant challenge. As people age, they are more likely to experience increased vulnerability—both physically, as various organ systems begin to be compromised, and psychologically, with losses in areas such as social support (due to deaths of friends and relatives) and independence (due to lost driver's licences, increased hospitalizations, or relocations from home to institution).

Despite the fact that aging is associated with increases in biological and psychological vulnerabilities, there is actually good evidence to suggest that old age is generally a time of psychological resilience rather than poor mental health. In addition to evidence of decreases in the prevalence of most mental disorders with age (which we outline in the upcoming prevalence section), it appears that well-being, happiness, and life satisfaction increase after middle age. An impressive review of life satisfaction among individuals from 40 nations found remarkable stability in well-being across the lifespan (Diener, Suh, Lucas, & Smith, 1999). Another large study of 340 847 people in the United States found that well-being showed U-shaped age profiles with increased well-being after age 50 (Stone, Schwartz, Broderick, & Deaton, 2010). This same U-shaped pattern of improved well-being, happiness, and mental health from middle age to later life was found across more than 72 developed and developing nations using analyses that showed that the findings were not due to factors such as sociodemographics and income (Blanchflower & Oswald, 2008). Consistent with these findings, data from Statistics Canada indicate that in 2009, 97 percent of older adults reported being satisfied with life and 70 percent reported having either good or excellent mental health (Butler-Jones, 2010). Finally, a number of personality characteristics that are associated with positive health, such as conscientiousness, agreeableness, and emotional stability, increase across the adult lifespan (Roberts, Walton, & Viechtbauer, 2006; Srivastava, John, Gosling, & Potter, 2003). Together, this evidence of positive mental health among older adults who would normally be considered vulnerable has been coined the **paradox of aging** (Baltes & Baltes, 1990). Of course, it is important for us to keep in mind that older adults do tend to experience multiple losses and that there are wide individual differences in how loss is dealt with. As we will see in the next section, although older adults tend to be resilient in the face of these losses, many do go on to develop mental health problems.

Prevalence of Mental Disorders in Older Adults

Although we will discuss prevalence rates for individual disorders later in the chapter, it is helpful to begin with an understanding of age differences in overall rates of mental health problems. Awareness of both overall prevalence and prevalence rates for specific disorders can help practitioners, researchers, and policy-makers understand how common mental health problems are so that they can make informed decisions about how best to target prevention and treatment strategies to improve older people's mental health. The best evidence concerning the prevalence of mental disorders across the lifespan comes from large-scale community surveys conducted in the United States (Kessler et al., 2005; Mackenzie, Pagura, & Sareen, 2010; Reynolds, Pietrzak, El-Gabalawy, Mackenzie, & Sareen, 2015), Australia (Henderson, 2002), Europe (Alonso & Lepine, 2007), and Canada (Streiner, Cairney, & Veldhuizen, 2006).

These surveys have provided three very important pieces of information. First, mental health problems are extremely common in the general population. Although there is variability across studies, they suggest that 25 to 50% of people will have a mental disorder at some point in their lifetimes, and 12 to 30% will have a mental disorder in a given year. Second, these surveys suggest that, with the exception of dementia and sleep disorders, mental disorders are less common among older adults. For example, the European Study of the Epidemiology of Mental Disorders found the highest 12-month prevalence of any mental disorder among 18- to 24-year-olds (16.5%), rates of about 12% among middle-aged Europeans, and the lowest prevalence (7.8%) among those aged 65 and older. Similarly, data from the Canadian Community Health Survey of 36 984 adults from across the country found linear decreases after age 55 in lifetime rates of combined major depression, bipolar disorder, social phobia, agoraphobia, and panic disorder (Streiner, Cairney, & Veldhuizen, 2006). Our research group has shown similar findings among older Americans, although prevalence rates of anxiety and mood problems increased slightly among men over 85 (Reynolds et al., 2015). Third, gender differences occur in the prevalence of mental health problems. Women are generally more likely to have diagnosable mood and anxiety disorders, and men are more likely to have diagnosable substance and personality disorders. However, gender differences tend to decrease with increasing age (see Figure 16.2; Reynolds et al., 2015; Streiner et al., 2006).

Let us consider the evidence we have just reviewed demonstrating that aging is associated with lower rates of common mental disorders, higher levels of well-being, and positive changes in personality. Can this really be true? It certainly seems to contradict the commonly held belief that we discuss in the misconceptions of treating older adults section below, which states that it is sad and depressing to get older. In fact, there are reasons why many people (including some researchers) don't believe these data for the following three reasons. First, when they take part in community surveys to measure rates of mental disorders, older individuals may be less likely than younger individuals to remember having symptoms of disorders, less likely to report them, or more likely to express psychological

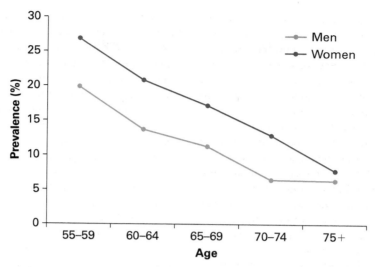

FIGURE 16.2 Prevalence of Lifetime Mental Disorders for Men and Women Aged 55 and Older

Source: Republished with permission of SAGE Publications, from "The epidemiology of psychological problems in the elderly." *Canadian Journal of Psychiatry*, 51 (3), 185–191. 2006; permission conveyed through Copyright Clearance Center, Inc.

symptoms in somatic ways (e.g., as aches and pains rather than as depression). Second, older adults with severe mental health problems may be excluded from surveys or refuse to participate in them because of homelessness or institutionalization. Third, there is likely a survivor effect in these surveys due to the fact that individuals with mental disorders have higher mortality rates, so that only the healthiest members of society survive to old age. However, although each of these factors likely has some influence, it is unlikely that they are strong enough to reverse clear and reliable age effects we have just reviewed (Streiner et al., 2006).

Before leaving this section it is important to briefly consider why, on average, older adults are mentally healthier than their younger counterparts. Most of the data pointing to mental health resiliency is cross-sectional—it is based on surveys at a given point in time that are completed by young, middle-aged, and older adults. As a result, it is important to ask if these age-related benefits are due to the process of aging itself (known as **age effects**), if they are the result of difference between groups of people born at different times (known as **cohort effects**), or if they are the result of different age groups living through different periods in time that either increase their risk for mental health problems or make them more resilient (known as **period effects**). For example, it may be that the cohort of adults who were born prior to 1920 and who lived through the Great Depression and both world wars are more psychologically resilient than are individuals born after 1950 because of their experiences coping with these difficult times. It may also be, however, that the process of aging brings with it perspective, wisdom, and good mental health. Unfortunately, it is difficult for cross-sectional research to untangle age, period, and cohort effects. That is why we need good longitudinal studies like the CLSA (Raina et al., 2009).

Historical Perspective

Historically, older adults with mental disorders were typically seen as eccentric rather than ill. When older adults became too disruptive, they were isolated, either in a variety of institutions or at home. Such eccentricities were seen both as part of normal old age and as something about which nothing could be done. Starting in the 1930s, psychiatric treatment—psychosurgery and psychopharmacological agents—became available, although limited to the most disruptive of older adults suffering from mental disorders. More commonly, however, "treatment" for such people continued to be isolation in some form of institution.

The idea that mental disorders in older adults can and should be treated is relatively new. Kermis (1984) argued that as recently as 1972 the clinical psychology of aging was virtually nonexistent, and that even the most widely used assessment tools were not normed for people over age 65. Today, there is growing acceptance in clinical psychology and other health and mental health professions of assessing older adults with mental disorders using appropriate age-normed methods, and the value of treating them.

MISCONCEPTIONS ABOUT TREATING OLDER ADULTS

Gerontologists are professionals from a wide variety of disciplines with expertise in aging. In addition to treating older adults with health concerns, these professionals help dispel myths about aging. One such myth that is particularly common is that treatment for mental health problems in late life is unnecessary and/or ineffective. This myth exists for a number of reasons. First, consider the following commonly held (and untrue) negative stereotypes about older adults: (a) they are rigid and set in their ways, (b) you cannot teach an old dog new tricks, and (c) the lights are on but no one is home. It is easy to see why people who mistakenly view older adults as being stuck in their ways, unable to learn new information, and cognitively impaired would not believe that therapy could be effective for them. Second, many people mistakenly believe that the development of pathology must be accepted as a part of **normal aging** and therefore need not be treated (Birren & Renner, 1980). It is not uncommon for people to think that aging is a sad, unfortunate process during which individuals experience physiological, cognitive, and social losses. Why wouldn't an 82-year-old man who has disabling arthritis and mild memory problems and has attended the funerals of two close friends in the past year be depressed?

Third, the notion that aging is a sad process is strongly reinforced by our societal emphasis on youth and "anti-aging" marketing. Fourth, current thinking may be influenced by early lifespan developmental theories, which suggested that emotional experiences paralleled changes in cognition and physiology, peaking in the early twenties and then deteriorating (Banham, 1951; Frenkel-Brunswik, 1968). Finally, one of Freud's unfortunate legacies was his explicit position that psychotherapy with older adults was ill-advised. As a result of factors like this, as discussed in detail in Focus box 16.1, research in Canada and elsewhere has demonstrated that younger and older adults in the community (including older adults themselves) and mental health professionals have inaccurate beliefs

FOCUS 16.1

Older Adults: The Missing Clients

By any measure—admissions to psychiatric facilities, attendance at community health clinics, representation in therapist caseloads—older adults are disproportionately underrepresented as users of mental health services. We recently demonstrated, with a representative sample of community-dwelling adults from the United States, that in comparison to middle-aged adults aged 35 to 64, older adults aged 65+ are approximately half as likely to seek help for anxiety and mood disorders (Mackenzie, Reynolds, Cairney, Streiner, & Sareen, 2012). The same pattern is found here in Canada; only 37 percent of older adults with one or more mental disorder reported using mental health services in the past year (Cairney, Corna, & Streiner, 2010). According to Gatz and colleagues (1985), there are three possible reasons for this unsettling finding: client barriers, therapist barriers, and systemic barriers.

Client barriers are reasons why older adults might contribute to their own low rates of mental health service use due to factors such as negative attitudes toward seeking help, stigma, and lack of knowledge about mental health problems and treatments (which is known as mental health literacy; Jorm, 2012). Until fairly recently, gerontologists assumed that older people were more likely to experience stigma about mental health problems because they grew up in an era when seeing a psychiatrist, psychologist, or social worker was uncommon. Interestingly, research from our laboratory, shown in Figure 16.3, suggests that older adults' attitudes toward seeking psychological help are actually more positive than those of younger adults (Mackenzie, Scott, Mather, & Sareen, 2008). Even though their attitudes toward seeking help are quite positive, older adults have been shown to have poorer mental health literacy than younger adults (Veenker & Paans, 2016).

Therapist barriers are reasons why mental health professionals may be less willing or able to treat older adults due to factors such as lack of geriatric training and ageist attitudes, beliefs, and treatment practices. Support exists for this barrier to older adults' service use. Perhaps as a result of ageist attitudes in the general population (Kite, Stockdale, Whitley Jr., & Johnson, 2005) and lack of geropsychology training (to be discussed), psychologists, psychiatrists, and clinical psychology graduate students are reluctant to treat older adults and prefer to work with younger clients (DeRyck, Gekoski, Knox, & Zivian, 1996; Zivian, Larsen, Knox, Gekoski, & Hatchette, 1992). In addition to mental health

professionals, family physicians provide the majority of mental health treatment in North America and are gatekeepers to the mental health system. There is reason to think that they, too, contribute to the greater underservice of the older segment of the population. We surveyed Canadian family physicians, who indicated that they were less likely both to treat older patients and to refer them to mental health professionals. This finding is not surprising considering that these physicians reported being less prepared to identify and treat mental disorders in older adults than in younger adults (Mackenzie, Gekoski, & Knox, 1999).

Finally, systemic barriers are practical reasons why access to mental health services is limited, including government policies and regulations that disadvantage older mental health service users (Karel, Gatz, & Smyer, 2012; Karlin & Duffy, 2004), logistic impediments to using services such as transportation and mobility issues, and the help-seeking attitudes and beliefs of people in older adults' social support networks (Mackenzie, Knox, Smoley, & Gekoski, 2004). A particularly important systemic barrier to meeting older adults' mental health needs is an insufficient number of mental health professionals who specialize in assessing and treating them. Fortunately, there is growing awareness of the need to improve our detection and treatment of mental health problems among older adults. To address the growing demand for psychologists and other mental health professionals with expertise in aging, guidelines and models of geropsychology training have been published (American Psychological Association, 2004; Knight, Karel, Hinrichsen, Qualls, & Duffy, 2009) and the need for increased training opportunities for geropsychologists has been highlighted internationally (Karel et al., 2012; Pachana, Emery, Konnert, Woodhead, & Edelstein, 2010). Unfortunately, in Canada there are no doctoral programs with a formal concentration in geropsychology, and faculty resources and practicum experiences in clinical psychology programs are sparse. The situation is somewhat better when clinical psychology graduate students go on internship, 40 percent of whom have a major rotation and a further 48 percent a minor rotation in geropsychology (Konnert, Dobson, & Watt, 2009). So although there are training opportunities in geropsychology in Canada and internationally, it is very clear that there is and will continue to be a severe shortage of geriatric mental health professionals for the foreseeable future. Students thinking about career opportunities after graduation should take note! ●

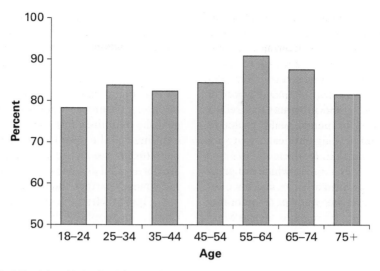

FIGURE 16.3 Prevalence of Positive Help-Seeking Attitudes Across the Adult Lifespan

and ageist attitudes concerning older adults' ability to benefit from treatment for mental disorders.

The belief that older adults cannot benefit from treatment is simply false. There is increasing evidence that psychotherapy and other psychosocial interventions are just as effective for older as for younger adults (Bartels et al., 2003; Jayasekara et al., 2015). There is also strong evidence that pharmacological treatments are equally effective for older and younger adults, although some antidepressant and antipsychotic medications tend to be tolerated less well in later life (Meyers & Jeste, 2010; Wolitzky-Taylor, Castriotta, Lenze, Stanley, & Craske, 2010). Finally, we published a recent study of 12 792 Canadians 55 years of age and older in which we found that the 664 older adults who used mental health services in the past year reported very good treatment outcomes. The majority were satisfied with treatment (88.5%) and perceived it as effective (84%), which is likely why only 15.5% had dropped out of treatment in the previous year (Lippens & Mackenzie, 2011).

② BEFORE MOVING ON

We have just reviewed several stereotypes of older adults, including the belief that older people are rigid and set in their ways, or that they cannot benefit from mental health services. What other stereotypes of older adults have you encountered—both negative and positive? In what way are these stereotypes helpful and harmful?

Age-Specific Issues of Diagnosis and Treatment

Recognizing and treating mental disorders in older adults is complicated by a number of factors particularly relevant to this population. Several of these factors are discussed in Focus box 16.1, including ageist attitudes and a dearth of mental health professionals with geriatric expertise. At least three other factors that can complicate diagnosis and

treatment are worth mentioning. First, symptoms of mental disorders can be attributed to age-related rather than psychological factors. For example, vegetative symptoms of depression, such as difficulty sleeping and loss of energy, that are likely to be accurately diagnosed in younger adults can be missed in older adults because of the perception that they are a "normal" part of aging. Second, correctly recognizing and diagnosing mental disorders in older adults is more difficult because over 90 percent of them have at least one chronic physical illnesses such as cardiovascular disease, arthritis, and gastrointestinal disease (Dall, Gallo, Chakrabarti, West, Semilla, & Storm, 2013; Fried, Ferrucci, Darer, Williamson, & Anderson, 2004). Not only can mental and physical health problems result in similar symptoms (e.g., fatigue caused by depression, sleep disorders, thyroid problems, chronic pain), but they also directly and indirectly influence one another (Lu & Ahmed, 2010; Scott et al., 2016). A longitudinal study from our laboratory with 10 409 adults aged over 55 found that having arthritis increased the risk of developing generalized anxiety disorder three years later. This study also found that having an anxiety disorder increased the risk of developing gastrointestinal disease three years later (El-Gabalawy, Mackenzie, Pietrzak, & Sareen, 2014). Finally, because health problems are increasingly common with advancing age, older adults are especially likely to be taking multiple medications for such illnesses. This concurrent use of multiple medications is known as **polypharmacy**. Both the symptoms of physical illness and the side effects of their treatments can mimic, or obscure, symptoms of mental disorders, making recognition and diagnosis more difficult. Comorbidity can also lead to problems for older adults if the appropriate treatment for one disorder is incompatible with the otherwise optimal treatment for the second. For example, a possible (anticholinergic) side effect of certain antidepressant medication is cognitive slowing and memory problems. These medications should be either avoided or used cautiously in individuals who have both dementia and depression.

In addition to providing professional mental health treatment to older adults who need it, there is increasing recognition of the importance of supplementing treatment with efforts to prevent age-related mental health problems and to promote older adults' mental health (Smyer, 1995; van't Veer-Tazelaar et al., 2009; Waters, 1995). One way to do this is by providing interventions and programs that reduce risk factors and vulnerabilities for mental health problems, such as those that increase and prolong physical activity and reduce isolation (Allen, Balfour, Bell, & Marmot, 2014). An example of such a program is Men's Sheds, which are grassroots community programs run primarily by and for older men (*http://menssheds.ca/*). Our recent study of 64 older men highlighted the need for community programs such as Men's Sheds that reduce isolation among older men, and suggested ways of increasing access to them (Nurmi, Mackenzie, Roger, Reynolds, & Urquhart, 2016).

Theoretical Frameworks of Aging

Because the way we conceptualize things has a strong influence on our actions, it is useful to look at theories that have been used or could be used to help us better understand mental health in older adults. There are two ways to approach the task of looking at theoretical frameworks for understanding mental health in later life. The first involves considering general theories that have been developed in an attempt to understand the causes of mental disorders, and asking what these theories have to say about mental disorders in older adults. The second approach involves considering theories developed specifically to understand aging and older adults, and asking what light they might shed on our understanding of mental health in later life.

With few exceptions, theorists have not extended, adapted, or refined any of the approaches outlined in Chapter 2 to specifically fit the clinical experience of older adults. It is not clear whether they have concluded that a particular framework can be applied without adaptation to older adults, or whether they have simply not asked the question. In contrast, there are several prominent theoretical approaches to understanding aging and old age that focus on how older adults adjust to or cope with age-related changes and may inform our thinking about mental disorders in later life. We will look at the following three approaches: the theory of selective optimization with compensation, socio-emotional selectivity theory, and strength and vulnerability integration theory.

SELECTIVE OPTIMIZATION WITH COMPENSATION

This theoretical framework (Baltes & Baltes, 1990) is one of the leading models in the field of gerontology in general, and successful aging in particular. The selective optimization with compensation (SOC) model holds that even within the context of normal aging and in the absence of pathology, old age brings losses of abilities and skills. According to

SOC, successful aging entails (1) selecting appropriate goals and goal priorities, (2) optimizing resources that facilitate these goals, and (3) compensating for losses by creatively using alternative means to achieving one's goals despite limited capacities. For example, my [Corey Mackenzie's] 98-year-old grandmother has the goal of continuing to play bridge—a cognitively demanding card game. To achieve this goal she optimizes her ability by playing frequently and by ensuring that she is well rested before playing. She also compensates for the fact that her memory and cognitive speed are not as good as when she was younger by relying more on her younger partner and by playing more slowly.

The SOC framework could be used to maximize functioning in people with mental disorders by building on strengths and avoiding weaknesses. For example, activities that do not make heavy demands on memory, such as bingo, will afford greater gratification to patients with dementia. This theoretical framework is attractive because it applies equally to all older adults, whether or not they suffer from physical or mental health problems. A review of nine studies using the SOC model with older adults found that compensation and optimization in particular were strongly associated with successful aging (Ouwehand, de Ridder, & Bensing, 2007).

SOCIO-EMOTIONAL SELECTIVITY THEORY

A second lifespan theory was originally developed to explain age differences in motivation, but has since been employed to better understand age differences in other factors such as mental health, emotion regulation, physical health, and cognitive functioning (Carstensen, Issacowitz, & Charles, 1999). The fundamental assumption of this theory is that when we perceive time as unlimited (as younger adults tend to), our goals will be future-oriented and we will focus our energy on seeking information and expanding our knowledge and horizons. In contrast, when we perceive time as limited (as older adults tend to), our goals become focused on short-term and emotionally meaningful matters. Figure 16.4 shows that as individuals progress from adolescence to middle age and eventually to old age, their goals shift from being knowledge focused to meaning focused, which has benefits for mental health.

A great deal of research supports socio-emotional selectivity theory (SST). Studies consistently show that older adults are more likely than younger adults to experience positive emotions, suggesting that they are better at regulating their emotions (Sims, Hogan, & Carstensen, 2015). Another interesting aspect of SST is the "positivity effect," whereby younger adults tend to focus on and remember negative information whereas older adults tend to focus on and remember positive information (Charles & Carstensen, 2009). Interestingly, having younger people imagine that they only had six more months to live resulted in their remembering more positive than negative pictures (Barber, Opitz, Martins, Sakaki, & Mather, 2016). Neuroscience research, using brain imaging technology, suggests that older participants actually process negative information less deeply than they do positive information (Carstensen, 2006).

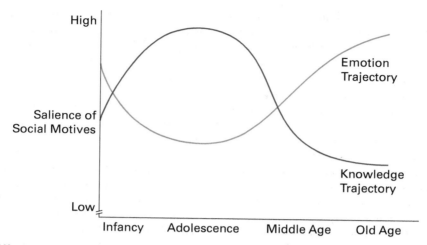

FIGURE 16.4 Age Differences in Social Goals Across the Lifespan According to Socio-Emotional Selectivity Theory

Source: Republished with permission of Springer Publishing Company, from *Annual Review of Geriatrics and Gerontology*, L. Carstensen, J. Gross, & H. Fung, Vol. 17 and 1997; permission conveyed through Copyright Clearance Center, Inc.

STRENGTH AND VULNERABILITY INTEGRATION THEORY

Building on the components of SST, Charles and Piazza (2009) proposed the strength and vulnerability integration (SAVI) theory. This theory also posits that aging is associated with an increased ability to regulate emotions and to avoid or mitigate exposure to negative experiences. Reasons for this are similar to those proposed by SST, including having a time-limited perspective characterized by a greater emphasis on emotionally meaningful goals; an increased present-moment awareness, which promotes strength-based appraisals of information and same-age social comparisons; a decrease in interpersonal conflict due to avoidance of difficult situations and the intentional pruning of peripheral social network members; and a greater focus on positive information and experiences. This theory suggests that older adults have had more opportunities to practise these strategies in dealing with the stress of daily life, and are therefore more effective and successful at applying them than younger and middle-aged adults. Both the change in perspective (time limited, present awareness, positive focused) and successful use of emotion regulation strategies (attentional and appraisal) allow older adults to avoid negative experiences and enhance their well-being, accounting for the gains in affective well-being across the lifespan (Charles, 2010). SAVI differs most significantly from SST in that it also acknowledges vulnerabilities associated with aging. Older adults have poorer cardiovascular (e.g., slower recovery of elevated blood pressure) and neuroendocrine (e.g., less efficient modulation of the hypothalamic-pituitary-adrenal axis) responses to stress. This leads to greater difficulty regulating emotional arousal and recovering from stressful events—especially when they are unavoidable, accompanied with high levels of arousal, and occur over a sustained amount of time (e.g., loss of a spouse, relative, or close friend; caregiver stress; illness). When this happens, age-related advantages in emotion regulation and well-being can be attenuated or even nullified or reversed (Charles, 2010; Charles & Luong, 2013).

③ BEFORE MOVING ON

Which of these theoretical models do you think best explains why the prevalence of depressive and anxiety disorders is lower among older adults than among middle-aged and younger individuals? What does your favourite model have that the others seem to be missing?

The remaining sections of this chapter focus on specific mental disorders, with an emphasis on disorders that are common in old age or that manifest differently in later life.

Depressive Disorders

Case Notes

Mrs. Sharma, aged 73, was referred by her family physician to an outpatient psychological clinic with symptoms of sleeplessness, appetite loss, and feelings of hopelessness and despair. Mrs. Sharma lost her husband of nearly 50 years about 18 months ago. Shortly thereafter, at her children's urging, she moved from the family home to a seniors' apartment complex. Now she thinks that the move might have been a mistake. Compared to her house, the apartment feels tiny and holds no fond memories. Mrs. Sharma reports that she is still depressed over her husband's death. She had spent much of the last several years caring for him and now has difficulty occupying her time. Mrs. Sharma worries that her memory might be failing, though tests show this not to be the case. She is also concerned that her children seem too busy with their own lives to spend enough time with her.

Perhaps because of the belief that older people have a lot to be depressed about—declining health, loss of those close to them, shrinking resources, reduced options—it is commonly assumed that they are most likely to experience depressive disorders. Yet the data show that quite the opposite is true for the key DSM-5 depressive disorders (i.e., *major depressive disorder* and *persistent depressive disorder*, which is also known as dysthymia). Major depressive disorder is nearly four times as common in younger adults as in older adults, and the more chronic form of the disorder, persistent depressive disorder, is approximately twice as common among younger than older individuals (Weissman et al., 1988). We published a study of 8012 older adults interviewed twice over a three-year period. Of all the depressive and anxiety disorders in this study, the most likely disorder to have a new onset within this three-year period was major depression: 3.3 percent of older adults had an incident of major depression (Chou, Mackenzie, Liang, & Sareen, 2011).

Depression in people over age 60 is more likely to be chronic than it is in younger adults (Benazzi, 2000). In fact, researchers at McGill University and the University of Montreal reviewed a dozen studies of depression in elderly community-residing populations and found that, overall, only 33 percent were well after two years (Cole, Bellavance, & Mansour, 1999). However, most of these people were not treated for their depression after it was detected. If they had been, the picture would likely have been better because older adults respond at least as well as younger people to most treatments for depression—a point we touch on elsewhere in the chapter. Nonetheless, the outlook for elderly depressed people is poorer than for younger individuals because of concurrent physical diseases, a higher death rate, and development of neurocognitive disorders such as Alzheimer's disease (Tuma, 2000). See Chapter 8 for a full discussion of depressive disorders and their symptoms.

SUICIDE

The risk of suicide is elevated in individuals with a variety of mental health problems, although it is a particular concern for those who are severely depressed (CCSMH, 2006a). How common is suicidal behaviour (a term that includes suicidal ideation or thoughts, as well as successful and unsuccessful attempts) among older adults? Before answering this question it is important to acknowledge that rates are likely underestimates as a result of reluctance to discuss this topic and to label deaths this way. If we begin with a broad definition of suicidal thoughts, research from the Canadian Community Health Survey found that more than 2 percent (246) of the 12 792 adults aged 55 and older had in the past year endorsed suicidal ideation (Corna, Cairney, & Streiner, 2010). With respect to rates of successful suicides, in 2002 Statistics Canada reported that 430 older Canadians took their own lives, 361 of whom were older men (CCSMH, 2006a). These numbers are consistent

with earlier Canadian data indicating that older men were five times more likely than older women to commit suicide, with an even greater sex ratio of 8:1 among adults 75 years of age and older (Heisel, 2006). Alarmingly, although younger people are more likely to attempt suicide (with a ratio of 200 attempts for every completed suicide), older individuals are more likely to be successful, with approximately 4 attempts per completed suicide (Blazer, 2003; De Leo et al., 2001). There are a number of potential explanations for increasing suicide success with age. In comparison to younger adults, older adults may have a greater intent to die; they often use more lethal methods; and they are more socially isolated, which decreases the chance of others intervening or rescuing them (Heisel, 2006; McIntosh, Santos, Hubbard, & Overholser, 1994).

Among older individuals, a number of factors increase the risk of suicide. The Canadian Coalition for Seniors' Mental Health (CCSMH, 2006a) guidelines for the assessment of suicidal risk and prevention of treatment outline the following risks: prior suicidal behaviour, mental illness and addiction, personality disorders, poor social support, including being divorced or widowed, recent negative life events such as financial or social losses, and impairment in the ability to carry out the activities of everyday life. Findings from the Canadian Community Health Survey revealed that chronic pain conditions, which are more common among older adults, were associated with both suicidal thoughts and attempts (Ratcliffe, Enns, Belik, & Sareen, 2008). Finally, a great deal of recent research has been directed at neurobiological vulnerabilities or biomarkers that increase risk for suicide. A recent review by the McGill Group for Suicide Studies suggests that cognitive deficits, especially those related to impaired decision making and reduced cognitive inhibition, may increase the risk of suicidal acts (Richard-Devantoy, Turecki, & Jollant, 2016). Identification of these risk factors is extremely important for suicide prevention initiatives. For example, research indicates that those who die from suicide are 30 times more likely than controls to have a history of suicidal behaviour. Thus, taking threats of suicide seriously, detecting and treating depression, and reducing access to firearms have been identified as some of the most important ways of preventing suicide in older adults (Unützer, 2007).

ETIOLOGY

What predisposes an older adult to depression? It seems that both physical health and social supports are involved; the combination of a weak support network and poor physical health places older individuals at particular risk (Blazer, 2003). However, the etiology of depression is not a simple matter. A variety of biological, psychological, social, and spiritual factors may play a greater or lesser role, depending on the particular depressive disorder and the age of the individual (see the discussion of risk factors in Chapters 2 and 7). For example, heredity has been shown to be important in the development of major depression and especially bipolar disorder (Escamilla & Zavala, 2008). However, when either of these disorders occurs for the first time later in life, hereditary factors are less likely to be a primary cause (Fiske, Wetherell, & Gatz, 2009). In contrast to the decreasing role of heredity in the etiology of late-life depression, there is an increasing role for medical illnesses such as cardiovascular disease, pain, and Parkinson's disease. These conditions increase the risk of depression across the lifespan and are more prevalent among older adults (Blazer, 2003; Lu & Ahmed, 2010). Stressful life events can also influence older adults differently than they do younger adults. For instance, an older person who loses a loved one is less likely to become depressed than is a younger widow or widower (George, Blazer, & Hughes, 1989). Whereas death can seem like a bolt out of the blue to younger adults, older people's resilience in the face of death is likely the result of the emotion regulation strategies outlined in the section on Theoretical Frameworks of Aging.

Let us turn now to a consideration of what we know about the main DSM-5 depressive disorders in older individuals.

DEPRESSIVE DISORDERS

Blazer's (2003) review of late-life depressive disorders begins by saying that "depression is perhaps the most frequent cause of emotional suffering in later life and significantly decreases the quality of life in older adults" (p. 249). Late-life depression is common, with 8 to 16% of community-dwelling older adults reporting clinically significant symptoms and up to 5% meeting criteria for major depressive disorder (MDD). As we discussed earlier in the chapter, however, older adults are more likely to experience common chronic health problems, and depression is more common in sick and frail older people. Rates of MDD are between 5 and 10% in primary care settings, between 11 and 14% in nursing homes, and as high as 37% following critical care hospitalizations (Taylor, 2014).

Persistent depressive disorder, which is also known as dysthymia, is a chronic form of depression lasting at least two years in adults (see Chapter 8). As with MDD, chronic forms of depression are more common in younger than older adults, and more common in women than men. Among women over age 65, prevalence is 2.3% as compared to 1% among males in the same age range (Weissman et al., 1988). Again, rates are much higher—between 4 and 8%—among the institutionalized (Blazer, 2003). Interestingly, research from our laboratory indicates that individuals with dysthymia are even more likely than those with major depression to seek professional help (Mackenzie et al., 2012). Although this finding may seem curious because this disorder is less acute than major depression, the most likely reason for it is the chronic nature of the mood problems that significantly reduce quality of life.

DIAGNOSTIC ISSUES What does MDD look like in older individuals? You will recall from Chapter 8 that, in addition to dysphoria (feeling sad) or anhedonia (a lack of ability to take pleasure in things), a diagnosis of MDD requires that four other symptoms be present from a list of affective (e.g., feelings of worthlessness or guilt), cognitive (e.g., difficulty concentrating or making decisions), and somatic (e.g., weight gain or loss, primary insomnia, fatigue) symptoms. MDD often looks different in older adults than it does in younger adults. Older clinically depressed individuals are more likely to report weight loss and other somatic symptoms and less likely to report feelings of sadness, worthlessness, or guilt (Blazer, 2003; Wallace & Pfohl, 1995). Given that either sadness or anhedonia is required for a diagnosis of MDD, older adults' reduced likelihood of reporting sadness when depressed may decrease the likelihood of their being diagnosed and treated.

In addition to the challenge of diagnosing depression in the absence of sadness, the Canadian Coalition for Seniors' Mental Health (CCSMH, 2006b) guidelines for the assessment and treatment of depression identify two other difficulties that clinicians face when assessing mood disorders in older adults. First, it can be difficult to diagnose depression among individuals with cognitive impairment. Depression and early-onset **neurocognitive disorders** (NCD) are very difficult to distinguish from one another because both have prominent mood and memory problems. Also, these disorders often coexist, and we now know that having a first depressive episode late in life is a risk factor for developing neurocognitive impairment (Chodosh, Kado, Seeman, & Karlamangla, 2007; Green et al., 2003; Taylor, 2014). Second, it is difficult to diagnose depression among individuals with somatic or physical problems, and older adults are at greater risk than younger adults for developing depression as a result of medical conditions. Depression can be found in 33 percent of stroke sufferers (Hachett, Yapa, Parag, & Anderson, 2005) and 20 to 40 percent of individuals with Parkinson's disease (Lieberman, 2006).

Because most older adults who seek mental health treatment start by visiting their family physician, it is important to consider factors that might make diagnosing depression in later life especially difficult. Mitchell (2011) outlines the following five major diagnostic issues faced by physicians concerning their older patients: (1) time constraints, which make it difficult to attend to verbal and nonverbal signs of depression; (2) complexity of late-life depression, including vague symptoms and patients' lack of knowledge about depressive symptoms; (3) lack of specific diagnostic criteria for older adults; (4) physical comorbidity masking depressive symptoms; and (5) lack of knowledge about available and effective treatment options for older adults, which leads physicians to question the utility of diagnosis.

TREATMENT Both MDD and persistent depressive disorder can be treated with lifestyle changes, psychotherapy, drug therapy, or some combination of these. With respect to lifestyle changes, a systematic review and meta-analysis of seven randomized controlled trials found that moderate-intensity exercise improved depressive symptoms (Bridle, Spanjers, Patel, Atherton, & Lamb, 2012). This suggestion and others, such as improving nutrition and encouraging social engagement, can help prevent clinical depression, but are unlikely to alleviate it in the absence of talk or drug therapies.

Earlier in this chapter, we made the point that, despite evidence to the contrary, older patients are commonly assumed to be poor candidates for psychotherapy. Meta-analyses (e.g., Cuijpers, van Straten, & Smit, 2006), reviews (e.g., Jayasekara et al., 2015), and expert consensus statements (e.g., Alexopoulous, Katz, Reynolds, Carpenter, & Docherty, 2001) converge to suggest that a variety of psychotherapeutic approaches are highly effective for depressed older adults, and that overall effectiveness of treatments is similar for older and younger individuals. Also, for individuals who require more intensive treatment, we have shown that depressed older adults attending a day hospital program at Toronto's Baycrest Centre for Geriatric Care for 3.5 days per week for four months experienced clinically significant improvement in mood (Mackenzie, Rosenberg, & Major, 2006).

As for drug therapy for late-life depression, the selective serotonin-reuptake inhibitors (SSRIs) are considered the first-line treatment for late-life depression despite mixed evidence from randomized controlled trials (RCTs) showing that they are more effective than placebo. When SSRIs are ineffective, physicians will often prescribe serotoninin-norepinephrine reuptake inhibitors (SNRIs) and older tricyclic antidepressants as second-line treatments. The latter class of drug has similar efficacy to SSRIs but worse side effects (Taylor, 2014). Reviews by Canadian researchers Alastair Flint (1994) at the University of Toronto and Marie-France Tourigny-Rivard (1997) at the University of Ottawa suggest that antidepressants and other chemical treatments are as effective in older patients as they are in younger ones. As these reviews also point out, however, these drugs often produce side effects that are tolerated less well, particularly among the frail elderly, than among younger patients. Natural age-related changes such as reduced renal clearance and more sensitive drug receptor sites in the brain can increase side effects and reduce drug tolerance. Furthermore, when polypharmacy is an issue for older adults, the interactive effects of multiple medications (referred to as **drug interactions**) can have unknown and dangerous consequences.

Another biological therapy that is effective for treating severe and treatment-resistant MDD in older adults is electroconvulsive therapy (ECT), with response rates of 60 to 80 percent (Unützer, 2007). Despite its effectiveness and usefulness in situations where the risk of harm is high due to factors such as suicidal ideation and psychosis, ECT often has side effects—most commonly headaches, temporary confusion, and memory impairment, but also occasionally amnesia for events surrounding treatment and falls immediately after sessions. Fortunately, a recent study of 380 patients with a mean age of 51 (30 percent of the sample was 60+) found good evidence of ECT effectiveness,

excellent tolerability among the older subsample, and only transient and not life-threatening adverse events (Damm et al., 2010). A newer potential alternative to ECT that does not require anesthesia and does not have side effects is transcranial magnetic stimulation. Relatively little research has examined its efficacy in older adults, although preliminary evidence suggests it is less effective than ECT and perhaps less effective in older than younger adults (Taylor, 2014).

How do various treatments for depression compare to one another? A meta-analysis of the two most common treatment approaches—talk and medication therapy—found that they are equally effective in younger and older adults (Pinquart, Duberstein, & Lyness, 2006). Given that talk therapy has far fewer side effects than biological treatments you might therefore expect it to be used more often for older patients. This is not so. Research from the United States found that 74 percent of older adults receiving treatment for depression received antidepressant medications (Marcus & Olfson, 2010). This strong bias toward biological treatments exists despite older adults' preference for psychotherapy over medication for the treatment of depression (Landreville, Landry, Baillargeon, Guerette, & Matteau, 2001).

Sleep–Wake Disorders

Case Notes

All her life Rose slept soundly, got up early, and was energetic. Now, in her seventies, things have changed. She often finds it hard to fall asleep and then often awakens in the middle of the night, worrying about her husband's worsening angina attacks, her daughter's marriage, and her son's difficulty finding a good job. Sometimes her husband wakes her because she is snoring. She feels guilty about her snoring waking him and yet resents being woken once she has finally fallen asleep. At the suggestion of friends, she has experimented with eating and drinking various supposedly sleep-inducing things before bed. So far, nothing has helped. Rose tries to sleep in, but finds it hard to sleep once it is light outside. When she gets up, she feels tired and often finds herself dozing off during the day. This has happened in church and in social situations, and has been very embarrassing. To avoid dozing off she has started to take naps during the day, but doing so has made it even more difficult to fall asleep at night. Finally, at her husband's urging, she has made an appointment to discuss the problem with her physician.

It is clear from the literature on sleep and sleep–wake disorders that older adults report much greater levels of dissatisfaction with the quality of their sleep than do younger adults. Epidemiological research suggests that between 30 and 60% of older adults complain of sleep problems

(Black, O'Reilly, Olmstead, Breen, & Irwin, 2015; McCurry, Logsdon, Teri, & Vitiello, 2007; Stepanski, Rybarczyk, Lopez, & Stevens, 2003). The primary complaints reported are light sleep, frequent awakenings during the night, decreased time spent asleep, awakening too early in the morning, and sleepiness during the day (Crowley, 2011). One reason why sleep problems appear to be more prevalent among older adults is that sleep disturbances often appear as a result of medical problems that are more common in later life (Gooneratne & Vitiello, 2014; McCurry et al., 2007). The literature also confirms that older adults use more sedatives or hypnotic medications than do younger adults. In the United States, 40% of the sedative or hypnotic medications prescribed were for the 12% of population who were older adults (Moran, Thompson, & Nies, 1988).

Importantly, sleep problems among older adults affect more than just their sleep. Individuals who fail to get the rest they need experience poorer daytime cognitive and functional performance (Yaffe, Falvey, & Haang, 2014), which can have serious consequences such as motor vehicle and other accidents (Stepanski et al., 2003). In addition, individuals with chronic sleep problems are more likely to have poor physical health and poor mental health, including an increased risk for developing depression, anxiety, and suicidal ideation (McCurry et al., 2007). In fact, older adults with insomnia increase their risk of developing depression by 23 percent (Jaussent, Bouyer, & Ancelin, 2011). The high prevalence of sleep problems in old age, and their negative consequences, highlights the importance of detecting and treating these conditions.

DIAGNOSTIC ISSUES

Unfortunately, most patients with sleep problems do not report them to their family physicians (Ancoli-Israel & Roth, 1999). This may be especially true for older adults. When sleep problems are reported, decisions about whether they warrant the diagnosis of sleep disorder depends on the quantity (intensity and/or persistence) and quality of the sleep disturbance. DSM-5 identifies 10 sleep disorder categories and provides diagnostic criteria for them. Several are extremely rare in older adults (e.g., narcolepsy), and so we will not discuss them here. Criteria for the most common sleep disorder among older adults, insomnia, are presented in Table 16.1.

Diagnosing and treating sleep disorders in older adults is complicated by the following factors (Vitiello & Prinz, 1994; Woodhouse, 1993):

- Information about sleep quantity and quality typically comes from self-reports, and so there is always a question as to whether they are distorted by unrealistic expectations.

- Sleep disturbance can be associated with a host of physical and mental disorders and medications for such disorders. Insomnia should be diagnosed only if it is severe enough to warrant clinical attention independent of related disorders or medical problems.

TABLE 16.1   DSM-5 DIAGNOSTIC CRITERIA FOR INSOMNIA DISORDER

A. A predominant complaint of dissatisfaction with sleep quantity or quality, associated with one (or more) of the following symptoms:
 1. Difficulty initiating sleep. (In children, this may manifest as difficulty initiating sleep without caregiver intervention.)
 2. Difficulty maintaining sleep, characterized by frequent awakenings or problems returning to sleep after awakenings. (In children, this may manifest as difficulty returning to sleep without caregiver intervention.)
 3. Early-morning awakening with inability to return to sleep.
B. The sleep disturbance causes clinically significant distress or impairment in social, occupational, educational, academic, behavioral, or other important areas of functioning.
C. The sleep difficulty occurs at least 3 nights per week.
D. The sleep difficulty is present for at least 3 months.
E. The sleep difficulty occurs despite adequate opportunity for sleep.
F. The insomnia is not better explained by and does not occur exclusively during the course of another sleep-wake disorder (e.g., narcolepsy, a breathing-related sleep disorder, a circadian rhythm sleep-wake disorder, a parasomnia).
G. The insomnia is not attributable to the physiological effects of a substance (e.g., a drug of abuse, a medication).
H. Coexisting mental disorders and medical conditions do not adequately explain the predominant complaint of insomnia.

Source: Reprinted with permission from the *Diagnostic and Statistical Manual of Mental Disorders, Fifth Edition.* (Copyright © 2013). American Psychiatric Association. All Rights Reserved.

- There are age-related changes in sleep that appear to be universal, and thus might be considered normal.

- Sleep characteristics and patterns vary widely between individuals; such differences may be especially great among older people.

- Sleep is affected by what sleep researchers and clinicians call sleep hygiene, which refers to habits surrounding sleep such as what time you go to bed; where you sleep; whom you sleep with; and how much eating, drinking, exercising, and screen time you engage in prior to going to sleep. These habits can change with age; for example, retirement can change an individual's bedtime. On the other hand, established sleep habits may no longer be conducive to quality sleep. For example, because sleep is lighter in older adults, sleeping with someone else in the bed may become a cause of frequent awakening and difficulty falling back to sleep.

Because of the multitude of factors that can affect sleep in older adults, it is essential that the complete 24-hour sleep–wake cycle be assessed when the diagnosis of insomnia is being considered. Unfortunately, such a thorough examination is rarely conducted.

NORMAL CHANGES IN SLEEPING PATTERNS

Sleep comprises five stages (Daly, 1989; Fetveit, 2009). In rapid eye movement (REM) sleep, electroencephalographic (EEG) activity is similar to that which occurs during waking activity, rapid conjugate eye movements occur (that is, the eyes move together), and muscle tone is decreased. REM sleep is also known as dream sleep. Non-rapid eye movement (NREM) sleep is divided into the remaining four stages. In stage 1, low-amplitude, fast-frequency, irregular EEG activity occurs. In stage 2, the activity is more synchronous (regular). Stages 3 and 4 are marked by slow EEG waves and are the deepest levels of sleep, because more intense stimulation is required to rouse someone at these stages. Most people progress through these stages, starting with stage 1 and ending in REM sleep, four to five times per night (Gooneratne & Vitiello, 2014). Laboratory studies have shown age-related changes of four types:

- *Total sleep time decreases.* Whereas babies and toddlers normally sleep from 10 to 14 hours per night, young adults average 6.5 to 8.5 hours per night, and older adults average 5 to 7 hours.

- *Changes in EEG activity.* Stage 2 EEG activity is less synchronous than in young adults; the slow waves in stages 3 and 4 are lower in amplitude and there are fewer of them.

- *Changes in the organization of sleep stages.* For example, although the number of REM sleep periods does not change, successive REM periods no longer increase in length.

- *Changes in the circadian rhythms, or sleep–wake cycles.* For example, older people may nap more and get up earlier in the morning than younger adults.

With respect to this fourth change, University of Toronto researcher Lynn Hasher and her colleagues (Hasher, Goldstein, & May, 2005) have demonstrated that there are changes with age in people's optimal times of day—the times at which they are most alert and functioning at the highest level both physically and cognitively. Their research indicates that only 6 percent of university-aged students consider themselves to be morning types (i.e., most alert and awake in the morning). The majority of young adults function better in the evening, which is why 8 a.m. classes in university are so unpopular. In contrast, nearly 75 percent of older adults in Hasher and colleagues' research classify themselves as morning types, reflecting a marked shift in circadian patterns with age.

Vitiello and Prinz (1994, p. 640) conclude:

Each of these age-related sleep changes—decreases in total sleep time, stage 4 sleep, and REM sleep; increases in wakefulness during the night, frequency of stage shifts, and sensitivity to environmental stimuli—may contribute to the characterization of the sleep of the elderly as "lighter" or more fragile than that of younger individuals. All of these changes may reflect normal, age-related neuronal alterations in brain areas controlling sleep physiology.

It is in distinction from these well-documented age-related changes in sleep that we must try to identify sleep disorders—pathologies that go beyond the normal age-related changes. Two of the most common sleep disorders in older adults are primary insomnia and sleep apnea. We will now consider each of these in turn.

INSOMNIA DISORDER

Insomnia disorder is typically defined in terms of both nocturnal and daytime symptoms. Nocturnal symptoms include difficulty falling asleep, frequent awakenings, shortened sleep, and non-restorative sleep. Daytime symptoms include fatigue, sleepiness, depression, and anxiety (Fetveit, 2009; Gooneratne & Vitiello, 2015). DSM-5 diagnostic criteria (see Table 16.1) require that symptoms be frequent, persistent, distressing, and not explained by lack of opportunity to sleep or other mental or physical health problems. The prevalence of insomnia is thought to increase with age, with most epidemiologic studies reporting prevalence rates of 20 to 40 percent (Gooneratne & Vitiello, 2014) and especially high prevalence rates found among women, adults over age 80, and individuals with comorbid physical and mental health problems (Crowley, 2011; Rodriguez et al., 2015).

ETIOLOGY A common framework for understanding how insomnia develops and is maintained is the 3-P model outlined in Figure 16.5 (Spielman, Caruso, & Glovinsky, 1987). According to this model, there are long-standing predisposing factors that increase the risk of older adults experiencing sleep problems, such as being female, having lower levels of education and income, and having poor health behaviours such as smoking and being sedentary. Precipitating factors are stressors that can acutely affect sleep, such as loss, pain, and mental health problems. Finally, perpetuating factors are cognitive and behavioural factors that maintain poor sleep in older adults once acute sleep problems have developed. These include things like excessive worry about sleep and daytime napping (Gooneratne, & Vitiello, 2014; Rodriguez, Dzierzewski, & Alessi, 2015).

TREATMENT Late-life insomnia can be treated with pharmacological, psychological, or combined strategies. In general, psychological strategies are considered the first-line treatments because there is a solid evidence base supporting their effectiveness, they are safe to use, and they have long-term benefits. Throughout this textbook you have read about cognitive behavioural treatments for mental health problems, and they also apply here. Cognitive behavioural therapy for insomnia (CBT-I) has been found to be superior to both drug treatments and combined psychological/pharmacological therapy in head-to-head trials (Morin et al., 2016). CBT-I produces reliable and lasting improvements in sleep efficiency and satisfaction with sleep, and reduces the use of sleep medications among older adults who are dependent on them. Generally, these approaches involve education (providing information about normal age-related changes in sleep and good sleep habits/hygiene), cognitive therapy (correcting dysfunctional thoughts and attitudes about sleep), stimulus control (strengthening the association between the bedroom and sleep by getting out of bed rather than tossing and turning, using the bedroom only for sleep and sex, and so on), sleep restriction (restricting the amount of time spent in bed to the actual amount of time the person with insomnia is sleeping), and relaxation (Gooneratne & Vitiello, 2014; Morin et al., 2006).

Despite the fact that sleep researchers and the American Academy of Sleep Medicine recommend CBT-I as the first-line treatment for insomnia, older adults with this disorder are commonly and routinely treated with sedatives or hypnotics prescribed by their family physicians (Schroeck et al., 2016). A Canadian nation-wide community survey by Stewart and colleagues (2006) found that whereas 5% of adults aged 25 to 34 with a diagnosis of insomnia received an anxiolytic or hypnotic prescription for sleep, that rate jumped to 16% among adults aged 65 to 74. Although a wide variety of medications are prescribed for insomnia in older adults (e.g., benzodiazepines, barbiturates, antihistamines), most are contraindicated for this age group. This is because older adults are "at particularly high risk for drug tolerance, dependence, drug interactions, hangover effects, and severe withdrawal reactions" (Daly, 1989, p. 485). Researchers have found that the number of medications consumed by older adults correlates positively with the severity of their sleep-disordered symptoms (Bliwise, 2004). In addition to using prescription and over-the-counter drugs for sleep problems, many older adults self-medicate with alcohol because of the common misconception that it is an effective treatment for insomnia. Although alcohol can help individuals fall asleep, it disrupts the normal sleep cycle and reduces the quality of sleep (Lydon, Ram, Conroy, Pincus, Geier, & Maggs, 2016). In addition, alcohol is contraindicated if an individual is taking any of a wide variety of medications. Indeed, 20% of all drug-related accidental or suicidal deaths are estimated to be the result of combining alcohol and drugs.

BREATHING-RELATED SLEEP DISORDERS

Sleep apnea involves episodes of cessation of breathing (apnea) that last at least 10 seconds. Diagnosis requires that there be at least five such episodes per hour of sleep, although most research studies on apnea use 15 or more events per hour as the diagnostic criteria (Gooneratne & Vitiello, 2014).

Sleep apnea results in hypoxemia (low blood oxygen saturation) and awakenings from sleep. Because quality and quantity of nighttime sleep is disturbed, during the day sufferers will typically have difficulty staying awake, take frequent naps, have difficulty waking up and getting going in the morning or after a nap, and often have a headache for an hour or two in the morning. Difficulty concentrating and remembering may also occur. If the disorder is severe or left untreated, weakened cardiac functioning can occur and can be fatal. Between 20 and 50 percent of older adults have sleep apnea, depending on whether 5 or 15 apnea episodes per hour are used to diagnose it (Gooneratne & Vitiello, 2014), and it is markedly more common in men than in women and with increasing age (Vitiello & Prinz, 1994).

ETIOLOGY The DSM-5 includes three breathing-related sleep disorders: (1) obstructive sleep apnea due to obstruction of the upper airway, generally indicated by snoring; (2) central sleep apnea due to impairment of respiratory control by the central nervous system, often caused by heart or renal failure or opioid use; and (3) sleep-related hypoventilation where respiration is decreased but not stopped, often due to medical conditions, medications, and obesity.

DIAGNOSIS The diagnosis of sleep apnea requires overnight polysomnography—usually in a sleep laboratory but increasingly there are portable testing options available. Obstructive apnea is the most common form, where sufferers have periods of no breathing followed by a restorative gasp and then a snore and sometimes a sharp muscle movement. Severity is typically related to obesity. This disorder is likely substantially underdiagnosed and undertreated in older adults (Gooneratne & Vitiello, 2014). Importantly, it is also likely to become increasingly prevalent given that the incidence of obesity in older adults has been increasing over time (Arterbutrn, Crane, & Sullivan, 2006).

TREATMENT For the most part, treatments for sleep apnea are identical for younger and older adults; they involve losing weight, learning to avoid sleeping on one's back (e.g., by wearing a T-shirt with tennis balls sewn into the back), and avoiding respiratory depressants such as alcohol and hypnotic medication. In addition, respiratory stimulants are often helpful. Treatment may also include continuous positive airway pressure (CPAP), which involves wearing a mask attached to an air compressor to keep the upper airways open while sleeping. As a last resort, surgery can modify the upper airway structures. Treatment can be effective, although compliance can be a problem with respect to weight loss and use of CPAP (Stepanski et al., 2003).

4 **BEFORE MOVING ON**

Given that diagnosing and treating sleep–wake disorders such as insomnia can be especially complicated when working with older adults, what kind of training do you think you would need above and beyond that needed to work with younger adults?

Anxiety Disorders

Case Notes

Mr. Wallace, a 68-year-old widower, came to the psychological clinic at the insistence of his sister. Since shortly after his retirement three years ago, he has been experiencing what he calls "attacks." During these attacks, his heart pounds and sometimes he has pain in his chest and trouble breathing. He trembles all over and feels that he is going to die. According to Mr. Wallace, the attacks were infrequent at first, occurring no more than once a month. Two years ago he suffered a mild heart attack, and since then the attacks have become more frequent, averaging one or two a week. His sister says that Mr. Wallace seems totally preoccupied with these attacks, worries continually about when the next one might occur, and has started leaving the house less and less. Their father died of a heart attack and Mr. Wallace is convinced that sooner or later one of his attacks will prove fatal too. A recent medical examination found no evidence of heart disease, blood pressure problems, or other medical conditions that might be producing his symptoms. Nonetheless, Mr. Wallace remains convinced that he has an undiagnosed life-threatening disorder and anticipates the next attack with dread.

Large community surveys in Canada and the United States that were reviewed in the prevalence section suggest that anxiety disorders occur approximately twice as often as depressive disorders among older adults. In fact, significant symptoms of anxiety and anxiety disorders are among the most common psychiatric problems experienced by older adults (Nordhus & Pallesen, 2003). Whereas about 4 percent of adults 55 and older had a depressive disorder (major depression or persistent depressive disorder) in the past year, somewhere between 7 and 12 percent had an anxiety disorder (Byers, Yaffe, Covinsky, Friedman, & Bruce, 2010; Mackenzie, Pagura, & Sareen, 2010).

Of the various anxiety disorders discussed in Chapter 5, the three most common in later life are social phobia, specific phobia, and generalized anxiety disorder (GAD; Mackenzie, Reynolds, Chou, Pagura, & Sareen, 2011). Although there has been far less research on anxiety than on mood disorders in later life, most of the anxiety disorder research has focused on GAD. GAD is a chronic and recurrent disorder with symptoms often lasting decades. Approximately half of the cases of GAD among older adults have their first onset later in life (Chou, 2009). Our study of 12 312 American adults 55 years of age and older found that 3 percent met criteria for GAD in the past year, but most of those individuals also had another anxiety, mood, or personality disorder (only 0.5 percent had GAD alone; Mackenzie et al., 2011).

Not only are anxiety disorders common in older adults, they are also associated with a number of negative outcomes. For example, Wetherell and colleagues (2011) found that chronic anxiety in older adults can lead to an increased risk of age-related conditions such as Alzheimer's disease. We also published a study of younger and older Canadians and Americans demonstrating that anxiety disorders are an independent risk factor for suicide ideation (Raposo, El-Gabalawy, Erickson, Mackenzie, & Sareen, 2014).

DIAGNOSTIC ISSUES

Accurately detecting and diagnosing anxiety disorders in adults can be problematic for a number of reasons. First, anxiety disorders can sometimes be overshadowed by depression. Research from Canada and Europe suggests that among older adults in the community with a diagnosis of major depression in the past year, between 23 and 46 percent also had a comorbid anxiety disorder (Ayers, Sorrell, Thorp, & Wetherell, 2007; Cairney, Corna, Veldhuizen, Hemnann, & Streiner, 2008). Second, anxiety is associated with a range of physical and psychological issues, and it is often difficult to determine which of these problems are causing anxiety, or vice versa (Ayers et al., 2007; Wolitzky-Taylor et al., 2010). Third, a common method of assessing anxiety symptoms involves having individuals complete questionnaires. With the exception of the Geriatric Anxiety Inventory (Pachana, Byrne, Siddle, Koloski, Harley, & Arnold, 2007), most anxiety measures have been normed and validated with younger adults, and so it is not clear that a score obtained by an elderly individual should be interpreted in the same way as it is for a younger person. For example, many of the symptoms on the typical anxiety scale are somatic (feelings of dizziness, heart palpitations, and so forth) and may be endorsed if people have symptoms of neurological, cardiovascular, respiratory, and endocrine disorders that are more common in later life.

TREATMENT

Although research on treatment of anxiety disorders in later life has lagged behind treatment of depression, there have been several reviews and meta-analyses of high-quality studies with anxious older adults randomly assigned to control groups or psychological treatments. This research suggests that cognitive-behavioural, supportive, and relaxation-based therapies are significantly more effective than wait-list or active controls (Ayers et al., 2007; Nordhus & Pallesen, 2003). Research by Mohlman and colleagues (2003) suggests that cognitive-behavioural therapy for older adults with anxiety might be more effective if tailored to suit the unique needs of older adults (e.g., by conducting reminder calls and weekly reviews of important concepts, strategies, and homework assignments). More recently, mindfulness training and acceptance and commitment therapy have been shown to be effective in the treatment of anxiety disorders among older adults (Helmes & Ward, 2015; Lenze & Wetherell, 2011).

Despite the apparent benefit of psychological treatment, benzodiazepine medications are commonly used to treat anxiety among older individuals, even though they are addictive, increase older adults' risk for falls, and can cause cognitive and psychomotor impairment (Wolitzky-Taylor et al., 2010). The first-line pharmacological treatments of anxiety in older adults are the SSRIs, which appear to be relatively effective and with favourable side effect profiles in comparison to benzodiazepines (Goncalves & Byrne, 2012). A randomized controlled trial by Wetherell and colleagues (2013) comparing SSRI with and without augmented CBT found that psychotherapy improved outcomes compared to the drug alone, and that both treatments prevented relapse compared to drug placebo. Despite the documented benefits of psychotherapy and SSRI medications for GAD in older adults, research suggests that elderly patients with anxiety disorders are roughly five times more likely to receive prescriptions for benzodiazepines than to receive psychotherapy (Hendriks, Oude Voshaar, Keijsers, Hoogduin, & van Balkom, 2008). Also, research evidence is limited or nonexistent with respect to therapy effectiveness for older adults with phobias, panic disorder, obsessive-compulsive disorder, and post-traumatic stress disorder (Ayers et al., 2007).

Finally, it is worth noting that despite the availability of effective treatments for at least some anxiety disorders in older adults, most older individuals suffering from clinical anxiety do not seek help. Research from our laboratory indicates that whereas 73% of older adults with both depression and anxiety sought professional help in the past year, only 43% with just a mood disorder alone sought help, and less than half that number (21%) with just an anxiety disorder sought professional treatment (Scott, Mackenzie, Chipperfield, & Sareen, 2010). Similarly, we found that although older individuals with GAD have significantly reduced physical and mental health–related quality of life, only 28% sought professional help in the past year (Mackenzie et al., 2010).

⑤ BEFORE MOVING ON

> Research now shows that for depressive disorders, anxiety disorders, and sleep–wake disorders, psychotherapy and pharmacotherapy appear to be relatively equally effective. What are some of the reasons why psychotherapy would be a preferable option to pharmacotherapy for older adults with these disorders? Conversely, what are some of the reasons why pharmacotherapy would be preferable? Would your reasons be the same for younger patients?

SCHIZOPHRENIA

As you will recall from Chapter 9, schizophrenia usually begins to manifest itself in the late teens or twenties. We will refer to this presentation of schizophrenia as the typical early onset subtype of the disorder. Early-onset schizophrenia becomes relevant to this chapter when these people age and become older adults. Unfortunately, many do not. People with early-onset schizophrenia have a higher death rate than

the general population, largely because of increased suicide rates (Allebeck, 1989). It was believed for many years that the disease followed a deteriorating course with age, so that those who did survive would have a poor long-term prognosis. More recent longitudinal studies do not support this view. On the contrary, it appears that symptoms of schizophrenia either disappear or decrease substantially over time in a significant number of patients (Harding, Brooks, Ashikaga, Strauss, & Breier, 1987; Harvey, 2001; Jeste, Manley, & Harris, 1991; Ruskin, 1990). In particular, as people with schizophrenia age, it appears that there is a decrease in positive symptoms, such as delusions and hallucinations, and an increase in negative symptoms, such as withdrawal and flattened affect (Ruskin, 1990).

In contrast to the typical onset of schizophrenia in young adulthood, at least 20 percent of individuals have a first onset of this disorder after age 40. Some researchers have proposed that this is a distinct subtype of schizophrenia known as **late-onset schizophrenia**.

DIAGNOSTIC ISSUES

The diagnostic criteria for late-onset schizophrenia are the same as those for early-onset schizophrenia, and despite the debate that has existed regarding the importance of age of onset the DSM-5 did not recognize late onset as a unique subtype. Early research suggested significant differences between early- and late-onset cases (Broadway & Mintzer, 2007). In contrast, a review of more recent studies suggests that early-onset and late-onset schizophrenia share fundamental clinical features (i.e., positive symptoms, negative symptoms, and functional deficits); but that late onset schizophrenia is more likely among women, has less severe positive symptoms, and lower average antipsychotic medication dose requirements (Maglione, Thomas, & Jeste, 2014).

Although one might think that schizophrenia in later life would be relatively easy to detect and diagnose, that is not necessarily the case. Because delusions of persecution are associated with a number of disorders that occur in older individuals—neurocognitive and delusional disorders, for example—differential diagnosis can be a problem (Howard, Castle, Wessely, & Murray, 1993; Jeste et al., 1988; Pearlson et al., 1989). To complicate matters, psychotic symptoms in this age group can also be caused by a number of medical illnesses, including Addison's disease, Parkinson's disease, and brain tumours.

TREATMENT

Neuroleptic (antipsychotic) drugs are the treatment of choice for schizophrenia and other causes of psychosis across the lifespan. Continuing with a common theme in this chapter, most of the research on antipsychotic medications has focused on younger adults. Several studies of both typical and the newer atypical antipsychotics with older adults suggest that they are generally well tolerated and effective (Broadway & Mintzer, 2007). Research on the effectiveness of cognitive-behavioural skills training for older adults with schizophrenia has shown increases in social activities, cognitive insight, and mastery of skills, as compared to an age-matched control group (Granholm et al., 2005). Similarly, a social skills intervention study carried out by Bartels and colleagues (2004) found evidence of increased social functioning and health management and decreases of inappropriate behaviour that remained one year following their intervention.

Delirium

Case Notes

Mrs. Chen is a 77-year-old woman who lives alone. She was brought to hospital by ambulance after she was found wandering and talking incoherently in a downtown department store. Her dazed appearance, and the fact that she was engaged in a rambling "conversation" with no one in particular, had attracted the attention of a security guard. When he attempted to question Mrs. Chen, she was unable to provide either her name or address or say why she was in the store. The security guard phoned 911 and an ambulance arrived. The ambulance attendants were also unable to obtain clear answers to their questions. She appeared anxious, confused, and frightened. When they arrived at the hospital, a nurse found several bottles of medication on Mrs. Chen, as well as her daughter's phone number. Consultation with her daughter and her primary care physician established that Mrs. Chen suffered from thyroid problems, and that her nutritional status was poor. Emergency room physicians diagnosed Mrs. Chen as suffering from delirium brought on by her poor nutritional status, in conjunction with her failure to take her thyroid medication. After several days in hospital, her symptoms began to abate. She was released to her daughter's care, with instructions to monitor her food and fluid intake, and her medication regimen.

Delirium is a neurocognitive disorder that has a sudden onset (developing over days or even hours), fluctuating course, and disturbances in levels of consciousness, attention, orientation, memory, thinking, perception, and behaviour (American Psychiatric Association, 2013). Although delirium can occur at any age, it is most common in older adults, as they are more likely to suffer from the various conditions that can precipitate its onset. As shown in the case example just described, delirium is especially common among medically ill older adults. According to the Canadian Coalition for Seniors' Mental Health National Guidelines for the Assessment and Treatment of Delirium (CCSMH, 2006c; Gage & Hogan, 2014), this disorder has been found in up to 50% of older people admitted as inpatients to acute care

settings. Surgery is also a risk factor for the development of delirium; it has been reported in 10 to 15% of older adults undergoing general surgery, in as many as 30% of older adults undergoing open-heart surgery, and in 50% of older adults receiving hip replacements.

Delirium usually has an acute onset. In some cases, however, there is a more gradual prodromal phase during which individuals experience mild, transient symptoms of fatigue, poor concentration, restlessness, and mild cognitive impairment. These disturbances may remain at this subacute level or progress to a full delirium. The hallmark symptom of full delirium is reduced or clouded consciousness, including fluctuating impairments in attention and orientation. The individual may move back and forth from lucidity to severe confusion. In addition to disorientation, delirium can also be manifested in incoherent speech, marked memory impairment, and confusion over simple things. Behaviourally, hallucinations, aggression, restlessness, and a dazed expression may be present (Cole, 2004).

ETIOLOGY

Although the exact cause of delirium is undetermined, known risk factors include a wide variety of organic factors that can be categorized as metabolic (e.g., hypothyroidism, nutritional deficits), infectious (e.g., tuberculosis, HIV-related dementia), or structural (e.g., Parkinson's disease, dementia, head injury). Other organic possibilities include drug overdose or withdrawal, acute strokes, and exposure to toxic substances. Delirium can also accompany functional disorders such as psychotic depression, mania, and schizophrenia.

DIAGNOSTIC ISSUES

Despite the rather striking symptoms associated with delirium, it is often undetected or misdiagnosed as a neurocognitive disorder or another psychiatric disorder such as depression (Cole, 2004). Because of the potentially lethal consequences of untreated delirium, the diagnostic challenge is to identify the underlying condition leading to the delirium in the individual case. Thus, it is essential that someone (family or friend) provide a detailed history of the patient to the diagnostician.

TREATMENT AND OUTCOMES

There are essentially three phases to the treatment of this disorder, according to the Canadian Coalition for Seniors' Mental Health National Guidelines (CCSMH, 2006; Gage & Hogan, 2014). The first phase focuses on preventative efforts to reduce the onset and severity of delirium. For example, low-dose melatonin may reduce the incidence of delirium in older patients admitted to acute medical units, and low-dose haloperidol may reduce the incidence and severity of post-operative delirium in older patients. The second phase of treatment for delirium involves low-dose and short-term psychotropic medications for individuals with delirium who are agitated or psychotic in order to prevent them from endangering themselves or others. When this is the case, the treatment of choice is usually the antipsychotic medication haloperidol, although the more recent atypical antipsychotic medications (e.g., olanzapine, quetiapine, risperidone) are now being used (Broadway & Mintzer, 2007; Gage & Hogan, 2014). The third and arguably most important phase of treatment, according to Cole (2004), is "the diagnosis and treatment of the conditions predisposing to, precipitating, or perpetuating the delirium" (p. 14). For example, in the case of Mrs. Chen, compliance with the medication regimen for her thyroid problem is essential.

In a recent editorial and review of this disorder, McGill University researchers Martin Cole and Jane McCusker (2016) describe that although most people with this disorder recover rather quickly (usually less than a week) and completely if the underlying cause is addressed, for a substantial minority the outcomes of delirium are chronic and poor. Individuals with subsyndromal delirium (who have some symptoms but not enough to meet diagnostic criteria) and who have persistent symptoms after partially recovering from it are at increased risk for cognitive impairment, functional disability, longer hospital stays, admission to long-term care institutions, or worse. If untreated, delirium can result in rapid deterioration and premature death; even with accurate diagnosis and treatment, the death rate is about 40 percent.

Neurocognitive Disorders (NCDs)

Case Notes

Mrs. Lorenzo was 76 when she and her family first noticed that she was beginning to be forgetful. In conversations, she would repeat things and be unable to answer questions about recent events. Soon she noticed that she was beginning to make errors at work, and so she retired from a part-time bookkeeping job that had been a great source of satisfaction for her. Mrs. Lorenzo's children convinced her and her husband to move from the family home to an apartment in a life-care centre. The children were surprised that their mother showed little emotion as she disposed of treasured possessions and left her home of many years. In the new apartment, Mrs. Lorenzo's forgetfulness worsened. Once a voracious reader, she stopped reading entirely and spent her days playing game after game of solitaire. Less than two years after the move, Mrs. Lorenzo's husband died. Although they had been married for 59 years and had been very close, she did not appear to grieve. She had trouble remembering that her husband was no longer alive. When her children phoned her, she would ask the same two or three questions over and over. Once fastidious, Mrs. Lorenzo rarely bathed or changed her clothes

without prompting. In the year following her husband's death, she was able to remain in her apartment with daily assistance from a homemaker and close monitoring by the life-care centre staff. This was not expected to be possible for very much longer, as her children were increasingly concerned about her health and safety.

NCDs are the most common mental disorders in older adults and, many argue, the cruellest, gradually robbing sufferers of their memory, judgment, and reason; their personal dignity; and, finally, their very sense of self. In the early stages, it may be almost as difficult for loved ones to stand helplessly by as it is for the sufferer; in the later stages, it is almost certainly more distressing for family, friends, and even professional caregivers.

The DSM-5 replaced the term *dementia* with *neurocognitive disorders*. Both of these broad labels refer to cognitive impairment that is caused by a variety of specific disorders that we discuss later in this section, which result in the loss of an individual's former level of cognitive functioning—that is, loss of memory, language, visuospatial, and reasoning abilities.

For a long time, NCDs were commonly known as senility or senile dementia because the mental deterioration was thought to be simply the result of the normal aging process (Blazer, 1990). We now know that this is not the case. Consequently, the terms *senile dementia* and *senility* are, quite appropriately, out of favour.

Although NCDs occur in younger people, they are rare and generally secondary to another disorder such as substance abuse or AIDS. As a primary mental disorder, neurocognitive disorders are clearly disorders of old age. The Canadian Study of Health and Aging has made significant contributions to our understanding of the prevalence of these disorders. More than 10 000 older Canadians living in the community (9008) and institutions (1255) were surveyed to identify its prevalence. The key findings from this survey, summarized in Table 16.2, are that (1) 8 percent of Canadians over the age of 65 have some form of major NCD, (2) prevalence rates increase sharply with age, and (3) prevalence rates are about twice as high among women as among men (Canadian Study of Health and Aging Working Group, 1994). Because of the dramatic growth of the older-adult segment of the population, unless prevalence rates change, we can expect about 600 000 cases of NCDs in the over-65 population by 2021. The prevalence of NCDs is even more startling on a global level. Current estimates suggest that worldwide about 24 million people have NCDs, with the number projected to double every 20 years (Qiu, de Ronchi, & Fratiglioni, 2007).

There are many causes of NCDs—the DSM-5 lists the following 11: Alzheimer's disease, vascular disease, frontotemporal lobar degeneration, Lewy body disease, Parkinson's disease, Huntington's disease, prion disease, HIV infection,

TABLE 16.2 PREVALENCE OF NEUROCOGNITIVE DISORDERS BY AGE (IN PERCENTAGES) IN CANADA

Age Group	All Causes	Alzheimer's Disease	Vascular Disease
65–74	2.4	1.0	0.6
75–84	11.1	6.9	2.4
85+	34.5	26.0	4.8
85–89	22.8	16.7	3.4
90–94	40.4	32.3	4.6
95+	58.6	43.3	6.7

Source: First three rows based on report of Canadian Study of Health and Aging Working Group (1994); last three rows based on Ebly, Parhad, Hogan, and Fung (1994).

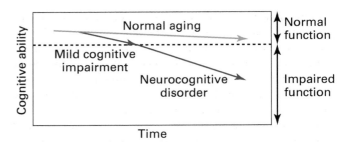

FIGURE 16.5 Theoretical Progression of Cognitive Ability over Time for Adults with Good Health, MCI, and Neurocognitive Disorders

traumatic brain injury, substances/medications, and other medical conditions. For the most part NDCs are progressive and not reversible. However, the term **pseudo-dementia** is used to describe symptoms of dementia that can be reversed (Foster & Martin, 1990). Depression, nutritional deficiency, thyroid disorder, and a number of other diseases can cause symptoms that mimic NCDs, such as forgetfulness, inability to concentrate, poor judgment, faulty reasoning, and lability or flattening of affect. Such symptoms may also occur as side effects from many medications, such as hypnotics, but are transient and disappear when their underlying cause is treated.

Another common way to distinguish among the various types of NCDs focuses on the areas of the brain that are primarily affected. Cummings and Benson (1992) separate cortical dementias, which primarily attack the cerebral cortex or grey matter, from subcortical dementias, which primarily attack the white matter and more primitive parts of the brain that are closer to the brain stem. This distinction is useful clinically because, depending on what brain regions are affected, different symptoms will be prominent. In cortical dementias (e.g., Alzheimer's disease, frontotemporal disease), the primary symptoms include problems learning new information and loss of short-term memory ability, visuospatial problems, language problems, and eventually poor reasoning and judgment. In subcortical dementias (e.g., vascular disease, Lewy body disease), the primary symptoms are cognitive slowing, problems retrieving information from memory, and difficulty with executive functioning (i.e., reasoning, judgment, and mental flexibility).

MILD NEUROCOGNITIVE DISORDERS

Before discussing the most common causes of neurocognitive disorders, we will focus briefly on attempts by clinicians and researchers to identify them at their earliest stages. The DSM-5 refers to this using the term *mild neurocognitive disorders*, but they are more commonly known using the term **mild cognitive impairment (MCI)**. The reason this concept has generated such clinical and theoretical interest is that,

as shown in Figure 16.5, it is thought to represent a transitional state between normal aging and NCDs (Knopman, Boeve, & Petersen, 2003; Petersen, Caracciolo, Brayne, Bauthier, Jelic, & Fratiglioni, 2014). Individuals who have MCI are between 5 and 10 times more likely to develop NCDs than are cognitively healthy adults. Another way of stating this is that healthy adults develop NCDs at a rate of about 1 to 2 percent per year. In comparison, individuals with MCI develop NCDs at a rate of about 10 to 15 percent per year, so that after five years, more than half of individuals diagnosed with MCI will progress to a diagnosis of NCDs (Petersen et al., 2001).

What exactly is MCI? According to a recent review article on this topic by the leading researchers in the world, including Ronald Petersen at the Mayo clinic who originally coined the term and Serge Gauthier at McGill (Petersen, et al., 2014), the construct has evolved tremendously over the past 10 years. Early definitions focused on memory complaints and objective mild memory impairment but otherwise normal cognitive, social, and occupational functioning. Since then, the criteria have expanded beyond just memory problems to include: (1) clinical concern raised by patients or informants, (2) cognitive impairment in one or more cognitive domains, (3) preserved functional independence, and (4) no dementia. If a diagnosis of MCI is made, patients can be further categorized as having amnestic MCI or non-amnestic MCI depending whether or not memory impairment exists. In the future, neuroimaging and biomarkers will play an increasingly important role in determining whether MCI is due to Alzheimer's disease or other causes.

Diagnosis is important because individuals with MCI are at very high risk of developing NCD, so identifying these individuals early in the process can help patients and their families begin to prepare for the likely onset of NCD. In addition, MCI is an obvious target for treatments aimed at improving symptoms and even preventing NCD. As we will discuss, there are medications that can slow the progression of NCD. Unfortunately, the first wave of clinical trials examining the ability of these drugs to slow the progression of MCI to NCD has been largely unsuccessful; additional trials are currently under way (Wilson, Peters, Ritchie, & Ritchie, 2011). Although drug-based interventions to prevent the progression of MCI have not yet been identified, exciting research by Krell-Roesch, Vemuri, & Pink (2017) suggests that lifestyle factors plus biomarkers might offer hope. These researchers assessed 1929 cognitively normal adults aged 70+ at baseline and then every 15 months afterward for four years. Individuals who did not have the APOE-4 gene and who engaged in mentally stimulating activities (e.g., game playing, crafts, computer use, and social activities) had the lowest risk of developing MCI. This study highlights the importance of lifestyle modifications and the need to look at other risk-reducing strategies such as controlling high blood pressure; maintaining low levels of cholesterol; eating a healthy, balanced diet; and engaging in exercise (Wilson et al., 2011).

ALZHEIMER'S DISEASE

It is estimated that 50 to 60% of NCDs are due exclusively to **Alzheimer's disease (AD),** 12 to 17% are due to vascular insults, 8 to 18% are due to a combination of AD and vascular pathology, and 10 to 20% are due to other causes (Zarit & Zarit, 1998). AD is a progressive, fatal, neurological disease with an average course of at least six years from diagnosis to death (Knopman et al., 2003), with some patients surviving after diagnosis for as long as 20 years (Zarit & Zarit, 1998). Although the course of the disease is progressive, slow, and steady, it is often helpful to conceptualize this decline in terms of three stages. The Alzheimer's Society of Canada refers to these as early, middle, and late stages.

In the early stage, individuals with AD exhibit problems with episodic memory (i.e., memory for recent events, such as what they talked about at a party they attended the previous day) and perhaps also problems with attention, concentration, and mild difficulty finding words. Stress and worry are common at this early stage and estimates of depression in AD patients are as high as 25 percent (Foster & Martin, 1990). Depressive disorders are more common in the early to middle phases of the disease; with progression of AD, patients typically lose insight into their difficulties so that later in the process the disease is more difficult for caregivers.

During the middle stage, existing symptoms become more severe and a wide range of additional symptoms may occur. In addition to worsening short-term memory problems (amnesia), language difficulties become more pronounced (aphasia), difficulty with purposeful motor movements appear so that individuals may have difficulty eating or getting dressed by themselves (apraxia), individuals have difficulty recognizing or naming people or things (agnosia), and problems with judgment, reasoning, and mental flexibility emerge (executive dysfunction). In addition, individuals with AD have problems in orientation as to time and place, sleep difficulties, difficulties in social situations, urinary incontinence, feelings of helplessness, flattening of affect, agitation, irritability, and wandering. Although at this point individuals with the disease are not yet bedridden, the caregiver's role becomes quite demanding.

In the late stage, cognitive impairments are profound. A variety of physical symptoms develop: stooped posture, increasing immobility, total incontinence, and increasing vulnerability to conditions such as pneumonia and congestive heart failure. In this stage, challenging behaviours include extreme symptoms such as delusions and hallucinations that occur in 30 to 50 percent of individuals with AD (Broadway & Mintzer, 2007).

DIAGNOSTIC CRITERIA Because AD is distinguished by distinct changes in the brain that are discussed in the next section, the gold standard for diagnosis is a histological examination at autopsy. However, neurologists, neuropsychologists, and other specialists have been shown to be quite accurate in their clinical diagnoses (Knopman et al., 2003). Table 16.3 lists the DSM-5 criteria used, but in many cases a definitive diagnosis is difficult because the same individual can suffer from multiple forms of NCD.

ETIOLOGY What causes the devastation of AD? It seems clear that the etiology is physiological. There are two dramatic differences between the brains of individuals with and without AD (Foster & Martin, 1990). The first is the presence of excessive amounts of beta amyloid plaques (collections within a nerve cell of nerve cell and supportive tissue debris suspended in a protein substance called amyloid) and neurofibrillary tangles (clusters of intertwined filaments in nerve cells that in the normal brain are not tangled). Greater numbers of plaques and tangles are related to poorer functioning and even death of nerve cells. The second difference, as shown in Figure 16.6, is substantial atrophy of the cortex in AD brains.

The question, of course, is what causes these changes. One hypothesis is genetic. The evidence for genetic involvement is twofold (Raskind & Peskind, 1992). First, individuals with Down syndrome (a genetic disorder) who live beyond age 40 generally show neuropathological indicators of AD. Second, AD has been shown to run in families. In such families, about 50% of those at risk develop the disease. The genetic influence is even stronger among identical twins, evidenced by a concordance rate of 78% (Bergem, Engedal, & Kringlen, 1997). However, familial AD is estimated to make up only 15% of all cases. Initially, there was thought to be an AD gene on chromosome 21, but more recent evidence has implicated chromosomes 1, 4, 9, 10, 11, 12, 14, 18, and 20 as well (Padilla & Isaacson, 2011; Rogaeva, Kawarai, & St. George-Hyslop, 2006; St. George-Hyslop, 2006). A certain form of the Apolipopritein E (APOE) gene, 4, increases the risk of developing AD, especially among women (Tsuang & Bird, 2002). Subsequent research has demonstrated that APOE is associated with an earlier onset of dementia and increased co-occurrence of other brain pathologies and disorders (Iacono et al., 2014). Although researchers have discovered many genes that are linked with AD, APOE remains the most reliable genetic association (Rogaeva et al., 2006). However, AD may have a number of forms, each associated with different genes or gene combinations. Non-genetic risk factors are described in further detail later in the text.

TABLE 16.3 DSM-5 DIAGNOSTIC CRITERIA FOR MAJOR OR MILD NEUROCOGNITIVE DISORDER DUE TO ALZHEIMER'S DISEASE

A. The criteria are met for major or mild neurocognitive disorder.

B. There is insidious onset and gradual progression of impairment in one or more cognitive domains (for major neurocognitive disorder, at least two domains must be impaired).

C. Criteria are met for either probable or possible Alzheimer's disease as follows:

For major neurocognitive disorder:

Probable Alzheimer's disease is diagnosed if either of the following is present; otherwise, **possible Alzheimer's disease** should be diagnosed.

1. Evidence of a causative Alzheimer's disease genetic mutation from family history or genetic testing.

2. All three of the following are present:

   a. Clear evidence of decline in memory and learning and at least one other cognitive domain (based on detailed history or serial neuropsychological testing).

   b. Steadily progressive, gradual decline in cognition, without extended plateaus.

   c. No evidence of mixed etiology (i.e., absence of other neurodegenerative or cerebrovascular disease, or another neurological, mental, or systemic disease or condition likely contributing to cognitive decline).

For mild neurocognitive disorder:

Probable Alzheimer's disease is diagnosed if there is evidence of a causative Alzheimer's disease genetic mutation from either genetic testing or family history.

Possible Alzheimer's disease is diagnosed if there is no evidence of a causative Alzheimer's disease genetic mutation from either genetic testing or family history, and all three of the following are present:

1. Clear evidence of decline in memory and learning.

2. Steadily progressive, gradual decline in cognition, without extended plateaus.

3. No evidence of mixed etiology (i.e., absence of other neurodegenerative or cerebrovascular disease, or another neurological or systemic disease or condition likely contributing to cognitive decline).

D. The disturbance is not better explained by cerebrovascular disease, another neurodegenerative disease, the effects of a substance, or another mental, neurological, or systemic disorder.

Source: Reprinted with permission from the *Diagnostic and Statistical Manual of Mental Disorders, Fifth Edition.* (Copyright © 2013). American Psychiatric Association. All Rights Reserved.

A second hypothesis regarding the cause of AD involves environmental and medical factors. Epidemiological research has identified numerous non-genetic risk factors for AD, many of which are preventable or reversible. These risk factors include vascular-related factors (e.g., high blood pressure, high cholesterol, cardiovascular problems, diabetes, stroke), depression, head trauma, lifestyle factors (e.g., poor nutrition, alcoholism, lack of regular physical activity, smoking), exposure to environmental toxins (e.g., pesticides, solvents, aluminum, mercury), lower levels of education, and manual labour jobs (Patterson, Feightner, Garcia, & MacKnight, 2007; Qiu et al., 2007).

With the exception of genetic causes of the relatively rare form of familial AD, there is still no known definite cause of the disease. It is important to highlight that genetic and environmental factors need not work in isolation. The interaction of these factors will likely receive increasing attention from researchers in years to come (Iacono et al., 2014; Kukull & Bowen, 2002). In addition to efforts aimed at finding the cause or causes of AD, research has also focused on possible protective factors. Many protective factors are simply the reverse of the risk factors identified above (e.g., whereas a high-fat diet is a risk factor, a low-fat vegetarian diet is considered protective).

Additional protective factors identified in the literature include regular and moderate consumption of red wine, dietary antioxidants such as vitamins C and E, exposure to certain prescription medications (e.g., lipid-lowering drugs and non-steroidal anti-inflammatory drugs such as Aspirin), and inoculations and vaccinations (e.g., tetanus, influenza). Interventions designed to prevent or delay dementia by focusing on remediable risk and protective factors represent an exciting direction for future research (Kukull & Bowen, 2002; Patterson et al., 2007; Qiu et al., 2007).

TREATMENT One approach to treating NCD has been to seek drugs that will reverse, stop, or at least slow its progression. Emphasis on seeking effective treatment has focused on AD because it is the most common type of dementia. Progress has been limited, and a "cure" remains elusive, but in recent years a particular class of drugs, cholinesterase inhibitors (ChEIs; e.g., Aricept), has been developed that may slow the progression and treat the symptoms of AD (Ihl et al., 2011). The benefit of the three "second-generation" ChEIs that have been approved for use in Canada (donepezil, galantamine, and rivastigmine) was examined by Dr. Krista Lanctot and her colleagues (2003) at Sunnybrook and

Denis Balibouse/Reuters

FIGURE 16.6 Normal Brain Tissue Contrasted with That of a Patient with Alzheimer's Disease
The image on the left side of the photo shows a normal brain; the image on the right shows a brain from a person with Alzheimer's disease.

Women's College Health Sciences Centre in Toronto. The outcome of their review and meta-analysis of 5159 treated patients compared to 2795 controls who received a placebo was that "treatment with ChEIs results in a modest but significant therapeutic effect and modestly but significantly higher rates of adverse events and discontinuation of treatment" (p. 557).

An additional approach to treatment has been to focus on secondary symptoms common in NCD, such as agitation, anxiety, and depression. For the most part, the antidepressants, antipsychotics, and neuroleptics that ameliorate these symptoms in other populations also work with AD patients. Some are contraindicated, however, because of undesirable side effects. For example, some drugs cause hyperactivity, which worsens AD symptoms such as wandering or agitation.

In addition to pharmacological approaches to treating secondary symptoms, effective non-pharmacological interventions have been developed to manage some of the challenging behaviours associated with AD and other NCDs (Cohen-Mansfield, 2001). A recent review of evidence-based treatments for behavioural disturbances in older adults with NCD found the most support for behavioural problem-solving therapies that increase pleasant activities and identify antecedents and consequences of challenging behaviours in patients with dementia (Logsdon, McCurry, & Teri, 2007). These interventions not only decrease challenging behaviours, but also reduce caregiver stress.

6 BEFORE MOVING ON

Recent research has demonstrated that individuals who have a particular genotype (APOE-4) are at increased risk for developing AD, although being APOE-positive does not mean that an individual will develop the disease. Would you want this test if it were available to you? What are arguments for and against genetic testing for a trait that increases your risk for developing a disease such as Alzheimer's, considering that no curative treatment is currently available?

VASCULAR NCD

The second most common cause of NCD is cerebrovascular damage. In vascular disease, the arteries that supply the brain are partly blocked. When blood flow is reduced beyond a certain point, a stroke occurs (Read, 1996). The area affected by a stroke can be large or small. An area of damaged cortex, referred to as a **brain lesion** or infarction, can lead to NCD. As shown in Table 16.3, the prevalence of **vascular NCD** increases with age and is higher among men than women.

DIAGNOSTIC ISSUES Vascular NCD can be diagnosed clinically and with the aid of neuroimaging (e.g., CT, PET, or MRI scans). Evidence of focal lesions or infarctions on scans is a telltale sign, although numerous small infarcts

Ronald Reagan

One of the most famous person to be affected by Alzheimer's disease is Ronald Reagan, the 40th president of the United States. Reagan left office in 1989 at age 78. Five years later, he issued a handwritten letter to the American public informing them of his diagnosis. Given the insidious and progressive nature of AD, there was speculation about whether he had exhibited early signs of the disease while he was president. Although his White House physicians stated publicly that they saw no evidence of the disease while he was in power, it is quite possible that Reagan experienced some degree of brain changes and clinical symptoms of the disease before he left office. Two factors complicate this issue. First, individuals who are highly intelligent are likely able to hide the effects of the disease longer than less intelligent people can. Second, six months after Reagan left office, he suffered significant head trauma after being thrown from a horse while in Mexico. As discussed earlier in this section, head trauma is a risk factor for NCD. As a result, it is possible that he showed no signs of the disease until this trauma, which may have triggered it or hastened its progression.

Library of Congress Prints and Photographs Division [LC-USZ62-13040]

(transient ischemic attacks, or TIAs) can be hard to detect on neuroimaging. Clinically, the onset of vascular NCD is often sudden (in comparison to the slow onset of AD) and patients will experience stepwise progression as they experience additional vascular insults. These individuals will also often have a history of stroke or stroke risk factors, such as obesity, diabetes, and smoking. The prognosis of vascular NCD is somewhat worse than for AD, with a faster progression and shorter survival times (Knopman et al., 2003). As mentioned, vascular NCD is a subcortical disease in which the first symptoms include cognitive slowing, problems retrieving short-term memories (that improve with cues, reminders, and so on), and executive dysfunction. As a result, its symptoms can be distinguished from "pure" AD, which is a cortical NCD in which the first symptoms are problems forming and recalling short-term memories (that do not improve with cues) and word-finding problems. Unfortunately, this distinction is frequently blurred by the fact that vascular NCD and AD often co-occur.

TREATMENT The most effective way of treating vascular NCD is by managing the risk factors for future cerebrovascular events. Such treatments include lifestyle changes as well as medications. Evidence suggests that the cholinesterase inhibitors also appear to benefit individuals with vascular NCD (Knopman et al., 2003). In addition, blood-thinning medication is often prescribed for vascular disease to lessen the likelihood of further strokes (Foster & Martin, 1990). In other respects, treatment focuses on management and is similar to that for AD.

OTHER FORMS OF NCD

Two additional types of NCDs—due to frontotemporal disease or Lewy bodies—are being recognized as distinct forms of disease that were formerly misclassified as AD (Kukull & Bowen, 2002). NCD is now recognized as occurring relatively frequently among older adults with Parkinson's disease. A key pathological change in the brains of patients with Parkinson's disease is filaments of protein with a dense core called Lewy bodies. Increasing awareness of a unique NCD syndrome associated with these pathological changes has led to the use of the term **NCD with Lewy bodies**. Like AD and vascular NCD, a diagnosis of NCD with Lewy bodies requires a progressive cognitive decline that interferes with social or occupational functioning. The diagnosis of this disorder differs from the others in that one or more of the following key symptoms are evident: (1) fluctuating cognition with pronounced variations in alertness and attention; (2) recurrent well-formed hallucinations; and (3) spontaneous features of Parkinsonism, including slowed body movement, muscle rigidity, resting tremor, and postural instability. In addition, patients with this type of NCD have neuroleptic sensitivity, meaning that they have extreme reactions to antipsychotic medications. Because of this feature, proper diagnosis is crucial due to the fact that if antipsychotics are prescribed to treat hallucinations, these patients can experience neuroleptic malignant syndrome, which can result in death (Ross & Bowen, 2002). As is the case with vascular NCD, the prognosis of NCD with Lewy bodies is poorer than for AD. Treatments for this type of dementia often focus on the proper medication management of Parkinson's symptoms with levodopa.

In addition, the cholinesterase inhibitors have shown promise for patients with this disease (Zarit & Zarit, 1998).

Frontotemporal NCD is a term used to describe a heterogeneous group of disorders, including Pick's disease (characterized by "Pick" bodies, spherical protein deposits found within neurons primarily in the frontal lobes of the brain at autopsy), that affect the frontal and temporal lobes of the brain. The key features of this type of NCD are changes in personality and judgment (Knopman et al., 2003). Patients with frontotemporal NCD often have relatively intact memory function until later in the disease process. In contrast to other types of NCD, they exhibit striking behaviour and personality changes such as disinhibition, impulsiveness, repetitiveness, poor judgment, social inappropriateness, loss of empathy, apathy, and reclusiveness. Because of their striking personality changes and lapses in judgment, individuals with frontotemporal NCD are often mistaken for having a psychiatric disorder, leading to under-recognition of this type of dementia. Age of onset tends to be younger than for AD and the course of frontotemporal NCD is variable, with certain patients living only three or four years and others living more than a decade.

CAREGIVER STRESS

Finally, it is important to recognize the impact that NCD has on family members, friends, and professional caregivers. Family caregivers, in particular, live their daily lives under chronically high levels of stress due to a variety of unpredictable physical and psychosocial demands. A growing body of research is clearly showing that caregivers have heightened levels of clinical depression and anxiety (Alzheimer's Disease International, 2009). More recent research continues to support this finding, indicating that compared to non-caregivers, caregivers have poorer perceived mental health and increased symptoms of depression and anxiety (Smith et al., 2014). In addition, caregivers have a higher risk of physical health problems (Vitaliano, Zhang, & Scanlan, 2003) and even premature mortality (Schulz & Beach, 1999). Finally, a small number of recent studies, including several from our laboratory, are finding that caregivers' cognitive abilities are also compromised by the daily stress they encounter (Mackenzie, Wiprzycka, Hasher, & Goldstein, 2009).

Importantly, the consequences of caregiving affect large numbers of North Americans; there are an estimated 6 to 7 million caregivers of older adults with NCD in the United States alone (Schulz & Martire, 2004), and the direct costs of NCD caregiving are estimated at more than US$50 billion per year south of the border (Leon, Cheung, & Neumann, 1998). The number of individuals providing care and the negative impact of this care are expected to grow as demographic shifts result in greater numbers of older adults over the next two decades. Fortunately, there is accumulating evidence of the effectiveness of cognitive-behavioural and multi-component programs aimed at reducing caregiver stress (Gallagher-Thompson & Coon, 2007). Our own research has demonstrated the effectiveness of self-efficacy and mindfulness-based interventions for professional caregivers (Mackenzie & Peragine, 2003; Mackenzie, Poulin, & Seidman-Carlson, 2006) and expressive writing for family caregivers (Mackenzie, Wiprzycka, Hasher, & Goldstein, 2007, 2008). The focus of recent research in caregiving interventions has been on the implementation of technology and the internet. Preliminary evidence suggests that their use will be of value in reaching a broader sample of caregivers and in decreasing the cost of treatment programs (Marziali, Mackenzie, & Tchernikov, 2015; Schulz & Martire, 2004). More generally, recent Canadian research has highlighted the association between older adults' use of the internet and greater feelings of self-efficacy, indicating its potential application in the treatment of a wide range of disorders among older adults (Erickson & Johnson, 2011).

CANADIAN RESEARCH CENTRE

Baycrest Centre for Geriatric Care

Baycrest is an academic health sciences centre affiliated with the University of Toronto. It began as the Toronto Jewish Old Folks Home in 1918 and has developed into one of the leading centres in North America with a focus on older adults' health and cognitive functioning. Key to the success of Baycrest's mission of improving the quality of life of the elderly are its efforts to integrate clinical care, research, and education. Clinically, Baycrest provides inpatient, outpatient, and day program services to more than 3000 older adults every day. As is the case in other university-affiliated hospitals in Canada and around the world, these clinical services both inform and are informed by a dizzying array of research activities.

Baycrest houses the internationally renowned Rotman Research Institute. Scientists at the institute study normal age-related changes in cognition, as well as the effects of abnormal processes such as NCD, stroke, traumatic brain injury, and other neuropsychiatric illnesses. In one example of a groundbreaking research carried out at the Rotman Research Institute, Ellen Bialystock, Fergus Craik, and Morris Freedman (2007) looked at the effects of speaking more than one language on the development of NCD. These scientists examined the clinical records of 184 patients referred to Dr. Freedman's memory clinic with memory complaints, half of whom were bilingual. Remarkably, patients who spoke only English developed NCD an average of four years sooner than those who spoke more than one language. Although this study did not examine why bilingualism appears to offer some protection against developing NCD, the researchers speculate that changes in the brain due to language learning enable it to better tolerate accumulated pathologies that eventually lead to diseases such as Alzheimer's.

SUMMARY

- People are living longer than they ever have, and the first of the baby boomers will soon be 70.

- Older adults are the fastest-growing segment of the population, and by 2036 nearly one quarter of Canadians will be 65 or older.

- As the number of older Canadians continues to grow, the physical and mental health of this segment of the population will become an increasingly important issue.

- Unfortunately, many health professionals, family members, and older people incorrectly believe that mental disorders such as depression are a normal and expected part of growing old, and that treatments for them are ineffective in older adults.

- Historical factors (e.g., the influence of Freud and early lifespan developmental theories), a societal emphasis on youth, and ageist beliefs on the part of older adults and health care professionals have all contributed to this inaccurate belief.

- The theoretical approaches to mental disorders covered in Chapter 2 typically do not take age into account and therefore provide little assistance in understanding mental health problems in older adults.

- In contrast, lifespan approaches such as selective optimization with compensation framework, socio-emotional selectivity theory, and strength and vulnerability integration theory suggest that mental healthy usually improves with age and offer testable hypotheses about how aging affects mental health.

- Mental disorders are generally more complicated to diagnose and treat in later life for a variety of reasons, including the tendency to attribute symptoms to age rather than to disorders, the fact that chronic physical health problems interact closely with mental health problems, and the possibility that medications used to treat health problems will mimic or obscure symptoms of mental disorders.

- There are also specific challenges in diagnosing and treating sleep–wake disorders, including the fact that self-reports of sleep problems are unreliable, that universal age-related changes in sleep are not always well understood, and that sleep characteristics and patterns vary widely, especially among older adults.

- Although more research has focused on depressive disorders than on anxiety and sleep–wake disorders among older adults, it is clear that depression, anxiety, and sleep problems are highly treatable. Psychological and pharmacological treatments appear to be just as effective for older adults as they are for younger adults.

- The final disorder we discussed in this chapter, neuro-cognitive disorder (NCD), is truly a disorder of aging, and the most prevalent form of NCD is Alzheimer's disease (AD).

- Risk factors for developing AD, and its precursor, mild cognitive impairment (MCI), are important for helping researchers, clinicians, and policy-makers target groups of people most likely to develop this disease so that they can develop prevention and early intervention programs for them and their caregivers.

- Certain known risk factors are not modifiable (e.g., chromosomes and genes that are implicated in the disease), some are more difficult to modify (e.g., exposure to environmental toxins, levels of education, and head trauma), and others are more easily modifiable (e.g., obesity, diet, activity levels, access to inoculations and vaccinations).

KEY TERMS

age effects (p. 415)

Alzheimer's disease (AD) (p. 431)

baby boomers (p. 413)

brain lesion (p. 433)

cohort effect (p. 415)

drug interactions (p. 422)

frontotemporal NCD (p. 435)

gerontologists (p. 415)

insomnia disorder (p. 424)

late-onset schizophrenia (p. 427)

mild cognitive impairment (MCI) (p. 430)

NCD with Lewy bodies (p. 434)

neurocognitive disorder (NCD) (p. 421)

normal aging (p. 416)

paradox of aging (p. 414)

period effects (p. 415)

polypharmacy (p. 417)

pseudo-dementia (p. 430)

sleep apnea (p. 425)

vascular NCD (p. 433)

JOHN HUNSLEY

•

CATHERINE M. LEE

CHAPTER
17

PaulaConnelly/E+/Getty Images

Therapies

LEARNING OBJECTIVES

AFTER READING THIS CHAPTER, STUDENTS WILL BE ABLE TO:

1 Describe issues in the use of electroconvulsive therapy for the treatment of depression.

2 Explain how psychotropic drugs are used in the treatment of different types of mental disorders.

3 Define psychotherapy and describe how the major theoretical approaches explain the development of problems and the strategies they use to facilitate change.

4 Identify the different modalities by which psychotherapy can be offered.

5 Explain how meta-analysis is used to synthesize results of several studies.

6 Explain how the effects of psychotherapy have been evaluated and give an overview of the conditions for which psychotherapy is helpful.

7 Identify the key issues in the development of evidence-based psychological practice.

When Jessica was 17 years old, her mother contacted a psychologist over concerns that Jessica was depressed: she had scratch marks on her forearms, always dressed in black, listened to music full of themes of despair and destruction, and had written about death in her personal diary.

Jessica's parents divorced when she was 10. She had appeared to adjust very well to the divorce; her school grades had remained excellent, she helped around the house, and her mother considered her to be a perfect child. Both of Jessica's parents remarried—her father when she was 13 and her mother when she was 14.

Jessica's mother and stepfather reported that since starting high school, Jessica had become moody and easily burst into tears. She accused them of being controlling and unreasonable about chores, and they now felt that they "walked on eggshells" around her. Jessica's father reported that she no longer seemed interested in visiting him and was disrespectful and sullen toward his new partner.

Jessica agreed to attend a first therapy session with her mother. When asked about herself, she gave only brief answers and seemed uncomfortable. She did, however, agree to meet individually with the psychologist. Jessica acknowledged that she was dissatisfied with her life, felt irritable and moody, and did not get along well with her family. She showed the psychologist scars on her arm from using a nail file to hurt herself. She said that she sometimes had thoughts that life was not worth living, but did not have plans to kill herself.

The psychologist first worked with Jessica to develop a safety plan, including crisis and emergency services she could phone if she had thoughts of hurting or killing herself. Jessica next began to monitor her mood. Together with the psychologist, she began to notice that her mood fluctuated with her activities, school pressures, tiredness, and family interactions.

The psychologist helped Jessica plan her weeks so that there was a mixture of work and enjoyable activities. She learned to problem-solve to manage the demands of schoolwork. Next, the psychologist invited Jessica's parents to attend a session. The family talked about reasonable expectations for a 17-year-old. When the parents became aware that they continued to negotiate and monitor chores as they had when Jessica was much younger, they were willing to experiment with discussing issues in regular household meetings. In one session, the family discussed how they could maintain contact in a way that fit Jessica's developmental needs for greater autonomy and more time with her friends. They began to experiment with developing a more mutually respectful style of interaction.

Over several months, Jessica's mood improved and family members found her more pleasant to be around. In therapy, Jessica worked to identify stressors that might make her prone to slip back into depression. She developed awareness of the early signs and planned ways to get back on track quickly. Short-term therapy that focused on Jessica's feelings, behaviours, and thoughts was successful in lifting her depression and helping her fight depression in the future.

Throughout this book, treatments have been discussed in relation to the various disorders. In this chapter, to more fully explore issues related to treatment, we re-examine the range of therapies available to treat mental disorders and the context within which these therapies are offered. Consistent with the tenets of evidence-based practice in health care (Sackett, Straus, Richardson, Rosenberg, & Haynes, 2000; Dozois et al., 2014), we will focus on the research evidence regarding the effects and outcomes of common treatments for mental disorders.

Biological Treatments

The first treatments for psychological disorders were biological (see Chapter 1). Practices such as bleeding, often by cuts to the body or application of leeches, were designed to correct biological imbalances presumed to underlie psychological symptoms. In the latter part of the nineteenth century, there was a proliferation of physical strategies designed to calm disturbed behaviour. For example, patients who were extremely distressed were protected from self-harm by physical restraints and were subjected to prolonged warm baths, or were placed under cold packs designed to pacify them.

Far more efficacious treatments are now available, and considerable attention is now paid to possible negative side effects of biological treatments. In the following sections, we will focus on two current treatment options, including one of the most controversial, electroconvulsive therapy, and the most common, psychopharmacology. However, there is a host of other biological treatment options that are the focus of intense research activity. For example, in the treatment of depression, light therapy, repetitive transcranial magnetic stimulation, and deep brain stimulation have all shown some encouraging results (e.g., Brunoni et al., 2016; Perera et al., 2016; Smith, 2014).

ELECTROCONVULSIVE THERAPY

In the 1930s, clinicians noticed that patients with schizophrenia who spontaneously experienced epileptic seizures subsequently showed a reduction in schizophrenic symptoms. They reasoned, therefore, that if seizures could be triggered, psychotic symptoms would be reduced. Seizures were provoked by the application of an electrical current to the patient's temples in a procedure now known as electroconvulsive therapy (ECT).

With the advent of efficacious antipsychotic medication, ECT was abandoned in the treatment of schizophrenia, but it is still used to treat severe depression that has not responded to other treatments (Milev et al., 2016). ECT used to be associated with serious side effects, including considerable disorientation and memory loss, broken bones, and, in rare cases (1 in 10 000), death due to cardiac failure (Avery, 1993). Adverse effects are now minimized through less intense, briefer currents, often delivered on only one side of the brain, and shorter courses of treatment. Now, the most

Electroconvulsive therapy (ECT) involves the application of an electrical current to the patient's temples.

commonly reported side effect is retrograde amnesia, and the mortality rate has been reduced to 1 death per 100 000 (Waite & Easton, 2013). Anaesthesia and muscle relaxants reduce distress and the risk of injury. Patients receive a full medical and neurological evaluation before receiving ECT and are monitored during the procedure. In Canadian hospitals up to 8100 people receive ECT each year (Martin et al., 2015).

A comprehensive review of randomized controlled trials found consistent evidence of the short-term efficacy of ECT in treating adult patients with depressive disorders (UK ECT Review Group, 2003; see Chapter 8). However, research has found that more than 50 percent of those treated with ECT are likely to relapse (Sackheim et al., 2000). Although there are concerns about risks of cognitive impairment due to the treatment, meta-analytic research indicates that such impairment is likely to diminish several days after the end of treatment (Semkovska & McLoughlin, 2010). Given these considerations, ECT is recommended for use only in the treatment of life-threatening severe depression that has not responded to other treatment (National Institute for Health and Clinical Excellence, 2016b).

① BEFORE MOVING ON

ECT may be seen by some people as a crude treatment with the risk of serious side effects, but by others as a life-saving intervention. What are the advantages and disadvantages of ECT in the treatment of depression?

PSYCHOPHARMACOLOGY

Pharmacological agents that affect the individual's psychological functioning are known as **psychotropic agents**. In Canada in 2015, individuals made over 7 900 000 visits to office-based physicians for problems related to depression, and over 6 700 000 for problems related to anxiety (IMS Brogan, 2016a). In the majority of these visits physicians offered psychopharmacological treatment for their symptoms of depression or anxiety (IMS Brogan, 2016a). Although not all individuals agree to take medication to address mental health issues, across all types of psychotropic drugs, a total of 84 432 000 prescriptions (new and refills) were issued in Canada in 2015. This is second only to the number of prescriptions issued to treat cardiovascular problems; the cost of psychopharmacological treatment of mental health problems in Canada was almost $2.9 billion in 2015 (IMS Brogan, 2016b).

The ideal method for developing new medications is first to understand the pathological process by which a disorder develops, then to identify an agent that will change that process. In reality, things rarely work out so neatly. Science has not clearly established biochemical mechanisms that account for most psychological disorders, and the discovery of classes of psychotropic drugs has often occurred serendipitously; that is, physicians carefully monitoring a patient's reaction to a drug have observed unanticipated benefits in other areas. After case studies show beneficial effects, medication trials are conducted to systematically assess drug efficacy (see Table 17.1; see also Chapter 4 for further discussion and example of blind trials). Nevertheless, there are important differences between the conditions in medication trials and the conditions in which these medications are subsequently prescribed (Verdoux & Bégaud, 2004; Zimmerman, Mattia, & Posternak, 2002). As a result, we cannot assume that drugs will have the same effects in general practice as they do in clinical trials. There is also evidence that some drugs that are effective in one age group may not be suitable for administration to other age groups, such as older adults (Fick et al., 2003).

Drugs can be classified in many ways. We group them here according to their application in the treatment of different types of disorder: antipsychotic, antidepressant, anxiolytic (anti-anxiety), mood-altering, and psycho-stimulant. However, as you can see in the following sections, many drugs are efficacious for disorders other than those for which they were originally prescribed. Commonly prescribed examples of these medications are listed in Table 17.2.

ANTIPSYCHOTICS Prior to the development of this class of drugs in the 1950s, patients diagnosed with schizophrenia typically spent their lives confined in psychiatric institutions. Those receiving chronic care had their physical needs met and were restricted to hospital grounds. The chances of return to the community were slender and, by the time their symptoms abated in middle and later life, they were ill-equipped for life in the community.

The development of phenothiazines and related major tranquilizers offered the possibility of reducing psychotic symptoms such as hallucinations. Freedom from debilitating and alarming symptoms offered relief to many patients. Following stabilization on the drug, formerly institutionalized patients were able to return to the community. This made possible the policy of deinstitutionalization, in which hospital stays were reserved for only the acute phase of the disorder, and patients were rapidly returned to the community. The economic benefits of this process are clear, and the advent of antipsychotic medication was heralded as a major breakthrough.

Because schizophrenia is a chronic disorder, patients must adhere to a long-term medication regimen. Antipsychotics do not cure schizophrenia; instead, they control its symptoms. Dosage must be carefully calibrated to maximize symptomatic control and to minimize side effects. Although drug maintenance reduces the risk of relapse, many patients are tempted to discontinue their medication when they are feeling symptom-free, increasing the risk of a relapse. To address this concern, medication can be delivered via long-acting intramuscular injection rather than as oral medication (Tiihonen et al., 2011).

Unfortunately, after a few weeks of taking major tranquilizers, some patients experience **extrapyramidal effects** similar to the symptoms of Parkinson's disease, including stooped posture, muscular rigidity, a distinctive shuffling gait, and occasional drooling. These side effects may be relieved by anti-Parkinsonian drugs, which in turn may have their own unpleasant side effects. After prolonged administration, patients may begin to show strange muscular movements such as eye twitching and tongue thrusting, which are evidence of another extrapyramidal effect known as tardive dyskinesia. Of concern, these symptoms may persist even after the medication has been discontinued.

Second-generation antipsychotic medications such as clozapine and olanzapine have fewer extrapyramidal effects, but are associated with other side effects such as weight gain. Although these second-generation antipsychotics were initially thought to be superior to the first-generation antipsychotics, the majority of studies comparing first- and second-generation antipsychotics yielded no evidence that the newer generation of drugs was more efficacious than the older (and less expensive) antipsychotics (Crossley, Constante, McGuire, & Power, 2010). The second-generation antipsychotics have mood-stabilizing properties

TABLE 17.1   MEDICATION TRIALS

- **Placebo:** An inert substance associated with alleviation of symptoms through expectancy effects
- **Active placebo:** A therapeutically inert substance with the same side effects as the medication
- **Placebo washout:** The first phase of a clinical trial, in which all participants are given a placebo and those who respond to the placebo are dropped from the study
- **Single-blind trial:** A clinical trial in which participants are unaware of whether they are receiving medication or placebo, but the clinician is aware
- **Double-blind trial:** A clinical trial in which both the participant and the clinician are unaware of whether the participant is receiving medication or placebo
- **Randomized controlled trial:** A clinical trial in which participants are randomly assigned to either a placebo or a medication condition, and the results of the two conditions are statistically compared

TABLE 17.2 COMMONLY PRESCRIBED PSYCHOTROPIC MEDICATIONS

Type/Generic Name	Brand Name	Treats	Side Effects
Antipsychotics			
Phenothiazines			
chlorpromazine	Thorazine	Psychotic symptoms (agitation, delusions, hallucinations, violent or aggressive behaviour), schizophrenia, possibly bipolar disorder	Variable efficacy, uncomfortable side effects, long-term possibility of tardive dyskinesia
thioridazine	Mellaril		
fluphenazine	Prolixin		
trifluoperazine	Stelazine		
Butyrophenone			
Haloperidol	Haldol		
Dibenzodiazepine			
clozapine	Clozaril		
olanzapine	Zyprexa		
risperidone	Risperdal		
Anxiolytics			
alprazolam	Xanax	Anxiety, tension, panic attacks	Drowsiness, lethargy, variable effectiveness
chlordiazepoxide	Librium		
diazepam	Valium		
lorazepam	Ativan		
oxazepam	Serax		
busiprone	BuSpar		
propranolol	Inderal		
meprobamate	Equinil, Miltown		
Antidepressants			
MAO Inhibitors			
isocarboxazid	Marplan	Depression, panic disorder	Dizziness, sleep disturbances, headaches, may be dangerous, special diet necessary
phenelzine	Nardil		
tranylcypromine	Parnate		
selegiline	Eldepryl		
Tricyclics			
amitriptyline	Elavil	Depression, panic disorder, OCD	Effects may take time, may cause discomfort
clomipramine	Anafranil		
doxepin	Sinequan		
imipramine	Tofranil		
nortriptyline	Pamelor		
SSRIs			
fluoxetine	Prozac	Depression, OCD, panic disorder, eating disorders	Relatively few side effects
sertraline	Zoloft		
paroxetine	Paxil		
fluvoxamine	Luvox		
SNRIs			
venlafaxine	Effexor	Depression, OCD	Relatively few side effects
duloxetine	Cymbalta	Depression	Relatively few side effects
buproprion	Wellbutrin		
Mood Stabilizers			
lithium carbonate	Eskalith, Lithane	Bipolar disorder	Possibility of toxicity
lithium citrate	Cibalith-S		
divalproex	Depakote	Bipolar disorder	Nausea, dizziness, visual problems
carbamazepine	Tegretol		
lamtrogine	Lamictal		
Stimulants			
dextroamphetamine	Dexedrine, Adderall	Hyperactivity, distractibility, learning disorders	Nervousness, insomnia, loss of appetite
methylphenidate	Ritalin		
pemoline	Cylert		

and are now frequently used, along with mood stabilizers (see page 443), in the treatment of bipolar disorder (Miller et al., 2014; Pillarella, Higashi, Alexander, & Conti, 2012). Evidence-based guidelines for the pharmacological treatment of schizophrenia indicate that the selection of the most appropriate antipsychotic medication(s) should be based on side effects experienced by the individual patient (Barnes & the Schizophrenia Consensus Group of the British Association for Psychopharmacology, 2011).

ANXIOLYTICS Anxiolytics are used to alleviate symptoms of anxiety and muscle tension by reducing activity in parts of the central nervous system, which lowers activity in the sympathetic nervous system, leading to lower respiration and heart rate and decreased muscle tension. An unfortunate property of barbiturates, the first class of anxiolytic drugs, is that patients develop tolerance for them, requiring larger doses over time to achieve the same effects. Large doses of barbiturates are highly toxic, which made them a common choice for suicide attempts.

A second class of anxiolytics, the benzodiazepines, offer effective control of anxiety without toxicity at high doses (see Chapter 5 for a discussion of possible mechanisms). Of concern, benzodiazepines are also addictive. After prolonged use of this class of drugs, sudden withdrawal can provoke convulsions that may be life-threatening. Consequently, as the dose is gradually reduced, patients must be monitored carefully. Like barbiturates, benzodiazepines are dangerous when taken in combination with alcohol. Clinical guidelines suggest that benzodiazepines should be used only for brief periods in the treatment of anxiety disorders (National Institute for Clinical Excellence, 2011).

ANTIDEPRESSANTS Drugs used in the treatment of depression fall into four major categories (see Chapter 8): the monoamine oxidase inhibitors (MAOIs), the tricyclics (TCAs), the selective serotonin reuptake inhibitors (SSRIs), and the serotonin-norepinephrine reuptake inhibitors (SNRIs). A major drawback of MAOIs is the severe dietary restrictions they require. In combination with MAOIs, common foods such as yeast, chocolate, and beer that contain the enzyme tyramine can cause a life-threatening increase in blood pressure. The TCAs, which were commonly used for many years, provoke many unpleasant side effects such as dry mouth, blurry vision, constipation, and light-headedness.

The most recently developed groups of antidepressants are the SSRIs and SNRIs. Extensive evidence suggests that, for adults, SSRIs are comparable in efficacy to TCAs (Bech et al., 2000). Although SSRIs may be better tolerated than TCAs (McGrath et al., 2000), they cause side effects such as nausea, diarrhea, headache, tremors, and sleepiness. Similar side effects can occur with SNRIs, and flu-like symptoms can occur if SNRIs are stopped abruptly. Concerns have been raised that the risk of adverse outcomes in older adults is greater with SSRIs than with TCAs (Coupland et al., 2011). Nevertheless, taking into account demonstrated treatment efficacy and common side-effect profiles, Canadian guidelines for the pharmacotherapy of depression recommend SSRIs and SNRIs as first-line medication options (Kennedy et al., 2016).

Because it takes time for antidepressants to reach beneficial levels in the blood, improvement is typically evident only after one to two weeks of treatment, with optimal response by the third or fourth week. Thirty to 50 percent of patients do not respond favourably to antidepressant medication, which may partly explain why most people discontinue the medication within three months of starting (Olfson, Marcus, Tedeschi, & Wan, 2006). However, 30 to 50 percent of those who do not respond to one class of antidepressants will respond favourably to another. Antidepressants bring symptomatic relief to many adults in the acute phase of a depressive disorder, but there is less evidence of their influence on relapse. Although the prescribing of antidepressant medication has markedly increased (Olfson & Marcus, 2009), the precise mode of action for antidepressants remains unclear. Furthermore, the benefits of antidepressants are most pronounced in those with severe depression, but only minimal or nonexistent at mild and moderate levels of symptom severity (Barbui, Cipriani, Ayuso-Mateos, & van Ommeren, 2011; Fournier et al., 2010). Importantly, for many years Health Canada has advised of potential risks to newborns when pregnant women are prescribed SSRIs (Health Canada, 2006). There is evidence that SSRIs may provide relief for adults diagnosed with eating disorders such as bulimia nervosa and binge-eating disorder, and for those diagnosed with anxiety and related disorders (Donovan, Glue, Kolluric, & Emir, 2010; Hay & Claudino, 2012).

As depression is a major risk factor for suicidal ideation and suicidal behaviour, considerable attention has been focused on suicidal risks in patients taking antidepressant medication. Ironically, because TCAs are toxic in overdose, a medication prescribed to alleviate depression can be used to attempt suicide. A major advantage of the SSRIs is their lower toxicity in overdose, but there have been suggestions in some research that the medication itself may increase the likelihood of suicidal ideation and behaviour. A number of studies showed that depressed children and adolescents were at greater risk for suicidal behaviour when taking SSRIs than when taking a placebo. As a result, drug regulatory agencies, including Health Canada, issued warnings about the use of SSRIs for depressed youth. These warnings that were designed to protect children and adolescents had unintended negative outcomes. In Canada, the rate of antidepressant prescriptions for youth dropped, but the total number of visits made to physicians because of symptoms of depression also dropped and the number of completed suicides among children and adolescents rose (Katz et al., 2008). A similar drop in the rate of SSRI prescriptions for youth occurred in the United States; the American data also showed that the change in prescription patterns was not offset by an increase in referrals for psychotherapy (Libby et al., 2007). Although a review of the treatment research concluded that the benefits of antidepressants for youth outweigh the risks of suicidal behaviour

(Bridge et al., 2007), the safety of using antidepressants with children and adolescents remains an open question for many mental health professionals. At present, no antidepressant is approved by Health Canada for use with patients under the age of 18, although current Canadian guidelines suggest that, with careful monitoring, treatment of youth with SSRIs may be appropriate (MacQueen et al., 2016).

MOOD STABILIZERS For decades lithium had been the medication of choice for bipolar disorder (see Chapter 8). The side effects of lithium at therapeutic dosages can include nausea, dizziness, weight gain, and mild diarrhea. Of greater concern is the fact that lithium has a narrow window of effectiveness, with low doses being ineffective and high doses being highly toxic. Physicians, therefore, must carefully monitor patients' blood lithium levels. For these reasons, the use of lithium has decreased in favour of other mood stabilizers (e.g., divalproex, carbamazepine, lamotrigine) and the newer antipsychotics (Scherk, Pajonk, & Leucht, 2007; Young & Hammond, 2007). Treatment of this complex disorder requires attention to hypomanic/manic episodes, depressive episodes, the cycling between the two types of episodes, and the prevention of these episodes. Recent clinical guidelines suggest that adding another medication to lithium or divalproex may provide superior results to the use of a single medication (Yatham et al., 2013). Although many of the mood stabilizers and second-generation antipsychotics listed in Table 17.2 have been found to affect one or more of these elements, there continues to be significant challenges finding the combination of medications that most effectively addresses the symptoms of each person (Keck & McElroy, 2015).

STIMULANTS Stimulants are the class of drugs most commonly used in the treatment of children and adults with attention deficit/hyperactivity disorder (ADHD; see Chapter 15). They are short-acting compounds with an onset of action within 30 to 60 minutes and peak clinical efficacy one to five hours after administration. Stimulants such as Ritalin reduce hyperactive and impulsive behaviour, permitting the individual to sustain attention. Compared to other classes of drugs, stimulants have received intense study. A review of 185 studies, including 12 245 children and adolescents diagnosed with ADHD (Storebø et al., 2015) found that methylphenidate was associated with improved teacher reports of ADHD symptoms and general behaviour, as well as parent reports of children's quality of life. A meta-analytic study on the use of pharmacotherapy for the treatment of adult ADHD found that it was associated with mild improvement in symptoms; adults were less likely to discontinue pharmacotherapy if they were also receiving psychological treatment (Cunill, Castells, Tobias, & Capellà, 2016). A systematic review of double-blind placebo trials found small to moderate effects on executive functioning; the pattern of findings was similar in samples of children and adults (Tamminga, Reneman, Huizenga, & Geurts, 2016). Common side effects of psychostimulants are appetite suppression and sleep disturbance. Less frequently, patients report mood disturbance, headaches, abdominal

discomfort, and fatigue. A meta-analytic review of 22 studies of 2385 children found that new onset or worsening of tics was reported with equal frequency in groups receiving psychostimulants and placebos (Cohen et al., 2015). Evidence-based clinical guidelines for the management of ADHD indicate that stimulants should not be prescribed to preschool age children; stimulants combined with psychological treatment should be the first-line treatment for severe ADHD in children and for moderate and severe ADHD in adults (National Institute for Health and Clinical Excellence, 2016a).

LIMITS ON EFFICACY Several classes of drugs have demonstrated efficacy in controlling diverse psychological symptoms. However, no class of drugs is efficacious for all people with a particular disorder, and it is not possible to predict who will respond to a particular class of drugs (Simon & Perlis, 2010). Psychotropic medication has freed many people from debilitating symptoms. However, medication does not necessarily enable the individual to learn new skills or to process information in a different way and, without concomitant psychological interventions, the person may be prone to relapse (e.g., Cuijpers, Hollon, van Straten, Bockting, Berking, Andersson, 2013). (See Focus box 17.1 for a discussion of whether psychologists should have the authority to prescribe medications.)

② BEFORE MOVING ON

> Psychotropic medications are prescribed at unprecedented rates to treat a range of debilitating mental disorders. It is impossible to predict who will respond positively to a particular drug. What issues should an informed consumer consider in making decisions about the advantages and disadvantages of taking a particular medication?

Psychotherapy: A Definition

Psychotherapy is typically defined as a process in which a professionally trained therapist systematically uses techniques derived from psychological principles to relieve another person's psychological distress or to facilitate growth. Psychotherapy is practised by professionals from many disciplines, including psychology, psychiatry, social work, medicine, and nursing. In most jurisdictions in Canada, the title *psychotherapist* is not licensed or restricted in any fashion; anyone can advertise his or her services as a psychotherapist.

Theoretical Orientations

Which types of psychotherapy are practised by therapists today? Surveys show the major schools of psychotherapy to be psychodynamic, cognitive-behavioural (including behavioural and cognitive approaches), humanistic-experiential, and integrative or eclectic (Hunsley, Ronson, & Cohen, 2013; Norcross, Karpiak, & Santoro, 2005). The theoretical assumptions of each approach were presented in Chapter 2.

FOCUS
17.1

Should Psychologists Prescribe Medication?

Since the 1980s, psychologists in the United States have debated the advantages and disadvantages of appropriately trained psychologists having the right to prescribe psychoactive medication. Some American jurisdictions (Guam, Illinois, Iowa, Louisiana, and New Mexico) and government departments now allow psychologists to prescribe psychoactive medication. Advocates of prescription privileges for psychologists argue that

1. Many major mental disorders (such as schizophrenia) are best treated with medication.

2. It might be more cost-effective for psychologists to prescribe for their patients rather than referring patients to psychiatrists or physicians.

3. Underserved groups such as the elderly, the chronically mentally ill, and those living in rural areas would benefit from expanded opportunities to receive psychopharmacological treatment from mental health professionals.

4. Psychologists can be at least as competent as other health care professionals in prescribing medication for psychological disorders. Most psychotropic medications are prescribed by general practitioners whose training in mental health issues is limited to a few weeks of placement with a psychiatrist.

Physicians have strongly opposed the extension of prescription privileges to psychologists, citing the importance of full medical training to understand the impact of psychotropic medication on other physical systems. Within psychology, critics argue that psychologists' distinctive expertise is in the development and application of evidence-based psychological assessment and psychological interventions. They express concern that the inclusion of adequate training in psychopharmacology would inevitably come at the expense of training in psychological issues.

Under Canada's publicly funded health care system, it is likely that the federal government would have concerns that additional numbers of practitioners eligible to prescribe expensive psychopharmacological treatments would contribute to mushrooming health care costs (Romanow & Marchildon, 2003). A Canadian Psychological Association (CPA) task force on prescriptive authority for psychology affirmed the importance of a biopsychosocial approach to the science and practice of psychology and emphasized the necessity for psychologists to work in a collaborative fashion with other health care professionals (CPA Task Force on Prescriptive Authority for Psychologists in Canada, 2010). The CPA task force recommended that training and continuing education in professional psychology ensure a basic understanding of psychopharmacology so that psychologists are equipped to work collaboratively with other professions in providing evidence-based services.

There is no plan for psychologists to seek prescriptive authority in Canada in the foreseeable future. A survey of Canadian students and professionals in psychology revealed that fewer than half of the clinical students polled indicated that they would seek prescription privileges if they were made available; among clinically oriented professionals, a little more than one-third indicated that they would seek prescription privileges (St. Pierre & Melnyk, 2004). The survey did not address the question of how much additional time students and professionals in psychology were willing to devote to acquiring competence in this field. However, these issues were considered in an American survey of psychology interns, residents, and psychologists (Fagan, Ax, Liss, Resnick, & Moody, 2007). Consistent with prior research, many respondents favoured psychologists having prescriptive authority and many were interested in obtaining this authority. However, respondents' interest in obtaining prescription privileges dropped dramatically when they learned that the required training would take two years or more and cost more than $10 000! ●

Because approaches to psychotherapy are constantly evolving, criticisms that may apply to an early form of a therapy may no longer apply to later forms of the therapy. As approaches evolve, there is considerable "cross-pollination" so that ideas from one approach are integrated into other approaches (e.g., Greenberg, 2008). The current emphasis on identifying and disseminating evidence-based treatments represents a shift in attention from theoretical debates toward a search to ensure that psychological interventions are helpful. So, instead of defending their own beliefs, psychologists focus on identifying what will help the patient. In the following pages, we provide an overview of some key aspects of common approaches to psychotherapy.

PSYCHODYNAMIC APPROACHES

Freud developed a theory that psychological problems have their roots in very early childhood and in unconscious conflicts (see Chapter 2). The main goal of Freudian

psychoanalysis is to help patients understand the unconscious factors that drive and control their behaviour. Classic psychoanalysis is an intensive process, generally entailing several visits each week over a period of years during which patients obtain insight into the nature of their problems and how past conflicts continue to affect them. Classic psychoanalysts rely heavily on five basic techniques:

1. *Free association.* The analyst requires the individual to say everything that comes to mind without censoring seemingly unimportant or embarrassing thoughts. The analyst helps the patient recognize unconscious motives and conflicts expressed in the spontaneous speech.

2. *Dream interpretation.* The analyst distinguishes between the manifest content of the dream (which is consciously remembered by the client) and the more important latent content (the unconscious ideas and impulses that have been disguised).

3. *Interpretation.* The analyst interprets what the client says or does. Slips of the tongue, forgetfulness, and the client's behaviour are presumed to reveal unconscious impulses, defence mechanisms, or conflicts. First, the analyst interprets behaviour that the client is already on the verge of understanding. Later, the therapist interprets the unconscious conflicts that induce defence mechanisms.

4. *Analysis of resistance.* During the process of free association or dream interpretation, clients may become resistant—for example, being unwilling to discuss certain topics, missing or arriving late for appointments, joking during the session, or remaining silent. Resistance prevents painful or difficult thoughts from entering awareness; thus, therapists must determine the source of resistance if the client is to deal effectively with the problem.

5. *Analysis of transference.* The core of psychoanalytic therapy is **transference**, which occurs when the client responds to the therapist as he or she responded to significant figures from his or her childhood (generally the parents). Freud believed that individuals unconsciously re-experience repressed thoughts during transference, making it essential to the resolution of the client's problems. By recognizing the transference relationship and remaining neutral, the therapist helps the client work through the conflict. The analyst is careful not to allow personal feelings, needs, or fears to interfere with the relationship with the client (counter-transference).

Throughout his life, Freud continued to modify his theories and his therapeutic strategies. In addition, many of his former disciples developed their own modifications of his work. This family of therapies is referred to as *psychoanalytic psychotherapy, psychoanalytically oriented therapy,* or *psychodynamic therapy.* Across these approaches, therapists engage in a blend of interpretive and supportive interventions (Henry, Strupp, Schacht, & Gaston, 1994). Interpretive interventions are designed to promote the client's development of insight into his or her wishes, emotions, and/or defence mechanisms; supportive interventions emphasize the setting of treatment goals and the strengthening of the client's psychosocial resources. The following are some examples of psychodynamic therapies.

BRIEF PSYCHODYNAMIC PSYCHOTHERAPY Primarily developed by Alexander and French (1946), this psychoanalytically oriented therapy uses Freudian techniques in an active, flexible manner. Therapy tends to be short term: sessions occur twice a week rather than daily. Goals are concrete, conversation replaces free association, therapists are empathic rather than emotionally detached, and interpretations focus on current life events rather than on childhood fears and conflicts.

EGO ANALYSIS Ego analysts, such as Karen Horney, Erik Erikson, Anna Freud, and Heinz Hartmann, argued that Freudian analysis was too focused on the unconscious sexual and aggressive motivation. They believed that individuals are capable of controlling their own behaviour. **Ego analysts** use Freudian techniques to explore the ego rather than the id. Therapists help clients understand how they have relied on defence mechanisms to cope with conflicts.

ADLER'S INDIVIDUAL PSYCHOLOGY Alfred Adler proposed that sexual and aggressive instincts are less important than the individual's striving to overcome personal weakness. Adler's individual psychology was based on the assumption that mental disorders are the consequence of deeply entrenched mistaken beliefs, which lead individuals to develop a maladaptive style of life that protects them from discovering their own imperfections. Adlerian therapists interpret dreams in terms of current behaviour, offer direct advice, and encourage new behaviours.

INTERPERSONAL PSYCHODYNAMIC PSYCHOTHERAPY Harry Stack Sullivan, the American psychiatrist who developed **interpersonal psychodynamic psychotherapy**, believed that mental disorders resulted from maladaptive early interactions between child and parent. This type of therapy is a variation of brief psychodynamic therapy and emphasizes the interactions between the client and his or her social environment. Interpersonal therapists provide feedback to help the client understand how his or her interpersonal styles (such as hostility or dependence) are perpetuating or provoking conflicts. The therapist also helps the client learn to interact with others in more flexible and positive ways and must be careful not to reinforce the client's maladaptive behaviours.

SHORT-TERM PSYCHODYNAMIC PSYCHOTHERAPIES Psychodynamic approaches such as **time-limited dynamic psychotherapy** (Binder, Strupp, & Henry, 1995) and **supportive-expressive psychotherapy** (Luborsky, 1984) retain an emphasis on analysis of transference as a central mechanism of therapeutic change but are much briefer interventions, with the client in face-to-face contact with the therapist. The therapist helps identify patterns of interaction with others that strengthen unhelpful thoughts about the self and others. Research in psychodynamic therapy has found the quality of the relationship between therapist and client is a predictor of therapy outcome. Consequently, these approaches place greater emphasis on interpersonal processes and the **therapeutic alliance** than did early psychoanalytic formulations. In short-term psychodynamic psychotherapies the therapist determines the appropriate balance of interpretive and supportive interventions needed to address the client's problems (Leichsenring et al., 2015).

HUMANISTIC-EXPERIENTIAL APPROACHES

Whereas psychodynamic approaches focus on the person's unconscious processes, humanistic and experiential approaches focus on the person's subjective experience, giving particular attention to emotional aspects of experience

(Greenberg, 2008). Humanistic-experiential approaches place emphasis on the person's current experience rather than on the past. In contrast to psychoanalytic formulations that view individuals as dominated by primitive urges that must be constrained, humanistic-experiential approaches value the individual's free will and encourage the client to take responsibility for personal choices. In addition to the growing evidence base for the efficacy of some humanistic approaches, a major contribution of the humanistic approaches has been the emphasis on the human qualities of the therapist. Research has established that therapists working with different approaches are more effective when their clients feel that they are genuine, that they make efforts to understand their experience, and that they accept them despite their problems (e.g., Greenberg, Elliott, & Lietaer, 1994).

CLIENT-CENTRED THERAPY Carl Rogers developed client-centred therapy in the 1940s as an alternative to psychoanalysis. **Client-centred therapy** emphasizes the warmth and permissiveness of the therapist and the tolerant climate in which the feelings of the client can be freely expressed. Rogers believed that psychological problems arise when personal growth is stunted by judgments imposed by others (see Chapter 2 for more on Rogers's theories). This creates conditions of worth in which the client believes that he or she must meet the standards of others in order to be a worthwhile person. Rogers defined the therapist qualities that facilitate the client's growth: genuineness, empathy, and "unconditional positive regard." The therapist strives to provide an environment in which the client feels accepted. It is theorized that self-acceptance follows, and this in turn leads to self-knowledge and dissipation of bad feelings. In the client-centred approach, clients are not diagnosed, evaluated, or given advice; rather, they are valued as unique individuals.

EXISTENTIAL THERAPY Existential therapists are inspired by the work of existential philosophers such as Sartre and Kierkegaard. Existential therapy focuses on the importance of the human situation as perceived by the individual, with the ultimate goal of making the client more aware of his or her own potential for growth and capacity for making choices. Existential therapists do not follow any particular procedures but emphasize the uniqueness of each individual. They challenge and confront the client on past and present choices. The therapist helps the client relate authentically to others through the therapeutic encounter. Existential therapists share themselves, their feelings, and their values with the client. This type of therapy examines the lack of meaning in a person's life, and is assumed to work best with those who are having conflicts regarding their existence, or those with anxiety or personality disorders rather than psychoses.

GESTALT THERAPY Gestalt therapy, developed by Frederich (Fritz) Perls, emphasized the idea that individuals have a distorted awareness of genuine feelings that leads to impairments in personal growth and behavioural problems. Gestalt therapists help clients become aware of feelings and

needs that have been ignored or distorted and recognize that these needs are a part of themselves and should be accepted. The key goal of Gestalt therapy is client awareness. To become aware, clients must integrate both their inner feelings and their external environments. Therapists encourage clients to experience what is going on in the here and now by asking questions such as "How do you feel when you think about that?" or "What thoughts are running through your head now?" Clients are instructed to communicate directly by talking *to* people rather than *about* them (using "I" statements). One of the most popular Gestalt techniques is the *empty chair technique*, used to make the client more aware of his or her genuine feelings. For example, a young woman with an unresolved conflict with her ex-boyfriend would be instructed to face an empty chair and imagine that her boyfriend was in it, and speak as though she were talking directly to him. Gestalt therapists often interpret dreams, looking at the importance of the dream to the client at that moment. They also attend to nonverbal cues and ask clients to focus on their body and the meaning that these paralinguistic cues are communicating.

EMOTION-FOCUSED THERAPY In recent years, there has been substantial growth in the range of humanistic-experiential approaches. Psychologist Dr. Les Greenberg and his colleagues at a number of Canadian universities, including the University of Ottawa, the University of Windsor, and York University, developed **emotion-focused therapy**, in which the client enters into an empathic relationship with a therapist who is directive and responsive to his or her experience (Elliot & Greenberg, 1995; Greenberg, 2008). Emotion-focused therapy, along with a number of similar humanistic-experiential therapies, was designed to address common psychological problems such as depression, trauma, and marital distress by enhancing and then focusing on clients' emotional reactions (Elliott, Greenberg, Watson, Timulak, & Freire, 2013).

COGNITIVE-BEHAVIOURAL APPROACHES

Although the distinctions between behavioural, cognitive, and cognitive-behavioural therapies continue to be debated, the overlap between them in both techniques and theoretical underpinnings is so great that the leading professional associations in the area (the Association of Behavioral and Cognitive Therapies and the Canadian Association of Cognitive and Behavioural Therapies) view them as a single orientation. The term **behaviour therapy** was first used in the 1950s to describe an operant conditioning treatment for psychotic patients (Lindsley, Skinner, & Solomon, 1954). Skinner's work produced dramatic changes in the behaviour of populations previously considered untreatable, such as the chronically mentally ill and individuals with what is now referred to as intellectual developmental disorder. Behavioural approaches emphasize that problem behaviours are learned behaviours and that faulty learning can be reversed through the application of learning principles (see Chapter 2).

From its roots in the application of classical and operant conditioning, the field of behaviour therapy has broadened to include research findings from areas such as perception, cognition, and the biological bases of behaviour. Behavioural therapists focus primarily on present thoughts and behaviours as opposed to childhood history. Accordingly, behavioural interventions focus on specific targets, such as dealing with social phobia, reducing the frequency of bulimic symptoms, and changing a host of other maladaptive behaviours. An essential feature is the application of scientifically derived principles in the treatment of problems. Throughout therapy, progress is assessed to determine whether the strategy should be modified. Behavioural treatment requires clear identification of goals and is oriented toward the future. Behaviour therapists are very active in evaluating the outcome of their interventions, but until recent decades have devoted less attention to studying the process of therapy or the role of the therapeutic relationship.

The idea that the way we think and feel influences our behaviour is not new. From the writings of the ancient Greeks onward, writers have suggested that the way we interpret our experience affects how we feel and behave (Meichenbaum, 1995). Albert Bandura drew attention to ways that learning could take place by observation and imitation (see Chapter 2). Bandura's work was first applied to children, but has been found to have important applications for adults as well. Bandura also focused on internal processes that facilitate skill development. He noted that in helping an individual to develop new behaviours, it is important to reward coping as well as mastery. For example, a person making fumbling attempts to learn to skate should be encouraged for persistence and effort, even in the absence of an accomplished performance. Self-efficacy, which refers to a person's sense of his or her own competence to learn and perform new tasks, is often found to be the best predictor of behaviour, such as approaching a phobic stimulus or attempting a new behaviour. Bandura's work laid the foundation for approaches that emphasize the importance of cognitions in mediating behavioural responses (Craighead, Craighead, & Ilardi, 1995).

Other, more purely cognitive approaches, such as Albert Ellis's **rational-emotive therapy** and Aaron Beck's **cognitive therapy** (see Chapter 2), are based on the assumption that an individual's perception of events, rather than the events themselves, affects adjustment. Consequently, they focus on identifying automatic thoughts and changing maladaptive patterns of thinking that are associated with distress, anxiety, and depression (Hollon & Beck, 1994). Like their behavioural "relatives," cognitive and cognitive-behavioural approaches rely on the application of empirically derived strategies in the treatment of diverse disorders, including depression, anxiety disorders, eating disorders, attention deficit/hyperactivity disorder, chronic pain, personality disorders, bipolar disorder, substance abuse, schizophrenia, and couple distress (Beck & Dozois, 2011; Beck et al., 2009). Cognitive approaches foster a collaborative relationship in which the therapist and client work together to identify problems, test hypotheses, and re-evaluate beliefs. Treatment response is continuously monitored and treatment is tailored to the needs of individual clients. Chapter 5 discusses in more detail cognitive techniques in the treatment of anxiety; Chapter 12 describes cognitive and behavioural treatments for personality disorders; and Chapter 8 discusses a cognitive approach to depression.

Developments in cognitive-behavioural approaches have shifted the focus away from an exclusive emphasis on challenging and changing maladaptive thoughts to attending to and accepting the presence of such thoughts (Dozois & Beck, 2011; Hayes, Villatte, Levin, & Hildebrandt, 2011). This is an example of the larger movement in cognitive-behavioural treatment to encourage clients to make improvements in overall well-being, accept some personal shortcomings and vulnerabilities, and use mindfulness of internal experiences as a strategy to deal with life stresses. These "third wave" cognitive-behavioural treatments (including acceptance and commitment treatment, dialectical behavioural therapy, and mindfulness-based cognitive therapy) focus on the way the person experiences and reacts to his or her thoughts and emotions (Hofmann, Sawyer, & Fang, 2010). So, for example, as part of promoting the client's awareness of the experience of self-denigrating thoughts, the client is taught to disengage from automatically responding to the thoughts. Rather than only learning to challenge a self-critical thought, a client is encouraged to be fully aware of the thought, understand its meaning and purpose, and then determine whether or not to take any action in response to the thought.

We now present examples of some commonly used behavioural, cognitive, and cognitive-behavioural interventions (Dobson & Dobson, 2016).

REINFORCEMENT Building on the robust phenomenon that a behaviour that is followed by a reward is more likely to be repeated, efforts to reinforce desirable behaviours are at the heart of behavioural approaches. They are core components of approaches in which parents learn to attend selectively to and reinforce appropriate behaviours in their children and to ignore undesirable behaviours. Systematic programs that use reinforcement to encourage and maintain effective behaviour work well in situations such as schools, residences, and institutions.

RESPONSE SHAPING Because many news skills are acquired gradually, **response shaping** is used to shape behaviour in gradual steps toward a goal. This method is used extensively with behaviour problems or difficulties across the lifespan. For example, a child with intellectual disability who is unable to get dressed independently can be taught the process gradually by being rewarded for putting on one item at a time until he or she is eventually able to handle the entire task. The method would also be used in treating a young child presenting with school refusal.

BEHAVIOURAL ACTIVATION Extensive research has demonstrated that depressed individuals are limited in the scope and nature of positive reinforcers. For example, they typically minimize interactions with others and avoid engaging in activities that they previously found enjoyable. The essence of behavioural activation in the treatment of depression is to help patients develop strategies to increase their overall activity and to counteract their tendencies to avoid activities. As clients begin to experience more natural reinforcers in their lives (such as enjoying going for a walk, watching a movie with a friend, going for coffee while shopping), their depressive symptoms begin to diminish (Dimidjian, Barrera, Martell, Muñoz, & Lewinsohn, 2011).

RELAXATION TRAINING Helping clients to relax, both physically and mentally, is a component of many treatments for anxiety disorders, as well as for interventions focused on helping people to cope with pain or manage stress. A range of relaxation strategies can be used with both children and adults, including visualization, breathing retraining, biofeedback, and progressive muscle relaxation. A key issue in all forms of relaxation training is ensuring that clients develop skills that are practical, so that they can be quickly and easily used when needed.

EXPOSURE Also called in vivo exposure, exposure involves gradually exposing the client to a series of increasingly anxiety-provoking situations or stimuli. This is the most commonly used technique based on the concept of extinction. Related to **exposure therapy** is systematic desensitization. Joseph Wolpe's work drew on classical conditioning processes, reasoning that pairing anxiety-provoking stimuli with responses incompatible with anxiety would eliminate the anxiety response. In the process of **systematic desensitization**, fear-inducing stimuli are arranged in a hierarchy. Next, individuals are trained in techniques to achieve deep muscle relaxation. They are then required to imagine the first item on the hierarchy while remaining relaxed. They gradually progress through the hierarchy while maintaining their relaxed state. If they become anxious, they stop visualizing until they have regained their relaxed state (see Chapter 5). Systematic desensitization is not used as frequently as it once was because in vivo exposure produces a better outcome than imaginal exposure and the addition of relaxation is no more effective than exposure alone (Antony & Barlow, 2002).

ASSERTIVENESS TRAINING Assertiveness training is designed to help clients who have difficulty in conflict situations. The desired behaviours are first rehearsed in the therapy session and are later applied in real-life situations. The therapist's role is to encourage and guide the client in practising new, more appropriate assertive behaviours and more effective interpersonal skills. For example, clients may learn "refusal skills," conversational skills, social problem solving, and appropriate responding to insults. Assertiveness training is offered to couples experiencing relationship problems, to aggressive individuals, and to shy, socially awkward individuals.

PROBLEM SOLVING Using models developed in information processing, D'Zurilla and Goldfried (1971) introduced a **problem-solving approach** that was applied in the treatment of diverse problems such as weight control, clinical depression, and social skills deficits. The key elements of problem solving in cognitive-behavioural treatments are problem definition and formulation, generating alternative solutions to deal with the problem, deciding on the best solution to implement, and implementing and evaluating the solution (D'Zurilla & Nezu, 2010).

COGNITIVE RESTRUCTURING Based on the assumption that many psychological and interpersonal problems are related to assumptions, expectations, attributions, and automatic thoughts, cognitive-behavioural therapists have developed a range of strategies for testing and changing people's thoughts and beliefs. The initial step of **cognitive restructuring** involves having people become more aware of their thoughts when they are experiencing strong emotions. The therapist questions the nature and accuracy of these thoughts, and patients are encouraged to conduct behavioural experiments to determine the validity and accuracy of these thoughts.

MINDFULNESS Drawing on well-established yoga and meditation techniques, mindfulness-based strategies are designed to help the person focus on the present moment. This focused awareness on current experience is nonjudgmental and open. Open awareness of one's experience is presumed to facilitate self-management and successful coping, in part by altering the person's usual unsuccessful attempts to avoid, ignore, or eliminate negative thoughts, memories, or emotions.

INTEGRATIVE APPROACHES

So far, we have highlighted the distinctive features of each approach to psychotherapy. This "compare and contrast" strategy illustrates how therapists who were dissatisfied with the dominant theories of the time split off from the mainstream and started new schools of thought. Ironically, the history of psychotherapy, a discipline devoted to helping people, has been marked by some bitter competition and intolerance of opposing views.

Over the years, a number of therapists have observed the similarities and overlaps between apparently different approaches. In his book, *Persuasion and Healing*, Jerome Frank (1961) looked not only at twentieth-century psychotherapy, but also at shamanism, religious conversion experiences, and placebo effects in drug treatment. He defined psychotherapy as a process whereby a person who was demoralized about some part of life sought help from a socially sanctioned healer. This separates psychotherapy from the conversations we may have with a friend or a hairdresser or in an online chat room. The first ingredient in healing is hope: either explicitly or implicitly, the therapist conveys an expectation that the client's life will change as a result of the psychotherapeutic process (Roberts, Kewman, Mercier, & Hovell, 1993). The second ingredient is an alternative explanation for the problem. Within specific orientations, the types of explanation differ; so, for example, a psychodynamic therapist works on the assumption that distress is related to early childhood experiences, whereas a cognitive therapist emphasizes the way the client thinks about the situation. According to Frank, these interpretations offer a way to understand the problems that the person is facing. The third ingredient is that the client is expected to think, feel, or act in a different way. Changes in thoughts, feelings, or behaviours have been found to have ripple effects, so that a person who engages in more pleasant activities may be less likely to feel depressed, or a person who thinks that a poor grade is unfortunate but not disastrous may be less likely to feel hopeless, and so on.

Frank was influential in promoting the development of new therapeutic practices and frameworks that draw on selected aspects of various dominant schools of therapy. The appeal of the resulting eclectic (that is, using techniques stemming from diverse orientations) or integrative (that is, developing a conceptual model to guide treatment based on elements of diverse orientations) approaches is evident in surveys of psychotherapists. Across numerous surveys in recent decades, at least one-third of therapists identify themselves as disciples of a particular school of therapy, but claim to have integrated aspects of diverse approaches (e.g., Cassin, Singer, Dobson, & Altmaier, 2007). In a climate of fiscal restraint, when health service providers are required to be accountable and furnish evidence that the service they offer is effective, therapists are increasingly motivated to attend to research findings (Goldfried & Norcross, 1995) and to combine the best elements of different schools of therapy.

One example of this trend is the increasing use of motivational interviewing strategies in different approaches to treatment. These strategies, largely derived from humanistic-experiential therapies, are used to explore the client's interest in making changes. As all psychological treatments require lifestyle changes, there is a potential benefit in any form of therapy to address the client's readiness to embark on such changes. Motivational interviewing has been found to be efficacious in addressing ambivalence to adopt lifestyle changes among people with diverse problems, including anxiety and related disorders, depression, eating disorders, and substance abuse (Arkowitz, Miller, & Rollnick, 2015).

③ BEFORE MOVING ON

> Given what you have learned about various theoretical approaches and their associated treatments, if a friend asked you what to expect in cognitive-behavioural therapy for the treatment of anxiety, what would you say?

Psychotherapy: Treatment Modalities

In addition to different theoretical approaches to therapy, there are distinctive modalities of delivering therapy—to individuals, couples, families, and groups.

INDIVIDUAL THERAPY

Early therapy was conducted exclusively in an individual format, with one person (the client or patient) and one therapist. Contacts with other family members were strictly avoided lest they contaminate the all-important therapeutic relationship. Individual therapy remains the most common treatment modality. Nevertheless, many psychologists find it useful to sometimes invite the client to include his or her significant others in treatment. Individual therapy is also practised with children and adolescents. Some forms of individual child psychotherapy appear very similar to adult "talk" therapy, whereas other approaches use activities and children's play as the medium of communication.

COUPLES THERAPY

In the nineteenth century, marriage was considered a lifetime commitment to live together and to raise a family. The personal qualities of each partner and the couple's enjoyment of life together were not relevant to the stability of the marriage. At the beginning of the twenty-first century, marriage is considered to be a partnership based on mutual interests and companionship. With the liberalization of Canadian divorce laws in 1968 and 1985, it became possible for one partner to end an unsatisfying marriage. At the same time as divorce became easier in Western countries, there was increased interest in developing therapies to help couples resolve their difficulties. Partners (who may be married, cohabiting, or dating, and may be of any sexual orientation) may have conjoint sessions but may also each meet separately with the therapist.

The goal in most forms of couples therapy is to enhance each partner's satisfaction with the relationship. Couples therapy is most effective when it is an early response to developing relationship problems. Couples treatments have also been found to be effective for problems originally thought of as individual, such as depression or alcoholism in adults and conduct disorder in children (Hunsley & Lee, 1995; Rohrbaugh, Shoham, Spungen, & Steinglass, 1995). Couples therapy may be based on different theoretical orientations, with the cognitive-behavioural forms of couples

The goals of family therapy are to improve interactions in the family.

Bruce Ayres/The Image Bank/Getty Images

Dr. Martin M. Antony

Martin Antony, PhD, is a professor of psychology at Ryerson University, has faculty appointments at McMaster University and the University of Toronto, and is the Director of Research at the Anxiety Treatment and Research Clinic at St. Joseph's Healthcare Hamilton. His research is on the assessment and treatment of anxiety-based problems such as obsessive-compulsive disorder, panic disorder, social anxiety disorder, specific phobia, generalized anxiety disorder (GAD), and perfectionism. He has published 29 books, including the *Handbook of Assessment and Treatment Planning for Psychological Disorders*, the *Oxford Handbook of Anxiety and Related Disorders*, and *Cognitive-Behavioral Treatment of Perfectionism*, and more than 200 scientific articles and book chapters. Dr. Antony has received a number of career awards for his contributions to research, training, and education; and is a Fellow of the American and Canadian Psychological Associations, the Association for Psychological Science, and the Royal Society of Canada. Dr. Antony has given more than 300 workshops and presentations to health care professionals from across North America, Europe, and Australia. In 2009–2010, Dr. Antony was President of the Canadian Psychological Association.

GAD is characterized by chronic, excessive, and uncontrollable worry about multiple events or life domains, and by a range of physiological symptoms of anxiety (e.g., restlessness, feeling on edge, muscle tension). For this reason it is often viewed as the prototypic anxiety disorder. Comorbidity with other mental disorders is very common, especially with mood and other anxiety disorders. Psychosocial impairment can be quite severe with this disorder, and it is often associated with both decreased work involvement and increased utilization of health care services (although not necessarily for anxiety problems). Applied relaxation strategies and cognitive-behaviour therapy (CBT) targeting worry and arousal

symptoms have been shown to be efficacious in the treatment of GAD. However, many GAD sufferers do not benefit from treatment, often because of their ambivalence about their anxiety. Although people with GAD recognize the substantial psychological and social impact of their chronic worrying, many mistakenly believe that the worry allows them to be prepared for potential negative outcomes and disruptive life events. For this reason some GAD sufferers are reluctant to fully engage in treatment, often holding back from attempting strategies that have been demonstrated to reduce anxiety and worry. Understanding this ambivalence and, then, developing treatment enhancements that address the reluctance to engage in therapy have become priorities for those who study GAD. Dr. Antony was recently involved in a clinical trial that examined these issues, in conjunction with collaborators at York University and the University of Massachusetts Amherst.

In this treatment study a total of 85 adults with severe GAD were recruited from the greater Toronto area, and then randomly assigned to one of two active treatments: standard CBT for GAD or CBT modified to incorporate motivational interviewing (MI) procedures. Both treatments included 15 weekly treatment sessions, followed by booster sessions one and three months following the completion of the weekly sessions. The CBT treatment included components dealing with psychoeducation about anxiety and worry, the use of relaxation strategies, cognitive restructuring, and behavioural strategies to reduce anxiety symptoms. The integrated MI and CBT treatment started with four sessions that explored a participant's feelings about making changes and readiness to change, with the remaining sessions emphasizing the "practical" strategies to promote change (i.e., the CBT strategies described previously). Additionally, whenever a participant's expressed ambivalence or reluctance about change during these change-focused sessions, the therapists

responded in an MI-consistent manner by exploring these reactions. Although there were no statistically significant group differences on measures of worry and general distress at the end of treatment, compared to those in the CBT condition, participants in the combined MI and CBT condition experienced symptom reductions at a faster rate and their symptoms were more likely to no longer meet diagnostic criteria for GAD at the end of treatment (Westra, Constantino, & Antony, 2016). The researchers also examined the process of treatment within the CBT condition. They found that the use of MI-like responses by therapists when addressing participant disagreements with aspects of treatment was associated with lower levels of participant worry at the end of treatment, even though therapists in the CBT condition had no formal training in MI (Aviram, Westra, Constantino, & Antony, 2016). They concluded that incorporating MI procedures into CBT improved the outcomes for the treatment of adults with GAD. Based on these and related findings, the researchers also suggested that therapists providing CBT for any mental disorder should include MI procedures in order to respond more flexibly to expressions of client resistance and ambivalence.

Photo by Will Pemulis. Courtesy of Dr. Martin M. Antony

therapy having the greatest research support (Shadish & Baldwin, 2005). In this form of treatment, therapists seek to enhance communication and conflict resolution skills, to help both partners to be realistic in their expectations about their relationship, and to promote intimacy. Canadian psychologists Drs. Sue Johnson and Les Greenberg developed and evaluated an **emotionally focused couples therapy**. Drawing on elements of experiential therapy and structural family therapy, the goal of the therapy is to modify distressed couples' constricted interaction patterns and emotional responses by fostering the development of a secure emotional bond (Johnson, Hunsley, Greenberg, & Schindler, 1999).

FAMILY THERAPY

Family therapy originated in social work and in the child guidance movement (Clarkin & Carpenter, 1995), but is now practised by therapists of diverse orientations, including cognitive-behavioural and psychodynamic. Although early family approaches viewed the family as the source of a family member's problems, many current family approaches make no such assumption but consider the family to be an important part of the solution to problems. A common task in family approaches is to identify interactions between family members that may inadvertently contribute to problems. The goals of family therapy are to enhance interactions in the family, so that each family member's well-being is promoted.

GROUP THERAPY

The cost of psychotherapy reduces its accessibility for many people. One obvious way to reduce the cost is to work with several clients in a group format. After the Second World War, therapy groups were developed to address the needs of various underprivileged groups. Many current cognitive-behavioural treatments, originally developed for use in

---

FOCUS 17.2

Technological Advances in the Provision of Psychological Treatments

Although there are now treatment protocols that have been demonstrated to be efficacious for many disorders and conditions, only a small proportion of those who could potentially benefit from services actually seek treatment. Those who do request services often face barriers such as long waiting lists and the high costs of services. In many countries there is a serious lack of trained practitioners who can deliver evidence-based psychological treatments (e.g., Hollinghurst et al., 2010). In this context, technological innovations that have become an integral part of the way we communicate, gather information, shop, and plan our activities also offer intriguing opportunities to make efficacious psychological services available to large numbers of people, who can access services at a time and location that is convenient to them.

Computerized and internet-based interventions that deliver evidence-based services with minimal contact with a clinician have produced promising results in the treatment of a range of disorders. Randomized controlled trials have now been conducted examining computerized treatments of anxiety for children (Khanna & Kendall, 2010), adolescents (Spence et al., 2011; Stallard, Richardson, Velleman, & Attwood, 2011), and adults (Reger & Gahm, 2009), and for the treatment of adults with insomnia (Ritterband et al., 2009) and post-traumatic stress disorder (Amstadter, Broman-Fulks, Zinzow, Ruggiero, & Cercone, 2009). Such investigations usually find that computerized and online services produce equivalent gains to those in individual CBT, with evidence that gains are maintained and sometimes enhanced at follow-up. Client ratings of treatment acceptability and satisfaction are comparable to regular CBT.

Other forms of treatments are also available for those who are far from a psychologist. The use of information technology and telecommunications to provide health care services at a distance is known as **telehealth**. Telehealth covers a range of delivery options, including telephone, videoconferencing, and computer-mediated communications (e.g., email, chat rooms, and internet-based services). There is, for example, a growing literature on the efficacy of videoconferencing psychotherapy showing that (a) treatment can be successfully delivered to a wide range of clients and (b) the outcomes are comparable with those of face-to-face psychotherapy (Backhaus et al., 2012). Most telehealth treatments currently available have adapted types of cognitive-behavioural therapies, and encouraging results have been obtained for adult disorders such as depression and anxiety disorders (e.g., Olthuis, Watt, Bailey, Hayden, & Stewart, 2015; Sloan, Gallagher, Feinstein, Lee, & Pruneau, 2011). Dr. Heather Hadjistavropoulos, at the University of Regina, has conducted extensive research on the value of providing cognitive-behavioural therapy via the internet (e.g., Hadjistavropoulos, Alberts, Nugent, & Marchildon, 2014)

Smartphone technology offers intriguing possibilities as an adjunct to psychological services. Rizvi, Dimeff, Skutch, Carroll, and Linehan (2011), for example, developed software called the DBT Coach that could be accessed via smartphone. Participants in a pilot project who were given smartphones with the DBT Coach app for a period of 10 to 14 days used the DBT Coach an average of 15 times, and found it helpful and user-friendly. Furthermore, use of the DBT Coach was associated with positive changes such as decreased emotional intensity and reduced urges to engage in maladaptive behaviour. Moving to a different problem area, Jones, Forehand, McKee, Cuellar, and Kincaid (2010) outlined numerous potential uses of smartphones as an adjunct to parenting interventions.

It is clear that we have only begun to explore the potential uses of communications technology in extending evidence-based psychological services to a wider population in a manner that is engaging, is cost-effective, and yields sustained gains. ●

individual therapy, have been modified for use in a group format. In addition to cost savings, there are important theoretical reasons for seeing clients in a group. In addition to the shared therapeutic experience of hope for change, the group context offers feedback from other people (Rosenbaum & Patterson, 1995) and a place to practise ways of relating to others. *Universality*—the awareness that other people share similar experiences or feelings—can reduce feelings of stigma (Ballinger & Yalom, 1995). Participation in a group offers exposure to solutions that have worked for others and may also lead to feelings of cohesion or belonging.

④ BEFORE MOVING ON

> Psychotherapy can be offered in different modalities. What are the advantages and disadvantages of each?

TABLE 17.3 INFORMED CONSUMERS: QUESTIONS TO ASK A POTENTIAL THERAPIST

1. What are your professional qualifications?
2. Have you worked with this kind of problem?
3. How would you describe the way you work?
4. What is the research evidence on the best treatment options for my problem?
5. Are there clinics or other practitioners who also work with problems like this?
6. How many times do you think it will be necessary for me to see you?
7. What can I expect from treatment? How will I be different at the end of treatment?
8. How much do you charge? Do you have a sliding fee scale?
9. How soon can I see you? How long is your waiting list?

The Context of Psychotherapy

WHO PROVIDES PSYCHOTHERAPY?

Clinical psychologists are among the main providers of psychotherapy. Surveys have consistently found that most clinical psychologists engage in the delivery of some form of therapeutic service, be it individual, couple, family, or group therapy. Although many clinical psychologists identify themselves as practising from a single orientation, others describe their practice as integrative. For example, in their survey of Canadian clinical psychologists, Hunsley and colleagues (2013) found that 80% described themselves as cognitive-behavioural, 31% as humanistic-experiential, and 26% as psychodynamic. As the total exceeds 100%, it is clear that many psychologists see themselves as having an integrative orientation. On average, survey respondents reported that they spent 41% of their professional time providing treatment services, with 85% of psychologists reporting that they provided individual psychotherapy services (other treatment modalities were offered by less than a third of respondents).

Research, to date, does not provide much evidence that therapists' professional training or years of experience are directly related to the outcome of treatment, although clients treated by professionally trained therapists, compared to those treated by non-professional therapists, are less likely to prematurely discontinue treatment and are more likely to improve by the end of treatment (Atkins & Christensen, 2001; Beutler et al., 2004). Accordingly, people seeking psychotherapy should adopt a "consumer rights" attitude, and before treatment they should question therapists about their training, experience, and therapeutic methods. Table 17.3 offers suggested questions to ask when seeking services.

WHO SEEKS PSYCHOTHERAPY?

People seek therapy for a multitude of reasons. Many have significant emotional distress that interferes with their daily functioning; previous chapters have described the range of disorders such individuals may be experiencing. Some seek therapy for advice and assistance in coping with the demands of social roles, such as parent, spouse, or employee. Some people may come to therapy for aid in coping with recent trauma (e.g., rape) or loss (e.g., death of a loved one). Some seek assistance in addressing questions related to personal identity, values, or self-knowledge. The use of mental health services has risen in the past few decades, but much of the increase in mental health service use is associated with the use of medication rather than psychotherapy (Olfson & Marcus, 2010). In a telephone survey conducted in Alberta, Esposito and colleagues (2007) examined the pattern of mental health treatment provided for depression. Among survey respondents meeting the diagnostic criteria for major depression, approximately 40 percent reported using antidepressant medication, whereas only 14 percent reported receiving some form of counselling or psychotherapy. Despite the fact that pharmacological treatment is provided more frequently than psychological treatment, decades of research has shown that people are three times more likely to prefer psychological treatment to medication for the treatment of mental disorders (McHugh, Whitton, Peckham, Welge, & Otto, 2013).

American epidemiological surveys indicate that some groups of people are more likely than others to seek psychotherapy (Vessey & Howard, 1993). For example, two-thirds of psychotherapy clients are female, half have university education, half are married, and the majority are young to middle-aged adults. Unfortunately, Vessey and Howard's analysis also suggested that many of those most in need of such services (that is, those suffering from a psychological disorder) never seek professional help. A similar picture is evident in Canada. Responses to the National Population Health Survey (NPHS) showed similar socio-demographic characteristics among those who reported consulting a psychologist for health or mental health reasons (Hunsley, Lee, & Aubry, 1999), as shown in Table 17.4. Users of psychological services experienced more stress and distress than did the population at large and were less satisfied with their life situation. Consistent with American data, Hunsley and colleagues' analysis found that, unfortunately, many who could

TABLE 17.4 CHARACTERISTICS OF CANADIANS WHO RECEIVE PSYCHOLOGICAL SERVICES

1. Women are twice as likely as men to consult a psychologist.
2. Although Canadians with university education make up 13% of the population, they make up 22% of the clientele of psychologists.
3. Although parents and children in single-parent families make up 8% of the Canadian population, they make up 20% of the clientele of psychologists.
4. People who experience pain that interferes with their daily lives are twice as likely as other Canadians to seek psychological services.
5. Canadians who receive psychological services also tend to be frequent users of other health care services.
6. Canadians who feel so unhappy that they believe life is not worthwhile are five times as likely as other Canadians to seek psychological services.
7. Whether measured by the number of stressful events in their past or the number of ongoing current stressors, users of psychological services are more likely than other Canadians to report high levels of stress.

benefit from therapy had not received it. For example, many Canadians suffering from depression had received neither therapy (from a psychologist, social worker, or other kind of counsellor) nor antidepressant medication. Data from the 2002 Canadian Community Health Survey examining the reasons why Canadian adults consulted a health professional for mental health reasons show that low income was a significant barrier to accessing the services of a psychologist (Vasiliadis, Tempier, Lesage, & Kates, 2009).

After Making an Appointment...

After someone has decided to seek psychotherapy or has been referred to a therapist, only half of them show up for their first appointment (Hampton-Robb, Qualls, & Compton, 2003; Wise, 2014). There are no psychological tricks that make problems go away overnight. It takes time and work for most people to see change. Unfortunately, the majority of people who receive psychotherapy attend fewer than 10 sessions. Across a range of therapy clinics, across European and North American settings, across a range of clients presenting problems, and over the past 60 years, the picture of the duration of psychotherapy is remarkably consistent (Owen et al., 2015; Phillips, 1991). A large minority of clients come for only one or two sessions, and the median number of therapy sessions ranges from 5 to 13 sessions. This means that many people who start treatment terminate before they have a chance to gain an optimal benefit from therapy. Data from hundreds of studies indicate that one in five clients end treatment prematurely (Swift & Greenberg, 2012). Although there have been many efforts to identify client characteristics that contribute to premature termination or to treatment failure, research has not established clear patterns (Hatchett & Park, 2003).

Evaluating the Effects of Psychotherapy
HISTORICAL CONTEXT

Prior to the 1960s there was little research examining whether or not psychotherapy worked. Since that time, though, there has been a dramatic increase in this line of research, so that there are now thousands of studies examining the effects of many different forms of therapy for many different types of problems. An important distinction in the research literature, and one that we use in the following sections, is between efficacy and effectiveness. **Treatment efficacy** is defined as evidence of treatment effects when delivered in the context of a controlled study, whereas **treatment effectiveness** is defined as the evidence of effects when the treatment is evaluated in a "real-world" context. Thought of in another way, efficacy relates to studies designed to maximize internal validity, and effectiveness relates to studies designed to maximize external validity.

As is often the case in science, research attention to a phenomenon is sparked by a controversy or a challenge to the accepted view. The current abundance of psychotherapy outcome research is due, in large part, to Hans Eysenck's 1952 article in which he argued that the rates of improvement among clients receiving psychodynamic or eclectic therapy were comparable to rates of remission of symptoms among untreated clients. On the basis of his review of the limited data available, he contended that about two-thirds of people with neurotic disorders (e.g., anxiety disorders, depression) would improve within two years, regardless of whether they were treated by psychotherapy. In other words, Eysenck argued that there was no evidence that psychotherapy had any demonstrable effect!

Not surprisingly, Eysenck's review evoked strong reactions from psychotherapists and psychotherapy researchers. Many critical responses to his review were published in scientific journals by leading proponents of psychotherapy. Perhaps the most important result of the ensuing debate was the emerging emphasis on the need for solid research design in evaluating psychotherapeutic effects. Vocal critics of Eysenck's position, such as Luborsky (1954) and Bergin (1971) pointed out errors in Eysenck's reasoning. For example, many of the studies lacked adequate control groups (that is, clients who did not receive treatment) and Eysenck's criteria for establishing clinical improvement were arbitrary and biased against finding positive therapeutic effects.

Throughout the 1970s, the debate about the impact of psychotherapy grew, as did the number of published studies on therapy outcome. By this time, behavioural therapies were being used by a growing number of psychologists. As empirical verification of outcome was a key element of the behavioural approach to treatment, there were soon many published studies examining the effect of these therapies. Researchers attempting to understand and integrate the burgeoning number of empirical articles on psychotherapy (including psychodynamic, behavioural, and other approaches) faced a formidable challenge in attempting to draw reasonable conclusions. As a result, the debate about the efficacy and effectiveness of therapy was muddied by the fact that proponents and critics of psychotherapy often drew on different studies to support their respective positions.

META-ANALYSIS

Chapter 4 reviewed the procedures generally used to evaluate the results of interventions in single studies. In attempting to reach conclusions derived from several studies, researchers can employ qualitative (that is, non-numerical) methods. In these, the reviewer provides a narrative account of the various studies—their strengths, weaknesses, and findings—and then draws conclusions about the state of knowledge. However, these methods are very limited in their ability to synthesize information across numerous studies using a number of different patient populations and a wide variety of outcome measures. For this reason, most literature reviews are now based on the results of a **meta-analysis**, which is simply a method of quantitatively summarizing the results of multiple research studies. An analogy to a typical research study may be helpful in understanding the nature of meta-analysis. As described in Chapter 4, a typical psychotherapy outcome study involves the collection of data from multiple research participants. These data are then summed and overall trends in the group of participants are examined with the use of statistical procedures such as analysis of variance. The same general process occurs in meta-analysis, except that the "participants" in a meta-analysis are research studies rather than individual clients.

In a single research study, similar data are collected from all participants. Obviously this is not possible in a meta-analysis, for the original research studies are likely to have employed a range of measures for assessing outcome. Therefore, in meta-analysis, the results of prior research are combined by developing a common metric (basically a z transformation) to be used across the studies. The metric is called an **effect size** and is calculated as the difference between the means of the experimental (that is, the treatment) group and the control group, divided by the standard deviation of either the control group or the pooled sample of both groups. In some instances, where two treatments are compared to one another, the effect size is the difference between the two treated groups, divided by the standard deviation of the control group or the pooled standard deviation of all groups (treated and untreated) in the study. Effect sizes can be calculated from raw data, group means, and standard deviations, or from inferential statistics reported in the original research studies (e.g., correlations, F-tests, t-tests).

Meta-analysis offers numerous advantages over traditional research reviews or single empirical studies. For example, statistical analyses, rather than the author's impressions, guide conclusions about a body of literature. Moreover, by including data from many studies, the number of research participants on whom conclusions are based is dramatically increased. This greatly enhances the meta-analyst's power to detect an effect in the literature and the generalizability of the conclusions drawn on the basis of the literature. As a result of these methodological and statistical strengths, meta-analysis is increasingly used to determine the current state of knowledge about the impact of psychotherapy and to assist in the development of health care policies regarding the provision of psychotherapy.

A BRIEF REVIEW OF META-ANALYTIC EVIDENCE

In the first meta-analysis of the treatment literature, Smith, Glass, and Miller (1980) reviewed 475 controlled studies of psychotherapy, including both studies published in scientific journals and unpublished dissertations. They concluded that psychotherapy, in general, was clearly efficacious, with an average effect size of 0.85; that is, the difference in the dependent variables (such as measures of symptomatology) between the treated and untreated groups was 0.85 standard deviation units. This value means that the average person receiving therapy was better off after therapy than 80 percent of people who did not receive therapy.

A subset of the studies they reviewed included direct comparisons of different forms of treatment. For example, there were 57 studies in which therapies they termed "verbal" (including psychodynamic, cognitive, and humanistic therapies) were compared with "behavioural" (behavioural and cognitive-behavioural therapies) treatments. An analysis of this subset of studies yielded an effect size of 0.77 for the verbal therapies and 0.96 for the behavioural therapies. Caution is required, however, in interpreting the differences among therapies, because clients treated by each differ in the type and severity of problems.

Since the initial meta-analysis of the effectiveness of psychotherapy, many hundreds of meta-analytic studies have been published. Initially, these studies focused on replicating the findings of Smith and colleagues (1980), and, indeed, other researchers obtained similar findings. Subsequent meta-analyses have had a narrower focus. For many researchers, the question of whether psychotherapy is efficacious has been answered with a resounding yes. Attention has therefore turned to the different effects of treatments on specific disorders (that is, what works for whom) and the effects of therapist and client characteristics on the process and outcome of treatment.

In an influential review of the literature, Luborsky, Singer, and Luborsky (1975) concluded that all psychotherapies produce equivalent effects. Quoting the dodo bird in *Alice in Wonderland*, they pronounced that "[e]verybody has won, and all must have prizes." Since the Luborsky and colleagues review, many psychotherapists and researchers have endorsed this view, citing meta-analytic findings such as Smith and colleagues (1980). Wampold and colleagues (1997) conducted a meta-analysis that included data from studies published between 1970 and 1995 that compared at least two bona fide treatments (i.e., the treatments were intended to be therapeutic and not simply to serve as a control condition). They reported an average effect size of 0.19 and suggested that this indicated that real treatments, regardless of orientation, do not differ in their efficacy. However, as the majority of studies included in the meta-analysis dealt with forms of cognitive-behavioural treatments, it would be more accurate to conclude that different cognitive-behavioural treatments have similar efficacy (Hunsley & Di Giulio, 2002). In their follow-up to the Wampold et al. (1997) study, Marcus, O'Connell, Norris, and Sawaqdeh (2014) conducted a meta-analysis on 51 comparative treatment studies published since Wampold and colleagues' meta-analysis. Depending on the outcome measure considered across studies, the average effect size difference between treatments ranged between 0.19 and 0.29.

Careful examination of comparative efficacy is crucial, because the acceptance of the equivalence of psychotherapies is tantamount to accepting the null hypothesis. Yet the failure to find a significant difference does not necessarily mean that no difference exists. Methodological limitations, such as small sample sizes, may limit the ability to draw conclusions. In fact, Kazdin and Bass (1989) found that almost half of the studies that found no differences between treatments had too few research participants to detect differences that may have existed.

Other methodological aspects of treatment studies can also be examined with meta-analysis. For example, in a series of meta-analyses, Westen and colleagues (e.g., Westen & Morrison, 2001) emphasized the importance of considering the number of potential participants excluded from studies because they failed to meet inclusion criteria. This type of information can be critical in determining the likely generalizability of the research findings.

Meta-analysis has also been used to evaluate the effects of psychological treatments for youth. Weiss and Weisz (1995) evaluated the relative efficacy of behavioural (including cognitive) versus non-behavioural (psychodynamic and humanistic) treatments for children and adolescents. Their meta-analysis examined 105 studies of treatments for problems, including anxiety disorders, depression, and social skills deficits. Past reviews of the literature had found that behavioural treatments tend to be superior to non-behavioural ones, but some researchers suggested that this may be due to superior study design rather than to the true strength of the behavioural treatment. When Weiss and Weisz statistically controlled for methodological quality of the studies, the effect sizes of the behavioural and non-behavioural treatments were 0.86 and 0.38, respectively. The difference was even stronger in the 10 studies in their sample that directly compared behavioural and non-behavioural treatments. More recent meta-analyses continue to find this significant difference between approaches in treatments for children and adolescents (Miller, Wampold, & Varhely, 2008).

Looking over all of these meta-analyses, can we conclude that cognitive-behavioural therapies are always the most efficacious? Not necessarily. It is accurate to say that there is more evidence to support the efficacy of this family of treatments than there is for any other approach. However, this is due, in large part, to the fact that cognitive-behaviourists have a tradition of empirically substantiating treatment effects. There may well be other effective approaches that have not been the object of as much empirical investigation.

Psychodynamic therapies, in particular, despite their widespread use, have received very little empirical attention. This has begun to change, largely through the efforts of prominent psychodynamic researchers/therapists such as Lester Luborsky and Hans Strupp (cf. Henry et al., 1994). Reviews and meta-analyses of a growing number of studies in which short-term psychodynamic therapy is systematically evaluated have yielded encouraging results (Gerber et al., 2011; Leichsenring et al., 2015). Researchers have been actively evaluating interpersonal therapy in the past few years, and indications are that it is an efficacious treatment for anxiety disorders, depression, and eating disorders (e.g., Cuijpers et al., 2011; Cuijpers, Donker, Weissman, Ravitz, & Cristea, 2016). Finally, meta-analytic evidence suggests that experiential therapies that are structured, directive, and short-term can be efficacious for treating symptoms of depression, anxiety, trauma, and marital distress (Elliott et al., 2013).

⑤ BEFORE MOVING ON

> Clinicians who wish to offer services need to keep up with the research literature. There are, however, so many studies that it can be bewildering to make sense of the results. How has meta-analysis been used in synthesizing results?

EFFECTS OF PSYCHOTHERAPY FOR SPECIFIC DISORDERS

Let us now turn to the effects of psychotherapy for specific disorders. There is now extensive evidence that there are effective psychotherapeutic treatments for many mental disorders and other health problems (Fonagy, Cottrell, Phillips, Bevington, Glaser, & Allison, 2015; Nathan & Gorman, 2015). The literature on psychosocial interventions that have been demonstrated to help children and adolescents who are dealing with diverse disorders and problems is expanding so rapidly that the *Journal of Clinical Child and Adolescent Psychology* now publishes an evidence-based update in each volume (Southam-Gerow & Prinstein, 2014). This encouraging picture must be balanced by the fact that, unfortunately, efficacious psychological treatments for various problems of childhood and adolescence are not routinely offered in standard care. Weisz et al. (2013) conducted a meta-analysis of 52 studies comparing evidence-based treatments to usual clinical care. They found superior results for evidence-based treatment compared to usual clinical care; youth receiving evidence-based care had a better outcome than 58 percent of those receiving usual care.

Efficacious treatments for children and youth often include the same core components as similar treatments for adult disorders, such as exposure for anxiety symptoms. Many treatments for children and youth disorders also involve training parents to respond in a way that encourages positive behaviour and discourages problematic behaviour (Manassis et al., 2014).

In this section, we provide a glimpse of the range of problems for which psychological treatment has been shown to be helpful.

ANXIETY AND RELATED DISORDERS It is now commonly accepted that efficacious treatment for specific phobias must involve an element of exposure. That is, the individual with a phobia must begin to confront the object of the phobia. The person is also encouraged (in various ways, depending on the exact nature of the treatment) to accept that the surge of anxiety he or she feels is normal, not life-threatening, and will soon diminish (see Chapter 5).

Fifty years of research have established a range of efficacious treatments for childhood anxiety disorders, including cognitive-behaviour therapy (CBT), exposure, modelling, and CBT with parents (Higa-McMillan, Francis, Rith-Najaran, & Chorpita, 2016). Similarly, there are many efficacious cognitive-behavioural treatments for anxiety disorders in adults (Hunsley, Elliott, & Therrien, 2014). For example, in the treatment of panic disorder, cognitive-behavioural treatments that combine cognitive restructuring (that is, challenging the beliefs and expectations held by the patient) and interoceptive exposure (that is, exposing the patient to bodily symptoms similar to those experienced in a panic disorder) are highly efficacious. Indeed, it is common to find that the majority of clients treated in this manner are panic-free by the end of treatment—and that this improvement is typically long term. Interestingly, the addition of medication to these forms of therapy does not appear to improve outcome rates (Furukawa, Watanabe, & Churchill, 2006).

Large effect sizes for two types of treatment of obsessive-compulsive disorder have been reported. The first involves a combination of exposure to the object of the obsession or compulsion and response prevention (e.g., the patient is encouraged to abstain from rituals such as washing or checking); the other is cognitive therapy. Individual exposure-based CBT and family-focused CBT have been found to be efficacious in treating obsessive-compulsive disorder in children and adolescents (Sánchez-Meca, Rosa-Alcázar, Iniesta-Sepúlveda, & Rosa-Alcázar, 2014), and individual CBT has been found to be efficacious in the treatment of adults (Rosa-Alcázar, Sánchez-Meca, Gómez-Conesa, & Marín-Martínez, 2008).

CBT has also been found to be efficacious in treating generalized anxiety disorder (GAD). Finally, evidence to date suggests trauma, trauma-focused CBT and school-based CBT are efficacious in the treatment of children and youth exposed to traumatic events (Silverman, Ortiz, et al. 2008). Trauma-focused CBT and a form of treatment known as eye movement desensitization and reprocessing (EMDR) are the psychological treatments of choice for adults with post-traumatic stress disorder (PTSD) (Ehring et al., 2014; Watts et al., 2013). It is worth noting that many PTSD researchers have suggested that, as is the case for many forms of CBT for anxiety disorders, the critical component of EMDR is the use of exposure.

DEPRESSIVE DISORDERS Researchers have found a number of psychologically based interventions to be efficacious in the treatment of clinical depression. Zhou et al. (2015) found that both interpersonal therapy and CBT were efficacious in treating depression in children and adolescents. In general, extensive research suggests that cognitive

The individual with a phobia must begin to confront the object of the phobia.

(and cognitive-behavioural) therapy is efficacious in treating depression, as is interpersonal psychotherapy and short-term psychodynamic therapy (Cuijpers, Andersson, Donker, & Van Straten, 2011). Importantly, there is also emerging evidence that cognitive therapy is efficacious in preventing relapse and recurrence of depression (Cuijpers et al., 2013). A number of treatments have been found to be efficacious in treating depression in older adults (Scogin, Welsh, Hanson, Stump, & Coates, 2005). These include several forms of CBT, short-term psychodynamic therapy, and reminiscence therapy (in which clients are encouraged to review their life and the ways in which they have dealt with challenges and stresses). In practice, it is relatively common for adult patients to receive both an antidepressant and some form of psychotherapy. Overall, the evidence suggests that adding an antidepressant to CBT treatment does not improve patient outcomes (Karyotaki et al., 2016), although this combined treatment may be slightly more efficacious for individuals who have chronic depression (de Maat, Dekker, Schoevers, & de Jonghe, 2007).

Many Canadian psychologists have been involved in developing cognitive-behavioural treatments for depression and for other disorders. After establishing the efficacy of this form of treatment, investigators attempted to separate the components of cognitive therapy to determine the "essential ingredient." Dr. Keith Dobson of the University of Calgary collaborated with American colleagues in a seminal study that randomly assigned people with major depression to one of three treatment conditions (Jacobson et al., 1996). A behavioural activation treatment focused only on increasing patients' physical activity, social interactions, and so on. The second treatment added interventions to help patients modify negative automatic thoughts. The full cognitive therapy condition included both of these components as well as work to alter the underlying dysfunctional beliefs that are hypothesized to make someone vulnerable to depression. Much to the researchers' surprise, there were no discernible differences between the three treatments, in either the short term or the long term, leading them to conclude that the active ingredient of cognitive therapy for depression may be behavioural activation (Gortner, Gollan, Dobson, & Jacobson, 1998). These findings have led to a dramatic growth in interest in developing and evaluating behavioural activation treatments for a range of client populations.

SLEEP–WAKE DISORDERS Psychotherapy researchers have been actively involved in devising interventions for sleep–wake disorders. To date, much of their attention has been devoted to insomnia disorder. As sedatives can lead to poor-quality sleep, possible addiction, and rebound insomnia on withdrawal, there is a pressing need for effective psychological interventions, especially for older adults (see Chapter 16). Treatments include strategies such as relaxation training, sleep restriction (that is, limiting the time spent in bed to the time a person is asleep), and stimulus control (e.g., going to bed only when sleepy, getting out of bed if unable to fall asleep). Canadian psychologist Dr. Charles Morin of Laval University has been at the forefront of work with adults suffering from insomnia (e.g., Morin & Espie, 2012). Given the very substantial effects that CBT interventions have on sleep–wake disorders, a great deal of attention is now focused on streamlining the treatments to make them as user-friendly as possible. For example, a randomized controlled trial found that a brief (two-hour) cognitive-behavioural intervention for young and middle-aged adults was more efficacious than either pharmacotherapy or combined cognitive-behavioural treatment and pharmacotherapy in the treatment of insomnia disorder (Jacobs, Pace-Shott, Stickgold, & Otto, 2004).

PERSONALITY DISORDERS Despite impressive breakthroughs in the treatment of psychological distress for many disorders, the majority of personality disorders have received relatively limited attention from psychotherapy researchers. The one major exception to this neglect of treatments for personality disorders is Linehan's multi-component dialectical behaviour therapy (including training in emotional awareness and control, problem solving, and stress management) for borderline personality disorder (e.g., Linehan, 1993; see Chapter 12). There is strong, replicated evidence that this treatment is efficacious; there is also some evidence that longer term (i.e., up to 18 months) forms of psychodynamic treatment can also be efficacious in the treatment of borderline personality disorder (Crits-Christoph & Barber, 2015). The development of efficacious and effective interventions for individuals with personality disorders continues to be a priority for many psychotherapy researchers.

SERIOUS MENTAL ILLNESS There is growing evidence that, for people with bipolar disorder, the addition of psychological interventions to the prescription of a mood stabilizer can enhance treatment outcome: CBT and group psychoeducation (and possibly family therapy) are efficacious in preventing relapse (Beynon, Soares-Weiser, Woolacott, Duffy, & Geddes, 2008). It appears that treatments focusing on medication adherence and the recognition of mood changes reduce manic symptoms, whereas treatments focusing on cognitive and interpersonal coping strategies reduce depressive symptoms (Miklowitz, 2008). There is evidence that the inclusion of CBT and family-based services in the treatment of early psychosis contributes to positive outcomes (Bird, Premkumar, Kendall, Whittington, Mitchell, & Kuipers, 2010). Psychological interventions, especially forms of CBT, have also been found to be important adjunctive treatments for individuals with schizophrenia (Jauhar et al., 2014; Wykes, Huddy, Cellard, McGurk, & Czobor, 2011). Given the severity of the deficits associated with this diagnosis, it is not surprising that no single form of psychotherapy has a positive impact on all aspects of a patient's psychosocial functioning. Nevertheless, when combined with efficacious medication, specific therapies yield important specific effects: social skills training improves social functioning, CBT reduces positive symptoms, cognitive remediation leads to improved cognitive functioning, and psychoeducational interventions with families decrease hospitalization and relapse rates (Pfammatter, Junghan, & Brenner, 2006).

COUPLE DISTRESS

The most widely studied couples therapy is behavioural marital therapy, developed by Jacobson and Margolin (1979). This therapy focuses on improving the communication between partners and encouraging more constructive interactions. This treatment, along with emotionally focused couples therapy, has been found to be efficacious in the treatment of couple distress (Halford, Pepping, & Petch, 2015). Interestingly, these forms of couples therapy, when used in the treatment for depressed clients who are maritally distressed, are also efficacious in diminishing depressive symptoms (Barbato & D'Avanzo, 2008).

MODULAR AND TRANSDIAGNOSTIC APPROACHES

Up until this point, we have highlighted the results of treatment research for specific disorders. However, children, adolescents, and adults who meet diagnostic criteria for one disorder frequently have other problems too, and often meet diagnostic criteria for one or more additional disorders. In an attempt to address this issue in services with youth, Chorpita and Daleiden (2009) examined the components or modules that were used in 322 randomized controlled trials of treatments (mainly CBT) for children and adolescents. They were able to identify groups of strategies consistently found to help in dealing with specific problems (e.g., in the treatment of anxiety, these include modules on psychoeducation, exposure, relaxation, cognitive interventions, and modelling). Chorpita and Daleiden recommended that clinicians consider individualizing treatments by selecting and integrating treatment modules that best correspond to the youth's presenting problems.

Importantly, Bernstein, Chorpita, Daleiden, Ebesuntani, and Rosenblatt (2015) found that this **modular approach** allowed for tailoring of services by combining practice elements to meet the needs of youth for whom there is no single evidence-based program.

A different approach to addressing the issue of comorbidity has been taken in developing treatments for adults. Instead of emphasizing modules that can be combined as needed, researchers have focused on developing treatments that address common problems typically observed across several diagnoses. Most commonly this **transdiagnostic approach** focuses on key aspects of anxiety and mood disorders. The Unified Protocol (Barlow et al., 2011), for example, was one of the first transdiagnostic approaches to be systematically evaluated (e.g., Farchione et al., 2012). Designed to target symptoms commonly found in mood, anxiety, and related disorders (e.g., depressed mood, anxiety, panic attacks, social anxiety, and obsessive thoughts), the treatment draws on both CBT and mindfulness strategies. Based on a meta-analysis of several different transdiagnostic approaches that draw heavily on CBT strategies, Newby, McKinnon, Kuyken, Gilbody, and Dalgleish (2015) found that these treatments were superior to "treatment as usual" and were comparable in efficacy to disorder-specific treatments for anxiety and mood disorders.

GENERALIZING TO CLINICAL SETTINGS

The evidence we have presented on the impact of psychotherapy in the preceding sections has one major potential limitation: almost all studies were conducted in a controlled research context. To meet the requirements of increasingly demanding experimental designs, researchers must carefully screen potential research participants to ensure that they fit criteria for their study, randomly assign participants to conditions, provide thorough training to therapists, and monitor the adherence of these therapists to the model of therapy they are supposed to use. The most important question, of course, is whether the results of such experimental studies generalize to the "real world" of clinical services. In the "real world" patients often have multiple problems rather than a single diagnosis, and they may receive untested services from therapists who are unlikely to be supervised as closely as those involved in randomized clinical trials.

Several reviews and analyses of the published literature have attempted to determine the extent to which the effects of research trials on psychotherapy for children, adolescents, and adults generalize to real clinical settings. In an early study on this issue, Jensen-Doss and Weisz (2006) examined 325 clinically referred young people aged 7 to 17 and found no evidence of poorer outcome in youth with multiple problems. Similarly, Kazdin and Whitley (2006) found that the presence of comorbidity was associated with greater change in young people with disruptive behaviour disorders who received evidence-based parent training or problem-solving treatments. These findings are encouraging in suggesting that evidence-based services are useful to those with more serious problems.

To determine whether such a conclusion applies also to treatments for adults, a group of psychotherapy researchers who had previously published meta-analytic studies joined forces to review the pertinent literature (Shadish et al., 1997). They were able to identify only 56 studies (out of approximately 1000 included in their own and other meta-analyses) that met criteria for clinical relevance (i.e., treatment provided in a non-university setting, with referred patients and experienced, professional therapists). Of those, only 15 met additional criteria for "treatment as usual." They did find a significant positive effect for psychotherapy for adults (effect sizes of 0.68 and 0.58 for the sets of 56 and 15 studies, respectively).

These studies pointed out a glaring gap in our knowledge of the benefits of psychotherapy. Researchers have steadily improved the internal validity of treatment studies by using randomized clinical trials and homogeneous groups of patients, and by training and monitoring the therapists. However, maximizing the internal validity of a study always comes with a cost—namely, a reduction in external validity (see Chapter 4 to review these concepts of validity). Psychotherapy researchers are increasingly aware of the need for research that has reasonable external validity without entirely sacrificing the controls necessary for sufficient internal validity. Accordingly, in a growing number of treatment studies, investigators conduct little or no screening of patients or provide no ongoing supervision of therapists (beyond an initial training workshop). These effectiveness trials are designed to explore treatment effects under truly "real-world" conditions.

Several reviews have examined the results of these effectiveness studies. Using a benchmarking strategy in which the results of efficacy trials are used as a point of comparison, Hunsley and Lee (2007) examined the results of effectiveness studies for adults and youth. Based on benchmarks for treatment completion and treatment outcome derived from meta-analyses of efficacy studies, they reported that, for the treatment of adult depression and anxiety disorders, it was typical for more than 75 percent of patients to follow the course of services to completion. This was comparable to completion rates reported in efficacy trials. With respect to treatment outcome, most of the effectiveness studies reported results that were comparable or superior to those obtained in efficacy studies. Almost identical results were obtained for effectiveness studies for child and adolescent mood and anxiety disorders. Lee, Horvath, and Hunsley (2013) followed up this review by examining 20 additional studies of treatments for disorders in children and adolescents conducted in regular clinical settings. All of these effectiveness studies reported that more than 75 percent of clients followed the course of services to completion. Improvement rates for treatment of internalizing problems were comparable to those reported in efficacy trials but, for parenting interventions to treat disruptive behaviour problems, some studies found results that were superior to the efficacy benchmark whereas others obtained results that were lower than the benchmark.

A meta-analysis of effectiveness studies of CBT for adult anxiety disorders found that the mean outcome of treatment in over 50 effectiveness studies was consistent with results obtained in efficacy studies (Stewart & Chambless, 2009). Treatment effectiveness appears to be slightly reduced, however, in the case of adult depression. Hans and Hiller (2013) conducted a meta-analysis on 34 CBT effectiveness studies; in all instances the studies included patients who sought treatment for depression and clinicians who worked in routine clinical settings. The researchers found compelling evidence for the effectiveness of both individual and group formats of CBT, with within-group effect sizes of approximately $d = 1.0$. Although substantial, these effectiveness results were somewhat less than what has been obtained in the highest quality RCTs of CBT for adult depression.

Although the evidence to date from various countries indicates that many evidence-based treatments for adults and youth can be very effective when used in regular practice settings, the picture is less encouraging for treatments dealing with couple distress. In their review of four effectiveness trials of couples therapy, Halford et al. (2015) reported that (a) over 50 percent of couples discontinued treatment before its completion, and (b) the success rates for couples (i.e., no longer being distressed in the couple relationship) were less than half of what has been reported in efficacy studies. The authors speculated that these disappointing results were likely due, at least in part, to the fact that relatively few therapists use either emotionally focused or cognitive-behavioural couples therapy.

⑥ BEFORE MOVING ON

> What are the common disorders for which there are efficacious treatments? Additionally, what are the common disorders with which we do not yet have efficacious treatments?

Evidence-Based Practice

Over the past three decades, health care systems in most Western countries have been restructured. Governments, insurance companies, and hospital health care professionals have recognized the importance of basing health care services on established scientific findings rather than on practitioners' assumptions. Psychotherapy is not exempt from this trend, and there is growing pressure to develop standards for **evidence-based practice**.

In professional psychology, the first step toward evidence-based practice was taken in 1993 when the American Psychological Association's Society of Clinical Psychology struck the Task Force on Promotion and Dissemination of Psychological Procedures to develop criteria to determine whether a psychosocial intervention had been demonstrated empirically to be efficacious. The criteria introduced by this task force for obtaining the designation as an **empirically supported therapy** included the repeated demonstration of efficacy in randomized controlled trials (or single-case design studies), the use of treatment manuals in the training of therapists and

the delivery of the treatment, and the clear description of the research participants who were involved in the treatment (Chambless et al., 1996). The first task force, along with two subsequent task forces, also released a list of treatments that were considered to have met these criteria.

Subsequently, an American Psychological Association (APA) presidential task force was struck to recommend APA policies and practices with respect to evidence-based practice (APA Presidential Task Force on Evidence-Based Practice, 2006). In its report, the task force defined evidence-based practice as the integration of the best available research and clinical expertise within the context of patient characteristics, culture, values, and treatment preferences. The evidence-based practice model was also endorsed by the Canadian Psychological Association (Dozois et al., 2014). To clarify the central role of research in evidence-based practice, the CPA Task Force stated that evidence-based practice relies on published, peer-reviewed research. The hierarchy of research evidence used to guide clinical practice is presented in Figure 17.1. To address all elements of evidence-based practice, psychologists are expected to openly and fully collaborate with clients in providing services and to monitor the effects of treatment on an ongoing basis in order to alter the treatment when indicated.

To provide you with a sense of the evidence-based treatments available for psychologists to use, Tables 17.5 and 17.6 summarize the disorders and conditions for which evidence-based psychotherapies are available (Lee & Hunsley, in press).

The momentum for evidence-based practice in psychology continues to grow. For example, the APA and the Canadian Psychological Association require that clinical psychology training programs and internships train students in some evidence-based treatments. However, not all psychologists are supportive of such moves. Drawing upon the substantial research base on the process of psychotherapy, the APA Division of Psychotherapy commissioned a task force to evaluate and disseminate information on

TABLE 17.5   CHILD AND ADOLESCENT MENTAL DISORDERS/CONDITIONS FOR WHICH THERE ARE EVIDENCE-BASED TREATMENTS

Anorexia Nervosa
Anxiety Disorders
Attention-Deficit/Hyperactivity Disorder
Autism Spectrum Disorder
Bipolar Spectrum Disorders
Depression
Disruptive Behaviour Disorders
Obesity
Obsessive-Compulsive Disorder
Post-traumatic Stress Disorder
Self-Injurious Behaviour
Substance Abuse

FIGURE 17.1 Hierarchy of Evidence Used to Guide Clinical Practice

Source: Canadian Psychology, Vol. 55, No. 3, page 157, Copyright ©2014 by The Canadian Psychological Association Inc. Reprinted by permission of The Canadian Psychological Association Inc.

the relevance of process-outcome research for evidence-based psychological practice (Norcross, 2002). A decade after this ground-breaking work, the APA Division of

Psychotherapy and the Society of Clinical Psychology collaborated in commissioning a task force to update the findings on **evidence-based therapy relationships** (Norcross, 2011). They concluded that the following elements of the therapeutic relationship are demonstrably or probably effective in influencing treatment outcome: therapeutic alliance (in individual adult therapy, therapy for youth, and family therapy), cohesion in group therapy, therapist empathy and positive regard, monitoring of client treatment progress, and patient–therapist goal consensus and collaboration. With respect to patient behaviours or characteristics, the task force found evidence that patient resistance, readiness for change, treatment preferences, cultural background, coping style, and treatment expectations were demonstrably or probably effective as factors for customizing therapy. Finally, one of the task force's main recommendations was that the concurrent use of evidence-based therapy relationship factors within the context of providing evidence-based treatments is likely to generate the best clinical outcome for patients.

Organizations such as the American Psychological Association and the Canadian Psychological Association have published guidelines on working with specific populations. Another important initiative with respect to evidence-based treatments is the development of **clinical practice guidelines**. Practice guidelines often draw together the research evidence for the assessment, diagnosis, and treatment of a specific disorder. Usually developed by an expert working group, these guidelines are meant to be used as tools for clinical training

TABLE 17.6 ADULT MENTAL DISORDERS/ CONDITIONS FOR WHICH THERE ARE EVIDENCE-BASED TREATMENTS

Mood Disorders
    Major Depressive Disorder
    Bipolar Disorder
Anxiety and Related Disorders
    Specific Phobias
    Social Anxiety Disorder
    Panic Disorder with and without Agoraphobia
    Generalized Anxiety Disorder
    Obsessive-Compulsive Disorder
    Post-traumatic Stress Disorder
Eating Disorders
    Anorexia Nervosa
    Bulimia Nervosa
    Binge-Eating Disorder
Substance-Related Disorders
Sleep Disorders
Sexual Disorders
Schizophrenia
Personality Disorders
    Avoidant Personality Disorder
    Borderline Personality Disorder

and service delivery. Such guidelines have been developed by a number of psychiatric associations and some government-sponsored health agencies; the American Psychological Association has begun to develop practice guidelines for specific disorders.

When people suffering from a psychological disorder decide to seek treatment, they often face a difficult decision—whether to take medication or to begin psychotherapy. As we have indicated in this chapter, there is evidence that both options can be helpful. Conversely, it is clear that neither option works for all people. Evidence-based clinical guidelines for the management of depression and anxiety offer authoritative recommendations on the treatment options (National Institute for Health and Care Excellence [NICE], 2011, 2016b). A key element of these guidelines is that the foundation of good treatment includes early detection, sound assessment, and person-centred care involving treatments that have been shown to be helpful for each level of symptom severity. For example, after reviewing the best available research on pharmacological treatment, psychological treatment, and combined treatments for depression, NICE made the following recommendations: (1) antidepressants should not be offered as the first treatment for mild depression, because the risk–benefit ratio is poor; (2) in the treatment of mild to moderate depression, patients should be offered a low-intensity cognitive-behavioural treatment (delivered as individual guided self-help, computerized CBT, or group CBT) or a structured group physical activity program; and (3) patients with moderate or severe depression should receive combined medication (SSRI) and high-intensity psychological intervention (CBT, behavioural activation, interpersonal psychotherapy, or behavioural couples therapy). In the treatment of anxiety, it is recommended that the first step is to communicate the diagnosis and explain the disorder. Next, individuals are offered a low-intensity psychological intervention, which could include self-help, with or without brief clinician facilitation, or participation in a psychoeducational group. Only individuals with more severe symptoms or those who have not responded to low-intensity psychological interventions are offered high-intensity cognitive-behavioural treatment or medication with an SSRI for anxiety disorders.

These guidelines do not assume that medication should be the first line of treatment for most psychological disorders. Although a pharmacological intervention may be the best first-line treatment for disorders such as schizophrenia and bipolar disorder, there is reason to be cautious in drawing this conclusion about psychopharmacological treatment in general. Moreover, psychotropic medication is commonly prescribed for conditions for which there are no supporting efficacy data. In the final analysis, it is unwise to think too generally about whether pharmaceutical or psychological treatments are best—instead, the evidence for the various treatment options must be examined. People's preferences must also be considered. Some individuals may not be good candidates for psychological interventions on the basis of their personal characteristics and social conditions. Likewise, some people may not be good candidates for psychotropic medication or may decide to discontinue medication because of side effects. A most reasoned, evidence-based approach to patient care should consider what treatment, or combination of treatments, might work best for a given individual at a particular point in time. In other words, research evidence, clinical expertise, and patient preferences are all key components of evidence-based practice for mental disorders that should be considered in any treatment decision.

In the eyes of many clinical psychologists, the field of psychotherapy research has matured sufficiently to warrant the promotion of psychotherapy as an evidence-based health service for many conditions and disorders. When combined with empirical evidence on important aspects of the therapeutic relationship, evidence-based treatments have a great deal to offer many people suffering from a range of health and psychological problems. In the relatively short time since Freud, psychotherapy has moved from being an esoteric set of practices based entirely on speculation and supposition to an essential health care service with substantial foundations in solid scientific knowledge.

7 BEFORE MOVING ON

For psychologists who wish to offer evidence-based services, which lines of research are most relevant?

SUMMARY

- ECT can be an efficacious treatment of last resort for severely depressed individuals who have not responded to other treatments and are at suicidal risk. ECT is associated with short-term benefits, but these must be balanced with the possibility of cognitive impairment side-effects.

- Psychotropic drugs have proven to be effective in treating a wide range of disorders.

- Psychopharmacological treatment includes phenothiazines and second generation antipsychotics used to treat psychotic disorders; anxiolytics for some anxiety disorders and anxiety-related disorders; MAOIs, TCAs, SRRIs, and SNRIs for depression, some anxiety disorders, and some anxiety-related disorders; mood stabilizers for bipolar disorders; and stimulants for ADHD.

- Psychotherapy is offered by diverse mental health professionals using a variety of theoretical orientations.
- There are efficacious psychological treatments for many mental disorders.
- Psychodynamic approaches are based on the assumption that much of the client's distress stems from patterns developed early in life and use both interpretive and supportive interventions.
- Humanistic-experiential approaches focus on emotional aspects of subjective experience, highlighting the impact of affect in the client's current life situation.
- Cognitive-behavioural approaches focus on internal (thoughts, images, emotions, bodily sensations) and external (fear-arousing objects, interpersonal interactions) stimuli in shaping the client's adaptive and maladaptive reactions.
- Individual therapy is the most common treatment modality.
- Couples therapy can be effective in treating relationship difficulties.
- Family therapy addresses the way that family patterns maintain or resolve problems.
- Group therapy is a cost-effective way to deliver services.
- Many efficacious psychological treatments can now be delivered at a distance via the internet, or via computerized self-help programs.
- Efficacy trials use highly controlled randomized clinical trials to establish that the treatment works.
- Effectiveness research examines whether the treatment can be just as useful when transported to a real-world context.
- Meta-analyses are an efficient way to synthesize results from diverse studies.
- Clinical practice guidelines are based on the best available data and often use a stepped-care approach.

KEY TERMS

behaviour therapy (p. 446)

client-centred therapy (p. 446)

clinical practice guidelines (p. 460)

cognitive restructuring (p. 448)

cognitive therapy (p. 447)

effect size (p. 454)

ego analysts (p. 445)

emotion-focused therapy (p. 446)

emotionally focused couples therapy (p. 451)

empirically supported therapy (p. 459)

evidence-based practice (p. 459)

evidence-based therapy relationships (p. 460)

exposure therapy (p. 448)

extrapyramidal effects (p. 440)

interpersonal psychodynamic psychotherapy (p. 445)

meta-analysis (p. 454)

modular approach (p. 458)

problem-solving approach (p. 448)

psychotropic agents (p. 439)

rational-emotive therapy (p. 447)

response shaping (p. 447)

supportive-expressive psychotherapy (p. 445)

systematic desensitization (p. 448)

telehealth (p. 451)

therapeutic alliance (p. 445)

time-limited dynamic psychotherapy (TLDP) (p. 445)

transdiagnostic approach (p. 458)

transference (p. 445)

treatment effectiveness (p. 453)

treatment efficacy (p. 453)

JULIAN HASFORD

•

ISAAC PRILLELTENSKY

CHAPTER

18

RISK AHEAD

Sergey Nivens/Shutterstock

Prevention and Mental Health Promotion in the Community

LEARNING OBJECTIVES

AFTER READING THIS CHAPTER, STUDENTS WILL BE ABLE TO:

1. Define and distinguish the major types of prevention and mental health promotion.

2. Provide a historical perspective on the field of prevention.

3. Explain and give examples of how the concepts of risk, resilience, and protection are important for prevention.

4. Describe the Strengths, Prevention, Empowerment, and Community Change conceptual framework for prevention.

5. Give examples of research on the high-risk and universal approaches to prevention.

6. Understand Canadian policy on prevention and mental health promotion.

7. Note some of the key issues in program implementation, dissemination, and social justice.

The birth of a baby is typically a joyous event for a family. However, after giving birth, some mothers become depressed, experiencing a condition commonly known as postpartum depression. This form of depression can be treated in various ways: with medication, talk therapies, diet and nutrition, home visitation by nurses, or other forms of social support. But can some of the far-reaching adverse consequences of postpartum depression be prevented? In seven Ontario communities, Dennis and colleagues (2009) studied a one-to-one peer support program designed to prevent postpartum depression. Women at risk for postpartum depression were randomly assigned to either standard postnatal care or standard postnatal care plus telephone-based peer support from a mother who previously experienced postpartum depression. Twelve weeks after the program started, 14 percent of the women who received peer support experienced high levels of depression, compared to a significantly higher rate of 25 percent among those who received only standard care.

In the field of abnormal psychology, the dominant emphasis has been on expanding our understanding of the nature and etiology of mental disorders and on developing effective treatments. Throughout this text, we have considered the manifestations and effects of specific disorders on individuals. But people do not live in isolation; they belong to families, communities, and societies. In this chapter, we consider the mental health not only of individuals but also of whole communities. We begin by briefly outlining the field of community psychology, which has highlighted the need for the prevention of mental disorders and the promotion of mental health.

Community Psychology

The term **community psychology** was first coined by Canadian psychologist William Line in 1951 (see Walsh-Bowers, 1998). In the United States, community psychology had its roots in clinical psychology during the 1960s, when some clinically trained psychologists began to question the appropriateness of an exclusive reliance on treatment approaches. They recognized that the prevalence of mental disorders far outstrips the availability of professional help.

Epidemiological studies have shown that the prevalence rate of mental disorders in Canada is approximately 20 percent, affecting over 6 million Canadians per year (Mental Health Commission of Canada [MHCC], 2013). Waddell and colleagues (2005) estimate that at any given time 14 percent of Canadian children aged 4 to 17 (i.e., more than 800 000) suffer from a mental disorder. Moreover, as discussed in Chapter 15, childhood disorders can often set the stage for ongoing problems in adulthood, which cause great misery to those afflicted

and to their families, and cost Canadians up to $50 billion annually (MHCC, 2013).

There are not, and never could be, enough trained mental health professionals to provide therapeutic interventions for the large number of children and adults worldwide who are afflicted with mental disorders (Albee, 1990). Indeed, as is clear from Chapter 17, no therapeutic intervention is 100 percent effective. Furthermore, most children with mental disorders do not receive treatment for their mental health problems (only 25 percent do, according to Waddell et al., 2005). As well, more than half of mental, emotional, and behavioural disorders begin in childhood or adolescence (O'Connell, Boat, & Warner, 2009). As Waddell, McEwan, Peters, Hua, and Garland (2007, p. 174) state:

> It is increasingly evident that treatment services alone cannot reduce the burden of illness. As well, the understanding that many mental disorders arise during childhood has encouraged a shift toward considering prevention. Preventing mental disorders requires placing children at the centre of a public mental health strategy.

For these reasons, much of the prevention and mental health promotion literature discussed in this chapter focuses on children and youth. It is important for the reader to know that only methods oriented toward prevention have been successful in reducing the prevalence of health problems: "[A]s the history of public health methods (that emphasize social change) has clearly established, no mass disease or disorder afflicting humankind has ever been eliminated by attempts at treating affected individuals" (Albee, 1990, p. 370).

In addition to its emphasis on prevention, community psychology has a number of other identifying features that distinguish it from clinical psychology (Nelson & Prilleltensky, 2010). Whereas clinical psychology has historically focused on the individual or micro level (e.g., the family) in diagnosis and treatment, community psychology applies an **ecological perspective** that stresses the interdependence of the individual, the family, the community, and society. Community psychologists believe that interventions for many problems should address multiple levels of analysis. For example, psychotherapy may be somewhat helpful to a family living in poverty, but social policies that reduce poverty may play an even more important role. Sensitivity to a person's social context and appreciation of diversity are key themes of community psychology (Bond, 2016)

Another difference is that, in contrast to the clinical psychology focus on deficits and on reducing maladaptive behaviours, community psychology tends to pay more attention to people's strengths and to the promotion of mental health and well-being (Prilleltensky & Prilleltensky, 2006). The community psychologist often functions as an enabler, a consultant, or a planner, rather than as an expert in diagnosis and treatment. The working style of the community psychologist emphasizes collaboration and participation of diverse groups from the community in planning, implementing, and evaluating interventions.

Community psychologists believe in the importance of informal social supports rather than an exclusive reliance on professional help. So, for example, community psychologists might help people who are experiencing a problem, such as depression, to form self-help/mutual aid groups. Research has shown that this alternative approach of supporting one another can be quite effective (Pistrang, Barker, & Humphreys, 2010).

Finally, with its U.S. roots in the 1960s, community psychology is oriented to social justice and social change. Community psychologists do not see themselves as value-neutral scientists, because to do so would be to accept the status quo of unjust social conditions. Rather, community psychology has a clear emphasis on values and social ethics (Nelson & Prilleltensky, 2010). The elimination of poverty, racism, sexism, and other forms of social injustice are viewed not only as important in preventing problems, but also as moral imperatives in the work of community psychology.

Prevention and Mental Health Promotion: Some Definitions
PRIMARY, SECONDARY, AND TERTIARY PREVENTION

Historically, the concept of **prevention** of mental disorders developed from the fields of physical disease, public health, and epidemiology. Graham (1994, p. 815) distinguished three levels of prevention:

By convention, three types of preventive activity are recognized. **Primary prevention** involves intervention that reduces the incidence of disorder. **Secondary prevention** comprises treatment that reduces the duration of the disorder, and **tertiary prevention** covers rehabilitative activity that reduces the disability arising from an established disorder.

In this chapter, we use the term *prevention* to mean primary prevention. There are three key features in our definition of prevention:

1. With successful prevention, new cases of a problem do not occur.
2. Prevention is not aimed at individuals but at populations; the goal is a decline in rates of disorder.
3. Preventive interventions intentionally focus on preventing mental health problems (Cowen, 1980).

UNIVERSAL, SELECTIVE, AND INDICATED PREVENTION

The typology of primary, secondary, and tertiary prevention has given way to a new typology of universal, selective, and indicated prevention developed by the U.S. Institute of Medicine (1994). The **universal approach** is designed to include all individuals in a particular geographical area (e.g., neighbourhood, city, province) or particular setting (e.g., school, workplace, public housing complex).

In contrast to universal prevention, **selective prevention**, also known as the high-risk approach, is based on the assumption that there are known risk factors for certain mental health problems, and prevention has the greatest effect in targeting individuals most exposed to these risk factors. Selective prevention targets participants on the basis of characteristics external to the participant (e.g., children whose parents have divorced) and/or on internal characteristics of the participant (e.g., cognitive vulnerability to anxiety or depression). Finally, several programs have selected participants who show mild or early-developing mental health problems (e.g., young children showing antisocial behaviour). These programs are sometimes referred to as **indicated prevention** programs, but might more appropriately be called early intervention, or what was previously called secondary prevention programs. In contrast, universal and selective prevention approaches are examples of what was previously called primary prevention.

MENTAL HEALTH PROMOTION

Complementary to prevention is the concept of **mental health promotion**. Whereas prevention, by definition, focuses on reducing problems, promotion focuses on enhancing well-being. Many people think of **mental health** in negative terms, as the absence of disorder. However, a broader view defines mental health, or well-being, in positive terms, as the presence of optimal social, emotional, and cognitive functioning (Peters, 1988). According to the Epp (1988, p. 7) report *Mental Health for Canadians: Striking a Balance*,

Mental health is the capacity of the individual, the group and the environment to interact with one another in ways that promote subjective well-being, the optimal development and use of mental abilities (cognitive, affective, and relational), the achievement of individual and collective goals consistent with justice and the attainment and preservation of conditions of fundamental equality.

In the Epp report, mental health and mental disorder are viewed as conceptually distinct. There is a mental disorder continuum ranging from severe mental disorder (e.g., florid schizophrenia) to the absence of mental disorder, and a mental health continuum ranging from minimal mental health (e.g., poor coping skills, low self-esteem) to optimal mental health (e.g., good coping skills, high self-esteem). Recent research in the United States has confirmed that mental health and mental disorder are two different dimensions (Westerhof & Keyes, 2010).

The Canadian Population Health Initiative (Canadian Institute for Health Information, 2009) has operationalized positive mental health in terms of five components: (1) the ability to enjoy life; (2) the ability to deal with life's challenges; (3) emotional well-being; (4) spiritual well-being; and (5) social connections and respect for culture, equity, social justice, and personal dignity.

Having identified the qualities of positive mental health, the question arises as to how mental health can be promoted. Cowen (1996) identifies four key characteristics of mental health promotion.

1. It is proactive; it seeks to promote mental health before mental health problems have taken root.

2. It focuses on populations, not individuals.

3. It is multi-dimensional, focusing on "integrated sets of operations involving individuals, families, settings, community contexts, and macrolevel societal structures and policies" (Cowen, 1996, p. 246).

4. It is ongoing, not a one-shot, time-limited intervention.

In practice, prevention and mental health promotion go together, and a program will normally involve elements of both, inextricably intertwined. Enhancing well-being will often prevent problems, and preventing problems may enhance well-being. The Canadian Institute for Health Information (CIHI, 2009, p. 47) has described mental health promotion as follows:

Mental health promotion typically emphasizes supporting individual resilience, creating supportive environments and addressing the influence of the broader determinants of mental health. Specific goals of mental health promotion include enhancing protective factors that help individuals, families and communities to deal with events, and increasing conditions, such as social cohesion, that reduce risk factors for diminished mental health among individuals, families and communities.

Moreover, CIHI emphasizes an **ecological approach** to mental health promotion, asserting that strategies to promote mental health can be implemented at the societal, community, and individual levels of analysis.

1. *Societal-level strategies.* The CIHI (2009) report underscored the importance of changing social policies to promote mental health. Two policy streams were identified. One stream involves social policies that indirectly affect positive mental health through distal socio-political conditions, such as economic inequality, housing, education, racism, and sexism—a range of factors increasingly referred as social determinants of health (World Health Organization [WHO], 2014). The other policy stream involves identifying the characteristics of more proximal supportive environments associated with positive mental health and instituting policies that create or enhance the supportive qualities of these environments (Cowen, 2000; Moos, 2003). This policy stream is aimed at more local settings, such as schools, neighbourhoods, places of worship, and workplaces.

2. *Community-level strategies.* The CIHI (2009) report suggests that empowering community residents is an important community-level strategy for promoting mental health. *Empowerment* refers to perceived and actual control over one's life (Rappaport, 1987; see also Chapter 7 for a discussion of the relationship between stress and control). Empowering interventions are those that enhance participants' "voice and choice" (self-determination and democratic participation) and that are directed and controlled by citizens (Prilleltensky, 1994a). The Better Beginnings, Better Futures project in Ontario, which is discussed later in the chapter, is a good example of how community residents can be empowered to improve their communities and the lives of their children and families (Peters, Bradshaw, et al., 2010). Building a strong sense of community and social support is also important for the promotion of mental health. Family, school, and workplace programs are important settings in which mental health can be enhanced (CIHI, 2009).

3. *Individual-level strategies.* The development of age-appropriate skills and competencies is an individual-level strategy for the enhancement of mental health (CIHI, 2009). Social competencies (e.g., social problem-solving skills, assertiveness, interpersonal skills), academic competencies, and work competencies are all important for mental health. Comprehensive, well-integrated, ongoing programs that are institutionalized in social settings show the most promise for the promotion of social competence and mental health (Weissberg & Greenberg, 1998). Also, the ability to cope effectively with stressful life events and conditions is another key pathway to mental health. Throughout life, we face both expected stressors, such as life transitions, and unexpected stressful events. Therefore, skills and resources to meet the challenges posed by stressors are essential

for mental health. Research has demonstrated that some individuals are extremely resilient and able to withstand life stressors (e.g., Rutter et al., 2015). Moreover, stressors are often seen as presenting an opportunity for growth. Programs that build up resources to cope with stress can potentially promote mental health.

① **BEFORE MOVING ON**

A program to prevent postpartum depression was described at the beginning of the chapter. What type of prevention program was this, and how might this program also promote mental health?

Historical Perspective

PRE–GERM THEORY ERA

In the eighteenth century, people believed that disease resulted from "miasmas," or noxious odours, that emanated from soil polluted with waste products. Miasmatists believed that the way to prevent disease was to clean up the environment (Bloom, 1984). Through the development of sewage disposal and sanitation campaigns, the rates of many diseases (e.g., typhoid fever, yellow fever, typhus) dropped dramatically. Some nutritional diseases were reduced without knowledge of the precise cause of the disease. For example, British sailors became known as "limeys" because they learned to prevent scurvy by eating citrus fruits, long before it was known that this disease resulted from a deficiency of vitamin C. This is a useful perspective for mental health, a field in which, as we have seen in almost every chapter of this book, etiology is usually complex and impossible to completely pin down.

PUBLIC HEALTH APPROACH

The next major impetus to the field of prevention was the public health approach, based on epidemiology (the study of the distribution and determinants of disease in a population; see Chapter 4).

The traditional **public health approach** is characterized by the following steps:

1. Identifying a disease and developing a reliable diagnostic method (descriptive epidemiology);
2. Developing a theory of the disease's course of development based on laboratory and epidemiological research (analytic epidemiology); and
3. Developing and evaluating a disease prevention program (experimental epidemiology) (Bloom, 1984).

Public health researchers tend to focus on three components: (1) characteristics of the host (that is, the person who contracts the disease); (2) characteristics of the environment (that is, stressors); and (3) the agent (that is, the

manner in which the disease is transmitted to the host). The thrust of public health promotion is generally twofold: to reduce environmental stressors while enhancing people's capacities to withstand those stressors. In the mental health field, for example, one could attempt to prevent substance abuse problems by strengthening the host (e.g., teaching teens how to deal with peer pressure to drink or take drugs), changing the environment (e.g., providing good alternative activities in the community for youth), and targeting the agent (e.g., regulating sales and reducing access to alcohol and drugs).

The public health approach has been very successful in reducing the incidence of many problems, including some mental health problems. For example, the incidence of general paresis, an organic psychosis resulting from syphilitic infection (see Chapter 1), has been greatly reduced as a result of this approach. Yet this approach is effective only with diseases that have a single identified precursor or cause, be it a vitamin deficiency or a germ. As shown throughout this book, very few mental health problems have a single cause (Albee, 1982).

SCHOOL-BASED APPROACH

While prevention of mental disorders was strongly influenced by the field of public health, prevention and mental health promotion have shifted more toward an educational, school-based approach. More specifically, there has been a great deal of interest recently in early childhood development (ECD) programs for preschool children as a method of prevention (Barnett, 2011). While ECD programs have been found to be successful in reaching their explicit goal of enhancing children's cognitive and academic outcomes (Camilli, Vargas, Ryan, & Barnett, 2010), long-term follow-up studies have found that these programs also have profound impacts on health (O'Nise, Lynch, Sawyer, & McDermott, 2010) and socio-emotional development, including lower rates of crime (Farrington, Gaffney, Lösel, & Ttofi, 2017). Although there are several examples of effective selective, or high-risk, ECD approaches in the United States (Camilli et al., 2010; Farrington et al., 2017), some European countries have implemented ECD programs universally (Melhuish, 2011). For example, France has had universal, free, preschool programs (l'école maternelle) starting at age three since the 1960s and 1970s. Not only has this program been effective in promoting success in school and the labour market, but it has also been shown to have a greater impact on children from economically disadvantaged families (Melhuish, 2011). ECD research has also had impacts on policies, with governments viewing ECD programs as a sound way to invest in the future (Gormley, 2011). For example, in 2010 the Ontario government began implementing a universal, full-day early learning program for kindergarten-age children, and early evidence suggests it is having a positive impact on students in several developmental domains, particularly among students who are most vulnerable (Ministry of Education, 2013).

The history of public health suggests that some health problems can be effectively prevented without knowing the precise cause of the problems. What are the implications of this observation for the prevention of mental health problems?

Resilience, Risk, and Protection
RESILIENCE, RISK, AND PROTECTIVE FACTORS

As mentioned earlier, a large body of evidence indicates that the onset and prevalence of mental disorders are significantly influenced by adversity within individuals' social environments, such as poverty, neighbourhood crime, poor housing, or familial conflict. Many individuals, however, have been found to function effectively, and even thrive, in spite of their exposure to adverse life situations. **Resilience** refers to the process of positive adaptation to significant adversity through the interaction of risk and protective factors (Rutter et al., 2015). **Risk factors** are the conditions or events that increase the likelihood of negative mental health outcomes, whereas **protective factors** are assets or resources that help to offset, or buffer, risk factors (Fergus & Zimmerman, 2005). For example, a person with a good social support network or good coping skills may adjust well to a stressful life event such as marital separation or job loss.

Over the past 30 years, a substantial amount of research has confirmed that most mental health problems are associated with many different risk and protective factors—most of which are, in turn, associated with many different types of mental health problems. Ecological studies of resilience have examined the interaction of risk and protective factors in context at the **microsystem** (e.g., small settings in which a child directly participates) and **macrosystem** (larger social systems of culture, norms, and so on) levels of analysis (Ungar, 2015; Ungar, Ghazinour, & Richter, 2013). For example, in the 1990s the U.S. Department of Housing and Urban Development sponsored the Moving to Opportunity for Fair Housing initiative, a large scale social experiment conducted with 4600 families in five U.S. cities. During the study, families who lived in high-poverty public housing areas were randomized to a control group or to one of two groups that received vouchers to move to neighbourhoods with lower levels of poverty. Long-term follow-up found that families and children who moved had better mental health, and did much better in school, than children who remained in deprived neighbourhoods (Graif, Acaya, & Roux, 2016; Kemp, Langer, & Thompson, 2016). No attempts were made to modify children's behaviour in the new environment. The new context of better-equipped schools with norms of high achievement accounted for the positive outcomes displayed, such as better rates of graduation, better college attendance, and better employment records. They also emphasize the impact of context on parenting. In high-risk contexts, a

controlling parenting style is more protective than is a permissive attitude toward teens. A number of studies have found similar relationships between protective factors in the environment and mental health among populations at risk (Carpiano, 2014; Shinn & Toohey, 2003). Some common risk factors and protective factors for mental health are presented in Tables 18.1 and 18.2.

INTERACTIONIST AND CONSTRUCTIONIST PERSPECTIVES ON RESILIENCE

As discussed in Chapter 2, as knowledge of any mental disorder grows, single-factor explanations are generally replaced by interactionist explanations that view behaviour as the product of the interaction of a variety of factors. The resilience approach reflects this complexity, focusing not on single factors but on many risk and protective factors. Researchers have recognized the need to go beyond identifying general risk and protective factors to understanding how these factors operate and how they interact in context.

Risk factors and protective factors do not affect everyone in the same way. Resilience researchers have considered how dimensions of human diversity shape resilience, and have found that characteristics such as gender, age, and ethnicity can influence the interactions between risk factors, protective factors, and mental health outcomes. For instance, it has been suggested that divorce affects young boys more strongly than it does young girls in the short term, but that girls suffer from "sleeper effects": they feel the consequences

TABLE 18.1 SOME GENERAL RISK FACTORS

Ecological Level	Domain	Risk Factor
Individual	Socio-emotional	Anxiety Social incompetence
	Cognitive	Attentional deficits Learning disabilities
	Biological	Sensory disabilities Perinatal complications
	Behavioural	Aggression Delinquency
Microsystem	Peers	Peer rejection Delinquent peers
	Families	Hostile parenting Single-parent status Mental illness in the family Family dysfunction Child abuse by parents Parental unemployment
	Schools	Poor school quality Scholastic demoralization
	Neighbourhood/ Community	Neighbourhood disorganization Neighbourhood disadvantage
Macrosystem	Socio-political	Social inequality Systemic discrimination

TABLE 18.2   SOME GENERAL PROTECTIVE FACTORS

Ecological Level	Domain	Protective Factor
Individual	Socio-emotional	Self-esteem Aspirations and an inclination to plan for the future
	Cognitive	High IQ Problem-solving abilities
	Biological	Attractiveness to peers and adults Easy temperament
	Behavioural	Prosocial behaviour
Microsystem	Relational	Positive role models
	Peers	Positive peer relations
	Families	Parental monitoring Parental education
	Schools	Positive school climate Positive classroom psycho-social environment
	Neighbourhood/Community	Social capital (feelings of trust and connection with people in the community) Community participation
Macrosystem	Socio-political	Democracy Healthy public policy

of parental divorce later in adolescence (Gore & Eckenrode, 1994). Another illustration of diversity concerns early parental loss. Losing a parent at a young age has been implicated in vulnerability to later psychiatric disorder. Brown and his colleagues found that girls who lost their mothers before age 11 were likely to experience depression later in life, but only if they did not have adequate care after the loss. This finding suggests that it is not so much the grief of losing a parent that predisposes children to psychiatric disorders as the fact that a child who has lost a parent is likely to receive poor care (Brown, Harris, & Bifulco, 1986).

At this point in our knowledge, it is difficult to connect specific risk factors and protective factors with specific forms of abnormal behaviour (see the discussion of the diathesis-stress and biopsychosocial models in Chapter 2 for an indication of how complex the relationships among factors can be). Furthermore, not all risk factors and protective factors have a direct impact on a person's mental health. Some have an immediate impact; others influence functioning indirectly.

Resilience is a dynamic concept that extends beyond the fixed characteristics or outcomes of individuals, and emerges from the process of interactions between individuals and their environments (Ungar, 2004). A critical examination of resilience phenomena indicates that it is highly complex, non-hierarchical, and contextualized. This is reflected, for instance, in the finding that some behaviours or disorders

that are typically considered maladaptive (e.g., oppositional defiance, aggression, or authoritarian parenting), can be protective factors depending on the context (Ungar, 2011). In addition, the nature of resilience is influenced by the ways in which people construct meaning from their experiences (Ungar, 2004). For example, a psychological sense of community is a characteristic that has often been associated with well-being and resilience (Sonn & Fisher, 1998). Some studies suggest, however, that a *negative* sense of community can be protective in some contexts (Brodsky, 1996). In a qualitative study of resilient African American single mothers living in impoverished neighbourhoods, Brodsky (1996) found that possessing a negative sense of community may have played a protective role in the lives of the women and their children, by enabling them to avoid perceived risks within the environment.

In a similar vein, an internal locus of control (the degree to which people believe they have control over events that influence their lives) is another personal characteristic that has been often associated with individual resilience by motivating more proactive coping responses to adversity (Luthar, 1991). Some research suggests, however, that the advantages of an internal locus of control are dependent on cultural context such as race. Ungar (2004) reviewed literature that suggests that although White children growing up in poverty have been shown to benefit from an internal locus of control, the same advantage may not extend to African American children in poverty. The difference may be in the prospects for mobility and nature of barriers faced by different groups, White children may be more likely to anticipate the possibility of future success that can be attributed it to their own effort or grit, while African American children may anticipate greater systemic barriers to economic security or higher education.

CUMULATIVE RISK

The effects of risk are cumulative: the more of these factors that are present, the more vulnerable a person is to a wide range of mental health problems. Research on **cumulative risk** has shown that the number of risk factors experienced by an individual often accounts for a greater proportion of the variation in outcomes than the sum of individual risk factors. In a study of rural children in the United States, Evans (2003) found that children with a greater number of environmental risk factors experienced higher levels of physiological and psychological distress and lower levels of self-worth than those exposed to fewer risk factors. Findings from a number of cumulative risk studies suggest that the likelihood of negative outcomes increases considerably when an individual has been exposed to three or more risk factors (e.g., Forehand, Biggar, & Kotchick, 1998). The effect of cumulative risk extends across the lifespan, with a large body of research indicating that experiencing multiple risk factors during childhood significantly increases negative outcomes during later life stages (Chartier, Walker, & Naimark, 2010).

In spite of the profound effects and widespread use of cumulative risk models, there remain a number of questions of and limitations to existing knowledge (McLaughlin & Sheridan, 2016). The most influential explanation for the mechanisms of multiple risk factors is the stress-response model, which postulates that multiple risk factors lead to frequent activations of the body's various stress-response systems, which contribute to physiological weathering over time (Evans, Li, & Whipple, 2013). The cumulative risk model, however, does not necessarily account for the unique or distinct effects of specific risks. The approach is based, in some respects, on an assumption that each risk (e.g., physical abuse, neglect, maternal depression, or poverty) has an equivalent impact on outcomes. Moreover, the stress-response model of cumulative risk does not necessarily account for developmental outcomes such as language delays (McLaughlin & Sheridan, 2016). More research is required to improve our understanding of the mechanisms of cumulative risk.

MECHANISMS OF RISK AND PROTECTION

Understanding the mechanisms of risk, protection, and resilience has important implications for prevention and promotion. According to Rutter (1987), there are four central mechanisms that can help people cope with adversity and develop positive mental health: (1) reducing risk impact, (2) interrupting unhealthy chain reactions stemming from stressful life events, (3) enhancing self-esteem and self-efficacy, and (4) creating opportunities for personal growth.

Risk impact may be reduced either by altering the risk factor itself or by altering exposure to the risk. Altering the risk means changing it in some way to minimize effects. For instance, facing a separation or a new situation without preparation constitutes a risk for young children. The risk for children who need hospitalization can be altered by taking them to visit the hospital before admission and by "practice separations" from parents in secure circumstances. Altering exposure means keeping the person away from the risky situation, or reducing involvement in its riskier aspects. For example, Rutter (1987) found that, in high-risk communities, strict parental supervision of children's activities outside the home can reduce the risk for delinquent behaviour. Placing limits on what children can do and how long they can stay outside the home minimizes exposure to the risky environment.

The mechanism of breaking a potentially damaging chain reaction can be seen in Brown and colleagues' (1986) study of parental loss: ensuring sustained, adequate care breaks the chain of harmful consequences. A nurturing environment can protect children from the consequences of loss, separation, and other risks. *Self-efficacy* can be fostered in children by offering age-appropriate tasks and sufficient rewarding experiences of control. Finally, opportunities for personal development may be created by teaching youth social skills that they can apply in various settings, and by

preventing school dropout. This last mechanism may be conceptualized as promoting beneficial chain reactions. A good education can lead to attractive jobs, a higher income, and the like. Similarly, adequate social skills can lead to friendships, which translate into social supports that have the effect of buffering stress (Gore & Eckenrode, 1994).

IMPLICATIONS OF RESILIENCE, RISK, AND PROTECTION FOR PREVENTION

Albee (1982) views the incidence of mental health problems as an equation involving risk and protective factors:

$$\text{Incidence} = \frac{\text{Risk factors}}{\text{Protective factors}} =$$

$$\frac{\text{Organic causes} + \text{Stress} + \text{Exploitation}}{\text{Coping skills} + \text{Self-esteem} + \text{Support systems}}$$

Prevention can be approached from both sides: by reducing risk factors and by increasing protective factors. Elias (1987), noting that Albee's equation tends to focus on the individual, formulated a prevention equation that focuses more on the social environment. Elias's equation is as follows:

$$\frac{\text{Stressors} + \text{Risk factors in the environment}}{\begin{array}{c}\text{Positive} \\ \text{socialization} \\ \text{experiences}\end{array} + \begin{array}{c}\text{Social support} \\ \text{resources}\end{array} + \begin{array}{c}\text{Opportunities for} \\ \text{positive relatedness} \\ \text{and connectedness}\end{array}}$$

The important implication for prevention from Elias's equation is that interventions designed to reduce the likelihood of behavioural and emotional problems should strive to change the social environment rather than the individual. For example, prevention programs should strive to reduce risk factors in the environment and increase the social support resources for people. The basic idea of this approach is that creating healthy environments will promote the healthy development of people and prevent mental health problems.

❸ BEFORE MOVING ON

Define risk factors, protective factors, and resilience, and give an example of how these concepts are important for prevention.

A Conceptual Framework for Prevention and Promotion

Prilleltensky (2005) developed a framework for the prevention of mental health problems and the promotion of well-being consisting of four complementary dimensions: ecological, temporal, capabilities, and participation. He has called this framework *SPEC*, which stands for Strengths, Prevention, Empowerment, and Community Change. The four dimensions belong in two fields. The contextual field

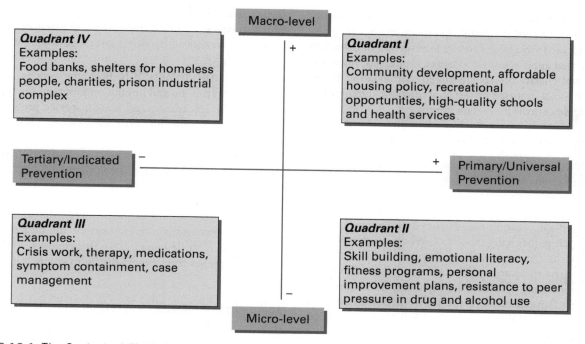

FIGURE 18.1 The Contextual Field: Intersection of Ecological and Temporal Dimensions in Prevention and Promotion

Source: Prilleltensky, I. Promoting well-being: Time for a paradigm shift in health and human services. *Scandinavian Journal of Public Health* 33(Suppl 66), pp. 53-60. Copyright © 2005 by Taylor & Francis. Reprinted by permission of SAGE Publications, Ltd.

consists of intersecting continua of temporal and ecological dimensions, creating four contextual quadrants. The affirmation field reflects the intersections of the participation and capabilities dimensions.

THE CONTEXTUAL FIELD

A contextual approach to well-being must account for the role of temporal and ecological variables. The ecological dimension covers the full range of interventions—from micro to macro levels (see Ecological Dimension). The temporal dimension, in turn, ranges from tertiary or indicated prevention to universal or primary prevention (see Temporal Dimension). When the two dimensions intersect, as illustrated in Figure 18.1, a contextual field with four quadrants is formed.

ECOLOGICAL DIMENSION Some prevention and mental health promotion programs focus narrowly on a small number of influences on behaviour, or on a tightly defined set of target outcome behaviours. A growing trend, however, is for more comprehensive programs that address a broad range of personal and environmental factors as well as a broad range of outcomes (Durlak et al., 2007). Thus, mental health problems are viewed in the context of characteristics of the individual (e.g., coping skills, personality traits), the microsystem (e.g., the family, the school), and the macrosystem (e.g., social norms, social class).

TEMPORAL DIMENSION The timing of the intervention is another important dimension of the conceptual framework of prevention and promotion. The early concepts of primary,

secondary, and tertiary prevention capture the issue of timing quite well. Primary prevention occurs before a problem has developed; secondary prevention involves early identification and intervention, as the problem is in its incipient stages of development; and tertiary prevention (treatment or rehabilitation) occurs well after the problem has developed. Thus, this dimension ranges from tertiary or indicated to primary or universal.

CONTEXTUAL QUADRANTS As seen in Figure 18.1, four quadrants are formed by the intersection of the temporal and ecological dimensions. Clockwise, Quadrant I is formed by the intersection of the positive ends of the x and y axes. Examples of collective and preventive approaches include affordable housing policies; provision of high-quality health care; incentives to achieve high educational standards; investments in education, family planning, and mental health; and progressive taxation policies that distribute wealth among the population.

Quadrant II represents interventions that are preventive but person-centred. Examples include skills building, emotional literacy, and education for proper eating and exercise to prevent physical illness. Many drug prevention programs that teach youth resistance skills and knowledge about the effects of alcohol, smoking, and illicit drugs fit into this quadrant.

Quadrant III reflects the medical model tradition whereby the intervention is aimed at containing symptoms and managing crises. Medications, therapy, and crisis intervention are the prototypical approaches in this quadrant. Practitioners wait until patients, clients, or community members complain of an ailment before intervening, usually in a medical clinic or a community agency setting.

Quadrant IV is created by the intersection of collective and indicated approaches. Food banks, shelters for homeless people, and charity efforts are aimed at alleviating the ill effects of social injustice or the unpredictable outcomes of economic downturns for certain groups.

THE AFFIRMATION FIELD

To experience well-being, human beings must first experience affirmation. Affirmation comes from an acknowledgment of a person's strengths, voice, and choice. Health and human services have been notorious for concentrating on deficits and for creating *clienthood* and *patienthood* instead of citizenship (McKnight, 1995). When empowerment and strengths are promoted, on the contrary, the experience of affirmation grows. The affirmation field consists of two intersecting continua: the capability dimension (see Capability Dimension) and the participation dimension (see Participation Dimension). Together, they create four distinct approaches to helping and healing.

CAPABILITY DIMENSION This dimension ranges from an exclusive focus on risk reduction and the prevention of deficits to an exclusive focus on the enhancement of protective factors and the promotion of strengths. Of course, it is possible to focus simultaneously on both prevention and promotion, which is captured by the middle range of the continuum.

PARTICIPATION DIMENSION Both the process and the content of prevention and promotion programs are typically controlled by researchers and human service professionals. Although community members increasingly participate in design and implementation, they still take a back seat. Professionals often operate on the basis of an expert model that (1) takes control away from the community, (2) promotes a power imbalance between professionals and citizens, (3) emphasizes deficits instead of strengths, and (4) limits the ability of people to help themselves (McKnight, 1995). A sense of ownership is important for the best outcomes (e.g., Peirson & Prilleltensky, 1994; Prilleltensky, 2005). This dimension ranges from expert-driven to community-driven participation.

AFFIRMATION QUADRANTS Quadrant I in Figure 18.2 represents interventions aiming to promote voice and choice in celebrating and building competencies. People are given an opportunity to exercise control over decisions affecting their lives, whereas modes of help build on former experiences of success.

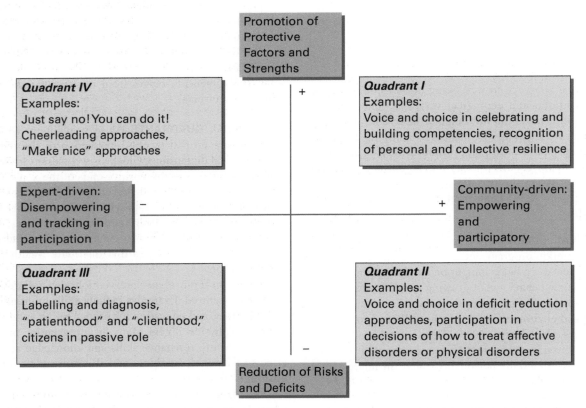

FIGURE 18.2 The Affirmation Field: The Intersection of the Capabilities and Participation Dimensions in the Promotion of Well-Being

Source: Prilleltensky, I. Promoting well-being: Time for a paradigm shift in health and human services. *Scandinavian Journal of Public Health* 33(Suppl 66), pp. 53-60. Copyright © 2005 by Taylor & Francis. Reprinted by permission of SAGE Publications, Ltd.

Quadrant II affords community members voice and choice in methods of deficit reduction. Citizens are made partners in the struggle to combat depression, stress, obesity, or infectious diseases.

Quadrant III is the epitome of clienthood and patienthood. Not only are people deprived of an opportunity to participate in helping and healing, but most of the focus is on diagnosis of pathology and labelling of maladaptive behaviour. Quadrant IV represents the unique combination of approaches that strives to be positive while keeping the person detached from the change process. Popular yet ineffective campaigns such as "just say no to drugs," or cheerleading efforts such as "you can do it if you want" represent vacuous promises of better health. While positive and effusive, such strategies fail to connect with the real-life experiences of youth growing up in drug-infested communities or with the struggle of many people to lower their weight despite lack of access to affordable and nutritious foods and vegetables.

4 BEFORE MOVING ON

> The conceptual framework for prevention and promotion that was presented includes four dimensions: an ecological dimension, a temporal dimension, a capability dimension, and a participation dimension. Discuss how each of these elements is relevant to prevention and promotion.

Research and Practice in Prevention and Promotion

Prevention activities may be either biological or psychological. As an example of biological primary prevention, encouraging pregnant women to avoid alcohol can prevent fetal alcohol syndrome (see Chapters 11 and 14). In fact, many prevention programs start with pregnant women, and include counselling on nutrition and substance use. An example of biological secondary prevention is the administration of special diets to children born with phenylketonuria (a genetic disorder characterized by an inability of the body to use an essential amino acid). As described in Chapter 14, this diet cannot correct the basic metabolic disorder, but it can prevent its most serious consequence, intellectual disability. Most prevention and mental health promotion programs, however, are primarily psychological or social in nature, and that is the type of program we will be discussing in this chapter.

Case Notes

The south side of Ypsilanti, Michigan, in the 1960s was a slum as most people probably picture slums in the United States; in fact, it was described as "one of the most congested slum areas in the state" (Schweinhart & Weikart, 1988). The children of the neighbourhood—Black and very poor—had difficulties when they entered school. They grew up into poverty and high rates of unemployment and imprisonment. The Perry Preschool Project set out to see whether the picture could be changed through a preschool educational program designed to give children the intellectual and social skills they needed for school. Selected participants were very poor three- and four-year-old children, with IQs between 60 and 90 (well below average), randomly assigned to experimental and control groups. For two school years, the children in the experimental program had two and a half hours a day of well-organized classroom activities. Each teacher worked with a group of five or six children. Also, every week during the school year, the teacher made a one-and-a-half-hour home visit to every mother and child, offering the mothers guidance in child-rearing skills.

What happened when these children started school? Initial results were encouraging: in kindergarten and Grade 1, the children in the experimental group showed more academic readiness and intellectual skills than those the control group. Disappointingly, by the time the children had reached Grades 3 and 4, differences in academic performance between the two groups had vanished.

Fortunately, the researchers continued to follow the children through their school-aged years and adulthood. The long-term effects of the Perry Preschool Project have been most interesting. At age 19, twice as many program participants as control children were employed, attending college, or receiving further training. High school graduation rates were 30% higher, and arrest and teen pregnancy rates were 40% lower. At age 27, program participants scored significantly higher than controls on literacy tests, and they were more likely to be employed (69% versus 56%) and own their own homes (27% versus 5%) (Schweinhart et al., 2005). Remarkably, the researchers were able to follow the participants in the Perry Preschool Project to age 40. Compared with participants in the control group, program participants at age 40 were less likely to be arrested five or more times (36% versus 55%) and more likely to be employed (70% versus 50%), earn $20 000 or more (60% versus 40%), and have a savings account (76% versus 50%). Moreover, the program was cost-effective. For every dollar invested in the 30-week program, there was a $14 return in savings from decreased special education, criminal justice, and welfare costs.

The Perry Preschool Project is one of the best known of the pioneering "first-generation" prevention and mental health promotion programs that began in the 1960s and 1970s. These early programs were often small and poorly funded and were rarely evaluated (Price, Cowen, Lorion, & Ramos-McKay, 1989). In 1982, the American Psychological

Association established a task force to study these prevention programs. The report of this task force profiled 14 soundly researched programs that had been effective in preventing a number of different problems (Price, Cowen, Lorion, & Ramos-McKay, 1988). These served as models for planning and redesigning "second-generation" programs in the 1980s and 1990s.

HIGH-RISK (SELECTIVE) PREVENTION PROGRAMS

Like the Perry Preschool Project, most of the early prevention programs—and, in fact, most programs being implemented today—are **high-risk programs**. Studies of these programs suggest that structured preschool experiences can give high-risk disadvantaged children a head start on their early academic performance. Although these gains in cognitive skills and academic performance diminish after several years, there are still enduring academic, health, and social impacts over the long term (Barnett, 2011; Camilli et al., 2010; Manning et al., 2010; Melhuish, 2011). For example, a preschool prevention program in North Carolina, called the Abecedarian Project, has been found to significantly reduce symptoms of depression when the participants reach 21 years of age (McLaughlin, Campbell, Pungello, & Skinner, 2007).

On the basis of the Perry Preschool Project and several other demonstration projects started in the early 1960s, the national Head Start project was established in the United States in 1966. This initiative provided one or two years of preschool experiences for nearly 1 million disadvantaged children. Although funding for the Head Start project has decreased over the years, and only one in five eligible disadvantaged children in the United States participates in the program, the long-term prevention effects of the Perry Preschool Project and other well-researched preschool projects have provided protection for Head Start through the period of severe cuts to social programs in the late 1980s and 1990s. In fact, the Head Start program has been extended to provide services to high-risk children from birth to three years of age (Early Head Start Benefits Children and Families, 2006; Ounce of Prevention Fund, 1994).

Another first-generation high-risk prevention project that has been well researched is the Prenatal Early Infancy Project. This project was initiated by David Olds in 1977 in Elmira, New York, a small, semi-rural community in upstate New York that was rated in the 1980 census as the most economically depressed area in the United States, and that had the highest rates of child abuse and neglect in the state. A major focus of the project was to prevent child abuse and neglect; it consisted of trained registered nurses carrying out home visits with first-time mothers from pregnancy through the child's second year of life (Olds, 1988, 1997).

Four hundred women were enrolled in the project before the thirtieth week of pregnancy, 85 percent of whom were considered to be high risk because they were low-income, unmarried, or teenaged. They were randomly assigned to the home visit program or to a control group that received transportation for health care and screening for health problems but no home visits.

The home visitation program was designed to improve three aspects of maternal and child functioning: (1) the outcomes of pregnancy, (2) quality of parenting, and (3) the mother's life course development (e.g., helping the mothers to return to school, find work, and plan future pregnancies). The nurses completed an average of 9 home visits during pregnancy, and 23 visits from birth through the second year of the child's life. Olds attempted to apply the ecological model described earlier in this chapter. Thus, the nurses were trained to attend to the immediate day-to-day needs of the mother and the child, as well as to other family and community concerns. This resulted in a very comprehensive program for fostering maternal and child development: nurses helped mothers learn about pregnancy, infant health, and child-rearing; helped them obtain support from families, friends, and community health and human services; and provided them with direct personal and emotional support.

The results of the evaluation research were striking. During the prenatal period, the women who received home visits improved the quality of their diets to a greater extent than did the women in the non-visited comparison group. By the end of pregnancy, nurse-visited women had fewer kidney infections, experienced greater informal social support, and made better use of formal community services. Two particularly high-risk groups showed especially strong benefits: among women who smoked, those who received home visits had 75 percent fewer preterm deliveries than did those in the control group, and among very young adolescents (aged 14 to 16), those who were nurse-visited had babies who were nearly 400 grams heavier.

During the first two years after delivery, 14% of the poor, unmarried teen mothers in the control group abused or neglected their children, in contrast to only 4% of the poor, unmarried teens visited by a nurse. Over a four-year period, the children of nurse-visited women were less likely to visit a physician or emergency department for injuries or ingestions. Among low-income, unmarried women, the rate of subsequent pregnancy was reduced by 42%, and the number of months that nurse-visited women participated in the workforce was increased by 83%. Kitzman, Olds, and colleagues (1997, 2000) conducted a replication of the Elmira study in Memphis, Tennessee, with a sample of predominantly African-American mothers, and reported similar positive results for the home visitation program (Olds, Kitzman, et al., 2004). In a nine-year follow-up of the Memphis study, Olds, Kitzman, and colleagues (2007) reported that nurse-visited women had longer intervals between the births of their first and second children and used welfare and food stamps less often than did women in the control condition. Moreover, the children born to nurse-visited women who were at particularly high risk (those with low psychological resources) had better Grade point averages and test scores in reading and math than did control children.

Moreover, in a 15-year follow-up of the Elmira study, Olds and colleagues (1997) found that the nurse-visited women had higher rates of employment than did the women in the control group, as well as lower rates of substance abuse; verified child abuse or neglect; and arrests, convictions, days in jail, use of welfare, and subsequent pregnancies. In the most recent follow-up when the youth were 19 years of age, Eckenrode et al. (2010) reported significantly lower rates of arrests and convictions for girls, but not boys, in the nurse home-visitation group compared with the control group.

In general, the effects of the Prenatal Early Infancy Project on preventing adverse outcomes tended to be concentrated on groups who were at highest risk for these problems—namely, poor, unmarried teenaged mothers and their children. The results of this project have fostered great interest in the use of home visits as an effective prevention approach for high-risk mothers and children. Subsequent reviews of the literature have reported positive impacts of home visitation programs in preventing child maltreatment (Geeraert, Van de Noortgate, Grietans, & Onghenea, 2004; MacLeod & Nelson, 2000; Sweet & Appelbaum, 2004).

UNIVERSAL PREVENTION AND PROMOTION PROGRAMS

A good example of a universal program is currently being implemented with children and families living in socio-economically disadvantaged neighbourhoods in eight communities in Ontario. This program, called Better Beginnings, Better Futures, is described in the Canadian Research Centre box.

CANADIAN RESEARCH CENTRE

Better Beginnings, Better Futures

The Better Beginnings, Better Futures project was announced in 1991 by the Ontario government as a 25-year longitudinal prevention research project focusing on children from birth to eight years of age and their families. The project has three major goals:

1. *Prevention.* To prevent serious social, emotional, behavioural, physical, and cognitive problems in young children.
2. *Promotion.* To promote the social, emotional, behavioural, physical, and cognitive development of these children.
3. *Community development.* To enhance the ability of socio-economically disadvantaged families and communities to provide for their children.

Funding was provided by the Ontario and federal governments to eight communities to provide services tailored to local circumstances for four years of program implementation. To determine both short-term and long-term effects, researchers will follow the progress of the children, their families, and their neighbourhoods until the children reach their mid-twenties. Five communities focused their programs on children from conception to four years of age (younger child sites), and three concentrated on the four- to eight-year-old age range (older child sites). Children and families from three communities that did not receive program funding are also being evaluated for comparison purposes. All

People participating in the Family Resource Centre, Highfield Community Enrichment Project (Better Beginnings, Better Futures) in Etobicoke, Ontario.

Courtesy of the Family Resource Centre/ Highfield Community Enrichment Project

communities offering programs followed the same model—one that is unique in several aspects:

- *A comprehensive ecological model.* Better Beginnings programs attempted to address this broad range of ecological influences on children. Unlike most prevention programs, the project was designed to address child development, parent/family development, and community development.
- *Local responsibility and significant parent–community involvement.* In most prevention projects, professionals plan, manage, and deliver services to parents, who are seen as receiving help. In Better Beginnings projects, professionals, parents, and other local community members worked collaboratively. Parents and other community

members were actively involved in all decisions about the local project, including program development, organization and management, staff hiring, and budgets. The transfer of this level of control and responsibility has the potential to empower community residents, who may have felt little control, individually or collectively, over their own lives and the lives of their children.

Project funding began in 1991, but it took each community at least two and a half years to develop such a comprehensive program, establish organization and management structures, and hire and train program staff, many of whom were local residents. Programs were implemented for four years from 1993 to 1997. Although the specific program activities differed somewhat across the eight communities, they generally had the following elements:

- *Home visits.* All projects for birth to four-year-olds included home visits to families during pregnancy and infancy. Drawing on Olds's work (just described), home visitors assisted all families in the neighbourhood with children four years of age or under who agreed to participate. Most of the home visitors were residents of the local neighbourhoods, and they worked with the families to meet basic needs, provide parent training and child development information, and link families with community health and social services and informal support resources.

- *Classroom enrichment.* The three project sites for the four- to eight-year-olds enriched children's formal educational experiences with social skills training, academic tutoring, and teacher support.
- *Child care enrichment.* All projects supplemented existing community child care with additional staff, resources, drop-in centres for at-home care providers, toy-lending libraries, and so on.
- *Other child-focused programs.* Other program elements, tailored to needs in each community, included play groups, breakfast programs, and school-based anti-bullying programs.
- *Family/parent-focused programs.* Again, a variety of activities were designed to meet community needs, including parent training and parent support groups, cooking classes, prenatal programs, and fathers' groups.
- *Community-focused programs.* A wide range of program activities were designed to create new resources in the community (e.g., food banks, crosswalks); activities for community members at large, designed to improve the quality of life in the community; and improved cultural awareness, relations, and pride. Included were such activities as neighbourhood safety working groups, cultural workshops and celebrations, and, for Indigenous people, a variety of healing activities and programs.

The Better Beginnings, Better Futures project is considered to be universal because it was offered to all children in a given age range and their families. The neighbourhoods selected for the program are "high risk" because they all have high concentrations of socioeconomically disadvantaged families, but all residents, regardless of their socioeconomic status, are actively encouraged to participate.

To adequately evaluate a program as comprehensive and broad-based as Better Beginnings requires a multidisciplinary approach. Project research includes extensive home interviews with parents; teacher ratings and direct assessments of the children's physical, cognitive, social, and mental development; descriptions of program activities and costs; and an evaluation of how well the programs were developed and implemented and whether they successfully involved community members as active decision makers.

Research on the short-term and medium-term impacts of the Better Beginnings Project at Grades 3, 6, and 9 indicated improved emotional, behavioural, and school functioning among children, and improved health for children in the older child sites (Peters, Bradshaw, et al., 2010). Also, parents reported better marital satisfaction and family functioning, improved social support, and improved neighbourhood quality. The percentage of students receiving special education services decreased, while the percentage of such students in schools in the control neighbourhoods increased. All Better Beginnings sites achieved at least 50 percent community member participation on planning and implementation committees. Community members from the eight sites volunteered 40 000 hours of their time in a year to local Better Beginnings projects.

The average cost of offering the Better Beginnings projects was between $1200 and $2000 per child per year. These expenditures are quite modest in comparison to other well-known prevention projects such as the High/Scope Perry Preschool Project, which averaged $8600 per child per year, and the Elmira nurse home visitation program, which averaged $4300 per child per year for two years (all costs are in 1997 Canadian dollars). Many prevention research projects have not reported average costs, making decisions by government policy-makers about which projects to fund at what cost very difficult. By Grade 12, it was estimated that for every dollar invested in Better Beginnings, there was a $2.50 savings in government spending (Peters, et al., 2016).

For current information on the Better Beginnings programs and current research results, see the Better Beginnings, Better Futures website: http://bbbf.queensu.ca.

In his review of the literature on mental health promotion and primary prevention, Cowen (1977) referred to progress as being made in "baby steps." Twenty years later, Cowen (1996) spoke of "lengthy strides." Clearly, the past few decades have seen tremendous growth in the research and practice bases of mental health promotion and prevention. In a meta-analytic review (see Chapter 17 for a discussion of meta-analysis) of 526 prevention and promotion programs for children and youth, Durlak and colleagues (2007) reported positive preventive impacts of these programs on children's emotional and behavioural problems.

Nation and colleagues (2003) conducted a review of prevention programs for children and youth. They concluded that the most effective prevention programs are those that

- are *comprehensive,*
- use *varied teaching methods,*
- provide *sufficient "dosage"* (i.e., the program is long and intensive enough to make a difference),
- are *theory-driven,*
- promote *positive relationships with adults and peers,*
- are *appropriately timed,*
- are *socio-culturally relevant,*
- use *outcome evaluation,* and
- have *well-trained staff.*

In Canada and the United States, prevention programs have been applied in a wide variety of settings to address many problems and disorders, including youth violence and bullying (Craig, Pepler, & Cummings, 2009; Crooks, Wolfe, Hughes, Jaffe, & Chiodo, 2008); criminal behaviour and conduct disorder (Farrington et al., 2017; Waddell, Hua, Garland, Peters, & McEwan, 2007); and depression and anxiety problems (Corrieri et al., 2014; Dozois & Dobson, 2004; Waddell, Hua, et al., 2007). In the United States, three influential reports, one by the Institute of Medicine (1994), one by the National Institute of Mental Health (Reiss & Price, 1996),

FOCUS 18.1

Preventing Substance Abuse and Dependence Among Canadian Children and Youth: Policy and Programs

Many children and youth experiment with drugs and alcohol. A study of nearly 30 000 youth in Grades 7 to 12 in British Columbia found that 54% had used alcohol and 30% had used marijuana (Smith et al., 2009). Excessive drug and alcohol use can lead to substance use disorder, one of the most prevalent mental disorders among young people (Waddell, Shephard, Schwartz, & Barican, 2014), which involves clinical impairment and distress, dependence, including tolerance and withdrawal (Children's Health Policy Centre, 2010). Within Canada's National Anti-drug Strategy, 70% of the funding goes toward law enforcement and treatment, while 30% is allocated to prevention programs (Department of Justice, 2012). However, other universal and selective prevention programs have been developed in Canada to prevent substance abuse disorders (Shamblen & Derzon, 2009).

We know from research what types of programs are ineffective and what types are effective in reducing rates of substance abuse (Stockings et al., 2016). Programs inspired by former U.S. First Lady Nancy Reagan's approach of "just say no to drugs" do not work (Tobler, 2000; Tobler et al., 2000). In spite of their popularity, non-interactive approaches in which adults lecture youth about drugs and alcohol to raise their awareness and knowledge (e.g., the police-developed project Drug Abuse Resistance Education [DARE]) have not been found to have any impact on youth's drug or alcohol use (West & O'Neal, 2004). What does work? Programs that are effective in reducing substance abuse use interactive formats with youth, including active participation with peers and youth-generated role plays, that focus on (1) knowledge and attitudes, including a critique of media influences; (2) drug-refusal interpersonal skills, such

as assertiveness and communication skills; and (3) intrapersonal skills such as goal setting, problem solving, and stress reduction (Sandler et al., 2014; Tobler, 2000; Tobler et al., 2000).

One evidence-based approach to substance abuse prevention is the Life Skills Training (LST) program (Botvin, 2000). LST is a universal prevention program that focuses on both general life skills and drug-refusal skills. Botvin, Baker, Dusenbury, Tortu, and Botvin (1990) evaluated LST in a randomized controlled trial of more than 4400 predominantly white Grade 7 students from 56 schools. The Grade 7 students attended 15 class periods during or after school, with ten booster class sessions in Grade 8 and five in Grade 9. At Grade 9, significant prevention effects were found for cigarette smoking, marijuana use, and immoderate alcohol use, and improvements were found in knowledge concerning substance use, interpersonal skills, and communication skills. Three years later, at Grade 12, more than 3500 students from the initial Grade 7 sample (60 percent of the original sample) were assessed again, and significant prevention effects were found for both drug and polydrug use (Botvin, Baker, Dusenbury, Botvin, & Diaz, 1995). Positive impacts of the LST combined with a universal, family-based program, the Strengthening Families Program, have also been reported (Spoth, Redmond, Trudeau, & Shin, 2002), and the economic benefits of LST have been found to outweigh its costs (Aos, Lieb, Mayfiel, Miller, & Pennucci, 2004).

If programs to prevent substance abuse and other mental, emotional, and behavioural problems are effective and save money in the long run, why do government policies such as the National Anti-Drug Strategy underinvest in them? ●

and one by the National Research Council and Institute of Medicine (O'Connell et al., 2009), have outlined how prevention strategies can be applied to a range of mental, emotional, and behavioural disorders.

⑤ BEFORE MOVING ON

> Describe one universal prevention program and one selective (high-risk) program, and report the findings from research on each of these programs.

Prevention and Promotion Policy in Canada

THE FEDERAL ROLE

Canada has been a leader in promoting the concept of prevention. In 1974, then federal Minister of Health Marc Lalonde released a report entitled *A New Perspective on the Health of Canadians*, which recognized the influence of

biological, lifestyle, and environmental factors on disease rates and argued for an increased emphasis on prevention and health promotion. The main message of the report was re-emphasized and expanded upon in two reports by subsequent federal Minister of Health Jake Epp, *Achieving Health for All* (1986) and *Mental Health for Canadians: Striking a Balance* (1988).

However, critics have argued that despite the rhetoric of prevention apparent in federal documents, little has changed in Canadian health systems (Hancock, 2011). Beginning in the late 1980s, the federal government began to drastically reduce transfer payments to the provinces, which are primarily responsible for health, education, and social services policies and programs. As Canada entered the twenty-first century, the federal government realized large budget surpluses and, under pressure from the public and the provinces, began to restore funding for health, education, and social services. In a review of Canadian programs, Waddell, Hua, and colleagues (2007) found that although there are several national and provincial ECD initiatives, only the Better Beginnings project has explicitly focused on the prevention of mental health problems and the promotion of mental health, and it is the only well-researched program that has demonstrated positive mental health outcomes for children.

When we compare Canada with several Western European countries, we find that Canada lags behind such countries in social policies that support families and children (Peters, Peters, Laurendeau, Chamberland, & Peirson, 2001). For example, France, Germany, the Netherlands, and the Scandinavian countries have implemented universal child care policies and, through various tax and transfer mechanisms, have dramatically reduced rates of child poverty, which is a significant risk factor in children's mental, emotional, and behavioural disorders. To address the gaps in Canadian mental health policy, the federal government created the Mental Health Commission of Canada (MHCC) in 2007. The MHCC is responsible for leading the development of innovative and collaborative mental health programs and policies, and released Canada's first mental health strategy in 2012 (MHCC, 2012). The strategy includes prevention and mental health promotion as the first of six strategic directions toward a transformed mental health system (MHCC, 2012). However, Canada has no national policy or funding mechanism for prevention or mental health promotion.

THE PROVINCIAL ROLE

Nelson, Prilleltensky, Laurendeau, and Powell (1996) surveyed mental health promotion and prevention in all provinces and territories. They found a good deal of support on paper for prevention, and many interesting projects. Nevertheless, they also reported that health funding has not been reallocated from treatment to prevention, and that funding for prevention remains very low in all provinces and territories. More recently, Kutcher, Hampton, and Wilson (2010) reported that while four of the 10 provinces have a child and adolescent policy or plan, little emphasis is placed on prevention and mental health promotion, except for suicide prevention.

There are more visible signs of prevention initiatives in some of the provinces, indicating that prevention is beginning to take root in provincial health, education, and social services. For example, Quebec has developed an infrastructure to support the growth of child care and prevention programs for children and youth (Laurendeau & Perreault, 1997), which has resulted in a diverse array of prevention programs being implemented (Chamberland et al., 1998). Several provinces have implemented home visitation programs (Waddell, McEwan, et al., 2007). In Ontario, McCain and Mustard (1999) completed a report entitled *Reversing the Real Brain Drain: Early Years Study—Final Report* (most recently updated in McCain, Mustard, and McCuaig, 2011), in which they argue that infant nurturing during the preschool years is essential for healthy child development and that preschool intervention programs can help parents provide such nurturing. Following from this report, Ontario Early Years Centres have been developed in many Ontario communities.

RETURN ON INVESTMENT

The sciences of prevention and early intervention have matured to the extent that it is now possible to compute the **return on investment (ROI)** of various programs and policies. Various states, such as Michigan, Connecticut, and Washington, have commissioned studies on the economic returns of high-quality programs in early childhood (see Focus box 18.2 for a list of reports on ROI).

Very reputable institutions such as the Brookings Institute, the Rand Corporation, the Federal Reserve Bank of Minneapolis, the Institute of Child Development at the University of Minnesota, and the Washington Institute for Public Policy have conducted state and national studies that demonstrate the human and financial benefits of investing in prevention.

In general, the research indicates that the economic returns for a variety of early intervention programs with families and children at risk range from $1.50 to $17.00 for every dollar invested. The savings come in the form of reduced attendance in costly special education programs,

FOCUS 18.2

Reports Documenting Return on Investment in Prevention

The following reports document the positive economic returns of early intervention and prevention programs in various American states. Returns usually vary from $1.50 to $17.00 for every dollar invested. They are presented alphabetically by state or by organization publishing the study.

1. Brookings Institution, www.brookings.edu/wp-content/uploads/2016/06/09_early_programs_isaacs.pdf
2. Chicago Parenting Centers,www.waisman.wisc.edu/cls/cbaexecsum4.html
3. Connecticut, www.cga.ct.gov/COC/PDFs/prevention/040207_stockportfolio_v1.pdf
4. Economic Policy Institute, www.epi.org/publication/book_enriching
5. Michigan, greatstartforkids.org/sites/default/files/file/ECIC_WilderStudy.pdf
6. Minneapolis, Federal Reserve Bank, www.minneapolisfed.org/~/media/files/publications/studies/earlychild/abc-part2.pdf
7. Rand Corporation, www.rand.org/pubs/research_briefs/RB9952.html
8. Washington State Institute for Public Policy, www.wsipp.wa.gov/pub.asp?docid=04-07-3901 ●

less contact with expensive social services, lower rates of incarceration and delinquency, and increased tax contributions through steady employment.

These findings, documented extensively in the reports listed in Focus box 18.2 and other academic publications, demonstrate that, indeed, one ounce of prevention is worth a pound—or more—of cure. Connecticut has passed a law requesting that all programs and agencies serving children invest at least 10 percent of their budgets in prevention.

A review of the economic benefits of early childhood development (ECD) programs came to the following conclusion:

> Investments in high-quality ECD programs consistently generate benefit-cost ratios exceeding 3-to-1—or more than a $3 return for every dollar invested—well above the 1-to-1 ratio needed to justify such investments. Even economists who are particularly skeptical about government programs make an exception for high-quality ECD programs.... This study demonstrates, for the first time, that providing all 20 percent of the nation's three- and four-year-old children who live in poverty with a high-quality ECD program would have a substantial payoff for governments and taxpayers in the future. (Lynch, 2004, pp. vii–viii)

⑥ BEFORE MOVING ON

How well do national and provincial policies in Canada support prevention and mental health promotion? Give an example to support your response.

Implementation, Dissemination, and Social Justice

While the outcomes of many prevention programs have been well documented, there is growing attention to three issues: program implementation, program dissemination, and social justice.

IMPLEMENTATION

Durlak (1998) has argued that **implementation** is important for understanding outcomes. If the outcomes of a prevention program are not achieved, this could be due either to problems with the program's theory of change or to poor implementation (Li-Grining & Durlak, 2014). Thus, it is important to determine how well a program is implemented. The study of implementation has been concerned with a program's fidelity, which has been defined as "the extent to which the innovation corresponds to the originally intended program" (Durlak & DuPre, 2008, p. 329), and a program's dosage, or the amount of the intervention that is delivered. Based on their review of prevention program implementation, Durlak and DuPre (2008) found that both program fidelity and dosage were related to outcomes. The higher the degree of fidelity and the more intensive the program, the better were the outcomes of the prevention program.

While fidelity appears to be important for outcomes, concern has been expressed that rigid adherence to a program model may lead to inappropriate applications of the program in some contexts. For example, suppose that a program has been developed to prevent problems in a predominantly White, rural population. The question arises as to how applicable, culturally sensitive, or relevant this model may be for other populations or communities, such as Indigenous children living on or off reserves or first generation immigrant South Asian youth. Some would argue that it is not only important but necessary to adapt and tailor programs to local conditions in order for them to be successful (Durlak & DuPre, 2008). While the debate about fidelity and adaptation has typically been framed as an "either-or" issue, it may be possible to ensure both fidelity and adaptation. Hawe, Shiell, and Riley (2004) have made a distinction between the form and function of a program, with form focusing on the specific way that the program is operated and function referring to the purpose or principles of the program. According to Hawe et al. (2004), this distinction suggests that it is possible to do the same program differently. For example, a parenting intervention might be delivered in different languages with unique cultural referents, while having a common set of principles. This distinction suggests that it is possible to have both fidelity and adaptation at the same time. Both are important, as Durlak and DuPre's (2008) review found that both fidelity and adaptation are associated with positive outcomes.

DISSEMINATION

Wandersman and colleagues (2008) have developed a model for the dissemination and adoption of prevention programs. They argue that **dissemination** is influenced by three interrelated systems: the prevention synthesis and translation system, the prevention delivery system, and the prevention support system.

First, the prevention synthesis and translation system acknowledges that scientific reports and journal articles are insufficient tools for transmitting knowledge about effective prevention programs. Rather, such information must be translated for practitioners, lay audiences, and policy-makers into user-friendly materials, as suggested by social marketing theory (Flay et al., 2005; Gormley, 2011; Wandersman et al., 2008). Second, the prevention support system includes individual, organizational, and community supports for prevention at the local level. There is growing evidence of the importance of the prevention support system for the adoption of prevention programs (Wandersman, Chien, & Katz, 2012). Good training materials and readiness for change are important, but must be reinforced by technical assistance and capacity-building such as training, networking, and consultation. The third component is the prevention delivery system, which includes stakeholders directly involved in implementing the program.

SOCIAL JUSTICE

Ample evidence suggests that many social and psychological ills can be traced to social injustice. If not the sole source, social injustice is at least a contributing factor; however, rarely do prevention or mental health promotion programs address issues of social justice (Prilleltensky, 1994b). **Social justice** "deals with the fair and equitable allocation of resources, obligations, and bargaining powers in society" (Prilleltensky & Nelson, 2013). A focus on social justice draws attention to issues of economic inequality, racism, sexism, and other societal sources of injustice. Joffe and Albee (1981) refer to these injustices as the "causes of the causes." The late George Albee (1996) was an outspoken advocate for the use of social and political action as a prevention tool. To date, however, most prevention programs focus on the individual or micro levels of analysis to the neglect of macro-level social injustices. In a review of 526 prevention studies, Durlak and colleagues (2007) found that none of the studies attempted to change community conditions.

Despite the call for a social justice approach to prevention (Albee, 1996; Joffe & Albee, 1981), to date there has been a lack of practical program models that exemplify such a perspective. A special issue of the *Journal of Primary Prevention* on social justice (Kenny & Hage, 2009) and a chapter by Prilleltensky and Nelson (2013) have attempted to bring together the concepts of social justice and prevention. Examples of this integration include Matthews and Adams's (2009) description of a project to prevent the negative consequences of heterosexism that included civic action and political awareness; Kivnick and Lymburner's (2009) description of a community program to promote social justice consciousness with youth through the arts; and Buhin and Vera's (2009) intervention to prevent racism at both the individual and policy levels. While research is needed on prevention programs that strive to create social justice, this is an important future direction for the field of prevention.

In summary, Canadian community psychologist, prevention researcher, policy advocate, and former Quebec politician Camil Bouchard (1994) noted the limitations of prevention programs that do not tackle issues of social injustice:

> Canadian families and children suffering the consequences of poverty are growing in number. In this context, the sole use of preventive psychosocial programs to counter the consequences of poverty without an equally important global strategy to reduce economic inequality or poverty itself seems incomplete, inefficient, and even cynical. (p. 44)

CULTURAL COMPETENCE AND ANTI-RACISM

Given the history of colonization, enslavement, and racial segregation in North America, issues of race, culture, and ethnicity are critical dimensions of social justice. The importance of race in understanding mental health is underscored by a large body of evidence that racialized people face significant inequities in mental health outcomes and their determinants (Paradies et al., 2015; Pieterse, Todd, Neville, & Carter, 2012). These health and social inequities are influenced by various types of racism experienced by racialized communities. **Internalized racism** refers to the psychological internalization of negative beliefs and stigma about a person's own racial or ethnic group (Sullivan & Cross, 2016). **Interpersonal racism** consists of relational interactions that convey hostility, disgust, or other forms of denigration of others according to their racial identity, and includes both overt and covert forms. Although overt forms of interpersonal racism are less common in today's society, there remain significant concerns about covert forms (also called **microaggressions**) (Sue et al., 2007). These unconscious, unintentional, subtle, and frequent acts (e.g., condescending statements, crossing the road when seeing a person of colour) have been shown to have significant negative effects on mental health (Wong, Derthick, David, Saw, & Okazaki, 2014). A third type of racism consists of **structural racism** (related concepts include systemic and institutional racism) involve collective beliefs, behaviours, practices, and policies of societies and institutions that function to disadvantage radicalized people and produce racial inequities between groups (Bailey et al., 2017).

There has been a growing recognition of the importance of cultural competence in the field of psychology as a way to respond to increasingly diverse and complex contexts. Historically, the emphasis in cultural competence approaches has been placed on educating practitioners about the cultural characteristics and beliefs of diverse clients, and the cultural adaptation of mainstream interventions. Although evidence suggests that cultural adaptation can contribute to improved outcomes for racialized or cultural minority groups (Hall, Ibaraki, Huang, Marti & Stice, 2016; Huey, Tilley, Jones, & Smith, 2014), such approaches do not necessarily address underlying issues of systemic racism or power relations between mainstream professionals and minority clients. There are increasing calls, therefore, for more critical (Christopher, Wendt, Marecek, & Goodman, 2014) and anti-racist/anti-oppressive (Corneau & Stergiopoulos, 2012) approaches to mental health practice and intervention that involve professionals critically examining their own power and privilege, and engaging clients in analyzing and challenging racism and other systems of oppression.

Another approach to culturally relevant intervention involves the use of Indigenous or culturally specific approaches (Barrera, Castro, & Steiker, 2014). These interventions use strategies that are grounded in the distinct cultural practices, values, and paradigms of ethnocultural groups, and often differ substantially from mainstream Western approaches. Such interventions are promising practices, because they not only potentially offer direct therapeutic benefit, but also create safe, alternative spaces for oppressed communities, where members can be exposed to positive socialization and identity development experiences (Jones & Neblett, 2016). For example, rights of passage programs have demonstrated considerable success in improving outcomes for youth of African descent (Okwumabua, Okwumabua, Peasant, Watson, & Walker, 2014). Rites of passage are a long-established tradition within various African (and other) cultures, during which adolescents undergo a ritualized initiation into adulthood, through an intensive educative process facilitated by community and elders (Harvey & Hill, 2004).

 BEFORE MOVING ON

> Using an example, describe the three systems that are important for program dissemination.

SUMMARY

- Universal, selective, and indicated prevention are approaches to prevent mental, emotional, and behavioural disorders. Mental health promotion strives to promote the ability to enjoy life, the ability to deal with life's challenges, emotional well-being, spiritual well-being, social connections, and respect for culture, equity, social justice, and personal dignity.

- Historically, the field of prevention has shifted from a pre–germ theory period to a public health approach to an educational approach.

- Risk, resilience, protection, and ecological levels of analysis are important theoretical constructs that serve to focus the strategies and goals of prevention programs.

- The Strengths, Prevention, Empowerment, and Community Change (SPEC) framework includes a contextual field, with ecological and temporal dimensions, and an affirmation field, with capability and participation fields, which are important for conceptualizing prevention programs.

- Both selective (high-risk) and universal approaches to prevention have been developed and found effective in preventing mental, emotional, and behavioural problems through evaluation research.

- While there is much rhetoric about the value of prevention and mental health promotion in federal and provincial policy in Canada, and considerable research attesting to the effectiveness of prevention programs, prevention and mental health promotion remain underfunded and underdeveloped.

- Issues in program implementation, program dissemination, and social justice are growing concerns in the prevention field that need further attention.

KEY TERMS

community psychology (p. 464)

cumulative risk (p. 469)

dissemination (p. 479)

ecological approach (p. 466)

ecological perspective (p. 465)

high-risk programs (p. 474)

implementation (p. 479)

indicated prevention (p. 465)

internalized racism (p. 480)

interpersonal racism (p. 480)

macrosystem (p. 468)

mental health (p. 465)

mental health promotion (p. 465)

microaggressions (p. 480)

microsystem (p. 468)

prevention (p. 465)

primary prevention (p. 465)

protective factors (p. 468)

public health approach (p. 467)

resilience (p. 468)

return on investment (ROI) (p. 478)

risk factors (p. 468)

secondary prevention (p. 465)

selective prevention (p. 465)

social justice (p. 480)

structural racism (p. 480)

tertiary prevention (p. 465)

universal approach (p. 465)

STEPHEN D. HART

•

RONALD ROESCH

CHAPTER

19

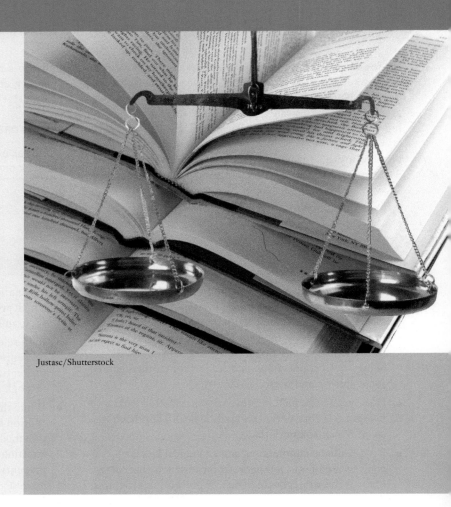

Justasc/Shutterstock

Mental Disorder and the Law

LEARNING OBJECTIVES

AFTER READING THIS CHAPTER, STUDENTS WILL BE ABLE TO:

1 Describe the basic structure of the Canadian legal system, including the primary sources of law in Canada.

2 Explain the law's assumptions regarding human nature and how mental disorder challenges these assumptions.

3 Explain the common law principles of police powers and *parens patriae* and how they provide a rationale for Canadian civil mental health law with respect to involuntary hospitalization and treatment.

4 Define and differentiate the concepts of mental state at the time of the offence and mental state at the time of trial in Canadian criminal law.

5 Describe some of the general and special ethical problems faced by psychologists who become involved in legal proceedings.

Scott Jeffery Schutzman was a man of considerable charm, intelligence, and creativity. Born in the United States, he moved to Canada with his family when he was about 13 years old. He skipped two grades in school, graduating from Ryerson (then a polytechnical school) with a diploma in electronics technology. He became a top salesman for an electronics firm. He was also an avid and skilled skier and a talented amateur physicist—yes, physicist. Despite a lack of formal education, he studied topics such as time measurement, anti-gravity, and relativity. He even collaborated with academics, such as a professor at Stanford University's SLAC National Accelerator Laboratory in the United States, who described his thinking as "years ahead of its time." He was given the nickname "Professor."

The "Professor" also had a serious mental disorder. Starting in 1985, when he was about 29 years old, he started to exhibit symptoms of psychosis. For example, he held some beliefs that were odd or eccentric, and others that were outright delusional. At various times, he claimed that he placed the last antenna on top of the CN Tower in Toronto; was married to celebrities such as Joan Rivers and Joan Collins; operated a business, the Starson Corporation, that was building a "starship"; communicated with extra-terrestrials; and was the next head of NASA. He considered himself to be the "son of the stars" and eventually changed his surname from Schutzman to Starson. His behaviour was also disorganized. He was overactive and had frequent outbursts of shouting and inexplicable laughter. He lost his job and his personal relationships suffered. He made repeated threats to kill others and engaged in other fear-inducing behaviour, including stalking Joan Rivers. He was hospitalized, arrested, and charged with criminal offences on many occasions. His symptoms improved when he was treated with antipsychotic medications, but he found that these medications also impaired his ability to think creatively. He considered this side effect "worse than death" and so refused treatment. His mental disorder worsened over the years.

***

In November 1998, Professor Starson was found not criminally responsible on account of mental disorder (NCRMD) on two counts of uttering death threats toward fellow residents of the Toronto townhouse in which he resided, and was subsequently detained in a secure facility. His psychiatrists proposed to treat him with medications, but he refused. The psychiatrists sought approval from the Ontario Consent and Capacity Board to treat Professor Starson involuntarily under that province's *Health Care Consent Act* (1996), arguing that he was not capable of making his own decisions about treatment—that is, unable to understand information relevant to making a decision about the treatment and to appreciate the reasonably foreseeable consequences of a decision. The board granted approval for involuntary treatment, finding that Professor Starson was in "almost total" denial of his mental disorder and failed to appreciate the consequences of his decision to refuse treatment. The board concluded that treatment was in Professor Starson's own best interests.

Professor Starson refused to accept the board's decision. He sought judicial review, first before the Ontario Superior Court of Justice, then the Court of Appeal of Ontario, and finally the Supreme Court of Canada (*Starson v. Swayze*, 2003). These courts reviewed the evidence and found the board had erred in its decision. First, although Professor Starson did not accept that his condition was a mental disorder, he recognized that his brain did not function normally. Second, there was no evidence that he failed to appreciate the potential risks and benefits of treatment (or lack thereof). Consequently, the board was wrong to conclude that he lacked the capacity to make a decision regarding his treatment. Furthermore, the courts found that the board, when it considered what was in his best interests, overstepped its legislative authority. Put simply, the board had no right to consider the wisdom of his ultimate decision regarding treatment, only to consider whether he was capable to make such a decision. The law must respect the dignity and autonomy of all Canadians, including those with mental health problems, by allowing them the freedom to make decisions that others might regard as foolish unless it is proven they are incapable of making such a decision.

The court decisions in this case, including the final one by the Supreme Court of Canada to uphold those by the lower courts, were praised by some as protecting the rights of those with mental disorder, and condemned by others as permitting mental disorder to ruin the lives of people who suffer from it. But the decisions were not easy for the courts to make. For example, the Supreme Court of Canada decision was split: six justices voted with the majority, but three dissented. One of the dissenters was the Chief Justice, the Right Honourable Beverley McLachlin, P.C. She later made a rare public commentary about the challenges posed by this case (McLachlin, 2005, n.p.):

> Professor Starson may well never recover from the illness that afflicts him and may spend the rest of his life in custody or under the significant control of the criminal justice system. Hence the cruel paradox—freedom to refuse "medication" may in fact result in institutional confinement and continued debilitation.... [O]ur law governing hospitalization and consent continues to grapple with the challenges of appropriately balancing the autonomy and dignity of mentally ill persons with their right to treatment and the important objective of protecting the public from dangerous individuals.... Laws cannot heal people ... [b]ut the law can create a social and regulatory environment that assists medical professionals in delivering their services in a manner that is both ethical and respectful of the rights and needs of the mentally ill.

The comments of Chief Justice McLachlin may strike some as idealistic rather than realistic. It came as little surprise to many that in the wake of the Supreme Court of Canada's decision, Professor Starson's symptoms persisted and worsened without treatment; he even began to refuse food. The hospital once again went before the Ontario Consent and Capacity Board, this time gathering and presenting incontrovertible evidence that he was incapable of making decisions about treatment and should be medicated involuntarily. The treatment led to a marked improvement in Professor Starson's mental health. He also regained his physical health. Once he was well enough to be deemed capable of making treatment decisions, he no longer resisted medications. With continued treatment, he eventually improved to the point that the Ontario Review Board was able to relax his conditions of detention and allow him greater freedoms. The Professor later sought absolute discharge, which would include the freedom to stop taking medications, on the grounds that he no longer posed a risk to public safety, but this request was denied by the Ontario Review Board—a decision supported by the Court of Appeal for Ontario—due to concerns he would quickly decompensate and again engage in intimidating behaviour. With the benefit of hindsight, then, we may conclude that Chief Justice McLachlin's comments were prescient. Ultimately, the law actually helped to make sure that Professor Starson received appropriate treatment, in a manner that respected his wishes as much as possible and that protected both his rights and freedoms and those of the public.

(Based on information presented in McLachlin, 2005; O'Neill & Fischer, 2005; Seymour, 2006; Schutzman (Re), 2013; *Starson v Swayze*, 2003.)

As the previous chapters have made clear, many forms of mental disorder are associated with social dysfunction or disability—problems getting along with other people, problems fulfilling social roles and obligations, and so forth. It should come as no surprise, then, that many people suffering from mental disorder find themselves in conflict with the law or involved in disputes with other people that end up in court. In many different societies and for many years, legal traditions have recognized this fact and made special provisions for handling disputes that involve people suffering from mental disorder. These legal traditions have also come to recognize that mental health professionals can play an important role by providing information about mental disorder to legal decision makers. In fact, all the major mental health professions—clinical psychology, psychiatry, and so on—now have forensic specialists, people whose work focuses primarily on topics related to mental disorder and the law.

The Starson case raises some fascinating questions about mental disorder and the law in Canada, as well as the role of psychologists in court. Should people suffering from mental disorders be held responsible for their behaviour and punished, or should they be found not responsible and treated? How should decisions of this sort be made? How much confidence should we have in psychologists when they state that people suffer from mental disorder that makes them incapable of making decisions about their own health care, not criminally responsible, or a risk of harm to others? How much weight should be accorded to the evidence presented by psychologists in court? Is the state of the science in psychology sufficiently developed to be used as the basis for making decisions that change the lives of others? Who do psychologists work for when they participate in legal proceedings—the people who are parties to a proceeding, the lawyers who represent them, or perhaps even the judges who preside over the proceedings?

To answer these and related questions, we will examine Canadian law as it relates to mental disorder and the practice of psychology in legal settings. The first part of the chapter is devoted to the issue of law. We start by outlining the structure of the Canadian legal system and discussing what various sources of law (constitutional, statutory, and common) have to say about mental disorder. We then take a closer look at two types of statutory law: civil mental health law and criminal law. We discuss the nature of the problem that the law is trying to address, the provisions it makes for special care and control of people suffering from mental disorder, and what research has revealed about the issue. The second part of the chapter is devoted to an examination of the role of psychology in the legal system. We begin by discussing the ways in which psychologists might become involved in legal proceedings. Next, we review ethical codes of psychology, focusing in particular on the ethical codes of forensic psychology, to see what guidance they offer. Finally, we examine the status of psychology in the law.

Mental Disorder in Canadian Law

Canadian law assumes that people can (and typically do) think and act in a reasoned, deliberate manner. People may be treated differently under the law when it is demonstrated that their thinking is irrational or their behaviour is involuntary. The inability to perceive accurately or reason correctly about the outside world is referred to as cognitive impairment; the inability to exert adequate controls on one's behaviour is sometimes referred to as volitional impairment (Hart, 2001). Canadian law recognizes that, in some cases, mental disorder may cause cognitive or volitional impairment. Courts and tribunals often call on mental health professionals to render opinions concerning the existence and impact of mental disorder in a given case, recognizing that they have special expertise in evaluating people and understanding human behaviour, especially abnormal behaviour.

 BEFORE MOVING ON

Why is mental disorder relevant in Canadian law?

The legal concept of mental disorder is not bound by psychological or medical definitions. The law typically defines mental disorder as any impairment of psychological functioning that is internal, stable, and involuntary in nature—that is, not a reflection of situational or contextual factors, not an ephemeral or transient state, and not a self-induced condition. Legal definitions of mental disorder, then, typically focus on acute and severe disturbances in thought, affect, or behaviour. Examples include cognitive disorders such as dementia; psychotic disorders such as schizophrenia; mood disorders such as major depressive disorder; developmental disorders such as autistic disorder; and intellectual disability. Mental disorders of this sort have been recognized in medicine and in law for millennia.

Although quite broad or general, the legal definition of mental disorder is much narrower than that used by mental health professionals. This means that some mental disorders that are recognized by mental health professionals and even included in the fifth edition of the *Diagnostic and Statistical Manual of Mental Disorders* (DSM-5; American Psychiatric Association, 2013) may not meet the legal definition of a mental disorder. One example is substance-related disorders, such as alcohol intoxication. Alcohol intoxication can result in severe disturbance of thought, affect, and behaviour. In most cases, however, intoxication is the result of voluntary behaviour—a conscious and deliberate decision to drink alcoholic beverages—and the disturbance in psychological functioning is temporary. For these reasons, the law typically does not consider alcohol intoxication to be a mental disorder. But what if the intoxication was involuntary? Perhaps a man who attends a party is given alcohol without his knowledge, or a woman who consumes a single drink of alcohol has an extreme reaction due to undiagnosed liver problems or the unanticipated effects of a new medication she is taking. And what if the intoxication is not temporary? It is possible that a person who drinks sufficient alcohol may suffer severe and long-lasting—even permanent—effects. In these latter scenarios, the law may consider people to have been suffering from a mental disorder.

In legal proceedings, triers of fact—those responsible for making decisions, such as judges, juries, or review boards—must determine whether or not a person who is party to the proceedings has a mental disorder, according to how mental disorder is defined in the relevant law. Mental health professionals act merely as consultants to triers of fact, providing expert observations and opinions. It is irksome to mental health professionals, but a fact of life, that their opinions may be accorded relatively little weight by triers of fact, or even disregarded entirely. The opinions of mental health professionals are most likely to be given weight when those opinions are based on an accurate understanding of the relevant law. We turn now to an overview of the Canadian legal system.

 BEFORE MOVING ON

> What are the primary differences between legal and psychological definitions of mental disorder in Canada?

The Canadian Legal System

Law, most generally, is a set of rules and procedures designed to regulate the behaviour of people (Melton, 1985). The fundamental goal of the law is to prevent and resolve, in a principled manner, conflicts among people. When people think about the law, they typically imagine lawyers arguing in front of a judge or jury in criminal court; yet people's encounters with the law take place, for the most part, outside court. Indeed, the law is so much a part of day-to-day life in modern society that we are rarely conscious of the extent to which it influences our actions. In Canada, there are three primary sources of law. **Constitutional law** comprises rules that govern the administration of Canada as a nation state. It both authorizes and limits the powers of the government vis-à-vis its citizens. **Statutory law** comprises written codes enacted by legislative authorities. Various statutes establish the law with respect to specific issues. **Common law** comprises legal precedent. It is the body of decisions made in past cases with respect to specific issues. Other sources of law include such things as international conventions and treaties.

CONSTITUTIONAL LAW

The development of Canada's legal system was strongly influenced by its historic ties to the United Kingdom. Canada has the same form of government as the United Kingdom, known as a constitutional monarchy. Under this system, the head of state is a monarch (king or queen), but day-to-day administration of the country is carried out by a government of parliamentary executives, who are in turn elected by the citizenry. The rights and responsibilities of the monarch, parliamentary executives, and citizenry are set out in a constitution. The Canadian constitution is a work in progress, with some parts as old as the country itself and other parts written and adopted within the last 30 years or so, but it enshrines the principles and precedents that were established in British law over the past thousand years and more. When questions arise about whether the government is living up to its responsibilities to care and provide for citizens, or whether it is overstepping its role and interfering in the private lives of citizens, it is the constitution that determines the answers. For this reason, constitutional law can be considered the single most important source of law in Canada.

The *Charter of Rights and Freedoms* (*Constitution Act*, 1982) sets out the fundamental freedoms of citizens, including freedom of conscience and religion; freedom of thought, belief, opinion, and expression; freedom of peaceful assembly; and freedom of association. It also sets out basic rights, including democratic rights, mobility rights, legal rights, equality rights, and language rights. Importantly, the *Charter* guarantees that the rights and freedoms enjoyed by ordinary citizens cannot be denied to others simply because they suffer from mental disorder. (Canada is unusual in this respect; even the *Universal Declaration of Human Rights* of the United Nations does not make such a guarantee.) Under the Equality Rights provision, section 15(1) of the *Charter*:

> Every individual is equal before and under the law and has the right to the equal protection and equal benefit of the law without discrimination and, in particular, without discrimination based on race, national or ethnic origin, colour, sex, age or mental or physical disability.

For people with mental disorders, the implications of section 15(1) are profound. Because the *Charter* prohibits discrimination on the basis of mental disability, they cannot be held against their will, prevented from expressing themselves, or denied opportunities for such things as employment or housing solely on the basis that they suffer from mental disorder. This minimizes the harm that may stem from stereotypical attitudes—sweeping and inaccurate generalizations—such as, "All people with mental disorder are at risk for violence" or "All people with mental disorder are incapable of making decisions about their health care." Thus, infringement of rights requires demonstration of a functional link—sometimes referred to in law as a causal nexus—between a person's mental disorder and some legally relevant impairment of cognitive or volitional capacity.

Constitutional law thus permits restriction of the rights and freedoms of people suffering from mental disorder. If people suffering from mental disorder are found to be incompetent to make important decisions about their lives—such as how to raise their children, what to do with their money, and how to care for their health and well-being—or incapable of controlling their behaviour, then others may make such decisions on their behalf or they may be detained and treated involuntarily (as we will discuss later). At the same time, the Constitution places strict limits on the extent to which rights and freedoms can be restricted, as well as the manner in which they can be restricted. The nature of the restrictions must be justified in light of any cognitive or volitional impairment resulting from mental disorder; they cannot be arbitrary or excessive. Also, the restrictions must be imposed in accord with the principles of fundamental justice, so that people are informed of the reasons for the restrictions and have the opportunity to challenge their imposition. In essence, the *Charter* demands that people suffering from mental disorder are treated fairly and retain as many of their rights and freedoms as possible.

STATUTORY LAW

In Canada, statutes are written and enacted by the government, with the support and approval of the monarch. If one considers federal, provincial, and municipal statutes together, there are literally hundreds of statutes in Canada that contain many thousands of rules governing the actions of citizens. Statutes set out what should and should not be done with respect to trade and commerce, health and safety, education, taxation, the environment—in fact, it is not an exaggeration to state that statutory law governs every aspect of the lives of Canadians, and every moment of their lives, from birth to death. Statutes are continually revised and updated to take into account changes in the world and the opinions and desires of citizens, but they must always be consistent with the Constitution. Mental disorder plays an important role in two types of statutory law in Canada: civil mental health law and criminal law. Civil mental health law differs across the provinces and territories, but criminal law does not (this is because the Canadian constitution gives the federal government primary authority with respect to setting criminal law, but gives provinces and territories primary authority with respect to health care).

Civil mental health law sets out the procedures under which people suffering from mental disorder can be involuntarily hospitalized or treated. These laws attempt to strike a balance between, on the one hand, the right of people suffering from mental disorder to receive the treatment of their choice—including the right not to receive treatment at all—and, on the other hand, the responsibility of the government to protect its citizens from harm. Although at first glance the mental health laws of the provinces and territories appear very similar, there are important differences among them. In fact, the same person would be treated in very different ways across the country, depending on the province or territory in which he or she lived.

Criminal law—specifically, the *Criminal Code* (*R.S.C.* 1985, c. C-46)—defines various criminal offences and sets out the procedures under which people can be arrested, tried, and sentenced for those offences. The *Criminal Code* includes provisions for dealing with people who may suffer from mental disorder that renders them not criminally responsible (i.e., not morally blameworthy and therefore undeserving of punishment) or that renders them unfit to stand trial (i.e., incapable of participating in the trial process). The provisions set out procedures for detaining people for assessment of their mental state, specify the nature of the impairment that must be evident before someone is deemed not criminally responsible or unfit to stand trial on account of mental disorder, and specify what happens to people who are found not criminally responsible or unfit to stand trial on account of mental disorder. The *Criminal Code* is intended to deal with people who are aged 18 or older; people in conflict with the law who are between the ages of 12 and 17 inclusive are dealt with under the *Youth Criminal Justice Act* (*R.S.C.* 2002, c. 1), which is similar to the *Criminal Code* but has a more rehabilitative philosophy in recognition of the special status and needs of young people.

COMMON LAW

Written laws, both constitutional and statutory, have important limitations. For example, it is impossible to anticipate every conflict that might arise between citizens, and so gaps in existing law become apparent over time. Also, it is impossible to write laws that are perfectly clear and unambiguous, so all existing laws must be interpreted and re-interpreted continually. What courts, tribunals, and review boards do on a day-to-day basis—the decisions they reach in particular cases, and the reasoning underlying those decisions—comprises common law, and is written down in legal journals. Decisions made at a local level may be reviewed by courts at a higher level; for example, the decision of a judge sitting on the bench of a provincial superior court may be reviewed by colleagues who sit on the provincial appellate court, or the decisions of a provincial appellate court may be reviewed by the highest court in the land, the Supreme Court of Canada. The outcomes of these reviews also become part of common law.

Common law may eventually become enshrined in statutory or even constitutional law. For example, common law has long recognized that the monarch has the duty—in reality, both the responsibility and the authority—to arrest, prosecute, and punish those who breach the peace and disturb subjects of the realm. In Canada, this common law principle of the police powers of the state is enshrined in constitutional and statutory law. Another ancient common law principle, **parens patriae**, recognizes that the monarch or state has the duty—again, both the responsibility and the authority—to care for citizens when they are unable to care for themselves. Historically, the monarch's duty extended to three major groups of people: children, those with what is now called intellectual disability (intellectual developmental disorder) in DSM-5, and those with serious mental disorders. The "care" offered by the monarch or state to people with intellectual disability or serious mental disorder could include involuntary detention in a hospital or asylum. In Canada, this common law principle is, in part, enshrined in the civil mental health laws of the provinces and territories.

In the domain of civil law, Quebec differs from the rest of Canada. It relies on a **civil code** instead of common law. The civil code is a comprehensive set of legal rules and principles that guides legal proceedings and decision making. Quebec's civil code was based on the Napoleonic code and reflects that province's historic ties to France. As in common law jurisdictions, previous court decisions may be considered when the law is silent or unclear regarding a particular issue.

A Closer Look at Civil Mental Health Law

Virtually every Canadian is touched by mental disorder in some way. According to the epidemiological research (Health Canada, 2002), at some point in our lives about 20% of Canadians—about five to six million of us—will experience a serious mental disorder, perhaps one as common as a major depressive disorder (lifetime prevalence of about 10 to 15%) or one as rare as a schizophrenic disorder, a bipolar mood disorder, or intellectual disability (each with a lifetime prevalence of about 1%). National surveys indicate that about 1 in 10 Canadians reported their mental health was only "fair" or even "poor" during the past year (Government of Canada, 2006), and about 1 in 6 reported they were in need of or had sought services to deal with mental or emotional problems in the past year (Sareen, Cox, Afifi, Clara, & Yu, 2005; Sunderland & Findlay, 2013).

Mental disorder is often associated with a call to action—it provokes in others the desire to help people who are suffering from mental disorder. Most of the time, people with mental disorder can and do function adequately while living in the community, either on their own, with personal support from family and friends, or with the assistance of health care professionals. What happens when mental disorder is so serious that it impairs people's daily functioning? Some people lack insight and cannot recognize that they suffer from mental disorder and may reject treatment or other assistance; others have symptoms so severe that they are unable to make rational decisions about their own care or unable to provide the necessities of life, such as food, clothing, or even basic hygiene, for themselves. There are no good estimates of the number of Canadians who are unable to care for themselves or to make decisions regarding their own care due to mental disorder, but anyone who has visited a big city like Montreal, Toronto, or Vancouver has seen some of these people living on the street or panhandling. What are we to do with people in this position—simply leave them to suffer on their own, or force care on them against their wishes?

INVOLUNTARY ADMISSION

The mental health acts of all 10 provinces and 3 territories permit involuntary admission of people suffering from mental disorder under specific conditions. Also known as involuntary hospitalization or **civil commitment**, this is the process of detaining people against their wishes on the grounds that they pose a risk to themselves or others on account of mental disorder. In general, the legal criteria are very similar insofar as they allow involuntary admission of people when three things are true: (1) they suffer from a mental disorder; (2) they pose a risk to their own health or safety, or to the health and safety of others, on account of this mental disorder; and (3) they are unwilling to consent or incapable of consenting to treatment on a voluntary basis.

But there are also some important differences across jurisdictions (Gray, Hastings, Love, & O'Reilly, 2016). First, some jurisdictions define mental disorder broadly, whereas others focus more narrowly on serious mental illness. Second, some jurisdictions define harm to self or others broadly to include physical or (serious) psychological harm, whereas others focus more narrowly on physical harm. Third, some jurisdictions permit involuntary admission when people pose a risk for deterioration in their physical or mental health due to mental disorder, even when they don't pose a direct risk for harm to self or others. Fourth, some jurisdictions also require that people have a need for treatment or incapacity to make decisions about their own treatment, in addition to risk of harm to self or others (or risk for deterioration). Fifth, a few jurisdictions require that the involuntary admission is to an inpatient treatment facility, where others permit treatment on an outpatient basis in the form of leave from an inpatient unit or a community treatment order. These differences are summarized in Table 19.1.

In addition, the length of time of initial and subsequent involuntary admission, the process for review or appeal of involuntary admission, and rules regarding involuntary treatment differ markedly across the jurisdictions.

Laws that allow involuntary hospitalization and treatment of physical illness or mental disorder clearly infringe on the basic rights and freedoms of citizens. But this infringement may be legally justified by the principle of police powers and the principle of *parens patriae* (Melton, Petrila, Poythress, & Slobogin, 2007; Morse, 2002, 2004; Schopp, 2001). The issue is, in essence, one of public safety: governments have a legal responsibility to protect citizens, and this includes the responsibility to protect citizens themselves from the harmful consequences of physical or mental illness (Gostin, 2005). In a very real sense, then, civil commitment is about containing dangerous illnesses, rather than dangerous people.

Involuntary hospitalization on the grounds of mental disorder is very different from **criminal commitment**, detention following conviction for a criminal offence. Criminal commitment is inherently and deliberately punitive. It is intended to make people suffer for harms they have perpetrated and for which they are morally culpable. In this respect, it is focused on the past, on what has already happened. But involuntary hospitalization as a form of civil commitment is preventive. It is intended to minimize potential harm, and so has its eye toward the future. Laws regarding involuntary hospitalization make no assumption that people are morally culpable for the risks they pose, and may

TABLE 19.1   COMPARISON OF CRITERIA FOR INVOLUNTARY ADMISSION IN THE MENTAL HEALTH ACTS OF CANADIAN PROVINCES AND TERRITORIES

Province/Territory	Definition of Mental Disorder	Definition of Harm to Self or Others	Includes Deterioration in Lieu of Harm	Requires Need for Treatment	Requires Incapacity to Make Treatment Decision	Permits CTO or Leave
Alberta	Narrow	Broad	Yes	No	No	CTO
British Columbia	Narrow	Broad	Yes	Yes	No	Leave
Manitoba	Narrow	Broad	Yes	Yes	No	Leave
New Brunswick	Narrow	Broad	No	No	No	No
Newfoundland & Labrador	Narrow	Broad	Yes	Yes	Yes	CTO
N.W.T.	Narrow	Narrow	No	No	No	No
Nova Scotia	Narrow	Broad	Yes	Yes	Yes	CTO
Nunavut	Narrow	Narrow	No	No	No	No
Ontario	Broad	Narrow	Partial	Partial	Partial	Both
Prince Edward Island	Narrow	Broad	No	No	No	Leave
Quebec	Broad	Narrow	No	No	No	CTO
Saskatchewan	Narrow	Broad	Yes	Yes	Yes	CTO
Yukon	Narrow	Narrow	No	No	Yes	Leave

Source: Adapted from Gray, J. E., Hastings, T. J., Love, S., & O'Reilly, R. L. (2016). Clinically significant difference among Canadian mental health acts: 2016. *Canadian Journal of Psychiatry, 61,* 222–226. Partial = in specific circumstances; CTO = community treatment order.

even assume that people are not culpable for the illnesses they suffer. For this reason, involuntary hospitalization is not punitive in nature, and in fact the procedures for and conditions of involuntary hospitalization must not be punitive if it is to be legally justified.

3   BEFORE MOVING ON

> Someone who suffers from a mental disorder and is believed to pose an imminent risk for serious harm to others may be involuntarily hospitalized for days or weeks—in theory, even for months or years. Isn't it simply unfair or unreasonable to punish someone for something he or she *hasn't done* but *might do*? How can this be justified?

INVOLUNTARY TREATMENT

Everyone committed to hospital receives a clean and safe place to stay where he or she is provided with the necessities of life, such as food, clothing, and care for physical illnesses or injury. In this sense, commitment may be considered therapeutic. But some people refuse active treatment in the form of psychoactive medications or psychotherapy.

When patients are committed and deemed incapable of making decisions about treatment, someone must make treatment decisions on their behalf. This person is sometimes referred to as a **temporary substitute decision maker**. In five jurisdictions (British Columbia, New Brunswick, Newfoundland and Labrador, Saskatchewan, and Quebec), the temporary substitute decision maker is an appointee of the

state, such as a physician, the director of a psychiatric unit, or a court or tribunal; in the other jurisdictions, the temporary substitute decision maker is a private representative of the patient (Gray et al., 2016). Private representatives may be people appointed by patients when they were mentally healthy and competent to make decisions, or they may be guardians or family members. If no private representative is available, the Public Trustee, an appointee of the state, makes the decision.

Regardless of who they are and how they were appointed, temporary substitute decision makers must exercise their judgment according to principles outlined in the mental health act. Two principles are used most commonly. The first is known as the **best interests principle**. Briefly, it holds that the temporary substitute decision maker should choose the treatment that maximizes the chances of a good outcome for the patient, taking into account the risks and benefits of all available treatments. Nine jurisdictions (Alberta, British Columbia, Manitoba, New Brunswick, Newfoundland and Labrador, Nova Scotia, Prince Edward Island, Saskatchewan, and Quebec) rely primarily or ultimately on this principle (Gray et al., 2016). The second is known as the **capable wishes principle**. It holds that a patient's personal wishes regarding treatment should be given the greatest weight in the decision-making process if these wishes were expressed when the patient was competent to make decisions about treatment. Four jurisdictions rely primarily or ultimately capable wishes principle (Northwest Territory, Nunavut, Ontario, and Yukon Territory), and in some of them a wish applicable to the circumstances expressed while a patient was capable cannot be overridden (Gray et al., 2016).

A relatively new trend in mental health law is the option of **compulsory treatment orders**, involuntary treatment on an outpatient basis (Gray & O'Reilly, 2005). Currently, six provinces have mental health acts that permit compulsory treatment orders (see Table 19.1); all require that the person has a history of recent psychiatric hospitalization. Compulsory treatment orders differ from conditional leave from hospital in that the latter require that a person was first involuntarily hospitalized and then released on the condition of continuing treatment in the community upon discharge.

A potential strength of compulsory treatment orders is that they provide a means of ensuring that patients will receive treatment that may relieve their distress and reduce the chances of relapse or re-hospitalization in a way that is less restrictive than involuntary hospitalization (Gray & O'Reilly, 2005). But compulsory treatment orders have several potential limitations as well. First, they are still coercive: people are legally required to receive a treatment they do not want, and face the threat of involuntary hospitalization if they fail to comply. In other jurisdictions, people under compulsory treatment orders may even lose their residence or financial support if they fail to comply (Bonnie & Monahan, 2005). Coercion may impair attempts to establish and maintain supportive and effective treatment relationships between people and their health care providers (Winick, 2008). Second, critics have expressed concern that compulsory treatment orders are used to coerce people into treatment who do not meet criteria for involuntary hospitalization because they pose a relatively low risk of harm to self or others. This means that compulsory treatment orders may actually increase, rather than decrease, the frequency with which people are subjected to coercive treatment, a result sometimes referred to as "net widening" (Geller, Fisher, Grudzinskas, Clayfield, & Lawlor, 2006). Finally, there is no convincing evidence from systematic reviews that compulsory treatment orders are effective in reducing health service use or improving clinical outcome and social functioning relative to traditional forms of treatment, voluntary or involuntary (Kisely, Campbell, Scott, Preston, & Xiao, 2006; Swartz & Swanson, 2004). Adequate mental health services must be available in the community for compulsory treatment orders to be effective, and it may be that providing high-quality voluntary outpatient services reduces or even eliminates the need for compulsory treatment orders (Greenfield, Stoneking, Humphreys, Sundby, & Bond, 2008).

REVIEWS AND APPEALS

Consistent with the *Charter*, every jurisdiction provides for quasi-judicial review of decisions regarding involuntary hospitalization and involuntary treatment. With respect to involuntary hospitalization, reviews typically take place at the end of each period of commitment and also, under certain circumstances, at the request of patients. The review board or panel will convene a hearing to consider evidence presented by the hospital to which the person was committed, as well as any evidence presented by the patients themselves; in most jurisdictions, patients have a specified right to be represented by legal counsel at the hearing. Patients or people acting on their behalf usually have the specified right to appeal their commitment to a court. Patients do not, however, have the right to be released from hospital while their commitment is under review or appeal. With respect to involuntary treatment, the procedures are very similar, except that treatment cannot begin until the matter is resolved, including any appeal.

SOME EXAMPLES OF RESEARCH ON MENTAL HEALTH LAW IN CANADA

WHO IS INVOLUNTARILY HOSPITALIZED? Somewhat surprisingly, no good statistics are readily available in Canada regarding the number of people who are involuntarily hospitalized or involuntarily treated. Better statistics are available concerning any hospitalization due to mental disorder. According to statistics for 2005–2006 collected by the Canadian Institute for Health Information, the hospitalization rate for mental disorder was 600 separations (that is, discharges from or deaths in hospital) per 100 000 people in the general population per year. About 1 in every 200 Canadians was released from the psychiatric ward of general hospitals, where the average length of stay was 16 days; about 1 in 1200 was released from a specialized psychiatric hospital, where the average length of stay was 100 days (Canadian Institute for Health Information, 2008). (Comparing these statistics to those collected over the past 30 years or so, there has been a major decrease in the rate of long-term hospitalization for mental disorder, referred to as **deinstitutionalization**, and a substantial increase in short-term and community-based treatments; see Canadian Institute for Health Information, 2008; Sealy & Whitehead, 2004; Stefan, 2006). Based on older national statistics (e.g., Riley & Richman, 1983) and studies that compared voluntary and involuntary admissions in smaller samples (e.g., Crisanti & Love, 2001; Malla, Norman, & Helmes, 1987; Tremblay, King, & Baines, 1994), it appears that up to 15 to 20 percent of all hospitalizations for mental disorder in Canada are involuntary. If this estimate is accurate, then the rate of involuntary hospitalization may be between 90 and 120 commitments per 100 000 people per year, or as many as 30 000 committals annually.

Comparisons of voluntary and involuntary admissions have found relatively few differences between the two groups. In one such study, Annette Crisanti and Edgar Love (2001) examined admissions to a psychiatric unit at Calgary General Hospital between 1987 and 1995. They reviewed the hospital records of large, representative samples of patients admitted either voluntarily ($n = 1007$) or involuntarily under Alberta's *Mental Health Act* ($n = 711$). Their results are summarized in Table 19.2. They found that the groups differed significantly with respect to age, length of stay, primary diagnosis, and criminal record: involuntary patients were more likely to be male, stayed in the hospital longer, were more likely to be diagnosed as schizophrenic

TABLE 19.2 COMPARISON OF VOLUNTARILY AND INVOLUNTARILY HOSPITALIZED PATIENTS ADMITTED TO CALGARY GENERAL HOSPITAL, 1987–1995

	Voluntarily Hospitalized (n = 1007)	Involuntarily Hospitalized (n = 711)
Sex		
Male	42%	54%
Female	58%	46%
Age (mean)	39 years	37 years
Length of Stay (median)	12 days	19 days
Primary Diagnosis		
Psychotic Disorder	23%	54%
Mood Disorder	36%	28%
Personality Disorder	28%	12%
Other Disorder	13%	6%
Criminal Record	16%	19%

Source: Based on Crisanti et al., "Characteristics of Psychiatric Inpatients Detained Under Civil Commitment Legislation: A Canadian Study," *International Journal of Law & Psychiatry*, Vol. 23, 2001, pp. 399–401.

(and less likely to be diagnosed as personality disordered), and more frequently had a criminal record prior to admission. The groups did not differ with respect to age, and also did not appear to differ with respect to education or employment history (although it was difficult to test these differences due to missing information).

A similar profile of involuntarily hospitalized patients has emerged from studies of patients who applied for a review of their detention. For example, Grant, Ogloff, and Douglas (2000) studied 279 patients at Riverview Hospital, a large psychiatric hospital in British Columbia that serves the entire province. They found that 60% of the patients were male, the average age was about 39 years, and 67% had a primary diagnosis of a psychotic disorder. Most also had a history of serious employment problems; in fact, only 4% were working prior to their admission. Consistent with a history of serious mental disorder, 91% of patients had a history of prior psychiatric hospitalizations. Grant and colleagues were also able to collect information about risk for harm to self or others. They found that 68% of the patients had a history of suicidal or other self-injurious behaviour prior to hospitalization, and 23% had engaged in self-harmful behaviour while hospitalized. Similarly, 64% of patients had a history of violence, including 23% with a history of arrests for violent offences and 49% who had committed violence in the two weeks prior to hospitalization.

What happens to people who are involuntarily hospitalized? A number of studies have examined the frequency with which patients apply for review of their committal. Gray, Clark, Higenbottam, Ledwidge, and Paredes (1985) examined 487 involuntary patients in British Columbia who applied for review and 2966 who did not. This suggests that in only 14 percent of cases was a review requested. Gray and colleagues also found some differences between people

who applied for review and those who did not with respect to demographic characteristics and mental health history. For example, those who applied for review were more often male, were younger, and had a history of more serious education and employment problems. Also, those who applied for review were more likely to have a diagnosis of schizophrenic disorder (and less likely to have a diagnosis of mental retardation) and had more previous hospitalizations. Similar findings were reported by Komer, O'Reilly, Cernovsky, and Dunbar (1999), who examined involuntarily hospitalized patients in Ontario. During a six-year period from 1987 to 1993, there were 31124 involuntary hospitalizations in the 10 provincial psychiatric hospitals in Ontario. A surprisingly small number of patients—4953, or 16% of all those involuntarily hospitalized—requested a review. Komer and colleagues also examined the outcome of the involuntary hospitalizations. Many of the cases in which applications were made were resolved prior to review: in 18% of cases, patients withdrew their request; in another 25%, physicians transferred patients to voluntary status; and in 1%, the period of commitment expired. Of the cases that actually went to review, the outcome was known in 2680 cases, and in only 343 cases was the patient released. This latter number reflects a tiny percentage of all involuntary hospitalization (1%); even looking only at cases that proceeded to review that had known outcomes, it reflects a very low "success rate" (13%).

Research by Higgenbottam et al. (1985) compared patients in British Columbia who were released after review to those who were not released. They found that patients who were released appeared to have less serious mental disorder, spent less time hospitalized, and were perceived to be at lower risk for harm to self. Also, they had better plans for release, insofar as they were more likely to be on the waiting list for placement in a boarding home. Furthermore, they were more likely to have been represented by legal counsel at the review.

Finally, there has been follow-up research examining the community adjustment of patients released from involuntary hospitalization. For example, Ledwidge and colleagues (1987) compared the post-release adjustment of 47 involuntary patients from British Columbia who were released after review with 47 patients released by their attending physicians. The two groups were matched on a number of key variables, including sex, age, primary diagnosis, and length of stay. The adjustment of both groups was rather poor: 45% were readmitted to hospital within a year, and most patients continued to have serious problems with employment and personal relationships. Poor adjustment after release was associated with more serious mental disorder and poor response to treatment before release. On a positive note, few patients engaged in suicidal or violent behaviour after release. Douglas and colleagues (Douglas, Ogloff, Nicholls, & Grant, 1999) conducted a retrospective file review of 193 involuntarily hospitalized patients who applied for review of their detention and were subsequently released, either after review or at the end of the period of committal. They examined adjustment in the community over a period of 20 months following release, focusing on violent acts that were documented in clinical files or resulted in arrest. Of the 193 patients, 38% committed at least one documented act of violence in the 20 months after their release from hospital, including 19% who committed at least one act of physical violence and 10% who were arrested for at least one violent criminal offence.

HOW CAN VIOLENCE RISK BE EVALUATED? Violence risk is a key element in decision making with respect to involuntary hospitalization. It is also important when making decisions about mentally disordered offenders (as we will discuss shortly). Until recently, psychologists trying to assess the violence risk posed by patients had few resources to guide them: little was known about the frequency of violence among psychiatric patients, the most important risk factors for violence, or the best ways to gather and combine information to reach decisions about violence risk. The past decade has seen major developments in this field, and Canadian researchers have made important contributions, including the development of procedures for the systematic assessment of violence risk.

There are two basic approaches to violence risk assessment: discretionary and nondiscretionary (see Guy, Douglas, & Hart, 2015). The discretionary approach is sometimes referred to as clinical, informal, or intuitive; whereas the nondiscretionary approach is sometimes referred to as actuarial, mechanistic, or algorithmic. The discretionary approach permits mental health professionals to exercise judgment in gathering relevant information and combining the information to make decisions about what kind of violence a patient might commit and how best to prevent the occurrence of violence or minimize the harm caused by the violence. The nondiscretionary approach imposes strict rules on the assessment process, instructing mental professionals as to exactly which information can and must be considered and exactly how the information should be weighted and combined to make decisions. The decisions here are typically estimates of the absolute or relative likelihood that someone will commit violence (e.g., the specific probability that someone will be arrested for a violent offence within six months of release from an institution). The two approaches have complementary strengths: the discretionary approach is flexible, or easily adapted to new and unusual situations, and idiographic, or responsive to the unique characteristics of the case at hand, whereas the nondiscretionary approach encourages consistency across cases.

One example of the discretionary approach to violence risk assessment is the Historical-Clinical-Risk Management—20, developed by a group of authors at or affiliated with Simon Fraser University that has included, over the years, Christopher D. Webster, Kevin S. Douglas, Derek Eaves, Stephen D. Hart, and Henrik Belfrage. The HCR-20 is a set of structured professional guidelines for assessing violence risk that was based on a comprehensive review of the scientific, professional, and legal literatures. The HCR-20 is a book or manual that discusses the concept of violence, recommends procedures for gathering relevant information, and describes 20 major risk factors for violence that should be considered, at a minimum, in every risk assessment. The 20 risk factors in the HCR-20 fall into three categories: there are 10 **H**istorical factors that reflect past or long-term functioning; 5 **C**linical factors that reflect recent or current functioning; and 5 **R**isk management factors that reflect potential adjustment problems based on the patient's plans for the future. The risk factors in the most recent edition of the HCR-20, Version 3 (Douglas, Hart, Webster, & Belfrage, 2013), are summarized in Table 19.3.

According to recent international surveys, the HCR-20 is the now the world's most widely used violence risk assessment tool (Singh et al., 2014). A large evidence base indicates that professionals can use the HCR-20 to make judgments concerning the presence and relevance of individual risk factors, as well as judgements regarding the overall risks posed by people, with good interrater reliability and predictive validity (for reviews, see Douglas & Reeves, 2010; Guy et al., 2015). For example, in their study of involuntarily committed civil psychiatric patients who were treated and then released, Douglas and colleagues (Douglas et al., 1999) found that ratings made using the HCR-20 had moderate to high predictive validity with respect to violent behaviour in the community. This was true when violence was defined broadly to include threatening or intimidating behaviour, and when it was defined more narrowly to include only physical violence or violence that resulted in criminal charges or convictions. They used a simple median split procedure to divide the patients into two groups: low risk (those with few HCR-20 risk factors) and high risk (those with many HCR-20 risk factors). Using event history analysis, they estimated that only 20 percent of the low-risk patients would commit violence within two years of release, compared to 60 percent of the high-risk patients. Based on these and

TABLE 19.3   THE HCR-20 VERSION 3 RISK FACTORS

Historical Factors: History of problems with...	Clinical Factors: Recent problems with...	Risk Management Factors: Future problems with...
H1. Violence	C1. Insight	R1. Professional services and plans
H2. Other antisocial behaviour	C2. Violent ideation or intent	R2. Living situation
H3. Relationships	C3. Symptoms of a major mental disorder	R3. Personal support
H4. Employment	C4. Instability	R4. Treatment and supervision response
H5. Substance use	C5. Treatment or supervision response	R5. Stress or coping
H6. Major mental disorder		
H7. Personality disorder		
H8. Traumatic experiences		
H9. Violent attitudes		
H10. Treatment or supervision response		

Source: Based on Douglas, K. S., Hart, S. D., Webster, C. D., & Belfrage, H. (2013). *HCR-20^V3; Assessing risk for violence.* Burnaby, Canada: Mental Health, Law, and Policy Institute, Simon Fraser University.

similar findings, it is not surprising that the HCR-20 has been translated into more than 20 languages and is used widely in civil psychiatric, forensic psychiatric, and correctional settings in many countries around the world.

A Closer Look at Mentally Disordered Offenders

People suffering from mental disorder are overrepresented among those who are arrested, charged with, or convicted of criminal offences. For example, Roesch and his colleagues (Roesch, 1995; see also Corrado, Cohen, Hart, & Roesch, 2000; Hart, Roesch, Corrado, & Cox, 1993) conducted large-scale epidemiological research in a pretrial jail in Vancouver, British Columbia. They screened 881 consecutive admissions to the institution in 1989 and 1990, all adult males. A total of 684 were willing and able to complete various interview-based screens for mental disorder; the findings indicated that about 10 to 20% of all admissions appeared to be suffering from symptoms of a serious mental disorder (Hart et al., 1993). A subsample of admissions completed the Diagnostic Interview Schedule, Version III-A (DIS; Robins & Helzer, 1985), which was used to make current and lifetime diagnoses of selected mental disorders according to the criteria contained in DSM-III (American Psychiatric Association, 1980). According to the DIS, 94% of admissions met diagnostic criteria for at least one DSM-III mental disorder, including 16% who met the criteria for at least one serious mental disorder (Corrado et al., 2000b; see also Table 19.4). People diagnosed with serious mental disorder were more likely to receive health care in the jail, including psychological counselling, psychoactive medications, transfer to the medical unit of the jail, and transfer out of the jail to a psychiatric hospital (Corrado et al., 2000b). Similar findings have been reported in epidemiological studies of people sentenced to provincial prisons (e.g., Bland, Newman, Dyck, & Orn, 1990)

or federal penitentiaries (e.g., Baudette, Power, & Stewart, 2015). Commentators, including the Correctional Investigator of Canada, have expressed concern for many years that the mental health needs of offenders in Canada exceed the capacity of its correctional systems to service those needs (e.g., Sapers, 2016), to the point that "Prisons and jails have become de facto 'treatment' facilities for people with mental illness" in Canada (Hart, 2006, p. 5).

TABLE 19.4   LIFETIME PREVALENCE OF MENTAL DISORDERS AMONG 192 ADULT MALES ADMITTED TO THE VANCOUVER PRETRIAL SERVICES CENTRE, 1989–1990

Disorder	Lifetime Prevalence
Major mental disorders	15.6% (2.6%)
Cognitive impairment	0.5% (0.5%)
Schizophrenic disorders	4.9% (1.6%)
Bipolar affective disorder	4.1% (1.4%)
Major depressive disorder	6.0% (1.7%)
Substance use disorders	85.9% (2.5%)
Alcohol use disorders	77.6% (3.0%)
Drug use disorders	63.7% (3.5%)
Other mental disorders	88.0% (2.4%)
Anxiety disorders	41.1% (3.6%)
Dysthymia	7.2% (1.9%)
Somatization disorder	0.7% (0.6%)
Bulimia	0.3% (0.4%)
Sexual disorders	27.0% (3.2%)
Antisocial personality disorder	64.3% (3.5%)
Any disorder	93.6% (1.8%)

Source: Corrado, R. R., Cohen, I., Hart, S. D., & Roesch, R. (2000). Comparative examination of the prevalence of mental disorders among jailed inmates in Canada and the United States. *International Journal of Law and Psychiatry, 23,* 633–647.

Municipal police are recognizing that a high proportion of police time is spent on responding to calls involving persons with mental health problems. For example, the city of Vancouver conducted a study in 2007 to assess the extent of this involvement (Wilson-Bates, 2008). Police contact data were obtained over a 16-day period. Police officers responding to the calls indicated whether the call involved a person with mental health problems. They found that of 1154 calls, 31 percent involved at least one mentally ill person. Certain areas of Vancouver, such as the Downtown Eastside, had percentages close to 50 percent. Many of these individuals are arrested due at least in part to the lack of alternative services in the community.

The fact that so many people who come into contact with police suffer from serious mental disorder poses tremendous problems for those responsible for the institutional and community management of offenders. It also poses a problem for the police, prosecutors, and triers of fact who are responsible for making decisions about when to arrest, charge, or convict people who suffer from mental disorder. Criminal law gives the state awesome powers, including the power to punish its citizens by stripping them of their fundamental rights and freedoms for the rest of their lives. However, criminal law is intended to be used only when people have committed acts that deserve punishment. It may not serve the public good to devote resources to punishing a crowd of ecstatic fans who hold an impromptu parade when their hockey team wins the league championship, someone who burns a flag during a political demonstration, or a person who "moons" someone in public on a dare, even though each of these things may technically constitute a criminal offence. Similarly, it may not serve the public good to punish a depressed person who creates a public disturbance while attempting to commit suicide by jumping off a bridge; a woman who kills her children while suffering from the delusion that they were possessed by the devil; or a man who walks naked in public while suffering from dementia but does not know the date, his wife's name, or where he resides. The *Criminal Code* includes special provisions for deciding whether people who committed offences while suffering from mental disorder should be held criminally responsible, as well as whether people currently suffering from mental disorder should be put on trial.

CRIMINAL RESPONSIBILITY: MENTAL STATE AT THE TIME OF THE OFFENCE

Under Canadian law, people can be convicted of criminal offences only when they commit a prohibited act with bad intention. The prohibited act is known as the *actus reus*; the bad intention as the *mens rea*. Among other things, the *Criminal Code* sets out the *actus reus* and the *mens rea* that constitute each criminal offence. It also sets out certain defences that might serve as acceptable explanations or excuses for what would otherwise be a criminal offence. A good example is self-defence; section 34 of the *Criminal Code* authorizes people to use force to protect themselves when they are unlawfully assaulted by another person; they are even authorized to cause the death of someone, if they have reasonable grounds to believe that person is attempting to kill them or to cause them grievous bodily harm. Similarly, section 16 of the *Criminal Code* sets out the defence of mental disorder, known popularly as the "insanity defence":

> 16. (1) No person is criminally responsible for an act committed or an omission made while suffering from a mental disorder that rendered the person incapable of appreciating the nature and quality of the act or omission or of knowing that it was wrong.
>
> (2) Every person is presumed not to suffer from a mental disorder so as to be exempt from criminal responsibility by virtue of subsection (1), until the contrary is proved on the balance of probabilities.
>
> (3) The burden of proof that an accused was suffering from a mental disorder so as to be exempt from criminal responsibility is on the party that raises the issue.

According to the *Criminal Code*, some people suffering from mental disorder, through no fault of their own, may have inaccurate perceptions of or irrational beliefs about the world that led them to commit a prohibited act, but without any bad intention—exactly in the same way that someone who raises the defence of self-defence admits the act, but denies the intent. In short, section 16 recognizes that mental disorder may negate or rule out *mens rea*.

The history of section 16 can be traced back across several millennia of Western history (e.g., Zapf, Golding, & Roesch, 2005). The laws of ancient civilizations, such as the Greeks and the Romans, as well as the philosophies of the Jewish, Christian, and Muslim faiths, recognized that people suffering from mental disorder are deserving of special care. This view was incorporated into English common law as far back as 1505, which was the first documented case of a person being found not guilty by reason of insanity. The current language of section 16, as well as the inclusion of provisions in the *Criminal Code* for the detention of people found legally insane—what we now call a finding of **not criminally responsible on account of mental disorder**, or **NCRMD**—dates back to the 1800s. That century saw two important cases in England involving people suffering from serious mental disorders who attempted to assassinate public figures, including the monarch and the prime minister. In the first, James Hadfield attempted to shoot King George III (*R. v. Hadfield*, 1800). He was charged with high treason but later acquitted due to mental disorder by a jury, after the defence led evidence indicating that he suffered from religious and nihilistic delusions that by killing the king he would hasten the end of the earthly world and the Second Coming of Jesus. In response to Hadfield's case, the English parliament passed the *Criminal Lunatics Acts of 1800*, which required that people acquitted due to mental disorder be detained in a secure facility for the rest of their lives. In the second case, Daniel M'Naghten attempted to shoot the prime minister, Robert Peel, mistakenly killing

Peel's private secretary instead (*R. v M'Naghten*, 1843). Like Hadfield before him, a jury heard evidence that M'Naghten was suffering from delusions—persecutory delusions that the government was involved in a conspiracy against him—and found him not guilty by reason of insanity. But following M'Naghten's acquittal, there was public outrage that he got away with murder. A panel of judges was convened to clarify the law, and the result was known as the **M'Naghten standard**. Briefly, it held that people could be acquitted due to mental disorder only if they suffered from a mental disorder that caused a specific cognitive impairment—namely, the inability to understand the nature and quality of their acts or the inability to understand that the acts were wrong. The original M'Naghten standard was included almost verbatim in the first Canadian *Criminal Code* in 1894 and has survived, virtually intact, to the present day. The M'Naghten standard also formed the basis for the insanity provisions of the criminal codes in most common law jurisdictions around the world, including the federal and most state codes in the United States.

Although the wording of section 16 has changed little in the last hundred years, there have been important developments in the insanity defence in Canada. One development was cases that led to clarification of key concepts in section 16(1). For example, in the Supreme Court of Canada's judgments in *Cooper v R.* (1980) and *Rabey v R.* (1980), it was confirmed that mental disorder includes any disturbance of the mind or its functioning that is internal (i.e., not the result of situational factors), intransient (i.e., not temporary or ephemeral), and involuntary (i.e., not self-induced). Thus, the law's definition of mental disorder is broad, and legal arguments therefore tend to focus on whether a person's mental disorder causes cognitive impairment, rather than whether the person's mental disorder is real or valid according to the law. In the cases of *Cooper v R.* (1980), *Kjeldsen v The Queen* (1981), and *R. v Abbey* (1982), it was confirmed that appreciating the nature and quality of an act requires full comprehension or understanding of the act's physical consequences. It is irrelevant, for example, if people suffer from a personality disorder that makes them unable to appreciate the emotional harm their victims suffer. And most recently, in the case of *R. v Chaulk* (1990), it was confirmed that knowing an act is wrong requires simple understanding or recognition that an act is legally and morally wrong.

A second development was major changes in the *Criminal Code* concerning the disposition of people detained for evaluation of criminal responsibility or found NCRMD in 1992. Prior to that time, defendants who were referred for evaluation of criminal responsibility were committed to a secure facility for 30 days, and they could easily be recommitted for further evaluation. Those acquitted by reason of insanity were committed to a secure facility indefinitely, or "at the pleasure of the Lieutenant Governor," according to the review procedures set out by each province or territory. In the case of *R. v Swain* (1991), the Supreme Court of Canada held that these procedures violated the *Charter*. In April 1992, Parliament passed Bill C-30, which addressed defects in the *Criminal Code* identified by the Supreme Court.

There were four major amendments. First, the *Criminal Code* now places a five-day limit on assessment orders, unless the defendant and prosecutor agree to a longer period not exceeding 30 days. Compelling circumstances can extend this to a maximum of 60 days. These evaluations can take place in a jail, an outpatient clinic, or an inpatient facility. Second, there have been changes to the disposition of an accused following a finding of NCRMD. People who are committed must undergo a regular review of their detention by a board, the composition and procedures of which are established under the provision of the *Code*. People may be committed only if they still present a risk of harm—in the case of *Winko v B.C. (Forensic Psychiatric Institute)* (1999), defined as a "significant threat" to public safety—due to mental disorder. At the initial disposition or after review, people found to be NCRMD may be detained in hospital, given a conditional discharge according to certain restrictions or requirements set out by the review board, or given an absolute or unconditional discharge. Third, there were changes regarding who may argue for acquittal under section 16. The *Criminal Code* now prohibits the prosecution from raising the issue of the accused's mental state unless the defence raises it at the time of the offence, or until after the accused is found guilty of an offence. This change recognizes that accused people should have the right to choose their own defence at trial. Finally, the *Criminal Code* amendments established "caps" or upper limits on the maximum length of time that people may be detained following a finding of NCRMD. In theory, this should prevent the possibility that people will be detained indefinitely for minor offences. The capping provisions, however, still have not yet been proclaimed.

A fourth and more recent development was the *Not Criminally Responsible Reform Act* (S.C. 2014, c. 6). This amendment to sec. 672.54 of the *Criminal Code* (and the corresponding section of the statute dealing with military justice) increases the involvement of victims of persons found NCRMD of unfit to stand trial (see following section) who are under the authority of Review Boards; tightens the review conditions for all persons under the authority of Review Boards; and creates a new designation, High Risk Accused, that places additional restrictions on the review conditions of people found NCRMD who are determined by courts to be at high risk for future violence. Supporters of the *Act* believe it will increase victims' rights in the justice system and enhance public safety, but critics are concerned it is an unnecessary and perhaps unjustifiable restriction of liberties, will be a barrier to effective rehabilitation and reintegration into the community of people found NCRMD, and may contribute to the general stigmatization of people with mental disorder (e.g., Lacroix, O'Shaughnessy, McNeil, & Binder, 2017). A particular concern is that the *Act* appears to have, at least in part, a reaction to a few high-profile NCRMD cases (Lacroix et al., 2017) and to be part of a more general "tough on crime" approach to criminal justice whose assumptions are contrary to a large body of social science research (e.g., Cook & Roesch, 2012).

COMPETENCY TO MAKE LEGAL DECISIONS: MENTAL STATE AT THE TIME OF TRIAL

According to principles of fundamental justice, people accused of crimes have the right to be present at their trial, to confront their accusers, and to make full answer and defence to the accusations against them (e.g., Zapf & Roesch, 2009). Proceeding to trial when people are suffering from a serious mental disorder and not fully "present" or lacking the capacity to defend themselves is not in the interests of justice: the risk of mistaken conviction increases, and even when people are guilty, any deterrent impact of punishment is diminished. When accused individuals suffer from a serious mental disorder, their trials may be suspended temporarily while they are transferred to hospital and treated.

Like the insanity defence, the doctrine of fitness or competency to stand trial has a long history in English common law. In the case of *R. v Pritchard* (1836), it was clarified that accused people must be able to make a plea to the indictment against them and must be of sufficient intellect to comprehend the course of the trial proceedings and the details of the evidence against them. In Canadian law, people who are unable to participate actively and effectively in their own defence due to mental disorder are referred to as **unfit to stand trial (UST)**. According to section 2 of the *Criminal Code*,

> "[U]nfit to stand trial" means unable on account of mental disorder to conduct a defence at any stage of the proceedings before a verdict is rendered or to instruct counsel to do so, and, in particular, unable on account of mental disorder to
> (a) understand the nature or object of the proceedings,
> (b) understand the possible consequences of the proceedings, or
> (c) communicate with counsel.

Only limited cognitive capacity is required for a person to be considered fit to stand trial (*R. v Taylor*, 1992; *R. v Whittle*, 1994). Defendants need to be able to recount to their attorneys the necessary facts relating to their offence in such a way that the attorneys can properly present their cases; it is not necessary that defendants have a rational understanding of their situation or that they can act in their own best interests.

The procedures governing the evaluation of fitness and the disposition of people who were found to be UST were revised in 1992 following the Supreme Court of Canada's decision in *Swain*. Briefly, defendants are presumed fit unless the court is satisfied, on the balance of probabilities, that they are UST. The issue of fitness can be raised before trial or at trial by the defendant, the prosecution (under certain circumstances), or the trial judge. Courts can order evaluations to assist in the determination of whether the defendant is UST. As is the case for criminal responsibility evaluations, there is a five-day limit on assessment orders, unless the defendant and Crown agree to a longer

period not exceeding 30 days; compelling circumstances can extend this to a maximum of 60 days. These evaluations can take place in a jail, an outpatient clinic, or an inpatient facility, although there is a presumption against custody. Despite this presumption, the majority of the evaluations are conducted in inpatient facilities, although the number of outpatient evaluations has increased since the passage of the 1992 *Criminal Code* revisions. The issue of unfitness is tried separately from the trial on the charge itself, and may be tried by judge or jury. If they are found fit to stand trial, defendants proceed to trial, although courts may order them to be detained until their trials are over to prevent deterioration of their mental state. If they are found to be UST, any pleas defendants may have made are set aside and they may be ordered to undergo inpatient or outpatient treatment. The cases of defendants found to be UST are considered by a review board formed under the *Criminal Code* at least once every two years. Defendants who become fit to stand trial are returned to court for the disposition of their case. At that point, defendants may go to trial, may plead guilty, or if sufficient evidence to obtain a conviction no longer exists, may be acquitted and released.

④ BEFORE MOVING ON

> A psychologist evaluates a person who has been arrested to determine if he is unfit to stand trial (UST). The psychologist concludes that the person is UST because he is experiencing severe symptoms of psychosis (e.g., conceptual disorganization, incoherent speech) that render him incapable of communicating with counsel. Does this mean that the psychologist should also conclude that the person was also not criminally responsible on account of mental disorder (NCRMD)? Why or why not?

SOME EXAMPLES OF RESEARCH ON MENTALLY DISORDERED OFFENDERS IN CANADA

HOW ARE FITNESS EVALUATIONS CONDUCTED? In Canada, as in other common law jurisdictions, research suggests that the opinions of mental health professionals regarding fitness are virtually dispositive—that is, courts rarely disagree with the opinions expressed by professionals (e.g., Hart & Hare, 1992; see also Cox & Zapf, 2004). Although the concept of fitness to stand trial is an old one, its definition has never been explicit in the law. This raises some interesting questions. How do mental health professionals interpret the law when determining whether a particular defendant is fit or unfit? What kinds of assessment techniques or procedures should be used?

Early research conducted in Canada and the United States suggested that mental health professionals based opinions regarding competency or fitness to stand trial on the seriousness of the mental disorder from which defendants were suffering, rather than on the seriousness of the functional deficits that stemmed from the mental disorder, such as inability to understand the proceedings or communicate with counsel. In fact, many evaluators seemed to equate psychosis with incompetency or unfitness (Roesch & Golding, 1980). These and similar findings prompted Canadian researchers to devote considerable effort to improving fitness evaluations over the three decades.

One example of how research has improved the practice of forensic psychology and psychiatry is the development of the revised Fitness Interview Test-Revised, or FIT-R, developed by Ron Roesch, Patricia Zapf, Christopher Webster, and Derek Eaves (1998). The FIT-R is a manual or reference book that presents guidelines concerning how to conduct brief evaluations of competency or fitness to stand trial, either in institutional or community settings. The FIT-R takes approximately 30 minutes to administer. It requires evaluators to make ratings of the defendant's functioning with respect to a number of specific psycho-legal abilities, each of which is defined in the manual. The FIT-R manual also presents questions that can be posed to defendants to help evaluators make their ratings. The items in the FIT-R fall into three main areas, consistent with the *Criminal Code:* (1) ability to understand the nature or object of the proceedings, or factual knowledge of criminal procedure, such as the defendant's understanding of the arrest process and the nature and severity of current charges; (2) the ability to understand the possible consequences of the proceedings, or the appreciation of personal involvement in and importance of the proceedings, such as the defendant's appreciation of the range and nature of possible penalties if found guilty; and (3) the ability to communicate with counsel, or to participate in the defence, such as the defendant's capacity to communicate facts to a lawyer. Each item is rated on a 3-point scale, where 2 means *definite or serious impairment*, 1 means *possible or mild impairment*, and 0 means *no impairment*. A sample item from the FIT-R is presented in Focus box 19.1.

In a number of studies, the FIT-R has been shown to help evaluators make reliable and valid decisions about fitness with adults. In one study, Zapf, Roesch, and Viljoen (2001) used the FIT-R to evaluate 145 defendants who had been remanded to an inpatient facility for a fitness evaluation. FIT-R evaluations were typically conducted within 24 hours of admission, and the interviews lasted less than 1 hour. Zapf and colleagues compared judgments based on the FIT-R with the clinical judgments of the forensic psychiatrists, made independent of the FIT-R. The clinical judgments were reached after an average length of stay of 21 days. Of the 145 evaluations, the FIT-R judgment and the hospital judgment were in full agreement that 106 of the defendants were fit to stand trial. Of the remaining 39 defendants, the FIT-R and the hospital agreed that 9 defendants were unfit. The other 30 defendants were considered possibly unfit by the FIT-R but were found to be fit by the hospital psychiatrists. The results show that the FIT-R works well as a screening instrument, in that it correctly identified defendants who were clearly fit and did not misclassify any defendants who were subsequently found to be unfit by the hospital evaluators. This study also shows that 73 percent (106 of 145) of the defendants could have been assessed without the need for inpatient evaluation, as the assessment can take place in a jail or other community setting rather than a forensic hospital. Defendants remanded to the forensic hospital were held an average of about 17 days. If decisions about a substantial portion of the defendants could be made on the basis of a brief assessment, the cost savings would be substantial—the cost of community-based evaluations is only a fraction of the cost of inpatient evaluations (see also Zapf & Roesch, 1997). More recently, the FIT-R has been shown to be useful in evaluating juveniles who have been charged with crimes (Viljoen & Roesch, 2007). Ensuring that the legal rights of adolescents are equally protected has become increasingly important due to changes in Canadian laws allowing for the imposition of adult sentences on juveniles convicted of certain offences.

FOCUS 19.1 A Sample Item from the FIT-R Manual

ITEM 12. CAPACITY TO PLAN LEGAL STRATEGY

This item calls for an assessment of the degree to which the accused can understand and cooperate with his/her counsel in planning a strategy for the defence that is consistent with the reality of his/her circumstances. Strategic issues such as agreeing to enter a guilty plea to a lesser offence, or the decision as to whether or not the accused should testify, may arise and require some participation from the accused.

- If your lawyer can get the Crown counsel [prosecutor] to accept a plea bargain wherein you plead guilty to a less serious charge in return for the Crown dropping a more serious charge, would you agree to it? Why/why not?

- If your lawyer decides that you should not testify, would you go along with him/her?
- What will you do if you disagree with your lawyer about how to handle your case?
- Should you talk with a lawyer before pleading guilty?
- What questions should you ask your lawyer if you are thinking about pleading guilty?
- Do you understand the consequences of being found unfit to stand trial?

Source: Roesch, R., Zapf, P. A., Webster, C. D., & Eaves, D. (1998). *The Fitness Interview Test.* Burnaby, BC: Mental Health, Law, & Policy Institute, Simon Fraser University.

WHO IS REFERRED FOR EVALUATION OF FITNESS OR CRIMINAL RESPONSIBILITY? Accused referred for fitness evaluations are often marginalized individuals. The majority are male, single, unemployed, with prior criminal histories, prior contact with mental health services, and past psychiatric hospitalizations (Zapf & Roesch, 1998; Zapf, Roesch, & Viljoen, 2001). Viljoen and Zapf (2002) compared 80 defendants referred for fitness evaluations with 80 defendants not referred and found that referred defendants were significantly more likely to meet diagnostic criteria for current psychotic disorder, be charged with a violent offence, and have impaired legal abilities, and less likely to have had previous criminal charges.

The public often views the *Criminal Code* provisions regarding mental disorder skeptically, believing they are used too frequently. This is a misconception; in fact, very few people charged with criminal offences raise the issue of mental disorder. Roesch and his colleagues (Roesch et al., 1997) examined patterns in the number of people in British Columbia who underwent evaluations of criminal responsibility or fitness in a two-year period between 1992 and 1994. In total, 653 defendants were referred for evaluation: 15% for evaluation of NCRMD, 61% for evaluation of fitness, and 24% for evaluation of both. In most of these evaluations, the outcome was a finding that the defendant was *not* NCRMD (recommended in about 61% of evaluations) or was *not* UST (recommended in about 79% of cases). A study by Grant (1997) found that fewer than 100 people were actually found NCRMD by courts in British Columbia in 1992 and 1993. In 1992 and 1993, the total number of charges laid for *Criminal Code* offences was more than 500 000 annually in British Columbia; thus, there were about 65 evaluations of mental state per 100 000 criminal charges per year, and the rate of "successful" NCRMD defences was about 10 per 100 000 criminal charges per year. This estimate is consistent with the findings of Hylton (1995), who estimated that a section 16 defence was raised in less than 0.2% of all cases coming before the courts in British Columbia. Similar results were found in a more recent study of all people found NCRMD in three provinces between May 2000 and April 2005 (Crocker et al., 2015). The number of NCRMD admissions was low overall, only about 360 per year, but varied considerably across provinces—about 219 per year Québec, about 97 per year in Ontario, and only about 44 per year in British Columbia.

Another misconception is that people found NCRMD or UST somehow "get off easy." In fact, the reality is that whereas virtually all defendants found guilty are given a fixed or determinate sentence, there is no limit on the length of time someone may be detained if found NCRMD or UST. Also, many people found NCRMD or UST will spend as much or even more time in a secure hospital than they would have spent in prison if they had been convicted. For example, Harris, Rice, and Cormier (1991) compared the length of detention among a cohort of insanity acquittees in Ontario to that of a group of men arrested for similar offences and with similar offence histories who were not found legally insane. They found that, on average, the insanity acquittees were detained for about 60 months whereas the men sentenced to prison were detained for about 50 months. Length of detention was similar for those men who had been arrested for serious offences such as murder or manslaughter, but men found legally insane for less serious offences were detained much longer than the sentenced men (e.g., 34 months versus 12 months, respectively, for those initially arrested for property crimes).

Despite a popular belief that the typical insanity acquittee has been charged with murder, research has demonstrated that only a minority has actually committed murder or even attempted murder. In Canada, a review of all insanity evaluatees in the province of British Columbia over a two-year period showed that although the majority of defendants had been charged with violent offences, less than 10 percent had been charged with murder or attempted murder (Roesch et al., 1997). More notably, in addition to the finding that murder charges are rare for insanity acquittees, approximately 35 percent of all charges in this population are for nonviolent minor offences, such as uttering threats, breach of probation, mischief, and possession of stolen property (Roesch et al., 1997).

The 1992 amendments to the *Criminal Code* appear to have had a small but significant impact on evaluations for NCRMD and UST. The number of evaluations appears to have increased in some provinces (e.g., British Columbia; see Grant 1997; Roesch et al., 1997) but not in others (e.g., Alberta; see Stuart, Arboleda-Florez, & Crisanti, 2001). A more consistent finding is that the number of short-term evaluations has increased, and an increasing number of evaluations are conducted in the defendant's community or in jail rather than a central forensic facility (Roesch et al., 1997; Stuart et al., 2001; Zapf & Roesch, 1998).

Psychology in the Legal System

Two types of psychologists are involved in the legal system. The first group comprises "accidental visitors" who are asked to provide opinions to a court or tribunal due to their specialized knowledge. For example, clinical or counselling psychologists who treat families may be subsequently called to court and asked to summarize the assessment findings and treatment outcome as part of custody and access hearings; or industrial-organizational psychologists may be asked to evaluate the hiring and promotion procedures of large companies as part of a sexual discrimination hearing. The second group comprises specialists in **forensic psychology**, whose work is primarily intended to assist proceedings in criminal or civil courts, or in front of quasi-judicial bodies such as administrative boards and tribunals. (Forensic—which derives from the Latin *forensis*, meaning forum—is an umbrella term used to describe any sort of legal proceeding.)

The field of forensic psychology is currently in a period of tremendous growth and expansion (for an overview, see Melton et al., 2007). Although its origins can be traced back more than a hundred years, it is only in the past 30 years or so that it has become recognized and accepted as a formal specialization. The field is very diverse, differing with respect to the primary focus (e.g., civil versus criminal issues) and the nature of the work (e.g., research versus practice). For example, forensic psychologists may

- Conduct a custody evaluation to determine what residential and access or visitation arrangements are most appropriate for children whose parents are in the midst of a divorce.

- Design a program for training correctional officers at a provincial prison to identify offenders who may be suicidal and in need of special care.

- Study the abilities of young children to accurately perceive and recognize faces in stressful situations, to help understand and improve the accuracy of their courtroom testimony.

- Evaluate the hiring and promotion practices of large organizations to determine whether there is evidence of discrimination on the basis of gender or age.

- Provide expert evidence in court concerning the assessment and management of violence risk in forensic psychiatric patients.

Psychological Ethics
GENERAL ETHICAL PRINCIPLES OF PSYCHOLOGY

The law is, in general, concerned with minimal standards of conduct: it focuses on identifying what constitutes bad or inappropriate behaviour and what actions should be taken in response to such behaviour. Put simply, the law tells us what *not* to do. To determine what psychologists *should* do in a given situation, they turn to **ethical codes**. Ethical codes are a fundamental part of the profession of psychology: they set out the core values that underlie the practice of psychology, thereby establishing an implied social contract between the psychologists and the public (Truscott & Crook, 2004). Ethical codes are primarily descriptive, in the sense that they reflect the actual or existing values of psychologists. But they are also aspirational, in the sense that they reflect the preferred values and highest ideals of psychologists. Similar to ethical codes in some respects are **professional standards**, which put forward expectations regarding the day-to-day practice or conduct of psychologists.

In Canada, the primary ethical code is the fourth edition of the *Canadian Code of Ethics for Psychologists*, published by the Canadian Psychological Association (2017). The *Code of Ethics* sets out four fundamental ethical principles, defines and discusses the principles, and presents a method for making ethical decisions. The four principles are as follows:

I. *Respect for the Dignity of Persons and People.* Psychologists strive to recognize and demonstrate their regard for the innate worth of every human being.

II. *Responsible Caring.* Psychologists strive to minimize risks and maximize benefits for others, particularly vulnerable people.

III. *Integrity in Relationships.* Psychologists strive to be honest, open, straightforward, and unbiased in their interactions with others.

IV. *Responsibility to Society.* Psychologists strive to promote the welfare of all people.

The principles in the *Code of Ethics* are, in many respects, a restatement of more general ethical principles: the **principle of autonomy**, or respect for self-determination; the **principle of nonmaleficence**, or avoiding harm; the **principle of beneficence**, or maximizing good; the **principle of fidelity**, or personal reliability; and the **principle of justice**, or fairness (e.g., Truscott & Crook, 2004). What makes the *Code of Ethics* different is that it ranks the principles in order of importance: Principle I is considered the most important, Principle II the next most important, and so forth. This ranking is useful when deciding what to do in situations where the principles are or may be in conflict.

The *Code of Ethics* presents many specific ethical standards derived from the four fundamental principles. Of most relevance to the practice of forensic psychology are ethical standards stating that psychologists should respect the human, legal, and civil rights of others (Ethical Standard I.5); clarify situations in which they have professional relationships with multiple parties, including situations in which the parties may include courts or police (Ethical Standard I.26); be aware of the knowledge and skills of other disciplines, including law, and make referrals or advise the use of such knowledge and skills to the benefit of others (Ethical Standard II.19); do everything possible to prevent harm to others, including notification of police or potential victims (Ethical Standard II.42); and familiarize themselves with relevant laws and regulations (Ethical Standard IV.17).

⑤ BEFORE MOVING ON

For the past year, a psychologist has been providing supportive psychotherapy to a client, the mother of two young children, to help her deal with adjustment problems related to marital and child-rearing stress. One day, the client informs the psychologist that she is seeking a divorce from her husband and sole custody of her children. She asks the psychologist to write a report assessing her parenting capacity for use in legal proceedings. What ethical concerns does this request raise? What should the psychologist do?

SPECIALIZED ETHICAL GUIDELINES

The *Code of Ethics* is very helpful for dealing with general ethical issues, but it does not deal much with the practice of forensic psychology or the special ethical dilemmas faced by forensic psychologists. Fortunately, two major professional organizations of forensic psychologists, the American Academy of Forensic Psychology and the

American Psychology-Law Society (Division 41 of the American Psychological Association), collaborated to fill this gap. Based on their work, the American Psychological Association developed and adopted the *Specialty Guidelines for Forensic Psychology* (American Psychological Association, 2013). As stated in the introduction (p. 7), the goals of the *Specialty Guidelines* are to "improve the quality of forensic psychological services; enhance the practice and facilitate the systematic development of forensic psychology; encourage a high level of quality in professional practice; and encourage forensic practitioners to acknowledge and respect the rights of those they serve."

The *Specialty Guidelines* have a dual nature: they are a blend of ethical principles and professional standards. They are intended to assist psychologists in applying more general ethical codes to the practice of forensic psychology. Several major themes are apparent in the *Specialty Guidelines*; we will focus our discussion on three of them. The first is the importance of objectivity and neutrality. Although psychologists in other areas of practice are expected to advocate for the people they are evaluating and treating, forensic psychologists are expected to reason, act, and communicate in an unbiased manner. This is reflected in statements such as, "Forensic practitioners strive for accuracy, honesty, and truthfulness in the science, teaching, and practice of forensic psychology and they strive to resist partisan pressures to provide services in any ways that might tend to be misleading or inaccurate" (Specialty Guideline 1.01) and "Forensic practitioners recognize the adversarial nature of the legal system and strive to treat all participants and weigh all data, opinions, and rival hypotheses impartially" (Specialty Guideline 1.02).

A second major theme is the importance of establishing, maintaining, and practising within one's area of competence. This is reflected in statements such as, "Forensic practitioners make ongoing efforts to develop and maintain their competencies" (Specialty Guideline 2.02) and "[F]orensic practitioners adequately and accurately inform all recipients of their services (e.g., attorneys, tribunals) about relevant aspects of the nature and extent of their experience, training, credentials, and qualifications, and how they were obtained" (Specialty Guideline 2.03).

A third major theme is the need for forensic psychologists to know and respect the laws that govern their areas of practice. Psychologists who do not know the law often fail to recognize that what may be acceptable in general practice may be unacceptable in forensic practice—indeed, it may even violate fundamental principles of law. One example here is the reliance of psychologists in general practice on oral or written self-report methods, such as interviews and questionnaires, in their assessments. In the law, it is a highly questionable practice to rely on uncorroborated statements made by parties to legal proceedings; key statements should be corroborated with third-party information obtained from collateral informants, official records, and so forth. Another example is the need to avoid asking unnecessary questions in certain situations, such as evaluating fitness to stand trial. Defendants should not be asked whether they "did it"—that

is, committed the offence(s) with which they have been charged. Not only is the answer irrelevant to the legal issue, but the question itself asks defendants to give up their constitutional rights against self-incrimination. The importance of understanding the law is reflected in statements such as, "Forensic practitioners recognize the importance of obtaining a fundamental and reasonable level of knowledge and understanding of the legal and professional standards, laws, rules, and precedents that govern their participation in legal proceedings and that guide the impact of their services on service recipients" (Specialty Guideline 2.04).

The practice of forensic psychology is a high-stakes arena. The potential consequences for parties to legal proceedings, as well as for the public, can be profound. Forensic psychologists must be familiar not only with general ethical codes, but with specialized ethical and professional standards. It is not sufficient for forensic psychologists to be "adequate" or "competent" with respect to their level of knowledge, skills, or expertise; they must be judged according to a higher standard of practice.

The Status of Psychology in the Legal System

Psychologists are often asked to give evidence before courts and tribunals as professionals (e.g., after conducting psychological assessments of such things as criminal responsibility, violence, risk, or parenting ability) or as scientists (e.g., after conducting research personally, or after preparing an *amicus curiae* brief that summarizes psychological research on a legal issue, such as the capacity of minors to consent to abortion or the impact that testimony might have on a child sexual abuse victim). But the role of psychologists is limited by law, and medical practitioners play a more dominant role in many areas in which mental health input is needed.

For example, in every province and territory, decisions regarding involuntary hospitalization and treatment must be made by one or more physicians—not necessarily psychiatrists, but any qualified medical practitioners. In no jurisdiction do psychologists have the legal authority to involuntarily hospitalize people. This is a rather curious state of affairs: psychologists—whose expertise in assessing, diagnosing, and treating mental disorder is recognized in law—cannot play a role in civil commitment; yet in some jurisdictions any physician, including a general practitioner, anaesthesiologist, or dermatologist, can involuntarily hospitalize someone under civil mental health law. This would seem to be of no benefit to citizens in terms of ensuring that they have access to appropriate health care.

The situation was similar with respect to criminal law, at least until recently. The *Criminal Code* had excluded psychologists from conducting court-ordered assessments of criminal responsibility and fitness to stand trial. Section 671.1 specified that these assessments must be conducted by "medical practitioners." The definition of "medical practitioners" includes both psychiatric and nonpsychiatric physicians, although in practice it is rare for a nonpsychiatric physician to evaluate criminal responsibility or fitness in Canada. The rationale for including nonpsychiatric physicians is that a psychiatrist may not be available in small or remote communities. A recent change to the *Criminal Code* allows the possibility that psychologists can conduct assessments of fitness and NCRMD. Section 671.1 now indicates that an assessment can be made by a medical practitioner or any other person who has been designated by the attorney general as being qualified to conduct an assessment of the mental condition of the accused. Thus, if the attorney general of a province designates psychologists as being qualified, they could then independently conduct these assessments.

The recent *Criminal Code* changes suggest that psychology's role in mental disorder assessments may gradually change in the coming years; it is important to note that psychologists have already been involved in evaluations related to involuntary hospitalization, fitness, or criminal responsibility (Viljoen, Roesch, Ogloff, & Zapf, 2003). In some cases, they are asked by psychiatrists to conduct an evaluation and prepare a report, which is in turn cited in or submitted together with a psychiatric report (Pollack & Webster, 1993). Although this role has sometimes been equated to playing "handmaiden" to psychiatrists (Bartholomew, Badger, & Milte, 1977), it is an important and valuable one that also serves as an opportunity for interdisciplinary collaboration (see Grisso, 1993).

Why have Canadian courts been reluctant to recognize the expertise of psychologists? It appears that they have doubts about the ability of psychologists to diagnose mental disorders. The case of *R. v F. D. M.* (1987) illustrates this concern. When asked about the defendant's sanity, a psychologist opined that the defendant had paranoid schizophrenia and was legally insane at the time of the crime. A psychiatrist diagnosed the same defendant with paranoid psychosis. Although these diagnoses are essentially equivalent in terms of symptomatology, the court emphasized the discrepancy. Monnin J., for the majority, stated, "Dr. Shane, a psychiatrist, did not support the schizophrenia portion of Dr. Ellis' assessment. Who are we to believe and whose testimony are we to accept—the psychologist or the psychiatrist? In my view, the only one qualified to testify is the psychiatrist" (p. 123). Surprisingly, in arguing that psychologists were unable to testify on the presence of mental disorder and the issue of criminal responsibility, he noted, "A general practitioner would not venture in this field. Nor would much weight be given to his testimony" (p. 123). Yet the *Criminal Code* itself permits general practitioners to make the venture!

Exclusion of psychological testimony with the claim that psychologists are unable to diagnose mental disorders is contrary to several provincial statutes governing the profession of psychology. Explicit references to the ability of psychologists to diagnose mental disorder are made in the psychology acts of Alberta, British Columbia, Nova Scotia, Ontario, Prince Edward Island, and Saskatchewan (Viljoen et al., 2003).

Although *R. v F. D. M.* (1987) did not recognize the ability of psychologists to diagnose schizophrenia, other cases have reached different conclusions. In *R. v J. A. P.* (2000, para. 33), Wheelan J. acknowledged the court's previous rejection of psychological testimony in *R. v F. D. M.* (1987) but noted:

> In this case the concern is with mental functioning due to brain injury and there has been ongoing reliance on the tests routinely used in assessing his level of functioning, including the ability to learn. This is a field in which it would seem that psychologists are particularly qualified.

Wheelan J. (para. 41) went on to say:

> Indeed it is my observation that the two disciplines in this case, psychiatry and psychology, have not communicated well and the gap in their approaches and opinions remains unexplained. I am particularly struck by the lack of objective testing by the psychiatrist and the routine way in which such tests were relied upon by the psychologists who found consistent results over several years and several occasions...

R. v J. A. P. (2000) appears to be an important case for Canadian psychologists, and may mark the era of expansion in the role of psychologists in legal proceedings.

CANADIAN RESEARCH CENTRE

Dr. Christopher Webster

Chris Webster received his Ph.D. in experimental psychology from Dalhousie University in 1967. After a few further years researching animal learning at the Addiction Research Foundation and teaching at the University of Toronto, he became interested in childhood autism and conduct disorder. This meant taking advantage of an offer by the Clarke Institute of Psychiatry to lead a program of research and clinical service for children suffering from autism and conduct disorders. In 1975 he became Director of the School of Child and Youth Care at the University of Victoria in British Columbia. The idea behind the school was, and remains, to prepare undergraduates from a variety of disciplines for careers in treatment centres, community projects, and remedial programs in schools and juvenile detention facilities.

A different kind of research opportunity beckoned in 1977 with the introduction of a new law and mental health assessment and treatment service within the Clarke Institute (now the Centre for Addiction and Mental Health). It was there that Chris began to undertake research and clinical work within the area of forensic psychology, clinical criminology, and psychiatry. This meant studying how to assess fitness for trial, criminal responsibility, and potential for violence.

In 1993 Chris became chair of the Department of Psychology at Simon Fraser University and began his collaboration with Steve Hart, Kevin Douglas, Derek Eaves, Randy Kropp, and others. Over the next four or five years the small group,

aided by some prominent international researchers and clinicians, published what has become known as the Historical/Clinical/Risk Management-20 (HCR-20). This clinical guide has now been researched extensively and has found practical application in the forensic and mental health fields, as well as in specialized aspects of correctional services.

In 1997 Chris again returned to Toronto. There he was able to return to his roots by joining a small group of clinicians and researchers at the Child Development Institute, all of whom were intent on creating structured professional

judgment guides for use with under-12 boys and girls with conduct disorders. These have become known as the Early Assessment Risk Lists (EARLs). He continues to research risk assessment issues and has become increasingly involved in devising and researching assessment schemes that are usable on an interdisciplinary basis, which are helpful to courts and review boards, and ethically sound. Chris believes that advances in his area of specialization are most likely to succeed when carried out by means of sustained, intense collaborations between researchers, clinicians, and policy-makers.

SUMMARY

- The fundamental goal of the law is to prevent and resolve, in a principled manner, conflicts among people. In Canada, which has a form of government known as a constitutional monarchy, there are three primary sources of law: constitutional law, statutory law, and common law (except in Quebec, which relies on a civil code). Each of these sources of law recognizes the potential relevance of mental disorder.

- Although Canadian law assumes that people typically think and act in a reasoned, deliberate manner, they may be treated differently when it is demonstrated that their thinking is irrational or their behaviour is involuntary. The legal concept of mental disorder is not bound by psychological or medical definitions. The law typically defines mental disorder as any impairment of psychological functioning that is internal, stable, and involuntary in nature. This definition of mental disorder is much narrower than that used by mental health professionals, so that some disorders that are recognized by mental health professionals may not meet the legal definition of a mental disorder. In legal proceedings, triers of fact must determine whether or not a person who is party to the proceedings has a mental disorder, according to how mental disorder is defined in the relevant law. Mental health professionals act merely as consultants to triers of fact, providing expert observations and opinions.

- Two common law principles are important with respect to mental health law in Canada. The first, the principle of police powers, recognizes that the state has the duty to protect its citizens from threats to their safety and security. The second, the principle of *parens patriae*, recognizes that the state has the duty to care for citizens when they are unable to care for themselves. These principles

provide a justification for the involuntary hospitalization and treatment of people suffering form mental disorder. Involuntary hospitalization, or civil commitment, is most often based on the patient's risk of harm to self or others; in some jurisdictions, it may also be based on the need for treatment, lack of capacity to make treatment decisions, or risk for deterioration in physical or mental health. When patients are committed and deemed incapable of making decisions about treatment, a temporary substitute decision maker may make treatment decisions on their behalf. Temporary substitute decision makers most often follow the best interests or capable wishes principles. Up to 15 to 20 percent of all hospitalizations for mental disorder in Canada may be involuntary.

- The *Criminal Code* includes special provisions for dealing with people suffering from mental disorder who are charged with offences. One important issue concerns whether these people are not criminally responsible on account of mental disorder (NCRMD). According to the *Criminal Code*, some people suffering from mental disorder, through no fault of their own, may have inaccurate perceptions of or irrational beliefs about the world that led them to commit a prohibited act, but without any bad intention—exactly in the same way that someone who raises the defence of self-defence admits the act but denies the intent. Another important issue concerns whether people suffering from mental disorder are unfit to stand trial (UST). According to the *Criminal Code*, some people suffering from mental disorder are unable to participate actively and effectively in their own defence. The key distinction is that decisions regarding NCRMD are based on mental disorder at the time an offence was committed (i.e., in the past), whereas decisions regarding UST are based on mental disorder at the time of trial (i.e., in the present).

- There are some ethical special challenges faced by psychologists whose work takes them inside the legal system. Ethical codes for psychologists set out the core values that underlie the practice of psychology, thereby establishing an implied social contract between the psychologists and the public. In Canada, this is the *Canadian Code of Ethics for Psychologists*, which sets out four fundamental ethical principles, defines and discusses the principles, and presents a method for making ethical decisions. Although ethical codes generally expect psychologists to advocate for the people they are evaluating and treating, psychologists who work in the legal system are expected to reason, act, and communicate in a neutral, unbiased manner. For this reason, specialty ethical guidelines for forensic psychologists have been developed.

KEY TERMS

actus reus (p. 494)

best interests principle (p. 489)

capable wishes principle (p. 489)

civil code (p. 488)

civil commitment (p. 488)

common law (p. 486)

compulsory treatment orders (p. 490)

constitutional law (p. 486)

criminal commitment (p. 488)

deinstitutionalization (p. 490)

ethical codes (p. 499)

forensic psychology (p. 498)

M'Naghten standard (p. 495)

mens rea (p. 494)

not criminally responsible on account of mental disorder (NCRMD) (p. 494)

parens patriae (p. 487)

principle of autonomy (p. 499)

principle of beneficence (p. 499)

principle of fidelity (p. 499)

principle of justice (p. 499)

principle of nonmaleficence (p. 499)

professional standards (p. 499)

statutory law (p. 486)

temporary substitute decision maker (p. 489)

unfit to stand trial (UST) (p. 496)

Glossary

ABAB Also called *reversal design*; a non-experimental investigative method, a variety of *single-subject design*, that requires the quantification of behaviour in its naturally occurring environment prior to any intervention. This constitutes the A phase or the baseline of the procedure. Next, in the B phase, the treatment is introduced in a controlled manner for a period of time. The next A phase constitutes the reversal, during which time the treatment is not provided, and the subject is exposed to the original baseline conditions. Finally, in the final B phase, the treatment is provided once again.

abstinence syndrome A reaction that many individuals experience during treatment for barbiturate abuse. It occurs at the stage at which the user is no longer dependent, and is characterized by insomnia, headaches, aching all over the body, anxiety, and depression, and can last for months.

acquired sexual dysfunction Any sexual dysfunction that the sufferer has developed after a dysfunction-free period of time.

actuarial approach An approach to evaluating and interpreting the data on patients, making predictions, and coming to decisions that relies exclusively on statistical procedures, empirical methods, and formal rules. *See also clinical approach.*

acquiescence The tendency to answer affirmatively.

actus reus In Canadian criminal law, the prohibited physical act that, together with the *mens rea*, defines a criminal offence.

age effects Changes that are due to the process of getting older or aging itself, rather than those that are the result of different age cohorts (cohort effects) or periods in time (period effects).

agonist drug A neurotransmitter that facilitates the inhibitory action of the neurotransmitter GABA at its receptors. Used as a pharmacological agent for the treatment of alcohol dependence.

agoraphobia An irrational fear of being in a situation where escape might be difficult or impossible.

alarm The first phase of the *general adaptation syndrome (GAS)*, a concept that was the first formal description and definition of stress as a consequence of adaptation to demands placed on the body. In the alarm phase, the body, faced with an adaptive challenge, mobilizes its defences. *See also resistance* and *exhaustion*.

alarm theory This theory proposes that a "true alarm" occurs when there is a real threat—our bodies produce an adaptive physiological response that allows us to face the feared object or flee from the situation. In some instances, this alarm system can be activated by emotional cues (in which case it is a "false alarm.")

alcohol dehydrogenase An enzyme that helps break down alcohol in the stomach. Women have significantly less of this enzyme than men.

alcohol expectancy theory A theory that proposes drinking behaviour is largely determined by the reinforcement that an individual expects to receive from it. Most of the subjective experiences actually felt are a function of expectation and attitude and not an effect of the alcohol.

alexithymia A personality characteristic in which an individuals has difficulty identifying and describing subjective feelings, difficulty distinguishing between feelings and bodily sensations of emotional arousal, constricted imaginal capacities, and an externally oriented cognitive style.

alters Refers to each of the unique personalities in an individual who has *dissociative identity disorder (DID)*. Alters may be very different from each other, with opposite personality traits (e.g., one very extraverted and another very introverted), and differences in the age, sex, race, and family history they claim to have.

alternate-form reliability An attribute of a test demonstrated by a high correlation between scores on two versions of a test. To circumvent the problem that one may improve on a test the second time around because of practice, test designers may prepare two forms of the same test—that is, they decide what construct they want their test to measure, think up questions (or items) that would test that construct, and then word those questions in a slightly different way in order to create a second test that measures the same construct as the first.

Alzheimer's disease The most common of the *primary dementias*. It progresses through three stages: *forgetfulness*, in which there are memory difficulties, problems with concentration, unclear thinking, difficulty finding words, and errors in judgment; *confusion*, in which existing symptoms become more severe and additional symptoms occur, such as language difficulties, problems in time and place orientation, sleep difficulties, employment or social difficulties, incontinence, feelings of helplessness, flattening of affect, agitation, irritability, and

wandering; and *dementia*, in which the ability to communicate is lost, memory impairment is profound, and a variety of physical symptoms develop, such as stooped posture, increasing immobility, total incontinence, increasing vulnerability to pneumonia, congestive heart failure, etc.

amenorrhea Failure to menstruate, a medical effect of *anorexia nervosa* and *bulimia nervosa*.

amniocentesis A procedure for prenatal screening for chromosomal abnormalities conducted between the eleventh and eighteenth weeks of pregnancy. With the assistance of ultrasound, a needle is inserted into the amniotic sac via the abdomen and a small amount of amniotic fluid withdrawn. Cells contained in the fluid are then cultured in the lab.

amotivational syndrome A continuing pattern of apathy, profound self-absorption, detachment from friends and family, and abandonment of career and educational goals evident in some long-term users of *cannabis*.

amphetamines Drugs that have effects on the body similar to those of the naturally occurring hormone adrenaline. Originally developed as a nasal decongestant and asthma treatment in the 1930s. In addition to shrinking mucous membranes and constricting blood vessels, they increase alertness and concentration. Chronic amphetamine use is associated with feelings of fatigue and sadness, as well as periods of social withdrawal and intense anger.

amygdala A small almond-shaped structure in the tip of the temporal lobe that plays a role in emotional behaviour.

analogue observational setting An artificial environment set up in an office or laboratory to elicit specific classes of behaviour in individuals. Used when *in vivo observation* in the natural environment is impractical because of time constraints and the unpredictability of modern family life.

androgens Male sex hormones (such as testosterone). Prenatal exposure to male-typical levels of androgens masculinizes postnatal behaviour, whereas underexposure to male-typical levels of androgens has the opposite effect.

anhedonia A loss of pleasure or interest in almost all activities or a lack of reactivity to usually pleasurable events.

anorexia nervosa An eating disorder characterized by the pursuit of thinness to dangerously low weight levels.

Antabuse Disulfiram, a drug that is used to make the experience of drinking extremely aversive. It blocks the action of the metabolizing enzyme acetaldehyde dehydrogenase, resulting in a build-up of acetaldehyde in the body. Like people who naturally lack this enzyme, people who drink alcohol after taking Antabuse experience increased heart rate, nausea, vomiting, and other unpleasant effects.

antagonist drug A neurotransmitter that inhibits the production of acetylcholine, a bodily substance that mediates the transmission of nerve impulses within the brain. Used as a pharmacological agent.

anxiety An emotion that leaves an individual feeling threatened by the potential occurrence of a future negative event.

anxiety sensitivity The tendency to catastrophically misinterpret arousal-related bodily sensations because one believes the sensations to have harmful consequences, such as death, insanity, or loss of control.

anxious/ambivalent *See anxious/ambivalent attachment.*

anxious/ambivalent attachment The interpersonal style of persons who strongly desire intimacy with others and persistently seek out romantic partners, but who, once they begin to get close to their partner, become anxious and back away; while they desire closeness, they appear to be afraid of it. People are considered to have developed these difficulties as a result of poor parent–child attachments that fail to instill the self-confidence and skills necessary for intimacy. Because this relationship style characterizes *borderline personality disorder (BPD)* patients, the features of borderline disorder may be seen as attempts to adjust to a desire for but distrust of intimacy.

appraisals In the *transactional model* of stress, evaluations that people constantly make about what is happening to them and its implications for themselves.

arrhythmias Disturbances in the normal pumping rhythm of the heart. Can result in *myocardial infarction*.

Asperger disorder A developmental disorder similar to *autism* but associated with fewer symptoms, higher functioning, and higher IQ. It is not known whether "core autism" (the full range and severity of symptoms) and Asperger disorder represent points on a continuum of severity, or whether they are related but different disorders.

asphyxiophilia *See autoerotic asphyxia.*

assessment A procedure in which information is gathered systematically in the evaluation of a condition; it serves as the preliminary to a *diagnosis*. A psychiatric assessment may include interviews with the patient or the patient's family, medical testing, psychophysiological or psychological testing, and the completion of self-report scales or other report rating scales.

assortative mating When individuals tend to mate with people who are like themselves in some respect.

asylum A place for treatment of the mentally ill. Units for the mentally ill were established within the great Arab hospitals in Baghdad in AD 800 and asylums were created in other Arab cities some 500 years before Europeans built their first asylums. Treatment in Arab asylums followed the tradition of care, support, and compassion.

atheoretical Not based on or concerned with a particular theory.

atherogenesis The development of *atherosclerosis*. Can occur as early as two years of age.

atherosclerosis A build-up of deposits, known as *plaques*, on the walls of the blood vessels. Atherosclerosis can narrow the openings of arteries enough to compromise the blood supply to the heart or the brain, leading to *myocardial infarction* or *stroke*.

attachment theory A development of the psychoanalytic approach by John Bowlby. According to this view, children form attachments with their parents that become the child's internalized model for all subsequent relationships. Difficulties in such attachments form the basis for later problems.

attention deficit/hyperactivity disorder (ADHD) A childhood disorder characterized by disruptive behaviour, an inability to control activity levels or impulses, or difficulty concentrating.

auditory hallucinations The experience of hearing sounds like voices that do not actually exist. A common symptom of schizophrenia.

autism From the Greek autos, meaning "self", autisms is characterized by difficulty in communicating and forming relationships with other people and in using language and abstract concepts.

autism spectrum disorder The best known of the *pervasive developmental disorders*. Autistic children exhibit a lack of social responsiveness or extreme autistic aloneness; very limited or unusual communication patterns; unusual patterns of behaviour such as a lack of eye contact; self-stimulation, including rocking, spinning, or flapping; self-injury, including head-banging or hand-biting; an obsessive interest in particular objects; and an obsessive need for sameness. From the Greek *autos*, "self."

autoerotic asphyxia A self-administered procedure for suppressing breathing so that unconsciousness occurs. Usually releasing procedures are built in to reinitiate breathing upon unconsciousness. This loss of consciousness is sexually arousing to the participant.

aversive drift In Meehl's theory, the tendency for people with a genetic predisposition for schizophrenia to be perceived negatively and subjected to personal rejection, leading progressively to social withdrawal and alienation.

avolition A loss of energy, motivation, or interest in activities, including grooming, education, or physical exertion.

B

baby boomer A person who was born during the post–Second World War baby boom between 1946 and 1964.

bedlam Any form of rowdy, chaotic behaviour. The noise and disruption among the residents of Bethlem Royal Hospital (as it is now known) prompted the use of the word (the local corruption of "Bethlem"). This asylum was established by Henry VIII in 1547 when he had the monastery of St. Mary of Bethlehem in London converted.

behavioural avoidance test (BAT) An assessment of a patient's avoidance whereby the person determines how close he or she can come to a feared object. During their approach, patients also provide ratings of their fear. This test is used to assess initial avoidance and behavioural change through therapy.

behavioural disinhibition A personality trait describing an inability to inhibit behavioural impulses, rebelliousness, aggressiveness, and risk-taking that are associated with the development of alcohol problems.

behavioural genetics The study of the way in which inherited features interact with the environment to produce behaviour.

behavioural inhibition A temperament in early childhood that may be related to anxiety disorders later in life, characterized by profound avoidance of others in preschool, and atypical autonomic nervous system responses to novelty.

behavioural medicine Application of the methods of behaviour modification to the treatment or prevention of disease—for example, the use of psychological techniques to control pain in patients undergoing medical procedures, or interventions to improve the diabetics' ability to control their blood glucose.

behavioural phenotype Characteristic patterns of motor, cognitive, linguistic, and social abnormalities commonly displayed by individuals with certain genetic disorders.

behavioural tolerance Through the principles of classical conditioning, cues in the environment can become conditioned stimuli to the effects of drug use. These cues cause the individual to anticipate the drug effects so that when the drug is actually administered the effects are diminished. Tolerance, or the need for a greater amount of drug for the same effect, is greatest when the conditioned environmental cues are present.

behaviourism A psychological approach to understanding abnormal behaviour devised by John B. Watson (1858–1935), which declared that psychology must be restricted to the study of observable features, that is, the behaviour of organisms. Watson considered abnormal functioning to be learned and so believed it could be unlearned. His model for learning was derived from Ivan Pavlov's (1849–1936) studies of classical conditioning.

behaviour therapy A treatment that emphasizes that problem behaviours are learned behaviours and that faulty learning can be reversed through the application of learning principles.

Bender Visual-Motor Gestalt Test The oldest and most commonly used of neuropsychological assessments often used to screen children for neuropsychological impairment. The test consists of a series of nine cards containing lines and shapes drawn in black on a piece of white cardboard. Children are asked first to copy the images on another card and then to draw them from memory. Errors in reproducing these lines and shapes may indicate neurological problems.

best interests principle In provincial mental health law, the doctrine that decisions made by others about the treatment of people suffering from mental disorders should maximize the chances of a good outcome, taking into account the risks and benefits of all available treatments.

biastophilia From Greek *biastes*, meaning rape; also referred to as paraphilic rape. Sexual arousal in response to non-consenting sex with, but not necessarily physical suffering of, victims.

binge eating/purging type A subtype of *anorexia nervosa* in which the afflicted person's dietary restraint breaks down fairly regularly and she/he binges and/or purges. About half of anorexia nervosa patients are of the binge eating/purging type. *See also restricting type*.

biological preparedness Refers to the idea that humans and animals are biologically prepared to fear certain stimuli as opposed to others. That is, evolution has "hard-wired" organisms to easily learn those associations that facilitate species survival.

biopsychosocial model A model proposing that behaviour is the result of the combined influence of biological, psychological, and social factors. Thus genetic endowment, neurological damage, and life experience (personal and social) all play a role in the emergence of behaviour.

bipolar and related disorders Mood disorders in which the change in mood occurs in both directions; that is, the patient at one time or another experiences both depression (mood lowering) and *mania* (mood elevation).

bipolar I disorder A subtype of the *bipolar disorders* in which there are one or more manic episodes and usually one or more depressive episodes. *See also bipolar II disorder*.

bipolar II disorder A subtype of the *bipolar disorders* in which there is at least one hypomanic episode and one or more episodes of major depression. *See also bipolar I disorder*.

birth-related complications Minor abnormalities at the time of birth, including extended labour, forceps delivery, and low weight, that may predispose a person to later illness.

blackouts Memory deficit caused by alcohol intoxication in which an interval of time passes for which a person cannot recall key details or entire events.

blood alcohol level (BAL) Alcohol level expressed as a percentage of blood volume. For example, if there are 80 milligrams of alcohol in 100 000 milligrams of blood, BAL is 0.08 percent.

body dysmorphic disorder (BDD) A disorder in which the individual is unusually and excessively preoccupied with some aspect of his or her personal appearance, which is not observable or appears minor to others. Classified in DSM-5 in the group of *obsessive-compulsive and related disorders*.

body mass index (BMI) A person's weight in kilograms over his or her height in metres squared, an indicator of how much fat one has on one's body.

brain lesion An area of brain tissue that appears abnormal.

brain plasticity The ability of intact brain cells to compensate for damaged cells and take over their function.

brief intervention One- to three-session treatments, offering time-limited and specific advice regarding the need to reduce or eliminate alcohol and other drug consumption or gambling behaviour.

bulimia nervosa An eating disorder characterized by a binge-purge syndrome in people who are generally in the normal weight range.

buprenorphine/naloxone (Narcan) A drug that blocks the effects of opioids, including depressed respiration and loss of consciousness, used to treat narcotic overdoses in emergency situations.

C

cannabis Hashish, which comes from the hemp plant *cannabis sativa*, indigenous to Asia but now grown in many parts of the world. Has psychoactive effects caused primarily by the chemical *THC*.

capable wishes principle In provincial mental health law, the doctrine that decisions made by others about the treatment of people suffering from mental disorders should reflect their personal wishes.

cardiac output The amount of blood pumped by the heart. One of the two major variables that determine blood pressure. Cardiac output is itself determined by two other variables: the rate at which the heart beats (commonly measured in beats per minute) and the amount of blood ejected from the heart (stroke volume). *See also total peripheral resistance.*

cardiovascular reactivity The degree of change in a cardiovascular function that occurs in response to psychologically significant events.

cardiovascular recovery Sustained cardiovascular activation above baseline levels during the post-stress recovery period, is associated with an increase in risk for hypertension and cardiovascular disease.

case study A non-experimental investigative method resulting in a description of the past and current functioning of a single individual, generally the result of information gathered through intense interactions over long periods. Variables such as family history, education, employment history, medical history, social relationships, and the patient's level of psychological adjustment are described. The goal is a description of an individual's current problem, and its relation to his or her past. A case study seeks to provide a theory concerning the etiology of a patient's problem or psychological makeup, and/or a course of treatment and outcome. The oldest approach to the study of abnormal behaviour.

catastrophic misinterpretation In the context of panic, when one misinterprets normal bodily sensations as signals that one is going to have a heart attack, go crazy, lose control, or die.

catatonic behaviour Rigid body positions assumed by people with schizophrenia.

categorical approach The diagnostic approach taken by the DSM, in which an individual is deemed either to have a disorder or not have a disorder.

cellular immunity One of the three general categories of immune response, based on the action of a class of blood cells called T-lymphocytes. The "T" designation refers to the locus of their production, the thymus gland. Cellular immunity results from a cascade of actions of various types of T-lymphocytes.

child molester An individual who sexually abuses a pre-pubescent child (or children) but does not necessarily have a sexual preference for children.

chlorpromazine The first true antipsychotic medication, introduced in the early 1950s.

chorionic villus sampling (CVS) A procedure for prenatal screening for chromosomal abnormalities that involves obtaining cells from the vagina and cervix. This test can be carried out earlier than amniocentesis—between the eighth and twelfth weeks of pregnancy—but may be less accurate.

civil code The written statement of law used in some jurisdictions to deal with matters of private law (i.e., disputes between individuals); in Canada, Quebec uses a civil code, whereas the other provinces and territories use common law.

civil commitment In provincial mental health law, the involuntary hospitalization of people suffering from mental disorder.

classical conditioning A type of learning described by the Russian physiologist Ivan Pavlov (1849–1936). In classical conditioning, a response is transferred from one stimulus to another. John B. Watson, an early behaviourist, took the view that classical conditioning was the basis for human behaviour, including abnormal behaviour. *See also operant conditioning.*

client-centred therapy A type of therapy developed by Carl Rogers as an alternative to psychoanalysis, based on his belief that psychological problems arose when personal growth was stunted by judgments imposed by others.

clinical approach An approach to evaluating and interpreting the data on patients, making predictions, and coming to decisions that relies on the clinician's experience and personal judgment, guided by intuition honed with professional experience rather than by formal rules. *See also actuarial approach.*

clinical practice guidelines Guidelines based on the best available empirical evidence that translate the knowledge gained from research into concrete guidelines intended to inform clinical practice.

clinical psychologists Persons who are initially trained in general psychology and then receive graduate training in the application of this knowledge to the understanding, diagnosis, and amelioration of disorders of thinking and behaviour. They have a thorough grounding in research methods, and some spend their careers doing research on abnormal functioning, although many also provide treatment. The treatment methods of clinical psychologists primarily involve psychological interventions of one kind or another.

clinical significance An attribute of research results, referring to the practical utility of the treatment studied, which does not follow automatically from the results' *statistical significance.*

cloak of competence The tendency to overestimate higher functioning individuals with disabilities by their "normal" appearance and verbal abilities.

clusters Groups of personality disorders. DSM-IV-TR lists 10 personality disorders in three clusters: (A) odd and eccentric disorders (paranoid, schizoid, and schizotypal); (B) dramatic, emotional, or erratic disorders (antisocial, borderline, histrionic, and narcissistic); and (C) anxious and fearful disorders (avoidant, dependent, and obsessive-compulsive).

coefficient alpha A method for evaluating *internal consistency*, calculated by averaging the intercorrelations of all the items on a given test. The higher the coefficient alpha, the higher the internal consistency.

coercive process A process in relationships in which aversive reactions are used to control the behaviour of another individual.

cognitive-behavioural theory A psychological theory that reflects the view that both thinking and behaviour are learned and can, therefore, be changed. It assumes that the way people view the world, including their beliefs and attitudes toward the world, themselves, and others, arises out of their experience and that these patterns of thinking and perceiving are maintained by consequences in the same way overt behaviour is maintained. Although this treatment approach incorporates some procedures derived from strictly cognitive therapy, it essentially follows the views expressed by Bandura's *social learning theory.*

cognitive-behaviour (behavioural) therapy (CBT) A form of psychotherapy that attempts to change maladaptive thoughts and behaviours.

cognitive distortions Thoughts about the self, world, or future that are distortions of the true state of affairs.

cognitive marker A disease marker that is cognitive in nature, typically involving a test of attention, memory, or reasoning.

cognitive restructuring A technique used by cognitive-behavioural therapists to encourage clients to become aware of, and to question, their assumptions, expectations, attributions, and automatic thoughts.

cognitive slippage The mental consequence of *hypokrisia*, namely loss of integrated thinking and coherent mental life.

cognitive therapy Based on the assumption that an individual's perception of events, rather than the events themselves, affects adjustment. This form of treatment focuses on identifying automatic thoughts and changing maladaptive patterns of thinking that are associated with distress (*also see cognitive-behavioural*).

cognitive triad Negative views of the self, world, and future, as part of Beck's cognitive model of depression.

cohort effect A cohort refers to people born at roughly the same time, and a cohort effect refers to differences in age cohorts (e.g., people born in 1930 versus those born in 1980) as a result of unique social and historical events they have experienced.

collective unconscious The concept that symbols and myths are shared among people in a culture, but remain beneath awareness. The Swiss psychiatrist C. G. Jung developed this concept more fully in his approach to dreams.

common law The law as stated in the decisions of the judges from the earliest times to the present.

community psychology A field of psychology that has highlighted the need for the prevention of mental disorders and the promotion of mental health, as opposed to exclusive reliance on treatment approaches; applies an ecological perspective that stresses the interdependence of the individual, the family, community, and society; embodies sensitivity to a person's social context and appreciation of diversity; pays more attention to people's strengths and the promotion of wellness, in contrast to the clinical psychology focus on deficits and reduction of maladaptive behaviours; stresses the importance of informal social supports, rather than relying solely on professional help; and is oriented to social justice and social change.

comorbidity The common situation in which an individual meets the criteria for more than one diagnostic condition. *See also overlap.*

compulsions Repetitive behaviours (overt actions or cognitive acts) performed in response to an obsession, or according to certain rules or in a stereotyped manner.

compulsory treatment order A court order requiring an individual to undergo treatment for his or her mental disorder.

computerized axial tomography (CAT) A brain imaging technique in which a narrow band of X-rays is projected through the head. The X-ray source and detector rotate very slightly and project successive images. The exposures are combined by a computer to produce a highly detailed cross-section of the brain.

concordance A concept used in behavioural research into the genetic bases of psychiatric disorders. When the disorder that characterizes one person, called the *index case* or *proband*, also occurs in another person, the two are said to display concordance. The degree of concordance is thought to reveal the influence of genetics.

concordant The similarity of diagnosis in a pair of twins—they are concordant if they both exhibit the same trait or disorder.

concurrent validity The ability of a diagnostic category to estimate an individual's present standing on factors related to the disorder but not themselves part of the diagnostic criteria. One of the major criticisms of the DSM is that it sheds little light on the non-symptom attributes of people with a given diagnosis.

conduct disorder (CD) A disorder of children who show a pattern of violating the rights of others and major age-appropriate societal norms or rules in a variety of settings.

confound In an experiment, what occurs when two or more variables exert their influence at the same time, making it impossible to accurately establish the causal role of either variable.

conscious In *psychodynamic* theory, the conscious contains information of which we are currently aware.

constitutional law The written statement of law that, among other things, defines the powers and limits of powers that can be exercised by the different levels and branches of government; in Canada, set out primarily in the *Constitution Act*.

constitutional vulnerability One model of how hostility might lead to health risk, which suggests that the link between hostility and poor health outcomes is the result of a third variable, constitutional vulnerability, with which they are both associated.

construct validity The validity of a test assuming a specific theoretical framework that relates the item the test measures, often rather abstract, to some other item that is more easily assessed. If the two sets of measurements correlate, the test is said to have construct validity.

content-specificity Distinct cognitive content is related to different types of disorders. For example, depression is related to thoughts of deprivation and loss, whereas anxiety is related to themes of threat and potential harm.

content validity When the content of a test includes a representative sample of behaviours thought to be related to the construct (that is, the concept or entity) the test is designed to measure.

control group In an experiment, the group that experiences all aspects of the experiment, including assessments, in a manner identical to the *experimental group*, except for the manipulation of the *independent variable*.

conversion disorder A disorder classified in the group of *somatic symptom and related disorders* in DSM-5, characterized by motor symptoms or disturbances in sensory functioning that appear to be a result of a neurological problem, but for which no physical cause can be found.

correlational method A nonexperimental investigative method that measures the degree of relationship between two variables; behaviour is not manipulated but quantitatively measured and then analyzed statistically. Following the measurement of the variables, a statistical quantity called a *correlation coefficient* is computed. Generally requires a large number of participants.

courtship disorder theory A theory of sexual offending advanced by Kurt Freund that postulates that sexual offending occurs when a person's sexual behaviour becomes fixated at one of the four phases of human sexual interactions: (1) looking for and appraising a potential partner; (2) posturing and displaying oneself to the partner; (3) tactile interaction with the partner; and (4) sexual intercourse. Fixation at stage 1 results in *voyeurism*; at stage 2 in *exhibitionism*; at stage 3 in *frotteurism*; and at stage 4 in *rape*.

criminal commitment A custodial sentence, or detention in a correctional facility following conviction for a criminal offence.

criterion validity An attribute of a test, when it gives higher scores to people already known to have greater ability in the area it tests. The concept arises because some qualities are easier to recognize than to define completely, such as artistic ability.

cross-fostering A type of adoption study in which one group comprises adopted children whose biological parents have a disorder and whose adoptive parents demonstrate no psychopathology, and the other group comprises adopted children whose biological parents have no disorder but whose adoptive parents develop psychopathology. The comparisons available in this design allow statements concerning the relative impact of genes and environment. Regarded as an improvement on the traditional adoption study.

culturally relative The functions and acceptability of various behaviours vary by culture, rather than being universal truths; as such, an individual's beliefs and activities should be understood in terms of his or her own culture.

cumulative liability The combined risk for developing an illness that accumulates over multiple factors and over time.

cumulative risk The summation of a person's risk for a disorder or disease up to a specified age.

cyclothymia *See cyclothymic disorder.*

cyclothymic disorder Mood disorder characterized by long-term (i.e., at least two years) repeated fluctuations in mood, varying from hypomanic symptoms to depressive symptoms that do not meet diagnostic criteria for *major depressive disorder*.

D

defence mechanisms According to Sigmund Freud, mechanisms through which the ego allows the expression of libidinal desires in a distorted or symbolic form.

deinstitutionalization The removal of people with disabilities from institutions and the provision of community-based accommodation and services.

delayed ejaculation A marked delay in ejaculation or a marked infrequency or absence of ejaculation, which is present in about 75 to 100 percent of sexual occasions and for a minimum duration of six months.

deliberate self-harm (DSH) When someone injures or harms him- or herself on purpose.

delusional thinking Implausible and unfounded beliefs and convictions not based in reality, as often experienced by people with schizophrenia and other psychotic disorders.

delusions False beliefs that are strongly held, even in the face of solid contradictory evidence. Such beliefs usually involve a misinterpretation of one's experiences.

delusions of grandeur False and implausible beliefs that focus on the possession of special powers, divinity, or fame.

dependent variable In an experiment, the behavioural response on measures the researchers hypothesize would be affected by the manipulation of the *independent variable*.

depersonalization A dissociative symptom in which one experiences a sense of unreality, detachment, or being an outside observer of one's own thoughts, feelings, bodily sensations, or actions.

depersonalization/derealisation disorder A dissociative disorder in which the individual has persistent or recurrent experiences of unreality or detachment from his or her own thoughts, feelings, bodily sensations, and/or surroundings. One's own sense of self and/or perceptions of other individuals or objects may be experienced as unreal, dreamlike, foggy, or distorted.

depressants Drugs that inhibit neurotransmitter activity in the central nervous system. Examples are alcohol, barbiturates ("downers"), and benzodiazepines.

depressive disorders Mood disorders in which the change in mood is only in the direction of depression or lowered mood, followed by a return to normal mood with recovery. *See also bipolar mood disorders.*

derealization A dissociative symptom in which one has a sense of unreality or detachment with respect to objects or other people in the environment, experiencing them as unreal, dreamlike, foggy, or distorted.

description The specification and classification of clinical phenomena; one of the primary goals of clinical research.

developmental dyscalculia A learning disorder that involves problems with recognizing and understanding numerical symbols, sequencing problems, and attention deficits. Also known as *mathematical disorder*. The number sense hypothesis suggests that learning disorder math difficulties reflect an inability to process numerical quantities, including making judgments about quantity and reasoning with symbolic representations of quantity. An alternate hypothesis suggests that math disorders reflect core deficits in working memory.

developmental dysgraphia Impairments in spelling, writing fluency, and written expression are thought to reflect deficits in multiple neuropsychological processes, including processing speed, working memory, and executive functioning.

diagnosis In the realm of medicine and abnormal psychology, a determination or identification of the nature of a person's disease or condition, or a statement of that finding. A diagnosis is made on the basis of a *diagnostic system*.

diagnostic overshadowing The problem of attributing emotional and behavioural difficulties of people with intellectual disability to the developmental disorder, causing real psychiatric disorders to be missed. The fact is that such people can develop all types of psychiatric disorders, including less common ones.

diagnostic system A system of rules for recognizing and grouping various types of abnormalities. Forms the basis for *diagnosis*.

dialectical behaviour therapy One of the cognitive-behavioural approaches to treatment of *borderline personality disorder (BPD)*, one of whose main features is the acceptance by the therapist of the patient's demanding and manipulative behaviours. In addition, several standard behavioural procedures are used, such as exposure treatment for the external and internal cues that evoke distress, skills training, contingency management, and cognitive restructuring.

diathesis A predisposition or vulnerability for the development of an illness or disorder.

diathesis-stress model A model that recognizes the combination of a diathesis (i.e., vulnerability) and sufficient amounts of life stress that, combined, are likely to produce a disorder.

diathesis-stress perspective The view that a predisposition to develop a disorder (the "diathesis"), interacting with the experience of stress, causes mental disorders. According to this perspective, the interaction underlies the onset of all disorders, although either the predisposition or the stress may be more important in a particular disorder, or in a particular person.

dignity of risk The right of individuals to choose to take some risk in engaging in life experiences and the consequences that are associated with those risks.

dimensional An approach to diagnosis that examines constructs on a continuum rather than as discrete categorical entities.

diminished emotional expression Lack of emotional expression and response.

disease markers Objective biological or behavioural traits or features of an individual that reliably reflect the presence of a medical or psychiatric disease or a predisposition to develop such a disease.

disgust sensitivity The degree to which people are disgusted by a variety of stimuli, such as bugs, types of food, and small animals.

disruptive mood dysregulation disorder A mood disorder in the DSM-5 that is characterized by severe recurrent verbal or behavioural outbursts that are disproportionate to the situation or provocation. This disorder represents a perfect intersect between externalizing and internalizing problems, highlighting once again, the complexity of mental problems in childhood and adolescence.

dissemination Scaling up of program to other settings for widespread adoption.

dissociation A disruption or breakdown in the integration of thoughts, feelings, experiences, behaviour, and/or identity in conscious awareness and memory.

dissociative amnesia A dissociative disorder characterized by sudden loss of memory for important autobiographical or personal information, which is not due to a neurological or other medical condition. Characterized by a sudden onset, typically in response to a traumatic event or extremely stressful experience, and by an equally sudden return of memory.

dissociative disorders Psychological problems characterized by *dissociation*.

dissociative fugue A type of *dissociative amnesia* in which an individual suddenly and unexpectedly travels away from home and may take up a new identity, accompanied by a loss of memory for his or her own identity or other important biographical information.

dissociative identity disorder (DID) The most severe and chronic of the dissociative disorders, characterized by the existence of two or more unique personalities in a single individual. Each personality may have its own constellation of behaviour, tone of voice, and physical gestures, and so on. *See also alters.*

dizygotic (DZ) twins Non-identical (or fraternal) twins, which result when two independent sperm separately fertilize two independent ova at approximately the same time. DZ twins, like non-twin siblings, have, on average, just 50 percent of their genes in common. From *di*, meaning "two."

dopamine A neurotransmitter associated with movement, attention, learning, and the brain's pleasure and reward system.

dopamine-blocking drugs Medication that acts by occupying receptors for dopamine in the brain, thereby reducing psychotic symptoms.

double-blind A procedure to help ensure that expectations of the subjects of a study do not influence the outcome, according to which neither the subjects nor the experimenters know who is getting the substance in question and who is getting a *placebo*.

Down syndrome The best-known chromosomal abnormality associated with intellectual disability.

drug interactions When another substance affects the activity of a drug (e.g., by increasing or decreasing its activity).

dual diagnosis The co-occurrence of serious behavioural or psychiatric disorders in people with developmental disabilities.

dualistic A view of mind and body as separate entities, subject to different laws. Nowadays avoided in DSM terminology, hence the substitution of the term *psychophysiological* for *psychosomatic.*

dyslexia A reading disorder that involves difficulties not only in the recognition but also in the comprehension of words. Reading is often very slow and characterized by omitted, substituted, or distorted words. Such difficulties often extend to spelling as well. Also referred to as *reading disorder.*

dysthymia *See persistent depressive disorder.*

E

Eating Disorder Examination (EDE) A structured clinical interview for diagnosing eating disorders.

eccentricity Generally describes behaviour that deviates from the norm and would be considered odd or whimsical.

echolalia One of the common characteristics of speech in autistic children, in which the child repeats another person's words or phrases, using the same or similar intonation.

ecological perspective A perspective on health promotion that considers nested levels of analysis, viewing mental health problems in the context of characteristics of the individual (for example, coping skills, personality traits); the *microsystem* (that is, the family and social network); the *exo-system*, which mediates between the individual, the family, and the larger society (for example, work settings, schools, religious settings, neighbourhoods); and the *macrosystem* (for example, social norms, social class).

effect size A common metric used to summarize the meaning of diverse studies in a *meta-analysis*. It is calculated as the difference between the means of the experimental (that is, the treatment) group and the control group, divided by the standard deviation of either the control group or the pooled sample of both groups.

ego In Sigmund Freud's theory, the structure that begins to develop in response to the fact that instinctual demands of the *id* are not always immediately met. The ego develops to curb the desires of id so that the individual does not suffer any unpleasant consequences.

ego analysts Psychoanalytically oriented therapists who use Freudian techniques to explore the ego rather than the id, and try to help clients understand how they have relied on defence mechanisms to cope with conflicts.

egodystonic Thoughts and behaviours that do not coincide with one's self-image (ego).

egodystonic homosexuality A disorder (not currently in use) in which the afflicted person is attracted to people of the same sex, but experiences conflict with his or her sexual orientation or wishes to change it.

egosyntonic Lack of emotional responsiveness to events or situations that would normally elicit a strong negative emotional response such as heightened anxiety or depression.

Electra complex The condition in which, according to Sigmund Freud, girls want to seduce their fathers to gain what they truly desire: a penis. By analogy to a character in several Greek tragedies.

electroconvulsive therapy (ECT) The use of electricity to induce a seizure in mental patients by placing electrodes on the skull and administering a convulsive rather than a lethal shock intensity.

emotional numbing The perception that one lacks, is without, or can't feel emotions; instead one feels "numb."

emotional responsiveness Reflecting a range of appropriate and contextual emotions to different situations and individuals.

emotionally focused couples therapy An experiential approach to couples therapy that aims to modify constricted interaction patterns and emotional responses by fostering the development of a secure emotional bond.

emotion-focused therapy A short-term psychotherapy approach that purports that emotions themselves are inherently adaptive and can help clients to change problematic emotional states or unwanted self-experiences.

empirically supported therapy Psychotherapeutic intervention that has been demonstrated empirically to be effective.

endogenous opiates The body's natural painkillers. *Opioids* mimic their effects.

endophenotypes A hereditary characteristic that is normally associated with some condition but is not a direct symptom of that condition.

epidemiology The study of the *incidence* and *prevalence* of disorders in a population.

epigenetics The study of modifications of gene expressions that are caused by mechanisms other than changes in the underlying DNA sequence.

equipotentiality premise The presumption that all stimuli have an equal chance of becoming acquired phobias.

erectile disorder A dysfunction characterized by difficulties with obtaining an erection during sexual activity, maintaining an erection until the completion of sexual activity, and/or a marked decrease in erectile rigidity in about 75 to 100 percent of sexual occasions over a period of at least six months, leading to distress.

estrogen A hormone (the so-called female sex hormone) that promotes the development and maintenance of female physical characteristics and that is involved in sexual activity and desire, variations in the level of which can lower or increase sex drive.

ethical codes Written statements that set out the core values that should guide decision making by members of a profession or other group.

ethyl alcohol The effective chemical compound in alcoholic beverages, which reduces anxiety and inhibitions, produces euphoria, and creates a sense of well-being.

etiology Causes or origins, especially of disease.

eugenics The science of improving a human population by controlled breeding to increase the occurrence of desirable heritable characteristics.

evidence-based practice Health care based on established scientific findings rather than practitioners' assumptions.

evidence-based therapy relationships (ESR) A task force of the APA Division of Psychotherapy reviewed the research literature to identify elements of effective therapy relationships and determine methods of tailoring therapy to individual patient characteristics.

excessive reassurance seeking Part of Coyne's model of depression where a depressed person seeks reassurance about him- or herself from non-depressed people.

exhaustion The third phase of the *general adaptation syndrome (GAS)*, a concept that was the first formal description and definition of stress as a consequence of adaptation to demands placed on the body. If the challenge persists beyond the *resistance* phase, the body can no longer maintain resistance, and characteristic tissue changes occur. At this point, the organism may succumb to a disease of adaptation, such as an ulcer. *See also alarm.*

exhibitionistic disorder A type of *paraphilic disorder* that is also a criminal offence, in which a person exposes his or her genitals to an unsuspecting stranger.

Exner system A way of standardizing the scoring of responses in a Rorschach examination in order to increase its reliability and validity. The Exner system may have greater clinical validity for testing schizophrenia than depression or personality disorders.

exogenous opiates Narcotics, which bind to receptor sites throughout the body, including the brain, spinal cord, and bloodstream, and reduce the body's production of *endogenous opiates.*

experiment A scientific procedure in which variables are manipulated and the effects on other variables are gauged. Large groups of subjects are generally used, and the results are analyzed statistically. In a true experiment, subjects are randomly assigned to *experimental* and *control groups*.

experimental effect The difference obtained in the dependent variable that occurs as a function of the manipulation of the *independent variable.*

experimental group In an experiment, the group exposed to a variable that is manipulated, the *independent variable.*

exposure therapy Any therapeutic procedure that repeatedly confronts the person with a stimulus that typically elicits an undesirable behaviour or an unwanted emotional response until the behaviour or response no longer occurs.

expressed emotion A measure of the amount of emotion displayed, typically within a family.

externalizing problems A type of disruptive behaviour disorder under the DSM-IV classification exhibited by children who behave disruptively, cannot control their activity levels or impulses, or have difficulty concentrating. These behaviours are usually more disturbing to others than to the children themselves.

external validity The generalizability of the findings in an investigation, or the degree to which the findings apply to other individuals in other settings.

extrapyramidal effects Severe side effects of the major tranquilizers.

eye-tracking The measurement of movements of the eyes as they follow a point of light or a waveform. Patients with schizophrenia often show jerky or irregular eye-tracking.

F

face validity An attribute of a test, when the items on it resemble the characteristics associated with the concept being tested for.

facilitated communication (FC) An alternative approach to teaching people with severe communication impairment, such as low-functioning children with *autism.* In FC, subjects pointed to pictures, letters, or objects while a facilitator provided various types of support to the hand or forearm, on the theory that physical support could overcome neuromotor problems. However, concerns were soon raised about the "ouija board effect"—that is, that facilitators were unintentionally influencing the subject by subtle body movements. Controlled studies confirmed that this was occurring and did not provide support for the emergence of hidden literacy skills.

factitious disorder A disorder characterized by faking or producing symptoms of illness or injury (e.g., by putting blood in a urine sample or swallowing a noxious substance) to gain a doctor's attention and thus satisfy a need to play the role of patient. Classified in DSM-5 within the group of *somatic symptom and related disorders.*

false memory syndrome Said to be exhibited by persons who claim to remember events that did not really take place, due to the influence of therapists who use leading questions, repeated suggestion, visualization, and hypnosis with the aim of recovering repressed memories.

familiality The extent to which a disorder occurs in members of the same family, including previous generations.

family-focused therapy (FFT) Adjunctive psychotherapy for bipolar and related disorders that focuses on educating the patient's family about the disorder and improving family communication.

family therapy A form of psychotherapy that focuses on work with families and couples in intimate relationships.

fear An emotion that occurs in response to a real or perceived current threat.

fear hierarchy A fear hierarchy is a list of feared situations or objects that are arranged in descending order according to how much they evoke anxiety. This list is then used in therapy for exposure exercises.

fearlessness hypothesis A theory that suggests that *psychopaths* have a higher threshold for feeling fear than other people. Events that make most people anxious (such as the expectation of being punished) seem to have little or no effect on psychopaths.

female orgasmic disorder A sexual dysfunction characterized by a woman's delay in, infrequency of, or absence of, orgasm and/or a reduction in the intensity of orgasmic sensations in all or almost all (75 to 100 percent) occasions of sexual activity for a minimum of six months, causing marked distress or interpersonal difficulty. Also known as *anorgasmia.*

female sexual interest/arousal disorder A sexual dysfunction characterized by a woman's lack of, or significantly reduced sexual arousal/interest (e.g., reduced sexual thoughts and sexual pleasure) for a minimum of six months in 75 to 100 percent of sexual occasions, and the presence of marked distress.

fetal alcohol syndrome disorder (FASD) Prenatal and postnatal growth retardation and central nervous system dysfunction due to alcohol consumption during pregnancy.

fetishisms Sexual behaviours/fantasies in which the presence of nonliving objects or excessive focus on non-genital body parts is usually required or strongly preferred for sexual excitement.

"fight or flight" response A term commonly used to describe the behavioural options of individuals (or organisms) experiencing fear; specifically, to either flee from a dangerous situation, or stand and fight.

flashback Unpredictable recurrences of some of the physical or perceptual distortions associated with drug use that occur when the person is no longer using the drug.

flooding (intense exposure) Flooding is intense exposure. This involves facing one's fears at a very high level of intensity rather than working gradually through the fear hierarchy.

forensic psychology An area of specialization in psychology that focuses on the application of research and practice to matters of law, including proceedings in criminal or civil courts or in front of quasi-judicial bodies such as administrative boards and tribunals.

fragile X syndrome A chromosomal abnormality characterized by a weakened or "fragile" site on the X chromosome.

frontal brain deficiency The idea that the frontal brain region is damaged or dysfunctional in schizophrenia.

frontal lobe The large brain region underlying the frontal part of the skull.

frontal lobotomy The surgical cutting of connecting fibres within the frontal brain.

frontotemporal neurocognitive disorder (NCD) A subtype of *dementia* characterized by striking changes in personality or social conduct (e.g., loss of initiative, lack of empathy, lapses in judgment) as well as deficits in higher-order cognitive abilities (i.e., executive functions).

frotteurism A form of *paraphilic disorder* that is also a criminal offence, in which a person touches or rubs against a nonconsenting person for the purpose of sexual pleasure.

functional magnetic resonance imaging (fMRI) A technique that allows observation of neurophysiological activity accompanying specific cognitive tasks.

G

gambling disorder Persistent and recurrent gambling despite harmful negative consequences or a desire to stop.

gender dysphoria Distress resulting from a disagreement between one's biological sex and one's gender identity.

gender identity A person's basic sense of self as, for example, male or female, the first signs of which appear between 18 and 36 months of age. *See also sexual orientation* and *gender role*.

gender role The collection of characteristics that a society defines as masculine or feminine. Because roles relate to social standards, ideas about gender role change over time and from culture to culture. *See also gender identity*.

gene–environment interactions A term used to describe the phenotypic effects (i.e., observable characteristics) that are due to interactions between the environment and genes.

general adaptation syndrome (GAS) A stereotyped pattern of bodily changes that occur in response to diverse challenges to the organism, first described by Hans Selye. The syndrome comprises three stages: *alarm, resistance,* and *exhaustion.* The GAS was the first formal description and definition of stress.

generalized sexual dysfunctions Any sexual dysfunction that is apparent in all sexual situations, including with the sufferer's sexual partners and during solitary sexual activity.

general paresis of the insane (GPI) A disorder evidenced by mania, euphoria, and grandiosity, followed by a progressive deterioration of brain functioning (called *dementia*) and paralysis. Now known to result from untreated infections by the syphilis spirochete.

genetic contribution The influence of genes on the development of a mental illness or disorder.

genetic linkage studies Studies in which researchers examine families that have a high incidence of a particular psychiatric disorder. Within these extended families the researchers look for the presence of particular traits (called genetic markers) that can be linked to the occurrence of the disorder.

genito–pelvic pain/penetration disorder A sexual dysfunction characterized by persistent or recurrent difficulties with one or more of the following: vaginal penetration during intercourse; marked vulvovaginal or pelvic pain during vaginal intercourse or penetration attempts; marked fear or anxiety about vulvovaginal or pelvic pain in anticipation of, during, or as a result of vaginal penetration; and marked tensing or tightening of the pelvic floor muscles during attempted vaginal penetration on 75 to 100 percent of sexual occasions for at least six months, resulting in distress.

genotype–environment interaction Refers to the fact that genes may influence behaviours that contribute to environmental stressors, which, in turn, increase the risk of psychopathology. In other words, there is a reciprocal relationship between genetic predisposition and environmental risk.

gerontologist A specialist in gerontology (a branch of science that deals with the study of the elderly).

glove anaesthesia A sensory symptom of *conversion disorder* involving a loss of feeling in the whole hand and wrist. Since this pattern is incompatible with the way nerves extend from the arm into the hand, it is clearly psychogenic in origin.

H

hallucinations False perceptions occurring in the absence of any relevant stimulus. Auditory hallucinations are the most common form, but they may occur within any sensory modality.

hallucinogens Drugs that change a person's mental state by inducing perceptual and sensory distortions or hallucinations. Also called *psychedelics,* from the Greek for "soul" and "to make manifest."

Halstead-Reitan Neuropsychological Test Battery A test that has screening components that include many similar measures to the *MoCA* and the *RBANS*. This measure also includes tests of sensory perceptions, such as sound and touch perception. This test can take several hours to complete and is not generally recommended as a screening test.

harm reduction approaches Approaches to treatment for alcohol and other drug abuse that focus on reducing the consequences of the use versus reducing or eliminating use.

health behaviour model One model of how hostility might lead to health risk, which suggests that hostile people may be more likely to engage in unhealthy behaviours (for example, smoking, drug use, high-fat diets) and less likely to have healthy practices, such as exercise.

health psychology Any application of psychological methods and theories to understand the origins of disease, individual responses to disease, and the dimensions and determinants of good health.

hermaphroditism A condition in which a person's reproductive structures are partly female and partly male.

heterogeneity The variability and diversity of clinical and biological features seen in schizophrenia.

heterosexual gender dysphoria A type of *gender identity disorder (GID)* in which the afflicted person is attracted to people of the opposite sex.

heterotypic comorbidity A disorder that is comorbid with another disorder in a different class of disorders (e.g., ODD and GAD).

heterotypic continuity An underlying (developmental) process or impairment stays the same, but how it is manifested may be different (e.g., prediction of a disorder by another disorder); in *homotypic continuity*, by contrast, the manifestations stay the same, but the underlying process changes.

high-risk children The children of parents with schizophrenia or other genetically influenced disorders who therefore have an increased risk of developing the disorder themselves.

high-risk program An intervention or prevention program that targets individuals (usually children or adolescents) at high risk for disorder or disease.

hippocampus A region of the middle part of the temporal lobe involved with memory formation.

HIV Human immunodeficiency virus (HIV) is a chronic disease that affects the immune system. Under normal circumstances, the immune system protects against infections and diseases; however, it becomes less efficient when weakened by HIV. The rate of deterioration of the immune system varies from rapid to slow. As the immune system deteriorates, other health problems, including opportunistic infections, are increasingly likely to occur.

homotypic comorbidity A disorder that is comorbid with another disorder in the same class of disorders (e.g., ODD and CD).

homotypic continuity An underlying (developmental) process or impairment may change, but the way it is manifested stays the same (e.g., the prediction of a disorder by the same disorder).

humoral immunity One of the three general categories of immune response, in which invading antigens are presented by macrophages to B-lymphocytes. ("B" stands for *bursa,* an organ in which such cells are produced in birds. B-lymphocytes derive from the liver and bone marrow in humans.) This causes the B-cells to reproduce—a process reinforced by the lymphokine secretion from the helper T-cells. Some of the activated B-cells remain as memory B-cells. Others go on to be plasma cells, secreting antibodies called immunoglobulins that neutralize antigens in a number of different ways, such as clumping, presenting the antigen to phagocytic cells, or rupturing the antigen.

humours Bodily fluids, disturbances of which, according to Hippocrates, resulted in psychological dysfunctioning.

hypersexuality Excessive interest or involvement in sexual activity at levels high enough to become clinically significant.

hypertension A characteristically high level of resting blood pressure (defined as a *systolic blood pressure/diastolic blood pressure* reading of more than 140/80 under precisely defined conditions). Can result from any of variety of causes, but in about 90 percent of cases it is "essential," meaning a simple cause cannot be identified. Hypertension is a *risk factor* for death due to cardiovascular disease.

hypochondriasis A *somatoform disorder* characterized by excessive preoccupation with fears of having a serious illness when there is no underlying illness. The most common diseases people worry about are cancer and heart disease. Often leads to "doctor shopping." From the Greek *hypochondria* for the region below the ribs, thought to be linked to changes in mood and mental functioning.

hypokrisia In Meehl's theory, the reduced selectivity with which nerve cells respond to stimuli, especially as seen in schizophrenia.

hypomania A less severe, less disruptive, and often shorter version of a manic episode.

hypothalamic-pituitary-adrenal (HPA) axis The biological stress response system responsible for the fight-or-flight response. It is overactive in major depression.

hypoxyphilia The practice of heightening the sexual experience by deliberately inducing unconsciousness in oneself by oxygen deprivation, produced by chest compression, strangulation, enclosing the head in a plastic bag, or various other techniques. Also known as *autoerotic asphyxia* and *asphyxiophilia.*

hysteria An outdated psychiatric term once used to describe a symptom pattern characterized by emotional excitability and physical symptoms (e.g., convulsions, paralyses, numbness, loss of vision) without any organic cause.

I

iatrogenic Refers to a symptom or disorder that is induced in a patient as the result of therapeutic treatment such as medication or psychotherapy (literally meaning "produced by treatment").

id In Sigmund Freud's theory, the structure present at birth that contains, or represents, the biological or instinctual drives that are not constrained at birth, demanding instant gratification without concern for the consequences either to the self or to others.

illness anxiety disorder A disorder characterized by preoccupation with having or acquiring a serious illness, even though the individual does not have any serious bodily symptoms. Individuals with this disorder are very preoccupied and anxious about their health, become easily alarmed by even mild symptoms, and perform excessive health-related behaviours such as repeatedly checking their body for signs of disease.

illness phobia An intense fear of developing a disease that the individual does not currently have. It is different from hypochondriasis, where the person believes that he or she *currently* has a disease or medical condition.

imagined loss Freudian theory that the individual unconsciously interprets all types of loss events (e.g., job loss) in terms of grief, thereby raising the risk for depression.

impairment of control A core symptom of substance dependence referring to a pattern of using more of the drug or using it longer than planned.

implementation How well a program is put into practice in a particular setting.

incidence The number of new cases of a disorder in a particular population over a specified time period, usually a year.

independent variable In an experiment, the variable that is manipulated.

indicated prevention Interventions that target high-risk individuals who have minimal but detectable symptoms of a disorder, or who exhibit vulnerability markers that indicate a predisposition to a disorder but do not currently meet diagnostic levels for the disorder.

insomnia disorder The most common sleep disorder in older adults, with nocturnal symptoms of difficulty falling asleep, frequent awakenings, shortened sleep, and non-restorative sleep, and daytime symptoms of fatigue, sleepiness, depression, and anxiety. DSM-IV diagnostic criteria require the symptoms to persist for at least one month, to be perceived as stressful, and to not be secondary to any other disorder.

instability In the context of personality disorders, describes an individual who has maladaptive interpersonal relationships and decisions and is generally unable to effectively regulate emotions or behaviour.

insulin coma A seizure and loss of consciousness induced by administration of insulin.

intellectual disability Significant limitations in intellectual functioning (i.e., IQ < 70; below the 2nd percentile) and adaptive behaviour, including communication, social, and community skills (i.e., below the 2nd percentile). The disability occurs before the age of 18.

intelligence quotient (IQ) A test of judgment, comprehension, and reasoning invented by the French psychologist Alfred Binet (1857–1911), in which a child's mental age, determined by the child's successful performance on age-grouped tests that had been normed, was divided by the child's chronological age, and the quotient multiplied by 100. Theoretically, IQ was a reflection of that person's performance compared with that of others the same age.

interactionist explanation A theory that views behaviour as the product of the interaction of a variety of factors.

internal consistency The degree of reliability within a test—the extent to which different parts of the same test yield the same results.

internal validity The degree to which the changes in the *dependent variable* of an experiment are a result of the manipulation of the *independent variable*. If no alternative explanations are possible, the experiment has strong internal validity.

internalized racism Refers to the psychological internalization of negative beliefs and stigma about a person's own racial or ethnic group.

internalizing problems Problems such as anxiety, depression, shyness, social withdrawal, and somatic complaints that are problematic for the individual who experiences them but pose few problems for the social partners surrounding that person.

interoceptive exposure Interoceptive exposure is exposure to bodily sensations (e.g., dizziness, shortness of breath, increased heart rate). It is a technique used to treat panic disorder.

interpersonal and social rhythm therapy (IPSRT) Adjunctive psychotherapy for bipolar disorder that focuses on regularizing patients' daily rhythms and routines.

interpersonal model Models that suggest that individuals who are depressed (or at risk for depression) behave in ways that bother or alienate others. As a result, depressed individuals are more likely to experience interpersonal rejection and relationship stress, thereby reducing social support and perpetuating their depression.

interpersonal psychodynamic psychotherapy A variation of brief psychodynamic therapy that emphasizes the interactions between the client and his or her social environment.

interpersonal psychotherapy (IPT) A therapy that uses a medical model to understand interpersonal conflicts and transitions as they relate to depression.

Interpersonal racism Consists of relational interactions that convey hostility, disgust, or other forms of denigration of others according to their racial identity, and includes both overt and covert forms.

inter-rater reliability The extent to which two or more clinicians agree on the *diagnosis* of a particular patient.

Intersex A variety of conditions in which a person is born with a reproductive or sexual anatomy that does not fit the typical definitions of "female" or "male."

intolerance of uncertainty (IU) An individual's discomfort with ambiguity and uncertainty.

intracavernous treatment Medication injected directly into the erectile tissue of the penis to stimulate an erection.

in vivo exposure (in vivo, "in the living being") A therapeutic technique for overcoming anxiety. In in vivo ("real life") exposure, patients face their feared objects or situations directly (this is often used gradually, whereby patients work their way progressively through their fear hierarchy).

in vivo observation (in vivo, "in the living being") A method used by behaviourally oriented therapists to determine how environmental variables affect a behaviour of concern, in which a clinician may record a running narrative of events, using pencil and paper, video, or still camera, in the client's everyday environment. More commonly, observations are made by *participant observers*, key people in the client's environment, and reported to the clinician. *See also analogue observational setting.*

ischemic heart disease A condition in which blood supply to the heart becomes compromised, leading to a *myocardial infarction*. One of the leading causes of death from diseases of the cardiovascular system in Western societies.

K

ketamine A pharmacological agent, a glutamate N-methyl-d-aspartate (NMDA) receptor antagonist, that has been explored as an agent that can rapidly reduce suicidal ideation, and thus may be useful in emergency situations of acute suicidality.

L

la belle indifférence A surprising nonchalance or lack of concern about the severity of one's symptoms, which was previously thought to be evidence of a *conversion disorder*.

labelling theory A point of view that suggests that when a person is identified as having a disorder, other people, particularly mental health workers, perceive that person as dysfunctional and different. This perception, which tends to persist even after recovery, results in these people being treated disadvantageously and even disrespectfully.

lanugo The fine white hair that grows on individuals with anorexia when they have no body fat left to keep themselves warm.

learning disabilities Significant difficulties learning and using academic skills (e.g., reading, mathematics, written expression).

left temporal lobe The brain region immediately beneath the left side of the skull and just above the ear.

lifelong sexual dysfunction Any sexual dysfunction that the sufferer has always experienced.

ligands Chemical labels that identify the presence of specific types of receptors in brain tissue.

lithium Lithium salt, used to treat mania and depression. Has the effect of flattening out the peaks and valleys of the illness, allowing sufferers to achieve some stability in their lives with less disruption for family members. Apparently lithium has preventive effects for both *unipolar mood disorders* and *bipolar mood disorders*, and lithium is considered the treatment of choice for bipolar disorder.

lobotomy *Psychosurgery* consisting of surgical removal, or disconnection, of the frontal lobes of the brain, intended to relieve all manner of mental and emotional disorders.

longitudinal study A scientific study in which a large number of people are evaluated with respect to the existence of psychological or behavioural features and are then followed up, often years or decades later, to determine whether they have developed a disease.

loosening of associations Loss of logical or conventional connections between ideas or words.

low-risk drinking guidelines A research-based definition of the upper limits on drinking that is not likely to lead to physical impairment in people in general.

lunacy A historical term for madness rooted in folk beliefs that the moon influenced mental states.

M

macrosystem A level of analysis in the *ecological perspective* that consists of social norms and social class.

madness A common term for irrational or uncontrolled behaviour as well as conditions like schizophrenia and bipolar disorder.

magnetic resonance imaging (MRI) Also called *nuclear magnetic resonance imaging*. A noninvasive technique for examining the structure and the functioning of the brain. A strong homogeneous magnetic field is produced around the head and brief pulses of radio waves are introduced. When the radio waves are turned off, radio waves of a characteristic frequency are emitted from the brain itself, which can be detected. The information gathered is integrated into a computer-generated image of the brain.

maintenance factor A variable that leads the symptoms to persist after their onset.

major depressive disorder (MDD) A *depressive disorder* characterized by persistent feelings of sadness, loss of interest or ability to feel pleasure, unexplained weight loss, difficulty sleeping, fatigue, difficulty concentrating, feelings of worthlessness or guilt, suicidal thoughts, and either agitation or slowing down. The person must not be suffering from other disorders that may present as depression, such as *schizoaffective disorder* or a *delusional disorder*.

male hypoactive sexual desire disorder A sexual dysfunction characterized by persistent or recurrent deficiency of sexual fantasies and desire for sex, causing marked distress or interpersonal difficulty.

malingering Pretending to be ill in order to achieve some specific objective. Not to be considered a *somatoform disorder*, in which the sufferer truly believes there is a serious physical problem.

mania A *bipolar mood disorder* characterized by flamboyance and expansiveness. A person experiencing a manic episode may go on shopping sprees, engage in sexually promiscuous behaviour, take on numerous, unrealistic work commitments, brag, and dominate others socially. In general, the person shows intolerance when the world does not cooperate with his or her momentary needs. Extreme or prolonged cases of mania are considered bona fide psychotic states, implying that the person is experiencing a break with reality. From the Greek *mainomai*, "to be mad." *See also hypomania.*

maternal serum screening (MSS) A blood test conducted during the second trimester of pregnancy. MSS detects alpha-fetoprotein (AFP), as well as two hormones produced by the placenta. The levels of these substances can help identify women at higher risk of having babies with chromosomal abnormalities like Down syndrome or neural tube defects like spina bifida. This test may be used to select women for diagnostic amniocentesis, which is a more invasive procedure.

mens rea In Canadian criminal law, the guilty mind or bad intent that, together with the *actus reus*, defines a criminal offence.

mental health Narrowly, the absence of disorder. In a broader view, the presence of optimal social, emotional, and cognitive functioning—also known as *wellness*.

Mental Health Commission of Canada (MHCC) A non-profit organization created to focus national attention on mental health issues and to work to improve the health and social outcomes of people living with mental illness.

mental health promotion A concept complementary to the concept of *prevention* in *community psychology* that focuses on the idea of enhancing the functioning of people.

mental hygiene movement A movement started by Dorothea Dix (1802–1887), a Boston schoolteacher, characterized by a desire to protect and provide humane treatment for the mentally ill. Her campaign resulted directly in the opening of 32 state hospitals, including 2 in Canada. Despite the noble aims, the asylums were overcrowded and the staff had no time to do more than warehouse and restrain the patients.

mental illness Often used to convey the same meaning as *psychological abnormality*, but implies a medical rather than psychological cause.

mental status examination The most frequently used semi-structured interview in psychiatric settings. Screens for patients' emotional, intellectual, and neurological functioning. Used in formal diagnosis or to plan treatment.

meta-analysis A method of quantitatively summing up previous research studies that have used different patient populations and outcome measures. The research results are combined by developing a common metric called an *effect size*.

methadone A heroin replacement used to treat heroin addicts, often to reduce the craving after initial withdrawal symptoms have abated. Methadone therapy appears to work best in conjunction with good individual and group psychological intervention programs, as well as ongoing peer support.

methylphenidate (Ritalin) The most frequently prescribed stimulant medication for children with *attention deficit hyperactivity disorder (ADHD)*.

microaggressions These are unconscious, unintentional, subtle, and frequent acts (e.g., condescending statements, crossing the road when seeing a person of colour) have been shown to have significant negative effects on mental health.

microsystem A level of analysis in the *ecological perspective* that consists of the family and the social network.

mild cognitive impairment (MCI) The boundary zone between normal cognitive functioning and *dementia*. Individuals with mild cognitive impairment have deficits in one cognitive domain (usually memory) but are able to function independently.

Millon Clinical Multiaxial Inventory (MCMI) An objective test of personality developed to help clinicians make diagnostic judgments within the multiaxial DSM system, especially in the personality disorders found on Axis II.

Minnesota model A residential treatment for alcohol dependence advocating a 12-step Alcoholics Anonymous philosophy and viewing alcoholism as a disease.

Minnesota Multiphasic Personality Inventory (MMPI) The most widely used objective test of personality. The adjective "multiphasic" means that it assesses many aspects of personality. The test contains 567 questions grouped to form 10 content scales plus additional scales to detect sources of invalidity such as carelessness, defensiveness, or evasiveness. The revised and updated version, called the MMPI-2, focuses primarily on the main clinical disorders.

M'Naghten standard A standard of insanity defined by the case of *Regina v. M'Naghten* (1843) that became the accepted rule in England, the United States, and Canada. In today's interpretation of the standard, (1) the accused must have been suffering from a mental disorder, and (2) he or she must not have known at least one of two things: the nature and quality of the act and that what he or she was doing was wrong. That is, inability to understand that an act is wrong can be sufficient even if the accused understands the act itself. Because the second element requires determination of the accused's thinking, the M'Naghten standard is referred to as a "cognitive" test of insanity.

modular approach An approach to treating mental health problems by choosing and tailoring specific modules that will be maximally effective for a particular person in his/her situation.

molecular biology A field in which researchers have been able to compare specific DNA segments, identify the genes that determine individual characteristics, and pinpoint the defective genes that cause various medical and psychological disorders.

modifiable risk factors Factors increasing the likelihood of disease, such as poor diet or smoking, that are under the control of the individual.

monoamine oxidase inhibitors (MAOIs) A class of medications used to treat major depression by inhibiting the enzyme monoamine oxidase, which breaks down monoamines such as dopamine and norepinephrine, thus allowing more of these neurotransmitters to accumulate in the presynaptic cell.

monozygotic (MZ) twins Identical twins, which result from the fertilization by a single sperm of a single ovum. This is followed by an unusual extra division into exactly matched zygotes, which subsequently develop into genetically identical fetuses. MZ twins have 100 percent of their genes in common. From *mono* meaning "one" and *zygote* meaning "fertilized egg."

Montreal Cognitive Assessment (MoCA) A screening instrument for evaluating mild cognitive impairment. It is a one-page, 30-point test that takes approximately 10 minutes to administer.

mood disorder An altered mood state severe enough to interfere with a person's social and occupational functioning (for example, ability to work or go to school) and whose range of symptoms is not limited to the person's feelings, but affects other bodily and behavioural systems as well.

moral therapy A form of treatment advocated by Philippe Pinel and his followers that held that the insane could be controlled without the use of physical or chemical restraints, by means of respect and quiet and peaceful surroundings, plenty of rest, a good diet, moderate exercise, and activities.

mosaicism A cause of *Down syndrome* in which cell division occurs unevenly, so that some cells have 45 chromosomes and some have 47. People with mosaic Down syndrome may have fewer physical characteristics, better speech, and higher intellectual functioning, depending upon the numbers of cells affected.

motivational interviewing A therapeutic approach that is client-centred and helps to engage intrinsic motivation for changing behaviour by creating discrepancy and exploring and resolving ambivalence within the client.

motivational-volitional model A model of suicide that states that cognitions of defeat, humiliation, and entrapment (i.e., an inability to escape) in response to stressful life events will result in a motivation for suicidal ideation when motivational moderators, such as feelings of thwarted belongingness and perceived burdensomeness, are high.

myocardial infarction Heart attack.

N

natural causes Causes that can be observed and examined. When mental afflictions are seen as being due to natural causes, they are treated in a way that addresses such causes.

neurocognitive disorder (NCD) The most common mental disorder in older adults, in which sufferers lose their memory, judgment, reason, personal dignity, and finally their sense of self.

neurocognitive disorder with Lewy bodies A subtype of *dementia* characterized by at least two of the following symptoms: (1) Parkinsonism (e.g., resting tremor, muscular rigidity, unstable posture); (2) visual hallucinations; (3) fluctuating alertness or cognition.

negative emotionality A personality trait describing the tendency to experience psychological distress, anxiety, and depression that is associated with the development of alcohol problems.

negative feedback seeking The tendency to actively seek out criticism and other negative interpersonal feedback from others.

negative symptoms Features of schizophrenia that comprise behavioural deficits, including loss of motivation, lack of emotional expression, and lack of interest in the environment.

neuroleptics Antipsychotic medication.

neuropsychological tests Tests of cognitive and motor ability that are sensitive to damage or dysfunction in different brain regions.

neurosis A nineteenth-century term for anxiety disorders and several other psychological problems (plural *neuroses*). Still in popular usage.

neurotransmitters The chemical substances that carry the messages from one neuron to the next in the complex pathways of nervous activity within the brain.

neutralizations Behavioural or cognitive acts used to prevent, cancel, or "undo" the feared consequences and distress caused by an obsession. While neutralizations can resemble *compulsions*, they are not the same thing (e.g., neutralizations are not necessarily repetitive).

nocturnal panic Panic attacks that occur during the night and awaken sufferers from their sleep.

nocturnal penile tumescence (NPT) A measure of nighttime erections in which the client sleeps in a laboratory over several nights with a device attached to his penis that records changes in its circumference as a result of blood inflow. The measurement technique is called *phallometry*.

nonassociative model A theory proposing that the process of evolution has endowed humans to respond fearfully to a select group of stimuli (e.g., water, heights, spiders), and thus no learning is necessary to develop phobias.

nonpurging type A subtype of *bulimia nervosa* characterized by the afflicted person's compensating for overeating by fasting or exercising to excess. The nonpurging type is encountered far less frequently than the *purging type*.

nonspecific immune responses One of the three general categories of immune response, in which circulating white cells called granulocytes and monocytes identify invading antigens and destroy them by *phagocytosis*: engulfing and digesting them. *See also cellular immunity and humoral immunity.*

nonsuicidal self-injury disorder (NSSID) Youth who would meet criteria for this disorder have less severe psychosocial impairment and fewer comorbid mental health disorders compared to youth who endorse a suicidal intent associated with self-injury.

normal aging A normal process of bodily systems slowing down that ultimately causes some systems to stop functioning, so that the person dies of old age rather than of any particular disease.

normative comparison An investigative approach meant to control for the potential irrelevance of statistical significance in research, in which treatment results are compared to those of non-disturbed samples.

not criminally responsible on account of mental disorder (NCRMD) In Canadian criminal law, not morally culpable for committing a prohibited act due to mental disorder at the time the act was committed.

null hypothesis Proposes that a prediction made from a given theory is false. Experiments (and other research strategies) are set up not to prove the worth of a theory, but rather to reject (or fail to reject) the null hypothesis. Thus, theories gain in strength because alternative explanations are rejected.

O

objective binge A large amount of food (larger than most individuals would eat) that is consumed in a specific time period (e.g., less than two hours).

obsessions Recurrent and uncontrollable thoughts, impulses, or ideas that an individual finds disturbing and anxiety-provoking.

Oedipal complex According to Sigmund Freud, a condition that occurs during the *phallic stage*, when boys are presumed to develop sexual desires for their mother and see their father as a competitor for their mother's love. The term is a reference to the character of Oedipus in the play by the Greek tragedian Sophocles.

olanzapine An "atypical" antipsychotic medication introduced in the late 1990s.

operant conditioning An idea developed by Burrhus F. Skinner (1904–1990), according to which it is the consequences of behaviour that are important. Some consequences encourage the repetition of the behaviour that produces them, while other consequences result in the opposite effect. *See also classical conditioning.*

opioids Also known as *narcotics*. A class of central nervous system *depressants* whose main effects are the reduction of pain and sleep inducement. Opium, the alkaloid from which opioids are derived, comes from the seeds of the opium poppy, which is indigenous to Asia and the Middle East.

oppositional behaviour Deliberate flouting of the expectations of others, even when it means certain punishment, and perhaps even because of it.

oppositional defiant disorder (ODD) A disorder of children who, more frequently than is usual, refuse to follow instructions, argue apparently just for the sake of arguing, and show hostility toward parents and teachers.

other-oriented perfectionism setting unrealistic standards for others.

overlap The similarity of symptoms in two or more different disorders (that is, some of the same criteria apply to different diagnoses), which creates problems with diagnosis. *See also comorbidity.*

P

pain disorder A *somatoform disorder* characterized by chronic pain with no known organic cause.

panic An extreme fear reaction that is triggered even though there is nothing to be afraid of (it is essentially a "false alarm").

panic attack A discrete period of intense fear or discomfort accompanied by at least 4 of 13 specific somatic, behavioural, and cognitive symptoms such as palpitations, shaking, chest pain, and fear of dying, going crazy, or losing control.

paradox of aging Positive mental health among older adults who would normally be considered vulnerable.

paraphilia A redirection of sexual desires toward what is generally considered to be an inappropriate or atypical object, or person, or behaviour. In the case of a paraphilia, there is no clinically significant impairment.

paraphilic disorder A paraphilia that is currently causing distress or impairment to the individual, or a paraphilia that causes personal harm, or risk of harm, to others when acted upon.

pathoplastic Variability in a symptom's specific form and content, shaped by events in a patient's life.

parens patriae The common law principle that recognizes the duty of the monarch or the state to care for citizens who are unable to care for themselves.

pedophile An adult who is sexually attracted to children.

pedophilia A form of *paraphilia* that is also a criminal offence, in which a person has recurrent fantasies or behaviours involving sexual activity with prepubescent children.

penetrance In genetics, the proportion of people with a given genetic endowment that actually express the effects of this endowment.

performance anxiety A state of nervousness that can occur when people perform sexually that can negatively affect their performance, because they are too busy worrying about and monitoring their own performance and their partners' responses.

period effect The influence of particular historical periods or events on people, such as the Great Depression or the September 11, 2001, attacks on the World Trade Center and the Pentagon.

persecutory delusions False and implausible beliefs that focus on being followed, chased, harassed, or threatened by other people or unseen forces.

perseverate To repeat mistakes or incorrect responses.

persistent depressive disorder A *unipolar mood disorder* that manifests many of the same symptoms as major depression, except that they are less severe. It persists for at least two years, with only brief interludes of normal mood. Also known as *dysthymia*.

personality disorders Personality styles that are characterized by inflexible and pervasive behavioural patterns, often cause serious personal and social difficulties, and impair general functioning.

person by situation interaction The impact of a person's surroundings on his or her behavioural characteristics, according to Walter Mischel's view that predicting a person's behaviour requires knowledge of both the person's typical behaviour patterns and the characteristics of the setting.

phallic stage Stage in which, according to Sigmund Freud, boys become focused on their penis and girls become aware that they do not have one. Girls are said to develop penis envy (that is, they desire to have a penis and feel cheated).

pharmacological dependence The indicators are tolerance and withdrawal. Tolerance means that the person needs increased amounts of the substance to achieve the same effect. Individuals suffering from withdrawal experience unpleasant and sometimes dangerous symptoms such as nausea, headache, or tremors when the addictive substance is removed from the body.

phenotype Any *observable* characteristic or trait of an organism.

phenylketonuria (PKU) The best known of several rare metabolic disorders that can cause intellectual disability. As a result of a recessive gene passed on from each parent, a liver enzyme is inactive, causing an inability to process or metabolize the amino acid phenylalanine. This substance builds up in the brain to toxic levels, leading to retardation.

phonological processing An auditory processing skill that involves detecting and discriminating differences in speech sounds under conditions of little or no distraction or distortion.

phototherapy Treatment for seasonal affective disorder that involves exposure to high-intensity full spectrum lighting.

placebo A substance that looks and feels like the substance being tested in an experiment, but does not contain the active ingredient.

placebo effect The phenomenon that individuals in treatment programs expect to get better, and as a result may feel an improvement, or that they report improvement to please the experimenter. From the Latin word meaning "I shall please."

polypharmacy Taking multiple medications concurrently, often practised by older adults.

polysubstance abuse The simultaneous misuse or dependence upon two or more substances.

polythetic An individual may be diagnosed with only a certain subset of symptoms without having to meet all criteria.

positive symptoms Abnormal additions to mental life, including the hallucinations, delusions, and disordered thought frequently experienced by patients with schizophrenia.

positron emission tomography (PET) A combination of *computerized axial tomography* and radioisotope imaging. Radiation is generated by injected or inhaled radioisotopes—that is, common elements or substances with the atom altered to be radioactive. As the substance is used in brain activity, radiation is given off and detected, allowing measurement of a variety of biological activities as the processes occur in the living brain.

post-test In an experiment, assessment of the subjects on several dependent variables judged to be important, in order to get a comprehensive picture of the effects of manipulating the *independent variable*.

potential years of life lost (PYLL) A measure of the impact of death on someone's lifespan calculated by subtracting age of death from his or her life expectancy.

preconscious In *psychodynamic* theory, the preconscious holds information that is not presently within our awareness but can readily be brought into awareness.

predictive validity The ability of a test to predict the future course of an individual's development. An essential requirement of a good *diagnostic system*.

premature (early) ejaculation A sexual dysfunction characterized by a man's ejaculating within approximately one minute of vaginal penetration during 75 to 100 percent of occasions of sexual activity for a minimum of six months, with marked distress.

pretest In an experiment, an assessment of subjects on many measures prior to manipulation of the *independent variable*. Done for descriptive purposes.

prevalence The frequency of a disorder in a population at a given point or period of time.

prevention A concept borrowed from the fields of physical disease, public health, and epidemiology and applied to mental disorders by *community psychology*. There are three categories of prevention activities: *primary prevention*, *secondary prevention*, and *tertiary prevention*.

primary appraisals In the *transactional model* of stress, an *appraisal*, which may occur quite unconsciously, that takes place when a person is faced with an event that may have adaptational significance. It is as if the individual asks: "Is this a threat to me?" The primary appraisal sets the stage for further events that may or may not lead to stress.

primary prevention A type of *prevention* practised prior to the biological origin of the disease (for example, immunization). See also *secondary prevention* and *tertiary prevention*.

principle of autonomy In ethics, the doctrine that stresses the importance of respect for people's right to self-determination when making decisions.

principle of beneficence In ethics, the doctrine that stresses the importance of maximizing good when making decisions.

principle of fidelity In ethics, the doctrine that stresses the importance of personal reliability when making decisions.

principle of justice In ethics, the doctrine that stresses the importance of fairness when making decisions.

principle of nonmaleficence In ethics, the doctrine that stresses the importance of avoiding or minimizing harm to people when making decisions.

proband In family studies, the patient, or the person who has come to the attention of the clinician or researcher. Also called the *index case*.

problem-solving approach A cognitive-behavioural treatment that involves the client in determining the problem definition and formulation, generating alternative solutions to deal with the problem, deciding on the best solution to implement, and then implementing and evaluating the solution.

professional standards Written statements that set out expectations regarding the day-to-day practice or conduct of members of a profession or other group.

projective test A type of psychological test that reveals information the person being tested cannot or will not report directly. Used to help clinicians form hypotheses about an individual's personality. See also *Rorschach inkblot test*.

prolactin A hormone that helps initiate and maintain breast milk production in pregnant and nursing women, and that is involved in sexual activity and desire, variations in the level of which can lower or increase sex drive.

pronoun reversal One of the common characteristics of speech in autistic children, in which the child often refers to him- or herself in the third person, perhaps because of trouble shifting reference between speaker and listener or a third party.

protective factors Events or circumstances that help to offset, or buffer, *risk factors*. Anything that lessens the likelihood of disease. For example, exercise is thought to be a protective factor for cardiovascular disease.

pseudo-dementia Cognitive impairment similar to that of *dementia* but reversible. May be brought on by depression, nutritional deficiency, thyroid disorder, or any one of a number of other diseases; symptoms may also occur as side effects from medications.

psychiatrists Persons trained in medicine prior to doing specialized training in dealing with mental illness. This specialized training focuses on diagnosis and medical treatment that emphasize the use of pharmacological agents in managing mental disorders. Most psychiatrists attend to the medical aspects and biological foundations of these disorders, although they usually also consider psychological and environmental influences.

psychotropic agents Pharmacological agents found to affect the individual's psychological functioning.

psychodynamic Denoting a school of psychology founded by Sigmund Freud. Psychodynamic theories claim that behaviour is controlled by unconscious forces of which the person is unaware.

psychological abnormality Behaviour, speech, or thought that impairs the ability of a person to function in a way generally expected of him or her, in the context in which the unusual functioning occurs.

psychological assessment A systematic gathering and evaluation of information pertaining to an individual with suspected abnormal behaviour.

psychological autopsy A research method used after someone dies by suicide and involves comprehensive (often structured) interviews with others in the life of the deceased (e.g., partners, family, friends) as well as those involved in their health care to obtain detailed information about the deceased individual and what might have contributed to the individual's suicide.

psychological disorder A specific manifestation of mental illness as described by some set of criteria established by a panel of experts.

psychoneuroimmunology A new field that studies the responsiveness of the immune system to psychosocial influences, and that has shown that the immune system can be affected by learning experiences, emotional states, and personal characteristics.

psychopathology Both the scientific study of psychological abnormality and the problems faced by people who suffer from such disorders.

psychopaths People who are considered to be predisposed via temperament to antisocial behaviour and whose primary characteristics include callousness and grandiosity combined with a history of poor self-regulation.

psychophysiological reactivity model One model of how hostility might lead to health risk, which suggests that hostile people are at higher risk for various diseases because they experience exaggerated autonomic and neuroendocrine responses during stress.

psychosis A mental state characterized by severe impairment or distortion in the experience of reality as seen in disorders like *schizophrenia*.

psychosocial vulnerability model One model of how hostility might lead to health risk, which suggests that hostile people experience a more demanding interpersonal life than others.

psychosurgery The use of brain surgery to alter behaviour, especially in relation to psychiatric disorders.

public health approach An approach to *community psychology* characterized by the following steps: (1) identifying a disease and developing a reliable diagnostic method (descriptive epidemiology); (2) developing a theory of the disease's course of development on the basis of laboratory and epidemiological research (analytic epidemiology); and (3) developing and evaluating a disease prevention program (experimental epidemiology). The thrust of the approach is to reduce environmental stressors while enhancing people's capacities to withstand those stressors.

public stigma The typical societal response that people have to stigmatizing attributes.

punishment In *operant conditioning*, what occurs when a behaviour decreases in frequency as a result of its consequences.

purging The engagement of compensatory behaviour intended to "undo" calories that have been consumed (e.g., vomiting, misuse of laxatives).

purging type A subtype of *bulimia nervosa* characterized by the afflicted person's compensating for overeating, most typically by self-induced vomiting or the use of laxatives, diuretics, or enemas. The purging type is encountered far more frequently than the nonpurging type.

Q

quality of life A recognized desirable goal in the field of developmental disabilities, about which there is a great deal of disagreement. What constitutes quality of life and how can it be measured? A number of different approaches have been taken. For example, the Quality of Life Interview Schedule (QUOLIS), designed specifically to address the needs of adults with severe and profound disabilities, involves interviews with two informants who know an individual well in different contexts, and quality of life is measured under 12 domains, such as health services and housing and safety. A second approach is reflected in the Quality of Life Project, a conceptual framework that includes three major components of quality of life, each divided into subcomponents.

quasi-experimental study One in which the subjects in the experimental group are not randomly assigned but selected on the basis of certain characteristics, and in which there is no manipulation of an *independent variable*.

R

random assignment A procedure that ensures each subject in an experiment has an equal probability of being in either the *experimental* or the *control group*, guaranteeing the equivalence of these groups.

rapport Mutual understanding or trust between people.

rational-emotive therapy A form of therapy developed by Albert Ellis that is concerned with how people interpret events and how these interpretations influence their responses. These interpretations, or mediating processes, are cognitive and result from the person's belief systems.

reactivity The change in behaviour often seen when people know they are being observed or filmed. One of the difficulties inherent in *in vivo observation* and *analogue observational settings*.

receptors Patches of sensitive membrane on nerve cells that bind to neurochemical messages from other nerve cells.

referential delusions The belief that common, meaningless occurrences have significant and personal relevance.

reframing A strategy in which problems are restated so that they can be more easily dealt with.

reinforcement In *operant conditioning*, what occurs when a behaviour increases in frequency as a result of consistent consequences.

relapse The return of an illness or disorder after a recovery.

reliability The ability of a measurement tool to give the same measurement for a given thing every time. Its usefulness partly depends on this attribute. *See also validity*.

religious delusions The belief that religious passages offer the way to destroy or save the world.

Repeatable Battery of the Assessment of Neuropsychological Status (RBANS) The RBANS is a brief, 12 subtest, standardized screening tool for measuring neuropsychological functioning in the areas of immediate and delayed memory, visuospatial/constructional skills, attention, and language. It can be used with adults ages 20 to 89 and takes approximately 30 minutes to administer.

repressed Referring to memories that a person cannot call into awareness, but which remain in the person's subconscious and can be retrieved under certain conditions or with the help of a psychotherapist.

resilience The capacity of people to "bounce back" and cope with stress and catastrophe.

resistance The second phase of the *general adaptation syndrome (GAS)*, a concept that was the first formal description and definition of stress as a consequence of adaptation to demands placed on the body. In the resistance phase, if the challenge of the *alarm* phase persists, the body actively fights or copes with the challenge through immune and neuroendocrine changes. These adaptive responses enhance the body's ability to ward off threats in the short term. *See also exhaustion*.

response shaping A process of shaping behaviour by gradual approximations of what is expected. For example, a child who is intellectual disability and may be unable to get dressed independently can be taught the process gradually by being rewarded for putting on one item at a time until he or she is eventually able to handle the entire task.

responsivity factor The circumstance that treatment must be responsive (or matched) to a particular client's needs and interpersonal style—that is, it must be of sufficient intensity and relevance, and seen by the patient as voluntary. Apparently, the efficacy of the treatment programs tend to be determined more by the orientation of the therapist or director.

restricting type A subtype of *anorexia nervosa* in which the afflicted person relies on a rigidly controlled, very low intake of food to maintain her low weight. About half of anorexia nervosa patients are of the restricting type. *See also binge eating/purging type*.

Rett syndrome A *pervasive developmental disorder* that is diagnosed primarily in females. Development before birth and up to the age of 5 months appears to be normal. However, between the ages of 5 and 30 months, the progress of development, including growth rate, slows, and the child loses speech and motor skills that have already developed. Social interaction diminishes and stereotyped wringing movements in the hands occur. Motor coordination problems increase and both expressive and receptive language are significantly impaired.

return on investment (ROI) A measurement used to evaluate the efficiency of an investment.

reversal design *See ABAB*.

risk factors Events or circumstances that increase the likelihood of later pathology.

risky use Continued substance use in situations that might be hazardous, such as driving or operating machinery.

risperidone An "atypical" antipsychotic medication with fewer side effects than *chlorpromazine*. It was introduced in the 1990s and is believed to influence serotonin as well as dopamine.

ritual prevention Intentionally refraining from maladaptive coping patterns. By doing so, the patient gradually and with repeated exposures experiences anxiety climb, peak, and then subsidence.

Rorschach inkblot test The oldest and probably the best known *projective test*. Based on the idea that people see different things in the same inkblot and that what they see reflects their personality. The blots are presented on separate cards and handed to the subject in a particular sequence.

rubella German measles, an infection that can affect infant development and cause mental retardation. Rubella-related problems have declined with routine vaccination.

Russell's sign An indication of bulimia in which scrapes or calluses occur on the back of the hands as a result of manually induced vomiting.

S

St. Vitus' dance An epidemic of mass hysteria, wherein groups of people would suddenly be seized by an irresistible urge to leap about, jumping and dancing, and sometimes convulsing.

savants Mentally deficient persons who nevertheless display islets of exceptional ability in areas such as mathematics, music, or art, or unusual feats of memory. A small proportion of those persons with *autism* who do not fall within the normal range of intelligence are savants.

schemas Mental structures used to organize information about the world.

schizophrenia One of the most serious psychological disorders, characterized by *delusions, hallucinations*, and *disorganized speech*. There are overall, adverse changes in thought, perception, emotion, and motor behaviour, and a feeling of *depersonalization*. Behaviour in some instances appears to be "autistic," in the sense of being governed by internal stimuli or private events. The individual may be unresponsive to environmental stimuli that would normally prompt reactions, or may respond in a way that suggests a distorted interpretation of the stimuli. Ordinary objects or events seem to take on a marked personal significance. There is pronounced disruption of cognitive transactions: thought and language appear to become loosened from the normal constraints that make for coherent sequences of ideas and distinguish fantasy from reality. Often, some notion or theme involving malevolent forces or inordinate personal power increasingly commands the individual's attention. Many people with schizophrenia appear to lose their intensity. Language may become impoverished, with little apparent effort or success at communication. They may become withdrawn socially and exhibit little interest in formerly enjoyable pursuits. Attention span may be markedly reduced. From the Greek *schizein*, "to split," and *phrenos*, "mind."

schizophrenogenic The unsupported theory that cold and rejecting behaviour causes *schizophrenia*.

schizotype In Meehl's theory, a person with the genetic liability for *schizophrenia*, but who may or may not progress to the full-blown psychotic illness.

science Knowledge obtained by observation and experimentation, critically tested, systematized, and brought under general principles. From the Latin *scientia* ("knowledge").

seasonal affective disorder (SAD) A *unipolar mood disorder* characterized by a vulnerability to environmental sunlight changes and a pattern of cyclic and time-limited mood problems.

secondary appraisals In the *transactional model* of stress, a set of *appraisals* that occur after a *primary appraisal* if the individual concludes there is an element of threat, equivalent to the question: "Is there anything I can do about this?"

secondary prevention A type of *prevention* practised after the disease is identified but before it has caused suffering and disability (for example, the control of blood sugar early in the course of diabetes to prevent systemic damage). *See also primary prevention* and *tertiary prevention.*

selective mutism A social anxiety disorder in which a person normally capable of speech is unable to speak in given situations, or to specific individuals.

selective serotonin reuptake inhibitors (SSRIs) One of the three known major classes of antidepressants. SSRIs, as their name suggests, delay the process of reuptake of neurotransmitters so that they remain available longer to maintain optimal neuronal firing rates. They include fluoxetine (Prozac), sertraline (Zoloft), and paraxetine (Paxil). *See also tricyclic antidepressants.*

selective prevention Interventions that target individuals whose risk of developing a disorder is greater than the average risk for that disorder within the general population.

self-actualization In Abraham H. Maslow's theory, an actualization of one's potential arrived at by satisfaction of a hierarchy of needs visualized as a pyramid. At the base are biological or survival needs; the next step up is the need for friendship and affiliation; finally, there is an assurance of self-worth, which comes from giving and receiving love and from an internalized sense of self-esteem. In Maslow's view, abnormal or dysfunctional behaviour results from a failure to attain the self-esteem necessary to achieve self-actualization.

self-oriented perfectionism Self-imposed high standards that are hard to achieve.

self-stigma The internalized psychological impact of public stigma.

sensate focus In sex therapy programs, a form of desensitization applied to sexual fears.

separation anxiety disorder (SAD) A children's disorder characterized by severe and excessive anxiety, even panic, at the prospect of separation from parents or others to whom the child is emotionally attached.

sexual masochism A sexual preference that involves sexual arousal from experiencing pain or humiliation inflicted by others.

sexual response cycle The sequence of changes that occur in the body with increased sexual arousal, orgasm, and the return to the unaroused state, noted by William Masters and Virginia Johnson.

sexual sadism A sexual preference that involves sexual arousal from inflicting pain or humiliation on others.

single-factor explanation A theory that attributes the supposed causal chain of dysfunctional behaviour to a single factor.

single-subject design A nonexperimental investigative method that, like the *case study*, is based on the intense investigation of an individual subject, but avoids many criticisms of the case study by using experimentally accepted procedures. It uses observable behaviours that are quantifiable, quantifies the presence of the behaviour prior to any intervention, systematically applies readily observable and quantifiable interventions, and measures the effects of the intervention on the behaviours of the subject.

situational sexual dysfunctions Any sexual dysfunction that is apparent only in a specific sexual situation, for example, with a certain sexual partner (for example, the client's spouse).

sleep apnea A sleep disorder characterized by episodes of cessation of breathing (apnea) that last at least 10 seconds. Diagnosis requires that there be at least five such episodes per hour of sleep.

social drift The tendency for people vulnerable to schizophrenia to "drift" down to lower social and economic levels.

social impairment A failure to fulfill major role obligations at work, home, or school.

social justice The fair and equitable allocation of burdens and privileges, rights and responsibilities, and pains and gains in society.

social learning theory As originally outlined by Bandura and Walters (1959), a theory that suggested that while *classical* and *operant conditioning* experiences are important, the majority of such experiences are primarily acquired vicariously—that is, by observation of others rather than direct personal experience. This theory has been extended to include not only direct observation of others but also information derived from books, movies, and television.

social skills training The teaching of appropriate and effective social communication and interpersonal behaviour.

social support An individual's perceived quality of support from close others (e.g., partner, friends, parent).

socially prescribed perfectionism Characterized by a propensity to impose high standards on others and blame them when the standards are not met. Also known as *other-oriented perfectionism.*

socio-cognitive model The theory that dissociative identity disorder is a form of role-playing in which individuals come to construe themselves as possessing multiple selves and then begin to act in ways consistent with their or their therapist's conception of the disorder.

sociopaths People who are considered to have normal temperament but who are weakly socialized because of environmental failures, including poor parenting, antisocial peers, and disorganized home and school experiences.

somatic delusions Beliefs related to the body.

somatic symptom and related disorders A set of disorders in DSM-5 that are characterized by bodily symptoms that may or may not have an identifiable medical explanation and are accompanied by significant distress and/or disability. Individuals with these disorders typically seek help in medical, rather than mental health, settings.

somatic symptom disorder A disorder characterized by one or more bodily symptoms that are distressing to the individual, result in significant disruption of daily life, and are accompanied by excessive worry and preoccupation, extreme anxiety, or disproportionate time and energy.

somatic symptom disorder with predominant pain A subtype of *somatic symptom disorder* in which the presenting bodily symptom involves pain (called *pain disorder* in previous editions of DSM).

somatogenesis The idea that psychopathology is caused by biological factors—*soma* meaning "body" in Latin.

SORC Four sets of variables that behavioural and cognitively oriented clinicians are concerned with. S stands for *stimuli*, environmental situations that preceded the problem, or in which the problem arose; O stands for *organismic*, factors within the individual that might increase the probability of a behaviour; R stands for overt *responses*—the problem behaviour itself; C stands for *consequences* of the behaviour, particularly those that might reinforce or punish it.

specifiers Further descriptors of a patient's condition that capture the natural variation in the expression of affective disturbances, and therefore increase the specificity of diagnoses by conveying important information about salient features that might be otherwise overlooked. For example, one specifier used in conjunction with a diagnosis of *major depressive disorder* is "with melancholic features."

split-half reliability A measure of *internal consistency*, often ascertained by comparing responses on odd-numbered test items with responses on even-numbered test items and seeing if the scores for these responses are correlated.

Stanford-Binet Intelligence Scales An intelligence test whose most recent version assesses four general kinds of ability: verbal reasoning, quantitative reasoning, abstract/visual reasoning, and short-term memory. It produces separate scores for each of these functions as well as a global IQ score that summarizes the child's ability. Developed from the work of French psychologist Alfred Binet (1857–1911).

statistical significance An attribute of research results when it is extremely unlikely that they could have occurred purely by chance. The standard by which most research is judged as valuable or worthy of being published.

statutory law A written or codified statement of the law in a given area, enacted by government.

stereotypy The repetition of meaningless gestures or movements. One of the manifestations of a developmental disorder.

stimulants A class of drugs that have a stimulating or arousing effect on the central nervous system, and create their effects by influencing the rate of uptake of the neurotransmitters dopamine and norepinephrine and serotonin at receptor sites in the brain.

stress Environmental and life events or stimuli that influence the development and onset of an illness or disorder.

stress generation hypothesis A theory of depression recurrence, which states that individuals with a history of depression have higher rates of stressful life events that are at least in part dependent on their own behaviour or characteristics than non-depressed individuals.

stress reactivity paradigm A viewpoint that sees the reaction to stress as important to an understanding of cardiovascular disease.

stroke A loss of brain functions that results from interruption of blood supply to the brain or hemorrhage of blood vessels in the brain and consequent death of the neural tissue on which the brain functions depend.

structural magnetic resonance imaging (MRI) A brain scanning technique that provides detailed pictures and information on neuroanatomical structures.

structural racism This involves collective beliefs, behaviours, practices, and policies of societies and institutions that function to disadvantage radicalized people and produce racial inequities between groups (related concepts include systemic and institutional racism).

substance use disorder Recurrent substance use that results in significant adverse consequences in social or occupational functioning, or use of a substance that impairs one's performance in hazardous situations, for example drinking and driving.

subtle avoidance Engaging in safety behaviours that serve to maintain anxiety. For example, an individual may be able to go into a movie theatre only if he or she sits in the back near the exit or is accompanied by a significant other. These subtle behaviours need to end in order for anxiety to really diminish over the long term.

suicide The intentional taking of one's life.

superego In Sigmund Freud's theory, the internalization of the moral standards of society inculcated by the child's parents.

supernatural causes Causes beyond the understanding of ordinary mortals, such as the influence of gods, demons, or magic. Psychological dysfunction in various historical periods was thought to result from either possession by demons or the witchcraft of evil people.

supportive expressive psychotherapy A psychodynamic approach, similar to time-limited dynamic psychotherapy, that is brief and involves the client in face-to-face contact with the therapist.

suspiciousness A generalized distrustful view of others and their motivations, but not sufficiently pathological to warrant a clinical diagnosis of paranoia.

switching The transition from one *alter* to another in an individual with *dissociative identity disorder*. Occurs suddenly and is often precipitated by stress or some other identifiable cue in the surrounding environment.

syndromes Groups of symptoms that tend to occur together.

synergistic Said of drugs whose combined effects exceed or are significantly different from the sum of their individual effects.

systematic desensitization A therapeutic technique whereby patients imagine the lowest feared stimuli and combine this image with a relaxation response. Patients gradually work their way up the fear hierarchy so that they can learn to handle increasingly disturbing stimuli.

systems theory A theory proposing that multiple interacting factors generate all behaviour, and that the effects of these factors are bidirectional; that is, the influence of each factor on another changes the other factors, which in turn then influence the original factor. The overall effect of these influences is said to be greater than the sum of the influence of each of the factors.

systolic blood pressure/diastolic blood pressure A measure of the pressure of the blood flowing through the vasculature. It is obtained by finding the number of millimetres of mercury displaced by a sphygmomanometer (blood pressure cuff).

T

telehealth A way of delivering healthcare that covers a range of delivery options, including telephone, videoconferencing, and computer-mediated communications (e.g., email, chat rooms, and internet-based services).

temporary substitute decision maker In provincial mental health law, someone authorized to make treatment decisions on behalf of a person who is civilly committed and deemed incapable of making such decisions.

tension-reduction A hypothesis which suggests that drinking is reinforced by its ability to reduce tension, anxiety, anger, depression, and other unpleasant emotions.

tertiary prevention A type of *prevention* practised after suffering or disability from the disease is being experienced, with the goal of preventing further deterioration. *See also primary prevention and secondary prevention.*

test-retest reliability The degree to which a test yields the same results when it is given more than once to the same person. Test-retest reliability can be evaluated by correlating a person's score on a given test with the same person's score on the same test taken at a later time. The higher the correlation between the two scores (as expressed in terms of a correlation coefficient) the more *reliable* it is.

testosterone A hormone (the so-called male sex hormone) that stimulates development of male secondary sexual characteristics and that is involved in sexual activity and desire, variations in the level of which can lower or increase sex drive.

thalidomide A drug prescribed for nausea in the 1950s and 1960s by European physicians that was found to cause limb deficiencies or malformations in infants.

THC The chemical delta-9-tetrahydrocannabinol, which causes the psychoactive effects of *cannabis*. Although the exact mechanisms by which THC exerts its influences is not fully understood, it appears as if it acts upon specific cannabinoid receptors in the body and mimics the effects of naturally occurring substances, including the *endogenous opiates*.

thematic apperception test (TAT) A psychological test using drawings on cards depicting ambiguous social interactions. Those being tested are asked to construct stories about the cards. It is assumed their tales reflect their experiences, outlook on life, and deep-seated needs and conflicts. Validity and reliability of scoring techniques are open to the same criticisms as those of the *Rorschach inkblot test*.

theory of mind The ability to attribute mental states (e.g., beliefs, intentions) to oneself and others and to understand that others have beliefs, desires, intentions, and perspectives that are different from one's own.

therapeutic alliance The relationship between therapist and client, recognized to be a predictor of therapy outcome. Recent research in psychodynamic therapy has underlined its importance.

thought-action fusion (TAF) The irrational tendency for individuals to believe their thoughts will increase the probability that a certain event will occur (Likelihood TAF), or to believe that their thoughts are the moral equivalent of actions (Moral TAF).

thought and speech disorder A psychotic symptom, often reported in schizophrenia, that involves disorganized and incoherent ideas and language, a kind of nonsensical "crazy talk."

time-limited dynamic psychotherapy (TLDP) A psychodynamic approach that tends to be brief and involve the client in face-to-face contact with the therapist. The TLDP therapist helps identify patterns of interaction with others that strengthen unhelpful thoughts about oneself and others.

tobacco nicotine An extremely potent central nervous system stimulant related to the *amphetamines*. The very small amount present in a cigarette is not lethal, and can increase alertness and improve mood. The pleasure centres of the brain seem to have receptors specific to it.

tolerance The need of a person for increased amounts of an addictive substance to achieve the desired effect.

total peripheral resistance The diameter of the blood vessels; one of the variables affecting blood pressure.

toxic psychosis Hallucinations, delirium, and paranoia caused by repeated high doses of *amphetamines*.

trait A personal quality that is characteristic of someone ("generous," "creative," etc.); that is, it is persistently displayed over time and in various situations. Every person manifests several traits, the combination of which makes up his or her personality.

transactional model (1) A model of stress that conceives of stress as a property neither of stimulus nor of response, but rather as an ongoing series of transactions between an individual and his or her environment. Central to this formulation is the idea that people constantly evaluate what is happening to them and its implications for themselves.

transactional model (2) One model of how hostility might lead to health risk, which suggests that the behaviour of hostile individuals constructs, by its natural consequences, a social world that is antagonistic and unsupportive, so that both interpersonal stressors and the lack of social support increase vulnerability. A hybrid of the *psychophysiological reactivity model* and the *psychosocial vulnerability model*.

transcranial magnetic stimulation (TMS) Treatment for severe depression that uses a magnet to excite neurons in the brain.

transdiagnostic approach An approach to treatment that addressed common problems typically observed across several diagnoses.

transference In the psychodynamic approach to therapy, the client's action of responding to the therapist as he or she responded to significant figures from his or her childhood (generally the parents). Considered the core of psychoanalytic therapy.

translocation A cause of *Down syndrome* in which part of the 21st chromosome of the human cell breaks off and attaches to another. Individuals with Down syndrome due to translocation have all of the features found in trisomy 21.

transvestite A person who wears the clothing associated with the opposite sex —in order to produce or enhance sexual excitement.

trauma model The theory that dissociative identity disorder is caused by severe childhood trauma, including sexual, physical, and emotional abuse, accompanied by personality traits that predispose the individual to employ dissociation as a defence mechanism or coping strategy.

treatment effectiveness Evidence that a treatment has been shown to work in real-world conditions (i.e., an emphasis on external validity).

treatment efficacy Evidence that a treatment has been shown to work under research conditions that emphasized internal validity.

trephination A prehistoric form of surgery possibly intended to let out evil spirits; it involved chipping a hole into a person's skull.

tricyclic antidepressants (TCAs) One of the three known major classes of antidepressants. Tricyclics enable more neurotransmitters to be released into the synaptic cleft. They include amoxapine (Asendin), amitriptyline (Elavil), imipramine (Tofranil), and doxepin (Sinequan).

trisomy 21 The most common type of *Down syndrome*, in which there is an extra chromosome on pair 21 of the 23 pairs of chromosomes in the human cell.

two-factor theory The most influential theory of fear and phobias during the 1960s and 1970s. The model proposed that fears are acquired by *classical conditioning*, but maintained by *operant conditioning*.

Type A A syndrome of behaviours that includes hyperalertness and arousability, a chronic sense of time-urgency, competitiveness, hostility, and job-involvement.

U

unconscious In *psychodynamic* theory, the unconscious contains the majority of our memories and drives, which can only be raised to awareness with great difficulty and typically only in response to special techniques (that is, psychoanalytic procedures).

unfit to stand trial (UST) In Canadian criminal law, incapable of participating in the trial process due to mental disorder at the time of trial.

universal approach An approach to *prevention* programs designed to include all individuals in a certain geographical area (for example, the neighbourhood, the city, the province) or a certain setting (for example, school, the workplace, a public housing complex).

V

vagus nerve stimulation (VNS) Treatment for severe depression that electrically stimulates the vagus nerve by way of an implanted stimulator.

validity The ability of a measurement tool to measure what it purports to measure. A rigid ruler would be *reliable*, but it would be useless as a measure of temperature.

vascular neurocognitive disorder (NCD) The second most common cause of *dementia* (second to *Alzheimer's disease*) that results from brain damage due to cerebrovascular disease.

vasculature The system of arteries, arterioles, capillaries, venules, and veins responsible for circulation of the blood to all parts of the body and its return to the heart.

vicarious learning Learning that takes place by observing others. Also called *modelling*.

voyeurism A form of *paraphilic disorder* that is also a criminal offence, in which a person is sexually aroused from watching unsuspecting individuals who are naked, disrobing, or engaged in sexual activity.

W

WAIS-IV The most recent version of the *Wechsler Adult Intelligence Scale*, published in 2008.

waxy flexibility A state wherein a person's limbs and posture can be "moulded" into different positions as if the person were made of wax. Occasionally seen in *schizophrenia*.

Wechsler Adult Intelligence Scale, or WAIS. The most widely used IQ tests, designed to measure diverse aspects of intelligence. Developed by David Wechsler (1896–1981). *See also WAIS-IV*.

Wernicke-Korsakoff syndrome A chronic disease related to alcohol dependence characterized by impaired memory and a loss of contact with reality.

Wisconsin Card Sorting Test A neuropsychological test that requires sorting cards into categories based on colour, shape, or quantity depending on corrective feedback from the examiner. One of the most frequently used tests in schizophrenia research.

withdrawal Unpleasant and sometimes dangerous symptoms such as nausea, headache, or tremors experienced when an addictive substance is removed from the body.

worry imagery exposure Identifying the patient's main areas of worry, vividly imagining these unpleasant scenes, and concentrating on them while conjuring up images of the worst possible outcome. After holding these graphic images in their minds for a period of time, patients are then encouraged to generate as many alternatives as possible to the worst scenario.

References

Aaron, P. G., Phillips, S., & Larsen, S. (1988). Specific reading disability in historically famous persons. *Journal of Learning Disabilities, 21* (9), 523–538.

Abbott, A. (2001). Into the mind of a killer. *Nature, 410,* 296–298.

Abel, E. L. (1984). *Fetal alcohol syndrome and fetal alcohol effects.* New York, NY: Plenum Press.

Abel, G. G., Becker, J. V., Mittelman, M. S., Cunningham-Rathner, J., Rouleau, J. L., & Murphy, W. D. (1987). Self-reported sex crimes of nonincarcerated paraphiliacs. *Journal of Interpersonal Violence, 2,* 3–25.

Abel, G. G., Blanchard, E. B., & Becker, J. V. (1978). An integrated treatment program for rapists. In R. T. Rada (Ed.), *Clinical aspects of the rapist* (pp. 161–214). New York: Grune & Stratton.

Abel, G., & Rouleau, J. L. (1990). The nature and extent of sexual assault. In W. L. Marshall, D. R. Laws, & E. H. Bartarce (Eds.), *Handbook of sexual assault* (pp. 9–21). New York, NY: Plenum.

Abramowitz, J. S. (2008). Obsessive-compulsive disorder. In W. E. Craighead, D. J. Miklowitz, & L. W. Craighead (Eds.), *Psychopathology: History, diagnosis, and empirical foundations* (pp. 159–197). Hoboken, NJ: Wiley.

Abramowitz, J. S., Deacon, B. J., & Valentiner, D. P. (2007). The short health anxiety inventory: Psychometric properties and construct validity in a non-clinical sample. *Psychology and Neuroscience, 31,* 871–883.

Abramowitz, J. S., Deacon, B. J., & Whiteside, S. P. H. (2011). *Exposure therapy for anxiety: Principles and practice.* New York, NY: Guilford.

Abrams, K., Kushner, M., Medina, K. L., & Voight, A. (2001). The pharmacologic and expectancy effects of alcohol on social anxiety in individuals with social phobia. *Drug and Alcohol Dependence, 64*(2), 219–231.

Achenbach, T. M., & Edelbrock, C. (1983). *Manual for the child behavior checklist and revised child behavior profile.* Burlington, VT: University of Vermont.

Achenbach, T. M., & Rescorla, L. A. (2001). *Manual for ASEBA school-age forms & profiles.* Burlington, VT: University of Vermont, Research Center for Children, Youth, & Families.

Ackerknecht, E. H. (1968). *Short history of psychiatry.* (S. Wolff, Trans.). New York, NY: Hafner.

Ackerly, S. S., & Benton, A. L. (1948). Report of a case of bilateral frontal lobe defect. *Research and Publications of the Association for the Research of Nervous and Mental Disease, 27,* 479–504.

Acocella, J. (1999). *Creating hysteria: Women and multiple personality disorder.* San Francisco, CA: Jossey-Bass.

Adamson, S. J., & Sellman, J. D. (2001). Drinking goal selection and treatment outcome in out-patients with mild-moderate alcohol dependence. *Drug and Alcohol Review, 20,* 351–359.

Addiction Research Foundation. (1992). Abstinence and reduced drinking: Two approaches to alcohol treatment. *Best advice.* Toronto: Author.

Addiction Research Foundation. (1997). *Addiction Research Foundation website.* Retrieved from www.arf.org. Now the Centre for Addiction and Mental Health, www.camh.net

Addington, J. (2007). The promise of early intervention. *Early Intervention in Psychiatry, 1,* 294–307.

Addington, J., Cornblatt, B. A., Cadenhead, K. S., Cannon, T. D., McGlashan, T. H., Perkins, D. O., . . . Heinssen, R. (2011). At clinical high risk for psychosis: Outcome for nonconverters. *American Journal of Psychiatry, 168,* 800–805.

Adelson, N. (2005). The embodiment of inequity: Health disparities in Aboriginal Canada. *Canadian Journal of Public Health,* (suppl 2), S45–S61.

Ader, R., Felten, D. L., & Cohen, N. (Eds.). (2001). *Psychoneuroimmunology* (Vols. 1–2, 3rd ed.). San Diego, CA: Academic Press.

Adlaf, E. M., Demers, A., & Gliksman, L. (Eds.). (2005). *Canadian campus survey 2004.* Toronto: Centre for Addiction and Mental Health.

Agras, S., Brandt, H. A., Bulik, C. M., Dolan-Sewell, R., Fairburn, C. G., Halmi, K. A., et al. (2004). Report of the National Institutes of Health Workshop on overcoming barriers to treatment research in anorexia nervosa. *International Journal of Eating Disorders, 35,* 509–521.

Agras, S., Hammer, L., & McNicholas, F. (1999). A prospective study of the influence of eating-disordered mothers on their children. *International Journal of Eating Disorders, 25,* 253–262.

Agras, W. S. (2001). The consequences and costs of the eating disorders. *Psychiatric Clinics of North America, 24,* 371–379.

Agras, W. S., Walsh, T., Fairburn, C. G., Wilson, G. T., & Kraemer, H. C. (2000). A multicenter comparison of cognitive-behavioral therapy and interpersonal psychotherapy for bulimia nervosa. *Archives of General Psychiatry, 57,* 459–466.

Agrawal, A., & Lynskey, M. T. (2008). Are there genetic influences on addiction: Evidence from family, adoption and twin studies. *Addiction, 103,* 1069–1081.

Ainscow, M. (2000). Reaching out to all learners: Some lessons from international experience. *School Effectiveness and School Improvement, 11,* 1–9.

Ainsworth, M. D. S., & Bowlby, J. (1991). An ethological approach to personality development. *American Psychologist, 46,* 333–34

Akagi, H., & House, A. (2001). The epidemiology of hysterical conversion. In P. Halligan, C. Bass, & J. Marshall (Eds.), *Contemporary approaches to the study of hysteria.* Oxford, UK: Oxford University Press.

Albee, G. W. (1982). Preventing psychopathology and promoting human potential. *American Psychologist, 37,* 1043–1050.

Albee, G. W. (1990). The futility of psychotherapy. *Journal of Mind and Behavior, 11,* 369–384.

Albee, G. W. (1996). Revolutions and counterrevolutions in prevention. *American Psychologist, 51,* 1130–1133.

Alberta Alcohol and Drug Abuse Commission. (2004). *Tobacco basics handbook.* Edmonton: Author.

Alda, M. (1997). Bipolar disorder: From families to genes. *Canadian Journal of Psychiatry, 42,* 378–387.

Alden, L. (1989). Short-term structured treatment for avoidant personality disorder. *Journal of Consulting and Clinical Psychology, 57,* 756–764.

Alden, L. E., & Taylor, C. T. (2004). Interpersonal processes in social phobia. *Clinical Psychology Review, 24,* 857–882.

Aldersey, H. M., Turnbull, A. P. & Minnes P. (2017). Providing support that enhances a family's quality of life. In Wehmeyer, M. L., Brown, I, Percy, M., Shogren, K. A., & Fung, W. L. A. (Eds.), *A Comprehensive guide to intellectual and developmental disabilities* (2nd ed.) New York, NY: Brookes Publishing.

Alexander, F. (1950). *Psychosomatic medicine: Its principles and applications.* New York, NY: Norton.

Alexander, F., & French, T. M. (1946). *Psychoanalytic therapy: Principles and application.* New York, NY: Ronald Press.

Alexander, M. G., & Fisher, T. D. (2003). Truth and consequences: Using the bogus pipeline to examine sex differences in self-reported sexuality. *The Journal of Sex Research, 40*(1), 27–35.

Alexopoulous, G. S., Katz, I. R., Reynolds, C. F., Carpenter, D., & Docherty, J. P. (2001). The Expert Consensus Guideline Series: Pharmacotherapy of depressive disorders in older patients. *Postgraduate Medicine, 110,* 1–86.

Alford, B. A., & Beck, A. T. (1997). *The integrative power of cognitive therapy.* New York, NY: Guilford.

Allebeck, P. (1989). Schizophrenia: A life-shortening disease. *Schizophrenia Bulletin, 15,* 81–90.

Allen, J., Balfour, R., Bell, R., & Marmot, M. (2014). Social determinants of mental health. *International Review of Psychiatry, 26*(4), 392–407. doi:10.3109/09540261. 2014.928270

Allen, N. J., & Barres, B. A. (2009). Neuroscience: Glia—more than just brain glue. *Nature, 457,* 675-677.

Alloy, L. B., Abramson, L. Y., Keyser, J., Gerstein, R. K., & Sylvia, L. G. (2008). Negative cognitive style. In K. S. Dobson & D. J. A. Dozois (Eds.), *Risk factors in depression* (pp. 237–262). Oxford, UK: Elsevier/Academic Press.

Alloy, L. B., Abramson, L. Y., Whitehouse, W. G., Hogan, M. E., Panzarella, C., & Rose, D. T. (2006). Prospective incidence of first onsets and recurrences of depression in individuals at high and low cognitive risk for depression. *Journal of Abnormal Psychology, 115,* 145–156.

Alonso, J., & Lepine, J. (2007). Overview of key data from the European Study of the Epidemiology of Mental Disorders. *Journal of Clinical Psychiatry, 68* (Suppl. 2), 3–9.

Altamura, A. C., Bertoldo, A., Marotta, G., Paoli, R. A., Caletti, E., Dragogna, F., . . . Brambilla, P. (2013). White matter metabolism differentiates schizophrenia and bipolar disorder: A preliminary PET study. *Psychiatry Research: Neuroimaging, 214*(3), 410–414. doi:org/10.1016/j.pscychresns.2013.08.011

Alterman, A. I., & Cacciola, J. S. (1991). The antisocial personality disorder diagnosis in substance abusers. *Journal of Nervous and Mental Disease, 179*, 401–409.

Althof, S. E. (1995). Pharmacologic treatment of rapid ejaculation. *Psychiatric Clinics of North America, 18*(1), 85–94.

Althof, S. E. (2016). Psychosexual therapy for premature ejaculation. *Translational Andrology and Urology, 5*, 475–481.

Althof, S. E., & Needle, R. B. (2011). Psychological factors associated with male sexual dysfunction: Screening and treatment for the urologist. *Urologic Clinics of North America, 38*, 141–146.

Althof, S. E., & Seftel, A. D. (1995). The evaluation and management of erectile dysfunction. *Psychiatric Clinics of North America, 18*, 171–192.

Althof, S. E., & Turner, L. A. (1992). Self-injection therapy and external vacuum devices in the treatment of erectile dysfunction: Methods and outcome. In R. C. Rosen & S. R. Leiblum (Eds.), *Erectile disorders: Assessment and treatment* (pp. 283–309). New York, NY: Guilford.

Alzheimer's Disease International. (2009). *World Alzheimer report 2009.* Retrieved from http://alz.co.uk/research/worldreport

Aman, M. G., Lam, K. S. L., & Collier-Crespin, A. (2003). Prevalence and patterns of use of psychoactive medicines among individuals with autism in the Autism Society of Ohio. *Journal of Autism & Developmental Disorders, 33*, 527–534.

Ambrogne, J. A. (2002). Reduced drinking as a treatment goal: What clinicians need to know. *Journal of Substance Abuse Treatment, 22*, 45–53.

Ament, S. A., Szelinger, S., Glusman, G., Ashworth, J., Hou, L., Akula, N., . . . & Stittrich, A. B. (2015). Rare variants in neuronal excitability genes influence risk for bipolar disorder. *Proceedings of the National Academy of Science, 112*(11), 3576–3581.

American Association on Mental Retardation. (1992). *Mental retardation: Definition, classification and systems of support* (9th ed.). Washington, DC: Author.

American Dietetic Association. (2006). Position of the American Dietetic Association: Nutrition intervention in the treatment of anorexia nervosa, bulimia nervosa, and other eating disorders. *Journal of the American Dietetic Association, 106*, 2073. doi: 10.1016/j.jada.2006.09.007

American Psychiatric Association. (1968). *Diagnostic and statistical manual of mental disorders* (2nd ed.). Washington, DC: Author.

American Psychiatric Association. (1980). *Diagnostic and statistical manual of mental disorders* (3rd ed.). Washington, DC: Author.

American Psychiatric Association. (1987). *Diagnostic and statistical manual of mental disorders* (3rd ed. rev.). Washington, DC: Author.

American Psychiatric Association. (1994). *Diagnostic and statistical manual of mental disorders* (4th ed.). Washington, DC: Author.

American Psychiatric Association. (2000). *Diagnostic and statistical manual of mental disorders* (4th ed. rev.). Washington, DC: Author.

American Psychiatric Association. (2001). *Practice guidelines for the treatment of patients with borderline personality disorder.* Washington, DC: Author.

American Psychiatric Association. (2011). *DSM-5 development.* Retrieved from www.dsm5.org/Pages/Default.aspx

American Psychiatric Association. (2013). *Diagnostic and statistical manual of mental disorders* (5th ed.). Washington, DC: Author.

American Psychological Association. (2004). Guidelines for psychological practice with older adults. *American Psychologist, 59*, 236–260.

American Psychological Association (2007). Guidelines for psychological practice with girls and women. *American Psychologist, 62*, 949–979.

American Psychological Association Presidential Task Force on Evidence-Based Practice. (2006). Evidence-based practice in psychology. *American Psychologist, 61*, 271–285.

American Psychological Association. (2013). Specialty guidelines for forensic psychology. *American Psychologist, 68*, 7–19.

American Psychosomatic Society. (1996). Special Issue: Animal models in psychosomatic research. *Psychosomatic Medicine, 58*, 521–632.

Ames, E. (1992). Development of Romanian orphanage children adopted to Canada. *Canadian Psychology, 33*, 503.

Ames, E., Chisholm, K., Fisher, L., Morison, S. J., Thompson, S., Mainemer, H., ... & Savoie, L. A. (1997). *The development of Romanian orphanage children adopted to Canada.* [Final report to National Welfare Grants Program, Human Resources Development Canada]. Burnaby, BC: Simon Fraser University.

Ammari, N., Heinrichs, R. W., & Miles, A. A. (2010). An investigation of 3 neurocognitive subtypes in schizophrenia. *Schizophrenia Research, 121*, 1–3.

Amminger, G. P., Berger, G. E., Schafer, M. R., Klier, C., Friedrich, M. H., & Feucht, M. (2007). Omega 3 fatty acids supplementation in children with autism: A double-blind, randomized, placebo-controlled pilot study. *Biological Psychiatry, 61*, 551–553.

Amstadter, A. B., Broman-Fulks, J., Zinzow, H., Ruggiero, K. J., & Cercone, J. (2009). Internet-based interventions for traumatic-stress related mental health problems. *Clinical Psychology Review, 29*, 410–420.

An Act to Amend The Education Act, 1974, Ontario. (1980). c61.

Ancoli-Israel, S. (1989). Epidemiology of sleep disorders. *Clinics in Geriatric Medicine, 5*, 347–362.

Ancoli-Israel, S., & Roth, T. (1999). Characteristics of insomnia in the United States: I. Results of the 1991 National Sleep Foundation Survey. *Sleep, 22(Suppl. 2)*, 347–353.

Andersen, A. E., & DiDomenico, L. (1992). Diet vs. shape content of popular male and female magazines: A dose-response relationship to the incidence of eating disorders? *International Journal of Eating Disorders, 11*, 283–287.

Anderson, J. C., Williams, S., McGee, R., & Silva, P. A. (1987). DSM-III disorders in preadolescent children: Prevalence in a large sample from the general population. *Archives of General Psychiatry, 44*, 69–76.

Anderson, K. G., Deschênes, S. S., & Dugas. M. J. (2016). Experimental manipulation of avoidable feelings of uncertainty: Effects on anger and anxiety. *Journal of Anxiety Disorders, 41*(6), 50-58.

Anderson, S. W., Bechara, A., Damasio, H., Tranel, D., & Damasio, A. R. (1999). Impairment of social and moral behaviour related to early damage in human prefrontal cortex. *Nature Neuroscience, 2*, 1032–1037.

Anderson, S. W., Damasio, H., Jones, R. D., & Tranel, D. (1991). Wisconsin Card Sorting Test performance as a measure of frontal lobe damage. *Journal of Clinical and Experimental Neuropsychology, 13*, 909–922.

Anderssen, E. (2016, October 05). Why Starbucks Canada's investment in mental health therapy matters. Retrieved from www.theglobeandmail.com/life/health-and-fitness/health/why-starbucks-canadas-investment-in-mental-health-therapy-matters/article32252755/

Andreasen, N. C., & Flaum, M. (1991). Schizophrenia: The characteristic symptoms. *Schizophrenia Bulletin, 17*, 27–49.

Andrés, S., Lázaro, L., Salamero, M., Boget, T., Penadés, R., & Castro-Fornieles, J. (2008). Changes in cognitive dysfunction in children and adolescents with obsessive-compulsive disorder after treatment. *Journal of Psychiatric Research, 42*, 507–514.

Andrews, D. A., Bonta, J., & Wormith, J. S. (2011). The risk-need-responsivity (RNR) model: Does adding the good lives model contribute to effective crime prevention? *Criminal Justice and Behavior, 38*(7), 735–755.

Andrews, D.A. & Bonta, J. (2003). *The psychology of criminal conduct* (3rd ed.). Cincinnati, OH: Anderson.

Andrews, G., Brugha, T., Thase, M. E., Duffy, F. F., Rucci, P., & Slade, T. (2007). Dimensionality and the category of major depressive episode. *International Journal of Methods in Psychiatric Research, 16*, S41–S51.

Angold, A., & Costello, J. (1996). Toward establishing an empirical basis for the diagnosis of oppositional defiant disorder. *Journal of the American Academy of Child & Adolescent Psychiatry, 35*, 1205–1212.

Angold, A., Costello, E. J., & Erkani, A. (1999). Comorbidity. *Journal of Child Psychology and Psychiatry, 40*, 57–87.

Angus, L. E., & Marziali, E. (1988). A comparison of three measures for the diagnosis of borderline personality disorder. *American Journal of Psychiatry, 145*, 1453–1454.

Antony, M. M., & Barlow, D. H. (2002). Specific phobias. In D. H. Barlow (Ed.), *Anxiety and its disorders* (2nd ed., pp. 380–417). New York, NY: Guilford.

Antony, M. M., & Swinson, R. P. (1996). *Anxiety disorders and their treatment: A critical review of the evidence-based literature.* Ottawa, ON: Health Canada.

Antony, M. M., McCabe, R. E., Leeuw, I., Sano, N., & Swinson, R. P. (2001). Effect of distraction and coping style on in vivo exposure for specific phobia of spiders. *Behaviour Research & Therapy, 39*, 1137–1150.

Antony, M. M., Orsillo, S. M., & Roemer, L. (2001). *Practitioner's guide to empirically based measures of anxiety.* New York, NY: Kluwer Academic/Plenum.

Antony, M. M., Purdon, C. L., Huta, V., & Swinson, R. P. (1998). Dimensions of perfectionism across the anxiety disorders. *Behaviour Research & Therapy, 36*, 1143–1154.

Anxiety Review Panel. Evans, M., Bradwejn, J., & Dunn, L. (Eds.). (2000). *Guidelines for the treatment of anxiety disorders in primary care.* Toronto, ON: Queen's Printer of Ontario.

Aos, S., Lieb, R., Mayfiel, J., Miller, M., & Pennucci, A. (2004). *Benefits and costs of prevention and early intervention programs for youth.* (No. 04-07-3901). Olympia, WA: Washington State Institute for Public Policy.

APA. *See* American Psychiatric Association.

Arboleda-Florez, J., & Holley, H. L. (1991). Antisocial burnout: An exploratory study. *Bulletin of the American Academy of Psychiatry and Law, 19*, 173–183.

Arcelus, J., Mitchell, A. J., Wales, J., & Nielsen, S. (2011). Mortality rates in patients with anorexia nervosa and other eating disorders: A meta-analysis of 36 studies. *Archives of General Psychiatry, 68*, 724-731. doi: 10.1001/archgenpsychiatry.2011.74

Archer, J. (1991). The influence of testosterone on human aggression. *British Journal of Psychology, 82*, 1–28.

Archer, R. P. (2016). *Assessing adolescent psychopathology: MMPI-A/MMPI-A-RF* (4th ed.). New York, NY: Routledge.

Arieti, S. (1963). Psychopathic personality: Some views on its psychopathology and psychodynamics. *Comprehensive Psychiatry, 4*, 301–312.

Arkowitz, H., Miller, W. R., & Rollnick, S. (Eds.). (2015). *Motivational interviewing in the treatment of psychological problems* (2nd ed.). New York, NY: Guilford.

Arseneault, L., Cannon, M., Poulton, R., Murray, R., Caspi, A., & Moffitt, T. E. (2002). Cannabis use in adolescence and risk for adult psychosis: Longitudinal prospective study. *British Medical Journal, 325*, 1212–1213.

Arterbutrn, D. E., Crane, P. K., & Sullivan, S. D. (2006). The coming epidemic of obesity in elderly Americans. *Journal of the American Geriatrics Society, 52*, 1907–1912.

Asadi-Pooya, A. A., Emami, Y., & Emami, M. (2014). Psychogenic non-epileptic seizures in Iran. *Seizure, 23*(3), 175–177.

Åsberg, M. (1976). Treatment of depression with tricyclic drugs—Pharmacokinetic and pharmacodynamic aspects. *Pharmacopsychiatry and Neuropsychopharmacology, 9*, 18–26.

Ashbaugh, A. R., & Radomsky, A. S. (2009). Interpretations of and memory for bodily sensations during public speaking. *Journal of Behavior Therapy and Experimental Psychiatry, 40*, 399-411.

Ashbaugh, A. R., & Radomsky, A. S. (2011). Memory for physiological feedback in social anxiety disorder: The role of fear of bodily sensations. *Cognitive Therapy and Research, 35*, 304-316.

Ashcroft, M. H., Krause, J. A., & Hopko, D. R. (2007). Is math anxiety a mathematical learning disability? In D. B. Berch & M. Mazzacco (Eds.), *Why is math so hard for some children? The nature and origins of mathematical learning difficulties and disabilities* (pp. 329–348). Baltimore, MD: Paul H. Brookes.

Ashkenazi, S., Black, J. M., Abrams, D. A., Hoeft, F., & Menon, F. (2013). Neurobiological underpinnings of math and reading learning disabilities. *Journal of Learning Disabilities, 46*(6), 549–569.

Ashton, H. (2005). The diagnosis and management of benzodiazepine dependence. *Current Opinion in Psychiatry, 18*, 249–255.

Assembly of First Nations and First Nations Information Governance Committee. (2007). *First Nations Regional Longitudinal Health Survey (RHS) 2002/03: Results for adults, youth and children living in First Nations communities.* Ottawa, ON: Author.

Asseraf, M., & Vaillancourt, T. (2015). Longitudinal links between perfectionism and depression in children. *Journal of Abnormal Child Psychology, 43*, 895–908. doi.org/10.1007/s10802-014-9947-9

Astley, S. J., Bailey, D., Talbot, C., & Clarren, S. K. (2000). Fetal alcohol syndrome (FAS) primary prevention through FAS diagnosis: Identification of high-risk birth mothers through the diagnosis of their children. *Alcohol, 35* (5), 499–508.

Atkins, D. C., & Christensen, A. (2001). Is professional training worth the bother? A review of the impact of psychotherapy training on client outcome. *Australian Psychologist, 36*, 122–130.

Atkinson, L., & Feldman, M. (1994). Survey of aberrant behaviour and its treatment in persons with developmental disabilities in Ontario. [Report submitted to Ontario Ministry of Community and Social Services]. Toronto, ON: Ontario Mental Health Foundation.

Avery, D. H. (1993). Electroconvulsive therapy. In D. L. Dunner (Ed.), *Current psychiatric therapy* (pp. 524–528). Philadelphia, PA: W. B. Saunders.

Aviram, A., Westra, H.A., Constantino, M.J., & Antony, M.M. (2016). Responsive management of resistance in cognitive-behavioral therapy for generalized anxiety disorder. *Journal of Consulting and Clinical Psychology, 84*, 783–794.

Aybek, S., Kanaan, R. A., & David, A. S. (2008). The neuropsychiatry of conversion disorder. *Current Opinion in Psychiatry, 21*, 275–280.

Ayers, C. R., Sorrell, J. T., Thorp, S. R., & Wetherell, J. L. (2007). Evidence-based psychological treatments for late-life anxiety. *Psychology and Aging, 22*, 8–17.

Azevedo, F. A., Carvalho, L. R., Grinberg, L. T., Farfel, J. M., Ferretti, R. E., Leite, R. E., . . . & Herculano-Houzel, S. (2009). Equal numbers of neuronal and nonneuronal cells make the human brain an isometrically scaled-up primate brain. *Journal of Comparative Neurology, 513*, 532–541.

Azrin, N. H. (1976). Improvements in the community-reinforcement approach to alcoholism. *Behaviour Research and Therapy, 14*, 339–348.

Babiak, P., & Hare, R. D. (2006). *Snakes in suits: When psychopaths go to work.* New York, NY: Regan Books/HarperCollins.

Babor, T., de la Fuente, J. R., Saunders, J., & Grant, M. (1992). *The Alcohol Use Disorders Identification Test: Guidelines for use in primary health care.* Geneva, Switzerland: World Health Organization.

Bach, A. K., Brown, T. A., & Barlow, D. H. (1999). The effects of false negative feedback on efficacy expectancies and sexual arousal in sexually functional males. *Behavior Therapy, 30*, 79–95.

Backenson, E., Holland, S. C., Kubas, H. A., Fitzer, K., Wilcox, G., Carmichael, . . . & Hale, J. B. (2015). Psychosocial and adaptive deficits associated with learning disability subtypes. *Journal of Learning Disabilities. 48*(5), 511–522

Backhaus, A., Agha, Z., Maglione, M. L., Repp, A., Ross, B., Zuest, D., et al. (2012). Video-conferencing psychotherapy: A systematic review. *Psychological Services, 9*, 111–131.

Bagley, C. (1991). Poverty and suicide among native Canadians: A replication. *Psychological Reports, 69*, 149–150.

Bailey, B. E., Wu, K. D., Valentiner, D. P., & McGrath, P. B. (2014). Thought–action fusion: Structure and specificity to OCD. *Journal of Obsessive-Compulsive and Related Disorders, 3*, 39–45.

Bailey, D. B., Jr., Raspa, M., & Olmsted, M. G. (2010). Using a parent survey to advance knowledge about the nature and consequences of Fragile X syndrome. *American Journal on Intellectual and Developmental Disabilities, 115*, 447–460.

Bailey, Z. D., Krieger, N., Agénor, M., Graves, J., Linos, N., & Bassett, M. T. (2017). Structural racism and health inequities in the USA: Evidence and interventions. *The Lancet, 389*(10077), 1453–1463.

Bajbouj, M., & Grimm, S. (2010). Efficacy of vagus nerve stimulation in the treatment of depression. *Expert Review of Neurotherapeutics, 10*, 87.

Baker, B. L. McIntyre, L.L., Blacher, J., Crnic, K., Edelbrock, C., & Low, C. (2003) Preschool children with and without developmental delay: Behavior problems and parenting stress over time. *Journal of Intellectual Disability Research. Special Issue on Family Research 47*, 217–230.

Baker, S. L., Patterson, M. D., & Barlow, D. H. (2002). Panic disorder and agoraphobia. In M. M. Antony & D. H. Barlow (Eds.), *Handbook of assessment and treatment planning for psychological disorders* (pp. 67–112). New York, NY: Guilford.

Baker-Morrissette, S., Bitran, S., & Barlow, D. H. (2010). Panic disorder and agoraphobia. In M. M. Antony & D. H. Barlow (Eds.), *Handbook of assessment and treatment planning for psychological disorders* (2nd ed., pp. 141–185). New York, NY: Guilford.

Bakkevig, J. F., & Karterud, S. (2010). Is the *Diagnostic and Statistical Manual of Mental Disorders, Fourth Edition*, histrionic personality disorder category a valid construct? *Comprehensive Psychiatry, 51*, 462–470. doi:10.1016/j.comppsych.2009.11.009

Balazs, J., Miklósi, M., Keresztény, Á., Hoven, C. W., Carli, V., Wasserman, C., . . . & Cotter, P. (2013). Adolescent subthreshold-depression and anxiety: Psychopathology, functional impairment and increased suicide risk. *Journal of Child Psychology and Psychiatry, 54*, 670–677.

Ballinger, B., & Yalom, I. (1995). Group therapy in practice. In B. Bongar & L. E. Beutler (Eds.), *Comprehensive textbook of psychotherapy: Theory and practice* (pp. 189–204). New York, NY: Oxford University Press.

Balter, R. E., Cooper, Z. D., & Haney, M. (2014). Novel pharmacologic approaches to treating cannabis use disorder. *Current addiction reports, 1*(2), 137–143.

Baltes, P. B., & Baltes, M. M. (1990). Psychological perspectives on successful aging: The model of selective optimization with compensation. In P. B. Baltes & M. M. Baltes (Eds.), *Successful Aging* (pp. 1–34). Cambridge, UK: Cambridge University Press.

Bancroft, J. (1989). *Human sexuality and its problems* (2nd ed.). New York, NY: Churchill Livingstone.

Bancroft, J. (2000, October). *Sexual wellbeing of women in heterosexual relationships: A national survey.* Paper presented at Female Sexual Function Forum: New perspectives in the management of female sexual dysfunction. Boston, MA.

Bancroft, J., & Janssen, E. (2000). The dual control model of male sexual response: A theoretical approach to centrally mediated erectile dysfunction. *Neuroscience and Biobehavioral Reviews, 24*, 571–579.

Bancroft, J., Graham, C. A., Janssen, E., Sanders, S. A. (2009). The dual control model: Current status and future directions. *The Journal of Sex Research, 46*, 121–142.

Bandettini, P., & Wong, E. (2015). The future of functional MRI. In K. Uludag, K. Ugurbil, & L. Berliner (Eds.), *fMRI: From nuclear spins to brain functions* (pp. 895–929). Boston, MA: Springer. Retrieved from http://dx.doi.org/10.1007/978-1-4899-7591-1_30

Bandura, A. (1973). *Aggression: A social learning analysis.* Englewood Cliffs, NJ: Prentice Hall.

Bandura, A. (1976). *Social learning theory.* Englewood Cliffs, NJ: Prentice Hall.

Bandura, A. (1977). Self-efficacy: Toward a unifying theory of behavioral change. *Psychological Review, 84,* 191–215.

Bandura, A. (2000a). Exercise of human agency through collective efficacy. *Current Directions in Psychological Science, 9,* 75–78.

Bandura, A. (2000b). Social cognitive theory: An agentic perspective. *Annual Review of Psychology, 52,* 1–26.

Bandura, A., & Menlove, F. L. (1968). Factors determining vicarious extinction of avoidance behavior through symbolic modelling. *Journal of Personality and Social Psychology, 8,* 99–108.

Bandura, A., & Walters, R. H. (1959). *Adolescent aggression.* New York, NY: Ronald Press.

Bandura, A., & Walters, R. H. (1963). *Social learning and personality development.* New York, NY: Holt, Rinehart & Winston.

Bandura, A., Ross, D., & Ross, S. A. (1961). Transmission of aggression through imitation of aggressive models. *Journal of Abnormal and Social Psychology, 63,* 575–582.

Bandura, A., Ross, D., & Ross, S. A. (1963). Imitation of film-mediated aggressive models. *Journal of Abnormal and Social Psychology, 66,* 3–11.

Banerjee, T. D., Middleton, F., & Faraone, S. V. (2007). Environmental risk factors for attention-deficit hyperactivity disorder. *Acta Paediatrica, 96*(9), 1269–1274.

Banham, K. M. (1951). Senescence and the emotions: A genetic theory. *Journal of Genetic Psychology, 78,* 175–183.

Barasch, A., Frances, A., Hurt, S., Clarkin, J., & Cohen, S. (1985). Stability and distinctness of borderline personality disorder. *American Journal of Psychiatry, 142,* 1484–1486.

Barbaree, H. E., & Seto, M. C. (1997). Pedophilia: Assessment and treatment. In D. R. Laws & W. O'Donohue (Eds.), *Sexual deviance: Theory, assessment, and treatment* (pp. 175–193). London, UK: Guilford.

Barbaree, H., Seto, M., Serin, R. C., Amos, N., & Preston, D. L. (1994). Comparisons between sexual and non-sexual rapist sub-types. *Criminal Justice & Behavior, 21,* 95–114.

Barbato, A., & D'Avanzo, B. (2008). Efficacy of couple therapy as a treatment for depression: A meta-analysis. *Psychiatric Quarterly, 79,* 121–132.

Barber, S. J., Opitz, P. C., Martins, B., et al. (2016). Thinking about a limited future enhances the positivity of younger and older adults' recall: Support for socioemotional selectivity theory. *Memory & Cognition, 44*(6), 869-882. doi:10.3758/s13421-016-0612-0

Barbui, C., Patel, V., Ayuso-Mateos, L., & van Ommeren, M. (2011). Efficacy of antidepressants and benzodiazepines in minor depression: A systematic review and meta-analysis. *British Journal of Psychiatry, 198,* 11–16. doi:10.1192/bjp.109.076448

Barefoot, J. C. (1992). Developments in the measurement of hostility. In H. S. Friedman (Ed.), *Hostility, coping and health* (pp. 13–31). Washington, DC: American Psychological Association.

Barefoot, J. C., Dodge, K. A., Peterson, B. L., Dahlstrom, W. G., & Williams, R. B. (1989). The Cook-Medley Hostility Scale: Item content and ability to predict survival. *Psychosomatic Medicine, 51,* 46–57.

Bar-Haim, Y., Dan, O., Eshel, Y., & Sagi-Schwartz, A. (2007). Predicting children's anxiety from early attachment relationships. *Journal of Anxiety Disorders, 21,* 1061–1068.

Barkley, R. A. (1997). Behavioral inhibition, sustained attention, and executive functions: Constructing a unified theory of ADHD. *Psychological Bulletin, 121*(1), 65–94.

Barkley, R. A., & Benton, C. M. (1998). *Your defiant child: Eight steps to better behavior.* New York, NY: Guilford.

Barlow, D. H. (2002). *Anxiety and its disorders* (2nd ed.). New York, NY: Guilford.

Barlow, D. H., & Durand, V. M. (1995). Substance-related disorders. In *Abnormal psychology: An integrated approach.* New York, NY: Brooks/Cole.

Barlow, D. H., Farchione, T. J., Fairholme, C. P., Ellard, K. K., Boisseau, C. L. Allen, L. B. & Ehrenreich-May, J. (2011). *The unified protocol for transdiagnostic treatment of emotional disorders: Therapist guide.* New York, NY: Oxford University Press.

Barlow, D. H., Gorman, J. M., Shear, M. K., & Woods, S. W. (2000). Cognitive-behavioral therapy, imipramine, or their combination for panic disorder: A randomized controlled trial. *Journal of the American Medical Association, 283,* 2529–2536.

Barlow, M. R., & Freyd, J. J. (2009). Adaptive dissociation: Information processing and response to betrayal. In P. F. Dell & J. A. O'Neil (Eds.), *Dissociation and the dissociative disorders: DSM-V and beyond* (pp. 93–105). New York, NY: Routledge.

Barnes, T. E., & the Schizophrenia Consensus Group of the British Association for Psychopharmacology. (2011). Evidence-based guidelines for the pharmacological treatment of schizophrenia: Recommendations from the British Association for Psychopharmacology. *Journal of Psychopharmacology, 25,* 567–620. doi:10.1177/0269881110391123jop. sagepub.com

Barnett, P. A., Spence, J. D., Manuck, S. B., & Jennings, J. R. (1997). Psychological stress and the progression of carotid artery disease. *Journal of Hypertension, 15,* 49–55.

Barnett, W. S. (2011). Effectiveness of early educational intervention. *Science, 333*(6045), 975-978.

Baroff, G. S. (1986). *Mental retardation: Nature, cause and management* (2nd ed.). Washington, DC: Hemisphere.

Baron, M., Risch, N., Levitt, M., & Gruen, R. (1985). Familial transmission of schizotypal and borderline personality disorders. *American Journal of Psychiatry, 142,* 927–934.

Baron, R. A., & Byrne, D. (1977). *Social psychology: Understanding human interaction* (2nd ed.). Boston, MA: Allyn and Bacon.

Barrera, M., Castro, F. G., & Steiker, L. K. H. (2011). A critical analysis of approaches to the development of preventive interventions for subcultural groups. *American Journal of Community Psychology, 48*(3–4), 439–454.

Barrett, F. M. (1980). Sexual experience, birth control usage, and sex education of unmarried Canadian university students: Changes between 1968 and 1978. *Archives of Sexual Behavior, 9,* 367–390.

Barry, S. J. E., Gaughan, T. M., & Hunter, R. (2012). Schizophrenia. Systematic review 1007. *BMJ Clinical Evidence.* Retrieved from http://clinicalevidence.bmj.com/x/systematic-review/1007/overview.html

Barsky, A. J. (1992). Amplification, somatization, and the somatoform disorders. *Psychosomatics, 33,* 28–34.

Bartels, S. J., Dums, A. R., Oxman, T. E., Schneider, L., Areán, P., Alexopoulos, G., et al. (2003). Evidence-based practices in geriatric mental health care: An overview of systematic reviews and meta-analyses. *Psychiatric Clinics of North America, 26,* 971–990.

Bartels, S. J., Forester, B., Mueser, K. T., Miles, K. M., Dums, A. R., Pratt, S. I., et al. (2004). Enhanced skills training and health care management for older persons with severe mental illness. *Community Mental Health Journal, 40*(1), 75–90.

Barth, J., Schumacher, M., & Herrmann-Lingen, C. (2004). Depression as a risk factor for mortality in patients with coronary heart disease: A meta-analysis. *Psychosomatic Medicine, 66,* 812–813.

Bartholomew, A. A., Badger, P., & Milte, K. L. (1977). The psychologist as an expert witness in the criminal courts. *Australian Psychologist, 12,* 133–150.

Bartholomew, K. (1989). Attachment styles in young adults: Implications for self-control and interpersonal functioning. Unpublished doctoral dissertation, Stanford University, Stanford, CA.

Bartholomew, K. (1990). Avoidance of intimacy: An attachment perspective. *Journal of Personal and Social Relationships, 7,* 147–178.

Bartlett, C. P., Vowels, C. L., & Saucier, D. A. (2008). Meta-analyses of the effects of media images on men's body-image concerns. *Journal of Social and Clinical Psychology, 27,* 279–310.

Bartlett, P. (2000). Structures of confinement in 19th-century asylums: A comparative study using England and Ontario. *International Journal of Law and Psychiatry, 23,* 1–13.

Bastiaansen, J. A., Servaas, M. N., Marsman, J. B., Ormel, J., Nolte, I. M., Riese, H., & Aleman, A. (2014). Filling the gap: Relationship between the serotonin-transporter-linked polymorphic region and amygdala activation. *Psychological Science, 25*(11), 2058–2066.

Basu, J. (2014). Psychologists' ambivalence toward ambiguity: Relocating the projective test debate for multiple interpretative hypotheses. *SIS Journal of Projective Psychology & Mental Health, 21*(1), 25–36.

Bates, M. E., Bowden, S. C., & Barry, D. (2002). Neurocognitive impairment associated with alcohol use disorders: Implications for treatment. *Experimental and Clinical Psychopharmacology, 10,* 193–212.

Bathje, G. J., & Pryor, J. B. (2011). The relationships of public and self-stigma to seeking mental health services. *Journal of Mental Health Counseling, 33,* 161–177.

Batshaw, M. L., & Perret, Y. M. (1986). *Children with handicaps: A medical primer.* Baltimore, MD: Paul Brookes.

Battle, C., Shea, M., Johnson, D., Yen, S., Zlotnick, C., Zanarini, M., et al. (2004). Childhood maltreatment associated with adult personality disorders: Findings from the Collaborative Longitudinal Personality Disorders Study. *Journal of Personality Disorders, 18* (2), 193–211.

Bauer, N. S., & Webster-Stratton, C. (2007). Prevention of behavioral disorders in primary care. *Current Opinions in Pediatrics, 18,* 654–660.

Baumeister, E. A., Storch, E., & Geffken, G. (2008). Peer victimization in children with learning disabilities. *Child and Adolescent Social Work Journal, 25,* 11–23.

Baxter, L. R., Phelps, M. E., Mazziotta, J. C., Guze, B. H., Schwartz, J. M., & Selin, C. E. (1987). Local cerebral glucose metabolic rates in obsessive-compulsive disorder. *Archives of General Psychiatry, 44,* 211–218.

Baydala, L., Dasmussen, C., Birch, J., Sherman, J., Wikman, E., Charchun, J., Kennedy, M., & Bisanz, J. (2009). Self-beliefs and behavioural development as related to academic achievement in Canadian Aboriginal children. *Canadian Journal of School Psychology, 24,* 19–33.

Baym, C. L., & Gonsalves, B. D. (2010). Comparison of neural activity that leads to true memories, false memories, and forgetting: An fMRI study of the misinformation effect. *Cognitive, Affective, and Behavioral Neuroscience, 10,* 339–348.

Bazzo, G., Nota, L., Soresi, S., Ferrari, L., & Minnes, P. (2007). Attitudes of social service providers towards the sexuality of individuals with intellectual disability. *Journal of Applied Research in Intellectual Disabilities, 20,* 110–115.

Beail, N. & Jackson, T. (2012). The practice of individual psychodynamic psychotherapy with people who have intellectual disabilities. *Psychoanalytic Psychotherapy, 27*(2), 108–123.

Beail, N., & Jahoda, A. (2012). Working with people: Direct interventions. *Clinical psychology and people with intellectual disabilities, 97,* 121.

Beaudette, J. N., Power, J., & Stewart, L. A. (2015). *National prevalence of mental disorders among incoming federally-sentenced men offenders* (Research Report, R-357). Ottawa, ON: Correctional Service Canada.

Bebko, J. M., Perry, A., & Bryson, S. E. (1996). Multiple method validation study of Facilitated Communication: II. Individual differences and subgroup results. *Journal of Autism and Developmental Disorders, 26,* 19–42.

Beblo, T., Driessen, M., Mertens, M., Wingenfeld, K., Piefke, M., Rullkoetter, N., et al. (2006). Functional MRI correlates of the recall of unresolved life events in borderline personality disorder. *Psychological Medicine, 36,* 845–856.

Bech, P., Cialdella, P., Haugh, M. C., Birkett, M. A., Hours, A., Boissel, J. P., & Tollefson, G. D. (2000). Meta-analysis of randomised controlled trials of fluoxetine v. placebo and tricyclic antidepressants in the short-term treatment of major depression. *British Journal of Psychiatry, 176,* 421–428.

Beck, A. T. (1963). Thinking and depression: I. Idiosyncratic content and cognitive distortions. *Archives of General Psychiatry, 9,* 36–46.

Beck, A. T. (1967). *Depression: Causes and treatment.* Philadelphia, PA: University of Pennsylvania Press.

Beck, A. T. (1976). *Cognitive therapy and the emotional disorders.* New York, NY: International Universities Press.

Beck, A. T. (1983). Cognitive therapy of depression: New perspectives. In P. J. Clayton & J. E. Barrett (Eds.), *Treatment of depression: Old controversies and new approaches* (pp. 265–290). New York, NY: Raven.

Beck, A. T. (1996). Beyond belief: A theory of modes, personality, and psychopathology. In P. M. Salkovskis (Ed.), *Frontiers of cognitive therapy* (pp. 1–25). New York, NY: Oxford University Press.

Beck, A. T., & Dozois, D. J. A. (2011). Cognitive therapy: Current status and future directions. *Annual Review of Medicine, 62,* 397–409. doi:10.1146/annurev-med-052209-100032

Beck, A. T., & Dozois, D. J. A. (2014). Cognitive theory and therapy: Past, present and future. In S. Bloch, S. A. Green, & J. Holmes (Eds.), *Psychiatry – past, present and prospect* (pp. 366-382). Oxford, England: Oxford University Press.

Beck, A. T., & Emery, G. (1985). *Anxiety disorders and phobias: A cognitive perspective.* New York, NY: Basic Books.

Beck, A. T., & Rector, N. A. (2000). Cognitive therapy of schizophrenia: A new therapy for the new millennium. *American Journal of Psychotherapy, 54*(3), 291–300.

Beck, A. T., Davis, D. D., & Freeman, A. (2015). *Cognitive therapy of personality disorders* (3rd ed.). New York, NY: Guilford.

Beck, A. T., Freeman, A., & Davis, D. D. (2004). *Cognitive therapy of personality disorders* (2nd ed.). New York: Guilford.

Beck, A. T., Freeman, A., Pretzer, J., Davis, D. D., Fleming, B., Ottaviani, R., et al. (1990). *Cognitive therapy of personality disorders.* New York, NY: Guilford.

Beck, A. T., Rector, N. A., Stolar, N., & Grant, P. (2009). *Schizophrenia: Cognitive theory, research, and therapy.* New York, NY: Guilford.

Beck, A. T., Rush, P. J., Shaw, B. F., & Emery, G. (1979). *Cognitive therapy of depression.* New York, NY: Guilford.

Beck, A. T., Ward, C. H., Mendelson, M., Mock, J. E., & Erbaugh, J. K. (1962). Reliability of psychiatric diagnosis: II. A study of consistency of clinical judgements and ratings. *American Journal of Psychiatry, 119,* 351–357.

Beck, J. C. (1978). Social influences on the prognosis of schizophrenia. *Schizophrenia Bulletin, 4*(1), 86–101.

Beck, J. G. (1993). Vaginismus. In W. O'Donohue & J. G. Greer (Eds.), *Handbook of sexual dysfunctions: Assessment and treatment* (pp. 381–397). Boston, MA: Allyn and Bacon.

Becker, E. S., Rinck, M., Turke, V., Kause, P., Goodwin, R., Neumer, S., & Margraf, J. (2007). Epidemiology of specific phobia subtypes: Findings from the Dresden Mental Health Study. *European Psychiatry, 22,* 69–74.

Becker, J. B., Breedlove, S. M., Crews, D., & McCarthy, M. M. (Eds.). (2002). *Behavioral endocrinology.* Cambridge, MA: MIT Press.

Becker, K. A. (2003). *History of the Stanford-Binet Intelligence Scales: Content and psychometrics.* (Stanford-Binet Intelligence Scales, Fifth Edition Assessment Service Bulletin No. 1). Itasca, IL: Riverside.

Becker, K., El-Faddagh, M., Schmidt, M. H., Esser, G., & Laucht, M. (2008). Interaction of dopamine transporter genotype with prenatal smoke exposure on ADHD symptoms. *Journal of Pediatrics, 152,* 263–269. doi:10.1016/j.jpeds.2007.07.004

Becker-Blease, K. A., Deater-Deckard, K., Eley, T., Freyd, J. J., Stevenson, J., & Plomin, R. (2004). A genetic analysis of individual differences in dissociative behaviors in childhood and adolescence. *Journal of Child Psychology and Psychiatry, 45,* 522–532.

Beery, K. E., & Beery, N. A. (2010). *The Beery–Buktenica developmental test of visual-motor integration (6th ed.).* Bloomington, MN: Pearson Inc.

Beevers, C. G., Strong, D. R., Meyer, B., Pilkonis, P. A., & Miller, I. W. (2007). Efficiently assessing negative cognition in depression: An item response theory analysis of the Dysfunctional Attitude Scale. *Psychological Assessment, 19*(2), 199.

Beirness, D. J., Beasley, E., & LeCavalier, J. (2009). The accuracy of evaluations by Drug Recognition Experts in Canada. *Canadian Society of Forensic Sciences Journal, 42,* 75–79.

Beirness, D. J., LeCavalier, J., & Singhal, D. (2007). Evaluation of the Drug Evaluation and Classification program: A critical review of the evidence. *Traffic Injury Prevention, 8,* 368–376.

Belanger, A., Martel, L., & Caron-Malenfant, E. (2005). *Population projections for Canada, provinces and territories: 2005–2031.* Statistics Canada Demography Division. Catalogue no. 91-520-XIE.

Bellani, M., Marzi, C. A., Savazzi, S., Perlini, C., Cerruti, S., Ferro, A., et al. (2010). Laterality effects in schizophrenia and bipolar disorder. *Experimental Brain Research, 201* (2), 339–344. doi:10.1007/s00221-009-2021-0

Belsky, J. (1997). Theory testing, effect-size evaluation, and differential susceptibility to rearing influence: The case of mothering and attachment. *Child Development, 68,* 598–600. doi:10.2307/1132110

Bemporad, J. R. (1992). *Psychoanalytically orientated psychotherapy.* New York, NY: Guilford.

Bemporad, J. R. (1997). Cultural and historical aspects of eating disorders. *Theoretical Medicine, 18,* 401–420.

Ben-Porath, Y. S., & Tellegen, A. (2008). *Minnesota Multiphasic Personality Inventory—2 Restructured Form; Manual for administration, scoring, and interpretation.* Minneapolis, MN: University of Minnesota Press.

Benazzi, F. (2000). Late-life chronic depression: A 399-case study in private practice. *International Journal of Geriatric Depression, 15,* 1–6.

Bender, L. (1938). The Visual Motor Gestalt Test and its clinical use. *Archives of Neurology and Psychiatry, 30,* 514–537.

Bender, W. N., & Wall, M. E. (1994). Social-emotional development of students with learning disabilities. *Learning Disability Quarterly, 17*(4), 323–341.

Bennett, A. E. (1947). Mad doctors. *Journal of Nervous and Mental Disease, 106,* 11–18.

Bennett, M. E., Wilson, A. L., Genderson, M., & Saperstein, A. M. (2013). Smoking cessation in people with schizophrenia. *Current Drug Abuse Reviews, 6*(3), 180–190.

Benowitz, N. (1990). Clinical pharmacology of caffeine. *Annual Review of Medicine, 41,* 277–288.

Bentall, R. P. (1994). Cognitive biases and abnormal beliefs: Towards a model of persecutory delusions. In A. S. David & J. C. Cutting (Eds.), *The neuropsychology of schizophrenia* (pp. 337–360). Brain damage, behaviour and cognition series. London, UK: Lawrence Erlbaum.

Berard, G. (1993). *Hearing equals behavior.* New Canaan, CT: Keats.

Bergem, A. L., Engedal, K., & Kringlen, E. (1997). The role of heredity in late-onset Alzheimer disease and vascular dementia: A twin study. *Archives of General Psychiatry, 54*(3), 264–270.

Bergeron, S., Brown, C., Lord, M. J., Oala, M., Binik, Y. M., & Khalifé, S. (2002). Physical therapy for vulvar vestibulitis syndrome: A retrospective study. *Journal of Sex and Marital Therapy, 28,* 183–192.

Bergeron, S., Pukall, C. F., & Mailloux, G. (2008). Vulvar pain syndrome: Treatment and quantitative sensory testing. In A. P. Baranowski, P. Abrams, & M. Fall (Eds.), *Urogenital pain in clinical practice* (pp. 295–307). New York, NY: Informa Healthcare.

Bergin, A. E. (1971). The evaluation of therapeutic outcomes. In A. E. Bergin & S. L. Garfield (Eds.), *The evaluation of therapeutic outcomes* (pp. 217–270). New York, NY: Wiley.

Beringer, V.W., Richards, T.L., & Abbot, R.D. (2015). Differential diagnosis of dysgraphia, dyslexia, and OWL LD: behavioral and neuroimaging evidence. *Read Writ 28*, 1119–1153.

Berkman, L. F., & Syme, S. L. (1979). Social networks, host resistance, and mortality: A nine-year follow-up study of Alameda County residents. *American Journal of Epidemiology, 109*, 186–204/

Berkman, L. F., Blumenthal, J., Burg, M., Carney, R. M., Catellier, D., Cowan, M.J., ... & Kaufmann, P. G. (2003). Effects of treating depression and low perceived social support on clinical events after myocardial infarction: the Enhancing Recovery in Coronary Heart Disease Patients (ENRICHD) Randomized Trial. *Journal of the American Medical Association 289*(23), 3106–3116.

Berman, L. A., Berman, J. R., Chhabra, S., & Goldstein, I. (2001). Novel approaches to female sexual dysfunction. *Expert Opinion on Investigating Drugs, 10*, 85–95.

Berman, W. H., & Sperling, M. B. (1994). The structure and function of adult attachment. In M. B. Sperling & W. H. Berman (Eds.), *Attachment in adults: Clinical and developmental perspectives* (pp. 3–28). New York, NY: Guilford.

Bernstein, A., Chorpita, B. F., Daleiden, E. L., Ebesutani, C. K., & Rosenblatt, A. (2015). Building an evidence-informed service array: Considering evidence-based programs as well as their practice elements. *Journal of Consulting and Clinical Psychology, 83*, 1085–1096.

Bernstein, D. P., Cohen, P., Velez, C. N., Schwab-Stone, M., Siever, L. J., & Shinsato, L. (1993). Prevalence and stability of the DSM-III-R personality disorders in a community-based survey of adolescents. *American Journal of Psychiatry, 50*, 1237–1243.

Bernstein, S. M., Steiner, B. W., Glaiser, J. T. D., & Muir, C. F. (1981). Changes in patients with gender identity problems after parental death. *American Journal of Psychiatry, 138*, 41–45.

Berrios, G. (1995). Mental retardation [clinical section II]. In G. Berrios & R. Porter (Eds.), *A history of clinical psychiatry* (pp. 225–238). London, UK: Athlone Press.

Berry-Kravis, E., Raspa, M., Loggin-Hester, L., Bishop, E., Holiday, D., & Bailey, D. B., Jr. (2010). Seizures in Fragile X syndrome: Characteristics and comorbid diagnoses. *American Journal on Intellectual and Developmental Disabilities, 115*, 461–472.

Berry, S. M., Broglio, K., Bunker, M., Jayewardene, A., Olin, B., & Rush, A. J. (2013). A patient-level meta-analysis of studies evaluating vagus nerve stimulation therapy for treatment-resistant depression. *Medical Devices (Auckl), 6*, 17-35.

Bertero, E. B., & Antunes, D. L. (2015). Surgical treatment of erectile dysfunction. *Sexual Medicine Reviews, 3*, 316-327.

Bethell, L. (1984). *The Cambridge history of Latin America: Vol. I. Colonial Latin America.* New York, NY: Cambridge University Press.

Betz, N. E., Mintz, L., & Speakmon, G. (1994). Gender differences in the accuracy of self-reported weight. *Sex Roles, 30*, 543–551.

Beutler, L. E., Malik, M., Alimohamed, S., Harwood, T. M.,Talebi, H., Noble, S., et al. (2004). Therapist variables. In M. J.Lambert (Ed.), *Bergin and Garfield's handbook of psychotherapy and behavior change* (5th ed., pp. 227–306). New York:, NY Wiley.

Bewernick, B. H., Hurlemann, R., Matusch, A., Kayser, S., Grubert, C., Hadrysiewicz, B., et al. (2010). Nucleus accumbens deep brain stimulation decreases ratings of depression and anxiety in treatment-resistant depression. *Biological Psychiatry, 67*, 110–116.

Beynon, S., Soares-Weiser, K., Woolacott, N., Duffy, S., & Geddes, J. R. (2008). Psychosocial interventions for the prevention of relapse in bipolar disorder: Systematic review of controlled trials. *British Journal of Psychiatry, 192*, 5–11.

Bialystok, E., Craik, F. I. M., & Freedman, M. (2007). Bilingualism as a protection against the onset of symptoms of dementia. *Neuropsychologia, 45*, 459–464.

Bianchi, K. N, & Carter, M. M. (2012). An experimental analysis of disgust sensitivity and fear of contagion in spider and blood injection injury phobia. *Journal of Anxiety Disorders, 26*(7), 753–761. doi: 10.1016/j.janxdis.2012.06.004.

Biedel, D. C., & Turner, S. M. (1988). Comorbidity of test anxiety and other anxiety disorders in children. *Journal for Abnormal Child Psychology, 16*, 275–287.

Biederman, J., Petty, C. R., Dolan, C., Hughes, S., Mick, E., Monuteaux, M. C., & Faraone, S. V. (2008). The long-term longitudinal course of oppositional defiant disorder and conduct disorder in ADHD boys: Findings from a controlled 10-year prospective longitudinal follow-up study. *Psychological Medicine, 38*, 1027–1036. doi:10.1017/S0033291707002668

Biederman, J., Petty, C. R., Evans, M., Small, J., & Faraone, S. V. (2010). How persistent is ADHD? A controlled 10-year follow-up study of boys with ADHD. *Psychiatry Research, 177*(3), 299–304. doi:10.1016/j.psychres.2009.12.010

Billings, J. H., Scherwitz, L. W., Sullivan, R., Sparler, S., & Ornish, D. M. (1996). The Lifestyle Heart Trial: Comprehensive treatment and group support therapy. In R. Allen & S. Scheidt (Eds.), *Heart and mind: The practice of cardiac psychology* (pp. 233–253). Washington, DC: American Psychological Association.

Binder, J. L., Strupp, H. S., & Henry, W. P. (1995). Psychodynamic therapies in practice: Time-limited psychodynamic psychotherapy. In B. Bongar & L. E. Beutler (Eds.), *Comprehensive textbook of psychotherapy: Theory and practice* (pp. 48–63). New York, NY: Oxford University Press.

Binik, Y. M. (2010a). The DSM diagnostic criteria for dyspareunia. *Archives of Sexual Behavior, 39*, 292–303.

Binik, Y. M. (2010b). The DSM diagnostic criteria for vaginismus. *Archives of Sexual Behavior, 39*, 278–291.

Binik, Y. M., Bergeron, S., & Khalifé, S. (2007). Dyspareunia and vaginismus: So-called sexual pain. In S. R. Leiblum (Ed.), *Principles and practices of sex therapy* (4th ed., pp. 124–156). New York, NY: Guilford.

Birbaumer, N., Wolfgang, G., Diedrich, O., Klose, U., Erb, M., Lotze, M., et al. (1998). fMRI reveals amygdala activation to human faces in social phobics. *Neuroreport, 9*, 1223–1226.

Birchall, H. (1999). Interpersonal psychotherapy in the treatment of eating disorders. *European Eating Disorders Review, 7*, 315–320.

Bird, V., Premkumar, T., Kendall, C., Whittington, C., Mitchell, J., & Kuipers, E. (2010). Early intervention services, cognitive-behavioural therapy and family intervention in early psychosis: Systematic review. *British Journal of Psychiatry, 197*(5), 350–356.

Birmaher, B., Axelson, D., Strober, M., Gill, M. K., Valeri, S., Chiappetta, L., et al. (2006). Clinical course of children and adolescents with bipolar spectrum disorders. *Archives of General Psychiatry, 63*, 175–183.

Birmaher, B., Ryan, N. D., Williamson, D. E., Brent, D. A., Kaufman, J., Dahl, R. E., et al. (1996). Childhood and adolescent depression: A review of the past 10 years: Part 1. *Journal of the Academy of Child and Adolescent Psychiatry, 35*, 1427–1439.

Birnbaum, K. (1914). *Die psychopathischen verbrecher* (2nd ed.). Leipzig, Germany: Thième.

Birren, J. E., & Renner, V. J. (1980). Concepts and issues of mental health and aging. In J. E. Birren & R. B. Sloane (Eds.), *Handbook of mental health and aging* (pp. 3–33). Englewood Cliffs, NJ: Prentice-Hall.

Bishop, M., & Felming, A. R. (2015). Rational emotive behavior therapy. In F. Chan, N. L. Berven, & K. R. Thomas (Eds.), *Counseling theories and techniques for rehabilitation and mental health professionals* (2nd ed., pp. 109–132). New York, NY: Springer Publishing Company.

Bishop, S., Gahagan, S., & Lord, C. (2007). Re-examining the core features of autism: A comparison of autism spectrum disorder and fetal alcohol spectrum disorder. *Journal of Child Psychology and Psychiatry, 48*, 1111–1121.

Bishop, S. L., Havdahl, K. A., Huerta, M., & Lord, C. (2016). Subdimensions of social-communication impairment in autism spectrum disorder. *Journal of Child Psychology and Psychiatry, 57*, 909–916.

Bittner, A., Egger, H. L., Erkanli, A., Costello, E. J., Foley, D. L., & Angold, A. (2007).What do childhood anxiety disorders predict? *Journal of Child Psychology and Psychiatry, 48*, 1174–1183.

Bjorntorp, P. (2001). Do stress reactions cause abdominal obesity and comorbidities? *Obesity Reviews, 2*, 73–86.

Black, D. N., Seritan, A. L., Taber, K. H., & Hurley, R. A. (2004). Conversion hysteria: Lessons from functional imaging. *Journal of Neuropsychiatry & Clinical Neuroscience, 16*, 245–251.

Black, D. S., O'Reilly, G. A., Olmstead, R., Breen, E. C., Irwin, M. R. (2015). Mindfulness meditation and improvement in sleep quality and daytime impairment among older adults with sleep disturbances: A randomized clinical trial. *JAMA Intern Med. 175*(4), 494–501. doi:10.1001/jamainternmed.2014.8081

Black, D. W. (2000). The epidemiology and phenomenology of compulsive sexual behavior. *CNS Spectrums, 5*, 26–72.

Blackburn, R. (1992). Criminal behavior, personality disorder, and mental confusion: The origins of confusion. *Criminal Behavior and Mental Health, 2*, 66–77.

Blackburn, S. (2014). *Maternal, fetal, & neonatal physiology, fourth edition.* Maryland Heights, MO: Elsevier Health Sciences.

Blain-Arcaro, C., & Vaillancourt, T. (2017; In press). Longitudinal associations between externalizing problems and symptoms of depression in children and adolescents. *Journal of Clinical Child and Adolescent Psychology*, 1–12. doi: 10.1080/15374416.2016.1270830

Blair, R. J. R. (2001). Neurocognitive models of aggression, the antisocial personality disorders, and psychopathy. *Journal of Neurology, Neurosurgery, & Psychiatry, 71*, 727–731.

Blair, R. J. R. (2003). Neurobiological basis of psychopathy. *British Journal of Psychiatry, 182*, 5–7.

Blair, R. J. R., Peschardt, K. S., Budhani, S., Mitchell, D. G. V., & Pine, D. S. (2006). The development of psychopathy. *Journal of Child Psychology and Psychiatry, 47*, 262–275.

Blais, M. A., Baity, M. R., & Hopwood, C. J. (Eds.). (2010). *Clinical applications of the Personality Assessment Inventory*. New York, NY: Taylor & Francis.

Blake, D. D., Weathers, F. W., Nagy, L. M., Kaloupek, D. G., Klauminzer, G., Charney, D. S., et al. (1990). A clinician rating scale for assessing current and lifetime PTSD: The CAPS-1. *The Behavior Therapist, 13*, 187–188.

Blake, E., Dobson, K. S., Sheptycki, A. R., & Drapeau, M. (2016). Changes in cognitive errors over the course of cognitive therapy for depression. *Journal of Cognitive Psychotherapy, 30*(1), 16–34.

Blanchard, R. (2013). A dissenting opinion on DSM-5 pedophilic disorder. *Archives of Sexual Behavior, 42*, 675.

Blanchard, R., & Hucker, S. (1991). Age, transvestism, bondage, and concurrent paraphilic activities in 117 fatal cases of autoerotic asphyxia. *British Journal of Psychiatry, 159*, 371–377.

Blanchard, R., Christensen, B. K., Strong, S. M., Cantor, J. M., Kuban, M. E., Klassen, P., et al. (2002). Retrospective self-reports of childhood accidents causing unconsciousness in phallometrically diagnosed pedophiles. *Archives of Sexual Behavior, 31*, 511–526.

Blanchard, R., Klassen, P., Dickey, R., Kuban, M.E., & Blak, T. (2001). Sensitivity specificity of the phallometric test for pedophilia in nonadmitting sex offenders. *Psychological Assessment, 13*, 118–26.

Blanchard, R., Kolla, N. J., Cantor, J. M., Klassen, P. E., Dickey, R., Kuban, M. E., & Blak, T. (2007). IQ, handedness, and pedophilia in adult male patients stratified by referral source. *Sexual Abuse: A Journal of Research and Treatment, 19*, 285–309.

Blanchflower, D. G., & Oswald, A. J. (2008). Is well-being U-shaped over the life cycle? *Social Sciences and Medicine, 66*, 1733–1749.

Bland, R., Newman, S., Dyck, R., & Orn, H. (1990). Prevalence of psychiatric disorders and suicide attempts in a prison population. *Canadian Journal of Psychiatry, 35*, 407–413.

Blankstein, K. R., Lumley, C. H., & Crawford, A. (2007). Perfectionism, hopelessness, and suicide ideation: Revisions to diathesis-stress and specific vulnerabiltiy models. *Journal of Rational-Emotive and Cognitive-Behavior Therapy, 25*, 279–319.

Blatt, B., & Kaplan, F. M. (1966). *Christmas in purgatory: A photographic essay on mental retardation*. Boston, MA: Allyn and Bacon.

Blatt, S. J. (2004). *Experiences of depression: Theoretical, clinical, and research perspectives*. Washington, DC: American Psychological Association.

Blatt, S. J., Quinlan, D. M., Chevron, E. S., McDonald, C., & Zuroff, D. (1982). Dependency and self-criticism: Psychological dimensions of depression. *Journal of Consulting and Clinical Psychology, 50*, 113–124.

Blazer, D. (1990). *Emotional problems in later life*. New York, NY: Springer.

Blazer, D. G. (2003). Depression in late life: Review and commentary. *Journal of Gerontology: Medical Sciences, 58A*, 249–265.

Bleuler, E. (1950). *Dementia praecox, or the group of schizophrenias* (J. Zinkin, Trans.). New York, NY: International Universities Press. (Original work published 1911).

Bliwise, D. L. (2004). Sleep disorders in Alzheimer's disease and other dementias. *Clinical Cornerstone, 6*(1), S16–S28.

Blonigen, D. M., Carlson, S. R., Krueger, R. F., & Patrick, C. J. (2003). A twin study of self-reported psychopathic personality traits. *Personality and Individual Differences, 35*, 179–197.

Blonigen, D. M., Hicks, B. M., Krueger, R. F., Patrick, C. J., & Iacono, W. G. (2005). Psychopathic personality traits: Heritability and genetic overlap with internalizing and externalizing psychopathology. *Psychological Medicine, 35*, 637–648.

Bloom, B. L. (1984). *Community mental health* (2nd ed.). Monterey, CA: Brooks/Cole.

Bloom, D.E., Cafiero, E.T., Jané-Llopis, E., Abrahams-Gessel, S., Bloom, L.R., Fathima, S., . . . Weinstein, C. (2011). *The global economic burden of noncommunicable diseases*. Geneva, Switzerland: World Economic Forum.

Blum, H. P. (1991). Sadomasochism in the psychoanalytic process, within and beyond the pleasure principle: Discussion. *Journal of the American Psychoanalytic Association, 39*, 431–450.

Blumenthal, S. (1990, December 26). Youth suicide: The physician's role in suicide prevention. *Journal of the American Medical Association, 264*, 3194–3196.

Boak, A., Hamilton, H. A., Adlaf, E. M., & Mann, R.E. (2015). Drug use among Ontario students 2015. CAMH Research Document No. 41. Toronto, ON: Centre for Addiction and Mental Health.

Boardman, L. A., & Stockdale, C. K. (2009). Sexual pain. *Clinical Obstetrics and Gynecology, 52*, 682–690.

Bockoven, J. S. (1963). *Moral treatment in American psychiatry*. New York: Springer.

Boehme, S., Miltner, W., & Staube, T. (2015). Neural correlates of self-focused attention in social anxiety. *Scan, 10*, 856–862.

Boelen, P. A., & Reijntjes, A. (2009). Intolerance of uncertainty and social anxiety. *Journal of Anxiety Disorders, 23*, 130–135.

Boer, D. P., Tough, S., & Haaven, J. (2004). Assessment of risk manageability of intellectually disabled sex offenders. *Journal of Applied Research in Intellectual Disabilities, 17*(4), 275–283.

Boerma, T., Harrison, J., Jakob, R., Mathers, C., Schmider, A., & Weber, S. (2016). Revising the ICD: Explaining the WHO approach. *The Lancet, 388*, 2476–2477.

Bögels, S. M., & Mansell, W. (2004). Attention processes in the maintenance and treatment of social phobia: Hypervigilance, avoidance and self-focused attention. *Clinical Psychology Review, 24*, 827–856.

Boggs, C. D., Morey, L. C., Skodol, A. E., Shea, M., Sanislow, C. A., Grilo, C. M., et al. (2005). Differential impairment as an indicator of sex bias in DSM-IV criteria for four personality disorders. *Psychological Assessment, 17*, 492–496. doi:10.1037/1040-3590.17.4.492.

Bolognesi, F., Baldwin, D. S., & Ruini, C. (2014). Psychological interventions in the treatment of generalized anxiety disorder: A structured review. *Journal of Psychopathology, 20*, 111126.

Bond, I., & Evans, D. (1967). Avoidance therapy: Its use in two cases of underwear fetishism. *Canadian Medical Association Journal, 96*, 1160–1162.

Bond, M. A. (2016). Leading the way on diversity: Community psychology's evolution from invisible to individual to contextual. *American Journal of Community Psychology, 58*(3–4), 259–268.

Bonnie, R., & Monahan, J. (2005). From coercion to contract: Reframing the debate on mandated community treatment for people with mental disorders. *Law & Human Behavior, 29*, 485–503.

Book, A. S., Quinsey, V. L., & Langford, D. (2007). Psychopathy and the perception of affect and vulnerability. *Criminal Justice and Behavior, 34*, 531–544. doi:10.1177/0093854806293554

Booth, T., & Booth, W. (1996). Sounds of silence: Narrative research with inarticulate subjects. *Disability and Society, 11*, 55–69.

Bora, E., Lin, A., Wood, S. J., Yung, A. R., McGorry, P. D., & Pantelis, C. (2014). Cognitive deficits in youth with familial and clinical high risk to psychosis: A systematic review and meta-analysis. *Acta Psychiatrica Scandinavica, 130*(1), 1–15.

Borduin, C. M., Mann, B. J., Cone, L. T., Henggeler, S. W., Fucci, B. R., Blaske, D. M., & Williams, R. A. (1995). Multisystemic treatment of serious juvenile offenders: Long-term prevention of criminality and violence. *Journal of Consulting and Clinical Psychology, 63*, 569–578.

Borkovec, T. D., & Hu, S. (1990). The effect of worry on cardiovascular response to phobic imagery. *Behaviour Research and Therapy, 28*, 69–73.

Borkovec, T. D., & Inz, J. (1990). The nature of worry in generalized anxiety disorder: A predominance of thought activity. *Behaviour Research and Therapy, 28*, 153–158.

Borkovec, T. D., & Roemer, L. (1995). Perceived functions of worry among generalized anxiety disorder subjects: Distraction from more emotionally distressing topics? *Journal of Behavior Therapy and Experimental Psychiatry, 26*, 25–30.

Borkovec, T. D., Abel, J. L., & Newman, H. (1995). Effects of psychotherapy on comorbid conditions in generalized anxiety disorder. *Journal of Consulting and Clinical Psychology, 63*, 479–483.

Borkovec, T. D., Lyonsfields, J. D., Wiser, S. L., & Deihl, L. (1993). The role of worrisome thinking in the suppression of cardiovascular response to phobic imagery. *Behaviour Research and Therapy, 31*, 321–324.

Borkovec, T. D., Ray, W. J., & Stober, J. (1998). Worry: A cognitive phenomenon intimately linked to affective, physiological, and interpersonal behavioral processes. *Cognitive Therapy and Research, 22*, 561–576.

Bornovalova, M. A., Hicks, B. M., Iacono, W. G., & McGue, M. (2009). Stability, change, and heritability of borderline personality disorder traits from adolescence to adulthood: A longitudinal twin study. *Development and Psychopathology, 21*, 1335–1353. doi:10.1017/S0954579409990186

Bornstein, M. H., & Lamb, M. E. (2010). *Developmental science: An advanced textbook*. New York, NY: Psychology Press.

Bornstein, R. F. (2011). Toward a multidimensional model of personality disorder diagnosis: Implications for DSM-5. *Journal of Personality Assessment, 93*, 362–369. doi:10.1080/00223891.2011.577474

Bornstein, R. F., & Gold, S. H. (2008). Comorbidity of personality disorders and somatization disorder: A meta-analytic review. *Journal of Psychopathology and Behavioral Assessment, 30*(2), 154–161.

Borruto, F., Comparetto, C., Acanfora, L., Bertini, G., & Rubaltelli, F. F. (2002). Role of ultrasound evaluation of nuchal translucency in prenatal diagnosis. *Clinical Experimental Obstetrics & Gynecology, 29*, 235–241.

Borthwick-Duffy, S. A. (1994). Epidemiology and prevalence of psychopathology in people with mental retardation. *Journal of Consulting and Clinical Psychology, 62*, 17–27.

Bosanac, P., & Castle, D. J. (2013). Schizophrenia and depression. *The Medical Journal of Australia, 199*(6 Suppl), S36–39.

Boscarino, J. A. (1997). Diseases among men 20 years after exposure to severe stress: Implications for clinical research and medical care. *Psychosomatic Medicine, 59*, 605–614.

Boscarino, J. A. (2008). A prospective study of PTSD and early-age heart disease mortality among Vietnam veterans: Implications for surveillance and prevention. *Psychosomatic Medicine, 70*, 668–676.

Bosch, J. A., de Geus, E. J. C., Ligtenberg, T. J. M., Nazmi, K., Veerman, E. C. I., Hoogstraten, J., & Amerongen, A. V. N. (2000). Salivary MUC5B-mediated adherence (Ex Vivo) of *Helicobacter pylori* during acute stress. *Psychosomatic Medicine, 62*, 40–49.

Botha, F. B., Shamblaw, A. L., & Dozois, D. J. A. (2017). Reducing the stigma of depression among Asian students: A social norm approach. *Journal of Cross-Cultural Psychology, 48*, 113–131.

Botvin, G. J. (2000). *Life skills training.* Princeton, NJ: Princeton Health Press.

Botvin, G. J., Baker, E., Dusenbury, L., Botvin, E. M., & Diaz, T. (1995). Long-term follow-up results of a randomized drug abuse prevention trial in a white middle-class population. *Journal of the American Medical Association, 273*(14), 1106–1112.

Botvin, G. J., Baker, E., Dusenbury, L., Tortu, S., & Botvin, E. M. (1990). Preventing adolescent drug abuse through a multimodal cognitive-behavioral approach: Results of a three-year study. *Journal of Consulting and Clinical Psychology, 58*, 437–446.

Bouaboula, M., Rinaldi, M., Carayon, P., Carillon, C., Delpech, B., Shire, D., Le-Fur, G., & Casellas, P. (1993). Cannabinoid-receptor expression in human leukocytes. *European Journal of Biochemistry, 214*(1), 173–180.

Bouchard, C. (1994). Discours et parcours de la prévention de la violence: Une réflexion sur les valeurs en jeu. *Canadian Journal of Community Mental Health, 13*(2), 37–46.

Bouma, E. M. C., Ormel, J., Verhulst, F. C., & Oldehinkel, A. J. (2008). Stressful life events and depressive problems in early adolescent boys and girls: The influence of parental depression, temperament and family environment. *Journal of Affective Disorders, 105*(1–3), 185–193.

Bouton, M. E., Mineka, S., & Barlow, D. H. (2001). A modern learning theory perspective on the etiology of panic disorder. *Psychological Bulletin, 108*, 4–32.

Bowden, S., Saklofske, D. H., & Weiss, L. G. (2011). Augmenting the core battery with supplementary subtests: Wechsler Adult Intelligence Scale-IV measurement invariance across the United States and Canada. *Assessment, 18*, 133–140.

Bowen, R. C., Offord, D. R., & Boyle, M. H. (1990). The prevalence of overanxious disorder and separation anxiety disorder: Results from the Ontario Child Health Study. *Journal of the American Academy of Child and Adolescent Psychiatry, 29*(5), 753–758.

Bowie, C. R., Leung, W. W., Reichenberg, A., McClure, M. M., Patterson, T. L., Heaton, R. K., & Harvey, P. D. (2008). Predicting schizophrenia patients' real world behavior with specific neuropsychological and functional capacity measures. *Biological Psychiatry, 63*, 505–511.

Bowie, C. R., McGurk, S. R., Mausbach, B., Patterson, T. L., & Harvey, P. D. (2012). Combined cognitive remediation and functional skills training for schizophrenia: Effects on cognition, functional competence, and real-world behavior. *American Journal of Psychiatry, 169*(7), 710–718.

Bowlby, J. (1973). *Attachment and loss.* New York, NY: Basic Books.

Bowlby, J. (1977). The making and breaking of affectional bonds: 1. Aetiology and psychopathology in the light of attachment theory. *British Journal of Psychiatry, 30*, 301–210.

Bowlby, J. (1988). *A secure base: Parent-child attachment and healthy human development.* New York, NY: Basic Books.

Boyce, W. T., & Ellis, B. J. (2005). Biological sensitivity to context: A. An evolutionary–developmental theory of the origins and functions of stress reactivity. *Development and Psychopathology, 17*, 271–301.

Boylan, K., Vaillancourt, T., Boyle, M., & Szatmari, P. (2007). Comorbidity of internalizing disorders in children with oppositional defiant disorder. *European Journal of Child and Adolescent Psychiatry, 16* (8), 484–494.

Boyle, M., & Offord, D. (1990). Primary prevention of conduct disorder: Issues and prospects. *Journal of the American Academy of Child and Adolescent Psychiatry, 29*, 227–233.

Boyle, M. H., & Offord, D. R. (1991). Psychiatric disorder and substance use in adolescence. *Canadian Journal of Psychiatry, 36*, 699–705.

Boysen, G. A., & VanBergen, A. (2013a). A review of dissociative identity disorder research: Response to critics. *The Journal of Nervous and Mental Disease, 201*(5), 440–443.

Boysen, G. A., & VanBergen, A. (2013b). A review of published research on adult dissociative identity disorder: 2000–2010. *Journal of Nervous and Mental Disease, 201*(1), 5–11.

Boysen, G., & VanBergen, A. (2014). Simulation of multiple personalities: A review of research comparing diagnosed and simulated dissociative identity disorder. *Clinical Psychology Review, 34*(1), 14–28.

Braamhorst, W., Lobbestael, J., Emons, W. H. M., Arntz, A., Witteman, C. L. M., & Bekker, M. H. J. (2015). Sex bias in classifying borderline and narcissistic personality disorder. *Journal of Nervous and Mental Disease, 203*, 804–808.

Brabban, A., Tai, S., & Turkington, D. (2009). Predictors of outcome in brief cognitive behavior therapy for schizophrenia. *Schizophrenia Research, 35*(5), 859–864.

Braden, M. L. (1989). *Logo reading system.* Obtainable at 219 East St. Vrain, Colorado Springs, CO.

Bradford, J. M. (2000). The treatment of sexual deviation using a pharmacological approach. *Journal of Sex Research, 37*, 248–257.

Bradford, J. M. (2001). The neurobiology, neuropharmacology, and pharmacological treatment of paraphilias and compulsive sexual behavior. *Canadian Journal of Psychiatry, 46*, 26–34.

Bradley, E., & Lofchy, J. (2005). Learning disability in the accident and emergency department. *Advances in Psychiatric Treatment, 11*(1), 45–57.

Bradley, E. A., & Summers, J. (2003). Developmental disability and behavioral, emotional and psychiatric disturbances. In I. Brown & M. Percy (Eds.), *Developmental disability in Ontario* (2nd ed., pp. 751–774). Toronto, ON: Ontario Association on Developmental Disability.

Bradley, E. A., Bolton, P. F., & Bryson, S. (2004). Psychiatric co-morbidity in persons with intellectual disabilities with and without autism. *Journal of Intellectual Disability Research, 48*, 296.

Bradley, E. A., Summers, J., Brereton, A. V., Einfeld, S. L., Havercamp, S. M., Holt, G., et al. (2007). Intellectual disabilities and behavioural, emotional and psychiatric disturbances. In I. Brown & M. Percy (Eds.), *A comprehensive guide to intellectual and developmental disabilities* (pp. 645–666). London, UK: Paul Brookes.

Bradley, S. J., & Zucker, K. J. (1997). Gender identity disorder: A review of the past 10 years. *Journal of the American Academy of Child and Adolescent Psychiatry, 36*, 872–880.

Braff, D. L., Freedman, R., Schork, N. J., & Gottesman, I. I. (2007). Deconstructing schizophrenia: An overview of the use of endophenotypes in order to understand a complex disorder. *Schizophrenia Bulletin, 33*(1), 21–32.

Bramon-Bosch, E., Troop, N., & Treasure, J. L. (2000). Eating disorders in males: A comparison with female patients. *European Eating Disorders Review, 8*, 321–328.

Brand, B., Loewenstein, R. J., & Spiegel, D. (2013). Disinformation about dissociation: Dr. Joel Paris's notions about dissociative identity disorder. *Journal of Nervous and Mental Disease, 201*(4), 354–356.

Brand, B. L., McNary, S. W., Myrick, A. C., Classen, C. C., Lanius, R., Loewenstein, R., . . . & Putnam, F. W. (2013). A longitudinal naturalistic study of patients with dissociative disorders treated by community clinicians. *Psychological Trauma: Theory, Research, Practice, and Policy, 5*(4), 301–308.

Brand, M., Snagowski, J., Laier, C., & Maderwald, S. (2016). Ventral striatum activity when watching preferred pornographic pictures is correlated with symptoms of internet pornography addiction. *Neuroimage, 129*, 224–232.

Brannigan, G. G., & Decker, S. L. (2003). *The Bender visual-motor gestalt test, second edition.* Itasca, IL: Riverside Publishing.

Bratland-Sanda, S., & Sundgot-Borgen, J. (2013). Eating disorders in athletes: Overview of prevalence, risk factors and recommendations for prevention and treatment. *European Journal of Sport Science, 13*, 499–508. doi: 10.1080/17461391.2012.740504

Braun, D. L., Sunday, S. R., Huang, A., & Halmi, K. A. (1999). More males seek treatment for eating disorders. *International Journal of Eating Disorders, 25*, 415–424.

Brekke, J. S., Prindle, C., Bae, S. W., & Long, J. D. (2001). Risks for individuals with schizophrenia who are living in the community. *Psychiatric Services, 52*, 1358–1366.

Bremner, J. D. (1999). Does stress damage the brain? *Biological Psychiatry, 45*, 797–805.

Bremner, J. D. (2001). A biological model for delayed recall of childhood abuse. In J. J. Freyd & A. P. DePrince (Eds.), *Trauma and cognitive science: A meeting of minds, science, and human experience* (pp. 165–183). New York, NY: Haworth Press.

Bremner, J. D., Randall, P., Vermetten, E., Staib, L., Bronen R. A., Mazure C., et al. (1997). Magnetic resonance imaging-based measurement of hippocampal volume in posttraumatic stress disorder related to childhood physical and sexual abuse: A preliminary report. *Biological Psychiatry, 41*, 23–32.

Bremner, J. D., Vythilingam, M., Vermetten, E., Southwick, S. M., Mcglashan, T., Nazeer, A., . . . Charney, D. S. (2003). MRI and PET study of deficits in hippocampal structure and function in women with childhood sexual abuse and posttraumatic stress disorder. *American Journal of Psychiatry, 160*(May), 924–932.

Brendgen, M., Vitaro, F., Boivin, M., Dionne, G., & Perusse, D. (2006). Genetic and environmental effects on reactive versus proactive aggression. *Developmental Psychology, 42*, 1299–1312.

Brent, B. K., Thermenos, H. W., Keshavan, M. S., & Seidman, L. J. (2013). Gray matter alterations in schizophrenia high-risk youth and early-onset schizophrenia: A review of structural MRI findings. *Psychosis in Youth, 22*(4), 689–714. doi.org/10.1016/j.chc.2013.06.003

Brent, D., Kales, R., Edelbrock, C., Costello, A. J., Dulcan, M. K., & Conover, N. (1996). Psychopathology and its relation to suicidal ideation in childhood and adolescence. *Journal of the American Academy of Child & Adolescent Psychiatry, 25*, 666–673.

Bresnahan, M., & Susser, E. (2003). Investigating socioenvironmental influences in schizophrenia: Conceptual and design issues. In R. M. Murray, P. B. Jones, E. Susser, J. Van Os, & M. Cannon (Eds.), *The epidemiology of schizophrenia* (pp. 5–17). Cambridge, UK: Cambridge University Press.

Breton, J. J., Bergeron, L., Valla, J. P., Berthiaume, C., Gaudet, N., Lambert, J., et al. (1999). Quebec child mental health survey: Prevalence of DSM-III-R mental health disorders. *Journal of Child Psychology and Psychiatry, 40*, 375–384.

Breuer, J., & Freud, S. (1955). *Studies on hysteria.* (J. Strachey, trans. & ed.). (The Standard Edition of the Complete Psychological Works of Sigmund Freud, Vol. II.). London, UK: Hogarth Press.

Brewerton T. D. (1999). Binge eating disorder: Diagnosis and treatment options. *CNS Drugs, 11*, 351–361.

Brewerton, T. D. (1995). Toward a unified theory of serotonin dysregulation in eating and related disorders. *Psychoneuroendocrinology, 20*, 561–590.

Brewerton, T. D. (2007). Eating disorders, trauma, and comorbidity: Focus on PTSD. *Eating Disorders: The Journal of Treatment & Prevention, 15*, 285–304.

Brewin, C. (2011). The nature and significance of memory disturbance in posttraumatic stress disorder. *Annual Review of Clinical Psychology, 7*, 203–227.

Brewin, C. R., Dalgleish, T., & Stephen, J. (1996). A dual representation theory of posttraumatic stress disorder. *Psychological Review, 103*, 670–686.

Brezo, J., Barker, E. D., Paris, J., Hebert, M., Vitaro, F., Tremblay, R. E., & Turecki, G. (2008). Childhood trajectories of anxiousness and disruptiveness as predictors of suicide attempts. *Archives of Pediatrics and Adolescent Medicine, 162*(11), 1015–1021. doi:10.1001/archpedi.162.11.1015

Brickner, R. M. (1934). An interpretation of frontal lobe function based upon the study of a case of partial bilateral frontal lobectomy. *Research and Publications of the Association for the Research of Nervous and Mental Disease, 13*, 259–351.

Brickner, R. M. (1936). *The intellectual functions of the frontal lobes.* New York, NY: Macmillan.

Bridge, J. A., Iyengar, S., Salary, C. B., Barbe, R. P., Birmaher, B., Pincus, H. A., et al. (2007). Clinical response and risk for reported suicidal ideation and suicide attempts in pediatric antidepressant treatment: A meta-analysis of randomized controlled trials. *Journal of the American Medical Association, 297*, 1683–1696.

Bridle, C., Spanjers, K., Patel, S., Atherton. N. M., Lamb, S. E. (2012). Effect of exercise on depression severity in older people: Systematic review and meta-analysis of randomized controlled trials. *British Journal of Psychiatry, 201*, 180–185.

Brien, S., Grenier, L., Kapral, M. E., Kurdyak, P., Vigod, S. (2015). *Taking Stock: A report on the quality of mental health and addictions services in Ontario.* An HQO/ICES Report. Toronto, ON: Health Quality Ontario and the Institute for Clinical Evaluative Sciences.

Briere, J., & Zaidi, L. Y. (1989). Sexual abuse histories and sequelae in female psychiatric emergency room patients. *American Journal of Psychiatry, 146*, 1602–1606.

Briken, P., Nika, E., & Berner, W. (2001). Treatment of paraphilia with luteinizing hormone-releasing hormone agonists. *Journal of Sex & Marital Therapy, 27*, 45–55.

Brisch, R., Saniotis, A., Wolf, R., Bielau, H., Bernstein, H. G., Steiner, J., . . . & Henneberg, M. (2014). The role of dopamine in schizophrenia from a neurobiological and evolutionary perspective: Old fashioned, but still in vogue. *Frontiers in Psychiatry, 5*(47), 1–11.

Broadway, J., & Mintzer, J. (2007). The many faces of psychosis in the elderly. *Current Opinions in Psychiatry, 20*, 551–558.

Brodie, D. A. (1971). Stress ulcer as an experimental model of peptic ulcer disease. In C. J. Pfeiffer (Ed.), *Peptic ulcer* (pp. 71–83). Philadelphia, PA: Lippincott.

Brodsky, A. E. (1996). Resilient single mothers in risky neighborhoods: Negative psychological sense of community. *Journal of Community Psychology, 24*(4), 347–363.

Broekman, B. F. P., Olff, M., & Boer, F. (2007). The genetic background to PTSD. *Neuroscience & Biobehavioral Reviews, 31*, 348–362.

Bronfenbrenner, U. (1977). Ecology of the family as a context for human development: Research perspectives. *Developmental Psychology, 22*, 723–742.

Brotman, M. A., Schmajuk, M., Rich, B. A., Dickstein, D. P., Guyer, A. E., Costello, E. J., et al. (2006). Prevalence, clinical correlates, and longitudinal course of severe mood dysregulation in children. *Biological Psychiatry, 60*, 991–997. doi:10.1016/j.biopsych.2006.08.042

Brotto, L. A. (2010a). The DSM diagnostic criteria for hypoactive sexual desire disorder. *Archives of Sexual Behavior, 39*, 221–239.

Brotto, L. A. (2010b). The DSM criteria for sexual aversion disorder. *Archives of Sexual Behavior, 39*, 271–277.

Brower, M. C., & Price, B. H. (2001). Neuropsychiatry of frontal lobe dysfunction in violent and criminal behaviour: A critical review. *Journal of Neurology, Neurosurgery, and Psychiatry, 71*, 720–727.

Brown, G. K., Henriques, G. R., Ratto, C., & Beck, A. T. (2002) *Cognitive Therapy Treatment Manual for Suicide Attempters.* Philadelphia, PA: University of Pennsylvania.

Brown, G. K., Ten Have, T., Henriques, G. R., Xie, S. X., Hollander, J. E., & Beck, A. T. (2005). Cognitive therapy for the prevention of suicide attempts: A randomized controlled trial. *Journal of the American Medical Association, 294*, 563–570.

Brown, G. W., & Harris, T. O. (1989). Depression. In G. W. Brown & T. O. Harris (Eds.), *Life events and illness* (pp. 49–93). New York, NY: Guilford.

Brown, G. W., Harris, T. O., & Bifulco, A. (1986). Long-term effects of early loss of parent. In M. Rutter, C. E. Izard, & P. B. Read (Eds.), *Depression in young people: Developmental and clinical perspectives* (pp. 251–298). New York, NY: Guilford.

Brown, I., & Percy, M. E. (2011). *Developmental disabilities in Ontario* (3rd ed.). Toronto, ON: Ontario Association on Developmental Disabilities

Brown, I., & Radford, J. P. (2007). Historical overview of intellectual and developmental disabilities. In I. Brown & M. Percy (Eds.), *A comprehensive guide to intellectual and developmental disabilities* (pp. 17–34). London, UK: Paul Brookes.

Brown, J. (1985). Historical perspective on child abuse. In A. Downer (Ed.), *Prevention of child sexual abuse: A trainer's manual.* Seattle, WA: Seattle Institute for Child Advocacy Committee for Children.

Brown, R. I. (Ed.). (1997). *Quality of life for people with disabilities: Models, research and practice* (2nd ed.). Cheltenham, UK: Stanley Thornes.

Brown, R. I., & Brown, I. (2004). *Quality of life and disability: An approach for community practitioners.* London: Jessica Kingsley.

Brown, R. J., Cardena, E., Nijenhuis, E., Sar, V., & van der Hart, O. (2007). Should conversion disorder be reclassified as a dissociative disorder in DSM-V? *Psychosomatics, 48*, 369–378.

Brown, T. A., & Barlow, D. H. (2009). A proposal for a dimensional classification system based on the shared features of the DSM-IV anxiety and mood disorders: Implications for assessment and treatment. *Psychological Assessment, 21*, 256–271.

Brown, T. A., & Barlow, D. H. (2014). *Anxiety and related disorders interview schedule for DSM-5, adult and lifetime version: Clinician manual.* Oxford, England: Oxford University Press.

Browne, E. G. (1921). *Arabian medicine.* New York, NY: Macmillan.

Brownmiller, S. (1975). *Against our will: Men, women, and rape.* New York, NY: Bantam Books.

Bruce, K., & Steiger, H. (2006). Prognostic implications of personality disorders in eating disorders. In R. A. Sansone & J. L. Levitt (Eds.), *Personality disorders and eating disorders: Exploring the frontier* (pp. 247–262). New York, NY: Routledge.

Bruce, K. R., Steiger, H., Ng Yin Kin, N. M. K., & Israel, M. (2006). Reduced platelet [^{3}H]paroxetine binding in anorexia nervosa: Relationship to eating symptoms and personality pathology. *Psychiatry Research, 142*, 225–232.

Bruce, L. C., & Heimberg, R. G. (2014). Social anxiety disorder. In J. A. J. Smits (Vol. Ed.), *Specific disorders,* (S. G. Hofmann, series ed.), *The Wiley handbook of cognitive-behavioral therapy* (Vol 3, pp. 895–915). Oxford, UK: Wiley-Blackwell.

Bruch, H. (1978). *The golden cage.* Cambridge, MA: Harvard University Press.

Bruininks, R. H., Woodcock, R. W., Weatherman, R. F., & Hill, B. K. (1996). *The Scales of Independent Behavior—Revised.* Itasca, IL: Riverside.

Brunelle, C., Assaad, J. M., Barrett, S. P., Ávila, C., Conrod, P. J., Tremblay, R. E., & Pihl, R. O. (2004). Heightened heart rate response to alcohol intoxication is associated with a reward-seeking personality profile. *Alcoholism: Clinical and Experimental Research, 28*(3), 394–401.

Brunner, R., Henze, R., Parzer, P., Kramer, J., Feigl, N., Lutz, K., et al. (2010). Reduced prefrontal and orbitofrontal gray matter in female adolescents with borderline personality disorder: Is it disorder specific? *Neuroimage, 49*, 114–120. doi:10.1016/j.neuroimage. 2009.07.070

Brunoni, A. R., Moffa, A. H., Fregni, F., Palm, U., Padberg, F., Blumberger, D. M.,…Loo, C. K. (2016). Transcranial direct current stimulation for acute major depressive episodes: Meta-analysis of individual patient data. *British Journal of Psychiatry, 208*, 522–531.

Bryan, S., & Walsh, P. (2004). Physical activity and obesity in Canadian women. In Canadian Institute for Health Information, BMC *Women's Health*, Women's Health Surveillance Report, *4*(Suppl 1), S6.

Bryan, T., Burstein, K., & Ergul, C. (2004). The social-emotional side of learning disabilities: A science-based presentation of the state of the art. *Learning Disability Quarterly, 27*, 45–51.

Bryant, R. A., Harvey, A. G., Guthrie, R. M., & Moulds, M. L. (2000). A prospective study of psychophysiological arousal, acute stress disorder, and posttraumatic stress disorder. *Journal of Abnormal Psychology, 109*, 341.

Bryer, J. B., Nelson, B. A., Miller, J. B., & Krol, P. K. (1987). Childhood sexual and physical abuse as factors in adult psychiatric illness. *American Journal of Psychiatry, 144*, 1426–1430.

Bryson, S. E. (1996). Brief report: Epidemiology of autism. *Journal of Autism and Developmental Disorders, 26*, 165–167.

Buchanan, R. W., & Carpenter, W. T. (2000). Schizophrenia: Introduction and overview. In B. J. Sadock & V. A. Sadock (Eds.), *Kaplan and Sadock's comprehensive textbook of psychiatry* (7th ed., Vol. 1, pp. 1096–1110). Philadelphia, PA: Lippincott Williams & Wilkins.

Budney, A. J., Moore, B. A., Vandrey, R. G., & Hughes, J. R. (2003). The time course and significance of cannabis withdrawal. *Journal of Abnormal Psychology, 112*, 393–402.

Buhin, L., & Vera, E. (2009). Preventing racism and promoting social justice: Person-centered and environment-centered interventions. *Journal of Primary Prevention, 30*, 43–59.

Bukatko, D., & Daehler, M. W. (2012). *Child development: A thematic approach* (6th ed.). Belmont, CA: Wadsworth.

Bulik, C. M., & Kendler, K. S. (2000). I am what I (don't) eat: Establishment of an identity independent of an eating disorder. *American Journal of Psychiatry, 157*, 1755–1760.

Bulik, C. M., Berkman, N. D., Brownley, K. A., Sedway, J. A., & Lohr, K. N. (2007). Anorexia nervosa treatment: A systematic review of randomized controlled trials. *International Journal of Eating Disorders, 40*, 310–320.

Bullough, V. L. (1976). *Sexual variance in society and history.* Chicago, IL: University of Chicago Press.

Bulmash, E., Harkness, K. L., Stewart, J. G., & Bagby, R. M. (2009). Personality, stressful life events, and treatment response in major depression. *Journal of Consulting and Clinical Psychology, 77*, 1067–1077.

Burbidge, J. & Minnes, P. (2014). Relationship quality in adult siblings with and without developmental disabilities. *Family Relations 63*, 148–162 DOI:10.1111/fare.12047

Burgess, H. J., Fogg, L. F., Young, M. A., & Eastman, C. I. (2004). Bright light therapy for winter depression—is phase advancing beneficial? *Chronobiology International, 21*, 759–775.

Burke, J. D., Loeber, R., & Birmaher, B. (2002). Oppositional defiant disorder and conduct disorder: A review of the past 10 years, Part II. *Journal of the Academy of Child and Adolescent Psychiatry, 41* (11), 1275–1293.

Burmeister, M., McInnis, M. G., & Zöllner, S. (2008). Psychiatric genetics: Progress amid controversy. *Nature Reviews Genetics, 9*(7), 527–540.

Burns, A. M., Erickson, D. H., & Brenner, C. A. (2014). Cognitive-behavioral therapy for medication-resistant psychosis: A meta-analytic review. *Psychiatric Services, 65*(7), 874–880.

Burns, J. F. (2010, May 25). British Medical Council bars doctor who linked vaccine with autism. *The New York Times*, p. A4.

Burton, R. (1621/1977). *Anatomy of melancholy.* New York, NY: Vintage.

Butcher, J. N. (2010). Personality assessment from the nineteenth to the early twenty-first century: Past achievements and contemporary challenges. *Annual Review of Clinical Psychology, 6*, 1–20.

Butcher, J. N., Dahlstrom, W. G., Graham, J. R., Tellegen, A., & Kaemmer, B. (1989). *Minnesota Multiphasic Personality Inventory: MMPI-2: Manual for administration and scoring.* Minneapolis, MN: University of Minnesota Press.

Butcher, J. N., Mineka, S., Hooley, J. M., Taylor, S., & Antony, M. M. (2010). *Abnormal Psychology* (Canadian ed.). Toronto, ON: Pearson Canada.

Butcher, J. N., Williams, C. L., Graham, J. R., Archer, R., Tellegen, A., Ben-Porath, Y. S., & Kaemmer, B. (1992). *MMPI-A: Manual for administration, scoring, and interpretation.* Minneapolis:MN University of Minnesota Press.

Butler, A. C., Chapman, J. E., Forman, E. M., & Beck, A. T. (2006). The empirical status of cognitive-behavioral therapy: A review of meta-analyses. *Clinical Psychology Review, 26*, 17–31.

Butler-Jones, D. (2010). *The Chief Public Health Officer's report on the state of public health in Canada: Growing older—adding life to years.* Retrieved from http://publichealth.gc.ca/CPHOreport

Butt, P., Beirness, F., Gliksman, L., Paradis, C., & Stockwell, T. (2011). *Alcohol and health in Canada: A summary of evidence and guidelines for low risk drinking.* Ottawa, ON: Canadian Centre on Substance Abuse.

Butterworth, B., Varma, S., & Laurillard, D. (2011). Dyscalculia: From brain to education. *Science, 332*(6033), 1049–1053.

Buttner, G., & Hasselhorn, M. (2011). Learning disabilities: Debates on definitions, causes, subtypes, and responses. *International Journal of Disability, Development and Education, 58*(1), 75–87.

Byer, C., Shainberg, L., & Galliano, G. (2002). *Dimensions of human sexuality.* New York, NY: McGraw-Hill.

Byers, A. L., Yaffe, K., Covinsky, K. E., Friedman, M. B., & Bruce, M. L. (2010). High occurrence of mood and anxiety disorders among older adults: The National Comorbidity Survey Replication. *Archives of General Psychiatry, 67*(5), 489–496.

Byers, E. S., & Grenier, G. (2003). Premature or rapid ejaculation: Heterosexual couples' perceptions of men's ejaculatory behavior. *Archives of Sexual Behavior, 32*(3), 261–270.

Byers, E. S., Henderson, J., & Hobson, K. M. (2009). University students' definitions of sexual abstinence and having sex. *Archives of Sexual Behavior, 38*, 665–674.

Byers, E. S., Price, L., & Dating Violence Research Team. (1997). A multidisciplinary collaborative approach to understanding dating violence. In J. Proulx & W. Josephson (chairs), *Dating violence research in Canada: Problem, projects, prevention.* Symposium presented at the meeting of the Canadian Psychological Association, Toronto. [Abstract published in *Canadian Psychology, 38*, 137–138.]

Byrne, S. M., Fursland, A., Allen, K. L., & Watson, H. (2011). The effectiveness of enhanced cognitive behavioural therapy for eating disorders: An open trial. *Behaviour Research and Therapy, 49*, 219–226.

Cabrera, I., Montorio, I., & MacLeod, C. (in press). Anxiety-linked differences in older adults' interpretation of ambiguous information. *Cognitive Therapy and Research.*

Cacioppo, J. T., & Berntson, G. G. (1992). Social psychological contributions to the decade of the brain. *American Psychologist, 47*, 1019–1028.

Cadman, D., Boyle, M., Szatmari, P., & Offord, D. R. (1987). Chronic illness, disability, and mental and social well–being: findings of the Ontario Child Health Study. *Pediatrics, 79*(5), 805–813.

Cairney, J., Corna, L. M., & Streiner, D. L. (2010). Health care use in later life: Results from a national survey of Canadians. *Canadian Journal of Psychiatry, 55* (3), 157–164.

Cairney, J., Corna, L. M., Veldhuizen, S., Hemnann, N., & Streiner, D. L. (2008). Comorbid depression and anxiety in later life: Patterns of association, subjective well-being, and impairment. *American Journal of Geriatric Psychiatry, 16*, 201–208.

Cairns, J. C., Styles, L. D., & Leichner, P. (2007). Evaluation of meal support training for parents and caregivers using a video and a manual. *Journal of the Canadian Academy of Child and Adolescent Psychiatry, 16*, 164–166.

Cairns, R. B., Cairns, B. D., Neckerman, H. J., Gest, S. D., & Gariepy, J. L. (1988). Social networks and aggressive behaviour: Peer support or peer rejection? *Developmental Psychology, 24*, 815–823.

Cairo, T. A., Woodward, T. S., & Ngan, E. T. C. (2006). Decreased encoding efficiency in schizophrenia. *Biological Psychiatry, 59*(8), 740–746.

Caldwell, A. (1978). History of psychopharmacology. In W. G. Clark & J. del Giudice (Eds.), *Principles of psychopharmacology* (2nd ed., pp. 9–40). New York, NY: Academic Press.

Caldwell, J. & Heller, T. (2007). Longitudinal outcomes of a consumer-directed program supporting adults with developmental disabilities and directed program supporting adults with developmental disabilities and their families. *Intellectual and Developmental Disabilities, 45*, 161–173.

Cambor, R., & Millman, R. B. (1991). Alcohol and drug abuse in adolescence. In M. Lewis (Ed.), *Child and adolescent psychiatry: A comprehensive textbook* (pp. 736–754). Baltimore, MD: Williams & Wilkins.

Camilli, G., Vargas, S., Ryan, S., & Barnett, W. S. (2010). Meta-analysis of the effects of early education interventions on cognitive and social development. *Teachers College Record, 112*, 579–620.

Campbell, E. (1990). The psychopath and the definition of "mental disease of defect" under the Model Penal Code test of insanity: A question of psychology or a question of law? *Nebraska Law Review, 69*, 190–229.

Campbell, M., Adams, P., Small, A. M., Kafantaris, V., Silva, R. R., Shell, J., et al. (1995). Lithium in hospitalized aggressive children with conduct disorder: A double-blind and placebo-controlled study. *Journal of the American Academy of Child and Adolescent Psychiatry, 34*, 397–534.

Campbell, M. A. (2003). The relative contribution of psychopathy and traditional risk factors in predicting young offender recidivism. Unpublished doctoral dissertation. Dalhousie University, Halifax, NS.

Campbell, M. A., Porter, S., & Santor, D. (2004). Psychopathic traits in adolescent offenders: An evaluation of criminal history, clinical, and psychosocial correlates. *Behavioral Sciences and the Law, 22*, 23–47.

Campbell, S., Chong, S., Ewen, V., Toombs, E., Tzalazidiz, R., & Maranza, K. A. (2016). Social media policy for graduate students: Challenges and opportunities for professional psychology training programs. *Canadian Psychology, 57*, 202–210.

Canadian Association for Suicide Prevention. (2004). *Blueprint for a Canadian national suicide prevention strategy.* Edmonton, AB: Author.

Canadian Association for Suicide Prevention. (2009). *The CASP blueprint for a Canadian national suicide prevention strategy* (2nd ed.).Edmonton, AB: Author.

Canadian Broadcasting Corporation. (2013, December 19). *Saint Mary's pro-rape chant sparks 20 new recommendations.* Retrieved from www.cbc.ca/news/canada/nova-scotia/saint-mary-s-pro-rape-chant-sparks-20-new-recommendations-1.2469851

Canadian Centre on Substance Abuse. (2004a). *Canadian Addiction Survey (CAS) highlights.* Ottawa: Canadian Centre on Substance Abuse.

Canadian Centre on Substance Abuse. (2004b). *Needle exchange programs (NEPs): FAQs.* Ottawa: Canadian Centre on Substance Abuse.

Canadian Centre on Substance Abuse. (2015). *Deaths involving fentanyl in Canada, 2009 – 2014.* Retrieved from www.ccsa.ca/Resource%20Library/CCSA-CCENDU-Fentanyl-Deaths-Canada-Bulletin-2015-en.pdf

Canadian Coalition for Seniors' Mental Health. (2006a). Canadian Coalition for Seniors' Mental Health national guidelines for seniors' mental health: Assessment of suicide risk and prevention of suicide. Retrieved from http://ccsmh.ca/en/natlguidelines/initiative.cfm

Canadian Coalition for Seniors' Mental Health. (2006b). Canadian Coalition for Seniors' Mental Health national guidelines for seniors' mental health: The assessment and treatment of depression. Retrieved from http://ccsmh.ca/en/natlguidelines/initiative.cfm

Canadian Coalition for Seniors' Mental Health. (2006c). National guidelines for seniors' mental health: The assessment and treatment of delirium. Available at http://ccsmh.ca/wp-content/uploads/2016/03/NatlGuideline_Delirium.pdf

Canadian Coalition for Seniors' Mental Health. (2014). Update guideline. Retrieved from http://ccsmh.ca/projects/delirium/

Canadian Institute for Health Information. (2008). *Hospital mental health services in Canada, 2005–2006.* Ottawa: Author.

Canadian Institute for Health Information. (2009). *Improving the health of Canadians: Exploring positive mental health.* Ottawa: Author.

Canadian Longitudinal Study on Aging. (n.d.) Retrieved from www.clsa-elcv.ca/about-us/about-clsa-research-platform

Canadian Medical Association. (2008). *8th annual national report card on health care.* Ipsos Reid Public Affairs. Retrieved from www.cma.ca/multimedia/CMA/Content_Images/Inside_cma/Annual_Meeting/2008/GC_Bulletin/National_Report_Card_EN.pdf

Canadian Medical Association. (2014, September 16). Take Home Naloxone program in BC saves lives. *Canadian Medical Association Journal, 186*(13), 995.

Canadian Partnership for Responsible Gambling. (2016). Canadian gambling digest 2014–2015. Available from www.cprg.ca/Digests/ViewMainCards?yearId=e0e02df2-2ea4-e511-97fa-1abbb38a3094

Canadian Psychological Association Task Force on Prescriptive Authority for Psychologists in Canada. (2010). *Report to the Canadian Psychological Association Board of Directors.* Retrieved from www.cpa.ca

Canadian Psychological Association. (2000). *Canadian code of ethics for psychologists* (3rd ed.). Ottawa, ON: Canadian Psychological Association.

Canadian Psychological Association. (2009, August 4). *Canadian Psychological Association (CPA) position on publication and dissemination of psychological tests.* Retrieved from www.cpa.ca/cpasite/userfiles/Documents/Practice_Page/2009_CPAPsychologicaltest_statement.pdf

Canadian Psychological Association. (2017). *Canadian code of ethics for psychologists* (4th ed.). Ottawa, ON: Author.

Canadian Psychological Association. (2017). www.cpa.ca/docs/File/Press%20Release/CPA_Starbucks_PressRelease.pdf

Canadian Psychological Association. (2017). *The Canadian psychological association applauds manulife for making mental health care accessible to all employees.* (2017). Unpublished manuscript. Ottawa, ON: Author.

Canadian Study of Health and Aging Working Group. (1994). Canadian Study of Health and Aging: Study methods and prevalence of dementia. *Canadian Medical Association Journal, 150*, 899–912.

Cannon, M., Jones, P. B., & Murray, R. M. (2002). Obstetric complications and schizophrenia: Historical and meta-analytic review. *American Journal of Psychiatry, 159*, 1080–1092.

Cannon, M., Jones, P. B., & Murray, R. M. (2002). Obstetric complications and schizophrenia: Historical and meta-analytic review. *American Journal of Psychiatry, 159*(7), 1080–1092.

Cannon, W. B. (1942). "Voodoo" death. *American Anthropologist, 44*, 169.

Canton, J., Scott, K. M., & Glue, P. (2012). Optimal treatment of social phobia: systematic review and meta-analysis. *Neuropsychiatric Disease and Treatment, 8*, 203.

Cantor, J. (2000). Media violence. *Journal of Adolescent Health, 27*(2), 30–34.

Cantor, J. M., Blanchard, R., Christensen, B. K., Dickey, R., Klassen, P. E., Beckstead, A. L., et al. (2004). Intelligence, memory, and handedness in pedophilia. *Neuropsychology, 18*, 3–14.

Cantor, J. M., Kabani, N., Christensen, B. K., Zipursky, R. B., Barbaree, H. E., Dickey, R. et al. (2008). Cerebral white matter deficiencies in pedophilic men. *Journal of Psychiatric Research, 42*, 167–83.

Cantor, J. M., Klein, C., Lykins, A., Rullo, J. E., Thaler, L., & Walling, B. R. (2013). A treatment-oriented typology of self-identified hypersexuality referrals. *Archives of Sexual Behavior, 42*(5), 883–893.

Cantor-Graae, E. (2007). The contribution of social factors to the development of schizophrenia: A review of recent findings. *Canadian Journal of Psychiatry, 52*, 277–286.

Cantwell, D. P. (1996). Classification of child and adolescent psychopathology. *Journal of Child Psychology and Psychiatry and Allied Disciplines, 37*, 3–12.

Capaldi, D. M. (1991). Co-occurrence of conduct problems and depressive symptoms in early adolescent boys: I. Familial factors and general adjustment at Grade 6. *Development and Psychopathology, 3*, 277–300. doi:10.1017/S095457940000531

Capaldi, D. M. (1992). Co-occurrence of conduct problems and depressive symptoms in early adolescent boys: II. A 2-year follow-up at Grade 8. *Development and Psychopathology, 4*, 125–144. doi:10.1017/S0954579400005605

Capaldi, D. M., & Stoolmiller, M. (1999). Co-occurrence of conduct problems and depressive symptoms in early adolescent boys: III. Prediction to young-adult adjustment. *Development and Psychopathology, 11*, 59–84. doi:10.1017/S0954579499001959

Caplan, G. (1964). *Principles of preventive psychiatry.* New York, NY: Basic Books.

Carey, G. (1992). Twin imitation for antisocial behaviour: Implications for genetic and family environment research. *Journal of Abnormal Psychology, 101*(1), 18–25.

Cariaga-Martinez, A., Saiz-Ruiz, J., & Alelú-Paz, R. (2016). From linkage studies to epigenetics: what we know and what we need to know in the neurobiology of schizophrenia. *Frontiers in Neuroscience, 10*, 1-17.

Carlat, D. J., Camargo, C. A., Jr., & Herzog, D. B. (1997). Eating disorders in males: A report on 135 patients. *American Journal of Psychiatry, 154*, 1127–1132.

Carlbring, P., Degerman, N., Jonsson, J., & Andersson, G. (2012). Internet-based treatment of pathological gambling with a three-year follow-up. *Cognitive behaviour therapy, 41*(4), 321–334.

Carlson, E. A., Yates, T. M., & Sroufe, L. A. (2009). Dissociation and development of the self. In P. F. Dell & J. A. O'Neil (Eds.), *Dissociation and the dissociative disorders: DSM-V and beyond* (pp. 39–52). New York, NY: Routledge.

Carlson, E. N., Vazire, S., & Oltmanns, T. F. (2011). You probably think this paper's about you: Narcissists' perceptions of their personality and reputation. *Journal of Personality and Social Psychology, 101*, 185–201. doi:10.1037/a0023781

Carlson, G. A., & Cantwell, D. P. (1980). Unmasking masked depression in children and adolescents. *The American Journal of Psychiatry, 137*, 445–449.

Carmassi, C., Akiskal, H. S., Yong, S. S., Stratta, P., Calderani, E., Massimetti, E., ... Dell'Osso, L. (2013). Post-traumatic stress disorder in DSM-5: Estimates of prevalence and criteria comparison versus DSM-IV-TR in a non-clinical sample of earthquake survivors. *Journal of Affective Disorders, 151*(3), 843–848.

Carmen, B., Angeles, M., Ana, M., & María, A. J. (2004). Efficacy and safety of naltrexone and acamprosate in the treatment of alcohol dependence: a systematic review. *Addiction, 99*(7), 811828.

Carmody, J., Baer, R. A., Lykins, E. L. B., & Olendzki, N. (2009). An empirical study of the mechanisms of mindfulness in a mindfulness-based stress reduction program. *Journal of Clinical Psychology, 65*, 613–626.

Carnes, P. (1983). *Out of the shadows: Understanding sexual addiction.* Minneapolis, MN: Compcare.

Carnes, P. (1989). *Contrary to love: Helping the sex addict.* Minneapolis, MN: Compcare.

Carney, R. M., Blumenthal, J. A., Catellier, D., Freedland, K. E., Berkman, L. F., Watkins, L. L., & Jaffe, A. S. (2003). Depression as a risk factor for mortality after acute myocardial infarction. *The American Journal of Cardiology, 92*(11), 1277-1281.

Carney, S., Cowen, P., Dearness, K., Eastaugh, J., Freemantle, N., Geddes, J., et al. (2003). Efficacy and safety of electroconvulsive therapy in depressive disorders: A review. *The Lancet, 361*, 9360.

Caron, J., & Liu, A. (2010). A descriptive study of the prevalence of psychological distress and mental disorders in the Canadian population: Comparison between low-income and non-low-income populations. *Chronic Diseases in Canada, 30*, 84–94.

Carpiano, R. M. (2014). The neighborhood and mental life: Past, present, and future sociological directions in studying community context and mental health. In Johnson, R. J., Turner, R. J., & Link, B. G. (Eds.), *Sociology of Mental Health* (pp. 101–123). Boston, MA: Springer International Publishing.

Carr, E. G., Horner, R. H., Turnbull, A. P., Marquis, J. G., Magito-McLaughlin, D., McAtee, M. L., et al. (1999). *Positive behavior support for people with developmental disabilities: A research synthesis* [Monograph]. Washington, DC: American Association on Mental Retardation.

Carragher, N., Krueger, R. F., Eaton, N. R., & Slade, T. (2015). Disorders without borders: Current and future directions in the meta-structure of mental disorders. *Social Psychiatry and Psychiatric Epidemiology, 50*, 339–350.

Carrington, S. J., Kent, R. G., Maljaars, J., Le Couteur, A., Gould, J., Wing, L., . . . & Leekam, S. R. (2014). DSM-5 Autism Spectrum Disorder: In search of essential behaviours for diagnosis. *Research in Autism Spectrum Disorders, 8*(6), 701–715.

Carroll, D., Ginty, A. T., Der, G., Hunt, K., Benzeval, M., & Phillips, A. C. (2012). Increased blood pressure reactions to acute mental stress are associated with 16-year cardiovascular disease mortality. *Psychophysiology, 49*(10), 1444–1448.

Carroll, D., Ginty, A. T., Whittaker, A. C., Lovallo, W. R., & de Rooij, S. R. (2017). The behavioural, cognitive, and neural corollaries of blunted cardiovascular and cortisol reactions to acute psychological stress. *Neuroscience & Biobehavioral Reviews, 77*, 74-86. doi: 10.1016/j.neubiorev.2017.02.025

Carroll, R. A. (2007). Gender dysphoria and transgender experiences. In S. R. Leiblum (Ed.), *Principles and practices of sex therapy* (4th ed., pp. 477–508). New York, NY: Guilford.

Carstensen, L. L. (2006). The influence of a sense of time on human development. *Science, 312*, 1913–1915.

Carstensen, L. L., Isaacowitz, D. M., & Charles, S. T. (1999). Taking time seriously: A theory of socioemotional selectivity. *The American Psychologist, 54*, 165–181.

Carter, A. S., Wagmiller, R. J., Gray, S. A. O., McCarthy, K. J., Horwitz, S. M., & Briggs-Gowan, M. J. (2010). Prevalence of DSM-IV disorder in a representative, healthy birth cohort at school entry: Sociodemographic risks and social adaptation. *Journal of the American Academy of Child & Adolescent Psychiatry, 49* (7), 686–698. doi:10.1097/00004583-201007000-00009

Carter, J. C. (2002). Self-help books in the treatment of eating disorders. In C. G. Fairburn & K. D. Brownell (Eds.), *Eating disorders and obesity* (pp. 358–361). New York, NY: Guilford.

Carter, J. C., Bewell, C., Blackmore, E., & Woodside, D. B. (2006). The impact of childhood sexual abuse in anorexia nervosa. *Child Abuse & Neglect, 30*, 257–269.

Carter, J. C., & Fairburn, C. G. (1998). Cognitive-behavioral self-help for binge eating disorder: A controlled effectiveness study. *Journal of Consulting and Clinical Psychology, 66*, 616–623.

Carter, J. C., Olmsted, M. P., Kaplan, A. S., McCabe, R. E., Mills, J. S., & Aimé, A. (2003). Self-help for bulimia nervosa: A randomized controlled trial. *American Journal of Psychiatry, 160*, 973–978.

Cartwright-Hatton, S., Roberts, C., Chitsabesan, P., Fothergill, C., & Harrington, R. (2004). Systematic review of the efficacy of cognitive behaviour therapies for childhood and adolescent anxiety disorders. *British Journal of Clinical Psychology, 43*, 421–436.

Carver, C. (1998). Premature ejaculation: A common and treatable concern. *Journal of the American Nurses Psychiatric Association, 4*(6), 199–204.

Case, R. B., Moss, A. J., Case, N., McDermott, M., & Eberly, S. (1992). Living alone after myocardial infarction: Impact on prognosis. *Journal of the American Medical Association, 267*, 515–519.

Cash, F., Morrow, J. A., Hrabosky, J. I., & Perry, A. A. (2004). How has body image changed? A cross-sectional investigation of college women and men from 1983 to 2001. *Journal of Consulting and Clinical Psychology, 72*, 1081–1089. doi: 10.1037/0022-006X.72.6.1081

Caslini, M., Bartoli, F., Crocamo, C., Dakanalis, A., Clerici, M., & Carrà, G. (2016). Disentangling the association between child abuse and eating disorders: A systematic review and meta-analysis. *Psychosomatic Medicine, 78*, 79–90. doi: 10.1097/PSY.0000000000000233

Caspi, A., McClay, J., Moffitt, T. E., Mill, J., Martin, J., Craig, I. W., et al. (2002). Role of genotype in the cycle of violence in maltreated children. *Science, 297*, 851–854.

Caspi, A., Moffitt, T. E., Newman, D. L., & Silva, P. A. (1996). Behavioral observations at age 3 predict adult psychiatric disorders: Longitudinal evidence from a birth cohort. *Archives of General Psychiatry, 53*, 1033–1039.

Caspi, A., Sugden, K., Moffitt, T. E., Taylor, A., Craig, I. W., Harrington, H., et al. (2003). Influence of life stress on depression: Moderation by a polymorphism in the 5-HTT gene. *Science, 301*, 386–389.

Cassin, S. E., & von Ranson, K. M. (2005). Personality and eating disorders: A decade in review. *Clinical Psychology Review, 25*, 895–916. doi: 10.1016/j.cpr.2005.04.012

Cassin, S. E., Singer, A. R., Dobson, K. S., & Altmaier, E. M. (2007). Professional interests and career aspirations of graduate students in professional psychology: An exploratory study. *Training and Education in Professional Psychology, 1*, 26–37.

Castel, P. (2014). Toward a more constructive (and historical) view of the harmful dysfunction theory? *Philosophy, Psychiatry, & Psychology, 21*, 357–360.

Castle, D. J., & Rossell, S. L. (2006). An update on body dysmorphic disorder. *Current Opinion in Psychiatry, 19*, 74–78.

Cavendish, W. (2013). Identification of learning disabilities: Implications of proposed DSM-5 criteria for school-based assessment. *Journal of Learning Disabilities, 46*(1), 52–57.

Cawley, R. (1974). Psychotherapy and obsessional disorders. In H. R. Beech (Ed.), *Obsessional states* (pp. 259–290). London, UK: Methuen.

CCSMH. *See* Canadian Coalition for Seniors' Mental Health.

Center for Behavioral Health Statistics and Quality. (2016). *2015 National survey on drug use and health: Detailed tables.* Substance Abuse and Mental Health Services Administration, Rockville, MD: Author.

Centers for Disease Control. *See* United States Centers for Disease Control.

Chadwick, P., Birchwood, M., & Trower, P. (1996). *Cognitive therapy for delusions, voices, and paranoia.* West Sussex, UK: Wiley.

Chamberland, C., Dallaire, N., Lindsay, J., Hébert, J., Fréchette, L., Beaudoin, G., & Cameron, S. (1998). Les conditions de réussite en prévention hr/promotion en enfance-famille-jeunesse: Une question de justification et de faisabilité. *Revue Canadienne de Santé Mentale Communautaire, 17*(1), 37–59.

Chambless, D. L., Sanderson, W. C., Shoham, V., Johnson, S. B., Pope, K. S., Crits-Christoph, P., et al. (1996). An update on empirically validated therapies. *The Clinical Psychologist, 49*(2), 5–18.

Champion, H., & Furnham, A. (1999). The effect of the media on body satisfaction in adolescent girls. *European Eating Disorders Review, 7*, 213–228.

Chan, R. C., Xu, T., Heinrichs, R. W., Yu, Y., & Wang, Y. (2009). Neurological soft signs in schizophrenia: A meta-analysis. *Schizophrenia Bulletin, 36*, 1-16.

Chan, R. C., Xu, T., Heinrichs, R. W., Yu, Y., & Wang, Y. (2010). Neurological soft signs in schizophrenia: A meta-analysis. *Schizophrenia Bulletin, 36*, 1089–1104.

Chandler, J. J., & Lalonde, C. (1998). Cultural continuity as a hedge against suicide in Canada's First Nations. *Transcultural Psychiatry, 35*, 191–219.

Chanen, A. M., & McCutcheon, L. K. (2008). Personality disorder in adolescence: The diagnosis that dare not speak its name. *Personality and mental health, 2*(1), 35–41.

Chanen, A. M., & McCutcheon, L. (2013). Prevention and early intervention for borderline personality disorder: current status and recent evidence. *The British Journal of Psychiatry, 202*(s54), s24–s29.

Chanen, A. M., Jackson, H. J., McGorry, P. D., Allot, K. A., Clarkson, V., & Yuen, H. P. (2004). Two-year stability of personality disorder in older adolescent outpatients. *Journal of personality disorders, 18*(6), 526–541.

Chanen, A. M., Jovev, M., & Jackson, H. J. (2007). Adaptive functioning and psychiatric symptoms in adolescents with borderline personality disorder. *Journal of Clinical Psychiatry, 68*(2), 297.

Chanen, A. M., Jovev, M., McCutcheon, L. K., Jackson, H. J., & McGorry, P. D. (2008). Borderline personality disorder in young people and the prospects for prevention and early intervention. *Current Psychiatry Reviews, 4*(1), 48–57.

Chapman, R. J., & Hesketh, L. (2000). Behavioral phenotype of individuals with Down syndrome. *Mental Retardation and Developmental Disabilities Research Reviews, 6*, 84–95.

Charavustra, A., & Cloitre, M. (2008). Social bonds and posttraumatic stress disorder. *Annual Review of Psychology, 59*, 301–328.

Charles, S. T. (2010). Strength and vulnerability integration: A model of emotional well-being across adulthood. *Psychological Bulletin, 136*(6), 1068–1091.

Charles, S. T., & Carstensen, L. L. (2009). Social and emotional aging. *Annual Review of Psychology*, 61, 383–409.

Charles, S. T., & Luong, G. (2013). Emotional experience across adulthood: The theoretical model of strength and vulnerability integration. *Current Directions in Psychological Science*, 22(6), 443–448. doi:10.1177/0963721413497013

Charles, S. T., & Piazza, J. R. (2009). Strength and vulnerability across the lifespan: An integration of literature on aging, emotional well-being and emotion regulation. *Social and Personality Psychology Compass*, 3(5),711–724.

Charney, D. S., Barlow, D. H., Botteron, K., Cohen, J. D., Goldman, S., Gur, R. E., et al. (2002). Neuroscience research agenda to guide development of a pathophysiologically based classification system. In D. J Kupfer, M. B. First, & D. A. Regier (Eds.), *A research agenda for DSM-V* (pp. 31–83). Washington, DC: American Psychiatric Association.

Chartier, M. J., Walker, J. R., & Naimark, B. (2010). Separate and cumulative effects of adverse childhood experiences in predicting adult health and health care utilization. *Child Abuse & Neglect*, 34(6), 454–464.

Charuvastra, A., & Cloitre, M. (2008). Social bonds and posttraumatic stress disorder. *Annual Review of Psychology*, 59, 301–328.

Chassin, L., Flora, D. B., & King, K. M. (2004). Trajectories of alcohol and drug use and dependence from adolescence to adulthood: the effects of familial alcoholism and personality. *Journal of abnormal psychology*, 113(4), 483.

Chatfield, J. (2002). AAP guideline on treatment of children with ADHD. *American Family Physician*, 65, 726–728.

Cheetham, T., Gitta, M., & Morrison, B. (2003). Some common syndromes associated with developmental disabilities. In I. Brown & M. Percy (Eds.), *Developmental disabilities in Ontario* (2nd ed., pp. 145–170). Toronto, ON: Ontario Association on Developmental Disabilities.

Chen C-C., Culhane, D. P., Metraux, S., Park, J. M., Venable, J. C., & Burnett, T. C. (2016). They're not all at home: residential placements of early adolescents in special education. *Journal of Emotional and Behavioral Disorders*. 24(4), 247–256

Chen, Y., Nettles, M. E., & Chen, S. (2009). Rethinking dependent personality disorder: Comparing different human relatedness in cultural contexts. *Journal of Nervous and Mental Disease*, 197, 793–800. doi:10.1097/NMD.0b013e3181be76ae

Chen, Z., Li, S., Subramaniam, S., Shyy, J. Y.-J., & Chien, S. (2017). Epigenetic regulation: A new frontier for biomedical engineers. *Annual Review of Biomedical Engineering*, 19(1), 195–219.

Cherner, R. A. & Reissing, E. D. (2013). A psychophysiological investigation of sexual arousal in women with lifelong vaginismus. *The Journal of Sexual Medicine*, 10, 1291–1303.

Chesler, P. (1972). *Women and Madness*. New York, NY: Doubleday.

Chick, J., Anton, R., Checinski, K., Croop, R., Drummond, D. C., Farmer, R., … & Peters, T. (2000). A multicentre, randomized, double-blind, placebo-controlled trial of naltrexone in the treatment of alcohol dependence or abuse. *Alcohol and alcoholism*, 35(6), 587–593.

Chida, Y., & Mao, X. (2009). Does psychological stress predict symptomatic herpes simplex virus recurrence? A meta-analytic investigation on prospective studies. *Brain, Behavior and Immunity*, 23, 917–925.

Chida, Y., & Steptoe, A. (2009). The association of anger and hostility with future coronary heart disease: A meta-analytic review of prospective evidence. *Journal of the American College of Cardiology*, 53, 936–946.

Chida, Y., & Steptoe, A. (2010). Greater cardiovascular responses to laboratory mental stress are associated with poor subsequent cardiovascular risk status. *Hypertension*, 55(4), 1026–1032.

Chien, H. C., Ku, C. H., Lu, R. B., Chu, H., Tao, Y. H., & Chou, K. R. (2003). Effects of social skills training on improving social skills of patients with schizophrenia. *Archives of Psychiatric Nursing*, 17(5), 228–236.

Children's Health Policy Centre. (2010). Preventing substance abuse in children and youth. *Children's Mental Health Research Quarterly*, 4(2), 1–16.

China Daily (2004, March 31). "Suicide attempts on the rise in China."

Chisholm, D., Sweeny, K., Sheehan, P., Rasmussen, B., Smit, F., Cuijpers, P., & Saxena, S. (2016). Scaling-up treatment of depression and anxiety: A global return on investment analysis. *The Lancet Psychiatry*, 3, 415-424.

Chiswick, D. (1992). Compulsory treatment of patients with psychopathic disorder: An abnormally aggressive or seriously irresponsible exercise. *Criminal Behavior and Mental Health*, 2, 106–113.

Chivers, M. L. (2017). The specificity of women's sexual response and its relationship with sexual orientations: A review and ten hypotheses. *Archives of Sexual Behavior*, 46(5), 1161–1179. doi: 10.1007/s10508-016-0897-x. Epub 2017 Jan 10.

Chivers, M. L., & Bailey, J. M. (2005). A sex difference in features that elicit genital response. *Biological Psychology*, 70, 115–120. doi:10.1016/j.biopsycho.2004.12.002

Chivers, M. L., Bouchard, K., & Timmers, A. D. (2015). Straight but not narrow; Within-gender variation in the gender-specificity of women's sexual response. *PLOS One*, 12, e0142575.

Chivers, M. L., Reiger, G., Latty, E., & Bailey, J. M. (2004). A sex difference in the specificity of sexual arousal. *Psychological Science*, 15, 736–744.

Chivers, M. L., Seto, M. C., Lalumière, M. L., Laan, E., & Grimbos, T. (2010). Agreement of self-reported and genital measures of sexual arousal in men and women: A meta-analysis. *Archives of Sexual Behavior*, 39, 5–56. doi:10.1007/s10508-009-9556-9

Chodosh, J., Kado, D. M., Seeman, T. E., & Karlamangla, A. S. (2007). Depressive symptoms as a predictor of cognitive decline: MacArthur studies of successful aging. *American Journal of Geriatric Psychiatry*, 15, 406–415.

Chokshi, N. (2017, February 14). Disney drops PewDiePie and YouTube distances itself after reports of anti-Semitic videos. Retrieved from www.nytimes.com/2017/02/14/business/pewdiepie-youtube-disney.html?_r=0

Chong, S. L., & Siegel, L. S. (2008). Stability of computational deficits in math learning disability from second through fifth grades. *Developmental Neuropsychology. Special Issue: Mathematics ability, performance, and achievement*, 33, 300–317.

Chorpita, B. F., & Daleiden, E. L. (2009). Mapping evidence-based treatments for children and adolescents: Application of the distillation and matching model to 615 treatments from 322 randomized trials. *Journal of Consulting and Clinical Psychology*, 77, 566–579.

Chou, K. L, Mackenzie, C. S., Liang, K., & Sareen, J. (2011). Three-year incidence and predictors of first-onset of DSM-IV mood, anxiety, and substance disorders in older adults: Results from Wave 2 of the National Epidemiologic Survey of Alcohol and Related Conditions. *Journal of Clinical Psychiatry*, 72(2), 144–155.

Chou, K. L. (2009). Age at onset of generalized anxiety disorder in older adults. *American Journal of Geriatric Psychiatry*, 17, 455–464.

Choy, Y., Fyer, A. J., & Lipsitz, J. D. (2007). Treatment of specific phobia in adults. *Clinical Psychology Review*, 27, 266–286.

Christensen, D. L. (2016). Prevalence and characteristics of autism spectrum disorder among children aged 8 years—autism and developmental disabilities monitoring network, 11 sites, United States, 2012. MMWR. *Surveillance Summaries*, 65.

Christianson, S., Forth, A. E., Hare, R. D., Strachan, C., Lidberg, L., & Thorell, L. (1996). Remembering details of emotional events: A comparison between psychopathic and nonpsychopathic offenders. *Personality and Individual Differences*, 20, 437–443.

Christopher, J. C., Wendt, D. C., Marecek, J., & Goodman, D. M. (2014). Critical cultural awareness: Contributions to a globalizing psychology. *American Psychologist*, 69(7), 645

Chronis-Tuscano, A., Degnan, K. A., Pine, D. S., Perez-Edgar, K., Henderson, H. A., Diaz, Y., et al. (2009). Stable early maternal report of behavioral inhibition predicts lifetime social anxiety disorder in adolescence. *Journal of the American Academy of Child & Adolescent Psychiatry*, 48(9), 928–935. doi:10.1097/CHI.0b013e3181ae09df

Chrousos, G. P., & Kino, T. (2007). Glucocorticoid action networks and complex psychiatric and/or somatic disorders. *Stress: The International Journal on the Biology of Stress*, 10, 213–219.

Chudley, A. E., Conry, J., Cook, J. L., Loock, C., Rosales, T., & LeBlanc, N. (2005). Fetal alcohol spectrum disorder: Canadian guidelines for diagnosis. *Canadian Medical Association Journal*, 172(5, Suppl.), S1–S21.

Chugani, D. C. (2002). Role of altered brain serotonin mechanisms in autism. *Molecular Psychiatry*, 7(Suppl. 2), S16–S17.

Cicchetti, D., & Beeghly, M. (1990). *Children with Down syndrome: A developmental perspective*. New York, NY: Cambridge University Press.

Claassen-van Dessel, N., van der Wouden, J. C., Dekker, J., & van der Horst, H. E. (2016). Clinical value of DSM IV and DSM 5 criteria for diagnosing the most prevalent somatoform disorders in patients with medically unexplained physical symptoms (MUPS). *Journal of Psychosomatic Research*, 82, 4–10.

Clark, D. A. (2014). Cognitive restructuring. In Dozois, D. J. A. (Vol. Ed.), S. G. Hofmann (Series Ed.), CBT: General Strategies. *The Wiley handbook of cognitive-behavioral therapy* (Vol I, pp. 23–44). Oxford: Wiley-Blackwell.

Clark, D. A., & Beck, A. T. (1999). *Scientific foundations of cognitive theory and therapy of depression*. New York, NY: Wiley.

Clark, D. A., & Beck, A. T. (2010a). Cognitive theory and therapy of anxiety and depression: Convergence with neurobiological findings. *Trends in Cognitive Sciences*, 14, 418–424.

Clark, D. A., & Beck, A. T. (2010b). *Cognitive therapy of anxiety disorders: Science and practice*. New York, NY: Guilford.

Clark, D. A., & Brown, G. P. (2014). Cognitive clinical assessment: Contributions and impediments to progress. In G. P. Brown & D. A. Clark (Eds.), *Assessment in cognitive therapy* (pp. 3–26). New York, NY: Guilford.

Clark, D. A., & Purdon, C. (2009). Mental control of unwanted intrusive thoughts: A phenomenological study of nonclinical individuals. *International Journal of Cognitive Therapy, 2,* 267–281.

Clark, D. A., Beck, A. T., & Alford, B. A. (1999). *Scientific foundations of cognitive theory and therapy of depression.* Philadelphia, PA: Wiley.

Clark, D. B., Birmaher, B., Axelson, D., Monk, K., Kalas, C., Ehmann, M., et al. (2005). Fluoxetine for the treatment of childhood anxiety disorders: Open-label, long-term extension to a controlled trial. *Journal of the American Academy of Child and Adolescent Psychiatry, 44*(12), 1263–1270.

Clark, D. M. (1986). A cognitive approach to panic. *Behaviour Research and Therapy, 24,* 461–470.

Clark, D. M. (1996). Panic disorder and social phobia. In D. M. Clark & C. G. Fairburn (Eds.), *Science and practice of cognitive-behaviour therapy* (pp. 119–154). New York, NY: Oxford University Press.

Clark, E., Lutke, J., Minnes, P., & Ouellette-Kuntz, H. (2004). Secondary disabilities among adults with fetal alcohol spectrum disorder in British Columbia. *Journal of Fetal Alcohol Syndrome International, 2,* 1–12.

Clark, L., & Lewis, D. (1977). *Rape: The price of coercive sexuality.* Toronto, ON: Women's Educational Press.

Clarkin, J. F., & Carpenter, D. (1995). Family therapy in historical perspective. In B. Bongar & L. E. Beutler (Eds.), *Comprehensive textbook of psychotherapy: Theory and practice* (pp. 205–227). New York, NY: Oxford University Press.

Clarren, S., Lutke J., Sherbuck, M. (2011). The Canadian guidelines and the interdisciplinary clinical capacity of Canada to diagnose fetal alcohol spectrum disorder. *Journal of Population Therapeutics and Clinical Pharmacology, 18,* 494–499.

Cleckley, H. (1941). *The mask of sanity.* St. Louis, MO: Mosby.

Clement, S., Schauman, O., Graham, T., Maggioni, F., Evans-Lacko, S., Bezborodovs, N., ... & Thornicroft, G. (2015). What is the impact of mental health-related stigma on help-seeking? A systematic review of quantitative and qualitative studies. *Psychological Medicine, 45*(1), 11–27.

Clement, U. (2002). Sex in long-term relationships: A systemic approach to sexual desire problems. *Archives of Sexual Behavior, 31*(3), 241–246.

Cloitre, M. (2009). Effective psychotherapies for posttraumatic stress disorder: A review and critique. *CNS Spectrums, 14,* 32–43.

Cloninger, C. R., Svrakic, D. M., & Przybeck, T. (1993). Psychobiological model of temperament and character. *Archives of General Psychiatry, 50,* 975–990.

Cobham, V. E., Dadds, M. R., & Spence, S. H. (1998). The role of parental anxiety in the treatment of childhood anxiety. *Journal of Consulting and Clinical Psychology, 66,* 893–905. doi:0022-006X/98

Coccaro, E. F. (1996). Neurotransmitter correlates of impulsive aggression in humans. *Annals of the New York Academy of Sciences, 794,* 82–89.

Coffman, D. L., Balantekin, K. N., & Savage, J. S. (2016). Using propensity score methods to assess causal effects of mothers' dieting behavior on daughters' early dieting behavior. *Childhood Obesity, 12,* 334-340. doi: 10.1089/chi.2015.0249

Cohen, N. (2009, July 28). A Rorschach cheat sheet on Wikipedia. *The New York Times,* p. A1.

Cohen, P., Cohen, J., & Brook, J. (1993). An epidemiology study of disorder in late childhood and adolescence: II. Persistence of disorder. *Journal of Child Psychology and Psychiatry, 34,* 869–877.

Cohen, P., Crawford, T. N., Johnson, J. G., & Kasen, S. (2005). The children in the community study of developmental course of personality disorder. *Journal of Personality Disorders, 19,* 466–486.

Cohen, S. C., Mulqueen, J. M., Ferracioli-Oda, E., Stuckelman, Z. D., Coughlin, C. G., Leckman, J. F., & Bloch, M. H. (2015). Meta-analysis of tics associated with stimulant use in randomized, placebo-controlled trials. *Journal of the American Academy of Child and Adolescent Psychiatry, 54,* 728-736.

Cohen, S., & Herbert, T. B. (1996). Health psychology: Psychological factors and physical disease from the perspective of human psychoneuroimmunology. *Annual Review of Psychology, 47,* 113–142.

Cohen, S., & Wills, T. A. (1985). Stress, social support, and the buffering hypothesis. *Psychological Bulletin, 98,* 310–357.

Cohen, S., Frank, E., Doyle, W. J., Skoner, D. P., Rabin, B. S., & Gwaltney, J. M. (1998). Types of stressors that increase susceptibility to the common cold in healthy adults. *Health Psychology, 17,* 214–223.

Cohen, S., Kaplan, J. R., Cunnick, J. E., Manuck, S. B., & Rabin, B. S. (1992). Chronic social stress, affiliation and cellular immune response in nonhuman primates. *Psychological Science, 3,* 301–304.

Cohen, S., Tyrrell, D. A. J., & Smith, A. P. (1993). Negative life events, perceived stress, negative affect and susceptibility to the common cold. *Journal of Personality and Social Psychology, 64,* 131–140.

Cohen-Kettenis, P. T., & Arrindell, W. A. (1990). Perceived parental rearing style, parental divorce and transsexualism: A controlled study. *Psychological Medicine, 20,* 613–620.

Cohen-Kettenis, P. T., & Gooren, L. J. (1999). Transsexualism: A review of etiology, diagnosis, and treatment. *Journal of Psychosomatic Research, 46*(4), 315–333.

Cohen-Kettenis, P. T., & Pfäfflin, F. (2010). The DSM diagnostic criteria for gender identity in adolescents and adults. *Archives of Sexual Behavior, 39,* 499–513.

Cohen-Kettenis, P. T., Owen, A., Kaijser, V. G., Bradley, S. J., & Zucker, K. J. (2003). Demographic characteristics, social competence, and behavior problems in children with gender identity disorder: A cross-national, cross-clinic comparative analysis. *Journal of Abnormal Child Psychology, 31,* 41–53.

Cohen-Mansfield, J. (2001). Nonpharmacologic interventions for inappropriate behaviors in dementia. *American Journal of Geriatric Psychiatry, 9,* 361–381.

Coid, J., & Ullrich, S. (2010). Antisocial personality disorder is on a continuum with psychopathy. *Comprehensive Psychiatry, 51,* 426–433. doi:10.1016/j.comppsych.2009.09.006

Colapinto, J. (2000). *As nature made him: The boy who was raised as a girl.* New York, NY: HarperCollins.

Colder, C. R., Campbell, R. T., Ruel, E., Richardson, J. L., & Flay, B. R. (2002). A finite mixture model of growth trajectories of adolescent alcohol use: Predictors and consequences. *Journal of consulting and clinical psychology, 70*(4), 976.

Cole, D. A., Nick, E. A., Zelkowitz, R. L., Roeder, K. M., & Spinelli, T. (2017). Online social support for young people: Does it recapitulate in-person social support; can it help?. *Computers in Human Behavior, 68,* 456-464.

Cole, J. O., Saloman, M., Gunderson, J., Sunderland, P., & Simmonds, P. (1984). Drug therapy for borderline patients. *Comprehensive Psychiatry, 25,* 249–254.

Cole, M. G. (2004). Delirium in elderly patients. *American Journal of Geriatric Psychiatry, 12,* 7–21.

Cole, M. G., Bellavance, F., & Mansour, A. (1999). Prognosis of depression in elderly community and primary care populations: A systematic review and meta-analysis. *American Journal of Psychiatry, 156,* 1182–1187.

Cole, M.G. & McCusker, J. (2016) Delirium in older adults: a chronic cognitive disorder? *International Psychogeriatrics, 28*(8): 1229–1233. doi: 10.1017/S1041610216000776.

Colebunders, B., Brondeel, S., D'Arpa, S., Hoebeke, P., & Monstrey, S. (2017). An update on the surgical treatment for transgender patients. *Sexual Medicine Reviews, 5,* 103–109.

Coleman, E. (2003). Compulsive sexual behavior: What to call it, how to treat it? *SIECUS Report, 31*(5), 12–16.

Coles, M. E., Radomsky, A. S., & Horng, B. (2006). Exploring the boundaries of memory distrust from repeated checking: Increasing external validity and examining thresholds. *Behaviour Research and Therapy, 44,* 995–1006.

Collimore, K. C., Asmundson, G. J. G., Taylor, S., & Abramowitz, J. S. (2009). Classification of hypochondriasis and other somatoform disorders. In D. McKay, J. S. Abramowitz, S. Taylor, & G. J. G. Asmundson (Eds.), *Current perspectives on the anxiety disorders: Implications for DSM-V and beyond* (pp. 431–451). New York, NY: Springer.

Collins, A. (1988). *In the sleep room: The story of the CIA brainwashing experiments in Canada.* Toronto, ON: Lester & Orpen Dennys.

Collins, K. A., Westra, H. A., Dozois, D. J. A., & Burns, D. D. (2004). Gaps in accessing treatment for anxiety and depression: Challenges for the delivery of care. *Clinical Psychology Review, 24,* 583–616.

Comer, J. S., Kendall, P. C., Franklin, M. E., Hudson, J. L., & Pimental, S. S. (2004). Obsessing/worrying about the overlap between obsessive-compulsive disorder and generalized anxiety disorder in youth. *Clinical Psychology Review, 24,* 663–683.

Comer, R. J. (1997). Substance-related disorders. In *Abnormal Psychology* (3rd ed., pp. 427–457). New York, NY: Freeman.

Compton, W. M., & Cottler, L. B. (2004). The Diagnostic Interview Schedule (DIS). In M. Hersen (Series Ed.), D. L. Segal & M. Hilsenroth (Vol. Eds.), *Comprehensive handbook of psychological assessment: Vol. 2. Personality assessment and psychopathology* (pp. 153–162). New York, NY: Wiley.

Conason, A. H., Klomek, A. B., & Sher, L. (2006). Recognizing alcohol and drug abuse in patients with eating disorders. *Quarterly Journal of Medicine, 99,* 335–339.

Condillac, R. A. (2007). Behavioral intervention and intellectual disabilities. In I. Brown & M. Percy (Eds.), *A comprehensive guide to intellectual and developmental disabilities* (pp. 363–372). London, UK: Paul Brookes.

Connolly, K. M., Olatunji, B. O., & Lohr, J. M. (2008). Evidence for disgust sensitivity mediating the sex differences found in blood-injection-injury phobia and spider phobia. *Personality and Individual Differences, 44,* 898–908.

Connolly, J. A., Boriakchanyavat, S., & Lue, T. F. (1996). Ultrasound evaluation of the penis in the assessment of impotence. *Journal of Clinical Ultrasound, 24,* 481–486.

Constitution Act, Schedule B to the Canada Act. (U. K.) 1982, c. 11.

Cook, A. N., & Roesch, R. (2012). "Tough on crime" reforms: What psychology has to say about the recent and proposed justice policy in Canada. *Canadian Psychology, 53,* 217–225.

Cook, J. L., Green, C. R., Lilley, C. M., Anderson, S. M., Baldwin, M. E., Chudley, A. E., . . . & Mallon, B. F. (2016). Fetal alcohol spectrum disorder: a guideline for diagnosis across the lifespan. *Canadian Medical Association Journal, 188*(3), 191–197.

Cook, W., & Medley, D. (1954). Proposed hostility and pharisaic virtue scaled for the MMPI. *Journal of Applied Psychology, 38,* 414–418.

Coolidge, F. L., Thede, L. L., & Jang, K. L. (2001). Heritability of personality disorders in childhood: A preliminary investigation. *Journal of Personality Disorders, 15,* 33–40.

Coolidge, F. L., Thede, L. L., & Young, S. E. (2002). The heritability of gender identity disorder in a child and adolescent twin sample. *Behavior Genetics, 32,* 251–257.

Coons, P. M. (1986). The prevalence of multiple personality disorder. *Newsletter of the International Society for the Study of Multiple Personality and Dissociation, 4,* 6–8.

Coons, P. M. (1998). The dissociative disorders: Rarely considered and underdiagnosed. *The Psychiatric Clinics of North America, 21,* 637–648.

Coons, P. M. (1999). Psychogenic or dissociative fugue: A clinical investigation of five cases. *Psychological Reports, 84,* 881–886.

Cooper v R. (1980), 1 S.C.R. 1149.

Cooper, K., Martyn-St James, M., Kaltenthaler, E., Dickinson, K., Cantrell, A., Wylie, K., et al. (2015). Behavioral therapies for management of premature ejaculation: A systematic review. *Sexual Medicine, 3,* 174–188.

Cooper, M., Corrado, R., Karlberg, A. M., & Adams, L. P. (1992). Aboriginal suicide in British Columbia: An overview. *Canada's Mental Health, 40,* 19–23.

Cooper, S. A., & Bailey, N. M. (2001). Psychiatric disorders amongst adults with learning disabilities-prevalence and relationship to ability level. *Irish Journal of Psychological Medicine, 18*(2), 45–53.

Cooper, S. A., Morrison, J., Melville, C., Finlayson, J., Allan, L., Martin, G., & Robinson, N. (2006). Improving the health of people with intellectual disabilities: Outcomes of a health screening programme after 1 year. *Journal of Intellectual Disability Research, 50*(9), 667–677.

Cooper, S. A., Smiley, E., Morrison, J., Williamson, A., & Allan, L. (2007). Mental ill-health in adults with intellectual disabilities: prevalence and associated factors. *The British Journal of Psychiatry, 190*(1), 27–35.

Cooper, Z., & Fairburn, C. G. (2011). The evolution of "enhanced" cognitive behavior therapy for eating disorders: Learning from treatment nonresponse. *Cognitive and Behavioral Practice, 18,* 394–402.

Copeland, J., Clement, N., & Swift, W. (2014). Cannabis use, harms and the management of cannabis use disorder. *Neuropsychiatry, 4*(1), 55–63.

Corcoran, R., Cahill, C., & Frith, C. D. (1997). The appreciation of visual jokes in people with schizophrenia: A study of "mentalizing" ability. *Schizophrenia Research, 24*(3), 319–327.

Corna, L. M., Cairney, J., & Streiner, D. L. (2010). Suicide ideation in older adults: Relationship to mental health problems and service use. *The Gerontologist, 50*(6), 785–797.

Corneau, S., & Stergiopoulos, V. (2012). More than being against it: Anti-racism and anti-oppression in mental health services. *Transcultural Psychiatry, 49*(2), 261–282.

Cornell, D. G., Warren, J., Hawk, G., Stafford, E., Oram, G., & Pine, D. (1996). Psychopathy in instrumental and reactive violent offenders. *Journal of Consulting and Clinical Psychology, 64,* 783–790.

Corrado, R. R., Cohen, I., Hart, S. D., & Roesch, R. (2000b). Diagnosing mental disorders in offenders: Conceptual and methodological issues. *Criminal Behaviour and Mental Health, 10,* 29–39.

Corrice, A. M., & Glidden, L. M. (2009). The Down syndrome advantage: Fact or fiction? *American Journal on Intellectual and Developmental Disabilities, 114,* 254–268.

Corrieri, S., Heider, D., Conrad, I., Blume, A., König, H. H., & Riedel-Heller, S. G. (2014). School-based prevention programs for depression and anxiety in adolescence: A systematic review. *Health Promotion International, 29*(3), 427–441.

Corrigan, P. W. (2004). How stigma interferes with mental health care. *American Psychologist, 59,* 614–625.

Corrigan, P. W., Druss, B. G., & Perlick, D. A. (2014). The impact of mental illness stigma on seeking and participating in mental health care. *Psychological Science in the Public Interest, 15,* 37–70.

Corrigan, P. W., Morris, S. B., Michaels, P. J., Rafacz, J. D., & Rüsch, N. (2012). Challenging the public stigma of mental illness: A meta-analysis of outcome studies. *Psychiatric Services, 63*(10), 963–973.

Costa, R., & Colizzi, M. (2016). The effect of cross-sex hormonal treatment on gender dysphoria individuals' mental health: A systematic review. *Neuropsychiatric Disease and Treatment, 2016,* 1953–1966.

Costello, E. J., Angold, A., Burns, B. J., Stangl, D. K., Tweed, D. L., Erkanli, A., et al. (1996). The Great Smokey Mountains study of youth: Goals, design, methods, and the prevalence of DSM-III-TR disorders. *Archives of General Psychiatry, 53,* 1129–1136.

Costello, E. J., Mustillo, S., Erkanli, A., Keeler, G., & Angold, A. (2003). Prevalence and development of psychiatric disorders in childhood and adolescence. *Archives of General Psychiatry, 60,* 837–844.

Costello, R. M. (1975). Alcoholism treatment and evaluation: In search of methods. *International Journal of the Addictions, 10,* 251–275.

Côté, G., & Hodgins, S. (1990). Co-occurring mental disorders among criminal offenders. *Bulletin of the American Academy of Psychiatry and Law, 18,* 271–281.

Cote, S. M., Vaillancourt, T., Barker, E. D., Nagin, D., & Tremblay, R. E. (2007). The joint development of physical and indirect aggression: Predictors of continuity and change during childhood. *Development and Psychopathology, 19,* 37–55.

Cotugno, A. J. (2009). Social competence and social skills training and intervention for children with autism spectrum disorders. *Journal of Autism and Developmental Disorders, 39,* 1268–1277.

Cougle, J.R., Resnick, H., & Kilpatrick, D.G. (2009). A prospective examination of PTSD symptoms as risk factors for subsequent exposure to potentially traumatic events among women. *Journal of Abnormal Psychology, 118,* 405–411.

Coupland, C., Dhiman, P., Morriss, R., Arthur, A., Barton, G., & Hippisley-Cox, J. (2011). Antidepressant use and risk of adverse outcomes in older people: Population based cohort study. *British Medical Journal.* doi:10.1136/bmj.d4551

Couturier, J., Kimber, M., & Szatmari, P. (2013). Efficacy of family-based treatment for adolescents with eating disorders: A systematic review and meta-analysis. *International Journal of Eating Disorders, 46,* 3–11. doi: 10.1002/eat.22042

Covin, R., Ouimet, A. J., Seeds, P. M., & Dozois, D. J. A. (2008). A meta-analysis of CBT for pathological worry among clients with GAD. *Journal of Anxiety Disorders, 22,* 108–116.

Cowen, E. L. (1977). Baby-steps toward primary prevention. *American Journal of Community Psychology, 5,* 1–16.

Cowen, E. L. (1980). The wooing of primary prevention. *American Journal of Community Psychology, 8,* 258–284.

Cowen, E. L. (1996). The ontogenesis of primary prevention: Lengthy strides and stubbed toes. *American Journal of Community Psychology, 24,* 235–249.

Cowen, E. L. (2000). Psychological wellness: Some hopes for the future. In D. Cicchetti, J. Rappaport, I. Sandler, & R. P. Weissberg (Eds.), *The promotion of wellness in children and adolescents.* Washington, DC: Child Welfare League of America Press.

Cox, B. J., Pagura, J., Stein, M. B., & Sareen, J. (2009). The relationship between generalized social phobia and avoidant personality disorder in a national mental health survey. *Depression and Anxiety, 26,* 354–362. doi:10.1002/da.20475

Cox, D. J. (1988). Incidence and nature of male genital exposure behavior as reported by college women. *Journal of Sex Research, 24,* 227–234.

Cox, M. L., & Zapf, P. A. (2004). An investigation of discrepancies between mental health professionals and the courts in decisions about competency. *Law and Psychology Review, 28,* 109–132.

Coyne, J. C. (1976). Toward an interactional description of depression. *Psychiatry, 39,* 2840.

CPA. *See* Canadian Psychological Association.

Craig, W., Pepler, D., & Cummings, J. (Eds.). (2009). *Rise up for respectful relationships: Prevent bullying. PREVNet Series, Vol. 2.* Kingston, ON: PREVNet Inc.

Craighead, W. E., Craighead, L. W., & Ilardi, S. S. (1995). Behavior therapies in historical perspective. In B. Bongar & L. E. Beutler (Eds.), *Comprehensive textbook of psychotherapy: Theory and practice* (pp. 64–83). New York, NY: Oxford University Press.

Craske, M. G., & Barlow, D. H. (2001). Panic disorder and agoraphobia. In D. H. Barlow (Ed.), *Clinical handbook of psychological disorders* (3rd ed., pp. 1–59). New York, NY: Guilford.

Craske, M. G., & Barlow, D. H. (2014). Panic disorder and agoraphobia. In D. H. Barlow (Ed.), *Clinical handbook of psychological disorders* (5th ed., pp. 1–61). New York, NY: Guilford.

Craske, M. G., Treanor, M., Conway, C., Zbozinek, T., & Vervliet, B. (2014). Maximizing exposure therapy: An inhibitory learning approach. *Behaviour and Research Therapy, 58,* 10–23. doi: 10.1016/j.brat.2014.04.006

Crawford, T. N., Cohen, P., Johnson, J. G., Kasen, S., First, M. B., Gordon, K., et al. (2005). Self-reported personality disorder in the children in the community sample: Convergent and prospective validity in late adolescence and adulthood. *Journal of Personality Disorders, 19,* 30–52.

Creed, F., & Barsky, A. (2004). A systematic review of the epidemiology of somatisation disorder and hypochondriasis. *Journal of Psychosomatic Research, 56,* 391–408.

Crick, N., & Dodge, K. (1994). A review and reformulation of social information-processing mechanisms in children's social adjustment. *Psychological Bulletin, 115,* 74–101.

Criminal Code of Canada, R.S.C. 1985, c. C-46.

Crisanti, A. S., & Love E. J. (2001). Characteristics of psychiatric inpatients detained under civil commitment legislation: A Canadian study. *International Journal of Law and Psychiatry, 24,* 399–410.

Crits-Christoph, P., & Barber, J. P. (2015). Psychological treatments for personality disorders. In P. E. Nathan & J. M. Gorman (Eds.), *A guide to treatments that work* (4th ed., pp. 851–870). New York, NY: Oxford University Press.

Crocker, A. C. (1992). Symposium: Prevention of mental retardation and related disabilities. Introduction: Where is the prevention movement? *Mental Retardation, 30,* iii–v.

Crocker, A. G., Nicholls, T. L., Seto, M. C., Charette, Y., Côté, G., & Caulet, M. (2015). The National Trajectory Project of individuals found Not Criminally Responsible on Account of Mental Disorder in Canada. Part 2: The people behind the label. *Canadian Journal of Psychiatry, 60,* 106–116.

Croizet, J. C., & Dutrévis, M. (2004). Socioeconomic status and intelligence: Why test scores do not equal merit. *Journal of Poverty, 8,* 91–107.

Crooks, C. V., Wolfe, D. A., Hughes, H., Jaffe, P. G., & Chiodo, D. (2008). Development, evaluation, and national implementation of a school-based program to reduce violence and related risk behaviours: Lessons from the Fourth R. *Institute for the Prevention of Crime Review, 2,* 109–135.

Crossley, N. A., Constante, M., McGuire, P., & Power, P. (2010). Efficacy of atypical v. typical antipsychotics in the treatment of early psychosis: Meta-analysis. *British Medical Journal, 196,* 434–439.

Crossley, R. (1992). Getting the words out: Case studies in facilitated communication. *Topics in Language Disorders, 12,* 1–4.

Crowe-Salazar, N. (2007). Exploring the experiences of an elder, a psychologist and a psychiatrist: How can traditional practices and healers complement existing practices in mental health? *First Peoples Child & Family Review, 3,* 83–95.

Crowley, K. (2011). Sleep and sleep disorders in older adults. *Neuropsychology Review, 21,* 41–53.

Cruise, K. R, Evans, L. J., & Pickens, I. B. (2011). Integrating mental health and special education needs into comprehensive service planning for juvenile offenders in long-term custody settings. *Learning and Individual Differences, 21*(1), 30–40.

CTV Television Network. (2011, January 13). Dire Straits' song should be censored, council rules. Retrieved from www.ctvnews.ca/dire-straits-song-should-be-censored-council-rules-1.595566

CTV Television Network. (2005, November 23). MP wants rapper 50 Cent banned from Canada. Retrieved from www.ctv.ca

Cui, Y., Shooshtari, S., Forget, E. L., Clara, I., & Cheung, K. F. (2014). Smoking during pregnancy: Findings from the 2009–2010 Canadian Community Health Survey. *PloS one, 9*(1), e84640.

Cuijpers, P., Andersson, G., Donker, T., & Van Straten, A. (2011). Psychological treatment of depression: Results of a series of meta-analyses. *Nordic Journal of Psychiatry, 65,* 354–364.

Cuijpers, P., de Beurs, D. P., van Spijker, B. A., Berking, M., Andersson, G., & Kerkhof, A. J. (2013). The effects of psychotherapy for adult depression on suicidality and hopelessness: A systematic review and meta-analysis. *Journal of Affective Disorders, 144,* 183–190

Cuijpers, P., Donker, T., Weisssman, M. M., Ravitz, P., & Cristea, J. A. (2016). Interpersonal psychotherapy for mental health problems: A comprehensive meta-analysis. *American Journal of Psychiatry, 173,* 680–687.

Cuijpers, P., Geraedts, A. A., van Oppen, P., Andersson, G., Markowitz, J. C., & van Straten, A. (2011). Interpersonal psychotherapy for depression: A meta-analysis. *American Journal of Psychiatry, 168,* 581–592.

Cuijpers, P., Hollon, S. D., van Straten, A., Bockting, C., Berking, M., & Andersson, G. (2013). Does cognitive behaviour therapy have an enduring effect that is superior to keeping patients on continuation pharmacotherapy? A meta-analysis. *BMJ Open, 26.* doi: 10.1136/bmjopen-2012-002542e002542

Cuijpers, P., van Straten, A., & Smit, F. (2006). Psychological treatment of late-life depression: A meta-analysis of randomized controlled trials. *International Journal of Geriatric Psychiatry, 21,* 1139–1149.

Culbert, K. M., Racine, S. E., & Klump, K. L. (2015). Research review: What we have learned about the causes of eating disorders–a synthesis of sociocultural, psychological, and biological research. *Journal of Child Psychology and Psychiatry, 56,* 1141–1164.

Cummings, J. L., & Benson, D. F. (1992). *Dementia: A clinical approach* (2nd ed.). Stoneham, MA: Butterworth-Heinemann.

Cummins, R. A., & Lau, A. L. D. (2003). Community integration or community exposure? A review and discussion in relation to people with an intellectual disability. *Journal of Applied Research in Intellectual Disabilities, 16,* 145–157.

Cunill, R., Castells, X., Tobias, A., & Capellá, A. (2016). Efficacy, safety and variability in pharmacotherapy for adults with attention deficit hyperactivity disorder: a meta-analysis and meta-regression in over 9000 patients. *Psychopharmacology, 233,* 187–197.

Cunningham, C. (2006). COPE: Large-group, community-based, family-centered parent training. In R. A. Barkley (Ed.), *Attention-deficit hyperactivity disorder: A handbook for diagnosis and treatment* (pp. 480–498). New York, NY: Guilford.

Cunningham, C. E. (2007). A family-centered approach to planning and measuring the outcome of interventions for children with attention-deficit/hyperactivity disorder. *Journal of Pediatric Psychology, 32*(6), 676–694.

Cunningham, C. E., Boyle, M., Offord, D., Racine, Y., Hundert, J., Secord, M., et al. (2000). Tri-ministry study: Correlates of school-based parenting course utilization. *Journal of Consulting and Clinical Psychology, 68,* 928–933.

Cunningham, C. E., Bremner, R., & Boyle, M. (1995). Large group community-based parenting programs for families of preschoolers at risk for disruptive behaviour disorders: Utilization, cost effectiveness, and outcome. *Journal of Child Psychology and Psychiatry, and Allied Disciplines, 36*(7), 1141–1159.

Cunningham, C. E., Cunningham, L. J., Martorelli, V., Tran, A., Young, J., & Zacharias, R. (1998). The effects of primary division, student-mediated conflict resolution programs on playground aggression. *Journal of Child Psychology and Psychiatry, 39,* 653–662.

Cunningham, J. A., & Breslin, F. C. (2004). Only one in three people with alcohol abuse or dependence ever seek treatment. *Addictive Behaviors, 29,* 221–223.

Cunningham, J., Yonkers, K. A., O'Brien, S., Eriksson, E. (2009). Update on research and treatment of premenstrual dysphoric disorder. *Harvard Review of Psychiatry, 17,* 120–137.

Cunningham, S. J., McGrath, P. J., Ferguson, H. B., Humphreys, P., D'Astous, J. D., Latter, J., et al. (1987). Personality and behavioural characteristics in pediatric migraine. *Headache, 27,* 16–20.

Currie, C. L. (2013). Epidemiology of adolescent Salvia divinorum use in Canada. *Drug and alcohol dependence, 128*(1), 166–170.

Currier, D., & Mann, J. J. (2008). Stress, genes and the biology of suicidal behavior. *Psychiatric Clinics of North America, 31,* 247–269.

Currin, L., Schmidt, U., Treasure, J., & Jick, H. (2005). Time trends in eating disorder incidence. *British Journal of Psychiatry, 186,* 132–135.

Cuskelly, M., & Bryde, R. (2004). Attitudes towards the sexuality of adults with an intellectual disability: Parents, support staff and a community sample. *Journal of Intellectual and Developmental Disability, 29,* 255–264.

Cuskelly, M., & Dadds, M. (1992). Behavioural problems in children with Down's syndrome and their siblings. *Journal of Child Psychology and Psychiatry, 33,* 749–761.

Custer, R. L. (1982). An overview of compulsive gambling. In P. A. Carone, S. F. Yolles, S. N. Kieffer, & L. W. Krinsky (Eds.), *Addictive disorders updated* (pp. 107–124). New York, NY: Human Sciences Press.

Cyranowski, J. M., Frank, E., Cherry, C., Houck, P., & Kupfer, D. J. (2004). Prospective assessment of sexual function in women treated for recurrent major depression. *Journal of Psychiatric Research, 38,* 267–273.

D'Onise, K., Lynch, J. W., Sawyer, M. G., & McDermott, R. A. (2010). Can preschool improve child health outcomes? A systematic review. *Social Science and Medicine, 70,* 1423–1440.

D'Onofrio, B. M., Slutske, W. S., Turkheimer, E., Emery, R. E., Harden, K. P., Heath, A. C., et al. (2007). Intergenerational transmission of childhood conduct problems: A children of twins study. *Archives of General Psychiatry, 64*(7), 820–829. doi:10.1001/archpsyc.64.7.820

D'Zurilla, T. J., & Goldfried, M. R. (1971). Problem solving and behavior modification. *Journal of Abnormal Psychology, 78,* 107–126.

D'Zurilla, T. J., & Nezu, A. M. (2010). Problem-solving therapy. In K. S. Dobson (Ed.), *Handbook of cognitive-behavioral therapies* (3rd ed., pp. 197–225). New York, NY: Guilford.

Dalenberg, C. J., Brand, B. L., Gleaves, D. H., Dorahy, M. J., Loewenstein, R. J., Cardena, . . . & Spiegel, D. (2012). Evaluation of the evidence for the trauma and fantasy models of dissociation. *Psychological Bulletin, 138*(3), 550–588.

Dalenberg, C. J., Brand, B. L., Loewenstein, R. J., Gleaves, D. H., Dorahy, M. J., Cardena, . . . & Carlson, E. B. (2014). Reality versus fantasy: Reply to Lynn et al. (2014). *Psychological Bulletin, 140*(3), 911–920.

Dalgleish, T. (2004). Cognitive approaches to posttraumatic stress disorder: The evolution of multirepresentational theorizing. *Psychological Bulletin, 130,* 228–260.

Dall, T.M., Gallo, P.D., Chakrabarti, R., West, T., Semilla, A.P., Storm, M.V. (2013). An aging population and growing disease burden will require a large and specialized health care workforce by 2025. *Health Affairs, 32*(11), 2013–2020. http://dx.doi.org/10.1377/hlthaff.2013.0714

Dalton, A. J., & McLachlan, D. R. (1986). Clinical expression of Alzheimer's disease in Down's syndrome. *Psychiatric Clinics of North America, 9,* 659–670.

Daly, B. P., Creed, T., Xanthopoulos, M., & Brown, R. T. (2007). Psychosocial treatments for children with attention deficit/hyperactivity disorder. *Neuropsychology Review, 17,* 73–89. doi:10.1007/s11065-006-9018-2

Daly, M. (1989). Sleep disorders in the elderly. *Primary Care, 16,* 475–488.

Damm, J., Eser, D., Schule, C., Obermeier, M., Moller, H., Rupprecht, R., et al. (2010). Influence of age on effectiveness and tolerability of electroconvulsive therapy. *Journal of ECT, 26*(4), 282–288.

Darke, J. L. (1990). Sexual aggression: Achieving power through humiliation. In W. L. Marshall, D. R. Laws, & H. E. Barbaree (Eds.), *Handbook of sexual assault: Issues, theories, and treatment of the offender* (pp. 55–72). New York, NY: Plenum Press.

Darke, S., Ross, J., & Cohen, J. (1994). The use of benzodiazepines among regular amphetamine users. *Addiction, 89,* 1683–1690.

Das, A. (2007). Masturbation in the United States. *Journal of Sex & Marital Therapy, 33,* 301–317.

Daum C., Hubschmid M., & Aybek S. (2014). The value of 'positive' clinical signs for weakness, sensory and gait disorders in conversion disorder: A systematic and narrative review. *Journal of Neurology, Neurosurgery & Psychiatry 85*(2), 180–190.

Davidson, L., & Heinrichs, R. W. (2003). Quantification of brain imaging findings on the frontal and temporal lobes in schizophrenia: A meta-analysis. *Psychiatry Research: Neuroimaging, 122*(2), 69–87.

Davidson, M. (1982). *Uncommon sense: The life and thought of Ludwig von Bertalanffy (1901–1972), father of general systems theory.* Boston, MA: Houghton Mifflin.

Davidson, M., Reichenberg, A., Rabinowitz, J., Weiser, M., Kaplan, Z., & Mark, M. (1999). Behavioral and intellectual markers for schizophrenia in apparently healthy male adolescents. *American Journal of Psychiatry, 156,* 1328–1335.

Davidson, P., Cain, N., Sloane-Reeves, J., Giesow, V. E., Quijano, L. E., Van Heyningen, J., & Shoham, I. (1995). Crisis intervention for community-based individuals with developmental disabilities and behavioral and psychiatric disorders. *Mental Retardation, 33,* 21–30.

Davidson, P., Cain, N., Sloane-Reeves, J., Van Speybroeck, A., Segel, J., Gutkin, J., et al. (1994). Characteristics of community-based individuals with mental retardation and aggressive behavioral disorders. *American Journal on Mental Retardation, 98,* 704–716.

Davies, D. K., Stock, S. E., Holloway, S., & Wehmeyer, M. L. (2010). Evaluating a GPS-based transportation device to support independent bus travel by people with intellectual disability. *Intellectual and Developmental Disabilities, 48,* 454–463.

Davis, C., Shuster, B., Blackmore, E., & Fox, J. (2004). Looking good—Family focus on appearance and the risk for eating disorders. *International Journal of Eating Disorders, 35,* 136–144.

Davis, K. L., Kahn, R. S., Ko, G., & Davidson, M. (1991). Dopamine in schizophrenia: A review and reconceptualization. *American Journal of Psychiatry, 148,* 1474–1486.

Davis, M. (1989). Gender and sexual development of women with mental retardation. *The Disabilities Studies Quarterly, 9*(3), 19–20.

Dawson, F., Shanahan, S., Fitzsimons, E., O'Malley, G. , MacGiollabhui, N. & Bramham, J. (2016). The impact of caring for an adult with intellectual disability and psychiatric intellectual disability and psychiatric comorbidity on career stress and psychological distress. *Journal of Intellectual Disability Research, 60*(6), 553–563.

Dawson, G., & Watling, R. (2000). Interventions to facilitate auditory, visual and motor integration in autism: A review of the evidence. *Journal of Autism and Developmental Disorders, 30,* 423–426.

Dawson, S., Bannerman, B., & Lalumiere, M. (2016). Paraphilic interests: An examination of sex differences in a nonclinical sample. *Sexual Abuse-a Journal of Research and Treatment, 28,* 20–45.

Day, N. L., Leech, S. L., Richardson, G. A., Cornelius, M. D., Robles, N., & Larkby, C. (2002). Prenatal alcohol exposure predicts continued deficits in offspring size at 14 years of age. *Alcoholism: Clinical and Experimental Research, 26,* 1584–1591.

De Leo, D., & Heller, T. S. (2008). Social modelling in the transmission of suicidality. *Crisis, 29,* 11–19.

De Leo, D., Padoani, W., Scocco, P., Lie, D., Bille-Brahe, U., Arensman, E., . . . Faria, S. (2001). Attempted and completed suicide in older subjects: Results from the WHO/EURO multicenter study of suicidal behaviour. *International Journal of Geriatric Psychiatry, 16,* 300–310. doi:10.1002=gps.337.abs

de Leon, J., & Diaz, F. J. (2005). A meta-analysis of worldwide studies demonstrates an association between schizophrenia and tobacco smoking behaviors. *Schizophrenia Research, 76,* 135–157.

De Los Reyes, A., & Kazdin, A. E. (2005). Informant discrepancies in the assessment of childhood psychopathology: A critical review, theoretical framework, and recommendations for further study. *Psychological Bulletin, 131,* 483–509. doi:10.1037/0033-2909.131.4.483

de Maat, S. M., Dekker, J., Schoevers, R. A., & de Jonghe, F. (2007). Relative efficacy of psychotherapy and combined therapy in the treatment of depression: A meta-analysis. *European Psychiatry, 22,* 1–8.

De Oliveira-Souza, R., Hare, R. D., Bramati, I. E., Garrido, G. J., Ignacio, F. A., Tovar-Moll, F., et al. (2008). Psychopathy as a disorder of the moral brain: Fronto-temporo-limbic grey matter reductions demonstrated by voxel-based morphometry. *Neuroimage, 40,* 1202–1213.

De Vries, A.M., Forni, V., Voellinger, R. & Stiefel, F. (2012). Alexithymia in cancer patients: Review of the literature. *Psychotherapy and Psychosomatics, 81,* 79 – 86.

Deacon, B., & Abramowitz, J. S. (2008). Is hypochondriasis related to obsessive-compulsive disorder, panic disorder, or both? An empirical evaluation. *Journal of Cognitive Psychotherapy, 22,* 115–127.

Dean, R. R., Kelsey, J. E., Heller, M. R., & Ciaranello, R. D. (1993). Structural foundations of illness and treatment: Receptors. In D. L. Dunner (Ed.), *Current psychiatric theory.* Philadelphia, PA: Saunders.

DeBakey, M., & Gotto, A. (1977). *The living heart.* New York, NY: Grosset & Dunlap.

Deeley, Q., Surgurladze, S., Tunstall, N., Mezey, G., Beer, D., Ambikapathy, A., et al. (2006). Facial emotion processing in criminal psychopathy. *British Journal of Psychiatry, 189,* 533–539.

Delis, D., Kaplan, E., & Kramer, J. (2001). *Delis-Kaplan executive function system.* San Antonio, TX: The Psychological Cooperation.

Denckla, M. (1996). Brain mechanisms. In M. M. Bristol, D. J. Cohen, E. J. Costello, M. Denckla, T. J. Eckberg, R. Kallen, H. C. Kraemer, et. al., State of the science in autism: Report to the National Institutes of Health. *Journal of Autism and Developmental Disorders, 26,* 134–140.

Dennerstein, L., Dudley, E., Lehert, P., & Burger, H. G. (2000, October). *Sexual functioning during the menopausal transition.* Paper presented at Female Sexual Function Forum: New perspectives in the management of female sexual dysfunction, Boston, MA.

Dennerstein, L., Smith, A. M., Morse, C. A., & Burger, H. G. (1994). Sexuality and the menopause. *Journal of Psychosomatic Obstetrics and Gynecology, 15,* 59–66.

Dennis, C. L., Hodnett, E., Kenton, L., Weston, J., Zupancic, J., Stewart, D. E., & Kiss, A. (2009). Effect of peer support on prevention of postnatal depression among high risk women: Multisite randomised controlled trial. *British Medical Journal, 338.* doi:10.1136/bmj.a3064

Denys, D., Van Nieuwerburgh, F., Deforce, D., & Westenberg, H. G. M. (2007). Prediction of response to paroxetine and venlafaxine by serotonin-related genes in obsessive-compulsive disorder in a randomized, double-blind trial. *The Journal of Clinical Psychiatry, 68,* 747–753.

Deonarine, A., Amlani, A., Ambrose, G., & Buxton, J. A. (2016). Qualitative assessment of take-home naloxone program participant and law enforcement interactions in British Columbia. *Harm reduction journal, 13*(1), 17.

Department of Health, UK. (2001). Treatment choice in psychological therapies and counselling: Evidence based clinical practice guideline. Retrieved from www.dh.gov.uk/assetRoot/04/05/82/45/04058245.pdf

Department of Justice, Canada. (2012). *National anti-drug strategy evaluation: Final report.* Retrieved from www.justice.gc.ca/eng/rp-pr/cp-pm/eval/rep-rap/12/nas-sna/

Depla, M. F. I. A., ten Have, M. L., van Balkom, A. J. L. M., & de Graaf, R. (2008). Specific fears and phobias in the general population: Results from the Netherlands mental health survey and incidence study (NEMESIS). *Social Psychiatry and Psychiatric Epidemiology, 43,* 200–208.

Depue, R. A. (2009). Genetic, environmental, and epigenetic factors in the development of personality disturbance. *Development and Psychopathology, 21,* 1031–1063.

Depue, R. A., Luciana, M., Arbisi, P., Collins, P., & Leon, A. (1994). Dopamine and the structure of personality: Relation of agonist-induced dopamine activity to positive emotionality. *Journal of Personality and Social Psychology, 67,* 485–498.

DeRubeis, R. J., Hollon, S. D., Amsterdam, J. D., Shelton, R. C., Young, P. R., Salomon, R. M., et al. (2005). Cognitive therapy vs medications in the treatment of moderate to severe depression. *Archives of General Psychiatry, 62,* 409–416.

DeRyck, B., Gekoski, W. L., Knox, V. J., & Zivian, M. T. (1996, October). *Mental disorders in older adults: The beliefs and attitudes of clinical psychology graduate students.* Quebec, QC: Canadian Association on Gerontology.

Deschênes, S. S., Dugas, M. J., & Gouin, J. P. (2016). Intolerance of uncertainty, worry catastrophizing, and heart rate variability during worry-inducing tasks. *Personality and Individual Differences, 90*(2), 199–204.

Deschênes, S. S., Dugas, M. J., Anderson, K. G., & Gouin, J. P. (2015). Effects of anger induction on worry and cognitive vulnerabilities underlying generalized anxiety disorder. *Journal of Experimental Psychopathology, 6,* 138–148. doi: 10.5127/jep.042814

Deschênes, S. S., Dugas, M. J., Fracalanza, K., & Koerner, N. (2012). The role of anger in generalized anxiety disorder. *Cognitive Behaviour Therapy, 41,* 261–271. doi: 10.1080/16506073.2012.666564

DeStefano, F., Bhasin, T. K., Thompson, W. W., Yeargin-Allsopp, M., & Boyle, C. (2004). Age at first measles-mumps-rubella vaccination in children with autism and school-matched control subjects: A population-based study in metropolitan Atlanta. *Pediatrics, 113*(2), 259–266.

Deutsch, A. (1948). *The shame of the States.* New York, NY: Harcourt Brace.

DeWall, C., Buffardi, L. E., Bonser, I., & Campbell, W. (2011). Narcissism and implicit attention seeking: Evidence from linguistic analyses of social networking and online presentation. *Personality and Individual Differences, 51,* 57–62. doi:10.1016/j.paid.2011.03.011

Dhingra, K., Boduszek, D., & O'Connor, R. C. (2015). Differentiating suicide attempters from suicide ideators using the Integrated Motivational-Volitional model of suicidal behaviour. *Journal of Affective Disorders, 186,* 211–218.

Di Castelnuovo, A., Costanzo, S., Bagnardi, V., Donati, M. B., Iacoviello, L., & de Gaetano, G. (2006). Alcohol dosing and total mortality in men and women: An updated meta-analysis of 34 prospective studies. *Archives of Internal Medicine, 166,* 2437–2445.

Diamond, D. B. (1997). The fate of the ego in contemporary psychiatry with particular reference to etiologic theories of schizophrenia. *Psychiatry: Interpersonal and Biological Processes, 60,* 67–88.

Diamond, M. (1982). Sexual identity, monozygotic twins reared in discordant sex roles and a BBC follow-up. *Archives of Sexual Behavior, 11,* 181–186.

Diaz, J. H. (2004). The global epidemiology, syndromic classification, management, and prevention of spider bites. *The American Journal of Tropical Medicine and Hygiene, 71,* 239–250.

Dick, D. M., Agrawal, A., Keller, M. C., Adkins, A., Aliev, F., Monroe, S., . . . Sher, K. J. (2015). Candidate gene–environment interaction research: Reflections and recommendations. *Perspectives on Psychological Science, 10*(1), 37–59. doi.org/10.1177/1745691614556682

Dickerson, F. B., & Lehman, A. (2011). Evidence based psychotherapy for schizophrenia: 2011 update. *Journal of Nervous and Mental Disease, 199,* 520–526.

Dickerson, F., Stallings, C. R., Origoni, A. E., Vaughan, C., Khushalani, S., Schroeder, J., & Yolken, R. H. (2013). Cigarette smoking among persons with schizophrenia or bipolar disorder in routine clinical settings, 1999–2011. *Psychiatric Services, 64*(1), 44-50.

Dickey, R., & Steiner, B. W. (1990). Hormone treatment and surgery. In R. Blanchard & B. W. Steiner (Eds.), *Clinical management of gender identity disorders in children and adults* (pp. 139–158). Washington, DC: American Psychiatric Press.

Dickinson, D., Ramsey, M., & Gold, J. M. (2007). Overlooking the obvious: A meta-analytic comparison of digit symbol coding tasks and other cognitive measures in schizophrenia. *Archives of General Psychiatry, 64,* 532–542.

Dickson, H., Laurens, K. R., Cullen, A. E., & Hodgins, S. (2012). Meta-analyses of cognitive and motor function in youth aged 16 years and younger who subsequently develop schizophrenia. *Psychological Medicine, 42*(4), 743–755.

Dickstein, D. P., Towbin, K. E., Van Der Veen, J. W., Rich, B. A., Brotman, M. A., Knopf, L., et al. (2009). Randomized double-blind placebo-controlled trial of lithium in youths with severe mood dysregulation. *Journal of Child and Adolescence Psychopharmacology, 19,* 61–73. doi:10.1089/cap.2008.044

Diener, E., Suh, E. M., Lucas, R. E., & Smith, H. L. (1999). Subjective well-being: Three decades of progress. *Psychological Bulletin, 125,* 276–302.

Dimidjian, S., Barrera, M., Martell, C., Muñoz, R. F., & Lewinsohn, P. M. (2011). The origins and current status of behavioral activation for depression. *Annual Review of Clinical Psychology, 7,* 1–38.

Dimidjian, S., Hollon, S. D., Dobson, K. S., Schmaling, K. B., Kohlenberg, R. J., Addis, M. E., et al. (2006). Randomized trial of behavioral activation, cognitive therapy, and antidepressant medication in the acute treatment of adults with major depression. *Journal of Consulting and Clinical Psychology, 74,* 658–670.

Dimitrelis, K., & Shankar, R. (2016). Pharmacological treatment of schizophrenia–a review of progress. *Progress in Neurology and Psychiatry, 20*(3), 28–35.

Dimsdale, J. E., & Ziegler, M. G. (1991). What do plasma and urinary measures of catecholamines tell us about human response to stressors? *Circulation, 83*(Suppl. II), II-36–II-42.

Dingemans, A. E., & van Furth, E. F. (2012). Binge eating disorder psychopathology in normal weight and obese individuals. *International Journal of Eating Disorders, 45,* 135–138.

Dishion, T. J., & Patterson, S. G. (1996). *Preventive parenting with love, encouragement, and limits: The preschool years.* Eugene, OR: Castalia.

Diskin, K. M., & Hodgins, D. C. (2009). A randomized controlled trial of a single session motivational intervention for concerned gamblers *Behaviour Research and Therapy, 47,* 382–388.

Distel, M. A., Vink, J. M., Willemsen, G., Middeldorp, C. M., Merckelbach, H. L. G. J., & Boomsma, D. I. (2008). Heritability of self-reported phobic fear. *Behavior Genetics, 38,* 24–33.

Dixon, J. F., & Hokin, L. E. (1998). Lithium acutely inhibits and chronically up-regulates and stabilizes glutamate uptake by presynaptic nerve endings in mouse cerebral cortex. *Proceedings of the National Academy of Sciences, 95,* 8363–8368.

Dobson, D., & Dobson, K. S. (2016). *Evidence-based practice of cognitive-behavioral therapy* (2nd ed.). New York, NY: Guilford.

Dobson, J. C., Kushida, E., Williamson, M., & Friedman, E. G. (1976). Intellectual performances of 36 phenylketonuria patients and their nonaffected siblings. *Pediatrics, 58,* 53–58.

Dobson, K. S. (1989). A meta-analysis of the efficacy of cognitive therapy for depression. *Journal of Consulting and Clinical Psychology, 57,* 414–419.

Dobson, K. S., Hollon, S. D., Dimidjian, S., Schmaling, K. B., Kohlenberg, R. J., Gallop, R. J., et al. (2008). Randomized trial of behavioral activation, cognitive therapy, and antidepressant medication in the prevention of relapse and recurrence in major depression. *Journal of Consulting and Clinical Psychology, 76,* 468–477.

Docter, R. F., & Prince, V. (1997). Transvestism: A survey of 1032 cross-dressers. *Archives of Sexual Behavior, 26*(6), 589–605.

Dodge, K. A. (1986). A social information processing model of social competence in children. In M. Perlmutter (Ed.), *Minnesota symposium in child psychology* (Vol. 18, pp. 77–125). Hillsdale, NJ: Lawrence Erlbaum Associates.

Dols, M. W. (2006). Historical perspective: Medical madness. *Journal of Muslim Mental Health, 1,* 77–95.

Dominguez, M. G., Viechtbauer, W., Simons, C. J., van Os, J., & Krabbendam, L. (2009). Are psychotic psychopathology and neurocognition orthogonal? A systematic review of their associations. *Psychological Bulletin, 135*(1), 157.

Donegan, E., & Dugas, M. J. (2012). Generalized anxiety disorder: A comparison of symptom change in adults receiving cognitive-behavioral therapy or applied relaxation. *Journal of Consulting and Clinical Psychology, 80,* 490–496.

Donnellan, A. M., Mirenda, P. L., Mesaros, R. A., & Fassbender, L. L. (1984). Analyzing the communicative functions of aberrant behavior. *Journal of the Association of Persons with Severe Handicaps, 9,* 201–212.

Donovan, M. R., Glue, P., Kolluri, S., & Emir, B. (2010). Comparative efficacy of antidepressants in preventing relapse in anxiety disorders—A meta-analysis. *Journal of Affective Disorders, 123,* 9–16.

Dorey, G., Speakman, M., Feneley, R., Swinkels, A., Dunn, C., & Ewings, P. (2004). Randomised controlled trial of pelvic floor muscle exercises and manometric biofeedback for erectile dysfunction. *British Journal of General Practice, 54,* 819–825.

Douglas, K. S., & Reeves, K. A. (2010). Historical-Clinical-Risk Management-20 (HCR-20) violence risk assessment scheme: Rationale, application, and empirical overview. In R. K. Otto & K. S. Douglas (Eds.), *Handbook of violence risk assessment* (pp. 147–185). New York, NY: Routledge.

Douglas, K. S., Guy, L. S., & Hart, S. D. (2009) Psychosis as a risk factor for violence to others: a meta-analysis. *Psychology Bulletin, 135,* 679–706.

Douglas, K. S., Hart, S. D., Webster, C. D., & Belfrage, H. (2013). *HCR-20^{V3}: Assessing risk for violence.* Burnaby, BC: Mental Health, Law, and Policy Institute, Simon Fraser University.

Douglas, K. S., Ogloff, J. R. P., Nicholls, T., & Grant, I. (1999). Assessing risk for violence among psychiatric patients: The HCR-20 Violence Risk Assessment Scheme and the Psychopathy Checklist: Screening Version. *Journal of Consulting and Clinical Psychology, 67,* 917–930.

Douglas, K. S., Vincent, G. M., & Edens, J. F. (2007). Risk for criminal recidivism: The role of psychopathy. In C. J. Patrick (Ed.), *Handbook of psychopathy* (pp. 533–554). New York, NY: Guilford.

Douville, R., & Casanova, J. D. (1967). *La vie quotidienne des Indiens du Canada à l'époque de la colonisation Francaise.* Paris, France: Librarie Hachette.

Dowlati, Y., Herrmann, N., Swardfager, W., Liu, H., Sham, L., Reim, E. K., & Lanctôt, K. L. (2010). A meta-analysis of cytokines in major depression. *Biological Psychiatry, 67*(5), 446–457.

Dozois, D. J. A. (2011). From the president's desk—Training in professional psychology: The content and process of learning. *Psynopsis. 33*(4), 7–9.

Dozois, D. J. A. (2013). Presidential address—Psychological treatments: Putting evidence into practice and practice into evidence. *Canadian Psychology, 54*(1), 1–11.

Dozois, D. J. A., & Beck, A. T. (2008). Cognitive schemas, beliefs and assumptions. In K. S. Dobson & D. J. A. Dozois (Eds.), *Risk factors in depression* (pp. 123–145). Oxford, UK: Elsevier.

Dozois, D. J. A., & Beck, A. T. (2011). Cognitive therapy. In J. D. Herbert & E. M. Forman (Eds.), *Acceptance and mindfulness in cognitive behavioral therapy: Understanding and applying the new therapies* (pp. 26–56). New York, NY: Wiley.

Dozois, D. J. A., & Dobson, K. S. (2001a). Information processing and cognitive organization in unipolar depression: Specificity and comorbidity issues. *Journal of Abnormal Psychology, 110*, 236–246.

Dozois, D. J. A., & Dobson, K. S. (2001b). A longitudinal investigation of information processing and cognitive organization in clinical depression: Stability of schematic interconnectedness. *Journal of Consulting and Clinical Psychology, 69*, 914–925.

Dozois, D. J. A., & Dobson, K. S. (2010). Depression. In M. M. Antony & D. H. Barlow (Eds.), *Handbook of assessment and treatment planning for psychological disorders* (2nd ed., pp. 344–389). New York, NY: Guilford.

Dozois, D. J. A., & Dobson, K. S. (Eds.). (2004). *The prevention of anxiety and depression: Theory, research, and practice.* Washington, DC: American Psychological Association.

Dozois, D. J. A., Dobson, K. S., & Rnic, K. (in press). Historical and philosophical bases of the cognitive-behavioral therapies. In K. S. Dobson & D. J. A. Dozois (Eds.), *Handbook of cognitive-behavioral therapies* (4th ed.). New York, NY: Guilford.

Dozois, D. J. A., & Frewen, P. A. (2006). Specificity of cognitive structure in depression and social phobia: A comparison of interpersonal and achievement content. *Journal of Affective Disorders, 90*, 101–109.

Dozois, D. J. A., & Rnic, K. (2015). Core beliefs and self-schematic structure in depression. *Current Opinion in Psychology, 4*, 98–103.

Dozois, D. J. A., & Westra, H. A. (2004). The nature of anxiety and depression: Implications for prevention. In D. J. A. Dozois & K. S. Dobson (Eds.), *The prevention of anxiety and depression: Theory, research, and practice* (pp. 9–41). Washington, DC: American Psychological Association.

Dozois, D. J. A., Bieling, P. J., Evraire, L. E., Patelis-Siotis, I., Hoar, L., Chudzik, S., . . . Westra, H. A. (2014). Changes in core beliefs (early maladaptive schemas) and self-representation in cognitive therapy and pharmacotherapy for depression. *International Journal of Cognitive Therapy, 7*(3), 217–234.

Dozois, D. J. A., Bieling, P. J., Patelis-Siotis, I., Hoar, L., Chudzik, S., McCabe, K., & Westra, H. A. (2009). Changes in self-schema structure in cognitive therapy for major depressive disorder: A randomized clinical trial. *Journal of Consulting and Clinical Psychology, 77*(6), 1078–1088.

Dozois, D. J. A., Covin, R., & Brinker, J. K. (2003). Normative data on cognitive measures of depression. *Journal of Consulting and Clinical Psychology, 71*, 71–80.

Dozois, D. J. A., Dobson, K. S., & Westra, H. A. (2004). The comorbidity of anxiety and depression, and the implications of comorbidity for prevention. In D. J. A. Dozois & K. S. Dobson (Eds.), *The prevention of anxiety and depression: Theory, research, and practice* (pp. 261–280). Washington, DC: American Psychological Association.

Dozois, D. J. A., Mikail, S., Alden, L. E., Bieling, P. J., Bourgon, G., Clark, D. A., . . . Johnston, C. (2014). The CPA presidential task force on evidence-based practice of psychological treatments. *Canadian Psychology, 55*, 153–160.

Dozois, D. J. A., Seeds, P. M., & Collins, K. A. (2009). Transdiagnostic approaches to the prevention of depression and anxiety. *International Journal of Cognitive Psychotherapy: An International Quarterly, 23*, 44–59.

Dragt, S., Nieman, D. H., Veltman, D., Becker, H. E., van de Fliert, R., de Haan L., & Linszen, D. H. (2011). Environmental factors and social adjustment as predictors of a first psychosis in subjects at ultra high risk. *Schizophrenia Research, 125*, 69–76.

Drake, R. E., & Vaillant, G. E. (1985). A validity study of axis II of DSM-III. *American Journal of Psychiatry, 142*, 553–558.

Drapeau, M., Holmqvist, M., & Piotrowski, A. (2016). Psychology in Canada: Opportunities and challenges. *Canadian Psychology/Psychologie Canadienne, 57*, 143–148.

Drasgow, F. (2012). Intelligence and the workplace. In I. B. Weiner, N. W. Schmitt, & S. Highhouse (Eds.), *Handbook of psychology, industrial and organizational psychology* (pp. 184–210). London, UK: Wiley.

Drevets, W. C. (2000). Functional anatomical abnormalities in limbic and prefrontal cortical structures in major depression. *Progress in Brain Research, 126*, 413–431.

Drevets, W. C., Price, J. L., & Furey, M. L. (2008). Brain structural and functional abnormalities in mood disorders: implications for neurocircuitry models of depression. *Brain Structure and Function, 213*(1-2), 93118.

Dryden, W. (2012). Rational emotive behavior therapy (REBT). In W. Dryden (Ed.), *Cognitive behaviour therapies* (pp. 189–215). London, UK: Sage.

Dryden, W. (2013). On rational beliefs in rational emotive behavior therapy: A theoretical perspective. *Journal of Rational-Emotive and Cognitive-Behavior Therapy, 31*, 39–48.

Du, L. J., Chen, B. R., Kim, J. J., Kim, S., Shen, J. H., & Dai, N. (2016). Helicobacter pylori eradication therapy for functional dyspepsia: Systematic review and meta-analysis. *World Journal of Gastroenterology, 22*(12), 3486–3495.

Duckworth, A. L., & Seligman, M. E. (2005). Self-discipline outdoes IQ in predicting academic performance of adolescents. *Psychological Science, 16*(12), 939–944.

Dudeney, J., Sharpe, L., & Hunt, C. (2015). Attentional bias towards threatening stimuli in children with anxiety: A meta-analysis. *Clinical Psychology Review, 40*, 66–75.

Dugas, M. J., & Robichaud, M. (2007). *Cognitive-behavioral treatment for generalized anxiety disorder: From science to practice.* New York, NY: Routledge.

Dugas, M. J., Gagnon, F., Ladouceur, R., & Freeston, M. H. (1998). Generalized anxiety disorder: A preliminary test of a conceptual model. *Behaviour Research and Therapy, 36*(2), 215–226.

Dugas, M. J., Hedayati, M., Karavidas, A., Buhr, K., Francis, K., & Phillips, N. A. (2005). Intolerance of uncertainty and information processing: Evidence of biased recall and interpretations. *Cognitive Therapy and Research, 29*, 57–70.

Dugas, M. J., Marchand, A., & Ladouceur, R. (2005). Further validation of a cognitive-behavioural model of generalized anxiety disorder: Diagnostic and symptom specificity. *Journal of Anxiety Disorders, 19*, 329–343.

Dukes, E., & McGuire, B. E. (2009). Enhancing capacity to make sexuality-related decisions in people with intellectual disability. *Journal of Intellectual Disability Research, 53*, 727–734.

Dulude, L., Labelle, A., & Knott, V. J. (2010). Acute nicotine alteration of sensory memory impairment in smokers with schizophrenia. *Journal of Clinical Psychopharmacology, 30*(5), 541–548.

Dunbar, H. F. (1935). *Emotions and bodily changes.* New York, NY: Columbia University Press.

Dunn, L. M., & Dunn, D. M. (2007). *Peabody picture vocabulary test* (4th ed.). Minneapolis, MN: Pearson Assessments.

Durkheim, E. (1951). *Suicide: A study in sociology* (G. Simpson & J. A. Spaulding, trans.). New York: The Free Press.

Durkin, M. (2002). The epidemiology of developmental disabilities in low income countries. *Mental Retardation and Developmental Disabilities Research Reviews, 8*, 206–211.

Durlak, J. A. (Ed.). (1998). Program implementation in preventive trials [special issue]. *Journal of Prevention and Intervention in the Community, 17*(2).

Durlak, J. A., & DuPre, E. P. (2008). Implementation matters: A review of research on the influence of implementation on program outcomes and the factors affecting implementation. *American Journal of Community Psychology, 41*, 327–350.

Durlak, J. A., Taylor, R. D., Kawashima, K., Pachan, M. K., DuPre, E. P., Cello, C. I., et al. (2007). Effects of positive youth development programs on school, family, and community systems. *American Journal of Community Psychology, 39*, 269–286.

Dutton, D. G. (2002). The neurobiology of abandonment homicide. *Aggression and Violent Behavior, 7*, 407–421.

Dutton, D. G., & Starzomski, A. J. (1993). Borderline personality in perpetrators of psychological and physical abuse. *Violence and Victims, 8*, 327–337.

Dutton, D. G., Saunders, K., Starzomski, A., & Batholomew, K. (1994). Intimacy-anger and insecure attachment as precursors of abuse in intimate relationships. *Journal of Applied Social Psychology, 24*, 1367–1386.

Dvorak-Bertsch, J. D., Curtin, J. J., Rubinstein, T. J., & Newman, J. P. (2009). Psychopathic traits moderate the interaction between cognitive and affective processing. *Psychophysiology, 46*(5), 913–921. doi:10.1111/j.1469-8986.2009.00833.x

Dykens, E. M. (2000). Annotation: Psychopathology in children with intellectual disability. *Journal of Child Psychology and Psychiatry, 41*, 407–417.

Dykens, E. M., Hodapp, R. M., & Finucane, B. M. (2000). *Genetics and mental retardation syndromes: A new look at behavioral interventions.* Baltimore, MD: Paul H. Brookes.

Dykens, E. M., Hodapp, R. M., & Leckman, J. F. (1987). Strengths and weaknesses in the intellectual functioning of males with Fragile X syndrome. *American Journal of Mental Deficiency, 92,* 234–236.

Dykens, E. M., Hodapp, R. M., & Leckman, J. F. (1994). *Behavior and development in Fragile X syndrome.* London, UK: Sage.

Dykens, E. M., Leckman, J. F., Paul, R., & Watson, M. (1988). Cognitive, behavioral and adaptive functioning in Fragile X and non-Fragile X retarded men. *Journal of Autism and Developmental Disorders, 18,* 41–52.

Dykman, B. M., Horowitz, L. M., Abramson, L. Y., & Usher, M. (1991). Schematic and situational determinants of depressed and nondepressed students' interpretation of feedback. *Journal of Abnormal Psychology, 100,* 45–55.

Dyshniku, F., Murray, M. E., Fazio, R. L., Lykins, A. D., & Cantor, J. M. (2015). Minor physical anomalies as a window into the prenatal origins of pedophilia. *Archives of Sexual Behavior, 44,* 2151–2159.

Dzelme, K., & Jones, R. A. (2001). Male cross-dressers in therapy: A solution focused perspective for marriage and family therapists. *American Journal of Family Therapy, 29,* 293–305.

Early Head Start Benefits Children and Families. (2006). Retrieved from www.earlychildhoodrc.org/events/presentations/raikes.pdf

Ebly, E. M., Parhad, I. M., Hogan, D. B., & Fung, T. S. (1994). Prevalence and types of dementia in the very old: Results from Canadian Study of Health and Aging. *Neurology, 44,* 1593–1600.

Eccles, W. J. (1959). *Frontenac: The courtier governor.* Toronto, ON: McClelland & Stewart.

Eckenrode, J., Campa, M., Luckey, D. W., Henderson, C. R., Jr., Cole, R., Kitzman, H., ... & Olds, D. (2010). Long-term effects of the prenatal infancy nurse home visitation on the life course of youths: 19-year follow-up of a randomized trial. *Archives of Pediatric and Adolescent Medicine, 164,* 9–15.

Eddy, K. T., Dorer, D. J., Franko, D. L., Tahilani, K., Thompson-Brenner, H., & Herzog, D. B. (2008). Diagnostic crossover in anorexia nervosa and bulimia nervosa: Implications for DSM-V. *American Journal of Psychiatry, 165,* 245–250. doi: 10.1176/appi.ajp.2007.07060951

Edens, J. F., Marcus, D. K., & Morey, L. C. (2009). Paranoid personality has a dimensional latent structure: Taxometric analyses of community and clinical samples. *Journal of Abnormal Psychology, 118,* 545–553. doi:10.1037/a0016313

Edgerton, R. B. (1967). *The cloak of competence: Stigma in the lives of the mentally retarded.* Berkeley, CA: University of California.

Edgerton, R. B. (1993). *The cloak of competence.* Berkeley, CA: University of California Press.

Edwards, A. C., Bacanu, S. A., Bigdeli, T. B., Moscati, A., & Kendler, K. S. (2016). Evaluating the dopamine hypothesis of schizophrenia in a large-scale genome-wide association study. *Schizophrenia Research, 176*(2), 136–140.

Egan, S. K., & Perry, D. G. (1998). Does low self-regard invite victimization? *Developmental Psychology, 34,* 299–309. doi:10.1037/0012-1649.34.2.299

Ehlers, A., & Clark, D. M. (2000). A cognitive model of posttraumatic stress disorder. *Behaviour Research and Therapy, 38,* 319–345.

Ehlers, A., & Clark, D. M. (2003). Early psychological interventions for adult survivors of trauma: A review. *Biological Psychiatry, 53,* 817–826.

Ehring, T., Welboren, R., Morina, N., Wicherts, J. M., Freitage, J., & Emmelkamp, P. M. G. (2014). Meta-analysis of psychological treatments for posttraumatic stress disorder in adult survivors of childhood abuse. *Clinical Psychology Review, 34,* 645–657.

Ehrlich, S., Brauns, S., Yendiki, A., Ho, B. C., Calhoun, V., Schulz, S. C., ... & Sponheim, S. R. (2012). Associations of cortical thickness and cognition in patients with schizophrenia and healthy controls. *Schizophrenia Bulletin, 38*(5), 1050–1062.

Ejareh dar, M., & Kanaan, R. A. A. (2016). Uncovering the etiology of conversion disorder: Insights from functional neuroimaging. *Neuropsychiatric Disease and Treatment, 12,* 143–153.

El-Badri, S. R., & Robertshaw, B. A. (1998). Sexual fetishism associated with temporal lobe dysrhythmia and learning disability: Two case studies. *British Journal of Learning Disabilities, 26*(3), 110–114.

El-Gabalawy, R., Mackenzie, C. S., Pietrzak, R. H., & Sareen, J. (2014). A longitudinal examination of anxiety disorders and physical health conditions in a nationally representative sample of U.S. older adults. *Experimental Gerontology, 60,* 46–56. doi: 10.1016/j.exger.2014.09.012.

El-Sakka, A. (2006). Intracavernosal prostaglandin E$_1$ self vs office injection therapy in patients with erectile dysfunction. *International Journal of Impotence Research, 18,* 180–185.

El-Sakka, A. I. (2016). What is the current role of intracavernosal injection in management of erectile dysfunction? *International Journal of Impotence Research, 28,* 88–95.

Elias, M. J. (1987). Establishing enduring prevention programs: Advancing the legacy of Swampscott. *American Journal of Community Psychology, 15,* 539–553.

Elkin, I., Shea, M. T., Watkins, J. T., Imber, S. M., Sotsky, S. M., Collins, J. F., et al. (1989). National Institute of Mental Health Treatment of Depression Collaborative Research Program: General effectiveness of treatments. *Archives of General Psychiatry, 46,* 971–982.

Elliott, R., & Greenberg, L. S. (1995). Experiential therapy in practice: The process-experiential approach. In B. M. Bongar & L. E. Beutler (Eds.), *Comprehensive textbook of psychotherapy: Theory and practice* (pp. 123–139). New York, NY: Oxford University Press.

Elliott, R., Greenberg, L. S., Watson, J., Timulak, L., & Freire, E. (2013). Research on humanistic-experiential psychotherapies. In M. L. Lambert (Ed.), *Bergin and Garfield's handbook of psychotherapy and behavior change* (6th ed., pp. 495–540). Hoboken, NJ: Wiley.

Ellis, A. (1962). *Reason and emotion in psychotherapy.* New York: Lyle Stuart.

Ellis, A. (1991). *Reason and emotion in psychotherapy.* New York: Citadel.

Ellis, A. (1999). Early theories and practices of rational emotive behavior therapy and how they have been augmented and revised during the last three decades. *Journal of Rational-Emotive and Cognitive Therapy, 17,* 69–93.

Ellis, A. (2004). Why rational emotive behavior therapy is the most comprehensive and effective form of behavior therapy. *Journal of Rational-Emotive and Cognitive-Behavior Therapy, 22,* 85–92.

Ellis, A., & Ellis, D. J. (2014). Rational emotive behavior therapy. In D. Wedding & R. J. Corsini *Current Psychotherapies* (10th ed., pp. 151–192). Belmont, CA: Brooks/Cole, Cengage Learning.

Ellis, B. J., Boyce, W. T., Belsky, J., Bakermans-Kranenburg, M. J., & Van IJzendoorn, M. H. (2011). Differential susceptibility to the environment: An evolutionary-neurodevelopmental theory. *Development and Psychopathology, 23*(01), 7-28. doi: 10.1017/S0954579410000611

Elton-Marshall, T., Leatherdale, S. T., & Turner, N. E. (2016). An examination of internet and land-based gambling among adolescents in three Canadian provinces: Results from the youth gambling survey (YGS). *BMC Publish Health, 16, 277 (published online).* https://bmcpublichealth.biomedcentral.com/track/pdf/10.1186/s12889-016-2933-0?site=bmcpublichealth.biomedcentral.com

Emerson, E., & Hatton, C. (2007). Contribution of socioeconomic position to health inequalities of British children and adolescents with intellectual disabilities. *American Journal on Mental Retardation, 112,* 140–150.

Emerson, E., Glover, G., Turner, S., Greig, R., Hatton, C., Baines, S., ... & Welch, V. (2012). Improving health and lives: the learning disabilities public health observatory. *Advances in Mental Health and Intellectual Disabilities, 6*(1), 26–32.

Emerson, E., Hatton, C., Llewellyn, G., Blacher, J & Graham, H., (2006) Socioeconomic position, household composition, health status and indicators of the well-being of mothers of children with and without intellectual disabilities. *Journal of Intellectual Disability Research, 50,* 862–873.

Emerson, E., Llewellyn, G., Hatton, C., Hindmarsh, G., Robertson, J., Man, W. Y. N., & Baines, S. (2015). The health of parents with and without intellectual impairment in the UK. *Journal of Intellectual Disability Research, 59*(12), 1142–1154.

Emerson, E., Madden, R., Graham, H., Llewellyn, G., Hatton, C., & Robertson, J. (2011). The health of disabled people and the social determinants of health. *Public health, 125*(3), 145–147.

Endler, N. S., & Magnusson, D. (1976). *Interactional psychology and personality.* Washington, DC: Hemisphere.

Eng, M. Y., Luczak, S. E., & Wall, T. L. (2007). ALDH2, ADH1B, and ADH1C genotypes in Asians: A literature review. *Alcohol Research & Health, 30,* 22–27.

Engel, G. L. (1977). The need for a new medical model: A challenge for biomedicine. *Science, 196,* 129–136.

Epp, A., & Dobson, K. S. (2010). The evidence base for cognitive-behavioral therapy. In K. S. Dobson (Ed.), *Handbook of cognitive-behavioral therapies* (pp. 39–73). New York, NY: Guilford.

Epp, J. (1986). Achieving health for all: A framework for health promotion. *Canadian Journal of Public Health, 77,* 393–407.

Epp, J. (1988). *Mental health for Canadians: Striking a balance.* Ottawa, ON: Minister of Supplies and Services.

Eranti, S. V., MacCabe, J. H., Bundy, H., & Murray, R. M. (2013). Gender difference in age at onset of schizophrenia: A meta-analysis. *Psychological Medicine, 43*(1), 155–167.

Ergon. (2006, May 5). Stephen Wiltshire: The Human Camera. Retrieved from www.youtube.com/watch?v=a8YXZTlwTAU

Erickson, J., & Johnson, G. M. (2011). Internet use and psychological wellness during late adulthood. *Canadian Journal on Aging, 30,* 197–209.

Ericson, M., Tuvblad, C., Raine, A., Young-Wolff, K., & Baker, L. A. (2011). Heritability and longitudinal stability of schizotypal traits during adolescence. *Behavior Genetics, 41,* 499–511. doi:10.1007/s10519-010-9401-x

Erlenmeyer-Kimling, L., Rock, D., Roberts, S. A., Janal, M., Kestenbaum, C., Cronblatt, B., et al. (2000). Attention, memory, and motor skills as childhood predictors of schizophrenia-related psychoses: The New York High-Risk Project. *American Journal of Psychiatry, 157,* 1416–1422.

Esbensen, A. J. & Seltzer, M. M, (2011). Accounting for the "Down Syndrome Advantage." *American Journal on Intellectual and Developmental Disabilities 116,* 3–15. doi: http://dx.doi.org/10.1352/1944-7558-116.1.3

Esbjørn, B. H., Hoeyer, M., Dyrborg, J., Leth, I., & Kendall, P. C. (2010). Prevalence and co-morbidity among anxiety disorders in a national cohort of psychiatrically referred children and adolescents. *Journal of Anxiety Disorders, 24,* 866–872. doi:10.1016/j.janxdis.2010.06.009

Escamilla, M. A., & Zavala, J. M. (2008). Genetics of bipolar disorder. *Dialogues in Clinical Neuroscience, 10* (2), 141–152.

Esler, A. N., Bal, V. H., Guthrie, W., Wetherby, A., Weismer, S. E., & Lord, C. (2015). The autism diagnostic observation schedule, toddler module: standardized severity scores. *Journal of autism and developmental disorders, 45*(9), 2704–2720.

Esmaili, S. K., Shafaroodi, N., Mehraban, A. H., Parand, A., Qorbani, M., Yazdani, F., & Mahmoudpour, A. (2016). Prevalence of psychiatric symptoms and mental health services in students with specific learning disabilities in Tehran, Iran. *International Journal of Health and Addiction, 14,* 438–448

Esposito, E., Wang, J. L., Adair, C. E., Williams, J. V., Dobson, K., Schopflocher, D., et al. (2007). Frequency and adequacy of depression treatment in a Canadian population sample. *Canadian Journal of Psychiatry, 52,* 780–789.

Essau, C. A., Sasagawa, S., Ishikawa, S. I., Okajima, I., O'Callaghan, J., & Bray, D. (2012). A Japanese form of social anxiety (taijin kyofusho): Frequency and correlates in two generations of the same family. *International Journal of Social Psychiatry, 58,* 635–642.

Essex, M. J., Klein, M. H., Slattery, M. J., Goldsmith, H. H., & Kalin, N. H. (2010). Early risk factors and developmental pathways to chronic high inhibition and social anxiety disorder in adolescence. *The American Journal of Psychiatry, 167*(1), 40–46. doi:10.1176/appi.ajp.2009.07010051

Etkin, A., & Wager, T. D. (2007). Functional neuroimaging of anxiety: A meta-analysis of emotional processing in PTSD, social anxiety disorder, and specific phobia. *American Journal of Psychiatry, 164,* 1476–1488.

Eubig, P. A., Aguiar, A., & Schantz, S. L. (2010). Lead and PCBs as risk factors for attention deficit/hyperactivity disorder. *Environmental Health Perspectives, 118,* 1654–1667. doi:10.1289/ehp.0901852

Evans, G. W. (2003). A multimethodological analysis of cumulative risk and allostatic load among rural children. *Developmental Psychology, 39,* 924–933.

Evans, G. W., Li, D., & Whipple, S. S. (2013). Cumulative risk and child development. *Psychological Bulletin, 139*(6), 1342.

Evans, J., Jones, J., & Mansell, I. (2001). Supporting siblings evaluation of support groups for brothers and sisters of children with learning disabilities and challenging behaviour. *Journal of Intellectual Disabilities, 5*(1), 69–78.

Everson-Rose, S. A., & Lewis, T. T. (2005). Psychosocial factors and cardiovascular disease. *Annual Review of Public Health, 26,* 469–500.

Evins, A. E., Cather, C., Culhane, M. A., Birnbaum, A., Horowitz, J., Hsieh, ... & Goff, D. C. (2007). A 12-week double-blind, placebo-controlled study of bupropion sr added to high-dose dual nicotine replacement therapy for smoking cessation or reduction in schizophrenia. *Journal of Clinical Psychopharmacology, 27*(4), 380–386.

Evraire, L. E., & Dozois, D. J. A. (2011). An integrative model of excessive reassurance seeking and negative feedback seeking in the development and maintenance of depression. *Clinical Psychology Review, 31,* 1291–1303.

Evraire, L. E., & Dozois, D. J. A. (2014). If it be love indeed tell me how much: Early core beliefs associated with excessive reassurance seeking in depression. *Canadian Journal of Behavioural Science, 46,* 1–8.

Evraire, L. E., Dozois, D. J. A., & Hayden, E. P. (2015). Assessment of cognitive vulnerability to psychopathology: Issues in theory and practice. In G. Brown & D. A. Clark (Eds.), *Cognitive therapy assessment, diagnosis and case formulation* (pp. 94–120). New York, NY: Guilford.

Ewles, G., Clifford, T. & Minnes, P. (2014) Predictors of advocacy in parents of children with autism spectrum disorders. *Journal on Developmental Disabilities, 20,* 73–82.

Exner, J. E. (1993). *The Rorschach: A comprehensive system, Vol 1. Basic foundations* (3rd ed.). New York, NY: Wiley.

Exner, J. E. (2002). *The Rorschach: A comprehensive system, Vol. 1. Basic foundations and principles of interpretation* (4th ed.). New York, NY: Wiley.

Exner, J. E., & Erdberg, P. (2005). *The Rorschach: A comprehensive system, Vol. 2. Advanced interpretation* (3rd ed.). New York, NY: Wiley.

Eysenck, H. J. (1952). The effects of psychotherapy: An evaluation. *Journal of Consulting Psychology, 16,* 319–324.

Fabbri, S., Fava, G. A., Sirri, L., & Wise, T. (2007). Development of a new assessment strategy in psychosomatic medicine: the diagnostic criteria for psychosomatic research. *Advances in Psychosomatic Medicine, 28,* 1–20.

Fabrega, H. (2007). How psychiatric conditions were made. *Psychiatry, 70,* 130–153.

Fagan, T. J., Ax, R. K., Liss, M., Resnick, R. J., & Moody, S. (2007). Prescriptive authority and preferences for training. *Professional Psychology: Research and Practice, 38,* 104–111.

Fairburn, C. G. (2002). Cognitive-behavioral therapy for bulimia nervosa. In C. G. Fairburn & K. D. Brownell (Eds.), *Eating disorders and obesity* (pp. 358–361). New York, NY: Guilford.

Fairburn, C. G. (2008). *Cognitive behavior therapy and eating disorders.* New York, NY: Guilford.

Fairburn, C. G., & Bohn, K. (2005). Eating disorder NOS (EDNOS): An example of the troublesome "not otherwise specified" (NOS) category in DSM-IV. *Behaviour Research and Therapy, 43,* 691–701.

Fairburn, C. G., & Cooper, Z. (2011). Eating disorders, DSM-5, and clinical reality. *British Journal of Psychiatry, 198,* 8–10.

Fairburn, C. G., Bailey-Straebler, S., Basden, S., Doll, H. A., Jones, R., Murphy, R., ... & Cooper, Z. (2015). A transdiagnostic comparison of enhanced cognitive behaviour therapy (CBT-E) and interpersonal psychotherapy in the treatment of eating disorders. *Behaviour Research and Therapy, 70,* 64–71. doi: 10.1016/j.brat.2015.04.010

Fairburn, C. G., Cooper, Z., & O'Connor, E. (2008). Eating disorder examination (edition 16.0D). In *Cognitive behavior therapy and eating disorders* (pp. 265–308). New York, NY: The Guilford.

Fairburn, C. G., Cooper, Z., & Shafran, R. (2003). Cognitive behaviour therapy for eating disorders: A "transdiagnostic" theory and treatment. *Behaviour Research & Therapy, 41,* 509–528.

Fairburn, C. G., Cooper, Z., Doll, H. A., O'Connor, M. E., Palmer, R. L., & Dalle Grave, R. (2013). Enhanced cognitive behaviour therapy for adults with anorexia nervosa: A UK–Italy study. *Behaviour Research and Therapy, 51,* R2–R8. doi: 10.1016/j.brat.2012.09.010

Fairburn, C. G., Cooper, Z., Doll, H. A., O'Connor, M. E., Bohn, K., Hawker, D. M., et al. (2009). Transdiagnostic cognitive-behavioural therapy for patients with eating disorders: A two-site trial with 60-week follow-up. *American Journal of Psychiatry, 166,* 311–319.

Fairburn, C. G., Jones, R., Peveler, R. C., Hope, R. A., & O'Connor, M. E. (1993). Psychotherapy and bulimia nervosa: The longer-term effects of interpersonal psychotherapy, behavior therapy, and cognitive therapy. *Archives of General Psychiatry, 48,* 463–469.

Fairburn, C. G., Marcus, M. D., & Wilson, G. T. (1993). Cognitive-behavioral therapy for binge eating and bulimia nervosa: A comprehensive treatment manual. In C. G. Fairburn & G. T. Wilson (Eds.), *Binge eating: Nature, assessment and treatment* (pp. 361–404). New York, NY: Guilford.

Fairburn, C. G., Shafran, R., & Cooper, Z. (1998). A cognitive behavioural theory of anorexia. *Behaviour Research and Therapy, 37,* 1–13.

Falconer, D. S. (1960). *Introduction to quantitative genetics.* New York, NY: Ronald Press.

Fandiño, J., Moreira, R. O., Preissler, C., Gaya, C. W., Papelbaum, M., Coutinho, W. F., & Appolinario, J. C. (2010). Impact of binge eating disorder in the psychopathological profile of obese women. *Comprehensive Psychiatry, 51,* 110–114. doi: 10.1016/j.comppsych.2009.03.011

Faraone, S. V., & Khan, S. A. (2006). Candidate gene studies of attention-deficit/hyperactivity disorder. *The Journal of Clinical Psychiatry, 67*(Suppl. 8), 13–20.

Farb, N. A. S., Anderson, A. K., Bloch, R., & Segal, Z. V. (2011). Mood-linked responses in medial prefrontal cortex predict relapse in patients with recurrent unipolar depression. *Biological Psychiatry, 70,* 366–372.

Farb, N. A., Irving, J. A., Anderson, A. K., & Segal, Z. V. (2015). A two-factor model of relapse/recurrence vulnerability in unipolar depression. *Journal of Abnormal Psychology, 124,* 38.

Farchione, T. J., Fairholme, C. P., Ellard, K. K., Boisseau, C. L., Thompson-Hollands, J., Carl J. R., ... Barlow, D. H. (2012). The unified protocol for the transdiagnostic treatment of emotional disorders: A randomized controlled trial. *Behavior Therapy, 43,* 666–678.

Faris, R. E. L. & Dunham, H. W. (1939). *Mental disorders in urban areas: An ecological study of schizophrenia and other psychoses.* Chicago, IL: University of Chicago Press.

Faris, R. E. L. & Dunham, H. W. (1939). *Mental disorders in urban areas.* Chicago, IL: University of Chicago Press.

Farmer, A. E. (1996). The genetics of affective disorder. *International Review of Psychiatry, 8*, 369–372.

Farrington, D. P., Gaffney, H., Lösel, F., & Ttofi, M. M. (2017). Systematic reviews of the effectiveness of developmental prevention programs in reducing delinquency, aggression, and bullying. *Aggression and Violent Behavior, 33*, 91–106.

Farrington, D. P., Jolliffe, D., Loeber, R., Stouthamer-Loeber, M., & Kalb, L. M. (2001). The concentration of offenders in families, and family criminality in the prediction of boys' delinquency. *Journal of Adolescence, 24*, 579–596.

Farrington, D. P., Loeber, R., Elliot, D. S., Hawkins, J. D., Kandel, D. B., Klein, M. W., et al. (1990). Advancing knowledge about the onset of delinquency and crime. *Advances in Clinical Child Psychology, 13*, 283–342.

Fava, G. A., & Wise, T. N. (2007). Issues for DSM-V: psychological factors affecting either identified or feared medical conditions: A solution for somatoform disorders. *The American Journal of Psychiatry, 164*(7), 1002–1003.

Fava, G. A., Fabbri, S., & Sonino, N. (2002). Residual symptoms in depression: An emerging therapeutic target. *Progress in Neuro-Psychopharmacology and Biological Psychiatry, 26*, 1019–1027.

Fava, G. A., Freyberger, H. J., Bech, P., Christodoulou, G., Sensky, T., Theorell, T. & Wise, T. N . (1995). Diagnostic criteria for use in psychosomatic research. *Psychotherapy and Psychosomatics, 63*, 1–8.

Fazel, S., Gulati, G., Linsell, L., Geddes, J. R., & Grann, M. (2009). Schizophrenia and violence: Systematic review and meta-analysis. *PLOS Medicine, 6*, 1–15. doi:10.1371/journal.pmed.1000120

Federico, A., Tamburin, S., Maier, A., Faccini, M., Casari, R., Morbioli, L., & Lugoboni, F. (2016). Multifocal cognitive dysfunction in high-dose benzodiazepine users: A cross-sectional study. *Neurological Sciences, 38*(1), 137–142.

Fedoroff, J. P. (1993). Serotonergic drug treatment of deviant sexual interests. *Annals of Sex Research, 6*, 105–121.

Fehr, B., Samson, D., & Paulhus, D. L. (1992). The construct of Machiavellianism: Twenty years later. In C. D. Spielberger & J. N. Butcher (Eds.), *Advances in personality assessment* (Vol. 9., pp. 77–116). Hillsdale, NJ: Erlbaum.

Feinstein, S. B., Fallon, B. A., Petkova, E., & Liebowitz, M. R. (2003). Item-by-item factor analysis of the Yale-Brown Obsessive Compulsive Scale Symptom Checklist. *Journal of Neuropsychiatry and Clinical Neurosciences, 15*, 187–193.

Feldman, M. A., Condillac, R. A., Tough, S. E., Hunt, S., & Griffiths, D. (2002). Effectiveness of community positive behavioral intervention for persons with developmental disabilities and severe behavioral challenges. *Behavior Therapy, 33*, 377–398.

Feldman, M. B., & Meyer, I. H. (2007). Eating disorders in diverse lesbian, gay, and bisexual populations. *International Journal of Eating Disorders, 40*, 218–226.

Fenwick, M. E. Kubas, H. A, Witzke, J. W.,Fitzer, K. R Miller, D. C. Maricle, . . . Hale, JB, (2016). Neuropsychological profiles of written expression learning disabilities determined by concordance-discordance model criteria. *Applied Neuropsychology, Child 5*(2), 83–96.

Fergus, S., & Zimmerman, M. A. (2005). Adolescent resilience: A framework for understanding healthy development in the face of risk. *Annual Review of Public Health, 26*, 399–419.

Ferguson, C. J. (2013). In the eye of the beholder: Thin-ideal media affects some, but not most, viewers in a meta-analytic review of body dissatisfaction in women and men. *Psychology of Popular Media Culture, 2*, 20–37. doi: 10.1037/a0030766

Fernandez, Y., Harris, A. J., Hanson, R. K., & Sparks, J. (2014). Stable-2007 coding manual revised 2014. Unpublished manuscript. Ottawa, ON: Public Safety Canada.

Ferrara, P., Vitelli, O., Bottaro, G., Gatto, A., Liberatore, P., Binetti, P., & Stabile, A. (2013). Factitious disorders and Münchausen syndrome: The tip of the iceberg. *Journal of Child Health Care, 17*(4), 366–374.

Fetveit, A. (2009). Late-life insomnia: A review. *Geriatrics and Gerontology International, 9*, 220–234.

Fichter, M. M., & Quadflieg, N. (2007). Long-term stability of eating disorder diagnoses. *International Journal of Eating Disorders. Special Issue on Diagnosis and Classification, 40*, S61–S66.

Fichter, M., Cebulla, M., Quadflieg, N., & Naab, S. (2008). Guided self-help for binge eating/purging anorexia nervosa before inpatient treatment. *Psychotherapy Research, 18*, 594–603.

Fick, D. M., Cooper, J. W., Wade, W. E., Waller, J. L., MacLean, R., & Beers, M. H. (2003). Updating the Beers criteria for potentially inappropriate medication use in older adults. *Archives of Internal Medicine, 163*, 2716–2724.

Filipek, P. A., Steinberg-Epstein, R., & Book, T. M. (2006). Intervention for autistic spectrum disorders. *NeuroRx, 3*, 207–216.

Finlay, W. M. L., & Lyons, E. (2001). Methodological issues in interviewing and using self-report questionnaires with people with mental retardation. *Psychological Assessment, 13*(3), 319–335.

Finlay, W. M. L., & Lyons, E. (2002). Acquiescence in interviews with people who have mental retardation. *Mental Retardation, 40*, 14–29.

Finn, P. R., Zeitouni, N. C., & Pihl, R. O. (1990). Effects of alcohol on psychophysiological hyper reactivity to non-aversive and aversive stimuli in men at high risk for alcoholism. *Journal of Abnormal Psychology, 99*, 79–85.

Fioravanti, M., Bianchi, V., & Cinti, M. E. (2012). Cognitive deficits in schizophrenia: An updated metanalysis of the scientific evidence. *BMC Psychiatry, 12*, 1–20.

Firestone, P. (1976). The effects and side effects of time-out on an aggressive nursery school child. *Journal of Behavior Therapy and Experimental Psychiatry, 21*, 23–26

Firestone, P., & Ledingham, J. (2007). Behaviour and emotional disorders of childhood and adolescence. In P. Firestone and D. Dozois (Eds.), *Abnormal psychology: Perspectives* (3rd ed., pp. 365–387). Toronto, ON: Pearson Prentice Hall.

Firestone, P., Bradford, J. M. W., McCoy, M., Greenberg, D. M., Larose, M. R., & Curry, S. (1998). Recidivism factors in convicted rapists. *Journal of American Academy Psychiatry and Law, 26*(2), 185–200.

Firestone, P., Dixon, K. L., Nunes, K. L., & Bradford, J. M. W. (2005). A comparison of incest offenders based on victim age. *Journal of the American Academy of Psychiatry and the Law, 33*(2), 223–232.

Firestone, P., Kingston, D. A., Wexler, A., & Bradford, J. M. (2006). Long-term follow-up of exhibitionists. *Journal of the American Academy of Psychiatry and the Law, 34*, 349–359.

First, M. B., & Frances, A. (2008). Issues for DSM-V: Unintended consequences of small changes: The case of paraphilias. *The American Journal of Psychiatry, 165*, 1240–1241.

First, M. B., Williams, J. B. W., & Spitzer, R. L. (1996). *DTREE: The DSM-IV expert.* Toronto, ON: MHS.

First, M. B., Williams, J. B. W., Benjamin, L. S., & Spitzer, R. L. (2015). *Structured clinical interview for DSM-5 personality disorders.* Arlington, VA: American Psychiatric Association.

First, M. B., Williams, J. B. W., Karg, R. S., & Spitzer, R. L. (2015a). *Structured clinical interview for DSM-5, clinical trials version.* Arlington, VA: American Psychiatric Association.

First, M. B., Williams, J. B. W., Karg, R. S., & Spitzer, R. L. (2015b). *Structured clinical interview for DSM-5, clinician version.* Arlington, VA: American Psychiatric Association.

First, M. B., Williams, J. B. W., Karg, R. S., & Spitzer, R. L. (2015c). *Structured clinical interview for DSM-5, research version (SCID-5-RV).* Arlington, VA: American Psychiatric Association.

First Nations and Inuit Health Branch. (2004). *2004 baseline study among First Nations on-reserve and Inuit in the North: Final Report.* Ottawa, ON: Author.

First Nations Information Governance Committee. (2012). *First Nations Regional Health Survey (RHS) 2008/10: results for adults, youth and children living in First Nations communities.* Available from http://fnigc.ca/sites/default/files/docs/first_nations_regional_health_survey_rhs_2008-10_-_national_report.pdf

Fisak, B., & Grills-Taquechel, A. E. (2007). Parental modeling, reinforcement, and information transfer: Risk factors in the development of child anxiety? *Clinical Child and Family Psychology Review, 10*(3), 213–231.

Fish, J. M. (Ed.). (2002). *Race and intelligence: Separating science from myth.* Mahwah, NJ: Erlbaum.

Fischer, B., Cruz, M. F., & Rehm, J. (2006). Illicit opioid use and its key characteristics: A select overview and evidence from a Canadian multisite cohort of illicit opioid users (OPICAN). *Canadian Journal of Psychiatry, 51*, 624–634.

Fischer, D. B., Perez, D. L., Prasad, S., Rigolo, L., O'Donnell, L., Acar, D., . . . & Dworetzky, B. A. (2016). Right inferior longitudinal fasciculus lesions disrupt visual-emotional integration. *Social Cognitive and Affective Neuroscience, 11*(6), 945–951.

Fischtein, D., Herold, E. S., & Desmarais, S. (2007). How much does gender explain in sexual attitudes and behaviors? A survey of Canadian adults. *Archives of Sexual Behavior, 36*, 451–461.

Fisher, D. J., Grant, B., Smith, D. M., Borracci, G., Labelle, A., & Knott, V. J. (2012). Nicotine and the hallucinating brain: Effects on mismatch negativity (MMN) in schizophrenia. *Psychiatry Research, 196*(2), 181–187.

Fiske, A., Wetherell, J. L., & Gatz, M. (2009). Depression in older adults. *Annual Review of Clinical Psychology, 5*, 363–389.

Flanagan, E. H., Keeley, J., & Blashfield, R. K. (2008). An alternative hierarchical organization of the mental disorders of the DSM-IV. *Journal of Abnormal Psychology, 117*, 693–698.

Flay, B. R., Biglan, A., Boruch, R. F., Gonzalez Castro, R., Gottfredson, D., Kellam, S., et al. (2005). Standards of evidence: Criteria for efficacy, effectiveness and dissemination. *Prevention Science, 6*, 151–175.

Fletcher, R. J., Barnhill, J., McCarthy, J., & Strydom, A. (2016). From DSM to DM-ID. *Journal of Mental Health Research in Intellectual Disabilities, 9*(3), 189–204.

Fletcher, R. J., Loschen, E., & Stavrakaki, C. (Eds.). (2007). *DM-ID: diagnostic manual-intellectual disability: A textbook of diagnosis of mental disorders in persons with intellectual disability.* Kingston, NY: NADD Press.

Flett, G. L., & Hewitt, P. L. (2002). *Perfectionism: Theory, research, and treatment.* Washington, DC: American Psychological Association.

Flett, G.L. & Hewitt, P.L. (2014). A proposed framework for preventing perfectionism and promoting resilience and mental health among vulnerable children. *Psychology in the Schools, 51,* 899–912. doi: 10.1002/pits.21792

Flett, G. L., Hewitt, P. L., & Heisel, M. J. (2014). The destructiveness of perfectionism revisited: Implications for the assessment of suicide risk and the prevention of suicide. *Review of General Psychology, 18*(3), 156–172.

Flint, A. J. (1994). Epidemiology and comorbidity of anxiety disorders in the elderly. *American Journal of Psychiatry, 151,* 640–649.

Flory, K., Molina, B. S., Pelham, W. E., Jr., Gnagy, E., & Smith, B. (2006). Childhood ADHD predicts risky sexual behavior in young adulthood. *Journal of Clinical Child and Adolescent Psychology, 35*(4), 571–577.

Foa, E. B., & Kozak, M. J. (1995). DSM-IV field trial: Obsessive-compulsive disorder. *American Journal of Psychiatry, 152,* 90–96.

Foley, D. L., Pickles, A., Maes, H. M., Silberg, J. L., & Eaves, L. J. (2004). Course and short-term outcomes of separation anxiety disorder in a community sample of twins. *Journal of the American Academy of Child and Adolescent Psychiatry, 43*(9), 1107–1114.

Fombonne, E. (2003). Epidemiological surveys of autism and other pervasive developmental disorders: An update. *Journal of Autism and Developmental Disorders, 27,* 641–651.

Fombonne, E. (2008). Thimerosal disappears but autism remains. *Archives of General Psychiatry, 65*(1), 15–16.

Fonagy, P., Cottrell, D., Phillipps, J., Bevington, D., Glaser, D., & Allison, E. (2015). *What works for whom? A critical review of treatments for children and adolescents* (2nd ed). New York, NY: Guilford.

Fonseca-Pedrero, E., Lemos-Giráldez, S., Muñiz, J., García-Cueto, E., & Campillo-Álvarez, Á. (2008). Schizotypy in adolescence: The role of gender and age. *Journal of Nervous and Mental Disease, 196,* 161–165. doi:10.1097/NMD.0b013e318162aa79

Foote, B., Smolin, Y., Kaplan, M., Legatt, M. E., & Lipschitz, D. (2006). Prevalence of dissociative disorders in psychiatric outpatients. *American Journal of Psychiatry, 163,* 623–629.

Ford, M. R., & Widiger, T. A. (1989). Sex bias in the diagnosis of histrionic and antisocial personality disorders. *Journal of Consulting and Clinical Psychology, 57,* 301–305.

Fordyce, W. E. (1976). *Behavioural methods for chronic pain and illness.* St. Louis, MO: Mosby.

Forehand, R., Biggar, H., & Kotchick, B. A. (1998). Cumulative risk across family stressors: Short- and long-term effects for adolescents. *Journal of Abnormal Child Psychology, 26,* 119–128.

Forman, M. (Director). (1975). *One flew over the cuckoo's nest* [Motion picture]. USA: Fantasy Films.

Forsyth, J. P., & Chorpita, B. F. (1997). Unearthing the nonassociative origins of fears and phobias: A rejoinder. *Journal of Behaviour Therapy and Experimental Psychiatry, 28,* 297–305.

Fortes, I.S., Paula, C.S., Oliveira, M.C., Bordin, I.A., de Jesus Mari, J. & Rohdel, L.A. (2016). A cross-sectional study to assess the prevalence of DSM-5 specific learning disorders in representative school samples from the second to sixth grade in Brazil. *European Child and Adolescent Psychiatr, y 25,* 195–207

Forth, A. E., Kosson, D., & Hare, R. D. (2003). Manual for the youth version of the Hare Psychopathy Checklist-Revised (PCL-YV). Toronto, ON: Multihealth Systems.

Foster, J. R., & Martin, C. C. (1990). Dementia. In D. Bienenfeld (Ed.), *Verwoerdt's clinical geropsychiatry* (3rd ed., pp. 66–84). Baltimore, MD: Williams & Wilkins.

Fournier, J. C., DeRubeis, R. J., Hollon, S. D., Dimidjian, S., Amsterdam, J. D., Shelton, R. C., et al. (2010). Antidepressant drug effects and depression severity. *Journal of the American Medical Association, 303,* 47–53.

Fowler, D., Garety, P. A., & Kuipers, E. (1995). *Cognitive behaviour therapy for psychosis: Theory and practice.* Toronto, ON: Wiley.

Fox, A. S., Oler, J. A., Tromp, D. P. M., Fudge, J. L., & Kalin, N. H. (2015). Extending the amygdala in theories of threat processing. *Trends in Neurosciences, 38,* 319–329.

Fracalanza, K., Koerner, N., Deschênes, S. S., & Dugas, M. J. (2014). Intolerance of uncertainty mediates the relation between generalized anxiety disorder symptoms and anger. *Cognitive Behaviour Therapy, 43,* 122–132.

Frances, A. (1985). Validating schizotypal personality disorders: Problems with the schizophrenic connection. *Schizophrenia Bulletin, 11,* 595–597.

Frances, A., & Chapman, S. (2013). DSM-5 somatic symptom disorder mislabels medical illness as mental disorder. *Australian and New Zealand Journal of Psychiatry, 47*(5), 483–484.

Frank, E., Kupfer, D. J., Buysse, D. J., Swartz, H. A., Pilkonis, P. A., Houck, P., et al. (2007). Randomized trial of weekly, twice-monthly, and monthly interpersonal psychotherapy as maintenance treatment for women with recurrent depression. *American Journal of Psychiatry, 164,* 761–767.

Frank, E., Kupfer, D. J., Thase, M. E., Mallinger, A. G., Swartz, H. A., Fagiolini, A. M., et al. (2005). Two-year outcomes for interpersonal and social rhythm therapy in individuals with bipolar I disorder. *Archives of General Psychiatry, 62,* 996–1004.

Frank, E., Swartz, H. A., & Kupfer, D. J. (2000). Interpersonal and social rhythm therapy: Managing the chaos of bipolar disorder. *Biological Psychiatry, 48,* 593–604.

Frank, J. D. (1961). *Persuasion and healing.* Baltimore, MD: Johns Hopkins University Press.

Frankel, E. B., & Gold, S. (2007). Principles and practices of early intervention. In I. Brown & M. Percy (Eds.), *A comprehensive guide to intellectual and developmental disabilities* (pp. 451–466). London, UK: Paul Brookes.

Frankel, E. B., Hutchinson, N. L., Burbidge, J., & Minnes, P. (2014). Pre-service early childhood educators' and elementary teachers' perspectives on including young children with developmental disabilities: A mixed methods analysis. *Journal of Early Childhood Teacher Education 35,* 373–391. doi: 10.1080/10901027.2014.968300.

Frankl, V. E. (1962). *Man's search for meaning.* Boston, MA: Beacon Press.

Franklin, G., Carson, A. J., & Welch, K. A. (2016). Cognitive behavioural therapy for depression: Systematic review of imaging studies. *Acta Neuropsychiatrica, 28,* 61–74.

Franklin, J. C., Schiele, B. C., Brozek, J., & Keys, A. (1948). Observations of human behavior in experimental semistarvation and rehabilitation. *Journal of Clinical Psychology, 4,* 28–45.

Franklin, M. E., & Foa, B. (2014). Obsessive-compulsive disorder. In D. H. Barlow (Ed.), *Clinical handbook of psychological disorders* (5th ed., pp. 155–205). New York: Guilford.

Franklin, M. E., Abramowitz, J. S., Bux, D. A., Zoellner, L. A., & Feeny, N. C. (2002). Cognitive-behavioral therapy with and without medication in the treatment of obsessive-compulsive disorder. *Professional Psychology: Research and Practice, 33,* 162–168.

Frasure-Smith, N., Lesperance, F., & Talajic, M. (1993). Depression following myocardial infarction: Impact on 6-month survival. *Journal of the American Medical Association, 270,* 1819–1825.

Frasure-Smith, N., Lesperance, F., Juneau, M., Talajic, M., & Bourassa, M. G. (1999). Gender, depression and one-year prognosis after myocardial infarction. *Psychosomatic Medicine, 61,* 26–37.

Frazier, P., Anders, S., Perera, S., Tomich, P., Tennen, H., Park, C., & Tashiro, T. (2009). Traumatic events among undergraduate students: Prevalence and associated symptoms. *Journal of Counseling Psychology, 56,* 450–460.

Freedman, R. (2014). α7-nicotinic acetylcholine receptor agonists for cognitive enhancement in schizophrenia. *Annual Review of Medicine, 65,* 245–261.

Freeman, D., Pugh, K., & Garety, P. (2008). Jumping to conclusions and paranoid ideation in the general population. *Schizophrenia Research, 102,* 254–260.

Freeston, M. H., Rheaume, J., Letarte, H., Dugas, M. J., & Ladouceur, R. (1994). Why do people worry? *Personality and Individual Differences, 17,* 791–802.

Frenkel-Brunswik, E. (1968). Adjustments and reorientation in the course of the life span. In B. L. Neugarten (Ed.), *Middle age and aging* (pp. 77–84). Chicago, IL: University of Chicago Press.

Freud, S. (1905). Psychical (or mental) treatment. In J. Strachey (Ed.), *The complete psychological works* (Vol. 7). New York, NY: Norton.

Freud, S. (1971). Mourning and melancholia (J. Riviere, Trans.). In M. Khan (Ed.), *Collected papers* (Vol. 4, pp. 152–170). London, UK: Hogarth Press. (Original work published in 1917).

Freund, K. (1981). Assessment of pedophilia. In M. Cook & K. Howells (Eds.), *Adult sexual interest in children* (pp. 139–179). London, UK: Academic Press.

Freund, K. (1990). Courtship disorder. In W. L. Marshall, D. R. Laws, & H. E. Barbaree (Eds.), *Handbook of sexual assault: Issues, theories and treatment of the offender* (pp. 195–207). New York, NY: Plenum Press.

Frewen, P. A., & Lanius, R. (2015). *Healing the traumatized self: Consciousnes, neuroscience, and treatment.* New York, New York: W. W. Norton.

Frezza, M., Di Padova, C., Pozzato, G., Terpin, M., Baraona, E., & Lieber, C. S. (1990). High blood alcohol levels in women: The role of decreased gastric alcohol dehydrogenase activity and first-pass metabolism. *New England Journal of Medicine, 322*(2), 95–99.

Frick, P. J. (2002). Juvenile psychopathy from a developmental perspective: Implications for construct development and use in forensic assessments. *Law and Human Behavior, 26*, 247–253.

Frick, P. J. (2006). Developmental pathways to conduct disorder. *Child Psychiatric Clinics of North America, 15*, 311–332.

Frick, P. J., & Ellis, M. (1999). Callous-unemotional traits and subtypes of conduct disorder. *Clinical Child and Family Psychology Review, 2*, 149–168.

Frick, P. J., Barry, C. T., & Kamphaus, R. W. (2010). Projective techniques. In P. J. Frick, C. T. Barry, & R. W. Kamphaus (Eds.), *Clinical assessment of child and adolescent personality and behavior* (3rd ed., pp. 225–251). New York, NY: Springer.

Frick, P. J., Bodin, S. D., & Barry, C. T. (2000). Psychopathic traits and conduct problems in community and clinic-referred samples of children: Further development of the Psychopathy Screening Device. *Psychological Assessment, 12*, 382–393.

Fried, L.P., Ferrucci, L., Darer, J., Williamson, J.D., & Anderson, G., (2004). Untangling the concepts of disability, frailty, and comorbidity: implications for improved targeting and care. *Journals of Gerontology Series A Biological Sciences and Medical Sciences, 59*(3), 255–263.

Friedman, H. S., & Booth-Kewley, S. (1987). Personality, Type A behavior, and coronary heart disease: The role of emotional expression. *Journal of Personality and Social Psychology, 53*, 783–792.

Friedman, M. J. (2009). PTSD and other posttraumatic syndromes. In D. McKay, J. S. Abramowitz, S. Taylor, & G. J. G. Asmundson (Eds.), *Perspectives on the anxiety disorders: Implications for DSM-V and beyond* (pp. 377–409). New York, NY: Springer.

Friedman, M., & Rosenman, R. H. (1959). Association of specific behavior pattern with blood and cardiovascular findings. *Journal of the American Medical Association, 169*, 1286–1296.

Friedman, M., & Rosenman, R. H. (1974). *Type A behavior and your heart*. New York, NY: Knopf.

Friedman, M., Thoresen, C. E., Gill, J., Ulmer, D., Powell, L. H., Price, B. A., et al. (1986). Alteration of Type A behavior and its effect on cardiac recurrences in postmyocardial infarction patients: Summary results of the Recurrent Coronary Prevention Project. *American Heart Journal, 112*, 653–665.

Froehlich, T. E., Anixt, J. S., Loe, I. M., Chirdkiatgumchai, V., Kuan, L., & Gilman, R. C. (2011). Update on environmental risk factors for attention-deficit/hyperactivity disorder. *Current Psychiatry Reports, 13*, 333–344. doi:10.1007/s11920-011-0221-3

Fromm-Reichmann, F. (1959). *Psychoanalysis and psychotherapy: Selected papers*. Chicago, IL: University of Chicago Press.

Fuchs, D., & Fuchs, L. (2006). Introduction to response to intervention: What, why and how valid is it? *Reading Research Quarterly, 41*, 93–99.

Fuchs, D., Mock, D., Morgan, P. L., & Young, C. (2003). Responsiveness-to-instruction: Definitions, evidence, and implications for the learning disabilities construct. *Learning Disabilities Research and Practice, 18*, 157–171.

Fudge Schormans, A., & Mandamin-Cameron, R. (2007). The intersection of race, disability and child maltreatment: Aboriginal children with developmental disabilities and the child welfare system. *Journal on Developmental Disabilities, 13*, 1–21.

Fulero, S. M. (1995). Review of the Hare Psychopathy Checklist–Revised. In J. C. Conoley & J. C. Impara (Eds.), *Twelfth mental measurements yearbook* (pp. 453–454). Lincoln, NE: Buros Institute.

Fuller-Thomson, E., Battiston, M., Gadalla, T. M., & Brennenstuhl, S. (2014). Bouncing back: remission from depression in a 12-year panel study of a representative Canadian community sample. *Social Psychiatry and Psychiatric Epidemiology, 49*, 903–910.

Funkenstein, D., King, S., & Drolette, M. (1957). *Mastery of stress*. Cambridge, MA: Harvard University Press.

Furby, L., Weinrott, M. R., & Blackshaw, L. (1989). Sex offender recidivism: A review. *Psychological Bulletin, 105*, 3–30.

Furukawa, T. A., Watanabe, N., & Churchill, R. (2006). Psychotherapy plus antidepressant for panic disorder with or without agoraphobia: Systematic review. *British Journal of Psychiatry, 188*, 305–312.

Fusar-Poli, P., Bechdolf, A., Taylor, M. J., Bonoldi, I., Carpenter, W. T., Yung, A. R., & McGuire, P. (2013). At risk for schizophrenic or affective psychoses? A meta-analysis of DSM/ICD diagnostic outcomes in individuals at high clinical risk. *Schizophrenia Bulletin, 39*(4), 923–932.

Gabbard, G. O., & Coyne, L. (1987). Predictors of response of antisocial patients to hospital treatment. *Hospital and Community Psychiatry, 38*, 1181–1185.

Gadermann, A. M., Alonso, J., Vilagut, G., Zaslavsky, A. M., & Kessler, R. C. (2012). Comorbidity and disease burden in the National Comorbidity Survey Replication (NCS-R). *Depression and Anxiety, 29*, 797–806.

Gage, L., & Hogan, D. B. (2014). 2014 CCSMH guideline update: The assessment and treatment of delirium. Toronto, ON: Canadian coalition for seniors' mental health (CCSMH)

Gage, S. H., Hickman, M., & Zammit, S. (2016). Association between cannabis and psychosis: epidemiologic evidence. *Biological Psychiatry, 79*(7), 549–556.

Gagné, F., & St. Père, F. (2002). When IQ is controlled, does motivation still predict achievement? *Intelligence, 30*(1), 71–100.

Gallagher-Thompson, D., & Coon, D. W. (2007). Evidence-based psychological treatments for distress in family caregivers of older adults. *Psychology and Aging, 22*, 37–51.

Galligan, P. T. (1996, March 15). *Report to the Attorney General of Ontario on certain matters relating to Karla Homolka*. Toronto, ON: Government of Ontario.

Galsworthy-Francis, L., & Allan, S. (2014). Cognitive Behavioural Therapy for anorexia nervosa: A systematic review. *Clinical Psychology Review, 34*, 54–72. doi: 10.1016/j.cpr.2013.11.001

Garb, H. N. (1997). Race bias, social class bias, and gender bias in clinical judgment. *Clinical Psychology: Science and Practice, 4*, 99–120.

Garety, P. A., & Freeman, D. (1999). Cognitive approaches to delusions: A critical review of theories and evidence. *British Journal of Clinical Psychology, 38*, 113–154.

Garfinkel, P. E., Lin, E., Goering, P., Spegg, C., Goldbloom, D. S., Kennedy, S., et al. (1995). Bulimia nervosa in a Canadian community sample: Prevalence and comparison of subgroups. *American Journal of Psychiatry, 152*(7), 1052–1058.

Garner, D. M., Garfinkel, P. E., Schwartz, D. M., & Thompson, M. M. (1980). Cultural expectations of thinness of women. *Psychological Reports, 47*, 483–491.

Garner, D. M., Olmsted, M. P., & Polivy, J. (1983). Development and validation of a multidimensional eating disorder inventory for anorexia and bulimia. *International Journal of Eating Disorders, 2*, 15–34.

Garrick, T., Minor, R. T., Buack, S., et al. (1989). Predictable and unpredictable shock stimulates gastric contractility and causes mucosal injury in rats. *Behavioural Neuroscience, 103*, 124–130.

Garyfallos, G., Katsigiannopoulos, K., Adamopoulou, A., Papazisis, G., Karastergiou, A., & Bozikas, V. P. (2010). Comorbidity of obsessive-compulsive disorder with obsessive-compulsive personality disorder: Does it imply a specific subtype of obsessive-compulsive disorder? *Psychiatry Research, 177*, 156–160. doi:10.1016/j.psychres.2010.01.006

Gater, R., Tansella, M., Korten, A., Tiemens, B. G., Mavreas, V. G., & Olatawura, M. O. (1998). Sex differences in the prevalence and detection of depressive and anxiety disorders in general health care settings. *Archives of General Psychiatry, 55*, 405–413.

Gatz, M., Kasl-Godley, J. E., & Karel, M. J. (1996). Aging and mental disorders. In J. E. Birren & K. W. Schaie (Eds.), *Handbook of the psychology of aging* (pp. 365–382). San Diego, CA: Academic Press.

Gatz, M., Popkin, S. J., Pino, C. P., & Vanden Bos, G. R. (1985). Psychological interventions with older adults. In J. E. Birren & K. W. Schaie (Eds.), *Handbook of the psychology of aging* (2nd ed., pp. 755–785). New York, NY: Van Nostrand Reinhold.

Gawin, F. H., & Kleber, H. D. (1986). Abstinence symptomatology and psychiatric diagnosis in cocaine abusers. *Archives of General Psychiatry, 43*, 107–113.

Geary, D. C. (2011). Consequences, characteristics, and causes of mathematical learning disabilities and persistent low achievement in mathematics. *Journal of Developmental & Behavioral Pediatrics, 32*, 250–263.

Geary, D. C., Hoard, M. K., Nugent, L., & Byrd-Craven, J. (2008). Development of number line representations in children with mathematical learning disability. *Developmental Neuropsychology. Special Issue: Mathematics ability, performance, and achievement, 33*, 277–299.

Gedye, A. (1995). *The Dementia Scale for Down Syndrome manual*. Vancouver, BC: Gedye Research and Consulting.

Geer, J. H., Davison, G. C., & Gatchel, R. I. (1970). Reduction of stress in humans through nonveridical perceived control of aversive stimulation. *Journal of Personality and Social Psychology, 16*, 731–738.

Geeraert, L., Van de Noortgate, W., Grietans, H., & Onghenea, P. (2004). The effects of early prevention programs for families with young children at risk for physical child abuse and neglect: A meta-analysis. *Child Maltreatment, 9*, 277–291.

Gelernter, J., and Kranzler, H. R. (2009). Genetics of alcohol dependence. *Human Genetics, 126*, 91–99.

Gellatly, R. & Beck, A.T. (2016). Catastrophic thinking: A transdiagnostic process across psychiatric disorders. *Cognitive Therapy and Research, 40*, 441–452.

Geller, J. L., Fisher, W. H., Grudzinskas, A. J., Clayfield, J. C., & Lawlor, T. (2006). Involuntary outpatient treatment as "desinstitutionalized coercion": The net-widening concerns. *International Journal of Law and Psychiatry, 29*, 551–562.

Geller, J., Johnston, C., & Madsen, K. (1997). The role of shape and weight in self-concept: The shape and weight based self-esteem inventory. *Cognitive Therapy and Research, 21,* 5–24.

Gendall, K. A., Sullivan, P. E., Joyce, P. R., Carter, F. A., & Bulik, C. M. (1997). The nutrient intake of women with bulimia nervosa. *International Journal of Eating Disorders, 21,* 115–127.

Gendreau, P. (1996). The principles of effective intervention with offenders. In A. T. Harland (Ed.), *Choosing correctional options that work: Defining the demand and evaluating the supply* (pp. 117–130). Thousand Oaks, CA: Sage.

Gentes, E. L., & Ruscio, A. M. (2011). A meta-analysis of the relation of intolerance of uncertainty to symptoms of generalized anxiety disorder, major depressive disorder, and obsessive-compulsive disorder. *Clinical Psychology Review, 31,* 923–933.

Geoffroy, P. A., Houenou, J., Duhamel, A., Amad, A., De Weijer, A. D., Ćurčić-Blake, B., . . . & Jardri, R. (2014). The arcuate fasciculus in auditory-verbal hallucinations: A meta-analysis of diffusion-tensor-imaging studies. *Schizophrenia Research, 159*(1), 234–237.

George, L. K., Blazer, D. G., & Hughes, D. C. (1989). Social support and the outcome of major depression. *British Journal of Psychiatry, 154,* 478–485.

George, M. S., Rush, A. J., Marangell, L. B., Sackeim, H. A., Brannan, S. K., Davis, S. M., et al. (2005). A one-year comparison of vagus nerve stimulation with treatment as usual for treatment-resistant depression. *Biological Psychiatry, 58,* 364–373.

Gerber, A. J., Kocsis, J. H., Milrod, B. L., Roose, S. P., Barber, J. P., Thase, M. E., et al. (2011). A quality-based review of randomized controlled trials of psychodynamic psychotherapy. *American Journal of Psychiatry, 168,* 19–28.

Gerin, W., Davidson, K. W., Christenfeld, N. J., Goyal, T., & Schwartz, J. E. (2006). The role of angry rumination and distraction in blood pressure recovery from emotional arousal. *Psychosomatic Medicine, 68*(1), 64–72.

Germain, A., & Thase, M. E. (2008). Sleep dysregulation and related regulatory models. In K. S. Dobson & D. J. A. Dozois (Eds.), *Risk factors in depression* (pp. 91–117). Oxford, UK: Elsevier/Academic Press.

Gershon, A. A., Dannon, P. N., & Grunhaus, L. (2003). Transcranial magnetic stimulation in the treatment of depression. *American Journal of Psychiatry, 160,* 835–845.

Gershuny, B. S., & Thayer, J. F. (1999). Relations among psychological trauma, dissociative phenomena, and trauma-related distress: A review and integration. *Clinical Psychology Review, 19,* 631–657.

Gersten, R., Clarke, B., & Mazzacco, M. (2007). Historical and contemporary perspectives on mathematical learning disabilities. In D. B. Berch & M. Mazzacco (Eds.), *Why is math so hard for some children? The nature and origins of mathematical learning difficulties and disabilities* (pp. 7–27). Baltimore, MD: Paul H. Brookes.

Gerstley, L. J., McLellan, A. T., Alterman, A. I., Woody, G. E., Luborsky, L., & Prout, M. (1989). Ability to form an alliance with the therapist: A possible marker of prognosis for patients with antisocial personality disorder. *American Journal of Psychiatry, 146,* 508–512.

Ghaziuddin, M. (2008). Defining the behavioral phenotype of Asperger syndrome. *Journal of Autism and Developmental Disorders, 38,* 138–142.

Giancola, P. R. (2002). Alcohol-related aggression in men and women: the influence of dispositional aggressivity. *Journal of studies on alcohol, 63*(6), 696–708.

Gibbins, C., & Weiss, M. (2007). Clinical recommendations in current practice guidelines for diagnosis and treatment of ADHD in adults. *Current Psychiatry Reports, 9*(5), 420–426.

Gibson, D. R., Flynn, N. M., & Perales, D. (2001). Effectiveness of syringe exchange programs in reducing HIV risk behavior and HIV seroconversion among injecting drug users. *Aids, 15*(11), 1329–1341.

Giesen-Bloo, J., Van Dyck, R., Spinhoven, P., Van Tilburg, W., Dirksen, C., Van Asselt, T., et al. (2006). Outpatient psychotherapy for borderline personality disorder: Randomized trial of schema-focused therapy vs. transference-focused psychotherapy. *Archives of General Psychiatry, 63,* 649–658.

Gignac, G. E., & Szodorai, E. T. (2016). Effect size guidelines for individual differences researchers. *Personality and Individual Differences, 102,* 74–78. doi.org/10.1016/j.paid.2016.06.069

Gilbert, M. (1996, July 27). The movement to break the gender barrier. *The Globe and Mail,* p. C-7.

Gillberg, C., & Gillberg, C. (1989). Asperger syndrome—some epidemiological considerations: A research note. *Journal of Child Psychology and Psychiatry 30,* 631–638.

Gilmore, L., & Chambers, B. (2010). Intellectual disability and sexuality: Attitudes of disability support staff and leisure industry employees. *Journal of Intellectual & Developmental Disability, 35,* 22–28.

Gilpin, N. W., & Koob, G. F. (2008). Overview: Neurobiology of alcohol dependence with a focus on motivational mechanisms. *Alcohol Research & Health, 31,* 185–195.

Giltz, M. (2007, March 27). Second set. *The Advocate.* Retrieved from http://findarticles.com/p/articles/mi_m1589/is_/ai_n19039120

Gitlin, M. J. (1993). Pharmacotherapy of personality disorders: Conceptual framework and clinical strategies. *Journal of Clinical Psychopharmacology, 13,* 343–353.

Gitlin, M. J., Swendsen, J., Heller, T. L., & Hammen, C. L. (1995). Relapse and impairment in bipolar disorder. *American Journal of Psychiatry, 152,* 1635–1640.

Gittelman, R., Abicoff, H., Pollack, E., Klein, D., Katz, S., & Mattes, J. (1980). A controlled trial of behavior modification and methylphenidate in hyperactive children. In C. Whalen & B. Henker (Eds.), *Hyperactive children: The social ecology of identification and treatment* (pp. 221–246). New York, NY: Academic Press.

Gjedde, A., & Wong, D. F. (1987). Positron tomographic quantification of neuroreceptors in human brain in vivo—with special reference to the D_2 dopamine receptors in caudate nucleus. *Neurosurgical Review, 10,* 9–18.

Gladstone, J., Nulman, I., & Koren, G. (1996). Reproductive risks of binge drinking during pregnancy. *Reproductive Toxicology, 10,* 3–13.

Glanze, W. D., Anderson, K. N., & Anderson, L. E. (1985). *The Mosby medical encyclopedia.* New York, NY: American Library.

Glaser, R., Pearl, D. K., Kiecolt-Glaser, J. K., & Malarkey, W. B. (1994). Plasma cortisol levels and reactivation of latent Epstein-Barr virus in response to examination stress. *Psychoneuroendocrinology, 19,* 765–772.

Glausiusz, J. (1997, January). The genes of 1996. *Discover, 36.*

Gleaves, D. H. (1996). The sociocognitive model of dissociative identity disorder: A reexamination of the evidence. *Psychological Bulletin, 120,* 42–59.

Glenn, C. R., & Klonsky, E. D. (2013). Nonsuicidal self-injury disorder: An empirical investigation in adolescent psychiatric patients. *Journal of Clinical Child & Adolescent Psychology, 42*(4), 496–507.

Glick, A. R. (2015). The role of serotonin in impulsive aggression, suicide, and homicide in adolescents and adults: a literature review. *International Journal of Adolescent Medicine & Health, 27,* 143–150.

Glidden, L. M. (Ed.). (2001). Autism. *International Review of Research in Mental Retardation* (Vol. 23). San Diego, CA: Academic Press.

Goddard, H. (1912). *The Kallikak family: A study in the heredity of feeblemindedness.* New York, NY: Macmillan.

Goeree, R., Farahati, F., Burke, N., Blackhouse, G., O'Reilly, D., Pyne, J., & Tarride, J. E. (2005). The economic burden of schizophrenia in Canada in 2004. *Current Medical Research and Opinion, 21*(12), 2017–2028.

Goettmann, C., Greaves, G. B., & Coons, P. M. (1994). *Multiple personality and dissociation 1791–1992: A complete bibliography.* Atlanta, GA: Greaves.

Gola, M., Wordecha, M., Sescousse, G., Lew-Starowicz, M., Kossowski, B., Wypych, M., et al. (2016). Can pornography be addictive? An fMRI study of men seeking treatment for problematic pornography use. *bioRxiv,* 057083.

Goldapple, K., Segal, Z., Garson, C., Lau, M., Bieling, P., Kennedy, S., & Mayberg, H. (2004). Modulation of cortical-limbic pathways in major depression: Treatment-specific effects of cognitive behavior therapy. *Archives of General Psychiatry, 61,* 34–41.

Goldberg, E. M., & Morrison, S. L. (1963). Schizophrenia and social class. *The British Journal of Psychiatry, 109*(463), 785–802.

Goldberg, J. F., & Kocsis, J. H. (1996). Relapse during SSRI treatment for depression. *Medscape Psychiatry & Mental Health eJournal, 1.*

Goldberg, R. L., Mann, L. S., Wise, T. N., & Segall, E. R. (1985). Parental qualities as perceived by borderline personality disorder. *Hillside Journal of Clinical Psychiatry, 7,* 134–140.

Goldberg, S. C., Schulz, S. C., Schulz, P. M., Resnick, R. J., Hamer, R. M., & Friedel, R. O. (1986). Borderline and schizotypal personality disorder treated with low-dose thiothixene versus placebo. *Archives of General Psychiatry, 43,* 680–686.

Goldfinger, C., Pukall, C. F., Gentilcore-Saulnier, E., McLean, L., & Chamberlain, S. (2009). A prospective study of pelvic floor physical therapy: Pain and sexual outcomes in provoked vestibulodynia. *The Journal of Sexual Medicine, 6,* 1955–1968.

Goldfried, M. R., & Norcross, J. C. (1995). Integrative and eclectic therapies in historical perspective. In B. Bongar & L. E. Beutler (Eds.), *Comprehensive textbook of psychotherapy: Theory and practice* (pp. 254–273). New York, NY: Oxford University Press.

Goldman, M. S., Del Boca, F. K., & Darkes, J. (1999). Alcohol expectancy theory: The application of cognitive neuroscience. In K. E. Leonard & H. T. Blane (Eds.), *Psychological theories of drinking and alcoholism* (2nd ed., pp. 203–246). New York, NY: Guilford.

Goldstein, A. T., Pukall, C. F., Brown, C., Bergeron, S., Stein, A., & Kellogg-Spadt, S. (2016). Vulvodynia: Assessment and treatment. *The Journal of Sexual Medicine, 13,* 572–590.

Goldstein, G. (1990). Neuropsychological heterogeneity in schizophrenia: A consideration of abstraction and problem-solving abilities. *Archives of Clinical Neuropsychology, 5*(3), 251–264.

Goldstein, H., & Wickstrom, S. (1986). Peer intervention effects on communicative interaction among handicapped and nonhandicapped preschoolers. *Journal of Applied Behavior Analysis, 19,* 209–214.

Goldstein, T. F., Lue, T. F., Padma-Nathan, H., Rosen, R. C., Steers, W. D., & Wicker, P. A. (1998, May 14). Oral sildenafil in the treatment of erectile dysfunction. *New England Journal of Medicine, 338,* 1397–1404.

Goncalves, D. C., & Byrne, G. J. (2012). Interventions for generalized anxiety disorder in older adults: Systematic review and meta-analysis. *Journal of Anxiety Disorders, 26,*1–11.

González-Maeso, J., Ang, R. L., Yuen, T., Chan, P., Weusstaub, N. V., López-Giménez, J. F., et al. (2008). Identification of a serotonin/glutamate receptor complex implicated in psychosis. *Nature, 452,* 93–97.

Goodman, A. (1997). Sexual addiction: Diagnosis, etiology, and treatment. In J. H. Lowenstein, R. B. Millman, P. Ruiz, Langrod, J. G. (Eds), *Substance abuse: A comprehensive textbook* (3rd ed.) (pp. 340–354). Baltimore, MD: Williams & Wilkins.

Gooneratne, N. S., & Vitiello, M. V. (2014). Sleep in older adults: Normative changes, sleep disorders, and treatment options. *Clinics in Geriatric Medicine, 30*(3), 591–627. doi:http://dx.doi.org.uml.idm.oclc.org/10.1016/j.cger.2014.04.007

Gordon, B. (2004). The Wechsler Preschool and Primary Scale of Intelligence, Third Edition (WPPSI-III). *Canadian Journal of School Psychology, 19,* 205–220.

Gore, S., & Eckenrode, J. (1994). Context and process in research on risk and resilience. In R. J. Haggerty, L. R. Sherrod, N. Garmezy, & M. Rutter (Eds.), *Stress, risk, and resilience in children and adolescents: Processes, mechanisms, and interventions* (pp. 19–63). New York, NY: Cambridge University Press.

Gorman, D. A., Gardner, D. M., Murphy, A. L., Feldman, M., Bélanger, S. A., Steele, M. M., . . . & Ustina, J. (2015). Canadian guidelines on pharmacotherapy for disruptive and aggressive behaviour in children and adolescents with attention-deficit hyperactivity disorder, oppositional defiant disorder, or conduct disorder. *The Canadian Journal of Psychiatry, 60*(2), 62–76.

Gormley, W. T. (2011). From science to policy in early childhood education. *Science, 333,* 978–981.

Gortner, E. T., Gollan, J. K., Dobson, K. S., & Jacobson, N. S. (1998). Cognitive-behavioral treatment for depression: Relapse prevention. *Journal of Consulting and Clinical Psychology, 66,* 377–384.

Gorton, G., & Akhtar, S. (1990). The literature on personality disorders, 1985–1988: Trends, issues, and controversies. *Hospital and Community Psychiatry, 41,* 39–51.

Gostin, L. (2005). The future of communicable disease control: Toward a new concept in public health law. *Milbank Quarterly, 83*(4), 1–17.

Gotlib, L. H., & Joormann, J. (2010). Cognition and depression: Current status and future directions. *Annual Review of Clinical Psychology, 6,* 285–312.

Gotowiec, A., & Beiser, M. (1994). Aboriginal children's mental health: Unique challenges. *Canada's Mental Health, 49,* 7–11.

Gottesman, I. I. (1991). *Schizophrenia genesis: The origins of madness.* New York: Freeman.

Gottesman, I. I., McGuffin, P., & Farmer, A. E. (1987). Clinical genetics as clues to the "real" genetics of schizophrenia: A decade of modest gains while playing for time. *Schizophrenia Bulletin, 13,* 23–47.

Gottfredson, L. S., & Deary, I. J. (2004). Intelligence predicts health and longevity, but why? *Current Directions in Psychological Science, 13*(1), 1–4. https://doi.org/10.1111/j.0963-7214.2004.01301001.x

Gottlieb, L., Martinovich, Z., Meyers, K. M., & Reinecke, M. A. (2016). Treatment for depression enhances protection: Findings from the Treatment for Adolescents with Depression Study (TADS). *International Journal of Cognitive Therapy, 9*(1), 38–56. https://doi.org/10.1521/ijct_2016_09_02

Gould, R. A., Otto, M. W., & Pollack, M. H. (1995). A meta-analysis of treatment outcome for panic disorder. *Clinical Psychology Review, 15,* 819–844.

Gould, S. J. (1985). *The flamingo's smile: Reflections in natural history.* New York, NY: Norton.

Gourlay, D. L. (2000). Cocaine. In B. Brands (Ed.), *Management of alcohol, tobacco and other drug problems. A physician's manual* (pp. 175–187). Toronto, ON: Centre for Addiction and Mental Health.

Government of Alberta. (1999, November 2). News release. Retrieved from www.gov.ab.ca/acn/199911/8353.html

Government of Canada. (2006). *The human face of mental health and mental illness in Canada, 2006.* Ottawa, ON: Minister of Public Works and Government Services Canada.

Government of Canada. (2012). *A report on mental illnesses in Canada: Chapter 3 schizophrenia.* Retrieved from www.phac-aspc.gc.ca/publicat/miic-mmac/chap_3-eng.php

Grabe, S., Ward, L. M., & Shibley Hyde, J. (2008). The role of the media in body image concerns among women: A meta-analysis of experimental and correlational studies. *Psychological Bulletin, 134,* 460–476.

Grafman, J., Schwab, K., Warden, D., Pridgen, A., Brown, H. R., & Salazar, A. M. (1996). Frontal lobe injuries, violence, and aggression: A report of the Vietnam Head Injury Study. *Neurology, 46,* 1231–1238.

Graham, C. A. (2010a). The DSM diagnostic criteria for female orgasmic disorder. *Archives of Sexual Behavior, 39,* 256–270.

Graham, C. A. (2010b). The DSM diagnostic criteria for female sexual arousal disorder. *Archives of Sexual Behavior, 39,* 240–255.

Graham, D. Y., Lew, G. M., Klein, P. D., et al. (1992). Effect of treatment of *Helicobacter pylori* infection on long-term recurrence of gastric or duodenal ulcer: A randomized, controlled study. *Annals of Internal Medicine, 116,* 705–708.

Graham, P. (1994). Prevention. In M. Rutter, E. Taylor, & L. Hersov (Eds.), *Child and adolescent psychiatry* (3rd ed., pp. 815–828). Oxford, UK: Blackwell Scientific Publications.

Graif, C., Arcaya, M. C., & Roux, A. V. D. (2016). Moving to opportunity and mental health: Exploring the spatial context of neighborhood effects. *Social Science & Medicine, 162,* 50–58.

Granholm, E., McQuaid, J. R., McClure, F. S., Auslander, L. A., Perivoliotis, D., Pedrelli, P., et al. (2005). A randomized, controlled trial of cognitive behaviors social skills training for middle-aged and older outpatients with chronic schizophrenia. *American Journal of Psychiatry, 162*(3), 520–529.

Grant, B., Stinson, F. S., Dawson, D. A., Chou, P., Dufour, M., Compton, W., et al. (2004). Prevalence and co-occurrence of substance use disorders and independent mood and anxiety disorders: Results from the National Epidemiologic Survey on Alcohol and Related Conditions. *Archives of General Psychiatry, 61*(8), 807–816.

Grant, I. (1997). Canada's new mental disorder disposition provisions: A case study of the British Columbia Criminal Code Review Board. *International Journal of Law and Psychiatry, 20*(4), 419–443.

Grant, I., Ogloff, J. R. P., & Douglas, K. D. (2000). The British Columbia Review Panel: Factors influencing decision-making. *International Journal of Law and Psychiatry, 23,* 173–194.

Grant, J. E., & Phillips, K. A. (2004). Is anorexia nervosa a subtype of body dysmorphic disorder? Probably not, but read on . . . *Harvard Review of Psychiatry, 12,* 123–126.

Grant, P. M., Huh, G. A., Perivoliotis, D., Stolar, N. M., & Beck, A. T. (2012). Randomized trial to evaluate the efficacy of cognitive therapy for low-functioning patients with schizophrenia. *Archives of General Psychiatry, 69*(2), 121–127.

Gray, B. E., McMahon, R. P., & Gold, J. M. (2013). General intellectual ability does not explain the general deficit in schizophrenia. *Schizophrenia Research, 147*(2–3), 315–319.

Gray, J. E., & O'Reilly, R. L. (2005). Canadian compulsory community treatment laws: Recent reforms. *International Journal of Law and Psychiatry, 28,* 13–22.

Gray, J. E., Hastings, T. J., Love, S., & O'Reilly, R. L. (2016). Clinically significant differences among Canadian mental health acts: 2016. *Canadian Journal of Psychiatry, 61,* 222–226.

Gray, J., & McEwen, B. (2014). Neuroendocrinology and neurotransmitters. In P. Emmelkamp & T. Ehring (Eds.), *The Wiley handbook of anxiety disorders* (volume 1, pp. 254- 273). Malden, MA: Wiley.

Gray, J., Clark, A., Higenbottam, J., Ledwidge, B., & Paredes, J. (1985). Review panels for involuntary psychiatric patients: Which patients apply? *Canadian Journal of Psychiatry, 30,* 573–576.

Greaves, G. B. (1980). Multiple personality: 165 years after Mary Reynolds. *The Journal of Nervous and Mental Disease, 168,* 577–596.

Green, G. (1994). The quality of the evidence. In H. C. Shane (Ed.), *Facilitated Communication: The clinical and social phenomenon.* San Diego, CA: Singular.

Green, G. (1996). Early behavioral intervention for autism: What does the research tell us? In C. Maurice, S. Luce, & G. Green (Eds.), *Behavioral intervention for young children with autism* (pp. 29–44). Austin, TX: Pro Ed.

Green, M. F. (2001). *Schizophrenia revealed.* New York, NY: W. W. Norton.

Green, R. C., Cupples, L. A., Kurz, A., Auerbach, S., Go, R., Sadovnick, D., et al. (2003). Depression as a risk factor for Alzheimer disease: The mirage study. *Archives of Neurology, 60,* 753–759.

Green, R., & Blanchard, R. (1995). Gender identity disorders. In H. I. Kaplan & B. J. Sadock (Eds.), *Comprehensive textbook of psychiatry* (pp. 1345–1360). Baltimore, MD: Williams & Wilkins.

Green, R., & Fleming, D. T. (1990). Transsexual surgery follow-up: Status in the 1990s. *Annual Review of Sex Research, 1,* 163–174.

Greenberg, L. (2008). Emotion and cognition in psychotherapy: The transforming power of affect. *Canadian Psychology, 49,* 49–59.

Greenberg, L., Elliot, R., & Lietaer, G. (1994). Research on experiential therapies. In A. E. Bergin, & S. L. Garlfield, (Eds.), *Handbook of psychotherapy and behavior change* (4th ed., pp. 509–539). New York, NY: Wiley.

Greenberg, R. P., Bornstein, R. F., Zborowski, M. J., Fisher, S., & Greenberg, M. D. (1994). A meta-analysis of fluoxetine outcome in the treatment of depression. *Journal of Nervous and Mental Disease, 182,* 547–551.

Greenberger, D., & Padesky, C. A. (1995). *Mind over mood: Change how you feel by changing the way you think.* New York: Guilford.

Greenberger, D., & Padesky, C. A. (2015). *Mind over mood: Change how you feel by changing the way you think* (2nd ed.). New York, NY: Guilford.

Greenfield-Spira, E., & Fischel, J. E. (2005). The impact of preschool inattention, hyperactivity, and impulsivity on social and academic development: A review. *Journal of Child Psychology and Psychiatry, 46,* 755–773.

Greenfield, T. K., Stoneking, B. C., Humphreys, K., Sundby, E., & Bond, J. (2008). A randomized trial of a mental health consumer-managed alternative to civil commitment for acute psychiatric crisis. *American Journal of Community Psychology, 42,* 135–144.

Grein, K.A. & Glidden, L.M. (2015). Predicting well-being longitudinally for mothers rearing offspring with intellectual and developmental disabilities. *Journal of Intellectual Disability Research, 59,* 622–637.

Greisberg, S., & McKay, D. (2003). Neuropsychology of obsessive-compulsive disorder: A review and treatment implications. *Clinical Psychology Review, 23,* 95–117.

Griffiths, D. M., & Gardner, W. I. (2002). The integrated biopsychosocial approach to challenging behaviours. In D. M. Griffiths, C. Stavrakaki, & J. Summers (Eds.), *Dual diagnosis: An introduction to the mental health needs of persons with developmental disabilities* (pp. 81–114). Sudbury, ON: Habilitative Mental Health Resource Network.

Grigorenko, E. L. (2006). Learning disabilities in juvenile offenders. *Child & Adolescent Psychiatric Clinics of North America, 15,* 353–371.

Grilo, C. M., Masheb, R. M., & White, M. A. (2010). Significance of overvaluation of shape/weight in binge-eating disorder: Comparative study with overweight and bulimia nervosa. *Obesity, 18,* 499–504. doi: 10.1038/oby.2009.280

Grilo, C. M., Sanislow, C. A., Shea, M. T., Skodol, A. E., Stout, R. L., Pagano, M. E., et al. (2003). The natural course of bulimia nervosa and eating disorder not otherwise specified is not influenced by personality disorders. *International Journal of Eating Disorders, 34,* 319–330.

Grinker, R. R., Werble, B., & Drye, R. C. (1968). *The borderline syndrome.* New York, NY: Basic Books.

Grisso, T. (1993). The differences between forensic psychiatry and forensic psychology. *Bulletin of the American Academy of Psychiatry and the Law, 21,* 133–145.

Groesz, L. M., Levine, M. P., & Murnen, S. K. (2002). The effect of experimental presentation of thin media images on body satisfaction: A meta-analytic review. *International Journal of Eating Disorders, 31,* 1–16.

Grogan, S. (2008). *Body image: Understanding body dissatisfaction in men, women and children* (2nd ed.). New York, NY: Taylor & Francis.

Grohol, J. M., & Tartakovsky, M. (2013). *DSM-5 resource guide.* Retrieved from http://psychcentral.com/dsm-5/

Groschwitz, R. C., Kaess, M., Fischer, G., Ameis, N., Schulze, U. M., Brunner, R., . . . Plener P. L. (2015). The association of non-suicidal self-injury and suicidal behavior according to DSM-5 in adolescent psychiatric inpatients. *Psychiatry Research, 228,* 454–461

Gross-Isseroff, R., Blegon, A., Voet, H., & Weizman, A. (2002). The suicide brain: A review of postmortem receptor/transporter binding studies. *Neuroscience and Biobehavioral Reviews, 22,* 653–661.

Groth-Marnat, G. (2016). *Handbook of Psychological Assessment* (6th ed.). Toronto, ON: Wiley.

Grove, W. M., & Lloyd, M. (2006). Meehl's contribution to clinical versus statistical prediction. *Journal of Abnormal Psychology, 115,* 192–194. doi:10.1037/0021-843X.115.2.192

Gruenberg, A. M., & Goldstein, R. D. (2003). Multiaxial assessment in the twenty-first century. In K. A. Phillips, M. B. First, & H. A. Pincus (Eds.), *Advancing DSM: Dilemmas in psychiatric diagnosis* (pp. 145–152). Washington, DC: American Psychiatric Association.

Gu, J., Strauss, C., Bond, R., & Cavanagh, K. (2015). How do mindfulness-based cognitive therapy and mindfulness-based stress reduction improve mental health and wellbeing? A systematic review and meta-analysis of mediation studies. *Clinical Psychology Review, 37,* 1–12.

Gudjonsson, G. H., Murphy, G. H., & Clare, I. C. H. (2000). Assessing the capacity of people with intellectual disabilities to be witnesses in court. *Psychological Medicine, 30,* 307–314.

Gunderson, J. G., & Singer, M. T. (1975). Defining borderline patients: An overview. *American Journal of Psychiatry, 132,* 1–10.

Gunter, T. D., Vaughn, M. G., & Philibert, R. A. (2010). Behavioral genetics in antisocial spectrum disorders and psychopathy: a review of the recent literature. *Behavioral sciences & the law 28(2),* 148–173

Gunzerath, L., Faden, V., Zakhari, S., & Warren, K. (2004). National Institute on Alcohol Abuse and Alcoholism report on moderate drinking. *Alcoholism: Clinical and Experimental Research, 28,* 829–847.

Guo, G., Jia, K-R, Shi, Y., Liu, X-F, Liu, K-Y, Qi, W., et al. (2009). Psychological stress enhances the colonization of the stomach by *Helicobacter pylori* in the BALB/c mouse. *Stress, 12,* 478–485.

Guralnik, O., Giesbrecht, T., Knutelska, M., Sirroff, B., & Simeon, D. (2007). Cognitive functioning in depersonalization disorder. *Journal of Nervous and Mental Disease, 195(12),* 983–988.

Gutjahr, E., Gmel, G., & Rehm, J. (2001). Relation between average volume of alcohol consumption and disease: An overview. *European Addiction Research, 7,* 117–127.

Guy, L. S., Douglas, K. S., & Hart, S. D. (2015). Risk assessment and communication. In B. Cutler & P. Zapf (Eds.), *APA handbook of forensic psychology,* Vol. 1 (pp. 35–86). Washington, DC: American Psychological Association.

Guyton, A. C. (1991). *Textbook of medical physiology* (8th ed., pp. 365–384). Philadelphia, PA: Saunders.

Hachett, M. L., Yapa, C., Parag, V., & Anderson, C. S. (2005). Frequency of depression after stroke: A systematic review of observational studies. *Stroke, 36,* 1330–1340.

Hadjistavropoulos, H. D., Alberts, N., Nugent, M., Marchildon, G. (2014). Improving access to psychological services through therapist-assisted internet cognitive behaviour therapy. *Canadian Psychology, 55,* 303–311.

Hadjistavropoulos, H. D., Craig, K. D., & Hadjistavropoulos, T. (1998). Cognitive and behavioural responses to illness information: The role of health anxiety. *Behaviour Research and Therapy, 36(2),* 149–164.

Häfner, H., & an der Heiden, W. (1999). The course of schizophrenia in the light of modern follow-up studies: The ABC and WHO studies. *European Archives of Psychiatry and Clinical Neurosciences, 249* (Suppl. 4), 14–26.

Hagberg, B., Aicardi, J., Dias, K., & Ramos, O. (1983). A progressive syndrome of autism, dementia, ataxia, and loss of purposeful hand use in girls: Rett's syndrome: Report of 35 cases. *Annals of Neurology, 14,* 471–479.

Hagerman, R. (1987). Fragile X syndrome. *Current Problems in Pediatrics, 17,* 621–674.

Hagerman, R. J., Rivera, S. M., & Hagerman, P. J. (2008). The Fragile X family of disorders: A model for autism and targeted treatments. *Current Pediatric Reviews, 4,* 40–52.

Häkkänen-Nyholm, H., & Hare, R. D. (2009). Psychopathy, homicide, and the courts: Working the system. *Criminal Justice and Behavior, 36,* 761–777. doi:10.1177/0093854809336946

Haldipur, C. V. (1984). Madness in ancient India; Concept of insanity in Charaka Samhita (1st century A.D.). *Comprehensive Psychiatry, 25,* 335–344.

Hale, J. B., & Fiorello, C. A. (2004). School neuropsychology: A practitioner's handbook. New York, NY: Guilford.

Hale, J.B., et al., (57 other contributors). (2010). Critical issues in response-to-intervention, comprehensive evaluation, and specific learning disabilities identification and intervention: an expert white paper consensus. *Learning Disability Quarterly, 33,* 223–237.

Halford, W. K., Pepping, C. A., & Petch, J. (2015). The gap between couple therapy research efficacy and practice effectiveness. *Journal of Marital and Family Therapy, 42,* 3244.

Hall, G. C. N., Ibaraki, A. Y., Huang, E. R., Marti, C. N., & Stice, E. (2016). A meta-analysis of cultural adaptations of psychological interventions. *Behavior Therapy, 47(6),* 993–1014.

Halperin, J. M., & Schulz, K. P. (2006). Revisiting the role of the prefrontal cortex in pathophysiology of attention-deficit/hyperactivity disorder. *Psychological Bulletin, 132(4),* 560–581.

Hameed, M. A., & Lewis, A. J. (2016). Offspring of parents with schizophrenia: A systematic review of developmental features across childhood. *Harvard Review of Psychiatry, 24(2),* 104–117.

Hamilton, S., Rothbart, M., & Dawes, R. M. (1986). Sex bias, diagnosis, and DSM-III. *Sex Roles, 15*, 269–274.

Hammen, C. (1991). Generation of stress in the course of unipolar depression. *Journal of Abnormal Psychology, 101*, 45–52.

Hammen, C. (2006). Stress generation in depression: Reflections on origins, research, and future directions. *Journal of Clinical Psychology, 62*, 1065–1082.

Hammen, C., & Shih, J. H. (2008). Stress generation and depression. In K. S. Dobson & D. J. A. Dozois (Eds.), *Risk factors in depression* (pp. 409–428). Oxford, UK: Elsevier/Academic Press.

Hampton-Robb, S., Qualls, R. C., & Compton, W. C. (2003). Predicting first-session attendance: The influence of referral source and client income. *Psychotherapy Research, 13*, 223–233.

Hancock, J., Woodworth, M. T., & Porter, S. (2011, 2013). Hungry like the wolf: A word pattern analysis of the language of psychopaths. *Legal and Criminological Psychology, 18*, 102–114.

Hancock, T. (2011). Health promotion in Canada: 25 years of unfulfilled promise. *Health Promotion International, 26*(suppl 2), ii263–ii267.

Handley, T. E., Inder, K. J., Kelly, B. J., Attia, J. R., Lewin, T. J., Fitzgerald, M. N., & Kay-Lambkin, F. J. (2012). You've got to have friends: The predictive value of social integration and support in suicidal ideation among rural communities. *Social Psychiatry and Psychiatric Epidemiology, 47*, 1281–1290.

Hankin, B. L., Abramson, L. Y., Moffitt, T. E., Silva, P. A., McGee, R., Angell, K. E. (1998). Development of depression from preadolescence to young adulthood: Emerging gender differences in a 10-year longitudinal study. *Journal of Abnormal Psychology, 107*, 128–140.

Hans, E., & Hiller, W. (2013). Effectiveness of and dropout from outpatient cognitive behavioral therapy for adult unipolar depression: A meta-analysis of nonrandomized effectiveness studies. *Journal of Consulting and Clinical Psychology, 81*, 75–88.

Hans, S. L., Auerbach, J. G., Styr, B., & Marcus, J. (2004). Offspring of parents with schizophrenia: Mental disorders during childhood and adolescents. *Schizophrenia Bulletin, 30*, 303–315.

Hansen, P. E., Ravnkilde, B., Videbech, P., Clemmensen, K., Sturlason, R., Reiner, M., et al. (2011). Low-frequency repetitive transcranial magnetic stimulation inferior to electroconvulsive therapy in treating depression. *Journal of ECT, 27*, 26–32.

Hanson, R. K., & Bussière, M. T. (1998). Predicting relapse: A meta-analysis of sexual offender recidivism studies. *Journal of Consulting and Clinical Psychology, 66*, 348–362.

Hanson, R. K., & Morton-Bourgon, K. E. (2004). *Predictors of sexual recidivism: An updated metaanalysis*. Ottawa: Public Safety and Emergency Preparedness Canada.

Hanson, R. K., & Morton-Bourgon, K. E. (2005). The characteristics of persistent sexual offenders: A meta-analysis of recidivism studies. *Journal of Consulting and Clinical Psychology, 73*, 1154–1163.

Hanson, R. K., Gordon A., Harris, A. J., Marques, J. K., Murphy, W., Quinsey, V. L., & Seto, M. (2002). First report of the collaborative outcome data project on the effectiveness of psychological treatment for sex offenders. *Sexual Abuse: A Journal of Research and Treatment, 14*, 169–194.

Happé, F., & Frith, U. (1995). Theory of mind in autism. In E. Schopler & G. B. Mesibov (Eds.), *Learning and cognition in autism* (pp. 177–197). New York, NY: Springer.

Harari, D., Bakermans-Kranenburg, M. J., & van Ijzendoorn, M. J. (2007). Attachment, disorganization, and dissociation. In E. Vermetten, M. J. Dorahy, & D. Spiegel (Eds.), *Traumatic dissociation: Neurobiology and treatment* (pp. 31–54). Washington, DC: American Psychiatric Publishing.

Harburg, E., Davis, D. R., & Caplan, R. (1982). Parent and offspring alcohol use. *Journal of Studies on Alcohol, 43*, 497–516.

Harding, C. M., Brooks, G. W., Ashikaga, T., Strauss, J. S., & Breier, A. (1987). The Vermont longitudinal study of persons with severe mental illness. I. Methodology, study sample, and overall status 32 years later. *American Journal of Psychiatry, 144*, 18–26.

Harding, T. W. (1992). Psychopathic disorder: Time for a decent burial of a bad legal concept? *Criminal Behavior and Mental Health, 2*, vi–ix.

Hardy, J. D., & Smith, T. W. (1988). Cynical hostility and vulnerability to disease: Social support, life stress and physiological response to conflict. *Health Psychology, 7*, 447–459.

Hare, E. (1988). Schizophrenia as a recent disease. *British Journal of Psychiatry, 153*, 521–531.

Hare, R. D. (1970). *Psychopathy: Theory and research*. New York: Wiley.

Hare, R. D. (1980). A research scale for the assessment of psychopathy in criminal populations. *Personality and Individual Differences, 1*, 111–119.

Hare, R. D. (1983). Diagnosis of antisocial personality disorder in two prison populations. *American Journal of Abnormal Psychiatry, 140*, 887–890.

Hare, R. D. (1985). A comparison of procedures for the assessment of psychopathy. *Journal of Consulting and Clinical Psychology, 53*, 7–16.

Hare, R. D. (1991). *The Hare Psychopathy Checklist–Revised*. Toronto, ON: Multihealth Systems.

Hare, R. D. (1993). *Without conscience: The disturbing world of the psychopaths among us*. New York, NY: Simon & Schuster.

Hare, R. D. (1996). Psychopathy: A clinical construct whose time has come. *Criminal Justice and Behavior, 23*, 25–54.

Hare, R. D. (1998). Psychopathy and its nature: Implications for mental health and criminal justice systems. In T. Millon, E. Simonsen, M. Birkert-Smith, & R. D. Davis (Eds.), *Psychopathy: Antisocial criminal and violent behavior* (pp. 188–212). New York, NY: Guilford.

Hare, R. D. (2003). *The Hare Psychopathy Checklist–Revised* (2nd ed.). Toronto, ON: Multihealth Systems.

Hare, R. D., & Hare, A. S. (1967). Psychopathic behaviour: A bibliography. *Excerpta Criminologica, 7*, 365–386.

Hare, R. D., & Neumann, C. S. (2009). Psychopathy: Assessment and forensic implications. *The Canadian Psychiatric Association Journal / La Revue de l'Association des psychiatres du Canada, 54*, 791–802.

Hare, R. D., Hart, S. D., & Harpur, T. J. (1991). Psychopathy and DSM-IV criteria for antisocial personality disorder. *Journal of Abnormal Psychology, 100*, 391–398.

Hari, R. (2015). Magnetoencephalography studies of action observation. In P. F. Ferrari & G. Rizzolatti (Eds.), *New Frontiers in Mirror Neurons Research* (pp. 58–70). Oxford, UK: Oxford University Press.

Harkness, K. L. (2008). Life events and hassles. In K. S. Dobson & D. J. A. Dozois (Eds.), *Risk factors in depression* (pp. 317–341). Oxford, UK: Elsevier/Academic Press.

Harkness, K. L., & Lumley, M. N. (2007). Child abuse and neglect and the development of depression in children and adolescents. In J. Abela & B. Hankin (Eds.), *Depression in children and adolescents*. New York, NY: Guilford.

Harkness, K. L., Alavi, N., Monroe, S. M., Slavich, G. M., Gotlib, I. H., & Bagby, R. M. (2010). Sex differences in life events prior to onset of major depressive disorder: The moderating effect of age. *Journal of Abnormal Psychology, 119*, 791–803.

Harkness, K. L., Hayden, E. P., & Lopez-Duran, N. L. (2015). Stress sensitivity and stress sensitization in psychopathology: An introduction to the special section. *Journal of Abnormal Psychology, 124*, 1–3. Retrieved from www.apa.org/pubs/journals/features/abn-0000041.pdf

Harkness, K. L., Stewart, J. G., & Wynne-Edwards, K. E. (2011). Cortisol reactivity to social stress in adolescents: Moderation by depression severity and child maltreatment. *Psychoneuroendocrinology, 36*, 173–181.

Harley, M., Kelleher, I., Clarke, M., Lynch, F., Arseneault, L., Connor, D., et al. (2010). Cannabis use and childhood trauma interact additively to increase the risk of psychotic symptoms in adolescence. *Psychological Medicine, 40*, 1627–1634.

Harlow, B., Kunitz, C., Nguyen, R., Rydell, S., Turner, R., & MacLehose, R. (2014). Prevalence of symptoms consistent with a diagnosis of vulvodynia: Population-based estimates from 2 geographic regions. *American Journal of Obstetrics and Gynecology, 210*, 40.e1.

Harlow, J. M. (1848). Passage of an iron rod through the head. *Boston Medical and Surgical Journal, 39*, 389–393.

Harlow, J. M. (1868). Recovery from the passage of an iron rod through the head. *Publications of the Massachusetts Medical Society, 2*, 327–347.

Harper, S. (2011). An examination of structural dissociation of the personality and the implications for cognitive behavioural therapy. *The Cognitive Behaviour Therapist, 4*, 53–67.

Harpur, T. J., & Hare, R. D. (1994). The assessment of psychopathy as a function of age. *Journal of Abnormal Psychology, 103*, 604–609.

Harrington, A. (2008). *The cure within: A history of mind-body medicine*. New York, NY: Norton.

Harris, G. T. (1989). The relationship between neuroleptic drug dose and the performance of psychiatric patients in a maximum security token economy program. *Journal of Behavior Therapy and Experimental Psychiatry, 20*, 57–67.

Harris, G. T., Rice, M. E., & Cormier, C. A. (1991). Length of detention in matched groups of insanity acquittees and convicted offenders. *International Journal of Law and Psychiatry, 14*, 223–236.

Harris, G. T., Rice, M. E., & Quinsey, V. L. (1993). Violent recidivism of mentally disordered offenders: The development of a statistical prediction instrument. *Criminal Justice and Behavior, 20*, 315–335.

Harris, G. T., Rice, M. E., Quinsey, V. L., Lalumiere, M. L., Boer, D., & Lang, C. (2003). A multi-site comparison of actuarial risk instruments for sex offenders. *Psychological Assessment, 15*, 413–425.

Harris, J. C. (1995). Schizophrenia: A neurodevelopmental disorder. In J. C. Harris, *Developmental neuropsychiatry. Vol. II: Assessment, diagnosis, and treatment of developmental disorders* (pp. 332–333). Cambridge, UK: Cambridge University Press.

Harris, J. G., Kongs, S., Allensworth, D., Martin, L., Tregellas, J., Sullivan, B., Zerbe, G., & Freedman, R. (2004). Effects of nicotine on cognitive deficits in schizophrenia. *Neuropsychopharmacology: Official Publication of the American College of Neuropsychopharmacology, 29*(7), 1378–1385.

Harrison, A. & Holmes, A. (2012). Easier said than done: Operationalizing the diagnosis of learning disability for use at the postsecondary level in Canada. *Canadian Journal of School Psychology 27*(1), 12–34. doi/pdf/10.1177/ 0829573512437021

Harrison, A., de la Cruz, F., Enander, J., Radua, J. & Mataix-Cols, D. (2016). Cognitive-behavioral therapy for body dysmorphic disorder: A systematic review and meta-analysis of randomized controlled trials. *Clinical Psychology Review, 48*(8), 43–51.

Harrison, A.G. & Holmes, A. (2012). Easier said than done: Operationalizing the diagnosis of learning disability for use at the postsecondary level in Canada. *Canadian Journal of School Psychology, 27* (1), 12–34.

Harrison, P. J. (1999). The neuropathology of schizophrenia: A critical review of the data and their interpretation. *Brain, 122*, 593–624.

Harrison, P. J. (2015). Recent genetic findings in schizophrenia and their therapeutic relevance. *Journal of Psychopharmacology, 29*(2), 85-96.

Harrison, P. L., & Oakland, T. (2015). *ABAS-3.* Torrance, CA: Western Psychological Services.

Harrison, P., & Oakland, T. (2003). *Adaptive Behavior Assessment System* (2nd ed.). San Antonio, TX: The Psychological Corporation.

Harrow, M., Lanin-Kettering, L., & Miller, J. G. (1989). Impaired perspective and thought pathology in schizophrenic and psychotic disorders. *Schizophrenia Bulletin, 15*, 605–623.

Hart, S. D. (2001). Forensic issues. In J. Livesley (Ed.), *The handbook of personality disorders* (pp. 555–569). New York, NY: Guilford.

Hart, S. D. (2006). Mental illness and criminal justice: Where tolerance breaks down. *Visions, 2*(8), 4-5.

Hart, S. D., & Hare, R. D. (1989). Discriminant validity of the Psychopathy Checklist in a forensic psychiatric population. *Psychological Assessment: A Journal of Consulting and Clinical Psychology, 1*, 211–218.

Hart, S. D., & Hare, R. D. (1992). Predicting fitness to stand trial: The relative power of demographic, criminal, and clinical variables. *Forensic Reports, 5*, 53–65.

Hart, S. D., & Hare, R. D. (1997). Psychopathy: Assessment and association with criminal behavior. In D. Stoff, J. Breiling, & J. D. Maser (Eds.), *Handbook of antisocial behavior* (pp. 22–35). New York, NY: Wiley.

Hart, S. D., Roesch, R., Corrado, R. R., & Cox, D. N. (1993). The Referral Decision Scale: A validation study. *Law and Human Behavior, 17*, 611–623.

Hartmann, U., Heiser, K., Ruffer-Hesse, C., & Kloth, G. (2002). Female sexual desire disorders: Subtypes, classification, personality factors and new directions for treatment. *World Journal of Urology, 20*(2), 79–88.

Harvey, A. R., & Hill, R. B. (2004). Africentric youth and family rites of passage program: Promoting resilience among at-risk African American youths. *Social Work, 49*(1), 65–74.

Harvey, P. D. (2001). Cognitive and functional impairments in elderly patients with schizophrenia: A review of the recent literature. *Harvard Review of Psychiatry, 9*, 59–68.

Harvey, P. D., & Bowie, C. R. (2012). Cognitive enhancement in schizophrenia: Pharmacological and cognitive remediation approaches. *Psychiatric Clinics of North America, 35*(3), 683–698.

Harvey, P. D., & Keefe, R. S. E. (2001). Studies of cognitive change in patients with schizophrenia following novel antipsychotic treatment. *American Journal of Psychiatry, 158*, 176–184.

Harvey, P. D., Koren, D., Reichenberg, A., & Bowie C. R. (2006). Negative symptoms and cognitive deficits: What is the nature of their relationship? *Schizophrenia Bulletin, 32*, 250–258.

Hasher, L., Goldstein, D., & May, C. P. (2005). It's about time: Circadian rhythms, memory, and aging. In C. Izawa & N. Ohta (Eds.), *Human learning and memory: Advances in theory and application: The 4th Tsukuba International Conference on Memory* (pp. 199–217). Mahwah, NJ: Lawrence Erlbaum Associates.

Haslam, J. (1976). *Observations on madness and melancholy.* New York: Arno Press. (Original work published 1809.)

Hastings, R. P., & Taunt, H. M. (2002). Positive perceptions in families of children with developmental disabilities. *American Journal on Mental Retardation, 107*, 116–127.

Hatchett, G. T., & Park, H. L. (2003). Comparison of four operational definitions of premature termination. *Psychotherapy, 40*, 226–231.

Hathaway, S. R., & McKinley, J. C. (1943). Manual for the Minnesota Multiphasic Personality Inventory. New York, NY: Psychological Corporation.

Hatzimouratidis, K., & Hatzichristou, D. G. (2005). A comparative review of the options for treatment of erectile dysfunction: Which treatment for which patient? *Drugs, 65*, 1621–1650.

Hatzimouratidis, K., Salonia, A., Adaikan, G., Buvat, J., Carrier, S., El-Meliegy, A., et al. (2016). Pharmacotherapy for erectile dysfunction: Recommendations from the fourth international consultation for sexual medicine (ICSM 2015). *The Journal of Sexual Medicine, 13*, 465–488.

Haushofer, J., & Fehr, E. (2014). On the psychology of poverty. *Science, 344*, 862–867.

Hawco, C., Buchy, L., Bodnar, M., Izadi, S., Dell'Elce, J., Messina, K., ... & Lepage M. (2014). Source retrieval is not properly differentiated from object retrieval in early schizophrenia: An fMRI study using virtual reality. *Neuroimage: Clinical, 68*(9), 683–691.

Hawe, P., Shiell, A., & Riley, T. (2004). Complex interventions: How "out of control" can a randomized trial be? *British Medical Journal, 328*, 1561–1563.

Hawgood, J., & De Leo, D. (2008). Anxiety disorders and suicidal behaviour: An update. *Current Opinion in Psychiatry, 21*, 51–64.

Hawley, L. L., Zuroff, D. C., Brozina, K., & Dobson, K. S. (2014). Self-critical perfectionism and stress reactivity following cognitive behavioral therapy for depression. *International Journal of Cognitive Therapy, 7*, 287–303.

Haworth-Hoeppner, S. (2000). The critical shapes of body image: The role of culture and family in the production of eating disorders. *Journal of Marriage and the Family, 62*, 212–227.

Hawton, K., & Harriss, L. (2007). Deliberate self-harm in young people: Characteristics and subsequent mortality in a 20-year cohort of patients presenting to hospital. *Journal of Clinical Psychiatry, 68*, 1574–1583.

Hay, P. J., & Claudino, A. M. (2012). Clinical psychopharmacology of eating disorders: A research update. *International Journal of Neuropsychopharmacology, 15*, 209–222.

Hay, P., & Fairburn, C. G. (1998). The validity of the DSM-IV scheme for classifying bulimic eating disorders. *International Journal of Eating Disorders, 23*, 7–15.

Hayden, E. P., Dougherty, L. R., Maloney, B., Durbin, C. E., Olino, T. M., Nurnberger, J. I., Jr., et al. (2008). Temperamental fearfulness in childhood and the serotonin transporter promoter region polymorphism: A multimethod association study. *Psychiatric Genetics, 17*, 135–142.

Hayden, E. P., Dougherty, L. R., Maloney, B., Olino, T. M., Durbin, C. E., Sheihk, H. I., et al. (2008). Early-emerging cognitive vulnerability to depression and the serotonin transporter promoter region polymorphism. *Journal of Affective Disorders, 107*, 227–230.

Hayden, E. P., Klein, D. N., Dougherty, L. R., Olino, T. M., Durbin, C. E., Sheikh, H. I., & Singh, S. (2010a). The dopamine D_2 receptor gene and depressive and anxious symptoms in childhood: Associations and evidence for gene-environment correlation and gene-environment interaction. *Psychiatric Genetics, 20*, 304–310.

Hayden, E. P., Klein, D. N., Dougherty, L. R., Olino, T. M., Durbin, C. E., Sheikh, H. I., & Singh, S. (2010b). The role of BDNF genotype, parental depression, and relationship discord in predicting early-emerging negative emotionality. *Psychological Science, 21*, 1678–1685.

Hayden, E. P., Klein, D. N., Sheikh, H. I., Olino, T. M., Dougherty, L. R., Dyson, M. W., et al. (2010). The serotonin transporter promoter polymorphism and childhood positive and negative emotionality. *Emotion, 10*, 696–702.

Hayden, E. P., Olino, T. M., Bufferd, S. J., Miller, A., Dougherty, L. R., Sheikh, H. I., Singh, S. M., & Klein, D. N. (2013). The 5-HTTLPR and BDNF Val66Met polymorphisms and maternal history of depression: Associations with cognitive vulnerability to depression in childhood. *Development and Psychopathology, 25*, 587–598.

Hayes, D. J., & Greenshaw, A. J. (2011). 5-HT receptors and reward-related behaviour: A review. *Neuroscience & biobehavioral reviews, 35*(6), 1419–1449.

Hayes, S. C., Villatte, M., Levin, M., & Hildebrandt, M. (2011). Open, aware, and active: Contextual approaches as an emerging trend in the behavioural and cognitive therapies. *Annual Review of Clinical Psychology, 7*, 141–168.

He, W., Goodkind, D., Kowal, P. (2016). *An aging world: 2015.* U.S. Census Bureau International Population Reports, P95:16-1. Retrieved from www.census.gov/content/dam/Census/library/publications/2016/.../p95-16-1.pdf

Health and Welfare Canada. (1988). *The epidemiology of mental retardation.* Report of the Working Group. Ottawa, ON: Ministry of National Health and Welfare.

Health Canada. (1998). HIV and AIDS among women in Canada. *HIV/AIDS Epi Update.* Ottawa, ON: Author.

Health Canada. (1999). Measuring up: A health surveillance update on Canadian children and youth. Retrieved from www.hc-sc.gc.ca/pphb-dgspsp/publicat/meas-haut/mu_y_e.html

Health Canada. (2002). *A report on mental illnesses in Canada.* Ottawa: Health Canada Editorial Board. Retrieved from www.phac-aspc.gc.ca/publicat/miic-mmac/index.html

Health Canada. (2003). *Canadian community health survey: Mental health and well-being.* Ottawa, ON: Author.

Health Canada. (2006). New antidepressants linked to serious lung disorders in newborns. Retrieved from www.hc-sc.gc.ca/media/advisories-avis/_2006/2006_11-eng.php

Health Canada. (2010a). Canadian Alcohol and Drug Use Monitoring Survey (CADUMS). Retrieved from www.hc-sc.gc.ca/hc-ps/drugs-drogues/stat/_2010/summary-sommaire-eng.php

Health Canada. (2010b). Canadian Tobacco Use Monitoring Survey (CTUMS) 2010. Retrieved from www.hc-sc.gc.ca/hc-ps/tobac-tabac/research-recherche/stat/ctums-esutc_2010_graph-eng.php

Health Canada. (2010c). Health Canada reminds Canadians to manage caffeine consumption. Retrieved from www.hc-sc.gc.ca/ahc-asc/media/advisories-avis/_2010/2010_40-eng.php

Health Canada. (2011a). Caffeine in food. Retrieved from www.hc-sc.gc.ca/fn-an/securit/addit/caf/food-caf-aliments-eng.php

Health Canada. (2011b). *Honouring our strengths: A renewed framework to address substance use issues among First Nations people in Canada.* HC Pub.: 110114; Cat.: H14-65/2011E-PDF

Health Canada. (2015). *Canadian Tobacco, Alcohol and Drugs Survey (CTADS).* Retrieved from http://healthycanadians.gc.ca/science-research-sciences-recherches/data-donnees/ctads-ectad/summary-sommaire-2015-eng.php

Health Canada. (2016). *Understanding the new Access to Cannabis for Medical Purposes Regulations.* Retrieved from www.canada.ca/en/health-canada/services/publications/drugs-health-products/understanding-new-access-to-cannabis-for-medical-purposes-regulations.html#a5

Health Canada. (2017). *Canadian Tobacco, Alcohol and Drugs Survey (CTADS) 2015 Summary.* Retrieved from http://healthycanadians.gc.ca/science-research-sciences-recherches/data-donnees/ctads-ectad/summary-sommaire-2015-eng.php

Health Care Consent Act, S.O. 1996, c. 2, Sch. A, art. 4.

Health Quality Ontario. (2016). Repetitive transcranial magnetic stimulation for treatment- resistant depression: a systematic review and meta-analysis of randomized controlled trials. *Ontario Health Technology Assessment Series, 16,* (5).

Heatherton, T. F., & Baumeister, R. F. (1991). Binge-eating as escape from self-awareness. *Psychological Bulletin, 110,* 86–108.

Heaton, R. K., Chelune, G. J., Talley, J. L., Kay, G. G., & Curtiss, G. (1993). *Wisconsin Card Sorting Test manual: Revised and expanded.* Odessa, FL: Psychological Assessment Resources.

Hebb, D. O., & Penfield, W. (1940). Human behavior after extensive bilateral removals from the frontal lobes. *Archives of Neurology and Psychiatry, 44,* 421–438.

Heber, R. (1959). A manual on terminology and classification in mental retardation. *American Journal of Mental Deficiency, 56* (Monograph Suppl.).

Hebert, E. A., Dugas, M. J., Tulloch, T. J. & Holowka, D. W. (2014). Positive beliefs about worry: A psychometric evaluation of the why worry-II. *Personality and Individual Differences, 56*(1), 3–8.

Hechtman, L. (1996). Families of children with attention deficit hyperactivity disorder: A review. *Canadian Journal of Psychiatry, 41*(6), 350–360.

Hecker, M. H. L., Chesney, M., Black, G. W., & Frautschi, N. (1988). Coronary-prone behaviors in the Western Collaborative Group Study. *Psychosomatic Medicine, 50,* 153–164.

Heim, C., Newport, D. J., Heit, S., Graham, Y. P., Wilcox, M., Bonsall, R., et al. (2000). Pituitary-adrenal and autonomic responses to stress in women after sexual and physical abuse in childhood. *Journal of the American Medical Association, 284,* 592–597.

Heim, C., Newport, D., Wagner, D., Wilcox, M., Miller, A., & Nemeroff, C. B. (2002). The role of early adverse experience and adulthood stress in the prediction of neuroendocrine stress reactivity in women: A multiple regression analysis. *Depression & Anxiety, 15,* 117–125.

Heim, N., & Hursch, C. J. (1979). Castration for sex offenders: Treatment or punishment? A review and critique of recent European literature. *Archives of Sexual Behavior, 8,* 281–305.

Heimberg, M. E., & Magee, B. (2014). Social anxiety disorder. In D. H. Barlow (Ed.), *Clinical handbook of psychological disorders* (5th ed., pp. 114–154). New York: Guilford.

Heimberg, R. G., Hofmann, S. G., Liebowitz, M. R., Schneier, F. R., Smits, J. A. J., Stein, M. B., . . . & Craske, M. G. (2014). Social anxiety disorder in DSM-5. *Depression and Anxiety, 31,* 472–479.

Heinberg, L. J., Thompson, J. K., & Stormer, S. (1995). Development and validation of the sociocultural attitudes towards appearance questionnaire. *International Journal of Eating Disorders, 17,* 81–89.

Heinrichs, R. W. (2001). *In search of madness: Schizophrenia and neuroscience.* New York, NY: Oxford University Press.

Heinrichs, R. W. (2003). Historical origins of schizophrenia: Two early madmen and their illness. *Journal of the History of the Behavioral Sciences, 39*(4), 349–363.

Heinrichs, R. W. (2004). Meta-analysis and the science of schizophrenia: Variant evidence or evidence of variants? *Neuroscience and Biobehavioral Reviews, 28,* 379–394.

Heinrichs, R.W. (2005). The primacy of cognition in schizophrenia. *American Psychologist, 60,* 229–242.

Heinrichs, R. W. (2007). Cognitive improvement in response to antipsychotic drugs. *Archives of General Psychiatry, 64,* 631–632.

Heinrichs, R. W., & Awad, A. G. (1993). Neurocognitive subtypes of chronic schizophrenia. *Schizophrenia Research, 9*(1), 49–58.

Heinrichs, R. W., & Zakzanis, K. K. (1998). Neurocognitive deficit in schizophrenia: A quantitative review of the evidence. *Neuropsychology, 12,* 426–445.

Heinrichs, R. W., Ammari, N., Vaz, S. M., & Miles, A. A. (2008). Are schizophrenia and schizoaffective disorder neuropsychologically distinguishable?. *Schizophrenia Research, 99*(1), 149–154.

Heinrichs, R. W., Miles, A. A., Smith, D., Zargarian, T., McDermid Vaz, S., Goldberg, J. O., & Ammari, N. (2008). Cognitive, clinical, and functional characteristics of verbally superior schizophrenia patients. *Neuropsychology, 22,* 321–328.

Heinz, A., Deserno, L., & Reininghaus, U. (2013). Urbanicity, social adversity and psychosis. *World Psychiatry, 12*(3), 187–197.

Heisel, M. J. (2006). Suicide and its prevention among older adults. *Canadian Journal of Psychiatry, 51,* 143–154.

Helff, C.M. & Glidden, L. M. (1998). More positive or less negative? Trends in research on adjustment of families rearing children with developmental disabilities. *Mental Retardation, 36,* 457–64.

Hellekson, K. L. (2001). NIH consensus statement on phenylketonuria. *American Family Physician, 63,* 1430–1432.

Heller, T., & Arnold, C. (2010). Siblings of adults with developmental disabilities: Psychosocial outcomes, relationships, and future planning. *Journal of Policy and Practice in Intellectual Disabilities, 7,* 16–25.

Helmes, E., & Ward, B. G. (2015). Mindfulness-based cognitive therapy for anxiety symptoms in older adults in residential care. *Aging & Mental Health,21*(3), 1–7. doi:10.1080/13607863.2015.1111862

Hemphill, J. F., & Hare, R. D. (2004). Some misconceptions about the Hare PCL-R and risk assessment: A reply to Gendreau, Goggin, and Smith. *Criminal Justice and Behavior, 31*(2), 203–243.

Hemphill, J. F., Hare, R. D., & Wong, S. (1998). Psychopathy and recidivism: A review. *Legal and Criminological Psychology, 3,* 139–170.

Henderson, S. (2002). The National Survey of Mental Health and Well-Being in Australia: Impact on policy. *Canadian Journal of Psychiatry, 47,* 819–824.

Hendriks, G. J., Oude Voshaar, R. C., Keijsers, G. P. J., Hoogduin, C. A. L., & van Balkom, A. J. L. M. (2008). Cognitive-behavioural therapy for late-life anxiety disorders: A systematic review and meta-analysis. *Acta Psychiatrica Scandinavica, 117,* 403–411.

Hendriks, S. M., Spijker, J. Licht, C. M. M., Hardeveld, F., de Graaf, R., Batelaan, N. M., . . . Beekman, A. T. F. (2015). Long-term work disability and absenteeism in anxiety and depressive disorders. *Journal of Affective Disorders, 178,* 121–130.

Henggeler, S. W., & Schoenwald, S. K. (1993). Multisystemic therapy with juvenile offenders: An effective family-based treatment. *The Family Psychologist, 9,* 24–26.

Henke, P. G. (1988). Recent studies of the central nucleus of the amygdala and stress ulcers. *Neuroscience and Biobehavioral Reviews, 12,* 143–150.

Henke, P. G. (1990). Hippocampal pathway to the amygdala and stress ulcer development. *Brain Research Bulletin, 25,* 691–695.

Henke, P. G. (1992). Stomach pathology and the amygdala. In J. P. Aggleton (Ed.), *The amygdala: Neurobiological aspects of emotion, memory and mental dysfunction* (pp. 323–338). New York, NY: Wiley.

Henry, K., & Cohen, C. (1983).The role of labeling in diagnosing borderline personality disorder. *American Journal of Psychiatry, 140,* 1527–1529.

Henry, W. P., Strupp, H. H., Schacht, T. E., & Gaston, L. (1994). Psychodynamic approaches. In A. E. Bergin & S. L. Garfield (Eds.), *Handbook of psychotherapy and behavior change* (4th ed., pp. 467–508). New York, NY: Wiley.

Herbert, T. B., & Cohen, S. (1993). Stress and immunity in humans: A meta-analytic review. *Psychosomatic Medicine, 55,* 364–379.

Hergovich, A., & Süssenbach, S. (2015). The time trend of beauties: Detection of cross-cultural invariance in *Playboy* centerfolds. *Current Psychology, 34,* 666–671. doi: 10.1007/s12144-014-9279–5

Herman, J. P., Prewitt, C. M. F., & Cullinan, W. E. (1996). Neuronal circuit regulation of the hypothalamo-pituitary-adrenocortical stress axis. *Critical Reviews in Neurobiology, 10,* 371–394.

Herrnstein, R., & Murray, C. (1994). *The bell curve: Intelligence and class structure in American life.* New York, NY: The Free Press.

Hershkowitz, D. (1998). *The madness of epic: Reading insanity from Homer to Statius.* Oxford, UK: Oxford University Press.

Herzog, D. B., Greenwood, D. N., Dorer, D. J., Flores, A. T., Ekeblad, E. R., Richards, A., et al. (2000). Mortality in eating disorders: A descriptive study. *International Journal of Eating Disorders, 28,* 20–26.

Hesse, E., Main, M., Abrams, K. Y., & Rifkin, A. (2003). Unresolved states regarding loss or abuse can have "second-generation" effects: Disorganized, role-inversion and frightening ideation in the offspring of traumatized non-maltreating parents. In D. J. Siegel & M. F. Solomon (Eds.), *Healing trauma: Attachment, mind, body and brain* (pp. 57–106). New York, NY: Norton.

Hetrick, S., Merry, S., McKenzie, J., Sindahl, P., & Proctor, M. (2007). Selective serotonin reuptake inhibitors (SSRIs) for depressive disorders in children and adolescents. *Cochrane Database of Systematic Reviews, 3:* CD004851.

Hettema, J. M., Neale, M. C., & Kendler, K. S. (2001). A review and meta-analysis of the genetic epidemiology of anxiety disorders. *American Journal of Psychiatry, 158,* 1568–1578.

Hewitt, P. L., & Flett, G. L. (1991). Perfectionism in the self and social contexts: Conceptualization, assessment, and association with psychopathology. *Journal of Personality and Social Psychology, 60*(3), 456–470. http://doi.org/10.1037/0022-3514.60.3.456

Hickson, L., Khemka, I., Golden, H., & Chatzistyli, A. (2015). Randomized controlled trial to evaluate an abuse prevention curriculum for women and men with intellectual and developmental disabilities. *American journal on intellectual and developmental disabilities, 120*(6), 490–503.

Higa-McMillan, C. K., Francis, S. E., Rith-Najaran, L., & Chorpita, B. F. (2016). Evidence base update: 50 years of research on treatment of child and adolescent anxiety. *Journal of Clinical Child and Adolescent Psychology, 45,* 91–113.

Higgenbottam, J., Ledwidge, B., Paredes, J., Hansen, M., Kogan, C., & Lambert, L. (1985). Variables affecting the decision making of a review panel. *Canadian Journal of Psychiatry, 30,* 577–581.

Higgins, S. T., Budney, A. J., Bickel, W. K., Foerg, F. E., & Badger, G. J. (1994). Alcohol dependence and simultaneous cocaine and alcohol use in cocaine-dependent patients. *Journal of Addictive Diseases, 13*(4), 177–189.

Higgins, S. T., Budney, A. J., Bickel, W. K., Hughes, J., Foerg, F., & Badger, G. (1993). Achieving cocaine abstinence with a behavioral approach. *American Journal of Psychiatry, 150*(5), 763–769.

Hijazi, A. M., Lumley, M. A., Ziadni, M. S., Haddad, L., Rapport, L. T., & Arnetz, B. B. (2014). Brief narrative exposure therapy for posttraumatic stress in Iraqi refugees: A preliminary randomized clinical trial. *Journal of Traumatic Stress, 27,* 314–322. doi:10.1002/jts.21922

Hilgard, E. R. (1986). *Divided consciousness: Multiple controls in human thought and action* (expanded. ed.). New York, NY: Wiley.

Hill, A. B. (1965). The environment and disease: Association or causation? *Proceedings of the Royal Society of Medicine, 58,* 295–300.

Hill, S. K., Harris, M. S., Herbener, E. S., Pavuluri, M., & Sweeney, J. A. (2008). Neurocognitive allied phenotypes for schizophrenia and bipolar disorder. *Schizophrenia Bulletin, 34,* 743–759.

Hill, S. Y., & Steinhauer, S. R. (1993). Assessment of prepubertal and postpubertal boys and girls at risk for developing alcoholism with P300 from a visual discrimination task. *Journal of Studies on Alcohol, 54,* 350–358.

Hill, S. Y., Shen, S., Lowers, L., & Locke, J. (2000). Factors predicting the onset of adolescent drinking in families at high risk for developing alcoholism. *Biological psychiatry, 48*(4), 265–275.

Hinshaw, S. P., & Anderson, C. A. (1996). Conduct and oppositional defiant disorders. In E. J. Mash & R. A. Barkley (Eds.), *Child psychopathology* (pp. 113–149). New York, NY: Guilford.

Hinshaw, S. P., & Lee, S. S. (2003). Conduct and oppositional defiant disorders. In E. J. Mash & R. A. Barkley (Eds.), *Child psychopathology* (2nd ed., pp. 144–198). New York, NY: Guilford.

Hinzen, W., & Rosselló, J. (2015). The linguistics of schizophrenia: Thought disturbance as language pathology across positive symptoms. *Frontiers in Psychology, 6,* 1–17.

Hirsch, C. R., & Clark, D. M. (2004). Information-processing bias in social phobia. *Clinical Psychology Review, 24,* 799–825.

Hirschfeld, R. (2001). Comorbidity of major depression and anxiety disorders: Recognition and management in primary care. *Journal of Clinical Psychiatry, 3,* 244–254.

Hisfield-Becker, D. R., Micco, J. A., Simoes, N. A., & Henin, A. (2008). High risk studies and developmental antecedents of anxiety disorder. *American Journal of Medical Genetics Part C (Seminars in Medical Genetics), 148C,* 99–117.

Hobson, J., Shine, J., & Roberts, R. (2000). How do psychopaths behave in a prison therapeutic community? *Psychology, Crime, and Law, 6,* 139–154.

Hodgins, D. C. (2005). Can patients with alcohol use disorders return to social drinking? Yes, so what should we do about it? *Canadian Journal of Psychiatry, 50,* 264–265.

Hodgins, D. C., & Diskin, K. M. (2003). Alcohol problems. In M. Hersen & S. M. Turner (Eds.), *Diagnostic Interviewing* (3rd ed.). New York, NY: Kluwer.

Hodgins, D. C., & el-Guebaly, N. (2000). Natural and treatment assisted recovery from gambling problems: Comparison of resolved and active gamblers. *Addiction, 95,* 777–789.

Hodgins, D. C., & Makarchuk, K. (2002). *Becoming a winner: Defeating problem gambling.* Calgary, AB: Addiction Centre, Calgary Regional Health Authority.

Hodgins, D. C., Currie, S. R., & el-Guebaly, N. (2001). Motivational enhancement and self-help treatments for problem gambling. *Journal of Consulting and Clinical Psychology, 69,* 50–57.

Hodgins, D. C., Currie, S. R., Currie, G., & Fick, G. H. (2009). A randomized trial of brief motivational treatments for pathological gamblers: More is not necessarily better. *Journal of Consulting and Clinical Psychology, 77,* 950–960. doi:10.1037/a0016318

Hodgins, D. C., Currie, S. R., el-Guebaly, N., & Peden, N. (2004). Brief motivational treatment for problem gambling: 24 month follow-up. *Psychology of Addictive Behaviors, 18,* 293–296.

Hodgins, D. C., Leigh, G., Milne, R., & Gerrish, R. (1997). Drinking goal selection in behavioural self-management treatment of chronic alcoholics. *Addictive Behaviors, 22,* 247–255.

Hodgson, B., Kukkonen, T. M., Binik, Y. M., & Carrier, S. (2016). Using the dual control model to investigate the relationship between mood, genital and self-reported sexual arousal in men and women. *Journal of Sex Research, 53,* 979–993.

Hoek, H. W. (2006). Incidence, prevalence and mortality of anorexia nervosa and other eating disorders. *Current Opinion in Psychiatry, 19,* 389–394. doi: 10.1097/01.yco.0000228759.95237.78

Hoek, H. W., & van Hoeken, D. (2003). Review of the prevalence and incidence of eating disorders. *International Journal of Eating Disorders, 34,* 383–396.

Hoffman, E. J., & Mathew, S. J. (2008). Anxiety disorders: A comprehensive review of pharmacotherapies. *Mount Sinai Journal of Medicine: A Journal of Translational and Personalized Medicine, 75,* 248–262.

Hofmann, S. G., & Barlow, D. H. (2002). Social phobia (social anxiety disorder). In D. H. Barlow (Ed.), *Anxiety and its disorders* (2nd ed., pp. 454–476). New York, NY: Guilford.

Hofmann, S. G., Lehman, C. L., & Barlow, D. H. (1997). How specific are specific phobias? *Journal of Behavior Therapy and Experimental Psychiatry, 28,* 233–240.

Hofmann, S. G., Pollack, M. H., & Otto, M. W. (2006). Augmentation treatment of psychotherapy for anxiety disorders with D-Cycloserine. *CNS Drug Reviews, 12,* 208–217.

Hofmann, S. G., Sawyer, A. T., & Fang, A. (2010). The empirical status of the "new wave" of CBT. *Psychiatric Clinics of North America, 33,* 701–710.

Hofmann, S. G., Sawyer, A. T., Witt, A. A., & Oh, D. (2010). The effect of mindfulness-based therapy on anxiety and depression: A meta-analytic review. *Journal of Consulting and Clinical Psychology, 78,* 169–183.

Högberg, G., Antonuccio, D. O., & Healy, D. (2015). Suicidal risk from TADS study was higher than it first appeared. *International Journal of Risk & Safety in Medicine, 27*(2), 85–91.

Hollinghurst, S., Peters, T. J., Kaur, S., Wiles, N., Lewis, G., & Kessler, D. (2010). Cost-effectiveness of therapist-delivered online cognitive-behavioural therapy for depression: Randomized controlled trial. *British Journal of Psychiatry, 197,* 297–304.

Hollingshead, A. B., & Redlich, F. C. (1958). *Social class and mental illness: A community study.* New York, NY: Wiley.

Hollon, S. D., & Beck, A. T. (1994). Cognitive and cognitive behavioral therapies. In A. E. Bergin & S. L. Garlfield (Eds.), *Handbook of psychotherapy and behavior change* (4th ed., pp. 428–466). New York, NY: Wiley.

Hollon, S. D., & Kendall, P. C. (1980). Cognitive self-statements in depression: Development of an automatic thoughts questionnaire. *Cognitive Therapy and Research, 4*(4), 383–395. https://doi.org/10.1007/BF01178214

Hollon, S. D., DeRubeis, R. J., Shelton, R. C., Amsterdam, J. D., Salomon, R. M., O'Reardon, J. P., et al. (2005). Prevention of relapse following cognitive therapy vs medications in moderate to severe depression. *Archives of General Psychiatry, 62,* 417–422.

Hollon, S. D., Thase, M. E., & Markowitz, J. C. (2002). Treatment and prevention of depression. *Psychological Science in the Public Interest, 3,* 39–77.

Holmes, T. H., & Masuda, M. (1974). Life change and illness susceptibility. In B. S. Dohrenwend & B. P. Dohrenwend (Eds.), *Stressful life events: Their nature and effects.* New York, NY: Wiley.

Holmes, T. H., & Rahe, R. H. (1967). The Social Readjustment Rating Scale. *Journal of Psychosomatic Research, 11,* 213–218.

Holoch, K., Stein, Q., Flanagan, J., & Hansen, K. (2008). Premature ovarian failure: A phenotypic expression of Fragile X premutation. *South Dakota Medicine, 61*(1), 13–15.

Holt-Lunstad, J., Smith, T. B., & Layton, J. B. (2010). Social relationships and mortality risk: a meta-analytic review. *PLoS Med, 7*(7), e1000316. doi: 10.1371/journal.pmed.1000316

Holt-Lunstad, J., Smith, T. B., Baker, M., Harris, T., & Stephenson, D. (2015). Loneliness and social isolation as risk factors for mortality a meta-analytic review. *Perspectives on Psychological Science, 10*(2), 227–237.

Holt, C. S., Heimberg, R. G., & Hope, D. A. (1992). Avoidant personality disorder and the generalized subtype of social phobia. *Journal of Abnormal Psychology, 101,* 318–325. doi:10.1037/0021-843X.101.2.318

Holt, S. E., Meloy, J. R., & Stack, S. (1999). Sadism and psychopathy in violent and sexually violent offenders. *Journal of the American Academy of Psychiatry and Law, 27,* 23–32.

Homan, K. (2010). Athletic-ideal and thin-ideal internalization as prospective predictors of body dissatisfaction, dieting, and compulsive exercise. *Body Image, 7,* 240–245.

Hook, E. B., Cross, P. K., & Regal, R. R. (1990). Factual, statistical and logical issues in the search for a paternal age effect for Down syndrome. *Human Genetics, 85,* 387–388.

Hooley, J. M. (2007). Expressed emotion and relapse of psychopathology. *Annual Review of Clinical Psychology, 3,* 329–352.

Hoon, E. F., Hoon, P. W., Rand, K. H., Johnson, J., Hall, N. R., & Edwards, N. B. (1991). A psycho-behavioral model of genital herpes recurrence. *Journal of Psychosomatic Research, 35,* 25–36.

Hopcroft, R. L., & Bradley, D. B. (2007). The sex difference in depression across 29 countries. *Social Forces, 85,* 1111–1136.

Hopwood, C. J., Wright, A. G. C., Ansell, E. B., & Pincus, A. L. (2013). The interpersonal core of personality pathology. *Journal of Personality Disorders, 27*(3), 270–295.

Hor, K., & Taylor, M. (2010). Suicide and schizophrenia: A systematic review of rates and risk factors. *Journal of Psychopharmacology, 24,* 81–90.

Horen, S. A., Leichner, P. P., & Lawson, J. S. (1995). Prevalence of dissociative symptoms and disorders in an adult psychiatric inpatient population in Canada. *Canadian Journal of Psychiatry, 40,* 185–191.

Horner, R. H., Carr, E. G., Strain, P. S., Todd, A. W., & Reed, H. K. (2002). Problem behavior interventions for young children with autism: A research synthesis. *Journal of Autism and Developmental Disorders, 32,* 423–446.

Horney, K. (1945). *Our inner conflicts: A constructive theory of neurosis.* New York, NY: Norton.

Horowitz, A. V., & Wakefield, J. C. (2007). *The loss of sadness: How psychiatry transformed normal sorrow into depressive disorder.* New York, NY: Oxford University Press.

Hospers, H. J., & Jansen, A. (2005). Why homosexuality is a risk factor for eating disorders in males. *Journal of Social and Clinical Psychology, 24,* 1188–1201.

Hotopf, M., Wilson-Jones, C., Mayou, R., Wadsworth, M., & Wessely, S. (2000). Childhood predictors of adult medically unexplained hospitalisations. *The British Journal of Psychiatry, 176*(3), 273–280.

House, J. S., Landis, K. R., & Umberson, D. (1988). Social relationships and health. *Science, 241,* 540–545.

Howard, J. S., Sparkman, C. R., Cohen, H. G., Green, G., & Stanislaw, H. A. (2005). Comparison of intensive behavior analytic and eclectic treatments for young children with autism. *Research in Developmental Disabilities, 26,* 359–383.

Howard, R., Castle, D., Wessely, S., & Murray, R. (1993). A comparative study of 470 cases of early-onset and late-onset schizophrenia. *British Journal of Psychiatry, 163,* 352–357.

Howe A. S., Buttenschon, H. N., Bani-Fatemi, A., Maron, E., Otowa, T., Erhardt A., . . . De Luca, V. (2016). Candidate genes in panic disorder: Meta-analyses of 23 common variants in major anxiogenic pathways. *Molecular Psychiatry, 21,* 665–679. doi:10.1038/mp.2015.138

Howes, O. D., & Kapur, S. (2009). The dopamine hypothesis of schizophrenia: Version III—the final common pathway. *Schizophrenia Bulletin, 35,* 549–562.

Howes, O. D., McCutcheon, R., Owen, M. J., & Murray, R. M. (2017). The role of genes, stress, and dopamine in the development of schizophrenia. *Biological Psychiatry, 81*(1), 9–20.

Howlin, P., Gordon, K., Pasco, G., Wade, A., & Charman, T. (2007). A group randomised, controlled trial of the Picture Exchange Communication System for children with autism. *Journal of Child Psychology and Psychiatry, 48,* 473–481.

Howlin, P., Magiati, I., & Charman, T. (2009). Systematic review of early intensive behavioral interventions for children with autism. *American Journal on Intellectual and Developmental Disabilities, 114,* 23–41.

Huang, Y., Kotov, R., de Girolamo, G., Preti, A., Angermeyer, M., Benjet, C., et al. (2009). DSM-IV personality disorders in the WHO World Mental Health Surveys. *British Journal of Psychiatry, 195*(1), 46–53. doi:10.1192/bjp.bp.108.058552

Hudson, J. I., Hiripi, E., Pope, H. G., & Kessler, R. C. (2007). The prevalence and correlates of eating disorders in the National Comorbidity Survey Replication. *Biological Psychiatry, 61,* 348-358. doi: 10.1016/j.biopsych.2006.03.040

Huettell, S., Song, A. W., & McCarthy, G. (2008). *Functional magnetic resonance imaging* (2nd ed.). Sunderland, MS: Sinauer Associates.

Huey Jr., S. J., Tilley, J. L., Jones, E. O., & Smith, C. A. (2014). The contribution of cultural competence to evidence-based care for ethnically diverse populations. *Annual Review of Clinical Psychology, 10,* 305–338.

Hughes, M. W., Schuster, J. W., & Nelson, C. M. (1993). The acquisition of independent dressing skills by students with multiple disabilities. *Journal of Developmental and Physical Disabilities, 5,* 233–252.

Humphreys, K. (2003). A research-based analysis of the Moderation Management controversy. *Psychiatric Services, 54,* 621–622.

Humphreys, K., & Klaw, E. (2001). Can targeting nondependent problem drinkers and providing internet-based services expand access to assistance for alcohol problems? A study of the moderation management self-help/mutual aid organization. *Journal of Studies on Alcohol, 62*(4), 528–532.

Hunsley, J., & Di Giulio, G. (2002). Dodo bird, phoenix, or urban legend? The question of psychotherapy equivalence. *Scientific Review of Mental Health Practice, 1,* 11–22.

Hunsley, J., & Elliott, K. (2014). Implementing an evidence-based approach to cognitive-behavioral assessment. In G. P. Brown & D. A. Clark (Eds.), *Assessment in cognitive therapy* (pp. 121–145). New York, NY: Guilford.

Hunsley, J., & Lee, C. M. (1995). The marital effects of individually oriented psychotherapy: Is there evidence for the deterioration hypothesis? *Clinical Psychology Review, 15,* 1–22.

Hunsley, J., & Lee, C. M. (2007). Research-informed benchmarks for psychological treatments: Efficacy studies, effectiveness studies, and beyond. *Professional Psychology: Research and Practice, 38,* 21–33.

Hunsley, J., & Mash, E. J. (2011). Evidence-based assessment. In D. H. Barlow (Ed.), *Oxford Handbook of Clinical Psychology* (pp. 76–97). New York, NY: Oxford University Press.

Hunsley, J., Dobson, K., Johnston, C., & Mikail, S. (1999). Empirically supported treatments in psychology: Implications for Canadian professional psychology. *Canadian Psychology, 40,* 289–301.

Hunsley, J., Elliott, K. P., & Therrien, Z. (2013). The efficacy and effectiveness of psychological treatments. *Canadian Psychology, 55,* 153–160.

Hunsley, J., Elliott, K. P., & Therrien, Z. (2014). The efficacy and effectiveness of psychological treatments for mood, anxiety, and related disorders. *Canadian Psychology, 55,* 161–176.

Hunsley, J., Lee, C. M., & Aubry, T. D. (1999). Who uses psychological services in Canada? *Canadian Psychology, 40,* 232–240.

Hunsley, J., Ronson, A., & Cohen, K. R. (2013). Professional psychology in Canada: A survey of demographic and practice characteristics. *Professional Psychology: Research and Practice, 44,* 118–126.

Hunter, J. M., Shannon, G. W., & Sambrook, S. L. (1986). Rings of madness: Service areas of 19th century asylums in North America. *Social Science and Medicine, 23,* 1033–1050.

Hurd, H. M., Drewry, W. F., Dewey, R., Pilgrim, C. W., Blumer, G. A., & Burgess, T. J. W. (1916). *The institutional care of the insane in the United States and Canada.* Baltimore, MD: Johns Hopkins Hospital Press.

Hurley, S. F. (1997). The effectiveness of needle-exchange programs for the prevention of HIV infection. *The Lancet, 349,* 1797–1800.

Hutchinson, N. L., Minnes, P., Burbidge, J., Dods, J., Pyle, A., Dalton C. J. (2015). Perspectives of Canadian teacher candidates on inclusion of children with developmental disabilities: A mixed methods study. *Exceptionality Education International, 25,* 42–64

Hutton, P., & Taylor, P. J. (2014). Cognitive behavioural therapy for psychosis prevention: A systematic review and meta-analysis. *Psychological Medicine, 44*(3), 449-468.

Hylton, J. H. (1995). Care or control: Health or criminal justice options for the long-term seriously mentally ill in a Canadian province. *International Journal of Law and Psychiatry, 18,* 45–59.

Hyman, S. E. (2010). The diagnosis of mental disorders: The problem of reification. *The Annual Review of Clinical Psychology, 6*, 155–179.

Hymel, S., Schonert-Reichl, K. A., Bonanno, R. A., Vaillancourt, T., & Rocke-Henderson, N. (2009). Bullying and morality: Understanding how good kids can behave badly. In S. R. Jimerson, S. M. Swearer, & D. L. Espelage (Eds.), *The international handbook of school bullying*. Mahwah, NJ: Lawrence Erlbaum Associates.

Iacono, D., Volkman, I., Nennesmo, I., Pedersen, N. L., Fratiglioni, L., Johansson, B., . . Gatz, M. (2014). Neuropathologic assessment of dementia markers in identical and fraternal twins. *Brain Pathology, 24*(4), 317–333. Doi: 10.1111/bpa.12127

Iacono, W. G., Bassett, A. S., & Jones, B. D. (1988). Eye tracking dysfunction is associated with parital trisomy of chromosome 5 and schizophrenia. *Archives of General Psychiatry, 45*, 1140–1141.

Iacono, W. G., Malone, S. M., & McGue, M. (2003). Substance use disorders, externalizing psychopathology, and P300 event-related potential amplitude. *International Journal of Psychophysiology, 48*(2), 147–178.

IASSID, Families Special Interest Research Group (2014), Families supporting a child with intellectual or developmental disabilities: The current state of knowledge. *Journal of Applied Research in Intellectual Disabilities, 27*, 420–430. doi:10.1111/jar.12078

Ihl, R., Frolich, L., Winblad, B., Schneider, L., Burns, A., Moller, H-J., et al. (2011). World Federation of Societies of Biological Psychiatry (WFSBP) guidelines for the biological treatment of Alzheimer's disease and other dementias. *The World Journal of Biological Psychiatry, 12*, 2–32. doi:10.3109/15622975.2010.538083

IMS Brogan. (2016a). *Pharamceutical trends: Top 10 reasons for physician visits in Canada, 2015.* Retrieved from www.imshealth.com/files/web/Canada/About%20Us/Top%20Line%20Market%20Data/IMSH_Canada_Top10Reasons_2015.pdf.

IMS Brogan. (2016b). *Pharmaceutical trends: Top 10 therapeutic classes in Canada, 2015.* Retrieved from www.imshealth.com/files/web/Canada/About%20Us/Top%20Line%20Market%20Data/IMSH_Canada_Top10TherapeuticClasses_2015.pdf.

Ingram, R. E., Atchley, R. A., & Segal, Z. V. (2011). *Vulnerability to depression: From cognitive neuroscience to prevention and treatment.* New York, NY: Guildford Press.

Ingram, R. E., Miranda, J., & Segal, Z. V. (1998). *Cognitive vulnerability to depression.* New York, NY: Guilford.

Ingram, R. E., Nelson, T., Steidtmann, D. K., & Bistricky, S. L. (2007). Comparative data on child and adolescent cognitive measures associated with depression. *Journal of Consulting and Clinical Psychology, 75*, 390–403.

Institute for Health Metrics and Evaluation. (2015). *Global Burden of Diseases, Injuries, and Risk Factors Study, 2013.* Data retrieved from http://www.healthdata.org/data-visualization/gbd-compare

Institute of Medicine. (1994). *Reducing risks for mental disorders: Frontiers for preventive intervention research.* Washington, DC: National Academy Press.

Ironson, G., Taylor, C. B., Boltwood, M., Bartzokis, T., Dennis, C., Chesney, M., et al. (1992). Effects of anger on left ventricular ejection fraction in coronary artery disease. *American Journal of Cardiology, 70*, 281–285.

Irvine, J., & Logan, A. G. (1991). Relaxation behavior therapy as sole treatment for mild hypertension. *Psychosomatic Medicine, 53*, 587–597.

Irvine, J., & Ritvo, P. G. (1998). Health risk behavior change and adaptation in cardiac patients, *Clinical Psychology and Psychotherapy, 5*, 86–101.

Isaac, C., & Januel, D. (2016). Neural correlates of cognitive improvements following cognitive remediation in schizophrenia: A systematic review of randomized trials. *Socioaffective Neuroscience & Psychology, 6*, 1–18.

It's the End of the World as Clear Channel Knows It. (2001, September 17). Retrieved April 20, 2017, from http://www.slate.com/articles/news_and_politics/chatterbox/2001/09/its_the_end_of_the_world_as_clear_channel_knows_it.html

Ittermann, T., Völzke, H., Baumeister, S. E., Appel, K., & Grabe, H. J. (2015). Diagnosed thyroid disorders are associated with depression and anxiety. *Social Psychiatry and Psychiatric Epidemiology, 50*, 1417–1425.

Iyer-Eimerbrink, P.A. & Nurnberger Junior, J.I.(2104). Genetics of alcoholism. *Current Psychiatry Reports, 16*, 518–530.

Jääskeläinen, E., Juola, P., Hirvonen, N., McGrath, J. J., Saha, S., Isohanni, M., . . . & Miettunen, J. (2013). A systematic review and meta-analysis of recovery in schizophrenia. *Schizophrenia Bulletin, 39*(6), 1296–1306.

Jackson, A., Cavanagh, J., & Scott, J. (2003). A systematic review of manic and depressive prodromes. *Journal of Affective Disorders, 74*, 209–217.

Jackson, D. N., & Messick, S. (1961). Acquiescence and desirability as response determinants on the MMPI. *Education and Psychological Measurement, 21*, 771–790.

Jackson, S. W. (1986). *Melancholia and depression: From Hippocratic times to modern times.* New Haven, CT: Yale University Press.

Jacobs, G. D., Pace-Shott, E. F., Stickgold, R., & Otto, M. W. (2004). Cognitive behavior therapy and pharmacotherapy for insomnia. *Archives of Internal Medicine, 164*, 1888–1896.

Jacobson, J. W., Mulick, J. A., & Schwartz, A. A. (1995). A history of facilitated communication: Science, pseudoscience and antiscience. *American Psychologist, 50*, 750–765.

Jacobson, N. S., & Margolin, G. (1979). *Marital therapy: Strategies based on social learning and behavior exchange principles.* New York, NY: Brunner/Mazel.

Jacobson, N. S., & Truax, P. (1991). Clinical significance: A statistical approach to defining meaningful change in psychotherapy research. *Journal of Consulting and Clinical Psychology, 59*(1), 12–19.

Jacobson, N. S., Dobson, K. S., Truax, P. A., Addis, M. E., Koerner, K., Gollan, J. K., et al. (1996). A component analysis of cognitive-behavioral treatment for depression. *Journal of Consulting and Clinical Psychology, 64*, 295–304.

Jafari, S., Buxton, J. A., & Joe, R. (2015). Rising fentanyl-related overdose deaths in British Columbia. *Canadian Journal of Addiction, 6*(1), 4–6.

Jaffe, J. H. (1995). Drug addiction and drug abuse. In L. S. Goodman & A. Gilman (Eds.), *The pharmacological basis of therapeutic behaviour.* New York, NY: Macmillan.

Jaffee, S. R., Caspi, A., Moffitt, T. E., Dodge, K. A., Rutter, M., Taylor, A., et al. (2005). Nature x nurture: Genetic vulnerabilities interact with physical maltreatment to promote conduct problems. *Development and Psychopathology, 17*, 67–84.

Jager-Hyman, S., Cunningham, A., Wenzel, A., Mattei, S., Brown, G. K., & Beck, A. T. (2014). Cognitive distortions and suicide attempts. *Cognitive Therapy and Research, 38*, 369–374.

Jamison, K. R. (1995). *An unquiet mind.* New York: Vintage.

Jang, K. L., Paris, J., Zweig-Frank, H., & Livesley, W. J. (1998). Twin study of dissociative experience. *Journal of Nervous and Mental Disease, 186*, 345–351.

Jannini, E. A., Lombardo, F., & Lenzi, A. (2005). Correlation between ejaculatory and erectile dysfunction. *International Journal of Andrology, 28*, 40–45.

Janus, S. S., & Janus, C. L. (1993). *The Janus report on sexual behavior.* New York, NY: Wiley.

Jarcho, M. R., Slavich, G. M., Tylova-Stein, H., Wolkowitz, O. M., & Burke, H. M. (2013). Dysregulated diurnal cortisol pattern is associated with glucocorticoid resistance in women with major depressive disorder. *Biological Psychology, 93*(1), 150–158.

Jauhar, S., McKenna, P. J., Radua, J., Fung, E., Salvador, R., & Laws, K. R. (2014). Cognitive-behavioural therapy for the symptoms of schizophrenia: Systematic review and meta-analysis with examination of potential bias. *British Journal of Psychiatry, 204*, 20–29.

Jaussent, I., Bouyer, J., Ancelin, M. L., Akbaraly, T., Peres, K., Ritchie, K., . . . & Dauvilliers, Y. (2011). Insomnia and daytime sleepiness are risk factors for depressive symptoms in the elderly. *Sleep, 34*(8), 1103–1110.

Jay, E. L., Nestler, S., Sierra, M., McClelland, J., Kekic, M., & David, A. S. (2016). Ventrolateral prefrontal cortex repetitive transcranial magnetic stimulation in the treatment of depersonalization disorder: A consecutive case series. *Psychiatry Research, 240*, 118–122.

Jayasekara, R., Procter, N., Harrison, J., Skelton, K., Hampel, S., Draper, R., & Deuter, K. (2015). Cognitive behavioural therapy for older adults with depression: A review. *Journal of Mental Health, 24*(3), 168–171. doi:10.3109/09638237.2014.971143

Jenike, M. A. (1998). Theories of etiology. In M. A. Jenike, L. Baer, & W. E. Minichiello (Eds.), *Obsessive-compulsive disorders: Practical management* (3rd ed., pp. 203–221). St. Louis, MO: Mosby.

Jenkins, M. R., & Culbertson, J. L. (1996). Prenatal exposure to alcohol. In R. L. Adams, O. A. Pausons, & J. L. Culbertson (Eds.), *Neuropsychology for clinical practices: Etiology, assessment, and treatment of common neurological disorders* (pp. 409–452). Washington, DC: American Psychological Association.

Jensen-Doss, A., & Weisz, J. R. (2006). Syndrome co-occurrence and treatment outcomes in youth mental health clinics. *Journal of Consulting and Clinical Psychology, 74*, 416–425.

Jensen, A. R. (1997). Psychometric g and the race question. In J. Kingma & W. Tomic (Eds.), *Advances in cognition and educational practices: Reflections on the concept of intelligence* (Vol. 4). London, UK: Reed Elsevier.

Jensen, P. S. (2003). Comorbidity and child psychopathology: Recommendations for the next decade. *Journal of Abnormal Child Psychology, 31*, 293–300.

Jeste, D. V., del Carmen, R., Lohr, J. B., & Wyatt, R. J. (1985). Did schizophrenia exist before the eighteenth century? *Comprehensive Psychiatry, 26*, 493–503.

Jeste, D. V., Harris, M. J., Pearlson, G. D., Rabins, P., Lesser, I., Miller, B., et al. (1988). Late-onset schizophrenia: Studying clinical validity. *Psychiatric Annals of North America, 11*, 1–13.

Jeste, D. V., Manley, M., & Harris, M. J., (1991). Psychoses. In J. S. Sadavoy, L. W. Lazarus, & L. F. Jarvik (Eds.), *Comprehensive review of geriatric psychiatry* (pp. 353–368). Washington, DC: American Psychiatric Press, Inc.

Joe, G. W., Dansereau, D. F., & Simpson, D. D. (1994). Node-link mapping for counselling cocaine users in methadone treatment. *Journal of Substance Abuse*, 6(4), 393–406.

Joffe, J. M., & Albee, G. W. (Eds.). (1981). *Prevention through political action and social change*. Hanover, NH: University Press of New England.

Joffe, R. T., Swinson, R. P., & Regan, J. J. (1988). Personality features of obsessive-compulsive disorder. *American Journal of Psychiatry*, 145, 1127–1129.

Johnson, C. P., Myers, S. M., & the Council of Children with Disabilities. (2007). American Academy of Pediatrics: Identification and evaluation of children with autism spectrum disorders. *Pediatrics*, 120, 1183–1215.

Johnson, C., & Connors, M. E. (1987). *The etiology and treatment of bulimia nervosa*. New York: Basic Books.

Johnson, D. J., & Myklebust, H. R. (1971). *Learning disabilities*. New York, NY: Grune & Stratton.

Johnson, E. S., Humphrey, M., Mellard, D., Woods, K., Swanson, H. L. (2010). Cognitive processing deficits and students with specific learning disabilities: A selective meta-analysis of the literature. *Learning Disability Quarterly*, 33, 3–18.

Johnson, G. R. (2014). Toward uniform competency standards in telepsychology:A proposed framework for Canadian psychologists. *Canadian Psychology*, 55, 291–302

Johnson, J. A., Lavoie, K. L., Bacon, S. L., Carlson, L. E., & Campbell, T. S. (2012). The effect of trait rumination on adaptation to repeated stress. *Psychosomatic Medicine*, 74(3), 258–262.

Johnson, J. G., Cohen, P., Dohrenwend, B. P., Link, B. G., & Brook, J. S. (1999). A longitudinal investigation of social causation and social selection processes involved in the association between socioeconomic status and psychiatric disorders. *Journal of Abnormal Psychology*, 108, 490–499.

Johnson, J. G., Cohen, P., Kasen, S., & Brook, J. S. (2006). Dissociative disorders among adults in the community, impaired functioning, and Axis I and II comorbidity. *Journal of Psychiatric Research*, 40, 131–140.

Johnson, J., Weissman, M. M., & Klerman, G. L. (1990). Panic disorder and suicide attempts. *Archives of General Psychiatry*, 47, 805–808.

Johnson, S. L. (2005). Life events in bipolar disorder: Towards more specific models. *Clinical Psychology Review*, 25, 1008–1027.

Johnson, S. L., Cueller, A. K., Ruggero, C., Winett-Perlman, C., Goodnick, P., ... Miller, I. (2008). Life events as predictors of mania and depression in bipolar I disorder. *Journal of Abnormal Psychology*, 117, 268–277.

Johnson, S. L., Ruggero, C. L., & Carver, C. S. (2005). Cognitive, behavioral, and affective responses to reward: Links with hypomanic symptoms. *Journal of Social and Clinical Psychology*, 24, 894–906.

Johnson, S. L., Sandrow, D., Meyer, B., Winters, R., Miller, I., Solomon, D., & Keitner, G. (2000). Increases in manic symptoms after life events involving goal attainment. *Journal of Abnormal Psychology*, 109, 721–727.

Johnson, S. M., Hunsley, J., Greenberg, L., & Schindler, D. (1999). Emotionally focused couples therapy: Status and challenges. *Clinical Psychology: Science and Practice*, 6, 67–79.

Johnstone, E. C., Crow, T. J., Frith, C. D., Husband, J., & Kreel, L. (1976). Cerebral ventricular size and cognitive impairment in chronic schizophrenia. *Lancet*, 2, 924–926.

Johnstone, E., Frith, C. D., Crow, T. J., Husband, J., & Kreel, L. (1976). Cerebral ventricular size and cognitive impairment in chronic schizophrenia. *The Lancet*, 308(7992), 924–926.

Joiner, T. E., Jr., Katz, J., & Lew, A. (1997). Self-verification and depression among youth psychiatric inpatients. *Journal of Abnormal Psychology*, 106, 608–618.

Jones, D. J., Forehand, R., McKee, L. G., Cuellar, J., & Kincaid, C. (2010). Behavioral parent training: Is there an "App" for that? *The Behavior Therapist*, 3, 72–77.

Jones, J. (2007). Persons with intellectual disabilities in the criminal justice system: Review of issues. *International Journal of Offender Therapy and Comparative Criminology*, 51(6), 723–733.

Jones, J., & Passey, J. (2004). Family adaptation, coping and resources: Parents of children with developmental disabilities and behaviour problems. *Journal on Developmental Disabilities*, 11(1), 31–46.

Jones, J., McQueen, M., Lowe, S., Minnes, P., & Rischke, A. (2015). Interprofessional education in canada: addressing knowledge, skills, and attitudes concerning intellectual disability for future healthcare professionals. *Journal of Policy and Practice in Intellectual Disabilities*, 12(3), 172–180.

Jones, J., Minnes, P., Elms, J., Paret, L., & Vilela, T. (2007). Anger management group for persons with dual diagnosis: a pilot study. *Journal on Developmental Disabilities*, 13, 37–45.

Jones, J., Ouellette-Kuntz, H., Vilela, T., & Brown, H. (2008). Attitudes of community developmental services agency staff toward issues of inclusion for individuals with intellectual disabilities. *Journal of Policy and Practice in Intellectual Disabilities*, 5(4), 219226.

Jones, K. L., & Smith, D. W. (1973). Recognition of the Fetal Alcohol Syndrome in early infancy. *The Lancet*, 2, 999–1001.

Jones, S. C., & Neblett, E. W. (2016). Racial–ethnic protective factors and mechanisms in psychosocial prevention and intervention programs for Black youth. *Clinical Child and Family Psychology Review*, 19(2), 134–161.

Jones, W. R., & Morgan, J. F. (2010). Eating disorders in men: A review of the literature. *Journal of Public Mental Health*, 9, 23–31.

Joormann, J., & Stanton, C. H. (2016). Examining emotion regulation in depression: A review and future directions. *Contributions from Experimental Psychopathology to the Understanding and Treatment of Mental Disorders*, 86, 35–49. https://doi.org/10.1016/j.brat.2016.07.007

Joormann, J., Talbot, L., & Gotlib, I. H. (2007). Biased processing of emotional information in girls at risk for depression. *Journal of Abnormal Psychology*, 116, 135–143.

Jorm, A. F. (2012). Mental health literacy: Empowering the community to take action for better mental health. *American Psychologist*, 67(3), 231–243.

Joshi, I., Percy, M., & Brown, I. (2002). Advances in understanding causes of autism and effective interventions. *Journal on Developmental Disabilities*, 9, 1–28.

Joshi, R., Herman, C. P., & Polivy, J. (2004). Self-enhancing effects of exposure to thin-body images. *International Journal of Eating Disorders*, 35, 333–341.

Joyce, T., Globe, A., & Moody, C. (2006). Assessment of the component skills for cognitive therapy in adults with intellectual disability. *Journal of Applied Research in Intellectual Disability*, 19, 17–23.

Judah, M., Grant, D., Mills, A., & Lechner, W. (2013). The neural correlates of impaired attentional control in social anxiety: An ERP study of inhibition and shifting. *Emotion*, 13, 1096–1106.

Julien, R. M. (2007). *A primer of drug action: A concise, non-technical guide to the actions, uses and side effects of psychoactive drugs*. New York, NY: Henry Holt & Co.

Jung, C. G. (1956). Recent thoughts on schizophrenia. In H. Read, M. Fordham, G. Adler, & W. McGuire (Eds.), *The collected works of C. G. Jung* (R. F. C. Hull, Trans., pp. 250–255). Princeton, NJ: Princeton University Press.

Juodis, M., Starzomski, A., Porter, S., & Woodworth, M. (2014). A comparison of domestic and non-domestic homicides: Further evidence for distinct dynamics and heterogeneity of domestic homicide perpetrators. *Journal of Family Violence*, 29, 299–313.

Kabat-Zinn, J. (1994). *Wherever you go there you are: Mindfulness meditation in everyday life*. New York, NY: Hyperion.

Kabat-Zinn, J. (2003). Mindfulness-based interventions in context: Past, present, and future. *Clinical Psychology Science and Practice*, 10, 144–156.

Kaess, M., Brunner, R., & Chanen, A. (2014). Borderline personality disorder in adolescence. *Pediatrics*, 134(4), 782–793.

Kaess, M., von Ceumern-Lindenstjerna, I. A., Parzer, P., Chanen, A., Mundt, C., Resch, F., & Brunner, R. (2012). Axis I and II comorbidity and psychosocial functioning in female adolescents with borderline personality disorder. *Psychopathology*, 46(1), 55–62.

Kafka, M. P. (1997). Hypersexual desire disorder with males: An operational definition and clinical implications for males with paraphilias and paraphilia-related disorders. *Archives of Sexual Behavior*, 26, 505–526.

Kafka, M. P. (2007). Paraphilia-related disorders: The evaluation and treatment of nonparaphilic hypersexuality. In S. R. Leiblum (Ed.), *Principles and practices of sex therapy* (4th ed., pp. 442–476). New York, NY: Guilford.

Kafka, M. P. (2010a). The DSM criteria for fetishism. *Archives of Sexual Behavior*, 39, 357–362.

Kafka, M. P. (2010b). Hypersexual disorder: A proposed diagnosis for DSM-V. *Archives of Sexual Behavior*, 39, 377–400.

Kagan, J. (1995). *Galen's prophecy*. New York, NY: Basic Books.

Kagan, J., Reznick, J. S., Clarke, C., Snidman, N., & Garcia-Coll, C. (1984). Behavioural inhibition to the unfamiliar. *Child Development*, 51, 2212–2225.

Kahana, S., Drotar, D., & Frazier, T. (2008). Meta-analysis of psychological interventions to promote adherence to treatment in pediatric chronic health conditions. *Journal of Pediatric Psychology*, 33, 590–611.

Kalberg, W. O., & Buckley, D. (2007). FASD: What types of intervention and rehabilitation are useful? *Neuroscience and Biobehavioral Reviews*, 31, 278–285.

Kamphaus, R. W., & Kroncke, A. P. (2004). "Back to the future" of the Stanford-Binet intelligence scales. In M. Hersen (Series Ed.), G. Goldstein & S. R. Beers (Vol. Eds.), *Comprehensive handbook of psychological assessment: Vol. 1. Intellectual and neuropsychological assessment* (pp. 50–69). New York, NY: Wiley.

Kane, J. M. (1989). The current status of neuroleptic therapy. *Journal of Clinical Psychiatry*, 50, 322–328.

Kanner, A. D., Coyne, J. C., Schaefer, C., & Lazarus, R. S. (1981). Comparisons of two modes of stress measurement: Daily hassles and uplifts versus major life events. *Journal of Behavioral Medicine, 4,* 1–39.

Kanner, L. (1935). *Child psychiatry.* Springfield, IL: Charles C. Thomas.

Kanner, L. (1943). Autistic disturbances of affective contact. *Nervous Child, 2,* 217–250.

Kaplan, H. I., & Sadock, B. J. (1998). *Synopsis of psychiatry* (8th ed.). Baltimore, MD: Williams & Wilkins.

Kaplan, H. S. (1979). *Disorders of sexual desire and other new concepts and techniques in sex therapy.* New York, NY: Brunner/Mazel.

Kaplan, J. R., Manuck, S. B., Clarkson, T. B., Lusso, F. M., Taub, D. M., & Miller, E. W. (1983). Social stress and atherosclerosis in normocholesterolemic monkeys. *Science, 220,* 733–735.

Kaplan, M. (1983). A woman's view of the DSM-III. *American Psychologist, 38,* 786–792.

Kapur, S., Phillips, A. G., & Insel, T. R. (2012). Why has it taken so long for biological psychiatry to develop clinical tests and what to do about it. *Molecular Psychiatry, 17,* 1174–1179.

Kar, N. (2011). Cognitive behavioral therapy for the treatment of post-traumatic stress disorder: A review. *Neuropsychiatric Disease and Treatment, 7,* 167–181.

Karam, E. G., Maalouf, W. E., & Ghandour, L. A. (2004). Alcohol use among university students in Lebanon: prevalence, trends and covariates: The IDRAC University Substance Use Monitoring Study (1991 and 1999). *Drug and Alcohol Dependence, 76*(3), 273–286.

Karasek Jr, R. A. (1979). Job demands, job decision latitude, and mental strain: Implications for job redesign. *Administrative Science Quarterly, 24*(2), 285–308.

Karasek, R. A., Baker, D., Marxer, F., Ahlborn, A., & Theorell, T. (1981). Job decision latitude, job demands and cardiovascular disease: A prospective study of Swedish men. *American Journal of Public Health, 71,* 694–705.

Karasek, R. A., Theorell, T. G., Schwartz, J., Pieper, C., & Alfredsson, L. (1982). Job, psychological factors and coronary heart disease: Swedish prospective findings and U. S. prevalence findings using a new occupational inference method. *Advances in Cardiology, 29,* 62–67.

Karel, M. J., Gatz, M., & Smyer, M. A. (2012). Aging and mental health in the decade ahead: What psychologists need to know. *American Psychologist, 67*(3), 184–198.

Karg, K., Burmeister, M., Shedden, K., & Sen, S. (2011). The serotonin transporter promoter variant (5-HTTLPR), stress, and depression meta-analysis revisited: Evidence for genetic moderation. *Archives of General Psychiatry, 68,* 444–454.

Karlin, B. E., & Duffy, M. (2004). Geriatric mental health policy: Impact on service delivery and directions for effecting change. *Professional Psychology: Research and Practice, 35*(5), 509–519.

Karlsgodt, K. H., Sun, D., & Cannon, T. D. (2010). Structural and functional brain abnormalities in schizophrenia. *Current Directions in Psychological Science, 19*(4), 226–231.

Karnesh, L. J., & Zucker, E. M. (1945). *Handbook of psychiatry.* St. Louis, MO: Mosby.

Karon, B. P., & VandenBos, G. R. (1981). *Psychotherapy of schizophrenia: The treatment of choice.* New York, NY: Aronson.

Karon, B. P., & VandenBos, G. R. (1981). *Psychotherapy of schizophrenia: The treatment of choice.* Lanham, MD: Jason Aronson Inc.

Karyotaki, E., Smit, Y., Holdt Henningsen, K., Huibers, M. J., Robays, J., de Beurs, D., & Cuijpers, P. (2016). Combining pharmacotherapy and psychotherapy or monotherapy for major depression? A meta-analysis on the long-term effects. *Journal of Affective Disorders, 194,* 144–152.

Kasai, K., Iwanami, A., Yamasue, H., Kuroki, N., Nakagome, K., & Fukuda, M. (2002). Neuroanatomy and neurophysiology in schizophrenia. *Neuroscience Research, 43,* 93–110.

Kasari, C., Freeman, S., & Paparella, T. (2006). Joint attention and symbolic play in young children with autism: A randomized controlled intervention study. *Journal of Child Psychology and Psychiatry, 47,* 611–620.

Kaschak, E. (1992). *Engendered lives.* New York, NY: Basic Books.

Katterman, S. N., Kleinman, B. M., Hood, M. M., Nackers, L. M., & Corsica, J. A. (2014). Mindfulness meditation as an intervention for binge eating, emotional eating, and weight loss: A systematic review. *Eating Behaviors, 15*(2), 197–204.

Katz, J., Rosenbloom, B. N., & Fashler, S. (2015). Chronic pain, psychopathology, and DSM-5 somatic symptom disorder. *The Canadian Journal of Psychiatry, 60*(4), 160–167.

Katz, L. Y., & Cox, B. J. (2002). Dialectical behavior therapy for suicidal adolescent inpatients: A case study. *Clinical Case Studies, 1,* 81–92.

Katz, L. Y., Kozyrskyj, A. L., Prior, H. J., Enns, M. W., Cox, B. J., & Sareen, J. (2008). Effect of regulatory warnings on antidepressant prescription rates, use of health services and outcomes among children, adolescents and young adults. *Canadian Medical Association Journal, 178,* 1005–1011.

Katzir, R., Youngsuk, K., Wolf, M., O'Brien, B., & Kennedy, B. (2006). Reading fluency: The whole is more than the parts. *Annuals of Dyslexia, 56,* 51–82.

Kauer, S. D, Reid, S. C., Crooke, A. H. D, Khor, A., Hearps, S. J. C., Jorm, A. F., ... Patton, G. (2012). Self-monitoring using mobile phones in the early stages of adolescent depression: Randomized controlled trial. *Journal of Medical Internet Research, 14*(3), e67.

Kavale, K. A., & Forness, S. R. (1996). Social skill deficits and learning disabilities: A meta-analysis. *Journal of Learning Disabilities, 29,* 226–237.

Kaye, W. (2008). Neurobiology of anorexia and bulimia nervosa. *Physiology & Behavior, 94,* 121–135.

Kaye, W. H., Gendall, K., & Strober, M. (1998). Serotonin neuronal function and selective serotonin reuptake inhibitor treatment in anorexia and bulimia nervosa. *Biological Psychiatry, 44,* 825–838.

Kazarian, S. S., & Malla, A. K. (1992). Working with the families of long-term patients: An expressed emotion perspective. In E. Persad, S. S. Kazarian, & L. W. Joseph (Eds.), *The mental hospital in the 21st century* (pp. 91–106). Toronto, ON: Wall & Emerson.

Kazdin, A. E. (1992). *Methodological issues and strategies in clinical research.* Washington, DC: American Psychological Association.

Kazdin, A. E. (1993). Adolescent mental health: Prevention and treatment programs. *American Psychologist, 48,* 127–141.

Kazdin, A. E. (1997). Parent management training: Evidence, outcomes, and issues. *Journal of the American Academy of Child and Adolescent Psychiatry, 36,* 1349–1356.

Kazdin, A. E. (2003a). Clinical significance: Measuring whether interventions make a difference. In A. E. Kazdin (Ed.), *Methodological issues and strategies in clinical research* (3rd ed., pp. 691–710). Washington, DC: American Psychological Association.

Kazdin, A. E. (2003b). *Research design in clinical psychology* (4th ed.). Needham Heights, MA: Allyn & Bacon.

Kazdin, A. E., & Bass, D. (1989). Power to detect differences between alternative treatments in comparative psychotherapy outcome research. *Journal of Consulting and Clinical Psychology, 57,* 138–147.

Kazdin, A. E., & Whitley, M. K. (2006). Comorbidity, case complexity, and effects of evidence-based treatment for children referred for disruptive behavior. *Journal of Consulting and Clinical Psychology, 74,* 455–467.

Kazdin, A. E., Esveldt-Dawson, K., French, N. H., & Unis, A. S. (1987a). Effects of parent management training and problem solving skills training combined in the treatment of antisocial child behavior. *Journal of the American Academy of Child and Adolescent Psychiatry, 26*(3), 416–424.

Kazdin, A. E., Esveldt-Dawson, K., French, N. H., & Unis, A. S. (1987b). Problem solving skills training and relationship therapy in the treatment of antisocial child behavior. *Journal of Consulting and Clinical Psychology, 55*(1), 76–85.

Kazdin, A. E., Mazurick, J. L., & Siegel, T. C. (1994). Treatment outcome among children with externalizing disorder who terminate prematurely versus those who complete psychotherapy. *Journal of the American Academy of Child and Adolescent Psychiatry, 33,* 549–557.

Kazdin, A. E., Siegel, T. C., & Bass, D. (1990). Drawing upon clinical practice to inform research on child and adolescent psychotherapy: A survey of practitioners. *Professional Psychology: Research and Practice, 21,* 189–198.

Keck, P. E., & McElroy, S. L. (2015). Pharmacological treatments for bipolar disorder. In P. E. Nathan & J. M. Gorman (Eds.), *A guide to treatments that work* (4th ed., pp. 237-271). New York, NY: Oxford University Press.

Keck, P. E., Jr., & McElroy, S. L. (1997). The new antipsychotics and their therapeutic potential. *Psychiatric Annals, 27,* 320–331.

Keefe, R. S. E., Bilder, R. M., Davis, S. M., Harvey, P. D., Palmer, B. W., Gold, J. M., et al. (2007). Neurocognitive effects of antipsychotic medication in patients with chronic schizophrenia in the CATIE trial. *Archives of General Psychiatry, 64,* 633–647.

Keel, P. K., & Striegel-Moore, R. H. (2009). The validity and clinical utility of purging disorder. *International Journal of Eating Disorders, 42,* 706–719.

Keel, P. K., Brown, T. A., Holm-Denoma, J., & Bodell, L. P. (2011). Comparison of DSM-IV versus proposed DSM-5 diagnostic criteria for eating disorders: Reduction of eating order not otherwise specified and validity. *International Journal of Eating Disorders, 44,* 553–560.

Keel, P. K., Dorer, D. J., Franko, D. L., Jackson, S. C., & Herzog, D. B. (2005). Postremission predictors of relapse in women with eating disorders. *American Journal of Psychiatry, 162,* 2263–2268.

Keller, M. B., McCullough, J. P., Jr., Klein, D. N., Arnow, B. A., Dunner, D. L., Gelenberg, A. J., et al. (2000). A comparison of nefazodone, the cognitive behavioral analysis system of psychotherapy, and their combination for the treatment of chronic depression. *New England Journal of Medicine, 342*, 1462–1470.

Kelly, T., Soloff, P. H., Cornelius, J., George, A., Lis, J. A., & Ulrich, R. (1992). Can we study (treat) borderline patients? Attrition from research and open treatment. *Journal of Personality Disorders, 6*, 417–433.

Kelsoe, J. R. (1997). The genetics of bipolar disorser. *Psychiatric Annals, 27*, 285–292.

Kemp, G. N., Langer, D. A., & Tompson, M. C. (2016). Childhood mental health: An ecological analysis of the effects of neighbourhood characteristics. *Journal of Community Psychology, 44*(8), 962–979.

Kendall, P. C., & Hedtke, K. (2006). *The Coping CAT workbook* (2nd ed.). Ardmore, PA: Workbook Publishing.

Kendall, P. C., Marrs-Garcia, A., Nath, S. R., & Sheldrick, R. C. (1999). Normative comparisons for the evaluation of clinical significance. *Journal of Consulting and Clinical Psychology, 67*, 285–299.

Kendall-Tackett, M. (2010). *The psychoneuroimmunology of chronic disease: Exploring the links between inflammation, stress and illness.* Washington, DC: American Psychological Association.

Kendler, K. (1998). Boundaries of major depression: An evaluation of DSM-IV criteria. *American Journal of Psychiatry, 155*, 172–177.

Kendler, K. S. (1985). Diagnostic approaches to schizotypal personality disorder: A historical perspective. *Schizophrenia Bulletin, 11*, 538–553.

Kendler, K. S. (2000). Schizophrenia: Genetics. In B. J. Sadock & V. A. Sadock (Eds.), *Kaplan and Sadock's comprehensive textbook of psychiatry* (7th ed., Vol. 1, pp. 1147–1159). Philadelphia, PA: Lippincott Williams & Wilkins.

Kendler, K. S., Eaves, L. J., Loken, E. K., Pedersen, N. L., Middeldorp, C. M., Reynolds, C., et al. (2011). The impact of environmental experiences on symptoms of anxiety and depression across the life span. *Psychological Science, 22*(10), 1343–1352. doi:10.1177/0956797611417255

Kendler, K. S., Gallagher, T. J., Abelson, J. M., & Kessler, R. C. (1996). Lifetime prevalence, demographic risk factors, and diagnostic validity of nonaffective psychosis as assessed in a U.S. community sample: The National Comorbidity Survey. *Archives of General Psychiatry, 53*, 1022–1031.

Kendler, K. S., Gardner, C. O., Annas, P., & Lichtenstein, P. (2008). The development of fears from early adolescence to young adulthood: A multivariate study. *Psychological Medicine, 38*, 1–11.

Kendler, K. S., Heath, A. C., Martin, N. G., & Eaves, L. J. (1986). Symptoms of anxiety and depression in a volunteer twin population: The etiologic role of genetic and environmental factors. *Archives of General Psychiatry, 43*, 213–221.

Kendler, K. S., Kessler, R. C., Walters, E. E., MacLean, C., Neale, M. C., Heath, A. C., et al. (1995). Stressful life events, genetic liability, and onset of an episode of major depression in women. *American Journal of Psychiatry, 152*, 833–842.

Kendler, K. S., Masterson, C. C., & Davis, K. L. (1985). Psychiatric illness in first degree relatives of patients with paranoid psychosis, schizophrenia and medical controls. *British Journal of Psychiatry, 147*, 524–531.

Kendler, K. S., Neale, M. C., Kessler, R. C., Heath, A. C., & Eaves, L. J. (1992). Major depression and generalized anxiety disorder: Same genes, (partly) different environments? *Archives of General Psychiatry, 49*, 716–722.

Kendler, K. S., Walters, E. E., Truett, K. R., Heath, A. C., Neale, M. C., Martin, N. G., & Eaves, L. J. (1995). A twin-family study of self-report symptoms of panic-phobia and somatization. *Behavior Genetics, 25*(6), 499–515.

Keng, S. L., Smoski, M. J., & Robins, C. J. (2011). Effects of mindfulness on psychological health: A review of empirical studies. *Clinical Psychology Review, 31*, 1041–1056.

Kennedy, B. D., Silva, S. G., Tonev, S., Rohde, P., Hughes, J. L., Vitiello, B., et al. (2009). Remission and recovery in the Treatment for Adolescents with Depression Study (TADS): Acute and long-term outcomes. *Journal of the American Academy of Child and Adolescent Psychiatry, 48*, 186–195. doi:10.1097/CHI.0b013e31819176f9

Kennedy, P. J., Hicks, B. M., & Patrick, C. J. (2007). Validity of factors of the Psychopathy Checklist–Revised in female prisoners: Discriminant relations with antisocial behavior, substance abuse, and personality. *Assessment, 14*, 323–340.

Kennedy, S. H., Lam, R. W., McIntyre, R. S., Tourjman, S. V., Blier, P., Hasnain, M., ...CANMAT Depression Work Group. (2016). Canadian Network for Mood and Anxiety Treatments (CANMAT) 2016 clinical guidelines for the management of adults with major depressive disorder: Section 3. Pharmacological treatments. *Canadian Journal of Psychiatry, 61*, 540–560.

Kennedy, S.H., Lam, R.W., Cohen, N.L. & Ravindran, A. (2001). CANMAT Clinical Guidelines for the Treatment of Depressive Disorders: Section IV: Pharmacotherapy and Other Biological Treatments for Major Depressive Disorder. *Canadian Journal of Psychiatry, 46*, 38–58.

Kenny, M. E., & Hage, S. M. (2009). The next frontier: Prevention as an instrument of social justice. *Journal of Primary Prevention, 30*, 1–10.

Kermis, M. D. (1984). *The psychology of human aging.* Boston, MA: Allyn & Bacon.

Kernberg, O. F. (1967). Borderline personality organization. *Journal of the American Psychoanalytic Association, 15*, 641–685.

Kernberg, O. F. (1975). *Borderline conditions and pathological narcissism.* New York, NY: Jason Aronson.

Keski-Rahkonen, A., Hoek, H. W., Linna, M. S., Raevuori, A., Sihvola, E., Bulik, C. M., ... & Kaprio, J. (2009). Incidence and outcomes of bulimia nervosa: A nationwide population-based study. *Psychological Medicine, 39*, 823–831. doi: 10.1017/S0033291708003942

Keski-Rahkonen, A., Hoek, H. W., Susser, E. S., Linna, M. S., Sihvola, E., Raevuori, A., ... & Rissanen, A. (2007). Epidemiology and course of anorexia nervosa in the community. *American Journal of Psychiatry, 164*, 1259–1265. doi: 10.1176/appi.ajp.2007.06081388

Kessel, B. (2001). Sexuality in the older person. *Age and Ageing, 30*(2), 121–124.

Kessler, R. C., Aguilar-Gaxiola, S., Alonso, J., Chatterji, S., Lee, S., & Üstün, T. B. (2009). The WHO world mental health (WMH) surveys. *Psychiatrie, 6*, 5–9.

Kessler, R. C., Berglund, P., Demler, O., Jin, R., Merikangas, K. R., & Walters, E. E. (2005). Lifetime prevalence and age-of-onset distributions of DSM-IV disorders in the National Comorbidity Survey Replication. *Archives of General Psychiatry, 62*, 593–602.

Kessler, R. C., Chiu, W. T., Demler, O., & Walters, E. E. (2005). Prevalence, severity, and comorbidity of 12-month DSM-IV disorders in the National Comorbidity Survey Replication. *Archives of General Psychiatry, 62*, 617–627.

Kessler, R. C., McGonagle, K. A., Swartz, M., Blazer, D. G., & Nelson, C. B. (1993). Sex and depression in the National Comorbidity Survey I: Lifetime prevalence, chronicity and recurrence. *Journal of Affective Disorders, 29*, 85–96.

Kessler, R. C., Petukhova, M., Sampson, N. A., Zaslavsky, A. M., & Wittchen, H. (2012). Twelve-month and lifetime prevalence and lifetime morbid risk of anxiety and mood disorders in the United States. *International Journal of Methods in Psychiatric Research, 21*(3), 169–184. doi: 10.1002/mpr.1359

Kessler, R. C., Rubinow, D. R., Holmes, C., Abelson, J. M., & Zhao, S. (1997). The epidemiology of DSM-III-R bipolar I disorder in a general population survey. *Psychological Medicine, 27*, 1079–1089.

Kessler, R. C., Sonnega, A., Bromet, E., Hughes, M., & Nelson, C. B. (1995). Posttraumatic stress disorder in the National Comorbidity Survey. *Archives of General Psychiatry, 52*, 1048–1060.

Kessler, R. C., Zhao, S., Katz, S. J., Kouzis, A. C., Frank, R. G., Edlund, M., & Leaf, P. (2013). Past-year use of outpatient services for psychiatric problems in the National Comorbidity Survey. *American Journal of Psychiatry, 156*, 115–123.

Khan, R. S., Khroury, J., Nichols, W. C., & Lanphear, B. P. (2003). Role of dopamine transporter genotype and maternal prenatal smoking in childhood hyperactive-impulsive, inattentive, and oppositional behaviors. *The Journal of Pediatrics, 143*, 104–110.

Khandaker, G. M., Zimbron, J., Lewis, G., & Jones, P. B. (2013). Prenatal maternal infection, neurodevelopment and adult schizophrenia: A systematic review of population-based studies. *Psychological Medicine, 43*(2), 239–257.

Khanna, M. S., & Kendall, P. C. (2010). Computer-assisted cognitive-behavioral therapy for child anxiety: Results of a randomized clinical trial. *Journal of Consulting and Clinical Psychology, 78*, 737–745.

Khaykin, Y., Dorian, P., Baker, B., Shapiro, C., Sandor, P., Mironov, D., et al. (1998). Autonomic correlates of antidepressant treatment using heart-rate variability analysis. *Canadian Journal of Psychiatry, 43*, 183–186.

Kho, K. H., van Vreeswijk, M. F., Simpson, S., & Zwinderman, A. H. (2003). A meta-analysis of electroconvulsive therapy efficacy in depression. *The Journal of ECT, 19*, 139–147.

Kidd, P. M. (2002). Autism, an extreme challenge to integrative medicine. Part 2: Medical management. *Alternative Medicine Reviews, 7*(6), 472–499.

Kiecolt-Glaser, J. K., Loving, T. J., Stowell, J. R., Malarkey, W. B., Lemeshow, S., Dickinson, S. L., & Glaser, R. (2005). Hostile marital interactions, proinflammatory cytokine production, and wound healing. *Archives of General Psychiatry, 62*, 1377–1384.

Kiehl, K. A., Smith, A. M., Mendrek, A., Forster, B. B., Hare, R. D., & Liddle, P. (2004). Temporal lobe abnormalities in semantic processing by criminal psychopaths as revealed by functional magnetic resonance imaging. *Psychiatry Research: Neuroimaging, 130*, 297–312.

Kihlstrom, J. F. (2005). Dissociative disorders. *Annual Review of Clinical Psychology, 1*, 227–253.

Killeen, T. K., Brady, K. T., Gold, P. B., Simpson, K. N., Faldowski, R. A., Tyson, C., et al. (2004). Effectiveness of naltrexone in a community treatment program. *Alcoholism: Clinical and Experimental Research, 28*, 1710–1717.

Kim-Cohen, J., Arseneault, L., Caspi, A., Tomas, M. P., Taylor, A., & Moffitt, T. E. (2005). Validity of DSM-IV conduct disorder in 41/2–5-year-old children: A longitudinal epidemiological study. *American Journal of Psychiatry, 162,* 1108–1117.

Kim, M. J., Loucks, R. A., Palmer, A. L., Brown, A. C., Solomon, K. M., Marchante, A. N., & Whalen, P. J. (2011). The structural and functional connectivity of the amygdala: From normal emotion to pathological anxiety. *Behavioural Brain Research, 223,* 403–410.

Kim, S. H., Paul, R., Tager-Flusberg, H., & Lord, C. (2014). Language and communication in autism. *Handbook of Autism and Pervasive Developmental Disorders* (4th ed.). New York, NY: Wiley.

Kingdon, D. G., & Turkington, D. (2005). *Cognitive therapy of schizophrenia.* New York, NY: Guilford.

Kingston, D. A., & Yates, P. M. (2008). Sexual sadism: Assessment and treatment. In D. R. Laws & W. O'Donohue (Eds.), *Sexual deviance: Theory, assessment, and treatment* (2nd ed., pp. 231–249). New York, NY: Guilford.

Kingston, D. A., Firestone, P., Moulden, H. M., & Bradford, J. M. (2007). The utility of the diagnosis of pedophilia: A comparison of various classification procedures. *Archives of Sexual Behavior, 36,* 423–436.

Kinsey, A. C., Pomeroy, W. B., & Martin, C. E. (1948). *Sexual behavior in the human male.* Philadelphia, PA: Saunders.

Kinsey, A. C., Pomeroy, W. B., Martin, C. E., & Gebhard, P. H. (1953). *Sexual behavior in the human female.* Philadelphia, PA: Saunders.

Kinston, W. (1980). A theoretical and technical approach to narcissistic disturbance. *International Journal of Psychoanalysis, 61,* 383–393.

Kirby, M. (Chair). (2008, April 28). Homeless and mental illness: Solving the challenge. Mental Health Commission of Canada Collaboration for Change Forum, Playhouse Theatre, Vancouver, BC. Retrieved from www.mentalhealthcommission. ca/SiteCollectionDocuments/Homelessness/Speech_kirbyVan_Apr2808_ENG.pdf

Kirmayer, L. J. (1994). Suicide among Canadian Aboriginal peoples. *Transcultural Psychiatric Research Review, 31,* 3–58.

Kirmayer, L. J. (2001). Cultural variations in the clinical presentation of depression and anxiety: Implications for diagnosis and treatment. *Journal of Clinical Psychiatry, 62*(Suppl. 13), 22–28.

Kirmayer, L. J., & Looper, K. J. (2007). Somatoform disorders. In M. Hersen, S. M. Turner, & D. C. Beidel (Eds.), *Adult psychopathology and diagnosis* (5th ed., pp. 410–472). Hoboken, NJ: Wiley.

Kirmayer, L. J., Robbins, J. M., & Paris, J. (1994). Somatoform disorders: Personality and social matrix of somatic distress. *Journal of Abnormal Psychology, 103,* 125–136.

Kirsh, I., Deacon, B. J., Huedo-Medina, T. B., Scoboria, A., Moore, T. J., & Johnson, B. T. (2008). Initial severity and antidepressant benefits: A meta-analysis of data submitted to the Food and Drug Administration. *PLoS Medicine, 5,* 260–268.

Kisely, S., Campbell, L. A., Scott, A., Preston, N., & Xiao, J. (2006). Randomized and non-randomized evidence for the effect of compulsory community and involuntary out-patient treatment on health service use: Systematic review and meta-analysis. *Psychological Medicine, 37,* 3–14.

Kite, M. E., Stockdale, G. D., Whitley Jr., B. E., & Johnson, B. T. (2005). Attitudes toward younger and older adults: An updated meta-analytic review. *Journal of Social Issues, 61*(2), 241–266.

Kitzman, H., Olds, D. L., Henderson, C. R., Hanks, C., Cole, R., Tatlebaum, R., et al. (1997). Effect of prenatal and infancy home visitation by nurses on pregnancy outcomes, childhood injuries, and repeated childbearing: A randomized controlled trial. *Journal of the American Medical Association, 278,* 644–652.

Kitzman, H., Olds, D. L., Sidora, K., Henderson, C. R., Hanks, C., Cole, R., et al. (2000). Enduring effects of nurse home visitation on maternal life course: A 3-year follow-up of a randomized trial. *Journal of the American Medical Association, 283,* 1983–1989.

Kivimäki, M., & Kawachi, I. (2015). Work stress as a risk factor for cardiovascular disease. *Current Cardiology Reports, 17*(9), 74.

Kivimaki, M., Head, J., Ferrie, J. E., Brunner, E., Marmot, M. G., Vahterra, J., & Shipley, M. (2006). Why is evidence on job strain and coronary heart disease mixed? An illustration of measurement challenges in the Whitehall II study. *Psychosomatic Medicine, 68,* 398–401.

Kivnick, H., & Lymburner, A. (2009). CitySongs: Primary prevention in the field. *Journal of Primary Prevention, 30,* 61–73.

Kjeldsen v The Queen (1981), 2 S.C.R. 617.

Klein, D. A., & Walsh, B. T. (2004). Eating disorders: Clinical features and pathophysiology. *Physiology & Behavior, 81,* 359–374.

Klein, D. N. (2003). Patients' versus informants' reports of personality disorders in predicting 71/2-year outcome in outpatients with depressive disorders. *Psychological Assessment, 15,* 216–222.

Klein, D. N. (2008). Classification of depressive disorders in the DSM-V: Proposal for a two-dimension system. *Journal of Abnormal Psychology, 117,* 552–560.

Klein, D. N., Taylor, E. B., Dickstein, S., & Harding, K. (1988). Primary early-onset dysthymia: Comparison with primary nonbipolar nonchronic major depression on demographic, clinical, familial, personality, and socioenvironmental characteristics and short-term outcome. *Journal of Abnormal Psychology, 97,* 387–398.

Klein, D. N., Taylor, E. B., Harding, K., & Dickstein, S. (1988). Double depression and episodic major depression: Demographic, clinical, familial, personality, and socioenvironmental characteristics and short-term outcome. *American Journal of Psychiatry, 145,* 1226–1231.

Kleinstäuber M., Witthöft M., Steffanowski A., van Marwijk H., Hiller W., & Lambert M. J. (2014). Pharmacological interventions for somatoform disorders in adults. *Cochrane Database of Systematic Reviews, 11,* Art. No.: CD010628.

Klerman, G. L., Weissman, M. M., Rousanville, B. J., & Chevron, E. S. (1984). *Interpersonal psychotherapy of depression.* New York, NY: Basic Books.

Klonsky, E. D. (2007). The functions of deliberate self-injury: A review of the evidence. *Clinical Psychology Review, 27*(2), 226–239.

Klonsky, E. D., & Olino, T. M. (2008). Identifying clinically distinct subgroups of self-injurers among young adults: a latent class analysis. *Journal of Consulting and Clinical Psychology, 76*(1), 22.

Klonsky, E. D., Muehlenkamp, J. J., Lewis, S., & Walsh, B. (2011). *Non-suicidal self-injury.* Cambridge, MA: Hogrefe.

Klostermann, S., Connell, A., & Stormshak, E. A. (2014). Gender differences in the developmental links between conduct problems and depression across early adolescence. *Journal of Research on Adolescence, 26,* 76–89. doi:10.1111/jora.1270

Kluft, R. (1999). An overview of the psychotherapy of dissociative identity disorder. *American Journal of Psychotherapy, 53,* 289–319.

Kluft, R. P. (2001). The difficult-to-treat patient with dissociative disorder. In M. J. Dewan, & R. W. Pies (Eds.), *The difficult-to-treat psychiatric patient* (pp. 209–242). Washington, DC: American Psychiatric Publishing.

Klump, K. L., & Gobrogge, K. L. (2005). A review and primer of molecular genetic studies of anorexia nervosa. *International Journal of Eating Disorders, 37,* S43–S48.

Klump, K. L., Gobrogge, K. L., Perkins, P. S., Thorne, D., Sisk, C. L., & Breedlove, S. M. (2006). Preliminary evidence that gonadal hormones organize and activate disordered eating. *Psychological Medicine, 36,* 539–546.

Klump, K. L., Kaye, W. H., & Strober, M. (2001). The evolving genetic foundations of eating disorders. *Psychiatric Clinics of North America, 24*(2), 215–225.

Knight, B. G., Karel, M. J., Hinrichsen, G. A., Qualls, S. H., & Duffy, M. (2009). Pikes Peak model for training in professional geropsychology. *American Psychologist, 64*(3), 205–214.

Knight, R. (1953). Borderline states. *Bulletin of the Menninger Clinic, 17,* 1–12.

Knopman, D. S., Boeve, B. F., & Petersen, R. C. (2003). Essentials of the proper diagnosis of mild cognitive impairment, dementia, and major subtypes of dementia. *Mayo Clinic Proceedings, 78,* 1290–1308.

Knowles, J. B., Southmayd, S. E., Delva, N., MacLean, A. W., Cairns, J., & Letemendia, F. J. (1979). Five variations of sleep deprivation in a depressed woman. *British Journal of Psychiatry, 135,* 403–410.

Koch, R., Azen, C., Friedman, E. G., Fishler, K., Baumann-Frischling, C., & Lin, T. (1996). Care of the adult with phenylketonuria. *European Journal of Pediatrics, 155*(Suppl.), S90–S92.

Koegel, L. (2000). Interventions to facilitate communication in autism. *Journal of Autism and Developmental Disorders, 30*(5), 383–391.

Koegel, L. K. (1995). Communication and language intervention. In R. L. Koegel & L. K. Koegel (Eds.), *Teaching children with autism: Strategies for initiating positive interactions and improving learning opportunities* (pp. 17–32). Baltimore, MD: Paul H. Brookes.

Koerner, N., Dugas, M. J., Savard, P., Guadet, A., Turcotte, J., & Marchand, A. (2004). The economic burden of anxiety disorders in Canada. *Canadian Psychology, 45,* 191–201.

Kogan, C. S., Turk, J., Hagerman, R. J., & Kornish, K. M. (2008, September 5). Impact of the Fragile X mental retardation 1 (FMR1) gene premutation on neuropsychiatric functioning in adult males without fragile X-associated Tremor/Ataxia syndrome: A controlled study. *American Journal of Medical Genetics Part B Neuropsychiatric Genetics, 147B*(6), 859–872.

Kohut, H. (1977). *The restoration of the self.* New York, NY: International Universities Press.

Kolb, B., & Teskey, G. C. (2011). Paradoxical phenomena in brain plasticity. In N. Kapur (Ed.), *The paradoxical brain* (pp. 350–364). New York, NY: Cambridge University Press.

Kolb, B., Mychasiuk, R., & Gibb, R. (2014). Brain development, experience, and behavior. *Pediatric Blood & Cancer, 61,* 1720–1723.

Komer, W. J., O'Reilly, R. L., Cernovsky, Z., & Dunbar, S. (1999). Review board outcomes for involuntary patients in provincial psychiatric hospitals. *Canadian Journal of Psychiatry, 44,* 495–498.

Konnert, C., Dobson, K., & Watt, A. (2009). Geropsychology training in Canada: A survey of doctoral and internship programs. *Canadian Psychology, 50,* 255–260.

Konnopka, A., Leichsenring, F., Leibing, E., & König, H. H. (2009). Cost-of-illness studies and cost-effectiveness analyses in anxiety disorders: A systematic review. *Journal of Affective Disorders, 114,* 14–31.

Konopasky, R. J., & Konopasky, A. W. B. (2000). Remaking penile plethysmography. In D. R. Laws, S. M. Hudson, & T. Ward (Eds.), *Remaking relapse prevention with sex offenders* (pp. 257–284). London, UK: Sage.

Kop, W., & Plumhoff, J. E. (2011). Depression and coronary heart disease: Diagnosis, predictive value, biobehavioral mechanisms and intervention. In R. Allan & J. Fisher (Eds.), *Heart and mind: The practice of cardiac psychology* (2nd ed., pp. 143–168). Washington, DC: American Psychological Association.

Kopala-Sibley, D. C. & Zuroff, D. C. (2014). The developmental origins of personality factors from the self-definitional and relatedness domains: A review of theory and research. *Review of General Psychology, 18,* 137–155.

Kopala-Sibley, D. C., Zuroff, D. C., Hankin, B. L., & Abela, J. R. Z. (2015). The development of self-criticism and dependency in early adolescence and their role in the development of depressive and anxiety symptoms. *Personality and Social Psychology Bulletin, 41,* 1094–1109.

Kornhaber, S. (2015, September 5). When art is an immigration issue. Retrieved from www.theatlantic.com/entertainment/archive/2015/09/tyler-the-creator-banned-in-uk-hip-hop-rap/403690/

Koss, M. P. (1988). Stranger and acquaintance rape: Are there differences in the victim's experience? *Psychology of Women Quarterly, 12,* 1–24.

Koss, M. P. (1992). The underdetection of rape: Methodological choices influence incidence estimates. *Journal of Social Issues, 48,* 61–75.

Kovacs, M., & Devlin, B. (1998). Internalizing disorders in childhood. *The Journal of Child Psychology and Psychiatry, 39,* 47–63.

Kraan, T., Velthorst, E., Koenders, L., Zwaart, K., Ising, H. K., van den Berg, D., . . . van der Gaag, M. (2016). Cannabis use and transition to psychosis in individuals at ultra-high risk: Review and meta-analysis. *Psychological Medicine, 46*(4), 673–681. https://doi.org/10.1017/S0033291715002329

Kraepelin, E. (1896). *Psychiatrie: Ein lehrbuch für studierende und aerzte* (5th ed). Leipzig, Germany: Barth.

Kraepelin, E. (1913). *Psychiatry: A textbook.* Leipzig, Germany: Barth.

Kraepelin, E. (1915). *Psychiatrie.* Leipzig, Germany: Barth.

Kraepelin, E. (1919). *Dementia praecoxand paraphrenia* (R. M. Barclay, Trans.; G. M. Robertson, Ed.). Edinburgh, UK: E. & S. Livingstone.

Kraepelin, E., (1921/1976). *Manic depressive insanity and paranoia* (R. M. Barclay, Trans.), Salem, NH: Ayer Company.

Krafft-Ebing, R. V. (1901). *Psychopathia sexualia.* Stuttgart, Germany: Ferdinand Enke.

Krafft-Ebing, R. V. (1939). *Psychopathia sexualis* (12th ed., V. Robinson, Trans.). New York, NY: Pioneer. (Original work published in 1886)

Kral, M. (2003). Unikkaartuit: Meanings of well-being, sadness, suicide, and change in two Inuit communities. Final Report to the National Health Research and Development Programs. Project #6606-6231-002. Ottawa: Health Canada.

Krantz, D. S., & Manuck, S. B. (1984). Acute psychophysiologic reactivity and risk of cardiovascular disease: A review and methodologic critique. *Psychological Bulletin, 96,* 435–464.

Krantz, D. S., Contrada, R. J., Hill, D. R., & Friedler, E. (1988). Environmental stress and biobehavioral antecedents of coronary heart disease. *Journal of Consulting and Clinical Psychology, 56,* 333–341.

Kratochwill, T. R., Sheridan, S. M., Carlson, J., & Lasecki, K. L. (1999). Advances in behavioral assessment. In C. R. Reynolds & T. B. Gutkin (Eds.), *The handbook of school psychology* (3rd ed., pp. 350–382). New York, NY: Wiley.

Kreher, D. A., Holcomb, P. J., Goff, D., & Kuperberg, G. R. (2008). Neural evidence for faster and further automatic spreading activation in schizophrenia thought disorder. *Schizophrenia Bulletin, 34,* 473–482.

Kreher, D. A., Holcomb, P. J., Goff, D., & Kuperberg, G. R. (2008). Neural evidence for faster and further automatic spreading activation in schizophrenic thought disorder. *Schizophrenia Bulletin, 34*(3), 473–482.

Kreitman, N. (1976). The coal gas story—United Kingdom suicide rates, 1960–1971. *British Journal of Preventive Social Medicine, 30,* 86–93.

Krell-Roesch, J., Vemuri, P., Pink, A., Roberts, R. O., Stokin, G. B., Mielke, M. J., . . . & Geda, Y. E. (2017). Association between mentally stimulating activities in late life and the outcome of incident mild cognitive impairment, with an analysis of the APOE e4 Genotype. *JAMA Neurology, 74*(3), 332–338.

Kresin, D. (1993). Medical aspects of inhibited sexual desire disorder. In W. O'Donohue & J. H. Greer (Eds.), *Handbook of sexual dysfunctions: Assessment and treatment* (pp. 15–52). Boston, MA: Allyn & Bacon.

Kreuger, R. B. (2010a). The DSM diagnostic criteria for sexual masochism. *Archives of Sexual Behavior, 39,* 346–356.

Kreuger, R. B. (2010b). The DSM diagnostic criteria for sexual sadism. *Archives of Sexual Behavior, 39,* 325–345.

Krittayaphong, R., Cascio, W. E., Light, K. C., Sheffield, D., Golden, R. N., Finkel, J. B., et al. (1997). Heart rate variability in patients with coronary artery disease: Differences in patients with higher and lower depression scores. *Psychosomatic Medicine, 59,* 231–235.

Kroll, J., & Bachrach, B. (1984). Sin and mental illness in the Middle Ages. *Psychological Medicine, 14,* 507–514.

Kudo, M. F., Lussier, C. M., & Swanson, H. L. (2015). Reading disabilities in children: A selective meta-analysis of the cognitive literature. *Research in Developmental Disabilities, 40,* 51–62

Kuehn, B. M. (2007). CDC: Autism spectrum disorders common. *Journal of the American Medical Association, 297,* 940.

Kuhn, C. M. (1989). Adrenocortical and gonadal steroids in behavioral cardiovascular medicine. In N. Schneiderman, S. M. Weiss, & P. G. Kaufmann (Eds.), *Handbook of research methods in cardiovascular behavioral medicine.* New York, NY: Plenum.

Kühn, S., & Gallinat, J. (2016). Neurobiological basis of hypersexuality. *International Review of Neurobiology.* https://yourbrainonporn.com/neurobiological-basis-hypersexuality-2016

Kukkonen, T. M., Binik, Y. M., Amsel, R., & Carrier, S. (2007). Thermography as a physiological measure of sexual arousal in both men and women. *Journal of Sexual Medicine, 4,* 93–105.

Kukkonen, T. M., Binik, Y. M., Amsel, R., & Carrier, S. (2009). Hot or not? Examining age related differences in genital temperature during sexual arousal via thermography. *Journal of Sexual Medicine, 6*(s4), 378.

Kukkonen, T. M., Binik, Y. M., Amsel, R., & Carrier, S. (2010). An evaluation of the validity of thermography as a physiological measure of sexual arousal in a non-university adult sample. *Archives of Sexual Behavior, 39,* 861–873.

Kukull, W. A., & Bowen, J. D. (2002). Dementia epidemiology. *Medical Clinics of North America, 86,* 573–590.

Kumari, V., & Postma, P. (2005). Nicotine use in schizophrenia: the self medication hypotheses. *Neuroscience & Biobehavioral Reviews, 29*(6), 1021–1034.

Kuper, H., & Marmot, M. (2003). Job strain, job demands, decision latitude and risk of coronary heart disease within the Whitehall II study. *Journal of Epidemiology and Community Health, 57,* 147–153.

Kuperberg, G. R., Lakshmanan, B. M., Greve, D. N., & West, W. C. (2008). Task and semantic relationship influence both the polarity and localization of hemodynamic modulation during lexico-semantic processing. *Human Brain Mapping, 29,* 544–561.

Kuperberg, G. R., McGuire, P. K., & David, A. S. (1998). Reduced sensitivity to linguistic context in schizophrenic thought disorder: Evidence from on-line monitoring from words in linguistically anomalous sentences. *Journal of Abnormal Psychology, 107,* 423–434.

Kupfer, D. J., & Ehlers, C. L. (1989). Two roads to REM latency. *Archives of General Psychiatry, 46,* 945–948.

Kupfer, D. J., Kuhl, E. A., & Regier, D. A. (2013). DSM-5—The future arrived. *Journal of the American Medical Association, 309,* 1691–1692.

Kura, K. (2013). Japanese north–south gradient in IQ predicts differences in stature, skin color, income, and homicide rate. *Intelligence, 41*(5), 512–516. https://doi.org/10.1016/j.intell.2013.07.001

Kurtz, J. E., & Blais, M. A. (2007). Introduction to the special issue on the Personality Assessment Inventory. *Journal of Personality Assessment, 88,* 1–4.

Kurtz, M. M. (2015). Cognitive and social cognitive interventions for schizophrenia. In P. E. Nathan & J. M. Gorman (Eds.), *A guide to treatments that work* (4th ed., pp. 217- 236). New York, NY: Oxford University Press.

Kurtz, M. M., & Mueser, K. T. (2008). A meta-analysis of controlled research on social skills training for schizophrenia. *Journal of Consulting and Clinical Psychology, 76,* 491–504.

Kurtz, M. M., & Richardson, C. L. (2012). Social cognitive training for schizophrenia: A meta-analytic investigation of controlled research. *Schizophrenia Bulletin, 38*(5), 1092–1104.

Kutcher, M. J., Hampton, S., & Wilson, J. (2010). Child and adolescent mental health policy and plans in Canada: An analytical review. *Canadian Journal of Psychiatry, 55,* 100–107.

Kuyken, W., Byford, S., Taylor, R. S., Watkins, E., Holden, E., White, K., et al. (2008). Mindfulness-based cognitive therapy to prevent relapse in recurrent depression. *Journal of Consulting & Clinical Psychology*, 76, 966–978.

Kwok, H. W. (2003). Psychopharmacology in autism spectrum disorders. *Current Opinion in Psychiatry*, 16(5), 529–534.

Kwok, W. (2014). Is there evidence that social class at birth increases risk of psychosis? A systematic review. *International Journal of Social Psychiatry*, 60(8), 801–808.

Kyriakopoulos, M., Bargiotas, T., Barker, G. J., & Frangou, S. (2008). Diffusion tensor imaging in schizophrenia. *European Psychiatry*, 23, 255–273.

Laborit, H. (1950). *Physiologie et biologie du système nerveux végétif au service de la chirurgie*. Paris: G. Doin et Cie.

Labrie, V., Pai, S., & Petronis, A. (2012). Epigenetics of major psychosis: Progress, problems and perspectives. *Trends in Genetics*, 28(9), 427–435.

Lacroix, R., O'Shaughnessy, R., McNiel D. E., & Binder R. L. (2017). Controversies concerning the Canadian Not Criminally Responsible Reform Act. *Journal of the American Academy of Psychiatry and the Law*, 45, 44–51.

Lahaie, M., Boyer, S. C., Amsel, R., Khalifé, S., & Binik, Y. M. (2010). Vaginismus: A review of the literature on the classification/diagnosis, etiology and treatment. *Women's Health (London, England)*, 6, 705719.

Lahey, B. B., Pelham, W. E., Loney, J., Lee, S. S., & Willcutt, E. (2005). Instability of the DSM-IV subtypes of ADHD from preschool through elementary school. *Archives of General Psychiatry*, 62, 896–902.

Lally, J., ó Conghaile, A., Quigley, S., Bainbridge, E., & McDonald, C. (2013). Stigma of mental illness and help-seeking intention in university students. *The Psychiatrist Online*, 37, 253≠260.

Lalonde, J. K., Hudson, J. I., Gigante, R. A., & Pope, H. G., Jr. (2001). Canadian and American psychiatrists' attitudes toward dissociative disorders diagnoses. *Canadian Journal of Psychiatry*, 46, 407–412.

Lalumière, M. L., Harris, G. T., & Rice, M. E. (2001). Psychopathy and developmental instability. *Evolution & Human Behavior*, 22, 75–92.

Lalumière, M. L., Quinsey, V. L., Harris, G. T., Rice, M. E., & Trautrimas, C. (2003). Are rapists differentially aroused by coercive sex in phallometric assessments? In R. A. Prentky, E. S. Janus, & M. C. Seto (Eds.), *Sexually coercive behavior: Understanding and management* (pp. 211–224). New York, NY: The New York Academy of Sciences.

Lam, D. H., Watkins, E. R., Hayward, P., Bright, J., Wright, K., Kerr, N., et al. (2003). A randomized controlled study of cognitive therapy for relapse prevention for bipolar affective disorder outcome of the first year. *Archives of General Psychiatry*, 60, 145–152.

Lam, R. W., Kennedy, S. H., Parikh, S. V., MacQueen, G. M., Milev, R. V., Ravindran, A. V., ...CANMAT Depression Working Group. (2016). Canadian Network for Mood and Anxiety Canadian Network for Mood and Anxiety Treatments (CANMAT) 2016 clinical guidelines for the management of adults with major depressive disorder. *Canadian Journal of Psychiatry*, 61, S26–S43.

Lam, R., & Levitan, R. (2000). Pathophysiology of seasonal affective disorder: A review. *Journal of Psychiatry & Neuroscience*, 25, 469–480.

Lam, R., & Levitt, A. (1999). *Canadian consensus guidelines for the treatment of seasonal affective disorder*. Vancouver, BC: Clinical and Academic Publishing.

Lambert, M. T., & Silva, P. S. (1998). An update on the impact of gun control legislation on suicide. *Psychiatric Quarterly*, 69, 127–134.

Lanctot, K. L., Herrmann, N., Yau, K. K., Khan, L. R., Liu, B. A., LouLou, M. M., & Einarson, T. R. (2003). Efficacy and safety of cholinesterase inhibitors in Alzheimer's disease: A meta-analysis. *Canadian Medical Association Journal*, 16, 557–564.

Landreville, P., Landry, J., Baillargeon, L., Guerette, A., & Matteau, E. (2001). Older adults' acceptance of psychological and pharmacological treatments for depression. *The Journals of Gerontology Series B: Psychological Sciences and Social Sciences*, 56, P285–P291.

Lane, S. D., & Cherek, D. R. (2002). Marijuana effects on sensitivity to reinforcement in humans. *Neuropsychopharmacology*, 26, 520–529.

Lang, A. R., Goeckner, D. J., Adessor, V. J., & Marlatt, G. A. (1975). Effects of alcohol on aggression in male social drinkers. *Journal of Abnormal Psychology*, 84, 508–518.

Lang, R., Pugh, G., & Langevin, R. (1988). Treatment of incest and pedophilic offenders: A pilot study. *Behavioral Science and the Law*, 6, 239–255.

Lang, R., Rouget, A. C., & van Santen, V. (1988). The role of victim age and sexual maturity in child sexual abuse. *Annals of sex research*, 1, 467–484.

Langevin, R. (1983). *Sexual strands: Understanding and treating sexual anomalies in men*. Hillsdale, NJ: Erlbaum.

Langley, R. L. (2005). Animal-related fatalities in the United States: An update. *Wilderness & Environmental Medicine*, 16, 67–74.

Långström, N. (2010). The DSM criteria for exhibitionism, voyeurism, and frotteurism. *Archives of Sexual Behavior*, 39, 317–324.

Långström, N., & Hanson, R. K. (2006). High rates of sexual behavior in the general population: Correlates and predictors. *Archives of Sexual Behavior*, 35(1), 37–52.

Långström, N., & Zucker, K. J. (2005). Transvestic fetishism in the general population: Prevalance and correlates. *Journal of Sex and Marital Therapy*, 31, 87–95.

Lanius, R. A., Rabellino, D., Boyd, J. E., Harricharan, S., Frewen, P. A., & MacKinnon, M. C. (2017). The innate alarm system in PTSD: Conscious and subconscious processing of threat. *Current Opinion in Psychology*, 14, 1–7.

Lanius, R. A., Vermetten, E., Loewenstein, R. J., Brand, B., Schmahl, C., Bremner, J. D., & Spiegel, D. (2010). Emotion modulation in PTSD: Clinical and neurobiological evidence for a dissociative subtype. *American Journal of Psychiatry*, 167, 640–647.

Laroi, F., & Woodward, T. S. (2007). Hallucinations from a cognitive perspective. *Harvard Review of Psychiatry*, 15, 109–117.

Last, C. G., Strauss, C. C., & Francis, G. (1987). Comorbidity among childhood anxiety disorders. *Journal of Nervous and Mental Disease*, 175, 726–730.

Latthe, P., Latthe, M., Say, L., Gulmezoglu, M., & Khan, K. (2006). WHO systematic review of prevalence of chronic pelvic pain: A neglected reproductive health morbidity. *BMC Public Health*, 6, 177–177.

Laugeson, E. A., Frankel, F., Mogil, C., & Dillon, A. R. (2009). Parent-assisted social skills training to improve friendships in teens with autism spectrum disorders. *Journal of Autism and Developmental Disorders*, 39(4), 596–606.

Laumann, E. O., Gagnon, J. H., Michael, R. T., & Michaels, S. (1994). *The social organization of sexuality: Sexual practices in the United States*. Chicago, IL: University of Chicago Press.

Laumann, E. O., Paik, A., & Rosen, R. C. (1999). Sexual dysfunction in the United States: Prevalence and predictors. *Journal of the American Medical Association*, 281, 537–544.

Laurendeau, M. C., & Perreault, R. (1997). L'amorce du virage préventif en santé mentale au Québec: Enquête sur les politiques, les structures et les programmes de prévention en santé mentale. *Psychologie Canadienne*, 38, 13–24.

Laurin, C., Labrecque, M., Dupuis, G., Bacon, S. L., Cartier, A., & Lavoie, K. L. (2009). Chronic obstructive pulmonary disease patients with psychiatric disorders are at greater risk of exacerbations. *Psychosomatic Medicine*, 71(6), 667–674.

Lavigne, J. V., Gibbons, R. D., Christoffel, K. K., Arend, R., Rosenbaum, D., Binns, H., et al. (1996). Prevalence rates and correlates of psychiatric disorders among preschool children. *Journal of the American Academy of Child and Adolescent Psychiatry*, 35, 203–214.

Lavoie, K. L., Cartier, A., Labrecque, M., Bacon, S. L., Lemière, C., Malo, J. L., ...& Ditto, B. (2005). Are psychiatric disorders associated with worse asthma control and quality of life in asthma patients? *Respiratory Medicine*, 99(10), 1249–1257.

Lavoie, K. L., Fleet, R. P., Lespérance, F., Arsenault, A., Laurin, C., Frasure-Smith, N., & Bacon, S. L. (2004). Are exercise stress tests appropriate for assessing myocardial ischemia in patients with major depressive disorder? *American Heart Journal*, 148(4), 621–627.

Lawler, M., & Nixon, E. (2011). Body dissatisfaction among adolescent boys and girls: The effects of body mass, peer appearance culture and internalization of appearance ideals. *Journal of Youth and Adolescence*, 40, 59–71.

Lawrence, A. (2003). Factors associated with satisfaction or regret following male-to-female sex reassignment surgery. *Archives of Sexual Behavior*, 32(4), 299–315.

Lawrence, A. J., Luty, J., Bogdan, N. A., Sahakian, B. J., & Clark, L. (2009). Impulsivity and response inhibition in alcohol dependence and problem gambling. *Psychopharmacology*, 207(1), 163–172.

Lawrence, P. J., & Williams, T. I. (2011). Pathways to inflated responsibility beliefs in adolescent obsessive-compulsive disorder: A preliminary investigation. *Behavioural and Cognitive Psychotherapy*, 39, 229–234.

Lawson, G., Peterson, J. S., & Lawson, A. (1983). *Alcoholism and the family: A guide to treatment and prevention*. Rockville, MD: Aspen.

Lazarus, R. S., & Folkman, S. (1984). *Stress, appraisal and coping*. New York, NY: Guilford.

Learning Disabilities Association of Ontario. (2001). Operationalizing the new definition of learning disabilities for utilization within Ontario's educational system. Retrieved from www.ldao.ca/documents/Definition_and_Suporting%20Document_2001.pdf.

Learning Disabilities Association of Canada. (2002). Official definition of learning disabilities. Retrieved from www.ldac-acta.ca/learn-more/ld-defined/official-definition-of-learning-disabilities.

Learning Disabilities Association of Canada. (2007). Putting a Canadian face on learning disabilities. Retrieved from www.pacfold.ca

Leatherdale, S. T., & Burkhalter, R. (2012). The substance use profile of Canadian youth: exploring the prevalence of alcohol, drug and tobacco use by gender and grade. *Addictive Behaviors, 37*(3), 318–322.

LeBeau, R. T., Glenn, D., Liao, B., Wittchen, H. U., Beesdo-Baum, K., Ollendick, T., & Craske, M. G. (2010). Specific phobia: A review of DSM-IV specific phobia and preliminary recommendations for DSM-V. *Depression and Anxiety, 27,* 148–167.

Ledley, D. R., & Heimberg, R. G. (2005). Social anxiety disorder. In M. M. Antony, D. R. Ledley, & R. G. Heimberg (Eds.), *Improving outcomes and preventing relapse in cognitive-behavioral therapy* (pp. 38–76). New York, NY: Guilford.

LeDoux, J. E. (2000). Emotion circuits in the brain. *Annual Review of Neuroscience, 23,* 155–184.

Ledwidge, B., Glackman, W., Paredes, J., Chen, R., Dhami, S., Hansen, M., & Higenbottam, J. (1987). Controlled follow-up of patients released by a review panel at one and two years after separation. *Canadian Journal of Psychiatry, 32,* 448–453.

Lee, B. A., MacKenzie, J. J., & Holden, J. J. A. (2003). The nature of Fragile X syndrome. In I. Brown & M. Percy (Eds.), *Developmental disabilities in Ontario* (pp. 229–244). Toronto, ON: Ontario Association on Developmental Disabilities.

Lee, C. M., & Hunsley, J. (in press). *Introduction to clinical psychology: An evidence-based approach* (4th ed.). Toronto, ON: Wiley.

Lee, C. M., Horvath, C., & Hunsley, J. (2013). Does it work in the real world? The effectiveness of treatments for psychological problems in children and adolescents. *Professional Psychology: Research and Practice, 44,* 81–88.

Lee, T., & Seeman, P. (1980). Elevation of brain neuroleptic/dopamine receptors in schizophrenia. *American Journal of Psychiatry, 137,* 191–197.

Lee, Z., Klaver, J. R., Hart, S. D., Moretti, M. M., & Douglas, K. S. (2009). Short-term stability of psychopathic traits in adolescent offenders. *Journal of Clinical Child and Adolescent Psychology, 38,* 595–605. doi:10.1080/15374410903103536

Leekam, S. R., Nieto, C., Libby, S. J., Wing, L., & Gould, J. (2007). Describing the sensory abnormalities of children and adults with autism. *Journal of Autism and Developmental Disorders, 37*(5), 894–910.

Leeman, R. F., Kulesza, M., Stewart, D. W., & Copeland, A. L. (2012). Cluster Analysis of Undergraduate Drinkers Based on Alcohol Expectancy Scores. *Journal of Studies on Alcohol and Drugs, 73*(2), 238–249.

Legault, S. E., Langer, A., Armstrong, P. W., & Freeman, M. R. (1995). Usefulness of ischemic response to mental stress in predicting silent myocardial ischemia during ambulatory monitoring. *American Journal of Cardiology, 75,* 1007–1011.

Lehmann, H. E., & Hanrahan, G. E. (1954). Chlorpromazine: New inhibiting agent for psychomotor excitement and manic states. *Archives of Neurology and Psychiatry, 71,* 227–237.

Leibenluft, E., Blair, R. J., Charney, D. S., & Pine, D. S. (2003). Irritability in pediatric mania and other childhood psychopathology. *Annals of the New York Academy of Sciences, 1008,* 201–218. doi:10.1196/annals.1301.022

Leichner, P., Hall, D., & Calderon, R. (2005). Meal support training for friends and families of patients with eating disorders. *Eating Disorders, 13,* 407–411.

Leichsenring, F., Luyten, P., Hilsenroth, M. J., Abbass, A., Barber, J. P., Keefe, J. R., ...Steinert, C. (2015). Psychodynamic therapy meets evidence-based medicine: A systematic review using updated criteria. *Lancet Psychiatry, 2,* 648–660.

LeMoult, J., Joormann, J., Kircanski, K., & Gotlib, I. H. (2016). Attentional bias training in girls at risk for depression. *Journal of Child Psychology and Psychiatry, 57,* 1326–1333.

Lentz, V., Robinson, J., & Bolton, J. M. (2010). Childhood adversity, mental disorder comorbidity, and suicidal behavior in schizotypal personality disorder. *Journal of Nervous and Mental Disease, 198,* 795–801. doi:10.1097/NMD.0b013e3181f9804c

Lenze, E. J., & Wetherell, J. L. (2011). Anxiety disorders: New developments in old age. *American Journal of Geriatric Psychiatry, 19*(4), 301–304.

Lenzenweger, M. F., Lane, M. C., Loranger, A. W., & Kessler, R. C. (2007). DSM-IV personality disorders in the national comorbidity survey replication, *Biological Psychiatry, 62,* 553–564.

Leon, J., Cheung, C. K., & Neumann, P. J. (1998). Alzheimer's disease care: Costs and potential savings. *Health Affairs, 17,* 44–54.

Leonard, H., & Wen, X. (2002). The epidemiology of mental retardation: Challenges and opportunities in the new millennium. *Mental Retardation and Developmental Disabilities Research Reviews, 8,* 117–134.

Lepiece, B., Reynaert, C., Jacques, D., & Zdanowicz, N. (2015). Poverty and mental health: What should we know as mental health professionals? *Psychiatria Danubina, 27*(1), 92–96.

Lépine, J. (2001). Epidemiology, burden, and disability in depression and anxiety. *Journal of Clinical Psychiatry, 62*(Suppl. 13), 4–10.

Lequin, M., & Hendrikse, J. (2017). Advanced MR imaging in pediatric brain tumors, clinical applications. *Pediatric Brain Tumors Update, 27*(1), 167–190. https://doi.org/10.1016/j.nic.2016.08.007

Lerner, J. W., & Lerner, S. R. (1991). Attention deficit disorder: Issues and questions. *Focus on Exceptional Children, 24,* 1–17.

Lesch, K. P. (2004). Gene-environment interaction and the genetics of depression. *Journal of Psychiatry and Neuroscience, 29,* 174–184.

Levenson, J. S. (2004). Reliability of sexually violent predator civil commitment criteria. *Law and Human Behavior, 28,* 357–368.

Levenstein, S. (2000). The very model of a modern etiology: A biopsychosocial view of peptic ulcer. *Psychosomatic Medicine, 62,* 176–185.

Levenstein, S., Kaplan, G. A., & Smith, M. (1995). Sociodemographic characteristics, life stressors and peptic ulcer: A prospective study. *Journal of Clinical Gastroenterology, 21,* 185–192.

Levenstein, S., Rosenstock, S., Jacobsen, R. K., & Jorgensen, T. (2015). Psychological stress increases risk for peptic ulcer, regardless of Helicobacter pylori infection or use of nonsteroidal anti-inflammatory drugs. *Clinical Gastroenterology and Hepatology, 13*(3), 498–506.

Levine, S. B. (1989). Comprehensive and sexual health centers: Is it time? *Journal of Sex and Marital Therapy, 15,* 215–224.

Levitan, R. D., Kaplan, A. S., Masellis, M., Basile, V. S., Walker, M. L., Lipson, N., et al. (2001). Polymorphism of the serotonin 5-HT1B receptor gene (HTR1B) associated with minimum lifetime body mass index in women with bulimia nervosa. *Biological Psychiatry, 50,* 640–643.

Levitt, A., Boyle, M., Joffe, R., & Baumal, Z. (2000). Estimated prevalence of the seasonal subtype of major depression in a Canadian community sample. *Canadian Journal of Psychiatry, 45,* 650–654.

Levy, D. L., Holzman, P. S., Matthysse, S., & Mendell, N. R. (1993). Eye tracking dysfunction and schizoprhenia: A critical perspective. *Schizophrenia Bulletin, 19,* 461–536.

Levy, D. L., Holzman, P. S., Matthysse, S., & Mendell, N. R. (1993). Eye tracking dysfunction and schizophrenia: A critical perspective. *Schizophrenia Bulletin, 19*(3), 461–536.

Levy, H. C., Senn, J. M., & Radomsky, A. S. (2014). Further support for the acceptability-enhancing roles of safety behavior and a cognitive rationale in cognitive-behavior therapy for anxiety disorders. *Journal of Cognitive Psychotherapy, 28*(4), 303–316.

Levy, T. M. (2000). *Handbook of attachment interventions.* San Diego, CA: Academic Press.

Lewinsohn, P. M., Mischel, W., Chaplin, W., & Barton, R. (1980). Social competence and depression: The role of illusory self-perceptions. *Journal of Abnormal Psychology, 90,* 213–219.

Lewis, S. P., & Heath, N. L. (2015). Nonsuicidal self-injury among youth. *The Journal of Pediatrics, 166*(3), 526–530.

Lewis, S. P., Mahdy, J. C., Michal, N. J., & Arbuthnott, A. E. (2014). Googling self-injury: the state of health information obtained through online searches for self-injury. *JAMA pediatrics, 168*(5), 443–449.

Lewontin, R. C., Rose, S., & Kamin, L. J. (1984). *Not in our genes: Biology, ideology, and human nature.* New York, NY: Pantheon Books.

Ley, D. J. (2012). *The myth of sex addiction.* Lanham, MD: Rowman & Littlefield Publishers.

Lezak, M. D. (1995). *Neuropsychological assessment* (3rd ed.). New York, NY: Oxford University Press.

Li-Grining, C. P., & Durlak, J. A. (2014). The design and implementation of early childhood intervention programs: Informing efforts to address risk and promote resilience. *Journal of Prevention & Intervention in the Community, 42*(4), 243–247.

Liang, C. W., Tsai, J. L., & Hsu, W. Y. (2017). Sustained visual attention for competing emotional stimuli in social anxiety: An eye tracking study. *Journal of Behavior Therapy and Experimental Psychiatry, 54*(3), 178–185.

Liao, S., Chen, W. J., Lee, M., Lung, F. Lai, T. Liu, C. . . . . Chen, C. (2012). Low prevalence of major depressive disorder in taiwanese adults: Possible explanations and implications. *Psychological Medicine, 42,* 1227–1237.

Libby, A. M., Brent, D. A., Morrato, E. H., Orton, H. D., Allen, R., & Valuck, R. J. (2007). Decline in treatment of pediatric depression after FDA advisory on risk of suicidality with SSRIs. *American Journal of Psychiatry, 164,* 884–891.

Libby, P. (2002). Atherosclerosis: The new view. *Scientific American, May,* 46–55.

Lichtenstein, P., & Annas, P. (2000). Heritability and prevalence of specific fears and phobias in childhood. *Journal of Child Psychology and Psychiatry, 4,* 927–937.

Lieberman, A. (2006). Depression in Parkinson's disease: A review. *Acta Neurologica Scandinavica, 113,* 1–8.

Lieberman, A. F., Chu, A., van Horn, P., & Harris, W. W. (2011). Trauma in early childhood: Empirical evidence and clinical implications. *Development and Psychopathology, 23*, 397–410.

Lilenfeld, L. R. R., Wonderlich, S., Riso, L. P., Crosby, R., & Mitchell, J. (2006). Eating disorders and personality: A methodological and empirical review. *Clinical Psychology Review, 26*, 299–320.

Lilenfeld, L. R., Stein, D., Bulik, C. M., Strober, M., Plotnicov, K., Pollice, C., et al. (2000). Personality traits among currently eating disordered, recovered and never ill first-degree female relatives of bulimic and control women. *Psychological Medicine, 30*, 1399–1410.

Lilienfeld, S. O., & Landfield, K. (2008). Issues in diagnosis: Categorical vs. dimensional. In W. E. Craighead, D. J. Miklowitz, & L. W. Craighead (Eds.), *Psychopathology: History, diagnosis, and empirical foundations* (pp. 1–33). Hoboken, NJ: Wiley.

Lilienfeld, S. O., & Marino, L. (1995). Mental disorder as a Roschian concept: A critique of Wakefield's "harmful dysfunction" analysis. *Journal of Abnormal Psychology, 104*, 411–420.

Limosin, F., Rouillon, F., Payan, C., Cohen, J. M., & Strub, N. (2003). Prenatal exposure to influenza as a risk factor for adult schizophrenia. *Acta Psychiatrica Scandinavica, 107*, 331–335.

Linden, W., & Chambers, L. (1994). Clinical effectiveness of non-drug treatment of hypertension: A meta-analysis. *Annals of Behavioral Medicine, 16*, 35–45.

Linden, W., & Moseley, J. V. (2006). The efficacy of behavioral treatments for hypertension. *Applied Psychophysiology and Biofeedback, 31*, 51–63.

Lindh, J. A. (2015). *Comparing Exner's Comprehensive System and the Rorschach Performance Assessment System: A critical review of the literature.* La Mirada, CA: Biola University.

Lindsay, W. R. (2002). Research and literature on sex offenders with intellectual and developmental disabilities. *Journal of Intellectual Disability Research, 46*(s1), 74–85.

Lindsay, W. R., & Beail, N. (2004). Risk assessment: Actuarial prediction and clinical judgement of offending incidents and behaviour for intellectual disability services. *Journal of Applied Research in Intellectual Disabilities, 17*(4), 229–234.

Lindsay, W. R., Taylor, J. L., & Sturmey, P. (Eds.). (2004). *Offenders with developmental disabilities.* Chichester, UK: Wiley.

Lindsley, O. R., Skinner, B. F., & Solomon, R. L. (1954). A method for the experimental analysis of the behavior of psychotic patients. *American Psychologist, 9*, 419–420.

Linehan, M. M. (1987). Dialectical behavior therapy for borderline personality disorder. *Bulletin of the Menninger Clinic, 41*, 261–276.

Linehan, M. M. (1993). *Cognitive-behavioral treatment of borderline personality disorder.* New York, NY: Guilford.

Linehan, M. M. (2015). *DBT skills training manual.* New York, NY: Guilford.

Linehan, M. M., & Heard, H. L. (1992). Dialectical behavior therapy for borderline personality disorder. In J. F. Clarkin, E. Marziali, & H. Munroe-Blum (Eds.), *Borderline personality disorder: Clinical and empirical perspectives* (pp. 248–267). New York, NY: Guilford.

Linehan, M. M., Armstrong, H. E., Suarez, A., Allmon, D., & Heard, H. L. (1991). Cognitive-behavioral treatment of chronically parasuicidal borderline patients. *Archives of General Psychiatry, 48*, 1060–1064.

Linehan, M. M., Cochran, B. N., & Kehrer, C. A. (2001). Dialectical behavior therapy for borderline personality disorder.In D. H. Barlow (Ed.), *Clinical handbook of psychological disorders: A step-by-step treatment manual* (3rd ed., pp. 470–522). New York, NY: Guilford.

Linehan, M. M., Comtois, K. A., Murray, A. M., Brown, M. Z., Gallop, R. J., Heard, H. L., et al. (2006). Two-year randomized controlled trial and follow-up of dialectical behavior therapy vs therapy by experts for suicidal behaviors and borderline personality disorder. *Archives of General Psychiatry, 63*, 757–766.

Links, P. S. (1992). Family environment and family psychopathology in the etiology of borderline personality disorder. In J. F. Clarkin, E. Marziali, & H. Munroe-Blum (Eds.), *Borderline personality disorder: Clinical and empirical perspectives* (pp. 45–66). New York, NY: Guilford.

Linschoten, M., Weiner, L., & Avery-Clark, C. (2016). Sensate focus: A critical literature review. *Sexual and Relationship Therapy, 31*, 230–247.

Liotti, G. (2009). Attachment and dissociation. In P. F. Dell & J. A. O'Neil (Eds.), *Dissociation and the dissociative disorders: DSM-V and beyond* (pp. 53–65). New York, NY: Routledge.

Lippens, T., & Mackenzie, C. S. (2011). Treatment satisfaction, perceived treatment effectiveness, and dropout among older users of mental health services. *Journal of Clinical Psychology, 67*, 1197–1209.

Lissek, S., Kaczkurkin, A. N., Rabin, S., Geraci, M., Pine, D. S., & Grillon, C. (2014). Generalized anxiety disorder is associated with overgeneralization of classically conditioned fear. *Biological Psychiatry, 75*, 909–915.

Livesley, W. J. (1986). Trait and behavioral prototypes for personality disorder. *American Journal of Psychiatry, 143*, 728–732.

Livesley, W. J., & West, M. (1986). The DSM-III distinction between schizoid and avoidant personalities. *Canadian Journal of Psychiatry, 31*, 59–62.

Livesley, W. J., Jang, K. L., & Vernon, P. A. (2003). Genetic basis of personality structure. In Theodore Millon (Ed.), *Handbook of psychology: Personality and social psychology* (Vol. 5). New York, NY: Wiley.

Livesley, W. J., Schroeder, M. L., Jackson, D. N., & Jang, K. L. (1994). Categorical distinctions in the study of personality disorder: Implications for classification. *Journal of Abnormal Psychology, 103*, 6–17.

Lochner, C., du Toit, P. L., Zungu-Dirwayi, N., Marais, A., van Kradenburg, J., Seedat, S., et al. (2002). Childhood trauma in obsessive-compulsive disorder, trichotillomania, and controls. *Depression and Anxiety, 15*, 66–68.

Lochner, C., Fineberg, N. A., Zohar, J., van Ameringen, M., Juven-Wetzler, A., Altamura, A. C., . . . Stein, D. J. (2014). Comorbidity in obsessive-compulsive disorder (OCD): A report from the International College of Obsessive-Compulsive Spectrum Disorders (ICOCS). *Comprehensive Psychiatry, 7*(55), 1513–1519. doi: 10.1016/j.comppsych.2014.05.020.

Lochner, C., Serebro, P., van der Merwe, L., Hemmings, S., Kinnear, C., Seedat, S., & Stein, D. J. (2011). Comorbid obsessive–compulsive personality disorder in obsessive–compulsive disorder (OCD): A marker of severity. *Progress in Neuro-Psychopharmacology & Biological Psychiatry, 35*, 1087–1092. doi:10.1016/j.pnpbp.2011.03.006

Lock, J., & le Grange, D. (2005). Family-based treatment of eating disorders. *International Journal of Eating Disorders. Special Issue: Anorexia Nervosa, 37*, S64–S67.

Loeber, R. (1990). Development and risk factors of juvenile antisocial behavior and delinquency. *Clinical Psychology Review, 10*, 1–42.

Loeber, R., Burke, J. D., Lahey, B. B., Winters, A., & Zera, M. (2000). Oppositional defiant and conduct disorder: A review of the past 10 years, Part I. *Journal of the Academy of Child and Adolescent Psychiatry, 39*(12), 1468–1484.

Loeber, R., Keenan, K., Lahey, B. B., Green, S. M., & Thomas, C. (1993). Evidence for developmentally based diagnoses of oppositional defiant disorder and conduct disorder. *Journal of Abnormal Child Psychology, 21*, 377–410.

Loftus, E. F. (1993). When a lie becomes memory's truth: Memory distortion after exposure to misinformation. *Current Directions in Psychological Science, 1*, 121–123.

Loftus, E. F. (2003). Make-believe memories. *American Psychologist, 58*, 867–873.

Loftus, E. F., & Davis, D. (2006). Recovered memories. *Annual Review of Clinical Psychology, 2*, 469–498.

Loftus, E. F., & Pickrell, J. E. (1995). The formation of false memories. *Psychiatric Annals, 25*, 720–725.

Logsdon, R. G., McCurry, S. M., & Teri, L. (2007). Evidence-based psychological treatments for disruptive behaviors in individuals with dementia. *Psychology and Aging, 22*, 28–36.

Longnecker, M. P. (1994). Alcohol consumption and the risk of cancer in humans: An overview. *Alcohol, 12*, 87–96.

Lonigan, C. J. (2006). Development, assessment, and promotion of preliteracy skills. *Early Education and Development, 17*, 91–114.

LoPiccolo, J. (1990). Sexual dysfunction. In A. S. Bellack, M. Hersen, & A. Kazdin (Eds.), *International handbook of behavior therapy and modification* (2nd ed., pp. 547–564). New York, NY: Plenum.

Lord, C. (1993). The complexity of social behavior in autism. In S. Baron-Cohen, H. Tager-Flusberg, & D. Cohen (Eds.), *Understanding other minds: Perspectives from autism* (pp. 292–316). Oxford, UK: Oxford University Press.

Lord, C., & Paul, R. (1997). Language and communication in autism. In D. J. Cohen & F. R. Volkmar (Eds.), *Handbook of autism and pervasive developmental disorders* (pp. 195–225). New York, NY: Wiley.

Lord, C., & Schopler, E. (1987). Neurobiological implications of sex differences in autism. In E. Schopler & G. B. Mesibov (Eds.), *Neurobiological issues in autism* (pp. 192–211). New York, NY: Plenum.

Lord, C., Luyster, R., Gotham, K., & Guthrie, W. (2012). *Autism diagnostic observation schedule,* (2nd ed.). *(ADOS-2) Manual (Part II): Toddler module.* Torrence, CA: Western Psychological Services.

Lord, C., Risi, S., Lambrecht, L., Cook, E. H., Leventhal, B. L., DiLavore, P. C., et al. (2000). The Autism Diagnostic Observation Schedule-Generic: A standard measure of social and communication deficits associated with the spectrum of autism. *Journal of Autism and Developmental Disorders, 30*, 205–233.

Lord, C., Rutter, M., & Le Couteur, A. (1994). Autism Diagnostic Interview–Revised: A revised version of a diagnostic interview for caregivers of individuals with possible pervasive developmental disorders. *Journal of Autism and Developmental Disorders, 24*, 659–685.

Lösel, F. (1998). Treatment and management of psychopaths. In D. Cooke, A. E. Forth, & R. D. Hare (Eds.), *Psychopathy: Theory, research and implications for society*. Dordrecht, The Netherlands: Kluwer.

Lösel, F., & Schmucker, M. (2005). The effectiveness of treatment for sexual offenders: A comprehensive meta-analysis. *Journal of Experimental Criminology, 1*, 117–146.

Loukas, A., Fitzgerald, H. E., Zucker, R. A., & von Eye, A. (2001). Parental alcoholism and co-occurring antisocial behavior: Prospective relationships to externalizing behavior problems in their young sons. *Journal of Abnormal Child Psychology, 29*, 91–106.

Lovaas, O. I. (1977). *The autistic child: Language development through behavior modification*. New York, NY: Irvington.

Lovaas, O. I., & Smith, T. (1988). Intensive behavioral treatment with young autistic children. In B. B. Lahey & A. E. Kazdin (Eds.), *Advances in clinical child psychology* (Vol. 11, pp. 285–324). New York, NY: Plenum Press.

Lovaas, O. I., Koegel, R. L., Simmons, J. Q., & Long, J. S. (1973). Some generalization and follow-up measures on autistic children in behavior therapy. *Journal of Applied Behavior Analysis, 6*, 131–166.

Lovering, J. S. (2003). Down syndrome: Characteristics and health issues. In I. Brown & M. Percy (Eds.), *Developmental disabilities in Ontario* (2nd ed., pp. 171–193). Toronto, ON: Association on Developmental Disabilities.

Lovering, J. S., & Percy, M. (2007). Down syndrome. In I. Brown & M. Percy (Eds.), *A comprehensive guide to intellectual and developmental disabilities* (pp. 149–172). London, UK: Paul Brookes.

Lovett, B. J., & Sheffield, R. A. (2007). Affective empathy deficits in aggressive children and adolescents: A critical review. *Clinical Psychology Review, 27*, 1–13.

Löwe, B., Spitzer, R. L., Williams, J. B., Mussell, M., Schellberg, D., & Kroenke, K. (2008). Depression, anxiety and somatization in primary care: Syndrome overlap and functional impairment. *General Hospital Psychiatry, 30*(3), 191–199.

Lowenstein, L. (2002). Fetishes and their associated behavior. *Sexuality and Disability, 20*(2), 135–147.

Lu, B. Y., & Ahmed, I. (2010). The mind-body conundrum: The somatopsychic perspective in geriatric depression. *American Journal of Geriatric Psychiatry, 18*(5), 378–381.

Luborsky, L. (1984). *Principles of psychoanalytic psychotherapy: A manual for supportive expressive (SE) treatment*. New York, NY: Basic Books.

Luborsky, L. (1954). A note on Eysenck's article "The effects of psychotherapy: An evaluation." *British Journal of Psychology, 45*, 129–131.

Luborsky, L., Singer, B., & Luborsky, L. (1975). Comparative studies of psychotherapies: Is it true that "everybody has won and all must have prizes?" *Archives of General Psychiatry, 32*, 995–1008.

Lubs, H. A. (1969). A marker X chromosome. *American Journal of Human Genetics, 21*, 231–244.

Luckasson, R., Coulter, D. L., Polloway, E. A., Reiss, S., Schalock, R. L., Snell, M. E., et al. (2002). *Mental retardation: Definition, classification and systems of supports* (9th ed.). Washington, DC: American Association on Mental Retardation.

Lueger-Schuster, B., Butollo, A., Moy, Y., Jagsch, R., Glück, T., Kantor, V., ... & Weindl, D. (2015). Aspects of social support and disclosure in the context of institutional abuse–long-term impact on mental health. *BMC Psychology, 3*(19), 1–9.

Lumley, M. N., & Harkness, K. L. (2007). Specificity in the relations among childhood adversity, early maladaptive schemas, and symptom profiles in adolescent depression. *Cognitive Therapy and Research, 31*, 639–657.

Lumley, M. N., & Harkness, K. L. (2009). Childhood maltreatment and depressotypic cognitive organization. *Cognitive Therapy and Research, 33*, 511–522.

Lumley, M.A., Neely, L.C. & Burger, A.J. (2007). The assessment of alexithymia in medical settings: Implications for understanding and treating health problems. *Journal of Personality Assessment, 89*, 230–246.

Lund, C., Breen, A., Flisher, A. J., Kakuma, R., Corrigall, J., Joska, J. A., ... & Patel, V. (2010). Poverty and common mental disorders in low and middle income countries: A systematic review. *Social Science & Medicine, 71*, 517–528.

Lund, E. M., & Hammond, M. (2014). Single-session intervention for abuse awareness among people with developmental disabilities. *Sexuality and Disability, 32*(1), 99–105.

Lunsky, Y., Bradley, E., Durbin, J., Koegl, C., Canrinus, M., & Goering, P. (2003). *Dual diagnosis in provincial psychiatric hospitals: a population-based study*. Toronto, ON: Centre for Addiction and Mental Health.

Lunsky, Y., Lin, E., Balogh, R., Klein-Geltink, J., Wilton, A. S., & Kurdyak, P. (2012). Emergency department visits and use of outpatient physician services by adults with developmental disability and psychiatric disorder. *The Canadian Journal of Psychiatry, 57*(10), 601–607.

Luthar, S. S. (1991). Vulnerability and resilience: A study of high-risk adolescents. *Child development, 62*(3), 600.

Lydon, D. M., Ram, N., Conroy, D. E., Pincus, A. L., Geier, C. F., & Maggs, J. L. (2016). The within-person association between alcohol use and sleep duration and quality in situ: An experience sampling study. *Addictive Behaviors, 61*, 68-73. doi:http://dx.doi.org.uml.idm.oclc.org/10.1016/j.addbeh.2016.05.018

Lykken, D. T. (1957). A study of anxiety in the sociopathic personality. *Journal of Abnormal and Social Psychology, 55*, 6–10.

Lykken, D. T. (1995). *The antisocial personalities*. Hillsdale, NJ: Erlbaum.

Lynam, D. R. (1996). Early identification of chronic offenders: Who is the fledgling psychopath? *Psychological Bulletin, 120*(2), 209–234.

Lynam, D. R. (2002). Fledgling psychopathy: A view from personality theory. *Law and Human Behavior, 26*, 255–259.

Lynch, C. (2004). Psychotherapy for persons with mental retardation. *Mental Retardation, 42*, 399–405.

Lynch, R. G. (2004). *Exceptional returns: Economic, fiscal, and social benefits of investment in early childhood development*. Washington, DC: Economic Policy Institute.

Lynn, R. (2010). In Italy, north–south differences in IQ predict differences in income, education, infant mortality, stature, and literacy. *Intelligence, 38*(1), 93–100. https://doi.org/10.1016/j.intell.2009.07.004

Lynn, S. J., Lilienfeld, S. O., Merckelbach, H., Giesbrecht, T., McNally, R. J., Loftus, E., ... & Malaktaris, A. (2014). The trauma model of dissociation: Inconvenient truths and stubborn fictions. Comment on Dalenberg et al. (2014). *Psychological Bulletin, 140*(3), 896–910.

Lyon, D. R., & Ogloff, J. R. P. (2000). Legal and ethical issues in psychopathy assessment. In C. Gacono (Ed.), *The clinical and forensic assessment of psychopathy: A practitioner's guide* (pp. 139–173). Hillsdale, NJ: Erlbaum.

MacArthur, G. J., Minozzi, S., Martin, N., Vickerman, P., Deren, S., Bruneau, J., ... & Hickman, M. (2012). Opiate substitution treatment and HIV transmission in people who inject drugs: Systematic review and meta-analysis. *British Medical Journal, 345*, e5945.

Macdonald, A., Pukay-Martin, N. D., Wagner, A. C., Fredman, S. J., & Monson, C. M. (2016). Cognitive–behavioral conjoint therapy for PTSD improves various PTSD symptoms and trauma-related cognitions: Results from a randomized controlled trial. *Journal of Family Psychology, 30*(1), 157–162.

Machado, P. P., Goncalves, S., & Hoek, H. W. (2013). DSM-5 reduces the proportion of EDNOS cases: Evidence from community samples. *International Journal of Eating Disorders, 46*, 60–65.

Machado, P. P. P., Machado, B. C., Gonçalves, S., & Hoek, H. W. (2007). The prevalence of eating disorders not otherwise specified. *International Journal of Eating Disorders, 40*, 212–217.

Machalek, K., Brown, I., Birkan, R., Fung, M., & Percy, M. (2003). Prenatal and early life. In I. Brown & M. Percy (Eds.), *Developmental Disabilities in Ontario* (2nd ed.) Toronto, ON: Ontario Association on Developmental Disabilities.

Mackay, T. F. (2014). Epistasis and quantitative traits: Using model organisms to study gene-gene interactions. *Nature Reviews Genetics, 15*(1), 22–33.

Mackenzie, C. S., Gekoski, W. L., & Knox, V. J. (1999). Family physicians' beliefs and treatment intentions regarding mental disorders in older adults. *Family Physician, 45*, 1219–1224.

Mackenzie, C. S., Knox, V. J., Smoley, J., & Gekoski, W. L. (2004). The influence of age and gender on advice given to depressed people. *Journal of Mental Health and Aging, 10*, 311–324.

Mackenzie, C. S., Pagura, J., & Sareen, J. (2010). Correlates of help-seeking and perceived need for mental health services among older adults in the Collaborative Psychiatric Epidemiology Surveys. *American Journal of Geriatric Psychiatry, 18*, 1103–1115.

Mackenzie, C. S., & Peragine, G. (2003). Measuring and enhancing self-efficacy among professional caregivers of individuals with dementia. *American Journal of Alzheimer's Disease and Other Dementias, 18*, 291–299.

Mackenzie, C. S., Poulin, P., & Seidman-Carlson, R. (2006). A brief mindfulness-based stress reduction intervention for nurses and nurse aides. *Applied Nursing Research, 19*, 105–109.

Mackenzie, C. S., Reynolds, K., Cairney, J., Streiner, D. L., & Sareen, J. (2012). Disorder-specific mental health service use for mood and anxiety disorders: Associations with age, sex, and psychiatric comorbidity. *Depression and Anxiety, 29*, 234–242.

Mackenzie, C. S., Reynolds, K., Chou, K-L., Pagura, J., & Sareen, J. (2011). Prevalence and correlates of generalized anxiety disorder in a national sample of older adults. *American Journal of Geriatric Psychiatry, 19*(4), 305–315.

Mackenzie, C. S., Rosenberg, M., & Major, M. (2006). Evaluation of a psychiatric day hospital program for elderly patients with mood disorders. *International Psychogeriatrics, 18*, 631–641.

Mackenzie, C. S., Scott, T., Mather, A., & Sareen, J. (2008). Older adults' help-seeking attitudes and treatment beliefs concerning mental health problems. *American Journal of Geriatric Psychiatry, 16,* 1010–1019.

Mackenzie, C. S., Wiprzycka, U., Hasher, L., & Goldstein, D. (2007). Does expressive writing reduce stress and improve health for family caregivers of older adults? *The Gerontologist, 47,* 296–306.

Mackenzie, C. S., Wiprzycka, U., Hasher, L., & Goldstein, D. (2008). Seeing the glass half full: Optimistic expressive writing improves mental health among chronically stressed caregivers. *British Journal of Health Psychology, 13,* 73–76.

Mackenzie, C. S., Wiprzycka, U., Hasher, L., & Goldstein, D. (2009). Associations between psychological distress, learning and memory among spouse caregivers of older adults with dementia. *Journal of Gerontology: Psychological Sciences, 64B,* 742–746.

Mackenzie, K.H., Ouellette-Kuntz, H. & Blinkhorn, A.D. (2017). Out of school and into distress: families of young adults with intellectual and developmental disabilities. Developmental disabilities in transition. *Journal of Applied Research in Intellectual Disabilities, 30,* 774–781. doi: 10.1111/jar.12264

Mackie, F. L., Hemming, K., Allen, S., Morris, R. K., & Kilby, M. D. (2017). The accuracy of cell-free fetal DNA-based non-invasive prenatal testing in singleton pregnancies: a systematic review and bivariate meta-analysis. *BJOG: An International Journal of Obstetrics and Gynaecology, 124*(1), 32–46. https://doi.org/10.1111/1471-0528.14050

MacLeod, J., & Nelson, G. (2000). Programs for the promotion of family wellness and the prevention of child maltreatment: A meta-analytic review. *Child Abuse and Neglect, 24,* 1127–1149.

MacMillan, H. L., Fleming, J. E., Streiner, D. L., Lin, E., Boyle, M. H., Jamieson, E., . . .Beardslee, W. R. (2001). Childhood abuse and lifetime psychopathology in a community sample. *American Journal of Psychiatry, 158,* 1878–1883.

MacQueen, G. M., Frey, B. N., Ismail, Z., Jaworska, N., Steiner, M., Van Lieshout, R. J., . . . CANMAT Depression Work Group. (2016). Canadian Network for Mood and Anxiety Treatments (CANMAT) 2016 clinical guidelines for the management of adults with major depressive disorder: Section 6. Special populations: Youth, women, and the elderly. *Canadian Journal of Psychiatry, 61,* 588–603.

Madowitz, J., Matheson, B. E., & Liang, J. (2015). The relationship between eating disorders and sexual trauma. *Eating and Weight Disorders-Studies on Anorexia, Bulimia and Obesity, 20,* 281–293. doi: 10.1007/s40519-015-0195-y

Maehler, C., & Schuchardt, K. (2011). Working memory in children with learning disabilities: Rethinking the criterion of discrepancy. *International Journal of Disability, Development and Education, 58*(1), 5–17.

Maffei, C., Fossati, A., Agostoni, I., Barraco, A., Bagnato, M., Deborah, D., et al. (1997). Interrater reliability and internal consistency for the Structured Clinical Interview of DSM-IV Axis II Personality Disorders (SCID-II), version 2.i0. *Journal of Personality Disorders, 11,* 279–284.

Maglione, J. E., Thomas, S. E., & Jeste, D. V. (2014). Late-onset schizophrenia: Do recent studies support categorizing LOS as a subtype of schizophrenia? *Current Opinion in Psychiatry, 27*(3), 173–178. doi:10.1097/YCO.0000000000000049

Magnusson, D. (1988). *Individual development from an interactional perspective: A longitudinal study.* Hillsdale, NJ: Erlbaum.

Magnusson, D., & Bergman, L. R. (1990). A pattern approach to the study of pathways from childhood to adulthood. In L. N. Robins & M. Rutter (Eds.), *Straight and devious pathways from childhood to adulthood* (pp. 101–115). Cambridge, UK: Cambridge University Press.

Maher, W. B., & Maher, B. A. (1985). Psychopathology. 1. From ancient times to the eighteenth century. In G. A. Kimble & K. Schlesinger (Eds.), *Topics in the history of psychology* (Vol. 2). Hillsdale, NJ: Erlbaum.

Mahler, M. S., Pine, F., & Bergman, A. (1975). *The psychological birth of the human infant.* New York, NY: Basic Books.

Maia, T. V., & Frank, M. J. (2017). An integrative perspective on the role of dopamine in schizophrenia. *Biological Psychiatry, 81*(1), 52–66.

Maier, W., Lichtermann, D., Klingler, T., Heun, R., & Hallmayer, J. (1992). Prevalence of personality disorders (DSM-III-R) in the community. *Journal of Personality Disorders, 6,* 187–196.

Main, M., & Morgan, H. (1996). Disorganization and disorientation in infant strange situation behaviour: Phenotypic resemblance to dissociative states? In L. L. Michelson & W. J. Ray (Eds.), *Handbook of dissociation.* New York, NY: Plenum.

Malamuth, N. M. (1986). Predictors of naturalistic sexual aggression. *Journal of Personality and Social Psychology, 50,* 953–962.

Malamuth, N. M., Heavey, C. L., & Linz, D. (1993). Predicting men's antisocial behavior against women: The interactional model of sexual aggression. In G. C. N. Hall, R. Hirschman, J. R. Graham, & M. S. Zaragonzee (Eds.), *Sexual aggression: Issues in etiology, assessment and treatment* (pp. 63–99). Bristol, PA: Taylor & Francis.

Malarkey, W. B., Kiecolt-Glaser, J. K., Pearl, D., & Glaser, R. (1994). Hostile behavior during marital conflict alters pituitary and adrenal hormones. *Psychosomatic Medicine, 56,* 41–51.

Malian, I., & Nevin, A. (2002). A review of self-determination literature: Implications for practitioners. *Remedial and Special Education, 2,* 68–74.

Malik, N., Kingdon, D., Pelton, J., Mehta, R., & Turkington, D. (2009). Effectiveness of brief cognitive-behavioral therapy for schizophrenia delivered by mental health nurses: Relapse and recovery at 24 months. *Journal of Clinical Psychiatry, 70,* 201–207.

Malkoff-Schwartz, S., Frank, E., Anderson, B. P., Hlastala, S. A., Luther, J. F., Sherrill, J. T., et al. (2000). Social rhythm disruption and stressful life events in the onset of bipolar and unipolar episodes. *Psychological Medicine, 30,* 1005–1016.

Malkoff-Schwartz, S., Frank, E., Anderson, B., Sherrill, J. T., Siegel, L., Patterson, D., et al. (1998). Stressful life events and social rhythm disruption in the onset of manic and depressive bipolar episodes: A preliminary investigation. *Archives of General Psychiatry, 55,* 702–707.

Malla, A., Norman, R. M. G., & Helmes, E. (1987). Factors associated with involuntary admission to psychiatric facilities in Newfoundland. *Canadian Medical Association Journal, 136,* 1166–1171.

Malone, R. (2008, May 28). Can antipsychotic medication help my child? Retrieved from https://iancommunity.org/cs/therapies_treatments/antipsychotics_malone

Malone, R. P., Delaney, M. A., Luebbert, J. F., Cater, J., & Campbell, M. (2000). A double-blind placebo-controlled study of lithium in hospitalized aggressive children and adolescents with conduct disorder. *Archives of General Psychiatry, 57,* 649–654.

Malone, R. P., Sheikh, R., & Zito, J. M. (1999). Psychopharmacology: Novel antipsychotic medications in the treatment of children and adolescents. *Psychiatric Services, 50,* 171–174.

Mammarella, I., Hill, F., Devine, A., Caviola, S., & Szucs, D. (2015). Math anxiety and developmental dyscalculia: A study on working memory processes. *Journal of Clinical and Experimental Neuropsychology, 37*(8), 878–887.

Manassis, K., & Monga, S. (2001). A therapeutic approach to children and adolescents with anxiety disorders and associated comorbid conditions. *Journal of the American Academy of Child & Adolescent Psychiatry, 40,* 115–117.

Manassis, K., Lee, T. C., Bennett, K., Zhao, X. Y., Mendlowitz, S., Duda, S. . . .Wood, J. J. (2014). Types of parental involvement in CBT with anxious youth: A preliminary meta-analysis. *Journal of Consulting and Clinical Psychology, 82,* 1163–1172.

Mangweth, B., Pope, H. G., Jr., Hudson, J. I., Olivardia, R., Kinzl, J., & Biebl, W. (1997). Eating disorders in Austrian men: An intracultural and crosscultural comparison study. *Psychotherapy and Psychosomatics, 66,* 214–221.

Mann, J. J., Huang, Y. Y., Underwood, M. D., Kassir, S. A., Oppenheim, S., Kelly, T. M., et al. (2000). A serotonin transporter gene promoter polymorphism (5-HTTLPR) and prefrontal cortical binding in major depression and suicide. *Archives of General Psychiatry, 57,* 729–738.

Manning, M., Homel, R., & Smith, C. (2010). A meta-analysis of the effects of early developmental prevention programs in at-risk populations on non-health outcomes in adolescence. *Children and Youth Services Review, 32,* 506–519.

Mansell, S., Sobsey, D., & Calder, P. (1992). Sexual abuse treatment for persons with developmental disabilities. *Professional Psychology: Research and Practice, 23,* 404–409.

Manuck, S. B., & McCaffery, J. M. (2014). Gene-environment interaction. *Annual Review of Psychology, 65,* 41–70.

Manuck, S. B., Kaplan, J. R., & Clarkson, T. B. (1983). Behaviorally induced heart rate reactivity and atherosclerosis in cynomolgus monkeys. *Psychosomatic Medicine, 45,* 95–108.

Manuck, S. B., Kaplan, J. R., Adams, M. R., & Clarkson, T. B. (1989). Behaviorally elicited heart rate reactivity and atherosclerosis in female cynomolgus monkeys (*Macaca fascicularis*). *Psychosomatic Medicine, 51,* 306–318.

Marchetti, R. L., Kurcgant, D., Neto, J. G., Von Bismark, M. A., & Fiore, L. A. (2009). Evaluating patients with suspected nonepileptic psychogenic seizures. *Journal of Neuropsychiatry and Clinical Neurosciences, 21,* 292–298.

Marcus, D. K., O'Connell, D., Norris, A. L., & Sawaqdeh, A. (2014). Is the Dodo bird endangered in the 21st century? A meta-analysis of treatment comparison studies. *Clinical Psychology Review, 34,* 519–530.

Marcus, S. C., & Olfson, M. (2010). National trends in the treatment for depression from 1998 to 2007. *Archives of General Psychiatry, 67,* 1265–1273.

Margari, L., Buttiglione, M., Craig, F., Cristella, A., de Giambattista, C. (2013). Neuropathological comorbidities in learning disorders. *BMC Neurology, 13,* 198.

Markon, K. E. (2014). From comorbidity to constructs: Recurring and emergent issues in modeling comorbidity. In C. S. Richards, & M. W. O'Hara (Eds.), *The oxford handbook of depression and comorbidity* (pp. 29–45). New York, NY: Oxford University Press.

Markovitz, P. J., Calabrese, J. R., Schulz, C. S., & Meltzer, H. Y. (1991). Fluox-etine in the treatment of borderline and schizotypal personality disorders. *American Journal of Psychiatry, 148*, 1067–1076.

Marlatt, G. A., & Gordon, J. R. (Eds.). (1985). *Relapse prevention maintenance strategies in the treatment of addictive behaviors.* New York, NY: Guilford.

Marmot, M. G. (1986). Social inequalities in mortality: The social environment. In R. G. Wilkinson (Ed.), *Class and health: Research and longitudinal data.* London, UK: Tavistock.

Marmot, M. G., & Mustard, J. F. (1994). Coronary heart disease from a population perspective. In R. G. Evans, M. L. Barer, & T. R. Marmor (Eds.), *Why are some people healthy and others not?* (pp. 189–216). New York, NY: Aldine de Gruyter.

Marmot, M. G., & Theorell, T. G. (1988). Social class and cardiovascular disease: The contribution of work. *International Journal of Health Services, 18*, 659–674.

Marmot, M. G., Kogevinas, M., & Elston, M. A. (1987). Social/economic status and disease. *Annual Review of Public Health, 8*, 111–135.

Marmot, M. G., Siegrist, J., Theorell, T. G., & Feeney, A. (1999). Health and the psychosocial environment at work. In M. G. Marmot & R. B. Wilkinson (Eds.), *Social determinants of health* (pp. 105–131). New York, NY: Oxford University Press.

Marques, L., Alegria, M., Becker, A. E., Chen, C. N., Fang, A., Chosak, A., & Diniz, J. B. (2011). Comparative prevalence, correlates of impairment, and service utilization for eating disorders across US ethnic groups: Implications for reducing ethnic disparities in health care access for eating disorders. *International Journal of Eating Disorders, 44*, 412–420. doi: 10.1002/eat.20787

Marshall, B. J. (2001). One hundred years of discovery and rediscovery of Helicobacter pylori and its association with peptic ulcer disease. In H. L. T. Mobley, G. L. Mendz, & S. L. Hazell (Eds.), *Helicobacter pylori: Physiology and Genetics* (pp. 19–24). Washington, DC: ASM Press.

Marshall, K., & Wynne, H. (2003). Fighting the odds. *Perspectives on labour and income, 4*(12). Ottawa, ON: Statistics Canada.

Marshall, K., & Wynne, H. (2004). Fighting the odds. *Perspectives on labour and income, 16*(1), 7.

Marshall, L. A., & Cooke, D. J. (1995). The role of childhood experiences in the aetiology of psychopathy. *Issues in Criminological and Legal Psychology, 24*, 107–108.

Marshall, L. A., & Cooke, D. J. (1999). The childhood experiences of psycho-paths: A retrospective study of familial and societal factors. *Journal of Personality Disorders, 13*(3), 211–225.

Marshall, T., Jones, D. P., Ramchandani, P. G., Stein, A., & Bass, C. (2007). Intergenerational transmission of health beliefs in somatoform disorders. *The British Journal of Psychiatry, 191*(5), 449–450.

Marshall, W. L. (1982). A model of dysfunctional behavior. In A. S. Bellack, M. Hersen, & A. E. Kazdin (Eds.), *International handbook of behavior modification and therapy* (pp. 57–78). New York, NY: Plenum.

Marshall, W. L. (1992). The social value of treatment for sexual offenders. *Canadian Journal of Human Sexuality, 1*, 109–114.

Marshall, W. L. (1997). Pedophilia: Psychopathology and treatment. In D. R. Laws & W. O'Donohue (Eds.), *Sexual deviance: Theory, assessment, and treatment* (pp. 152–174). New York, NY: Guilford.

Marshall, W. L. (2007). Diagnostic issues, multiple paraphilias, and comorbid disorders in sexual offenders: Their incidence and treatment. *Aggression and Violent Behavior, 12*, 16–35.

Marshall, W. L., & Barbaree, H. E. (1984). Disorders of personality, impulse and adjustment. In S. M. Turner & M. Hersen (Eds.), *Adult psychopathology: A behavioral perspective* (pp. 406–449). New York, NY: Wiley.

Marshall, W. L., & Barbaree, H. E. (1988). The long-term evaluation of a behavioral treatment program for child molesters. *Behaviour Research and Therapy, 26*, 499–511.

Marshall, W. L., & Barbaree, H. E. (1990). An integrated theory of sexual offending. In W. L. Marshall, D. R. Laws, & H. E. Barbaree (Eds.), *Handbook of sexual assault: Issues, theories, and treatment of the offender* (pp. 257–275). New York, NY: Plenum.

Marshall, W. L., & Barrett, S. (1990). *Criminal neglect: Why sex offenders go free.* Toronto, ON: Doubleday. (Also reprinted in paperback by Seal/Bantam Books, 1992)

Marshall, W. L., & Eccles, A. (1993). Pavlovian conditioning processes in adolescent sex offenders. In H. E. Barbaree, W. L. Marshall, & S. M. Hudson (Eds.), *The juvenile sex offender* (pp. 118–142). New York, NY: Guilford.

Marshall, W. L., & Marshall, L. E. (2000). The origins of sexual offending. *Trauma, Violence & Abuse: A Review Journal, 1*, 250–263.

Marshall, W. L., Anderson, D., & Fernandez, Y.M. (1999). *Cognitive behavioral treatment of sexual offenders.* Chichester, UK: Wiley.

Marshall, W. L., Earls, C. M., Segal, Z. V., & Darke, J. L. (1983). A behavioral program for the assessment and treatment of sexual aggressors. In K. Craig & R. McMahon (Eds.), *Advances in clinical behavior therapy* (pp. 148–174). New York, NY: Brunner/Mazel.

Marshall, W. L., Eccles, A., & Barbaree, H. E. (1991). Treatment of exhibitionists: A focus on sexual deviance versus cognitive and relationship features. *Behaviour Research and Therapy, 29*, 129–135.

Marshall, W. L., Hudson, S. M., & Hodkinson, S. (1993). The importance of attachment bonds in the development of juvenile sex offending. In H. E. Barbaree, W. L. Marshall, & S. M. Hudson (Eds.), *The juvenile sex offender* (pp. 164–181). New York, NY: Guilford.

Marshall, W. L., Kennedy, P., & Yates, P. (2002). Issues concerning the reliability and validity of the diagnosis of sexual sadism applied in prison settings. *Sexual Abuse: A Journal of Research and Treatment, 14*, 301–311.

Marshall, W. L., Kennedy, P., Yates, P., & Serran, G. (2002). Diagnosing sexual sadism in sexual offenders: Reliability across diagnosticians. *International Journal of Offender Therapy and Comparative Criminology, 46*, 668–676.

Marshall, W. L., Marshall, L. E., Serran, G. A., & Fernandez, Y. M. (2006). *Treating sexual offenders: An integrative approach.* New York, NY: Brunner-Routledge.

Martel, M. M., Nikolas, M., Jernigan, K., Friderici, K., Waldman, I., & Nigg, J. T. (2011). The dopamine receptor D4 gene (DRD4) moderates family environmental effects on ADHD. *Journal of Abnormal Child Psychology, 39*, 1–10. doi:10.1007/s10802-010-9439-5

Martin, B. A., Devla, N. J., Graf, P., Gosselin, C., Enns, M. W., Gilron, I., . . .Chan, P. K. Y. (2015). Delivery of electroconvulsive therapy in Canada: A first national survey report on usage, treatment practice, and facilities. *Journal of ECT, 31*, 119–124.

Martin, J. P., & Bell, J. (1943). A pedigree of mental defect showing sex-linkage. *Journal of Neurological Psychiatry, 6*, 154–157.

Martin, S. L., Ramey, C. T., & Ramey, S. L. (1990). The prevention of intellectual impairment in children of impoverished families: Findings of a randomized trial of educational daycare. *American Journal of Public Health, 80*, 844–847.

Martinez, R. S., Nellis, L. M., White, S. E., Jochim, M. L., & Peterson, R. K. (2016). Learning disorders of childhood and adolescence. In Maddux, J. E. & Winstead, B.A. (Eds.), *Psychopathology: Foundations for a contemporary understanding* (4th ed) (pp. 419–430). New York, NY: Routledge/Taylor & Francis Group.

Martinot, J. L., Peron-Magnan, P., Huret, J. D., Mazoyer, B., Baron, J. C., Boulenger, J. P., et al. (1990). Striatal D_2 dopaminergic receptors assessed with positron emission tomography and [76Br] bromospiperone in untreated schizophrenic patients. *American Journal of Psychiatry, 147*, 44–50.

Martinot, M. L. P., Bragulat, V., Artiges, E., Dollé, F., Hinnen, F., Jouvent, R., et al. (2001). Decreased presynaptic dopamine function in the left caudate of depressed patients with affective flattening and psychomotor retardation. *American Journal of Psychiatry, 158*, 314–316.

Martınez-Taboas, A., Dorahy, M., Sar, V., Middleton, W., & Krüger, C. (2013). Growing not dwindling: International research on the worldwide phenomenon of dissociative disorders. *Journal of Nervous and Mental Disease, 201*, 353.

Marver, J. E., Galfalvy, H. C., Burke, A. K., Sublette, M. E., Oquendo, M. A., Mann, J. J., & Grunebaum, M. F. (in press). Friendship, depression, and suicide attempts in adults: Exploratory analysis of a longitudinal follow-up study. *Suicide and Life-Threatening Behavior.*

Marwaha, S., & Johnson, S. (2004). Schizophrenia and employment: A review. *Social Psychiatry and Psychiatric Epidemiology, 39*(5), 337–349.

Marziali, E. (1992). The etiology of borderline personality disorder: Developmental factors. In J. F. Clarkin, E. Marziali, & H. Munroe-Blum (Eds.), *Borderline personality disorder: Clinical and empirical perspectives* (pp. 27–44). New York, NY: Guilford.

Marziali, E., Mackenzie, C. S., & Tchernikov, I. (2015). Acceptability of an e-learning program to help nursing assistants manage relationship conflict in nursing homes. *American Journal of Alzheimer's Disease and Related Disorders, 30*(1), 55–60. doi: 10.1177/1533317514551482

Mash, E. J., & Barkley, R. A. (Eds.). (2007). *Assessment of childhood disorders* (4th ed.). New York, NY: Guilford.

Mash, E. J., & Barkley, R. A. (Eds.). (2014). *Child psychopathology.* New York, NY: Guilford.

Mash, E. J., & Dozois, D. J. A. (2003). Child psychopathology: A developmental-systems perspective. In E. J. Mash & R. A. Barkley (Eds.), *Child psychopathology* (2nd ed., pp. 3 – 71). New York, NY: Guilford.

Maslow, A. H. (1954). *Motivation and personality.* New York, NY: Harper & Row.

Masterpasqua, F. (2009). Psychology and epigenetics. *Review of General Psychology, 13*, 194–201. doi:10.1037/a0016301

Masters, W. H., & Johnson, V. E. (1966). *Human sexual response.* Boston: Little, Brown.

Masters, W. H., & Johnson, V. E. (1970). *Human sexual inadequacy.* Boston: Little, Brown.

Mataix-Cols, D., de la Cruz, L. F., Monzani, B., Rosenfield, D., Andersson, E., Perez-Vigil, A., ... Frumento, P. (2017). D-cycloserine augmentation of exposure-based cognitive behavior therapy for anxiety, obsessive-compulsive, and posttraumatic stress disorders: A systematic review and meta-analysis. *JAMA Psychiatry,* [epub ahead of print]. doi: 10.1001/jamapsychiatry.2016.3955

Mather, N., & Goldstein, S. (2001). *Learning disabilities and challenging behaviors: A guide to intervention and classroom management.* Baltimore, MD: Paul H. Brookes.

Maticka-Tyndale, E. (2001). Sexual health and Canadian youth: How do we measure up? *The Canadian Journal of Human Sexuality, 10,* 1–17.

Matson, J. L., & Neal, D. (2009). Psychotropic medication use for challenging behaviors in persons with intellectual disabilities: An overview. *Research in developmental disabilities, 30*(3), 572–586.

Matson, J. L., Benavidez, D. A., Compton, L. S., Paclawskyj, T., & Baglio, C. (1996). Behavioral treatment of autistic persons: A review of research from 1980 to the present. *Research in Developmental Disabilities, 17,* 433–465.

Matsunaga, H., Kaye, W. H., McConaa, C., Plotnicov, K., Pollice, C., & Rao, R. (2000). Personality disorders among subjects recovered from eating disorders. *International Journal of Eating Disorders, 27,* 353–357.

Matthews, C., & Adams, E. (2009). Using a social justice approach to prevent the mental health consequences of heterosexism. *Journal of Primary Prevention, 30,* 11–26.

Matusch, A., & Kroll, T. (2017). PET in neurological and psychiatric disorders: Technologic advances and clinical applications. In M. M. Khalil (Ed.), *Basic Science of PET Imaging* (pp. 485–535). Julich, Germany: Springer International Publishing.

Matusiewicz, A. K., Hopwood, C. J., Banducci, A. N., & Lejuez, C. W. (2010). The effectiveness of cognitive behavioral therapy for personality disorders. *Psychiatric Clinics of North America, 33,* 657–685. doi:10.1016/j.psc.2010.04.007

Mawani, F. N., & Gilmour, H. (2010). Validation of self-rated mental health. Statistics Canada Catalogue no. 82-003-X.

May, R. (Ed.) (1961). *Existential psychology.* New York, NY: Random House.

Mayberg, H. S., Brannan, S. K., Mahurin, R. K., McGinnin, S., Silva, J. A., Tekell, J. L., et al. (2000). Regional metabolic effects of fluoxetine in major depression: Serial changes and relationship to clinical response. *Biological Psychiatry, 48,* 830–848.

Mayberg, H. S., Lozano, A. M., Voon, V., McNeely, H. E., Seminowicz, D., Hamani, C., et al. (2005). Deep brain stimulation for treatment-resistant depression. *Neuron, 45,* 651–660.

Mayes, S. D., & Calhoun, S. L. (2005). Test of the definition of learning disability based on the difference between IQ and achievement. *Psychological Reports, 97*(1), 109–116.

Mayes, S. D., Calhoun, S. L., & Lane, S. E. (2005). Diagnosing children's written disabilities: Different tests give different results. *Perceptual and Motor Skills, 10,* 72–78.

Mayou, R., Kirmayer, L. J., Simon, G., Kroenke, K., & Sharpe, M. (2005). Somatoform disorders: Time for a new approach in DSM-V. *American Journal of Psychiatry, 162,* 847–855.

Mazur, E. (2006). Biased appraisals of parenting daily hassles among mothers of young children: Predictors of parenting adjustment. *Cognitive Therapy and Research, 30,* 161–175.

Mazzocco, M. M. M., & Holden, J. J. A. (2007). Fragile X syndrome. In I. Brown & M. Percy (Eds.), *A comprehensive guide to intellectual and developmental disabilities* (pp. 173–187). London, UK: Paul Brookes.

McBride, W. G. (1961). Thalidomide and congenital abnormalities. *The Lancet, 2,* 1358.

McBurnett, K., Lahey, B. B., Rathouz, P. J., & Loeber, R. (2000). Low salivary cortisol and persistent aggression in boys referred for disruptive behavior. *Archives of General Psychiatry, 57,* 38–43.

McCabe, M. P., Sharlip, I. D., Lewis, R., Atalla, E., Balon, R., Fisher, A. D., et al. (2016a). Incidence and prevalence of sexual dysfunction in women and men: A consensus statement from the fourth international consultation on sexual medicine 2015. *The Journal of Sexual Medicine, 13,* 144–152.

McCabe, M. P., Sharlip, I. D., Lewis, R., Atalla, E., Balon, R., Fisher, A. D., et al. (2016b). Risk factors for sexual dysfunction among women and men: A consensus statement from the fourth international consultation on sexual medicine 2015. *The Journal of Sexual Medicine, 13,* 153–167.

McCabe, R. E., Antony, M. M., Summerfeldt, L. J., Liss, A., & Swinson, R. P. (2003). Preliminary examination of the relationship between anxiety disorders in adults and self-reported history of teasing or bullying experiences. *Cognitive Behaviour Therapy, 32,* 187–193.

McCain, M. N., & Mustard, J. F. (1999). *Reversing the real brain drain: Early years study—Final report.* Toronto, ON: Publications Ontario.

McCain, M.N., Mustard, J.F., & McCuaig, K. (2011). *Early years study 3: Making decisions, taking action.* Toronto, ON: Margaret & Wallace McCain Family Foundation.

McCarthy, M. C. & Lumley, M. N. (2012). Sources of emotional maltreatment and the differential development of unconditional and conditional schemas. *Cognitive Behaviour Therapy, 41,* 288–297.

McCarthy, M., & Thompson, D. (1997). A prevalence study of sexual abuse of adults with intellectual disabilities referred for sex education. *Journal of Applied Research in Intellectual Disabilities, 10,* 105–124.

McClellan, A. T., Arndt, I. O., Metzger, D. S., Woody, G. E., & O'Brien, C. P. (1993). The effects of psychosocial services in substance abuse treatment. *Journal of the American Medical Association, 269,* 1953–1959.

McConnell, S. R. (2002). Children with autism: Review of available research and recommendations for educational intervention and future research. *Journal of Autism and Developmental Disorders, 32,* 399–409.

McCord, W., & McCord, J. (1964). *The psychopath: An essay on the criminal mind.* New York, NY: Van Nostrand.

McCrady, B. S., Horvath, A. T., & Delaney, S. I. (2003). Self-help groups. In R. K. Hester & W. R. Miller (Eds.), *Handbook of alcoholism treatment approaches effective alternatives* (3rd ed., pp. 165–187). Boston, MA: Allyn and Bacon.

McCreary, B., & Jones, J. (2015). *Intellectual disabilities and dual diagnosis.* Kingston, ON, and Montreal, QC: McGill-Queen's University Press.

McCullough, J. P. (2005). Cognitive behavioral analysis system of psychotherapy: Treatment for chronic depression. In J. C. Norcross & M. R. Goldfried (Eds.), *Handbook of psychotherapy integration* (2nd ed., pp. 281–298). London, UK: Oxford University Press.

McCurry, S. M., Logsdon, R. G., Teri, L., & Vitiello, M. V. (2007). Evidence-based psychological treatments for insomnia in older adults. *Psychology and Aging, 22,* 18–27.

McDermid Vaz, S., & Heinrichs, R. W. (2006). Stability and validity of memory-based subtypes of schizophrenia. *Journal of the International Neuropsychological Society, 12,* 782–791.

McDonell, M. G., Srebnik, D., Angelo, F., McPherson, S., Lowe, J. M., Sugar, A., ... & Ries, R. K. (2013). Randomized controlled trial of contingency management for stimulant use in community mental health patients with serious mental illness. *American Journal of Psychiatry, 170*(1), 94–101.

McDougall, P. & Vaillancourt, T. (2015). The long-term adult outcomes of peer victimization in childhood and adolescence: Pathways to adjustment and maladjustment. *American Psychologist, 70,* 300–310. doi: 10.1037/a0039174

McDougall, P., Hymel, S., Vaillancourt, T., & Mercer, L. (2001). The consequences of childhood peer rejection. In M. Leary (Ed.), *Interpersonal rejection* (pp. 213–247). New York, NY: Oxford University Press.

McDougle, C. J., Price, L. H., & Volkmar, F. R. (1994). Recent advances in the pharmacotherapy of autism and related conditions. *Child and Adolescent Psychiatric Clinics of North America, 3,* 71–89.

McDowell, I. (2006). *Measuring health: A guide to rating scales and questionnaires* (3rd ed.). New York, NY: Oxford.

McFarlane, T., Olmsted, M. P., & Trottier, K. (2008). Timing and prediction of relapse in a transdiagnostic eating disorder sample. *International Journal of Eating Disorders, 41,* 587–593.

McFarlane, T., Urbszat, D., & Olmsted, M. P. (2011). "I Feel Fat": An experimental induction of body displacement in disordered eating. *Behaviour Research and Therapy, 49,* 289–293. doi: 10.1016/j.brat.2011.01.008

McFarlane, W. R., Dixon, L., Lukens, E., & Lucksted, A. (2003). Family psychoeducation and schizophrenia: A review of the literature. *Journal of Marital & Family Therapy, 29*(2), 223–245.

McGee, G. G., Morrier, M. J., & Daly, T. (1999). An incidental teaching approach to early intervention for toddlers with autism. *Journal of the Association for Persons with Severe Handicaps, 24,* 133–146.

McGee, R., Feehan, M., Williams, S., & Anderson, J. (1992). DSM–III disorders from age 11 to age 15 years. *Journal of the American Academy of Child and Adolescent Psychiatry, 31,* 50–59.

McGlashan, T. H. (1994). What has become of the psychotherapy of schizophrenia? *Acta Psychiatrica Scandinavica, 90*(Suppl. 384), 147–152.

McGlashan, T. M. (1987). I. Testing DSM–III symptom criteria for schizotypal and borderline personality disorders. *Archives of General Psychiatry, 44,* 143–148.

McGrath, J., Saha, S., Chant, D., & Welham, J. (2008). Schizophrenia: A concise overview of incidence, prevalence, and mortality. *Epidemiologic Reviews, 30*(1), 67–76.

McGrath, P. J., Stewart, J. W., Janal, M. N., Petkova, E., Quitkin, F. M., & Klein, D. F. (2000). A placebo-controlled study of fluoxetine versus imipramine in the acute treatment of atypical depression. *American Journal of Psychiatry, 157,* 344–350.

McGue, M. (1999). Behavioral genetic models. In K. E. Leonard & H.T. Blane (Eds.), *Psychological theories of drinking and alcoholism* (2nd ed., pp. 372–421). New York, NY: Guilford.

McGue, M., & Gottesman, I. I. (1989). A single dominant gene still cannot account for the transmission of schizophrenia. *Archives of General Psychiatry, 46,* 478–479.

McGue, M., Slutske, W., & Iacono, W. G. (1999). Personality and substance use disorders: II. Alcoholism versus drug use disorders. *Journal of Consulting and Clinical Psychology, 67*(3), 394.

McGuffin, P., Katz, R., & Rutherford, J. (1991). Nature, nurture and depression: A twin study. *Psychological Medicine, 21,* 329–335.

McGuffin, P., Katz, R., Watkins, S., & Rutherford, J. (1996). A hospital-based twin register of the heritability of DSM-IV unipolar depression. *Archives of General Psychiatry, 53,* 129–136.

McGuffin, P., Owen, M. J., O'Donovan, M. C., Thapar, A., & Gottesman, I. I. (1994a). Seminars in psychiatric genetics. *BMJ, 309*(6957), 818-819.

McGuffin, P., Owen, M. J., O'Donovan, M. C., Thapar, A., & Gottesman, I. I. (1994b). *Seminars in psychiatric genetics.* London: Gaskell.

McGuire, R. J., Carlisle, J. M., & Young, B. G. (1965). Sexual deviations as conditioned behaviour: A hypothesis. *Behaviour Research and Therapy, 2,* 185–190.

McGurk, S. R., Twamley, E. W., Sitzer, D. I., McHugo, G. J., & Mueser, K. T. (2007). A meta-analysis of cognitive remediation in schizophrenia. *American Journal of Psychiatry, 164,* 1791–1802.

McHugh, R. K., Whitton, S. W., Peckham, A. D., Welge, J. A., & Otto, M. W. (2013). Patient preference for psychological vs pharmacologic treatment of psychiatric disorders: A meta-analytic review. *Journal of Clinical Psychiatry, 74,* 595–602.

McIntosh, J. L., Santos, J. F., Hubbard, R. W., & Overholser, J. C. (1994). *Elder suicide: Research, theory and treatment.* Washington, DC: American Psychological Association.

McIntyre, L. L., & Brown, M. A. (2016). Utilization and usefulness of social support for families with children with autism spectrum disorder. *Journal of Intellectual & Developmental Disability.* http://dx.doi.org/10.3109/13668250. 2016.1262534

McKay, D., Abramowitz, J. S., Taylor, S., & Asmundson, G. J. G. (Eds.). (2009). *Perspectives on the anxiety disorders: Implications for DSM-V and beyond.* New York, NY: Springer.

McKenzie, K., Ouellette-Kuntz, H., Blinkhorn, A. and Démoré, A. (2017), Out of school and into distress: Families of young adults with intellectual and developmental disabilities in transition. *Journal of Applied Research in Intellectual Disabilities, 30,* 774–781. doi:10.1111/jar.12264

McKnight, J. (1995). *The careless society: Community and its counterfeits.* New York, NY: Basic Books.

McLachlin, B. (2005, February). *Medicine and the law: The challenges of mental illness.* Remarks at the Honourable Mr. Justice Michael O'Byrne/AHFMR Lecture on Law, Medicine and Ethics, sponsored by University of Alberta and University of Calgary, Alberta. Retrieved from www.scc-csc.gc.ca/court-cour/ju/spe-dis/bm05-02-17-eng.asp#note31

McLaughlin, A. E., Campbell, F. A., Pungello, E. P., & Skinner, M. (2007). Depressive symptoms in young adults: The influences of the early home environment and early educational child care. *Developmental Psychology, 78,* 746–756.

McLaughlin, K. A., & Sheridan, M. A. (2016). Beyond cumulative risk: a dimensional approach to childhood adversity. *Current Directions in Psychological Science, 25*(4), 239–245.

McLaughlin, K. A., Breslau, J., Green, J. G., Lakoma, M. D., Sampson, N. A., Zaslavsky, A. M., & Kessler, R. C. (2011). Childhood socio-economic status and the onset, persistence, and severity of DSM-IV mental disorders in a US national sample. *Social Science and Medicine, 73,* 1088–1096. doi:10.1016.j.socscimed.2011.06.011

McMain, S. F., Links, P. S., Gnam, W. H., Guimond, T., Cardish, R. J., Korman, L., & Streiner, D. L. (2009). A randomized trial of dialectical behavior therapy versus general psychiatric management for borderline personality disorder. *The American Journal of Psychiatry, 166,* 1365–1374. doi:10.1176/appi.ajp. 2009.09010039

McNally, R. J. (1994). *Panic disorder: A critical analysis.* New York, NY: Guilford.

McNally, R. J. (2002). Anxiety sensitivity and panic disorder. *Biological Psychiatry, 52,* 938–946.

McQueen, P. C., Spence, M. W., Garner, J. B., Pereira, L. H., & Winsor, E. J. T. (1987). Prevalence of major mental retardation and associated disabilities in the Canadian Maritime provinces. *American Journal of Mental Deficiency, 91,* 460–466.

McSherry, B. M. (2009). The United Nations Convention on the Rights of Persons with Disabilities. *Journal of Law and Medicine, 16,* 17–20.

McVey, G., Tweed, S., & Blackmore, E. (2007). Healthy Schools–Healthy Kids: A controlled evaluation of a comprehensive universal eating disorder prevention program. *Body Image, 4,* 115–136.

McVilly, K. R., & Rawlinson, R. B. (1998). Quality of life issues in the development and evaluation of services for people with intellectual disability. *Journal of Intellectual and Developmental Disability, 23,* 199–218.

Mealey, L. (1995). The sociobiology of sociopathy: An integrated evolutionary model. *Behavioral and Brain Sciences, 18,* 523–599.

Meana, M., Binik, Y. M., Khalife, S., & Cohen, D. R. (1997). Biopsychosocial profile of women with dyspareunia. *Obstetrics & Gynecology, 90,* 583–589.

Meehl, P. E. (1954). *Clinical versus statistical prediction: A theoretical analysis and review of the evidence.* Minneapolis, MN: University of Minnesota Press.

Meehl, P. E. (1959). Some ruminations on the validation of clinical procedures. *Canadian Journal of Psychology, 13,* 102–128.

Meehl, P. E. (1962). Schizotaxia, schizotypy, schizophrenia. *American Psychologist, 17,* 827–838.

Meehl, P. E. (1990). Toward an integrated theory of schizotaxia, schizotypy, schizophrenia. *Journal of Personality Disorders, 4,* 1–99.

Mehdizadeh, S. (2010). Self-presentation 2.0: Narcissism and self-esteem on Facebook. *Cyberpsychology, Behavior, and Social Networking, 13,* 357–364. doi:10.1089/cyber.2009.0257

Mehler, P. S. (2011). Medical complications of bulimia nervosa and their treatments. *International Journal of Eating Disorders, 44,* 95–104. doi: 10.1002/eat.20825

Mehlum, L., Tørmoen, A. J., Ramberg, M., Haga, E., Diep, L. M., Laberg S., . . . Grøholt, B. (2014). Dialectical behavior therapy for adolescents with repeated suicidal and self-harming behavior: a randomized trial. *Journal of the American Academy of Child and Adolescent Psychiatry, 53,* 1082–1091

Mehta, D., Klengel, T., Conneely, K. N., Smith, A. K., Altmann, A., Pace, T. W., . . .Binder, E. B. (2013). Childhood maltreatment is associated with distinct genomic and epigenetic profiles in posttraumatic stress disorder. *Proceedings of the National Academy of Sciences, 110,* 8302–8307.

Meichenbaum, D. (1974). *Cognitive behavior modification.* New York, NY: General Learning Corporation.

Meichenbaum, D. (1985). *Stress inoculation training.* New York, NY: Pergamon Press.

Meichenbaum, D. (1995). Cognitive behavioral therapy in historical perspective. In B. Bongar & L. E. Beutler (Eds.), *Comprehensive textbook of psychotherapy: Theory and practice* (pp. 140–158). New York, NY: Oxford University Press.

Meichenbaum, D. (1997). *Treating post-traumatic stress disorder.* Chichester, UK: Wiley.

Meichenbaum, D. (2002). *Treating individuals with anger control problems and aggressive behavior.* Waterloo, ON: Institute Press.

Meichenbaum, D. (2003). Cognitive-behavior therapy: Folktales and the unexpurgated history. *Cognitive Therapy & Research, 27,* 125–129.

Meichenbaum, D. (2007). Stress inoculation training: A preventative and treatment approach. In P. M. Lehrer, R. L. Woolfolk, & W. E. Sime (Eds.), *Principles and practice of stress management* (3rd ed., pp. 497–516). New York, NY: Guilford.

Meichenbaum, D., & Goodman, J. (1971). Training impulsive children to talk to themselves: A means of developing self-control. *Journal of Abnormal Psychology, 77,* 115–126.

Meichenbaum, D., & Turk, D. (1976). The cognitive behavioral management of anxiety, anger, and pain. In P. O. Davidson (Ed.), *The behavioral management of anxiety, depression, and pain.* New York, NY: Brunner/Mazel.

Melhuish, E. C. (2011). Preschool matters. *Science, 333,* 299–300.

Melton, G. B. (Ed.). (1985). *Nebraska symposium on motivation: Vol. 33. The law as a behavioral instrument.* Lincoln, NE: University of Nebraska Press.

Melton, G. B., Petrila, J., Poythress, N. G., & Slobogin, C. (2007). *Psychological evaluations for the courts: A handbook for mental health professionals and lawyers* (3rd ed.). New York, NY: Guilford.

Meltzer, H. Y. (1993). New drugs for the treatment of schizophrenia. *Psychiatric Clinics of North America, 16,* 365–385.

Meltzer, H., Gatward, R., Goodman, R., & Ford, T. (2000). *Mental health of children and adolescents in Great Britain.* London, UK: Stationery Office.

Melzack, R., & Wall, P. D. (1982). *The challenge of pain.* New York, NY: Basic Books.

Mendlewicz, J., & Rainer, J. D. (1977). Adoption study supporting genetic transmission in manic depresssive illness. *Nature, 268,* 327–329.

Menon, V. (2013). Developmental pathways to functional brain networks: Emerging principles. *Trends in Cognitive Sciences, 17*(12), 627–640.

Menon, V. (2016). Working memory in children's math learning and its disruption in dyscalculia. *Current Opinion in Behavioral Sciences, 10,* 125–132.

Mental Health Commission of Canada [MHCC]. (2009). *Toward recovery and well-being: A framework for a mental health strategy for Canada.* Ottawa, ON: National Library of Canada.

Mental Health Commission of Canada. (2011, April 29). *Formative evaluation: Final technical report.* Retrieved from www.mentalhealthcommission.ca/SiteCollectionDocuments/Evaluation/MHCC_Technical_Report_FINAL_ENG.pdf

Mental Health Commission of Canada. (2012). *Changing directions, changing lives.* Retrieved from http://strategy.mentalhealthcommission.ca/

Mental Health Commission of Canada. (2013). *Making the case for investing in mental health in Canada.* Retrieved from www.mentalhealthcommission.ca/English/document/5210/making-case-investing-mental-health-canada-backgrounder-key-facts.

Menzies, R. G., & Clarke, J. C. (1995). The etiology of phobias: A nonassociative account. *Clinical Psychology Review, 15,* 23–48.

Merikangas, K. R., & Weissman, M. M. (1986). Epidemiology of DSM-III Axis II personality disorders. In A. J. Frances & R. E. Hales (Eds.), *The American Psychiatric Association Annual Review* (pp. 49–74). Washington, DC: American Psychiatric Press.

Merikangas, K. R., He, J., Burstein, M., Swanson, S. A., Avenevoli, S., Cui, L., et al. (2010). Lifetime prevalence of mental disorders in U.S. adolescents: Results from the National Comorbidity Survey Replication-Adolescent Supplement (NCS-A). *Journal of the American Academy of Child & Adolescent Psychiatry, 49*(10), 980–989. doi:10.1016/j.jaac.2010.05.017

Merrick, J., Aspler, S., & Schwartz, G. (2001). Should adults with phenylketonuria have diet treatment? *Mental Retardation, 39,* 215–217.

Merskey, H. (1992). The manufacture of personalities: The production of multiple personality disorder. *British Journal of Psychiatry, 160,* 327–340.

Merskey, H. (1995). *The analysis of hysteria: Understanding conversion and dissociation* (2nd ed.). London, UK: Gaskell.

Messenger, J. C. (1993). Sex and repression in an Irish folk community. In D. N. Suggs & A. W. Miracle (Eds.), *Culture and human sexuality.* Pacific Grove, CA: Brooks/Cole.

Metz, M. E., Pryor, J. L., & Nesvacil, L. J. (1997). Premature ejaculation: A psychophysiological review. *Journal of Sex and Marital Therapy, 23,* 3–24.

Metzger, L. J., Carson, M. A., Lasko, N. B., Paulus, L. A., Orr, S. P., Pitman, R. K., & Yehuda, R. (2008). Basal and suppressed salivary cortisol in female Vietnam nurse veterans with and without PTSD. *Psychiatry Research, 161,* 330–335.

Meuret, A. E., Rosenfield, D., Wilhelm, F. H., Zhou, E., Conrad, A., Ritz, T., & Roth, W. T. (2011). Do unexpected panic attacks occur spontaneously? *Biological Psychiatry, 70,* 985–991.

Meyer, G. J., Erard, R. E., Erdberg, P., Mihura, J. L., & Viglione, D. J. (2011). *Rorschach Performance Assessment System: Administration, coding, interpretation, and technical manual.* Toledo, OH: Rorscharch Performance Assessment System.

Meyers, B. S., & Jeste, D. V. (2010). Geriatric psychopharmacology: Evolution of a discipline. *Journal of Clinical Psychiatry, 71,* 1416–1424.

Meyers, W. S., & Keith, C. R. (1991). Homosexual and preoedipal issues in the psychoanalytic psychotherapy of a female-to-male transsexual. In C. W. Socarides & V. D. Volkan (Eds.), *The homosexualities and the therapeutic process* (pp. 75–96). Adison, CT: International Universities Press.

Michael, T., Blechert, J., Vriends, N., Margraf, J., & Wilhelm, F. H. (2007). Fear conditioning in panic disorder: Enhanced resistance to extinction. *Journal of Abnormal Psychology, 116,* 612–617.

Miklowitz, D. J. (2008). Adjunctive psychotherapy for bipolar disorder: State of the evidence. *American Journal of Psychiatry, 165,* 1408–1419.

Miklowitz, D. J., George, E. L., Richards, J. A., Simoneau, T. L., & Suddath, R. L. (2003). A randomized study of family-focused psychoeducation and pharmacotherapy in the outpatient management of bipolar disorder. *Archives of General Psychiatry, 60,* 904–912.

Miklowitz, D. J., Otto, M. W., Frank, E., Reilly-Harrington, N. A., Wisniewski, S. R., Kogan, J. N., et al. (2007). Psychosocial treatments for bipolar depression: A 1-year randomized trial from the Systematic Treatment Enhancement Program. *Archives of General Psychiatry, 64,* 419–426.

Miles, C. (1977). Conditions predisposing to suicide: A review. *Journal of Nervous and Mental Disease, 164,* 231–246.

Miles, D. R., & Carey, G. (1997). Genetic and environmental architecture of human aggression. *Journal of Personality and Social Psychology, 72,* 207–217.

Miles, S. W., Sheridan, J., Russell, B., Kydd, R., Wheeler, A., Walters, C., . . . & Tuomola, P. (2013). Extended-release methylphenidate for treatment of amphetamine/methamphetamine dependence: a randomized, double-blind, placebo-controlled trial. *Addiction, 108*(7), 1279–1286.

Milev, R. V., Giacobbe, P., Kennedy, S. H., Blumberger, D. M., Daskalakis, Z. J., Downar, J., . . . CANMAT Depression Work Group. (2016). Canadian Network for Mood and Anxiety Treatments (CANMAT) 2016 clinical guidelines for the management of adults with major depressive disorder: Section 4. Neurostimulation treatments. *Canadian Journal of Psychiatry, 61,* 561–575.

Milich, R., Balentine, A. C., & Lynam, D. R. (2001). ADHD combined type and ADHD predominantly inattentive type are distinct and unrelated disorders. *Clinical Psychology, 8,* 463–488.

Millar, J. (1998). *Hepatitis and injection drug use in British Columbia—Pay now or pay later.* Vancouver, BC: Ministry of Health.

Miller, A. L., Muehlenkamp, J. J., & Jacobson, C. M. (2008). Fact or fiction: Diagnosing borderline personality disorder in adolescents. *Clinical psychology review, 28*(6), 969–981.

Miller, C. J., Li, M., Penfold, R. B., Lee, A. F., Smith, E. G., Osser, D. N., . . . Bauer, M. S. (2014). Patterns of initiation of second generation antipsychotics for bipolar disorder: A month-by-month analysis of provider behavior. *BMC Psychiatry, 14,* 339. doi: 10.1186/s12888-014-0339-z.

Miller, G. E., Chen, E., & Zhou, E. S. (2007). If it goes up, must it come down? Chronic stress and the hypothalamic-pituitary-adrenocortical axis in humans. *Psychological Bulletin, 133,* 25–45.

Miller, G. E., Dopp, J. M., Myers, H. F., Stevens, S. Y., & Fahey, J. L. (1999). Psychosocial predictors of natural killer cell mobilization during marital conflict. *Health Psychology, 18,* 262–271.

Miller, G. E., Rohleder, N., Stetler, C., & Kirschbaum, C. (2005). Clinical depression and regulation of the inflammatory response during acute stress. *Psychosomatic Medicine, 67,* 679–687.

Miller, G. E., Stetler, C. A., Carney, R. M., Freedland, K. E., & Banks, W. A. (2002). Clinical depression and inflammatory risk markers for coronary heart disease. *American Journal of Cardiology, 90,* 1279–1283.

Miller, M. N., & Pumariega, A. J. (2001). Culture and eating disorders: A historical and cross-cultural review. *Psychiatry—Interpersonal and Biological Processes, 64,* 93–110.

Miller, S., Wampold, B., & Varhely, K. (2008). Direct comparisons of treatment modalities for youth disorders: A meta-analysis. *Psychotherapy Research, 18,* 5–14.

Miller, T. Q., Smith, T. W., Turner, C. W., Guijarro, M. L., & Hallet, A. J. (1996). A meta-analytic review of research on hostility and physical health. *Psychological Bulletin, 119,* 322–348.

Miller, W. R., & Rollnick, S. (1991). *Motivational Interviewing: Preparing people to change addictive behavior.* New York, NY: Guilford.

Miller, W. R., & Rollnick, S. (2003). *Motivational interviewing: Preparing people to change addictive behavior* (2nd ed.). New York, NY: Guilford.

Miller, W. R., & Rollnick, S. (2013). *Motivational interviewing: Helping people change.* New York, NY: Guilford.

Miller, W. R., Wilbourne, P. L., & Hettema, J. E. (2003). What works? A summary of alcohol treatment outcome research. In R. K. Hester & W. R. Miller (Eds.), *Handbook of alcoholism treatment approaches effective alternatives* (3rd ed., pp. 13–63). Boston, MA: Allyn and Bacon.

Milligan, K., Badali, P., & Spiroiu, F. (2013). Using integra mindfulness martial arts to address self-regulation challenges in youth with learning disabilities: A qualitative exploration. *Journal of Child and Family Studies.* doi: 10.1007/s10826-013-9868-1

Milligan, K., Phillips, M. & Morgan, A. (2015). Tailoring social competence interventions for children with learning disabilities. *Journal of Child and Family Studies,* online Sep 03 2015.

Millon, G., Millon, C. M., Meagher, S. E., Grossman, S. D., & Ramnath, R. (2004). *Personality disorders in modern life* (2nd ed.). Hoboken, NJ: Wiley & Sons, Inc.

Millon, T. (1969). *Modern psychopathology: A biosocial approach to maladaptive learning and functioning.* Philadelphia, PA: Saunders.

Millon, T. (1981). *Disorders of personality: DSM-III: Axis II.* New York, NY: Wiley.

Millon, T. (1992). The borderline construct: Introductory notes on its history, theory, and empirical grounding. In J. F. Clarkin, E. Marziali, & H. Munroe-Blum (Eds.), *Borderline personality disorder: Clinical and empirical perspectives* (pp. 3–23). New York, NY: Guilford.

Millon, T. (1996). *Disorders of personality: DSM-IV and beyond* (2nd ed.). New York, NY: Wiley.

Millon, T., & Meagher, S. E. (2004). The Millon Clinical Multiaxial Inventory-III (MCMI-III). In M. Hersen (Series Ed.), M. J. Hilsenroth & D. L. Segal (Vol. Eds.), *Comprehensive handbook of psychological assessment: Vol. 2. Personality assessment* (pp. 108–121). Hoboken, NJ: Wiley.

Millon, T., Grossman, S., & Millon, C. (2015). *Millon Clinical Multiaxial Inventory–IV manual.* Minneapolis, MN: Pearson Assessments.

Millon, T., Simonsen, R., & Birket-Smith, M. (1998). Historical conceptions of psychopathy in the United States and Europe. In T. Millon, E. Simonsen, M. Birket-Smith, & R. D. Davis (Eds.), *Psychopathy: Antisocial, criminal, and violent behavior* (pp. 3–31). New York, NY: Guilford.

Mills, D. E., & Prkachin, K. M. (1993). Psychological stress reverses antiaggregatory effects of dietary fish oil. *Journal of Behavioral Medicine, 16,* 403–412.

Mills, J., Polivy, J., Herman, C. P., & Tiggemann, M. (2002). Effects of exposure to thin media images: Evidence of self-enhancement among restrained eaters. *Personality and Social Psychology Bulletin, 28,* 1687–1699.

Milner, B. (1963). Effects of different brain lesions on card sorting. *Archives of Neurology, 9,* 90–100.

Milner, B. (1964). Some effects of frontal lobectomy in man. In J. M. Warren & K. Akert (Eds.), *The frontal granular cortex and behavior* (pp. 313–331). New York, NY: McGraw-Hill.

Mincic, A., M. (2015). Neuroanatomical correlates of negative emotionality-related traits: A systematic review and meta-analysis. *Neuropsychologia, 77,* 97–118.

Minelli, A., & Maffioletti. E. (2014). Genetics of anxiety disorders. In S. A. Roman (Ed.), *Anxiety disorders: Risk factors, genetic determinants and cognitive-behavioral treatment* (pp. 67-92). New York, NY: Novinka/Nova Science Publishers.

Miner, J. (2009, October 8). Psychiatric pioneer, 86, slams too much reliance on drugs. *London Free Press.* Retrieved from www.lfpress.com

Ministry of Education, Government of Ontario. (2013). *A meta-perspective on the evaluation of full-day kindergarten during the first two years of implementation.* Retrieved from www.edu.gov.on.ca/kindergarten/FDKReport2013.pdf.

Minnes, P. M. (1992). Facilitated Communication: An overview and directions for research. *Journal of Developmental Disabilities, 1,* 57–67.

Minnes, P., & Woodford, L. (2004). Well-being in aging parents caring for an adult with a developmental disability. *Journal on Developmental Disabilities, 11,* 47–66.

Minnes, P., Perry, A., & Weiss, J. A. (2015). Predictors of distress and well-being in parents of young children with developmental delays and disabilities: The importance of parent perceptions. *Journal of Intellectual Disability Research, 59*(6), 551–560. doi: 10.1111/jir.12160

Minzenberg, M. J., Fan, J., New, A. S., Tang, C. Y., & Siever, L. J. (2007). Fronto-limbic dysfunction in response to facial emotion in borderline personality disorder: An event-related fMRI study. *Psychiatry Research, 155,* 231–243.

Mirenda, P. L., & Schuler, A. (1988). Augmenting communication for persons with autism: Issues and strategies. *Topics in Language Disorders, 9,* 24–43.

Mischel, W. (1968). *Personality and assessment.* New York, NY: Wiley.

Mishna, F. (2003). Learning disabilities and bullying: Double jeopardy. *Journal of Learning Disabilities, 36,* 336–347.

Mishna, F., Muskat, B., & Wiener, J. (2010). "I'm not lazy; it's just that I learn differently": Development and implementation of a manualized school-based group for students with learning disabilities. *Social Work with Groups, 33,* 139–159.

Mitchell, A. J. (2011). Why do physicians have difficulty diagnosing depression in the elderly? *Aging Health, 7*(1), 99–101.

Mitchell, D. G. V., Colledge, E., Leonard, A., & Blair, R. J. R. (2002). Risky decisions and response reversal: Is there evidence of orbitofrontal cortex dysfunction in psychopathic individuals? *Neuropsychologia, 40,* 2013–2033.

Mitchell, M. A., & Schmidt, N. B. (2014). An experimental manipulation of social comparison in social anxiety. *Cognitive Behaviour Therapy, 43,* 221–229. doi: 10.1080/16506073.2014.914078.

Mittal, V. A., Pelletier-Baldelli, A., Trotman, H., Kestler, L., Bollini, A., & Walker, E. (2016). Schizophrenia spectrum and other psychotic disorders. In J. E. Maddux & B. A. Winstead (Eds.) *Psychopathology: Foundations for a contemporary understanding* (4th ed., pp. 318-340). New York, NY: Routledge.

Moehle, K. A., & Levitt, E. E. (1991). The history of the concepts of fear and anxiety. In C. E. Walker (Ed.), *Clinical psychology: Historical and research foundations* (pp. 159–182). New York, NY: Plenum Press.

Moffitt, T. E. (1990a). Juvenile delinquency and attention deficit disorder: Boys' developmental trajectories from age 3 to age 15. *Child Development, 6,* 893–910.

Moffitt, T. E. (1990b). The neuropsychology of delinquency: A critical review. In M. Tonry & N. Morris (Eds.), *Crime and justice: A review of research* (pp. 99–169). Chicago, IL: University of Chicago Press.

Moffitt, T. E. (1993). Adolescence-limited and life-course-persistent antisocial behavior: A developmental taxonomy. *Psychological Review, 100,* 674–701.

Mohlman, J., Gorenstein, E. E., Kleber, M., de Jesus, M., Gorman, J. M., & Papp, L. A. (2003). Standard and enhanced cognitive-behavior therapy for late-life generalized anxiety disorder: Two pilot investigations. *American Journal of Geriatric Psychiatry, 11,* 24–32.

Mohr, D. C., & Beutler, L. E. (1990). Erectile dysfunction: A review of diagnostic and treatment procedures. *Clinical Psychology Review, 10,* 123–150.

Molendijk, M. L., Hoek, H. W., Brewerton, T. D., & Elzinga, B. M. (in press). Childhood maltreatment and eating disorder pathology: A systematic review and dose-response meta-analysis. *Psychological Medicine.* doi:10.1017/S0033291716003561

Molina, B., Flory, K., Hinshaw, S., Greiner, A. R., Arnold, L. E., Swanson, J. M., et al. (2007). Delinquent behavior and emerging substance use in the MTA at 36 months: Prevalence, course, and treatment effects. *Journal of the American Academy of Child and Adolescent Psychiatry, 46,* 1028–1040.

Möller, H. J., & Von Zerssen, D. (1995). Course and outcome of schizophrenia. In S. R. Hirsch & D. R. Weinberger (Eds.), *Schizophrenia* (pp. 106–127). Oxford, UK: Blackwell Science.

Mond, J. M., Hay, P. J., Rodgers, B., & Owen, C. (2007). Health service utilization for eating disorders: Findings from a community-based study. *International Journal of Eating Disorders, 40,* 399–408.

Money, J. (1984). Paraphilias: Phenomenology and classification. *American Journal of Psychotherapy, 38,* 164–179.

Money, J. (1987). Sin, sickness, or status: Homosexual gender identity and psychoneuroendocrinology. *American Psychologist, 42,* 384–399.

Monroe, S. M., & Harkness, K. L. (2005). Life stress, the "kindling" hypothesis, and the recurrence of depression: Considerations from a life stress perspective. *Psychological Review, 112,* 417–445.

Monroe, S. M., & Simons, A. D. (1991). Diathesis-stress theories in the context of life stress research: Implications for the depressive disorders. *Psychological Bulletin, 110,* 406–425.

Monroe, S. M., Kupfer, D. J., & Frank, E. (1992). Life stress and treatment course of recurrent depression. I. Response during index episode. *Journal of Consulting and Clinical Psychology, 60,* 718–724.

Monson, C. M., & Fredman, S. J. (2012). *Cognitive-behavioral conjoint therapy for posttraumatic stress disorder: Harnessing the healing power of relationships.* New York, NY: Guilford.

Moos, R. H. (2003). Social contexts: Transcending their power and their fragility. *American Journal of Community Psychology, 31*(1–2), 1–13.

Moosavi, J. (2009). The place of Avicenna in the history of medicine. *Avicenna Journal of Medical Biotechnology, 1,* 3–8.

Moran, M. G., Thompson, T. L., & Nies, A. S. (1988). Sleep disorders in the elderly. *American Journal of Psychiatry, 145,* 1369–1377.

Morel, C., Fattore, L., Pons, S., Hay, Y. A., Marti, F., Lambolez, B., . . . & Faure, P. (2014). Nicotine consumption is regulated by a human polymorphism in dopamine neurons. *Molecular psychiatry, 19*(8), 930–936.

Moreno, C., Laje, G., Blanco, C., Jiang, H., Schmidt, A. B., & Olfson, M. (2007). National trends in the outpatient diagnosis and treatment of bipolar disorder in youth. *Archives of General Psychiatry, 64,* 1032–1039.

Morey, L. C. (1988). Personality disorders in DSM-III and DSM-III-R: Convergence, coverage, and internal consistency. *American Journal of Psychiatry, 145,* 573–577.

Morey, L. C. (2007). *Personality assessment inventory professional manual* (2nd ed.). Lutz, FL: Psychological Assessment Resources.

Morgan, A. H. (1973). The heritability of hypnotic susceptibility in twins. *Journal of Abnormal Psychology, 82,* 55–61.

Morin, C. M., & Espie, C. A. (Eds.). (2012). *Oxford handbook of sleep and sleep disorders.* New York, NY: Oxford University Press.

Morin, C. M., Beaulieu-Bonneau, S., Bélanger, L., Ivers, H., Sánchez Ortuño, M., Vallières, A., . . . Mérette, C. (2016). Cognitive-behavior therapy singly and combined with medication for persistent insomnia: Impact on psychological and daytime functioning. *Behaviour Research and Therapy, 87,* 109–116. doi:http://dx.doi.org.uml.idm.oclc.org/10.1016/j.brat.2016.09.002

Morin, C., Bootzin, R., Buysse, D., Edinger, J., Espie, C., & Lichstein, K. (2006). Psychological and behavioral treatment of insomnia: Update of the recent evidence (1998–2004). *Sleep, 29*(11), 1390–1414.

Morina, N., Ijntema, H., Meyerbröker, K., & Emmelkamp, P. M. (2015). Can virtual reality exposure therapy gains be generalized to real-life? A meta-analysis of studies applying behavioral assessments. *Behaviour Research and Therapy, 74,* 18–24.

Morioka, T., Hashiguchi, K., Nagata, S., Miyagi, Y., Yoshida, F., Shono, T., . . . Sasaki, T. (2007). Additional hippocampectomy in the surgical management of intractable temporal lobe epilepsy associated with glioneuronal tumor. *Neurological Research, 29*(8), 807–815. https://doi.org/10.1179/016164107X223566

Morison, S. J., & Ellwood, A. L. (2000). Resiliency in the aftermath of deprivation: A second look at the development of Romanian orphanage children. *Merrill-Palmer Quarterly, 46*(4), 717–737.

Moritz, S., Pfuhl, G., Lüdtke, T., Menon, M., Balzan, R. P., & Andreou, C. (2017). A two-stage cognitive theory of the positive symptoms of psychosis. Highlighting the role of lowered decision thresholds. *Journal of Behavior Therapy and Experimental Psychiatry*, 56, 12–20.

Morris, B. H., & Rottenberg, J. (2015). Heightened reward learning under stress in generalized anxiety disorder: A predictor of depression resistance? *Journal of Abnormal Psychology*, 124, 115–127.

Morse, S. J. (2002). Uncontrollable urges and irrational people. *Virginia Law Review*, 88, 1025–1078.

Morse, S. J. (2004). Preventive confinement of dangerous offenders. *Journal of Law, Medicine, and Ethics*, 32, 56–72.

Mosher, L. R., & Keith, S. J. (1980). Psychosocial treatment: Individual, group, family, and community support approaches. *Schizophrenia Bulletin*, 6, 10–41.

Moss, H. B., Goldstein, R. B., Chen, C. M., & Yi, H. Y. (2015). Patterns of use of other drugs among those with alcohol dependence: Associations with drinking behavior and psychopathology. *Addictive behaviors*, 50, 192–198.

Moulden, H. M., Firestone, P., Kingston, D. A., & Bradford, J. M. (2009). Recidivism in pedophiles: An investigation using different different diagnostic methods. *Journal of Forensic Psychiatry & Psychology*, 20, 680–701.

Moullec, G., Labrecque, M., Beauchesne, M. F., & Pepin, V. (2014). Efficacy of brief motivational interviewing to improve adherence to inhaled corticosteroids among adult asthmatics: results from a randomized controlled pilot feasibility trial. *Patient Preference and Adherence*, 8, 1555–1569.

Mowrer, O. H. (1947). On the dual nature of learning—A reinterpretation of "conditioning" and "problem-solving." *Harvard Educational Review*, 17, 102–148.

Mudford, O. C., Cross, B. A., Breen, S., Cullen, C., Reeves, D., Gould, J., & Douglas, J. (2000). Auditory integration training for children with autism: No behavioral benefits detected. *American Journal on Mental Retardation*, 105, 118–129.

Muehlenkamp, J. J., Claes, L., Quigley, K., Prosser, E., Claes, S., & Jans, D. (2013). Association of training on attitudes towards self-injuring clients across health professionals. *Archives of Suicide Research*, 17(4), 462–468.

Mueser, K. T., & McGurk, S. R. (2004). Schizophrenia. *The Lancet*, 363, 2063–2072.

Mueser, K. T., Deavers, F., Penn, D. L., & Cassisi, J. E. (2013). Psychosocial treatments for schizophrenia. *Annual Review of Clinical Psychology*, 9, 465–497.

Müijen, M., & Hadley, T. R. (1995). Community care: Parts and systems. In S. R. Hirsch & D. R. Weinberger (Eds.), *Schizophrenia* (pp. 649–663). Oxford, UK: Blackwell Science.

Mulhall, J. P., Luo, X., Zou, K. H., Stecher, V., & Galaznik, A. (2016). Relationship between age and erectile dysfunction diagnosis or treatment using real-world observational data in the USA. *International Journal of Clinical Practice*, 70, 1012–1018.

Mulkens, S. A. N., de Jong, P. J., & Merckelbach, H. (1996). Disgust and spider phobia. *Journal of Abnormal Psychology*, 105, 464–468.

Mundy, P., Sigman, M., & Kasari, C. (1990). Joint attention, developmental level and symptom presentation in autism. *Development and Psychopathology*, 6, 389–401.

Munoz, L. C., & Frick, P. J. (2007). The reliability, stability, and predictive utility of the self-report version of the Antisocial Process Screening Device. *Scandinavian Journal of Psychology*, 48, 292–312.

Munro, J. D. (1986). Epidemiology and the extent of mental retardation. *Psychiatric Perspectives on Mental Retardation*, 9, 591–624.

Munroe, S. (2002). Medical marijuana regulations issued. Retrieved from www.canadaonline.about.com/library/weekly/aa070601a.htm

Murdoch, D. D., Gregory, A., & Eggleton, J. M. (2015). Why psychology? an investigation of the training in psychological literacy in nursing, medicine, social work, counselling psychology, and clinical psychology. *Canadian Psychology*, 56, 136–146.

Murphy, D. (2005). Can evolution explain insanity? *Biology and Philosophy*, 20, 745–766.

Murphy, G. H. (2003). Capacity to consent to sexual relationships in adults with learning disabilities. *Journal of Family Planning and Reproductive Health Care*, 29(3), 148–149.

Murray, C. J. L., & Lopez, A. D. (1996). *The global burden of disease*. Geneva, Switzerland: World Health Organization, Harvard School of Public Health, & World Bank.

Murray, J. L., & Minnes, P. M. (1994a). Staff attitudes towards the sexuality of persons with intellectual disability. *Australia and New Zealand Journal of Developmental Disabilities*, 19, 45–52.

Murray, J. L., & Minnes, P. M. (1994b). Persons with developmental disabilities who have AIDS: What are the attitudes of those employed in the field? *Journal of Developmental Disabilities*, 3, 734–784.

Murray, M. E. (1979). Minimal brain dysfunction and borderline personality adjustment. *American Journal of Psychotherapy*, 33, 391–403.

Murrie, D. C., & Cornell, D. G. (2000). The Millon Adolescent Clinical Inventory and psychopathy. *Journal of Personality Assessment*, 75, 110–125.

Murrough, J. W., Soleimani, L., DeWilde, K. E., Collins, K. A., Lapidus, K. A., Iacoviello, B. M., . . . Charney, D. S. (2015). Ketamine for rapid reduction of suicidal ideation: A randomized controlled trial. *Psychological Medicine*, 45, 3571–3580.

Musto, D. F. (1992). Cocaine's history, especially the American experience. In *Cocaine: Scientific and social dimensions*. Chichester, UK: Wiley.

Musty, R. E., & Kabak, L. (1995). Relationships between motivation and depression in chronic marijuana users. *Life Sciences*, 56, 2151–2155.

Myrtek, M. (2007). Type A behavior and hostility as independent risk factors for coronary heart disease. In J. Jordan, B. Bardé, & A. M. Zeiher (Eds.), *Contributions toward evidence-based psychocardiology: A systematic review of the literature* (pp. 159–183). Washington, DC: American Psychological Association.

Nachshen, J. S., & Minnes, P. (2005). Empowerment in parents of school-aged children with and without developmental disabilities. *Journal of Intellectual Disability Research*, 49, 889–904.

Nachshen, J., Garcin, N., & Minnes, P. (2005). Problem behaviour in children with intellectual disabilities: Parenting stress, empowerment, and school services. *Mental Health Aspects of Developmental Disabilities*, 8, 105–114.

Nachshen, J., Woodford, L., & Minnes, P. M. (2003). The Family Stress and Coping Interview: Interview for families of children with developmental disabilities: A lifespan perspective on family adjustment. *Journal of Intellectual Disability Research*, 47, 285–290.

Nagel, B., & Leiper, R. (1999). A national survey of psychotherapy with people with learning disabilities. *Clinical Psychology Forum*, 129, 14–18.

Nakdimen, K. A. (1986). A new formulation for borderline personality disorder? *American Journal of Psychiatry*, 143, 1069.

Narash-Eisikovits, O., Dierberger, A., & Westen, D. (2002). A multidimensional meta-analysis of pharmacotherapy for bulimia nervosa: Summarizing the range of outcomes in controlled clinical trials. *Harvard Review of Psychiatry*, 10, 193–211.

Nartin, B. A., Delva, N. J., Graf, P., Gosselin, C., Enns, M. W., Gilron. I., . . .Chan, P. K. (2015). Delivery of electroconvulsive therapy in Canada: A first national survey report on usage, treatment practice, and facilities. *Journal of ECT*, 31, 119–124.

Nasar, S. (1998). *A beautiful mind*. New York, NY: Simon & Shuster.

Nasreddine, Z. S., Phillips, N. A., Bédirian, V., Charbonneau, S., Whitehead, V., Collin, I., . . . Chertkow, H. (2005). The Montreal Cognitive Assessment, MoCA: A brief screening tool for mild cognitive impairment. *Journal of the American Geriatrics Society*, 53(4), 695–699.

Nathan, P. E., & Gorman, J. M. (Eds.). (2015). *A guide to treatments that work* (4th ed.). New York, NY: Oxford University Press.

Nation, M., Crusto, C., Wandersman, A., Kumpfer, K. L., Seybolt, D., Morrissey-Kane, E., & Davino, K. (2003). What works in prevention: Principles of effective prevention programs. *American Psychologist*, 58, 449–456.

National Institute for Health and Clinical Excellence. (2009, October). *Depression: The treatment and management of depression in adults. Clinical guideline 90*. Retrieved from www.nice.org.uk

National Institute for Health and Clinical Excellence. (2011, January). *Generalised anxiety disorder and panic disorder (with or without agoraphobia) in adults. Clinical guideline 113*. Retrieved from www.nice.org.uk

National Institute for Health and Clinical Excellence. (2016a). *Attention deficit hyperactivity disorder: Diagnosis and management*. National Clinical Guideline CG72. Retrieved from http://guidance.nice.org.uk

National Institute for Health and Clinical Excellence. (2016b). *Depression in adults: The treatment and management of depression in adults*. National Clinical Guideline CG90. Retrieved from http://guidance.nice.org.uk

National Institute of Mental Health Psychopharmacology Service Center Collaborative Study Group. (1964). Phenothiazine treatment in acute schizophrenia: Effectiveness. *Archives of General Psychiatry*, 10, 246–261.

National Institute of Mental Health. (2016). Research domain criteria (RDoC). Retrieved from https://www.nimh.nih.gov/research-priorities/rdoc/index.shtml

National Institute on Drug Abuse. (1992). *Alcohol Alert 15: Alcohol and AIDA*. Washington, DC: U.S. Government Printing Office.

Neece, C., & Baker, B. (2008) Predicting maternal parenting stress in middle childhood: the roles of child intellectual status, behaviouir problems and social skills. *Journal of Intellectual Disability Research*, 52, 1114–1128,

Neeleman, J. (1996). Suicide as a crime in the UK: Legal history, international comparisons and present implications. *Acta Psychiatrica Scandinavica*, 94, 252–257.

Nelson, G., & Prilleltensky, I. (2010). *Community psychology: In pursuit of liberation and well-being* (2nd ed.). New York, NY: Palgrave.

Nelson, G., Prilleltensky, I., Laurendeau, M. C., & Powell, B. (1996). The prevention of mental health problems in Canada: A survey of provincial policies, structures, and programs. *Canadian Psychology, 37,* 161–172.

Nelson, H. (1997). *Cognitive behavioural therapy with schizophrenia: A practice manual.* Cheltenham, UK: Stanley Thornes.

Nestadt, G., Romanoski, A. J., Chahal, R., Merchant, A., Folstein, J. F., Gruenberg, E. M., & McHugh, P. R. (1990). An epidemiological study of histrionic personality disorder. *Psychological Medicine, 20,* 413–422.

Neuman, R. J., Lobos, E., Reich, W., Henderson, C. A., Sun, L. W., & Todd, R. D. (2007). Prenatal smoking exposure and dopaminergic genotypes interact to cause a severe ADHD subtype. *Biological Psychiatry, 61,* 1320–1328.

Neumärker, K. (2000). Mortality rates and causes of death. *European Eating Disorders Review, 8,* 181–187.

Neumeister, A., Hu, X., Luckenbaugh, D. A., Schwarz, M., Nugent, A. C., Bonne, O., et al. (2006). Differential effects of 5-HTTLPR genotypes on the behavioral and neural responses to tryptophan depletion in patients with major depression and controls. *Archives of General Psychiatry, 63,* 978–986.

Neve, M., & Turner, T. (2001). A history of child and adolescent psychiatry. In M. Rutter & E. Taylor (Eds.), *Child and adolescent psychiatry* (4th ed., pp. 382–396). New York, NY: Blackwell Scientific.

Newby, J. M., McKinnon, A., Kuyken, W., Gilbody, S., & Dalgleish, T. (2015). Systematic review and meta-analysis of transdiagnostic psychological treatments for anxiety and depressive disorders in adulthood. *Clinical Psychology Review, 40,* 91–110.

Newcomb, M. D. (1994). Predictors of drug use and implications for the workplace. In S. MacDonald & D. Roman (Eds.), *Research advances in alcohol and drug problems: Vol. II. Drug testing in the workplace.* New York, NY: Plenum.

Newth, S., & Rachman, S. (2001). The concealment of obsessions. *Behaviour Research and Therapy, 39,* 457–464.

Nezu, A. M., & Nezu, C. M. (2014). Problem-solving stategies. In Dozois, D. J. A. (Vol. Ed.), S. G. Hofmann (Series Ed.), CBT: General strategies. *The Wiley handbook of cognitive-behavioral therapy* (Vol I, pp. 67–84). Oxford, UK: Wiley-Blackwell.

Nezu, A. M., Ronan, G. F., Meadows, E. A., & McClure, K. S. (2000). *Practitioner's guide to empirically based measures of depression.* New York, NY: Kluwer Academic/Plenum.

Nicholai, F. (1784). *Beschreibung einer reise durch Deutschland und die Schweitz im jahre 1781. Nebst Bemerkungen über Gelehrsamkeit, Industrie, Religion und Sitten,* (Vol. 3). Berlin & Stettin, Germany: n.pub.

Nietzel, M. T., Winett, R. A., Macdonald, M. L., & Davidson, W. S. (1977). *Behavioral approaches to community psychology.* New York, NY: Pergamon Press.

Nijenhuis, E. R. S., & den Boer, J. A. (2009). Psychobiology of traumatization and trauma-related structural dissociation of the personality. In P. F. Dell & J. A. O'Neil (Eds.), *Dissociation and the dissociative disorders: DSM-V and beyond* (pp. 337–365). New York, NY: Routledge.

Nijmeijer, J. S., Minderaa, R. B., Buitelaar, J. K., Mulligan, A., Hartman, C. A., & Hoekstra, P. J. (2008). Attention-deficit/hyperactivity disorder and social dysfunctioning. *Clinical Psychology Review, 28,* 692–708. doi:10.1016/j.cpr.2007.10.003

Nirje, B. (1969). The normalization principle and its human management implications. In R. Kugel & W. Wolfensberger (Eds.), *Changing patterns in residential services for the mentally retarded.* Washington, DC: Government Printing Office.

Niznikiewicz, M. A., Kubicki, M., & Shenton, M. E. (2003). Recent structural and functional imaging findings in schizophrenia. *Current Opinion in Psychiatry, 16,* 123–147.

Nock, M. K., Kazdin, A. E., Hiripi, E., & Kessler, R. C. (2007). Lifetime prevalence, correlates, and persistence of oppositional defiant disorder: Results from the National Comorbidity Survey Replication. *Journal of Child Psychology and Psychiatry, 48* (7), 703–713. doi:10.1111/j.1469-7610.2007.01733.x

Noland, J. S., Singer, L. T., Arendt, R. E., Minnes, S., Short, E. J., & Bearer, C. F. (2003). Executive functioning in preschool-age children prenatally exposed to alcohol, cocain and marijuana. *Alcoholism: Clinical and Experimental Research, 27,* 647–656.

Nolen-Hoeksema, S., Wisco, B. E., Lyubomirsky, S. (2008). Rethinking rumination. *Perspectives in Psychological Sciencce, 3,* 400–424.

Norasakkunkit, V., & Kalick, S. M. (2009). Experimentally detecting how cultural differences on social anxiety measures misrepresent cultural differences in emotional well-being. *Journal of Happiness Studies, 10,* 313–327.

Norberg, M. M., Diefenbach, G. J., & Tolin, D. F. (2008). Quality of life and anxiety and depressive disorder comorbidity. *Journal of Anxiety Disorders, 22,* 1516–1522.

Norcross, J. C. (Ed.). (2002). *Psychotherapy relationships that work.* New York, NY: Oxford University Press.

Norcross, J. C. (Ed.). (2011). *Psychotherapy relationships that work* (2nd ed.). New York, NY: Oxford University Press.

Norcross, J. C., Karpiak, C. P., & Santoro, S. O. (2005). Clinical psychologists across the years: The Division of Clinical Psychology from 1960–2003. *Journal of Clinical Psychology, 61,* 1467–1483.

Nordhus, I. H., & Pallesen, S. (2003). Psychological treatment of late-life anxiety: An empirical review. *Journal of Consulting and Clinical Psychology, 71,* 643–651.

Norlin, D., & Broberg, M. 2013) Couple relationship and individual well-being. *Journal of Intellectual Disability Research. 57,* 552–566

Norquist, G. S., & Narrow, W. E. (2000). Schizophrenia: Epidemiology. In B. J. Sadock & V. A. Sadock (Eds.), *Kaplan and Sadock's comprehensive textbook of psychiatry* (7th ed., Vol. 1, pp. 1110–1117). Philadelphia, PA: Lippincott Williams & Wilkins.

Norton, A. R., & Abbott, M. J. (2016). Self-focused cognition in social anxiety: A review of the theoretical and empirical literature. *Behaviour Change, 33*(1), 44–64. doi: 10.1017/bec.2016.2

Not Criminally Responsible Reform Act, S.C. 2014, c. 6

Nowakowski, M. E., Rogojanski, J., & Antony, M. M. (2014). Specific phobia. In J. A. J. Smits (Vol. Ed.), Specific Disorders, S. G. Hofmann (Series Ed.), *The Wiley handbook of cognitive-behavioral therapy* (Vol 3, pp. 979–999). Oxford, UK: Wiley-Blackwell.

Noyes, R., Jr., Langbehn, D. R., Happel, R. L., Stout, L. R., Muller, B. A., & Longley, S. L. (2001). Personality dysfunction among somatizing patients. *Psychosomatics, 42,* 320–309.

Nuechterlein, K. H., Green, M. F., Calkins, M. E., Greenwood, T. A., Gur, R. E., Gur, R. C., . . . & Siever, L. J. (2015). Attention/vigilance in schizophrenia: Performance results from a large multi-site study of the Consortium on the Genetics of Schizophrenia (COGS). *Schizophrenia Research, 163*(1), 38–46.

Nulman, I., Ickeowicz, I., Koren, G., & Knittel-Keren, D. (2007). Fetal alcohol spectrum disorder. In I. Brown & M. Percy (Eds.), *A comprehensive guide to intellectual and developmental disabilities* (pp. 213–228). London, UK: Paul Brookes.

Nunes, K. L., Hanson, R. K., Firestone, P., Moulden, H. M., Greenberg, D. M., & Bradford, J. M. (2007). Denial predicts recidivism for some sexual offenders. *Sexual Abuse: A Journal of Research and Treatment, 19*(2), 91–105.

Nurmi, M. A., Mackenzie, C. S., Roger, K., Reynolds, K., & Urquhart, J. (2016). Older men's perceptions of the need for and access to male-focused community programs such as Men's Sheds. Published online via First View in *Ageing & Society.* doi: 10.1017/S0144686X16001331.

Nussbaum, N. L., & Bunner, M. R. (2009). Halstead-Reitan neuropsychological test batteries for children. In C. R. Reynolds & E. Fletcher-Janzen (Eds.), *Handbook of clinical child neuropsychology: Critical issues in neuropsychology* (3rd ed., pp. 247–266). New York, NY: Springer.

O'Connell, M. E., Boat, T., & Warner, K. E. (Eds.). (2009). *Preventing mental, emotional, and behavioural disorders among young people: Progress and possibilities.* Washington, DC: National Academies Press.

O'Connor, R. C. (2011). The integrated motivational-volitional model of suicidal behavior. *Crisis, 32,* 295–298.

O'Donohue, W., Regev, L. G., & Hagstrom, A. (2000). Problems with the DSM-IV diagnosis of pedophilia. *Sexual Abuse: A Journal of Research and Treatment, 12,* 95–105.

O'Donovan, M. C., & Owen, M. J. (1992). Advances and retreats in the molecular genetics of major mental illness. *Annals of Medicine, 24,* 171–177.

O'Donovan, M. C., & Owen, M. J. (1996). The molecular genetics of schizophrenia. *Annals of Medicine, 28,* 541–546.

O'Hara, M. W. (1995). Postpartum depression. In L. B. Alloy (Ed.), *Series in psychopathology* (pp. 1–27). New York, NY: Springer-Verlag.

O'Hara, M. W., Neunaber, D. J., & Zekoski, E. M. (1984). A prospective study of postpartum depression: Prevalence, course, and predictive factors. *Journal of Abnormal Psychology, 91,* 158–171.

O'Neill, J., & Fischer, D. (2005, June 11). Fighting for the right to refuse treatment. *The Ottawa Citizen,* p. E1.

O'Nise, K., Lynch, J. W., Sawyer, M. G., & McDermott, R. A. (2010). Can preschool improve child health outcomes? A systematic review. *Social Science & Medicine, 70,* 1423–1440.

O'Reardon, J. P., Solvason, H. B., Janicak, P. G., Sampson, S., Isenberg, K. E., Nahas, Z., et al. (2007). Efficacy and safety of transcranial magnetic stimulation in the acute treatment of major depression: A multisite randomized controlled trial. *Biological Psychiatry, 62,* 1208–1216.

Oakley, A. (2015). *Sex, gender and society.* New York, NY: Routledge.

Oberle, I., Rousseau, F., Heitz, D., Kretz, C., Devys, D., Hanauer, A., et al. (1991). Instability of a 550-base pair DNA segment and abnormal methylation in Fragile X syndrome. *Science, 252,* 1097–1102.

Odom, S. L., Teferra, T., & Kaul, S. S. (2004). An overview of international approaches to early intervention for young children with special needs and their families. *Young Children, 59,* 38–43.

Oertel-Knöchel, V., Bittner, R. A., Knöchel, C., Prvulovic, D., & Hampel, H. (2011). Discovery and development of integrative biological markers for schizophrenia. *Progress in Neurobiology.* Advance online publication. www.elsevier.com/wps/find/journaldescription.cws_home/412/description#description

Offord, D. R., & Bennett, K. J. (1994). Conduct disorder: Long-term outcomes and intervention effectiveness. *Journal of the American Academy of Child and Adolescent Psychiatry, 33,* 1069–1078.

Offord, D. R., Alder, R. J., & Boyle, M. H. (1986). Prevalence and sociodemographic correlates of conduct disorder. *American Journal of Social Psychiatry, 6,* 272–278.

Offord, D. R., Boyle, M. H., Campbell, D., Cochrane, J., Goering, P., Lin, E., et al. (1994). *Mental health in Ontario: Selected findings from the Mental Health Supplement to the Ontario Health Survey.* Toronto, ON: Ontario Ministry of Health.

Offord, D. R., Boyle, M. H., & Racine, Y. (1989). Ontario child health study: Correlates of disorder. *Journal of the American Academy of Child & Adolescent Psychiatry, 28(6),* 856–860.

Offord, D. R., Boyle, M. H., Racine, Y. A., Fleming, J. E., Cadman, D. T., Blum, H. M., et al. (1992). Outcome, prognosis, and risk in a longitudinal follow-up study. *Journal of the American Academy of Child and Adolescent Psychiatry, 31,* 916–923.

Offord, D. R., Boyle, M. H., Racine, Y., Szatmari, P., Fleming, J. E., Sanford, M., & Lipman, E. L. (1996). Integrating assessment data from multiple informants. *Journal of the Academy of Child and Adolescent Psychiatry, 35,* 1078–1085.

Offord, D. R., Boyle, M. H., Szatmari, P., Rae-Grant, N. I., Links, P. S., Cadman, D. T., et al. (1987). Ontario Child Health Study: II. Six-month prevalence of disorder and rates of service utilization. *Archives of General Psychiatry, 44,* 832–836.

Ohayon, M. M., & Schatzberg, A. F. (2010). Social phobia and depression: Prevalence and comorbidity. *Journal of Psychosomatic Research, 68,* 235–243.

Okwumabua, T. M., Okwumabua, J., Peasant, C., Watson, A., & Walker, K. (2014). Promoting health and wellness in African American males through rites of passage training. *Journal of Human Behavior in the Social Environment, 24(6),* 702–712.

Olatunji, B. O., Deacon, B. J., & Abramowitz, J. S. (2009). Is hypochondriasis an anxiety disorder? *British Journal of Psychiatry, 194(6),* 481–482.

Olatunji, B. O., Kauffman, B. Y., Meltzer, S., Davis, M. L., Smits, J. A., & Powers, M. B. (2014). Cognitive-behavioral therapy for hypochondriasis/health anxiety: A meta-analysis of treatment outcome and moderators. *Behaviour Research and Therapy, 58,* 65–74.

Olds, D. L. (1988). The Prenatal/Early Infancy Project. In R. H. Price, E. L. Cowen, R. P. Lorion, & J. Ramos-McKay (Eds.), *Fourteen ounces of prevention: A casebook for practitioners* (pp. 9–23). Washington, DC: American Psychological Association.

Olds, D. L. (1997). The Prenatal Early Infancy Project: Preventing child abuse and neglect in the context of promoting maternal and child health. In D. A. Wolfe, R. J. McMahon, & R. DeV. Peters (Eds.), *Child abuse: New directions in prevention and treatment across the lifespan.* Thousand Oaks, CA: Sage.

Olds, D. L., Eckenrode, J., Henderson, C. R., Kitzman, H., Powers, J., Cole, R., et al. (1997). Long-term effects of home visitation on maternal life course and child abuse and neglect: Fifteen-year follow-up of a randomized trial. *Journal of the American Medical Association, 278,* 637–643.

Olds, D. L., Henderson, C., Cole, R., Eckenrode, J., Kitzman, H., Luckey, D., et al. (1998). Long-term effects of nurse home visitation on children's criminal and antisocial behavior. *Journal of the American Medical Association, 260,* 1238–1244.

Olds, D. L., Kitzman, H., Cole, R., Robinson, J., Sidora, K., Luckey, D. W., et al. (2004). Effects of nurse home-visiting on maternal life course and child development: Age 6 follow-up results of a randomized trial. *Pediatrics, 114,* 1550–1559.

Olds, D. L., Kitzman, H., Hanks, C., Cole, R., Anson, E., Sidora-Arcoleo, K., et al. (2007). Effects of nurse home visiting on maternal and child functioning: Age 9 follow-up of a randomized trial. *Pediatrics, 120,* 832–845.

Olds, D. L., Robinson, J., O'Brien, R., Lucky, D. W., Pettitt, L. M., Henderson, C. R., et al. (2002). Home visiting by paraprofessionals and nurses: A randomized, controlled trial. *Pediatrics, 110,* 486–496.

Olds, D. L., Robinson, J., Pettitt, L., Luckey, D. W., Holmberg, J., Ng, R. K., et al. (2004). Effects of home visits by paraprofessionals and by nurses: Age 4 follow-up results of a randomized trial. *Pediatrics, 114,* 1560–1568.

Olff, M., Langeland, W., Draijer, N., & Gersons, B. P. R. (2007). Gender differences in posttraumatic stress disorder. *Psychological bulletin, 133,* 183.

Olfson, M., & Marcus, S. C. (2009). National patterns in antidepressant medication treatment. *Archives of General Psychiatry, 66,* 848–856.

Olfson, M., & Marcus, S. C. (2010). National trends in outpatient psychotherapy. *American Journal of Psychiatry, 167,* 1456–1463.

Olfson, M., Marcus, S. C., Tedeschi, M., & Wan, G. J. (2006). Continuity of antidepressant treatment for adults with depression in the United States. *American Journal of Psychiatry, 163,* 101–108.

Olivardia, R., Pope, H. G., Jr., Mangweth, B., & Hudson, J. I. (1995). Eating disorders in college men. *American Journal of Psychiatry, 152,* 1279–1285.

Olmsted, M. P., MacDonald, D. E., McFarlane, T., Trottier, K., & Colton, P. (2015). Predictors of rapid relapse in bulimia nervosa. *International Journal of Eating Disorders, 48,* 337–340. doi: 10.1002/eat.22380

Olmsted, M. P., McFarlane, T., Carter, J. C., Trottier, K., Woodside, D. B., & Dimitropoulos, G. (2010). Inpatient and day hospital treatment for anorexia nervosa. In C. M. Grilo & J. E. Mitchell (Eds.), *The treatment of eating disorders: A clinical handbook* (pp. 198–211). New York, NY: Guilford.

Olmsted, M. P., McFarlane, T., Trottier, K., & Rockert, W. (2013). Efficacy and intensity of day hospital treatment for eating disorders. *Psychotherapy Research, 23,* 277–286. doi: 10.1080/10503307.2012.721937

Olsen, J., Pereira, A., & Olsen, S. F. (1991). Does maternal tobacco smoking modify the effect of alcohol on fetal growth? *American Journal of Public Health, 81,* 69–73.

Olson, R., & Byrne, B. (2005). Genetic and environmental influences on reading and language ability and disability. In H. W. Catts & A. G. Kamhi (Eds.), *The connections between language and reading disabilities* (pp. 173–200). Mahwah, NJ: Erlbaum.

Olsson, M.B. (2008). Understanding individual differences in adaptation in parents of children with intellectual disabilities: a risk and resilience perspective. *International Review of Research in Mental Retardation 36,* 282–315

Olthuis, J. V., Watt, M. C., Bailey, K., Hayden, J. A., & Stewart, S. H. (2015). Therapist-supported internet cognitive behavioural therapy for anxiety disorders in adults. *Cochrane Database of Systematic Reviews,* Article. No.: CD011565. DOI: 10.1002/14651858.CD011565.

Olzernov-Palchik, O., Xi, Y., Wang, Y., & Gaab, N. (2016). Lessons to be learned: how a comprehensive neurobiological framework of atypical reading development can inform educational practice. *Current Opinion in Behavioral Sciences, 10,* 45–58

Ones, D. S., Dilchert, S., & Viswesvaran, C. (2012). Cognitive ability. In N. Schmitt (Ed.), *Oxford handbook of ability and personnel assessment and selection* (pp. 179–224). Oxford, UK: Oxford University Press.

Ori, R., Amos, T., Bergman, H., Soares-Weiser, K., Ipser, J. C., & Stein, D. J. (2015). Augmentation of cognitive and behavioural therapies (CBT) with d-cycloserine for anxiety and related disorders. *Cochrane Database of Systematic Reviews, 5.* doi: 10.1002/14651858.CD007803.pub2.

Ornish D, Scherwitz, L. W., Billings, J. H., Brown, S. E., Gould, K. L., Merritt, T. A., . . . , & Brand, R. J. (1998). Intensive lifestyle changes for reversal of coronary heart disease. *JAMA, 280,* 2001–2007.

Orr, E. M. J., & Moscovitch, D. A. (2015). Blending in at the cost of losing oneself: Dishonest self-disclosure erodes self-concept clarity in social anxiety. *Journal of Experimental Psychopathology, 3,* 278–296.

Orsillo, S. M., Theodore-Oklota, C., Luterek, J. A., & Plumb, J. (2007). The development and psychometric evaluation of the emotional reactivity and numbing scale. *Journal of Nervous & Mental Disease, 195,* 830–836.

Orsmond, G. I., & Seltzer, M. M. (2000). Brothers and sisters of adults with mental retardation: Gendered nature of the sibling relationship. *American Journal on Mental Retardation, 105,* 486–508.

Osler, W. (1910). The Lumleian Lectures in angina pectoris. *The Lancet, 175,* 839–844.

Oswald, D. P., & Sonenklar, N. A. (2007). Medication use among children with autism-spectrum disorders. *Journal of Child and Adolescent Psychopharmacology, 17,* 348–355.

Ottawa Citizen. (2003, October). "The quiet epidemic: A nine-part series."

Ouellette-Kuntz, H., Shooshtari, S., Temple, B., Brownell, M., Burchill, C., Yu, C. T., Holden, J. J. A., & Hennen, B. (2009). Estimating administrative prevalence of intellectual disabilities in Manitoba. *Journal on Developmental Disabilities, 15(3),* 69–80.

Ougrin, D. (2011). Efficacy of exposure versus cognitive therapy in anxiety disorders: Systematic review and meta-analysis. *BMC Psychiatry, 11(1),* 200.

Ouimet, A. J., Covin, R., & Dozois, D. J. A. (2012). Generalized anxiety disorder. In P. Sturmey & M. Hersen (Eds.), *Handbook of evidence-based practice in clinical psychology. Volume II: Adult disorders* (pp. 651–680). New York, NY: Wiley.

Ounce of Prevention Fund (1994). *A head start on Head Start: Effective birth-to-three strategies.* Chicago, IL: Ounce of Prevention Fund.

Ouwehand, C., de Ridder, D. T. D., & Bensing, J. M. (2007). A review of successful aging models: Proposing proactive coping as an important additional strategy. *Clinical Psychology Review, 27*, 873–884.

Overstreet, N. M., Quinn, D. M., & Agocha, V. B. (2010). Beyond thinness: The influence of a curvaceous body ideal on body dissatisfaction in Black and White women. *Sex Roles, 63*, 91–103. doi: 10.1007/s11199-010-9792-4

Owen, J., Adelson, J., Budge, S., Wampold, B., Kopta, M., Minami, T., & Miller, S. (2015). Trajectories of change in psychotherapy. *Journal of Clinical Psychology, 71*, 817–827.

Owens, E. M., Bachman, P., Glahn, D. C., & Bearden, C. E. (2016). Electrophysiological endophenotypes for schizophrenia. *Harvard Review of Psychiatry, 24*(2), 129–147.

Ozonoff, S., Pennington, B. F., & Rogers, S. (1991). Executive function deficits in high-functioning autistic individuals: Relationship to theory of mind. *Journal of Child Psychology and Psychiatry, 32*, 1081–1105.

Pachana, N. A., Emery, E., Konnert, C. A., Woodhead, E., & Edelstein, B. A. (2010). Geropsychology content in clinical training programs: A comparison of Australian, Canadian, and U.S. data. *International Psychogeriatrics, 22*(6), 909–918.

Pachana, N., Byrne, G., Siddle, H., Koloski, N., Harley, E., & Arnold, E. (2007). Development and validation of the Geriatric Anxiety Inventory. *International Psychogeriatrics, 19*, 103–114. doi: 10.1017/S1041610206003504.

Padilla, C., & Isaacson, R. S. (2011). Genetics of dementia. *CONTINUUM Lifelong Learning in Neurology, 17*(2), 326–342.

Paglia-Boak, A., Adlaf, E. M., & Mann, R. E. (2011). *Drug use among Ontario students, 1977–2011: Detailed OSDUHS findings.* CAMH Research Document Series No. 32. Toronto, ON: Centre for Addiction and Mental Health.

Paglia-Boak, A., Mann, R. E., Adlaf, E. M., & Rehm, J. (2009). *Drug use among Ontario students, 1977–2009: Detailed OSDUHS findings* (CAMH Research Document Series No. 27). Toronto, ON: Centre for Addiction and Mental Health.

Paíno-Piñeiro, M., Fonseca-Pedrero, E., Lemos-Giráldez, S., & Muñiz, J. (2008). Dimensionality of schizotypy in young people according to sex and age. *Personality and Individual Differences, 45*, 132–138. doi:10.1016/j.paid.2008.03.011

Palacios, S., Menendez, C., Jurado, A. R., Castano, R., & Vargas, J. C. (1995). Changes in sex behaviour after menopause: Effects of tibolone. *Maturitas, 22*(2), 155–161.

Palmer, B. A., Pankratz, V. S., & Bostwick, J. M. (2005). The lifetime risk of suicide in schizophrenia: A reexamination. *Archives of General Psychiatry, 62*, 247–253.

Palombo, J. (2006). *Nonverbal learning disabilities: A clinical perspective.* New York: W. W. Norton.

Panayiotou, G., & Karekla, M. (2013). Perceived social support helps, but does not buffer the negative impact of anxiety disorders on quality of life and perceived stress. *Social Psychiatry and Psychiatric Epidemiology, 48*, 283–294.

Panicker, A. S., & Chelliah, A. (2016). Resilience and stress in children and adolescents with specific learning disability. *Journal of the Canadian Academy of Child and Adolescent Psychiatry, 25*(1), 17–23.

Panksepp, J. (1998). The sources of fear and anxiety in the brain. In J. Panksepp, *Affective neuroscience: The foundations of human and animal emotions* (pp. 206–224). New York, NY: Oxford University Press.

Pantony, K., & Caplan, P. J. (1991). Delusional dominating personality disorder: A modest proposal for identifying some consequences of rigid masculine socialization. *Canadian Psychology, 32*, 120–135.

Paradies, Y., Ben, J., Denson, N., Elias, A., Priest, N., Pieterse, A., . . . & Gee, G. (2015). Racism as a determinant of health: A systematic review and meta-analysis. *PloS One, 10*(9), e0138511.

Paris, J. (1996). A critical review or recovered memories in psychotherapy. Part I. Trauma and memory. *Canadian Journal of Psychiatry, 41*, 201–205.

Paris, J. (2009). The treatment of borderline personality disorder: Implications of research on diagnosis, etiology, and outcome. *Annual Review of Clinical Psychology, 5*, 277–290. doi:10.1146/annurev.clinpsy.032408.153457

Paris, J. (2012). The rise and fall of dissociative identity disorder. *Journal of Nervous and Mental Disease, 200*(12), 1076–1079.

Paris, J., & Frank, H. (1989). Perceptions of parental bonding in borderline patients. *American Journal of Psychiatry, 146*, 1498–1499.

Park, D. C., & Radford, J. P. (1998). From the case files: Reconstructing a history of involuntary sterilisation. *Disability and Society, 13*, 317–342.

Park, J. H., & Kim, K. W. (2011). A review of the epidemiology of depression in Korea. *Journal of the Korean Medical Association / Taehan Uisa Hyophoe Chi, 54*, 362–369.

Parker, G. (2014). Is borderline personality disorder a mood disorder? *British Journal of Psychiatry, 204*(4), 252–253

Parson, T. D., & Rizzo, A. A. (2008). Affective outcomes of virtual reality exposure therapy for anxiety and specific phobias: A meta-analysis. *Journal of Behavior Therapy and Experimental Psychiatry, 39*, 250–261.

Partridge, G. E. (1928). Psychopathic personalities among boys in a training school for delinquents. *American Journal of Psychiatry, 8*, 159–186.

Partridge, G. E. (1929). Psychopathic personality and personality investigation. *American Journal of Psychiatry, 8*, 1053–1055.

Partridge, G. E. (1930). Current conceptions of psychopathic personality. *American Journal of Psychiatry, 10*, 53–99.

Paschall, K. W., & Mastergeorge, A. M. (2016). A review of 25 years of research in bidirectionality in parent–child relationships: An examination of methodological approaches. *International Journal of Behavioral Development, 40*(5), 442–451.

Paterson, L. Q. P., Shuo Jin, E., Amsel, R., & Binik, Y. M. (2014). Gender similarities and differences in sexual arousal, desire and orgasmic pleasure in the laboratory. *Journal of Sex Research, 51*, 801–813.

Patrick, M., Hobson, R. P., Castle, D., & Howard, R. (1994). Personality disorder and the mental representation of early social experiences. *Development and Psychopathology, 6*, 375–388.

Patten, S. B., Williams, J. V. A., Lavorato, D. H., Wang, J. L., McDonald, K., & Bulloch, A. G. M. (2015). Descriptive epidemiology of major depressive disorder in Canada in 2012. *The Canadian Journal of Psychiatry, 60*(1), 23–30.

Patterson, C., Feightner, J., Garcia, A., & MacKnight, C. (2007). General risk factors for dementia: A systematic evidence review. *Alzheimer's & Dementia, 3*, 341–347.

Patterson, G. (1986). Performance models for antisocial boys. *American Psychologist, 44*, 432–444.

Patterson, G. R. (1982). *Coercive family process.* Eugene, OR: Castalia.

Pattison, E. M., Sobell, M. B., & Sobell, L. C. (1977). *Emerging concepts of alcohol dependence.* New York, NY: Springer.

Patton, J. R., Payne, J. S., & Beirne-Smith, M. (1986). *Mental retardation* (2nd ed.). Toronto, ON: Merrill.

Paulhus, D. L., & Williams, K. M. (2002). The Dark Triad of personality: Narcissism, Machiavellianism and psychopathy. *Journal of Research in Personality, 36*, 556–563. doi:10.1016/S0092-6566(02)00505-6

Paulsen, J. S., Heaton, R. K., Sadek, J. R., Perry, W., Delis, D. C., Braff, D., et al. (1995). The nature of learning and memory impairments in schizophrenia. *Journal of the International Neuropsychological Society, 1*, 88–99.

Payne, L. A., Ellard, K. K., Farchione, T. J., Fairholme, C. P., & Barlow, D. H. (2014). Emotional disorders: A unified transdiagnostic protocol. In D. H. Barlow (Ed.), *Clinical handbook of psychological disorders: A step-by-step treatment manual* (pp. 237–274). New York, NY: Guilford.

Peachey, D., Hicks, V., & Adams, O. (2013). *An imperative for change: Access to psychological services for Canada.* Unpublished manuscript. Ottawa, ON: Canadian Psychological Association.

Pearlson, G. D., Kreger, L., Rabins, P. V., Chase, G. A., Cohen, B., Wirth, J. B., et al. (1989). A chart review study of late-onset and early-onset schizophrenia. *American Journal of Psychiatry, 146*, 1568–1574.

Pearson, C., Janz, T., & Ali, J. (2013). *Mental and substance use disorders in Canada.* Ottawa, Ontario: Statistics Canada, Catalogue no. 82-624-X.

Peat, C., Mitchell, J. E., Hoek, H. W., & Wonderlich, S. A. (2009). Validity and utility of subtyping anorexia nervosa. *International Journal of Eating Disorders, 42*, 590–594. doi: 10.1002/eat.20717

Pedersen, W., & Mastekaasa, A. (2011). Conduct disorder symptoms and subsequent pregnancy, child-birth and abortion: A population-based longitudinal study of adolescents. *Journal of Adolescence, 34*, 1025–1033.

Peindl, K. S., Zolnik, E. J., Wisner, K. L., & Hanusa, B. H. (1995). Effects of postpartum psychiatric illnesses on family planning. *International Journal of Psychiatry Medicine, 25*, 291–300.

Peirson, L., & Prilleltensky, I. (1994). Understanding school change to facilitate prevention: A study of change in a secondary school. *Canadian Journal of Community Mental Health, 13*(2), 127–144.

Pelham, W. E., & Fabiano, G. A. (2008). Evidence-based psychosocial treatments for attention-deficit/hyperactivity disorder. *Journal of Clinical Child and Adolescent Psychology, 37*, 184–214. doi:10.1080/15374410701818681

Pendery, M. L., Maltzman, I. M., & West, L. J. (1982). Controlled drinking by alcoholics? New findings and reevaluation of a major affirmative study. *Science, 217*, 169–174.

Peng P & Fuchs, D. (2014). A meta-analysis of working memory deficits in children with learning difficulties: Is there a difference between verbal domain and numerical domain? *Journal of Learning Disabilities, 49*, 3–20.

Penn, D. L., Sanna, L. J., & Roberts, D. L., (2008). Social cognition in schizophrenia: An overview. *Schizophrenia Bulletin, 34*, 408–411.

Penner-Goeke, K., Henriksen, C. A., Chateau, D., Latimer, E., Sareen, J., & Katz, L. Y. (2015). Reductions in quality of life associated with common mental disorders: Results from a nationally representative sample. *The Journal of Clinical Psychiatry, 76*, 1506–1512.

Penner, J., Ford, K. A., Taylor, R., Schaefer, B., Théberge, J., Neufeld, R. W. J., . . . Williamson, P. C. (2016). Medial prefrontal and anterior insular connectivity in early schizophrenia and major depressive disorder: A resting functional MRI evaluation of large-scale brain network models. *Frontiers in Human Neuroscience, 10*, 132. https://doi.org/10.3389/fnhum.2016.00132

Percy, M., Lewkis, S. Z., & Brown, I. (2007). Introduction to genetics and development. In I. Brown & M. Percy (Eds.), *A comprehensive guide to intellectual and developmental disabilities* (pp. 87–108). London, UK: Paul Brookes.

Percy, M., Lewkis, S., & Brown, I. (2003). An introduction to genetics and development. In I. Brown & M. Percy (Eds.), *Developmental disabilities in Ontario* (2nd ed., pp. 89–116). Toronto, ON: Association on Developmental Disabilities.

Perera, S., Eisen, R., Bhatt, M., Bhatnagar, N., de Souza, R., Thabane, L., & Samaan, Z. (2016). Light therapy for non-seasonal depression: Systematic review and meta-analysis. *British Journal of Psychiatry Open, 2*, 116–126.

Pergamin-Hight, L., Naim, R., Bakermans-Kranenburg, M. J., van IJzendoorn, M. H., & Bar-Haim, Y. (2015). Content specificity of attention bias to threat in anxiety disorders: A meta-analysis. *Clinical Psychology Review, 35*, 10–18.

Perna, G., Alciati, A., Riva, A., Micieli, W., & Caldirola, D. (2016). Long-term pharmacological treatments of anxiety disorders: An updated systematic review. *Current Psychiatry Reports, 18*(3), 23.

Perry, A. (1991). Rett syndrome: A comprehensive review of the literature. *American Journal on Mental Retardation, 96*, 275–290.

Perry, A., Bryson, S. E., & Bebko, J. M. (1993). Multiple method validation study of facilitated communication: Preliminary group results. *Journal of Developmental Disabilities, 2*, 1–19.

Perry, A., Condillac, R. A., & Freeman, N. L. (2002). Best practices and practical strategies for assessment and diagnosis of autism. *Journal on Developmental Disabilities, 9*, 61–75.

Perry, A., Cummings, A., Dunn Geier, J., Freeman, N., Hughes, S., LaRose, L., . . . & Williams, J. (2008). Effectiveness of Intensive Behavioral Intervention in a large, community-based program. *Research in Autism Spectrum Disorders, 2*, 621–642.

Perry, A., Harris, K., & Minnes, P. (2004). Family environments and family harmony: An exploration across severity, age, and type of developmental disability. *Journal on Developmental Disability, 11*, 15–24.

Perry, J. C., & Klerman, G. L. (1978). The borderline patient: A comparative analysis of four sets of diagnostic criteria. *Archives of General Psychiatry, 35*, 141–150.

Perske, R., & Perske, M. (1973). *New Directions:For parents of persons who are retarded.* Nashville, TN: Abingdon Press.

Pert, L., Ferriter, M., & Saul, C. (2004). Parental loss before the age of 16 years: A comparative study of patients with personality disorder and patients with schizophrenia in a high secure hospital's population. *Psychology and Psychotherapy: Theory, Research, and Practice, 77*, 403–407.

Peters, R. D., Petrunka, K., Khan, S., Howell-Moneta, A., Nelson, G., Pancer, S. M., & Loomis, C. (2016). Cost-savings analysis of the Better Beginnings, Better Futures community-based project for young children and their families: A 10-year follow-up. *Prevention Science, 17*(2), 237–247.

Peters, R. DeV. (1988). Mental health promotion in children and adolescents: An emerging role for psychology. *Canadian Journal of Behavioural Science, 20*, 389–401.

Peters, R. DeV., Bradshaw, A. J., Petrunka, K., Nelson, G., Herry, Y., Craig, W., et al. (2010). The Better Beginnings, Better Futures Project: An ecological, community-based prevention approach—findings from Grade 3 to Grade 9. *Monographs of the Society for Research in Child Development, 75*(3), 1–176.

Peters, R. DeV., Nelson, G., Petrunka, K., Pancer, S. M., Loomis, C., Hasford, J., et al. (2010). *Investing in our future: Highlights of Better Beginnings, Better Futures research findings at grade 12.* Kingston, ON: Better Beginnings, Better Futures Research Coordination Unit, Queen's University.

Peters, R. DeV., Peters, J. E., Laurendeau, M. C., Chamberland, C., & Peirson, L. (2001). Social policies for promoting the well-being of Canadian children and families. In I. Prilleltensky, G. Nelson, & L. Peirson (Eds.), *Promoting family wellness and preventing child maltreatment: Fundamentals for thinking and action.* Toronto, ON: University of Toronto Press.

Petersen, J. L., & Hyde, J. S. (2010). A meta-analytic review of research in gender differences in sexuality, 1993–2007. *Psychological Bulletin, 136*(1), 21–38.

Petersen, R. C., & O'Brien, J. (2006). Mild cognitive impairment should be considered for DSM-V. *Journal of Geriatric Psychiatry and Neurology, 19*, 147–154.

Petersen, R. C., Caracciolo, B., Brayne, C., Gauthier, S., Jelic, V., & Fratiglioni, L. (2014). Mild cognitive impairment: A concept in evolution. *Journal of Internal Medicine, 275*(3), 214–228.

Petersen, R. C., Doody, R., Kurz, A., Mohs, R. C., Morris, J. C., Rabins, P. V., et al. (2001). Current concepts in mild cognitive impairment. *Archives of Neurology, 58*, 1985–1992.

Petersen, T., Papakostas, G. I., Mahal, Y., Guyker, W. M., Beaumont, E. C., Alpert, J. E., Fava, M., & Nierenberg, A. A. (2004). Psychosocial functioning in patients with treatment resistant depression. *European Psychiatry, 19*, 196–201.

Peterson, R. A., & Reiss, S. (1993). *Anxiety Sensitivity Index Revised test manual.* Worthington, OH: IDS Publishing Corporation.

Petronis, A. (2004). The origin of schizophrenia: Genetic thesis, epigenetic antithesis, and resolving synthesis. *Biological Psychiatry, 55*, 965–970.

Petronis, A. (2010). Epigenetics as a unifying principle in the aetiology of complex traits and diseases. *Nature, 465*, 721–727.

Pezawas, L., Meyere-Lindenberg, A., Drabant, E. M., Verchinski, B. A., Munoz, K. E., Kolachana, B. S., et al. (2005). 5-HTTLPR polymorphism impacts human cingulate-amygdala interactions: A genetic susceptibility mechanism for depression. *Nature Neuroscience, 8*, 828–834.

Pfammatter, M., Junghan, U. M., & Brenner, H. D. (2006). Efficacy of psychological therapy in schizophrenia: Conclusions from meta-analyses. *Schizophrenia Bulletin, 32*(Suppl. 1), S64–S80.

Pfohl, B., Coryell, W., Zimmerman, M., & Stangl, D. (1986). DSM-III personality disorders: Diagnostic overlap and internal consistency of individual DSM-III criteria. *Comprehensive Psychiatry, 27*, 21–34.

Pham, A. & Riviere, A. (2015). specific learning disorders and ADHD: Current issues in diagnosis across clinical and educational settings. *Current Psychiatry Reports 2015, 17*, 38.

Phenix, A., Helmus, L., & Hanson, R. K. (2015). Static-99R & Static-2002R evaluators' workbook. Published online www.static99.org/pdfdocs/Static-99RandStatic-2002R_EvaluatorsWorkbook-Jan2015.pdf

Phillips, E. L. (1991). George Washington University's international data on psychotherapy delivery systems: Modeling new approaches to the study of therapy. In L. E. Beutler & M. Crago (Eds.), *Psychotherapy research: An international review of programmatic studies* (pp. 263–273). Washington, DC: American Psychological Association.

Phillips, K. A. (2007). Suicidality in body dysmorphic disorder. *Primary Psychiatry, 14*, 58–66.

Phillips, K. A. (2009). *Understanding body dysmorphic disorder.* Oxford, UK: Oxford University Press.

Phillips, K. A., Pinto, A., Menard, W., Eisen, J. L., Mancebo, M., & Rasmussen, S. A. (2007). Obsessive-compulsive disorder versus body dysmorphic disorder: A comparison study of two possibly related disorders. *Depression and Anxiety, 24*, 399–409.

Piasecki, T. M., Richardson, A. E., & Smith, S. M. (2007). Self-monitored motives for smoking among college students. *Psychology of Addictive Behaviors, 21*, 328–337.

Piccinelli, M., & Wilkinson, G. (2000). Gender differences in depression: Critical review. *British Journal of Psychiatry, 177*, 486–492.

Piek, J., Lidke, G., & Terberger, T. (2011). The neolithic skull from Bölkendorf–Evidence for stone age neurosurgery? *Central European Neurosurgery, 72*, 42–43.

Piet, J., & Hougaard, E. (2011). The effect of mindfulness-based cognitive therapy for prevention of relapse in recurrent major depressive disorder: A systematic review and meta-analysis. *Clinical Psychology Review, 31*, 1032–1040.

Pieterse, A. L., Todd, N. R., Neville, H. A., & Carter, R. T. (2012). Perceived racism and mental health among Black American adults: A meta-analytic review. *Journal of Counseling Psychology, 59*(1), 1–9.

Pihl, R. O., & Peterson, J. B. (1991). Attention-deficit hyperactivity disorders, childhood conduct disorder and alcoholism: Is there an association? *Alcohol Health Research World, 15*, 25–31.

Pillarella, J., Higashi, A., Alexander, G. C., & Conti, R. (2012). Trends in use of second-generation antipsychotics for treatment of bipolar disorder in the United States, 1998–2009. *Psychiatric Services, 63*, 83–86.

Pine, D. S. (2007). Research review: A neuroscience framework for pediatric anxiety disorders. *Journal of Child Psychology and Psychiatry, and Allied Disciplines, 48*(7), 631–648.

Pinel, J. P. J. (1997). *Biopsychology* (3rd ed.). Needham Heights, MA: Allyn and Bacon.

Pinel, P. (1809). *Traite medico-phiosophique sur l'alienation mentale* (2nd ed.). Paris, France: Chez J. Ant. Brosson.

Pinquart, M., Duberstein, P. R., & Lyness, J. M. (2006). Treatments for later-life depressive conditions: A meta-analytic comparison of pharmacotherapy and psychotherapy. *American Journal of Psychiatry, 163,* 1493–1501.

Piotrowski, C. (2016). Bender-Gestalt Test usage worldwide: A review of 30 practice-based studies. *Journal of Projective Psychology and Mental Health, 23,* 73–81.

Piper, A., & Merskey, H. (2004a). The persistence of folly: A critical examination of dissociative identity disorder. Part I. The excesses of an improbable concept. *Canadian Journal of Psychiatry, 49,* 592–600.

Piper, A., & Merskey, H. (2004b). The persistence of folly: Critical examination of dissociative identity disorder. Part II. The defence and decline of multiple personality or dissociative identity disorder. *Canadian Journal of Psychiatry, 49,* 678–683.

Pistrang, N., Barker, C., & Humphreys, K. (2010). The contributions of mutual help groups for mental health problems to psychological well-being: A systematic review. In L. D. Brown & S. Wituk (Eds.), *Mental health self-help: Consumer and family initiatives* (pp. 61–85). New York, NY: Springer.

Pizzagalli, D. A., Iosifescu, D., Hallett, L. A., Ratner, K. G., & Fava, M. (2009). Reduced hedonic capacity in Major Depressive Disorder: Evidence from a probabilistic reward task. *Journal of Psychiatric Research, 43,* 76–87.

Plomin, R. (1990). The role of inheritance in behaviour. *Science, 248,* 183–188.

Plomin, R., & Neiderhiser J. M. (1992). Genetics and experience. *Current Directions in Psychological Science, 1,* 160–163.

Plomin, R., DeFries, J. C., Knopik, V. S., & Neiderhiser, J. M. (2016). Top 10 replicated findings from behavioral genetics. *Perspectives on Psychological Science, 11,* 3–23.

Pogue-Geile, M. F., & Gottesman, I. (1999). Schizophrenia: Study of a genetically complex phenotype. In B. C. Jones & P. Mormede (Eds.), *Neurobehavioral genetics: Methods and applications* (pp. 247–264). Boca Raton, FL: CRC Press.

Polan, M., Desmond, J., Banner, L., Pryor, M., McCallum, S., Atlas, S., et al. (2003). Female sexual arousal: A behavioural analysis. *Fertility and Sterility, 8*(6), 1480–1487.

Polanczyk, G., & Rohde, L. A. (2007). Epidemiology of attention-deficit/hyperactivity disorder across the lifespan. *Current Opinion in Psychiatry, 20*(4), 386–392.

Polanczyk, G., de Lima, M. S., Horta, B. L., Biederman, J., & Rohde, L. A. (2007). The worldwide prevalence of ADHD: A systematic review and metaregression analysis. *The American Journal of Psychiatry, 164*(6), 942–948.

Polanczyk, G.V., Salum,G.A., Sugaya,L.S., Caye, A., & Rohde, L.A. (2015). Annual Research Review: A meta-analysis of the worldwide prevalence of mental disorders in children and adolescents. *Journal of Child Psychology and Psychiatry, 56,* 345–365. doi:10.1111/jcpp.12381

Pole, N. (2007). The psychophysiology of posttraumatic stress disorder: A meta-analysis. *Psychological Bulletin, 133,* 725–746.

Polich, J. M., Armor, D. J., & Braiker, H. B. (1981). *The course of alcoholism: Four years after treatment.* New York, NY: Wiley.

Polivy, J., & Herman, C. P. (1987). The diagnosis and treatment of normal eating. *Journal of Consulting and Clinical Psychology, 55,* 635–644.

Polivy, J., & Herman, C. P. (2002). Causes of eating disorders. *Annual Review of Psychology, 53,* 187–213.

Polivy, J., & Herman, C. P. (2004). Sociocultural idealization of thin female body shapes: An introduction to the special issue on body image and eating disorders. *Journal of Social & Clinical Psychology. Special Issue: Body Image and Eating Disorders, 23,* 1–6.

Polivy, J., Herman, C. P., Mills, J., & Wheeler, H. B. (2003). Eating disorders in adolescence. In G. Adams & M. Berzonsky (Eds.), *The Blackwell handbook of adolescence* (pp. 523–549). Oxford, UK: Blackwell.

Pollack, A. L., & Webster, C. D. (1993). Psychology and the law: The emerging role of forensic psychology. In K. S. Dobson & D. J. G. Dobson (Eds.), *Professional psychology in Canada* (pp. 391–412). Toronto, ON: Hogrefe & Huber.

Polvan, N. (1969). Historical aspects of mental ills in Middle East discussed. *Roche Reports, 6,* 3.

Pomarol-Clotet, E., Salvador, R., Sarró, S., Gomar, J., Vila, F., Martinez, A., et al. (2008). Failure to deactivate in the prefrontal cortex in schizophrenia: Dysfunction of the default mode network? *Psychological Medicine, 38,* 1185–1193.

Pompoli, A., Furukawa, T. A., Imai, H., Tajika, A., Efthimiou, O., & Salanti, G. (2016). Psychological therapies for panic disorder with or without agoraphobia in adults: A network meta-analysis. *Cochrane Database of Systematic Reviews, 4.* doi: 10.1002/14651858.CD011004.pub2

Pope, H. G., Barry, S., Bodkin, A., & Hudson, J. I. (2006). Tracking scientific interest in the dissociative disorders: A study of scientific publication output 1984–2003. *Psychotherapy and Psychosomatics, 75,* 19–24.

Pope, H. G., Jr., Oliva, P., Hudson, J. I., Bodkin, J., & Gruber, A. (1999). Attitudes toward DSM-IV dissociative disorders diagnoses among board certified American psychiatrists. *American Journal of Psychiatry, 156,* 321–323.

Porcelli, P., Bagby, R.M., Taylor, G.J., De Carne, M., Leandro, G. & Todarello, O. (2003). Alexithymia as predictor of treatment outcome in patients with functional gastrointestinal disorders. *Psychosomatic Medicine, 65,* 911–918.

Porjesz, B., & Begleiter, H. (1997). Event-related potentials in COAs (children of alcoholics) (includes related article on COAs at risk of developing alcoholism). *Alcohol Health & Research World, 21*(3), 236–250.

Porporino, F. J., & Motiuk, L. L. (1995). The prison careers of mentally disordered offenders. *International Journal of Law and Psychiatry, 18,* 29–44.

Porter, R. (1995). Mood disorders [social section]. In G. Berrios & R. Porter (Eds.), *A history of clinical psychiatry* (pp. 409–420). London: Athlone Press.

Porter, R., & Wright, D. (Eds.). (2003). *The confinement of the insane: International perspectives, 1800–1965.* Cambridge, UK: Cambridge University Press.

Porter, S. (1996). Without conscience or without active conscience? The etiology of psychopathy revisited. *Aggression and Violent Behavior, 1,* 179–189.

Porter, S., & Porter, S. (2007). Psychopathy and violent crime. In H. Hervé & J. C. Yuille (Eds.), *The psychopath: Theory, research, and practice* (pp. 287–300). Mahwah, NJ: Erlbaum.

Porter, S., & Woodworth, M. (2007). I'm sorry I did it. . . but he started it: A comparison of the official and self-reported homicide descriptions of psychopaths and non-psychopaths. *Law and Human Behavior, 31,* 91–107.

Porter, S., Birt, A. R., & Boer, D. P. (2001). Investigation of the criminal and conditional release histories of Canadian federal offenders as a function of psychopathy and age. *Law and Human Behavior, 25,* 647–661.

Porter, S., Fairweather, D., Drugge, J., Hervé, H., Birt, A. R., & Boer, D. P. (2000). Profiles of psychopathy in incarcerated sexual offenders. *Criminal Justice & Behavior, 27,* 216–233.

Porter, S., ten Brinke, L., & Wilson, K. (2009). Crime profiles and conditional release performance of psychopathic and non-psychopathic sexual offenders. *Legal and Criminological Psychology, 14,* 109–118. doi:10.1348/135532508X284310

Porter, S., Woodworth, M., Earle, J., Drugge, J., & Boer, D. P. (2003). Characteristics of violent behavior exhibited during sexual homicides by psychopathic and non-psychopathic murderers. *Law and Human Behavior, 27,* 459–470.

Porter, S., Yuille, J. C., & Lehman, D. (1999). The nature of real, implanted, and fabricated memories for emotional childhood events: Implications for the recovered memory debate. *Law and Human Behavior, 23,* 517–538.

Posey, D. J., & McDougall, C. J. (2001). Pharmacotherapeutic management of autism. *Expert Opinion in Pharmacotherapy, 2,* 587–600.

Posey, D. J., Stigler, K. A., Erickson, C. A., & McDougle, C. J. (2008). Antipsychotics in the treatment of autism. *The Journal of Clinical Investigation, 118*(1), 6–14.

Poston, D., Turnbull, A., Park, J., Mannan, H., Marquis, J., & Wang, M. (2003). Family quality of life: A qualitative inquiry. *Mental Retardation, 41*(3), 313–328.

Potthoff, J. G., Holahan, C. J., & Joiner, T. E., Jr. (1995). Reassurance seeking, stress generation and depressive symptoms: An integrative model. *Journal of Personality and Social Psychology, 68,* 664–670.

Pötzl-Malikova, M. (1982). *Franz Xaver Messerschmidt.* Vienna, Austria: Jugend und Volk.

Pötzl-Malikova, M. (1987). Zur Beziehung Franz Anton Mesmer—Franz Xaver Messerschmidt. *Wiener Jahrbuch für Kunstgeschichte, Band XL,* 257–267.

Poulin, F., Dishion, T. J., & Haas, E. (1999). The peer influence paradox: Relationship quality and deviancy training within male adolescent friendships. *Merrill–Palmer Quarterly, 45,* 42–61.

Poulton, R., & Menzies, R. G. (2002). Fear born and bred: Toward a more inclusive theory of fear acquisition. *Behaviour Research and Therapy, 40,* 197–208.

Power, A. J., Colling, L. J., Mead, N., Barnes, L., & Gowsami, U. (2016). Neural encoding of the speech envelope by children with developmental dyslexia. *Brain & Language 160,* 1–10

Poythress, N. G., Skeem, J. L., & Lilienfeld, S. O. (2006). Associations among early abuse, dissociation, and psychopathy in an offender sample. *Journal of Abnormal Psychology, 115,* 288–297.

Prause, N., & Janssen, E. (2006). Blood flow: Vaginal photoplethysmography. In I. Goldstein et al. (Eds.), *Women's sexual function and dysfunction: Study, diagnosis and treatment* (pp. 359–367). New York, NY: Taylor and Francis.

Prause, N., Steele, V., Staley, C., Sabatinelli, D., & Hajcak, G. (2015). Modulation of late positive potentials by sexual images in problem users and controls inconsistent with "porn addiction." *Biological Psychology, 109,* 192–199.

Prendergast, M., Podus, D, Finney, J., Greenwell, L., & Roll, J. (2006). Contingency management for treatment of substance use disorders: A meta-analysis. *Addiction, 101*(11), 1546–1560.

Preston, D., & Carter, M. (2009). A review of the efficacy of the picture exchange communication system intervention. *Journal of Autism and Developmental Disorders, 39,* 1471–1486.

Price, E. L., McLeod, P. J., Gleich, S. S., & Hand, D. (2006). One-year prevalence rates of major depressive disorder in first-year university students. *Canadian Journal of Counselling, 40,* 68–81.

Price, J. M., & Zwolinski, J. (2010). The nature of child and adolescent vulnerability: history and definitions. In R. E. Ingram & J. M. Price (Eds.), *Vulnerability to psychopathology: Risk across the lifespan* (2nd ed., pp. 18-38). New York, NY: Guildford.

Price, R. H., Cowen, E. L., Lorion, R. P., & Ramos-McKay, J. (1989). The search for effective prevention programs: What we learned along the way. *American Journal of Orthopsychiatry, 59,* 49–58.

Price, R. H., Cowen, E. L., Lorion, R. P., & Ramos-McKay, J. (Eds.). (1988). *Fourteen ounces of prevention: A casebook for practitioners.* Washington, DC: American Psychological Association.

Prilleltensky, I. (1994a). Empowerment in mainstream psychology: Legitimacy, obstacles, and possibilities. *Canadian Psychology, 35,* 358–374.

Prilleltensky, I. (1994b). *The morals and politics of psychology: Psychological discourse and the status quo.* Albany, NY: State University of New York Press.

Prilleltensky, I. (2005). Promoting well-being: Time for a paradigm shift in health and human services. *Scandinavian Journal of Public Health, 33,* 53–60.

Prilleltensky, I. & Nelson, G. (2013). Critical psychology, prevention, and social justice. In E. Vera (Ed.), *The Oxford handbook of prevention in counseling psychology.* New York, NY: Oxford University Press.

Prilleltensky, I., & Prilleltensky, O. (2006). *Promoting well-being: Linking personal, organizational, and community change.* Hoboken, NJ: John Wiley and Sons.

Prince, J. B. (2006). Pharmacotherapy of attention-deficit hyperactivity disorder in children and adolescents: Update on new stimulant preparations, atomoxetine, and novel treatments. *Child and Adolescent Psychiatric Clinics of North America, 15*(1), 13–50.

Pringsheim, T., Hirsch, L., Gardner, D.M., & Gorman, D.A. (2015a). The pharmacological management of oppositional behaviour, conduct problems, and aggression in children and adolescents with attention-deficit hyperactivity disorder, oppositional defiant disorder, and conduct disorder: A systematic review and meta-analysis. Part 1: Psychostimulants, alpha-2 agonists, and atomoxetine. *Canadian Journal of Psychiatry, 60,* 42–51

Pringsheim, T., Hirsch, L., Gardner, D., & Gorman, D.A. (2015b). The pharmacological management of oppositional behaviour, conduct problems, and aggression in children and adolescents with attention-deficit hyperactivity disorder, oppositional defiant disorder, and conduct disorder: a systematic review and meta-analysis. Part 2: Antipsychotics and traditional mood stabilizers. *Canadian Journal of Psychiatry, 60,* 52–61.

Prior, M., & Cummins, R. A. (1992). Questions about facilitated communication and autism. *Journal of Autism and Developmental Disorders, 22,* 331–338.

Pritchard, J. C. (1835). *A treatise on insanity and other disorders affecting the mind.* London: Sherwood, Gilbert & Piper.

Pritchard, M., & Cramblitt, B. (2014). Media influence on drive for thinness and drive for muscularity. *Sex Roles, 71,* 208–218. doi: 10.1007/s11199-014-0397-1

Prkachin, K. M., & Silverman, B. (2002). Hostility and facial expression: Is social regulation more important than negative affect? *Health Psychology, 21,* 33–39.

Prkachin, K. M., Mills, D. E., Kaufman, F. L., & Carew, W. L. C. (1991). Cynical hostility, the perception of contingency and cardiovascular activity. *Canadian Journal of Behavioural Science, 23,* 455–468.

Prkachin, K. M., Mills, D. E., Zwaal, C., & Husted, J. (2001). Comparison of hemodynamic responses to social and nonsocial stress: Evaluation of an anger interview. *Psychophysiology, 38,* 879–885.

Public Health Agency of Canada. (2002). *A report on mental illnesses in Canada.* Retrieved from www.phac-aspc.gc.ca/publicat/miic-mmac

Public Health Agency of Canada. (2014). The chief public health officer's report on the state of public health in Canada, 2014: Public health in the future. Retrieved from www.phac-aspc.gc.ca/cphorsphc-respcacsp/2014/chang-eng.php#a1

Pueschel, S. M. (Ed.). (2006). *Adults with Down syndrome.* Baltimore, MD: Paul H. Brookes.

Pujol, J., Soriano-Mas, C., Alonso, P., Cardoner, N., Menchon, J., Deus, J., & Vellejo, J. (2004). Mapping structural brain alterations in obsessive-compulsive disorder. *Archives of General Psychiatry, 61,* 720–730.

Pukall, C. F., Goldstein, A. T., Bergeron, S., Foster, D., Stein, A., Kellogg-Spadt, S., & Bachmann, G. (2016). Vulvodynia: Definition, prevalence, impact, and pathophysiological factors. *Journal of Sexual Medicine, 13,* 291–304.

Pukall, C. F., Payne, K. A., Binik, Y. M., & Khalifé, S. (2003). Pain measurement in vulvodynia. *Journal of Sex and Marital Therapy, 29*(supp), 111–120.

Qiu, C., de Ronchi, D., & Fratiglioni, L. (2007). The epidemiology of the dementias: An update. *Current Opinions in Psychiatry, 20,* 380–385.

Quadland, M. C. (1983). Compulsive sexual behavior: Definition of a problem and an approach to treatment. *Journal of Sex and Marital Therapy, 11,* 121–132.

Quigley, B. M., & Leonard, K. E. (2006). Alcohol expectancies and intoxicated aggression. *Aggression and Violent Behavior, 11*(5), 484–496.

Quilty, L. C., Dozois, D. J., Lobo, D. S., Ravindran, L. N., & Bagby, R. M. (2014). Cognitive structure and processing during cognitive behavioral therapy vs. pharmacotherapy for depression. *International Journal of Cognitive Therapy, 7*(3), 235–250.

Quinsey, V. L. (1995). The prediction and explanation of criminal violence. *International Journal of Law and Psychiatry, 18,* 117–127.

Quinsey, V. L. (2010). Coercive paraphilic disorder. *Archives of Sexual Behavior, 39,* 405–410.

Quinsey, V. L., Book, A., & Skilling, T. A. (2004). A follow-up of deinstitutionalized men with intellectual disabilities and histories of antisocial behaviour. *Journal of Applied Research in Intellectual Disabilities, 17*(4), 243–253.

Quinsey, V. L., Harris, G. T., Rice, M. E., & Cormier, C. A. (2006). *Violent offenders: Appraising and managing risk* (2nd ed.). Washington, DC: American Psychological Association.

Quinsey, V. L., Harris, G. T., Rice, M. E., & Lalumière, M. L. (1993). Assessing treatment efficacy in outcome studies of sex offenders. *Journal of Interpersonal Violence, 8,* 512–523.

R. v Abbey (1982), 2 S.C.R. 24.

R. v Chaulk (1990), 3 S.C.R. 1303.

R. v F. D. M. (1987), 33 C.C.C. (3d) 116 (Man. C. A.).

R. v Hadfield (1800), 27 St. Tr. 1281, 1312.

R. v J. A. P. (2000), 192 Sask. R. 80 (Prov. Ct.).

R. v M'Naghten (1843), 10 Cl. & F. 200, 8 E.R. 718.

R. v Pritchard (1836), 7 Car. & P. 304.

R. v Swain (1991), 1 S.C.R. 933.

R. v Taylor (1992), 77 C.C.C. (3d) 551 (Ont. C.A.).

R. v Whittle (1994), 2 S.C.R. 914.

Rabey v R. (1980), 2 S.C.R. 513.

Rabinowitz Greenberg, S. R., Firestone, P., Bradford, J. M., & Greenberg, D. M. (2002). Prediction of recidivism in exhibitionists: Psychological, phallometric, and offence factors. *Sexual Abuse: A Journal of Research and Treatment, 14*(4), 329–347.

Rachman, S. (1977). The conditioning theory of fear-acquisition: A critical examination. *Behaviour Research and Therapy, 15,* 375–387.

Rachman, S. (1993). Obsessions, responsibility and guilt. *Behaviour Research and Therapy, 31,* 149–154.

Rachman, S. (1997). A cognitive theory of obsessions. *Behaviour Research and Therapy, 35,* 793–802.

Rachman, S. (1998). A cognitive theory of obsessions: Elaborations. *Behaviour Research and Therapy, 36,* 385–401.

Rachman, S. (2002). A cognitive theory of compulsive checking. *Behaviour Research and Therapy, 40*(6), 625–639.

Rachman, S., Radomsky, A. S., & Shafran, R. (2008). Safety behavior: A reconsideration. *Behaviour Research and Therapy, 46,* 163–173.

Rachman, S., Shafran, R., Mitchell, D., Trant, J., & Teachman, B. A. (1996). How to remain neutral: An experimental analysis of neutralization. *Behaviour Research and Therapy, 34,* 889–898.

Radden, J. (2004). Melancholia in the writing of a sixteenth-century Spanish nun. *Harvard Review of Psychiatry, 12,* 293–297.

Radomsky, A. S., & Alcolado, G. M. (2010). Don't even think about checking: Mental checking causes memory distrust. *Journal of Behavior Therapy and Experimental Psychiatry, 41,* 345–351.

Radomsky, A. S., Dugas, M. J., Alcolado, G. M., & Lavoie, S. L. (2014). When more is less: Doubt, repetition, memory, metamemory, and compulsive checking in OCD. *Behaviour Research and Therapy, 59,* 30–39. doi: 10.1016/j.brat.2014.05.008

Radomsky, A. S., Gilchrist, P. T., & Dussault, D. (2006). Repeated checking really does cause memory distrust. *Behaviour Research and Therapy, 44,* 305–316.

Raina, P. S., Wolfson, C., Kirkland, S. A., Griffith, L. E., Oremus, M., Patterson, ... & Brazil, K. (2009). The Canadian Longitudinal Study on Aging (CLSA). *Canadian Journal on Aging, 28*(3), 221–229.

Raine, A. (1993). *The psychopathology of crime: Criminal behavior as a clinical disorder.* San Diego, CA: Academic Press.

Raine, A., Lencz, T., Bihrle, S., LaCasse, L., & Colletti, P. (2000). Reduced prefrontal gray matter volume and reduced autonomic activity in antisocial personality disorder. *Archives of General Psychiatry, 57,* 119–127.

Raine, A., Lencz, T., Yaralian, P., Bihrle, S., LaCasse, L., Ventura, J., & Colletti, P. (2002). Prefrontal structural and functional deficits in schizotypal personality disorder. *Schizophrenia Bulletin, 28*(3), 501–513.

Raine, A., Venables, P. H., & Mednick, S. A. (1997). Low resting heart rate at age 3 years predisposes to aggression at age 11 years: Evidence from the Mauritius Child Health Project. *Journal of the American Academy of Child and Adolescent Psychiatry, 36,* 1457–1464.

Ramage-Morin, P. (2004). Panic disorder and coping. *Health Reports, 15*(Suppl.), 33–41 (Statistics Canada cat. no. 82-003). Retrieved from www.statcan.ca/english/freepub/82-003-SIE/2004000/panic.htm

Ramey, C. T., & Ramey, S. L. (1992). Effective early intervention. *Mental Retardation, 30,* 337–345.

Randolph, C., Tierney, M. C., Mohr, E., & Chase, T. N. (1998). The Repeatable Battery for the Assessment of Neuropsychological Status (RBANS): Preliminary clinical validity. *Journal of Clinical and Experimental Neuropsychology, 20*(3), 310–319. https://doi.org/10.1076/jcen.20.3.310.823

Rangaswamy, M., Porjesz, B., Chorlian, D. B., Wang, K., Jones, K. A., Kuperman, S., ... & Begleiter, H. (2004). Resting EEG in offspring of male alcoholics: Beta frequencies. *International Journal of Psychophysiology, 51*(3), 239–251.

Ranney, L., Melvin, C., Lux, L., McClain, E., Morgan, L., & Lohr, K. (2006). *Tobacco use: Prevention, cessation, and control* (Evidence Report/Technology Assessment No. 140). Rockville, MD: Agency for Healthcare Research and Quality.

Rapanaro, C., Bartu, A., & Lee, A. H. (2008). Perceived benefits and negative impact of challenges encountered in caring for young adults with intellectual disabilities in the transition to adulthood. *Journal of Applied Research in Intellectual Disabilities, 21,* 34–47.

Rapaport, M. H., Clary, C., Fayyad, R., & Endicott, J. (2005). Quality-of-life impairment in depressive and anxiety disorders. *American Journal of Psychiatry, 162,* 1171–1178.

Rapee, R. M. (2014). Preschool environment and temperament as predictors of social and nonsocial anxiety disorders in middle adolescence. *Journal of the American Academy of Child & Adolescent Psychiatry, 53*(3), 320–328.

Rapee, R. M., & Spence, S. H. (2004). The etiology of social phobia: Empirical evidence and an initial model. *Clinical Psychology Review, 24,* 737–767.

Raposo, S., El-Gabalawy, R., Erickson, J., Mackenzie, C. S., & Sareen, J. (2014). Associations between anxiety disorders, suicide ideation, and age in nationally representative samples of Canadian and American adults. *Journal of Anxiety Disorders, 28*(8), 823–829.

Rappaport, J. (1987). Terms of empowerment/exemplars of prevention: Toward a theory for community psychology. *American Journal of Community Psychology, 15,* 121–148.

Raskind, M. A., & Peskind, E. R. (1992). Alzheimer's disease and other dementing disorders. In J. E. Birren, R. B. Sloane, & G. D. Cohen (Eds.), *Handbook of mental health and aging* (2nd ed., pp. 478–513). San Diego, CA: Academic Press.

Raspa, M., Bailey, D. B., Jr., & Bishop, E. (2010). Obesity, food selectivity and physical activity in individuals with Fragile X syndrome. *American Journal on Intellectual and Developmental Disabilities, 115,* 482–495.

Rassin, E., Merckelbach, H., Muris, P., & Schmidt, H. (2001). The thought-action fusion scale: Further evidence for its reliability and validity. *Behaviour Research and Therapy, 39,* 537544.

Rastegar, D. A., Sharfstein Kawasaki, S., King, V. L., Harris, E. E., & Brooner, R. K. (2016). Criminal charges prior to and after enrollment in opioid agonist treatment: A comparison of methadone maintenance and office-based buprenorphine. *Substance Use & Misuse, 51*(7), 803–811.

Rastogi, M., Massey-Hastings, N., & Wieling, E. (2012). Barriers to seeking mental health services in the Latino/a community: A qualitative analysis. *Journal of Systemic Therapies, 31,* 1–17.

Ratcliffe, G. E., Enns, M. W., Belik, S., & Sareen, J. (2008). Chronic pain conditions and suicidal ideation and suicide attempts: An epidemiologic perspective. *Clinical Journal of Pain, 24*(3), 204–210.

Rathbone, B. J., & Healey, V. (Eds.). (1989). *Campylobacter pylori and gastroduodenal disease.* Oxford, UK: Blackwell.

Rauch, S. L., Whalen, P. J., Dougherty, D., & Jenike, M. A. (1998). Neurobiological models of obsessive-compulsive disorder. In M. A. Jenike, L. Baer, & W. E. Minichiello (Eds.), *Obsessive-compulsive disorders: Practical management* (3rd ed., pp. 222–253). St. Louis, MO: Mosby.

Rauschenberger, S. L., & Lynn, S. J. (1995). Fantasy proneness, DSM-III-R Axis I psychopathology, and dissociation. *Journal of Abnormal Psychology, 104,* 373–380.

Ray, O., & Ksir, C. (1990). *Drugs, society, & human behaviour.* St. Louis, MO: Times Mirror/Mosby College Publishing.

Raymond, N. C., Coleman, E., & Miner, M. H. (2003). Psychiatric comorbidity and compulsive/impulsive traits in compulsive sexual behavior. *Comprehensive Psychiatry, 44,* 370–380.

Read, S. (1996). The dementias. In J. S. Sadavoy, L. W. Lazarus, & L. F. Jarvik (Eds.), *Comprehensive review of geriatric psychiatry* (pp. 287–310). Washington, DC: American Psychiatric Press.

Reaves, J. (2001, February 7). Will Robert Downey Jr.'s case spark a change in drug sentencing? *Time.* Retrieved from www.time.com/time/nation/article/0,8599,98373,00.html

Reba-Harrelson, L., Von Holle, A., Hamer, R. M., Torgersen, L., Reichborn-Kjennerud, T., & Bulik, C. M. (2010). Patterns of maternal feeding and child eating associated with eating disorders in the Norwegian Mother and Child Cohort Study (MoBa). *Eating Behaviors, 11,* 54–61.

Rector, N. A., Seeman, M. V., & Segal, Z. V. (2003). Cognitive therapy for schizophrenia: A preliminary randomized controlled trial. *Schizophrenia Research, 63,* 1–11.

Reddy, L. F., Horan, W. P., Jahshan, C., & Green, M. F. (2014). Cognitive remediation for schizophrenia: A review of recent findings. *Current Treatment Options in Psychiatry, 1*(2), 121–133.

Reger, M. A., & Gahm, G. A. (2009). A meta-analysis of the effects of internet and computer-based cognitive-behavioral treatments for anxiety. *Journal of Clinical Psychology, 65,* 53–75.

Regier, D. A., Kuhl, E. A., & Kupfer, D. J. (2013). The DSM-5: Classification and criteria changes. *World Psychiatry, 12,* 92–98.

Rehm, J., Baliunas, S., Brochu, B., Sarnocinska-Hart, A., & Taylor, B. (2006). *The costs of substance abuse in Canada 2002: Highlights.* Ottawa, ON: Canadian Centre on Substance Abuse.

Reich, C. L., Young, D., & Fowler, R. C. (1986). San Diego suicide study: Young vs old subjects. *Archives of General Psychiatry, 43,* 577–582.

Reich, D., Zanarini, M. C., & Bieri, K. A. (2009). A preliminary study of lamotrigine in the treatment of affective instability in borderline personality disorder. *International Clinical Psychopharmacology, 24,* 270–275. doi:10.1097/YIC.0b013e32832d6c2f

Reich, J. (1987). Sex distribution of DSM-III personality disorders in psychiatric outpatients. *American Journal of Psychiatry, 144,* 485–488.

Reich, J. (1990). Comparison of males and females with DSM-III dependent personality disorder. *Psychiatry Research, 33,* 207–214.

Reich, J., & Green, A. I. (1991). Effect of personality disorders on outcome of treatment. *Journal of Nervous and Mental Disease, 179,* 74–82.

Reichard, S., & Tillman, C. (1950). Patterns of parent-child relationships in schizophrenia. *Psychiatry, 13,* 247–257.

Reid, D. H., Wilson, P. G., & Faw, G. D. (1983). Teaching self-help skills. In J. L. Matson & J. A. Mulick (Eds.), *Handbook of mental retardation.* New York, NY: Pergamon Press.

Reid, W. H., & Gacono, C. (2000). Treatment of antisocial personality, psychopathy, and other characterologic antisocial syndromes. *Behavioral Sciences & the Law, 18,* 647–662.

Reilly, D., Huws, J., Hastings, R., & Vaughan, F. (2010). Life and death of a child with Down syndrome and a congenital heart condition: Experiences of six couples. *Intellectual and Developmental Disabilities, 48,* 403–416.

Reinders, H. S. (2008). Persons with disabilities as parents: What is the problem? *Journal of Applied Research in Intellectual Disabilities, 21,* 308–314.

Reinisch, J. M., & Beasley, R. (1990). *Kinsey Institute new report on sex* (pp. 162–163). Bloomington, IN: Martin.

Reiss, D., & Price, R. H. (1996). National research agenda for prevention research: The National Institute of Mental Health Report. *American Psychologist, 51,* 1109–1115.

Reiss, F. (2013). Socioeconomic inequalities and mental health problems in children and adolescents: A systematic review. *Social Science & Medicine, 90,* 24–31.

Reiss, S. (1990). Prevalence of dual diagnosis in community-based day programs in the Chicago metropolitan area. *American Journal on Mental Retardation, 94,* 578–585.

Reissing, E. K., Binik, Y. M., Khalifé, S., Cohen, D., & Amsel, R. (2004). Vaginal spasm, pain, and behavior: An empirical investigation of the diagnosis of vaginismus. *Archives of Sexual Behavior, 33,* 5–17.

Reitan, R., & Wolfson, D. (1985). *The Halstead–Reitan neuropsychological test battery: Therapy and clinical interpretation.* Tucson, AZ: Neuropsychological Press.

Renaud, C. A., & Byers, E. S. (1999). Exploring the frequency, diversity and content of university students' positive and negative sexual cognitions. *Canadian Journal of Human Sexuality, 8*(1), 17–30.

Renshaw, D. (1998). When the patient's chief complaint is sexual disinterest. *Medical Update for Psychiatrists, 3*(5), 159–164.

Renwick, R., Brown, I., & Raphael, D. (1994). Quality of life: Linking a conceptual approach to service delivery. *Journal of Developmental Disabilities, 3*, 32–44.

Renwick, R., Goldie, R. S., & King, S. (1999). Children who have HIV. In I. Brown & M. Percy (Eds.), *Developmental disabilities in Ontario* (pp. 323–335). Toronto, ON: Front Porch.

Reschly, D. J. (2005). Learning disabilities identification: Primary intervention, secondary intervention, and then what? *Journal of Learning Disabilities, 38*, 510–515.

Reutens, S., Nielsen, O., & Sachdev, P. (2010). Depersonalization disorder. *Current Opinion in Psychiatry, 23*, 278–283.

Reynolds, K., Mackenzie, C. S., Medved, M., & Roger, K. (2015). The experiences of older male adults throughout their involvement in a community programme for men. *Ageing and Society, 35*(3), 531–551. doi:10.1017/S0144686X13000858

Reynolds, K., Pietrzak, R. H., El-Gabalawy, R., Mackenzie, C. S., & Sareen, J. (2015). Prevalence of psychiatric disorders in U.S. older adults: Findings from a nationally representative survey. *World Psychiatry, 14*(1), 74–81. http://doi.org/10.1002/wps.20193

Rhee, S. H., & Waldman, I. D. (2002). Genetic and environmental influences on antisocial behavior: A meta-analysis of twin and adoption studies. *Psychological Bulletin, 128*, 490–529.

Rice, M. E. (1997). Violent offender research and implications for the criminal justice system. *American Psychologist, 52*, 414–423.

Rice, M. E., & Harris, G. T. (1993). Treatment for prisoners with mental disorder. In J. H. Steadman & J. J. Cocozza (Eds.), *Mental illness in America's prisons* (pp. 91–130). Seattle, WA: National Coalition for the Mentally Ill in the Criminal Justice System.

Rice, M. E., & Harris, G. T. (1997a). Cross-validation and extension of the Violence Risk Appraisal Guide for child molesters and rapists. *Law and Human Behavior, 21*, 231–241.

Rice, M. E., & Harris, G. T. (1997b). The treatment of adult offenders. In D. M. Stoff, J. Breiling, & J. D. Maser (Eds.), *Handbook of antisocial behavior* (pp. 425–435). New York, NY: Wiley.

Rice, M. E., Harris, G. T., & Cormier, C. A. (1992). An evaluation of a maximum security therapeutic community for psychopaths and other mentally disordered offenders. *Law and Human Behavior, 16*, 399–412.

Rice, M. E., Harris, G. T., & Quinsey, V. L. (1996). Treatment of forensic patients. In B. Sales & S. Shah (Eds.), *Mental health and the law: Research, policy, and practice* (pp. 141–190). New York, NY: Carolina Academic Press.

Rice, M. E., Quinsey, V. L., & Harris, G. T. (1991). Predicting sexual recidivism among treated and untreated extrafamilial child molesters from a maximum security psychiatric institution. *Journal of Consulting and Clinical Psychology, 59*, 381–386.

Rich, C. L., Young, D., & Fowler, R. C. (1986). San Diego suicide study: Young vs old subjects. *Archives of General Psychiatry, 43*, 577–582.

Richard-Devantoy, S., Turecki, G., & Jollant, F. (2016). Neurobiology of elderly suicide. *Archives of Suicide Research, 20*(3), 291–313. doi:10.1080/13811118.2015.1048397

Richards, H. J., Casey, J. O., & Lucente, S. W. (2003). Psychopathy and treatment response in incarcerated female substance abusers. *Criminal Justice and Behavior, 30*, 251–276.

Richters, J. E., Arnold, L. E., Jensen, P. S., Abikoff, H., Conners, C. K., Greenhill, L. L., et al. (1995). NIMH collaborative multisite multimodal treatment study of children with ADHD: I. background and rationale. *Journal of the American Academy of Child and Adolescent Psychiatry, 34*(8), 987–1000.

Riley, D. (1994). *The harm reduction model: Pragmatic approaches to drug use form the area between intolerance and neglect.* Ottawa: Canadian Centre on Substance Abuse.

Riley, R., & Richman, A. (1983). Involuntary hospitalization in Canadian psychiatric inpatient facilities, 1970–1978. *Canadian Journal of Psychiatry, 28*, 536–541.

Rimland, B. (1991). Facilitated communication: Problems, puzzles and paradoxes: Six challenges for researchers. *Autism Research Review International, 5*, 3.

Rimland, B. (1993). Controlled evaluations of facilitated communication. *Autism Research Review International, 7*, 7.

Rimland, B., & Baker, S. M. (1996). Brief report: Alternative approaches to the development of effective treatments for autism. *Journal of Autism and Developmental Disorders, 26*, 237–241.

Ritterband, L. M., Thorndike, F. P., Gonder-Frederick, L. A., Mager, J. C., Bailey, E. T., Saylor, D. K., & Morin, C. M. (2009). Efficacy of internet-based behavioral intervention with insomnia. *Archives of General Psychiatry, 66*, 692–698.

Rivers, P. C. (1994). *Alcohol and human behavior: Theory, research, and practice.* Englewood Cliffs, NJ: Prentice-Hall.

Rizvi, S. L., Dimeff, L. A., Skutch, J., Carroll, D., & Linehan, M. (2011). A pilot study of the DBT coach: An interactive mobile phone application for individuals with borderline personality disorder and substance abuse disorder. *Behavior Therapy, 42*, 589–600.

Robert, M., Leblanc, L. & Boyer, T. (2014). When satisfaction is not directly related to the support services received: Understanding parents' varied experiences with specialised services for children with developmental disabilities *British Journal of Learning Disabilities. 43*, 168–177.

Roberts, A. H., Kewman, D. G., Mercier, L., & Hovell, M. (1993). The power of nonspecific effects in healing: Implications for psychosocial and biological treatments. *Clinical Psychology Review, 13*, 375–391.

Roberts, B. W., Walton, K. E., & Viechtbauer, W. (2006). Patterns of mean-level change in personality traits across the life course: A meta-analysis of longitudinal studies. *Psychological Bulletin, 132*, 1–25.

Roberts, G., & Boardman, J. (2013). Understanding 'recovery.' *Advances in Psychiatric Treatment, 19*, 400–409. doi: 10.1192/apt.bp.112.010355

Robichaud, M., & Dugas, M. J. (2015). *The generalized anxiety workbook: A comprehensive CBT guide for coping with uncertainty, worry, and fear.* Oakland, CA: New Harbinger.

Robins, C. J., & Chapman, A. L. (2004). Dialectical behaviour therapy: Current status, recent developments, and future directions. *Journal of Personality Disorders, 18*, 73–89.

Robins, L. N. (1966). *Deviant children grow up: A sociological and psychiatric study of sociopathic personality.* Baltimore, MD: Williams & Wilkins.

Robins, L. N., & Helzer, J. E. (1985). *Diagnostic Interview Schedule, Version III-A.* St. Louis, MO: Department of Psychiatry, Washington University School of Medicine.

Robins, L. N., & Regier, D. A. (1991). *Psychiatric disorders in America: The Epidemiological Catchment Area Study.* New York, NY: Free Press.

Robins, L. N., Cottler, L. B., Bucholz, K. K., Compton, W. M., North, C. S., & Rourke, K. M. (2000). *Diagnostic Interview Schedule for the DSM-IV (DIS-IV).* St. Louis, MO: Washington University Medical School.

Robins, L. N., Helzer, J. E., Croughan, J., & Ratcliff, K. S. (1981). National Institute of Mental Health Diagnostic Interview Schedule: Its history, characteristics, and validity. *Archives of General Psychiatry, 38*, 381–389.

Robinson, M., Oddy, W. H., Li, J., Kendall, G. E., Klerk, N. H., Silburn, S. R., et al. (2008). Pre- and postnatal influences on preschool mental health: A large-scale cohort study. *Journal of Child Psychology and Psychiatry, 49*, 1118–1128.

Robinson, S., Weiss, J. A., Lunsky, Y., & Ouellette-Kuntz, H. (2016). Informal support and burden among parents of adults with intellectual and/or developmental disabilities. *Journal of Applied Research in Intellectual Disabilities, 29*(4), 356–365.

Rockert, W., Kaplan, A. S., & Olmsted, M. P. (2007). Eating disorder not otherwise specified: The view from a tertiary care treatment center. *International Journal of Eating Disorders. Special Issue on Diagnosis and Classification, 40*, S99–S103.

Rodebaugh, T.L., Bielak, T., Vidovic, V., & Moscovitch, D.A. (2016). The effects of social anxiety on interpersonal evaluations of warmth and dominance. *Journal of Anxiety Disorders, 38*, 68–78.

Roder, V., Mueller, D. R., Mueser, K. T., & Brenner, H. D. (2006). Integrated Psychological Therapy (IPT) for schizophrenia: Is it effective? *Schizophrenia Bulletin, 32*(Suppl. 1), S81–S93.

Rodewald, F., Wilhelm-Gossling, C., Emrich, H. M., Reddemann, L., & Gast, U. (2011). Axis-I comorbidity in female patients with dissociative identity disorder and dissociative identity disorder not otherwise specified. *Journal of Nervous and Mental Disease, 199*, 122–131.

Rodrigues, H., Figueira, I., Lopes, A., Goncalves, R., Mendlowicz, M. V., Coutinho, E. S. F., & Ventura, P. (2014). Does d-cycloserine enhance exposure therapy for anxiety disorders in humans? A meta-analysis. *PLoS ONE, 9*(7), e93519. doi:10.1371/journal.pone.0093519

Rodriguez, J. C., Dzierzewski, J. M., & Alessi, C. A. (2015). Sleep problems in the elderly. *Medical Clinics of North America, 99*(2), 431–439. doi:http://dx.doi.org.uml.idm.oclc.org/10.1016/j.mcna.2014.11.013

Roeleveld, N., Zielhuis, G. A., & Gabreels, F. (1997). The prevalence of mental retardation: A critical review of recent literature. *Developmental Medicine and Child Neurology, 39*, 125–132.

Roelofs, K., Hoogduin, K. A., Keijsers, G. P., Naring, G. W., Moene, F. C., & Sandijck, P. (2002). Hypnotic susceptibility in patients with conversion disorder. *Journal of Abnormal Psychology, 111*, 390–395.

Roemer, L., Orsillo, S. M., & Barlow, D. H. (2002). Generalized anxiety disorder. In D. H. Barlow (Ed.), *Anxiety and its disorders* (2nd ed., pp. 477–515). New York, NY: Guilford.

Roesch, R. (1995). Mental health intervention in jails. In G. Davies, S. Lloyd-Bostock, M. McMurran, & C. Wilson (Eds.), *Psychology, law, and criminal justice* (pp. 520–531). New York, NY: Walter de Gruyter.

Roesch, R., & Golding, S. L. (1980). *Competency to stand trial.* Urbana, IL: University of Illinois Press.

Roesch, R., Ogloff, J. R. P., Hart, S. D., Dempster, R. J., Zapf, P. A., & Whittemore, K. E. (1997). The impact of Canadian Criminal Code changes on remands and assessments of fitness to stand trial and criminal responsibility in British Columbia. *Canadian Journal of Psychiatry, 42*, 509–514.

Roesch, R., Zapf, P. A., Webster, C. D., & Eaves, D. (1998). *The Fitness Interview Test.* Burnaby, BC: Mental Health, Law, & Policy Institute, Simon Fraser University.

Rogaeva, E., Kawarai, T., & St. George-Hyslop, P. (2006). Genetic complexity of Alzheimer's disease: Successes and challenges. *Journal of Alzheimer's Disease, 9*, 381–387.

Rogeness, G. A., Cepeda, C., Macedo, C. A., Fischer, C., & Harris, W. R. (1990). Differences in heart rate and blood pressure in children with conduct disorder, major depression, and separation anxiety. *Psychiatry Research, 33*, 199–206.

Rogers, C. R. (1961). *On becoming a person.* Boston, MA: Houghton Mifflin.

Rogers, R., Dion, K. L., & Lynett, E. (1992). Diagnostic validity of antisocial personality disorder. *Law and Human Behavior, 16*, 677–689.

Rogers, R., Duncan, J. C., Lynett, E., & Sewell, K. W. (1994). Prototypical analysis of antisocial personality disorder: DSM-IV and beyond. *Law and Human Behavior, 18*, 471–484.

Rogers, S. (2002). Interventions that facilitate socialization in children with autism. *Journal of Autism and Developmental Disorders, 30*, 351–372.

Rohrbaugh, M., Shoham, V., Spungen, C., & Steinglass, P. (1995). Family systems therapy in practice. In B. Bongar & L. E. Beutler (Eds.), *Comprehensive textbook of psychotherapy: Theory and practice* (pp. 228–253). New York, NY: Oxford University Press.

Roid, G. H. (2003). *Stanford-Binet intelligence scales* (5th ed.). Itasca, IL: Riverside.

Romanow, R. J., & Marchildon, G. P. (2003). Psychological services and the future of health care in Canada. *Canadian Psychology, 44*, 283–295.

Ronningstam, E., & Gunderson, J. G. (1990). Identifying criteria for narcissistic personality disorder. *American Journal of Psychiatry, 147*, 918–922.

Root, T. L., Pisetsky, E. M., Thornton, L., Lichtenstein, P., Pedersen, N. L., & Bulik, C. M. (2010). Patterns of co-morbidity of eating disorders and substance use in Swedish females. *Psychological Medicine, 40*, 105–115. doi: 10.1017/S0033291709005662

Rosa-Alcázar, A. I., Sánchez-Meca, J., Gómez-Conesa, A., & Marín-Martínez, F. (2008). Psychological treatment of obsessive-compulsive disorder: A meta-analysis. *Clinical Psychology Review, 28*, 1310–1325. doi:10.1016/j.cpr.2008.07.001

Rosen, R. C., & Leiblum, S. R. (1995). Treatment of sexual disorders in the 1990s: An integrated approach. *Journal of Consulting and Clinical Psychology, 63*, 877–890.

Rosenbaum, M., & Patterson, K. M. (1995). Group psychotherapy in historical perspective. In B. Bongar & L. E. Beutler (Eds.), *Comprehensive textbook of psychotherapy: Theory and practice* (pp. 173–188). New York, NY: Oxford University Press.

Rosenberg, D. R., & Keshavan, M. S. (1998). Toward a neurodevelopmental model of obsessive-compulsive disorder. *Biological Psychiatry, 43*, 623–640.

Rosenberger, P. H., & Miller, G. A. (1989). Comparing borderline definitions: DSM-III borderline and schizotypal disorders. *Journal of Abnormal Psychology, 92*, 161–169.

Rosenman, R. H., Brand, R. J., Jenkins, C. D., Friedman, M., Straus, R., & Wurm, M. (1975). Coronary heart disease in the Western Collaborative Group Study: Final follow-up experience of 8 1/2 years. *Journal of the American Medical Association, 233*, 872–877.

Rosenvinge, J. H., & Pettersen, G. (2015). Epidemiology of eating disorders part II: An update with a special reference to the DSM-5. *Advances in Eating Disorders: Theory, Research and Practice, 3*, 198–220. doi: 10.1080/21662630.2014.940549

Rösler, A., & Witztum, E. (1998). Treatment of men with paraphilia with a long-acting analogue of gonadotropin-releasing hormone. *New England Journal of Medicine, 338*, 416–422.

Rösler, A., & Witztum, E. (2000). Pharmacotherapy of paraphilias in the next millennium. *Behavioral Sciences and the Law, 18*, 43–56.

Ross, C. A. (1989). *Multiple personality disorder: Diagnosis, clinical features and treatment.* New York, NY: Wiley.

Ross, C. A. (1996). History, phenomenology, and epidemiology of dissociation. In L. K. Michelson & W. J. Ray (Eds.), *Handbook of dissociation* (pp. 3–24). New York, NY: Plenum.

Ross, C. A. (1997). Dissociative identity disorder: Diagnosis, clinical features, and treatment of multiple personality (2nd ed.). New York, NY: Wiley.

Ross, C. A., Anderson, G., Fleisher, W. P., & Norton, G. R. (1991). The frequency of multiple personality disorder among psychiatric inpatients. *American Journal of Psychiatry, 148*, 1717–1720.

Ross, C. A., Heber, S., Norton, G. R., Anderson, G., Anderson, D., & Barchet, P. (1989). The dissociative disorders interview schedule: A structured interview. *Dissociation, 2*, 169–189.

Ross, G. W., & Bowen, J. D. (2002). The diagnosis and differential diagnosis of dementia. *Medical Clinics of North America, 86*, 455–476.

Rossetti, Z. & Hall, S. (2015) Adult sibling relationships with brothers and sisters with severe disabilities. *Research and Practice for Persons with Severe Disabilities, 40*(2),120–137.

Rossiter, L., & Sharpe, D. (2001). The siblings of individuals with mental retardation: A quantitative integration of the literature. *Journal of Child and Family Studies, 10*, 65–84.

Rourke, B. P. (1989). *Nonverbal learning disabilities: The syndrome and the model.* New York, NY: Guilford.

Rourke, B. P., & Finlayson, M. A. (1978). Neuropsychological significance of variations in patterns of academic performance: Verbal and visual-spatial abilities. *Journal of Abnormal Child Psychology, 6*, 121–133.

Rourke, B. P., Ahmad, S. A., Hayman-Abello, S. E., & Warriner, E. M. (2002). Child clinical/pediatric neuropsychology: Some recent advances. *Annual Review of Psychology, 53*, 309–339.

Rowe, R., Costello, E. J., Angold, A., Copeland, W. E., & Maughan, B. (2010). Developmental pathways in oppositional defiant disorder and conduct disorder. *Journal of Abnormal Psychology, 119*(4), 726–738. doi:10.1037/a0020798

Roy, A., Nielsen, D., Rylander, G., Sarchiapone, M., & Segal, N. (1999). Genetics of suicide in depression. *Journal of Clinical Psychiatry 60*(Suppl. 2), 12–17.

Royal Canadian Mounted Police. (2000). *Designer drugs and raves.* Vancouver, BC: RCMP E Division.

Royal College of Psychiatrists. (2001). *DC-LD: Diagnostic criteria for psychiatric disorders for use with adults with learning disabilities/mental retardation* (Vol. 48). London, UK: Springer Science & Business.

Royer, J. M., & Walles, R. (2007). Influences of gender, ethnicity, and motivation on mathematical performance. In D. B. Berch & M. Mazzocco (Eds.), *Why is math so hard for some children? The nature and origins of mathematical learning difficulties and disabilities* (pp. 349–367). Baltimore, MD: Paul H. Brookes.

Rozanski, A., Bairey, C. N., Krantz, D. S., Friedman, J., Resser, K. J., Morell, M., et al. (1988). Mental stress and the induction of silent myocardial ischemia in patients with coronary artery disease. *New England Journal of Medicine, 318*, 1005–1012.

Rubia, K., Alegría, A. A., & Brinson, H. (2014). Brain abnormalities in attention-deficit hyperactivity disorder: A review. *Revista De Neurologia 58*(Supl 1), S3–S18

Rugulies, R. (2002). Depression as a predictor for coronary heart disease: a review and meta-analysis. *American Journal of Preventive Medicine, 23*, 51–61.

Ruscio, A., Brown, T., Chiu, W., Sareen, J., Stein, M., & Kessler, R. (2008). Social fears and social phobia in the USA: Results from the national comorbidity survey replication. *Psychological Medicine, 38*, 15–28.

Rush, A. J., Marangell, L. B., Sackeim, H. A., George, M. S., Brannan, S. K., Davis, S. M., et al. (2005). Vagus nerve stimulation for treatment-resistant depression: A randomized, controlled acute phase trial. *Biological Psychiatry, 58*, 347–354.

Rushton, J. P. (2002). Race, brain size, and IQ. *The General Psychologist, 37*(2), 28–33.

Ruskin, P. E. (1990). Schizophrenia and delusional disorders. In D. Bienenfeld (Ed.), *Verwoerdt's clinical geropsychiatry* (3rd ed., pp. 125–136). Baltimore, MD: Williams & Wilkins.

Russ, E., Heim, A., & Westen, D. (2003). Parental bonding and personality pathology assessed by clinician report. *Journal of Personality Disorders, 17*, 522–536.

Russek, L. G., & Schwartz, G. E. (1997). Perceptions of parental caring predict health status in midlife: A 35-year follow-up of the Harvard Mastery of Stress study. *Psychosomatic Medicine, 59*, 144–149.

Russell, S., & Nehra, A. (2003). The physiology of erectile dysfunction. *Herz, 28*(4), 277–283.

Rutherford, M. J., Cacciola, J. S., & Alterman, A. I. (1999). Antisocial personality disorder and psychopathy in cocaine-dependent women. *American Journal of Psychiatry, 156*, 849–856.

Rutter, M. (1987). Psychosocial resilience and protective mechanisms. *American Journal of Orthopsychiatry, 57*(3), 316–331.

Rutter, M., Bailey, A., Simonoff, E., & Pickles, A. (1997). Genetic influences and autism. In D. J. Cohen & F. R. Volkmar (Eds.), *Handbook of autism and pervasive developmental disorders* (pp. 370–387). New York, NY: Wiley.

Rutter, M., Le Couteur, A., & Lord, C. (2003). ADI-R. *Autism diagnostic interview revised. Manual.* Los Angeles, CA: Western Psychological Services.

Rutter, M., Thapar, A., Pine, D. S., Leckman, J. F., Scott, S., Snowling, M. J., & Taylor, E. (2015). Resilience: Concepts, findings, and clinical implications. In Rutter, M. J., Bishop, D., Pine, D., Scott, S., Stevenson, J. S., Taylor, E. A., & Thapar, A. (Eds.) *Rutter's Child and Adolescent Psychiatry* (pp. 341–351). Chichester, UK: Wiley.

Rutter, M., Tizard, J., Yule, W., Graham, P., & Whitmore, K. (1976). Research report: Isle of Wight Studies, 1964–1974. *Psychological Medicine, 6,* 313–332.

Ryan, R. M., & Deci, E. L. (2000). Self-determination theory and the facilitation of intrinsic motivation, social development, and well-being. *American Psychologist, 55*(1), 68–78.

Rynn, M. A., Siqueland, L., & Rickels, K. (2001). Placebo-controlled trial of sertraline in the treatment of children with generalized anxiety disorder. *American Journal of Psychiatry, 158*(12), 2008–2014.

Sabaté, E. (2003). *Adherence to long-term therapies: Evidence for action.* Geneva, Switzerland: World Health Organization.

Sachs, B. D., Rodriguiz, R. M., Siesser, W. B., Kenan, A., Royer, E. L., Jacobsen, J. P., . . . & Caron, M. G. (2013). The effects of brain serotonin deficiency on behavioural disinhibition and anxiety-like behaviour following mild early life stress. *International Journal of Neuropsychopharmacology, 16*(9), 2081–2094.

Sachs, G. S., & Gardner-Schuster, E. E. (2007). Adjunctive treatment of acute mania: A clinical overview. *Acta Psychiatrica Scandinavica, 116,* 27–34.

Sacker, A., Done, D. J., Crow, T. J., & Goldberg, J. (1995). Antecedents of schizophrenia and affective illness: Obstetric complications. *British Journal of Psychiatry, 166,* 734–741.

Sackett, D. L., Straus, S. E., Richardson, W. S., Rosenberg, W., & Haynes, R. B. (2000). *Evidence-based medicine: How to practice and teach EBM* (2nd ed.). New York, NY: Churchill Livingstone.

Sackeim, H. A., Prudic, J., Devanand, D. P., Nobler, M. S., Lisanby, S. H., Peyser, S., et al. (2000). A prospective, randomized, double-blind comparison of bilateral and right unilateral electroconvulsive therapy at different stimulus intensities. *Archives of General Psychiatry, 57,* 425–434.

Šagud, M., Mihaljević-Peleš, A., Mück-Šeler, D., Pivac, N., Vuksan-Ćusa, B., Brataljenović, T., & Jakovljević, M. (2009). Smoking and schizophrenia. *Psychiatria Danubina, 21*(3), 371–375.

Saklofske, D. H., van de Vijver, F. J. R., Oakland, T., Mpofu, E., & Suzuki, L. A. (2015). Intelligence and culture: History and assessment. In S. Goldstein, D. Princiotta & J. A. Naglieri (Eds.), *Handbook of intelligence: Evolutionary theory, historical perspective, and current concepts* (pp. 341–365). New York, NY: Springer.

Sala, M. M., Caverzasi, E. E., Lazzaretti, M. M., Morandotti, N. N., De Vidovich, G. G., Marraffini, E. E., et al. (2011). Dorsolateral prefrontal cortex and hippocampus sustain impulsivity and aggressiveness in borderline personality disorder. *Journal of Affective Disorders, 131,* 417–421. doi:10.1016/j.jad.2010.11.036

Saladin, M. E., & Santa Ana, E. J. (2004). Controlled drinking: More than just a controversy. *Current Opinion in Psychiatry, 17,* 175–187.

Salekin, R. T., & Frick, P. J. (2005). Psychopathy in children and adolescents: A developmental psychopathology perspective. *Journal of Abnormal Child Psychology, 33,* 403–409.

Salekin, R. T., Rogers, R., & Sewell, K. W. (1996). A review and meta-analysis of the Psychopathy Checklist and Psychopathy Checklist–Revised: Predictive validity of dangerousness. *Clinical Psychology: Science and Practice, 3,* 203–215.

Salkovskis, P. M. (1985). Obsessional-compulsive problems: A cognitive-behavioural analysis. *Behaviour Research and Therapy, 23,* 571–583.

Salkovskis, P. M. (1996). The cognitive approach to anxiety: Threat beliefs, safety-seeking behavior, and the special case of health anxiety and obsessions. In P. M. Salkovskis (Ed.), *Frontiers of cognitive therapy* (pp. 48–74). New York, NY: Guilford.

Salkovskis, P. M., & Warwick, H. M. C. (1986). Morbid preoccupations, health anxiety and reassurance: A cognitive-behavioural approach to hypochondriasis. *Behaviour Research and Therapy, 24,* 597–602.

Sallows, G. O., & Graupner, T. D. (2005). Intensive behavioral treatment for children with autism: Four-year outcome and predictors. *American Journal of Mental Retardation, 110,* 417–438.

Sampson, P. D., Streissguth, A. P., Bookstein, F. L., Little, R. E., Clarren, S. K., Dehaene, P., et al. (1997). Incidence of fetal alcohol syndrome and prevalence of alcohol-related neurodevelopmental disorder. *Teratology, 56,* 317–326.

Samuel, D. B., & Widiger, T. A. (2009). Comparative gender biases in models of personality disorder. *Personality and Mental Health, 3,* 12–25. doi:10.1002/pmh.61

Samuel, D. B., Lynam, D. R., Widiger, T. A., & Ball, S. A. (2011). An expert consensus approach to relating the proposed DSM-5 types and traits. *Personality Disorders: Theory, Research, and Treatment, 3,* 1–16. doi:10.1037/a0023787

Samuels, J., Eaton, W., Bienvenu, O., Brown, C., Costa, P., & Nestadt, G. (2002). Prevalence and correlates of personality disorders in a community sample. *British Journal of Psychiatry, 180*(6), 536–542.

Sánchez-Meca, J., Rosa-Alcázar, A. I., Iniesta-Sepúlveda, M., & Rosa-Alcázar, Á. (2014). Differential efficacy of cognitive-behavioral therapy and pharmacological treatments for pediatric obsessive-compulsive disorder: A meta-analysis. *Journal of Anxiety Disorders, 28,* 31–44.

Sánchez-Meca, J., Rosa-Alcázar, A. I., Marín-Martínez, F., & Gómez-Conesa, A. (2010). Psychological treatment of panic disorder with or without agoraphobia: A meta-analysis. *Clinical Psychology Review, 30,* 37–50.

Sandak, R., Mencl, W. E., Frost, S. J., & Pugh, K. R. (2004). The neurobiological basis of skilled and impaired reading: Recent findings and new directions. *Scientifica Studies of Reading, 8*(3), 273–292.

Sanday, P. R. (1981). The socio-cultural context of rape: A cross-cultural study. *Journal of Social Issues, 37,* 5–27.

Sanders, M. R. (2010). Adopting a public health approach to the delivery of evidence-based parenting interventions. *Canadian Psychology, 51,* 17–23.

Sandler, I., Wolchik S. A., Cruden, G., Mahrer, N. E., Ahn, S., Brincks, A., & Brown, C. H. (2014). Overview of meta-analyses of the prevention of mental health, substance use, and conduct problems. *Annual Review of Clinical Psychology, 10,* 243–273.

Sandnabba, N. K., Santtila, P., Alison, L., & Nordling, N. (2002). Demographics, sexual behavior, family background, and abuse experiences of practitioners of sadomasochistic sex: A review of recent research. *Sexual and Relationship Therapy, 17,* 39–55.

Sankar, A., Scott, J., Paszkiewicz, A., Giampietro, V. P., Steiner, H., & Fu, C. H. Y. (2015). Neural effects of cognitive–behavioural therapy on dysfunctional attitudes in depression. *Psychological Medicine, 45*(7), 1425–1433. https://doi.org/10.1017/S0033291714002529

Santtila, P., Sandnabba, N. K., Alison, L., & Nordling, N. (2002). Investigating the underlying structure in sadomasochistically oriented behavior. *Archives of Sexual Behavior, 31*(2), 185–196.

Sapers, H. (2016). *Annual report of the Office of the Correctional Investigator 2015-2016.* Ottawa, ON. Available at www.oci-bec.gc.ca/cnt/rpt/pdf/annrpt/annrpt20152016-eng.pdf

Sapolsky, R. M. (1989). Hypercortisolism among socially subordinate wild baboons originates at the CNS level. *Archives of General Psychiatry, 46,* 1047–1051.

Sapolsky, R. M. (1990). Stress in the wild. *Scientific American, 262,* 116–123.

Sapolsky, R. M. (1994). *Why zebras don't get ulcers: A guide to stress, stress-related diseases, and coping.* New York, NY: Freeman.

Sapolsky, R. M. (1995). Social subordinance as a marker of hypercortisolism. Some unexpected subtleties. *Annals of the New York Academy of Sciences,* Vol. 771, 626–639.

Sapolsky, R. M. (2000). Glucocorticoids and hippocampal atrophy in neuropsychiatric disorders. *Archives of General Psychiatry, 57,* 925–935.

Sapolsky, R., & Plotsky, P. M. (1990). Hypercortisolism and its possible neural basis. *Biological Psychiatry, 27,* 937–952.

Şar, V., Akyüz, G., Kundakçı, T., Kızıltan, E., & Doğan, O. (2004). Childhood trauma, dissociation, and psychiatric comorbidity in patients with conversion disorder. *American Journal of Psychiatry, 161*(12), 2271–2276.

Sarafino, E. P. (1997.) *Health psychology: Biopsychosocial interactions.* New York, NY: Wiley.

Sareen, J., Campbell, D. W., Leslie, W. D., Malisza, K. L., Stein, M. B., Paulus, M. P., et al. (2007). Striatal function in generalized social phobia: A functional magnetic resonance imaging study. *Biological Psychiatry, 61,* 396–404.

Sareen, J., Cox, B. J., Afifi, T. O., Clara, I., & Yu, B. N. (2005). Perceived need for mental health treatment in a nationally representative Canadian survey. *Canadian Journal of Psychiatry, 50,* 643–651.

Sariaslan, A., Fazel, S., D'onofrio, B. M., Långström, N., Larsson, H., Bergen, S. E., . . . & Lichtenstein, P. (2016). Schizophrenia and subsequent neighborhood deprivation: Revisiting the social drift hypothesis using population, twin and molecular genetic data. *Translational Psychiatry, 6*(5), 1–7.

Sarin, S., Amsel, R., & Binik, Y. M. (2014). How hot is he? A psychophysiological and psychosocial examination of the arousal patterns of sexually functional and dysfunctional men. *Journal of Sexual Medicine, 11,* 1725–1740.

Sarin, S., Amsel, R., & Binik, Y. M. (2016). A streetcar named derousal? A psychophysiological examination of the desire-arousal distinction in sexually functional and dysfunctional women. *Journal of Sex Research, 53,* 711–729.

Sattler, J. M. (2008). *Assessment of children: Cognitive applications* (5th ed.). La Mesa, CA: Author.

Savage, C. R., Baer, L., Keuthen, N. J., Brown, H. D., Rauch, S. L., & Jenike, M. A. (1999). Organizational strategies mediate nonverbal memory impairment in obsessive-compulsive disorder. *Biological Psychiatry, 45,* 905–916.

Scaini, S., Belotti, R., & Ogliari, A. (2014). Genetic and environmental contributions to social anxiety across different ages: A meta-analytic approach to twin data. *Journal of Anxiety Disorders, 28*, 650–656.

Scanlon, D. (2013). Specific learning disability and its newest definition: Which is comprehensive? And which is insufficient? *Journal of Learning Disabilities, 46*(1), 26–33.

Scarr, S., & McCartney, K. (1983). How people make their own environments: Environmental effects. *Child Development, 54*, 424–435.

Schaafsma, D., Kok, G., Stoffelen, J. M., Van Doorn, P., & Curfs, L. M. (2014). Identifying the important factors associated with teaching sex education to people with intellectual disability: A cross-sectional survey among paid care staff. *Journal of Intellectual and Developmental Disability, 39*(2), 157–166.

Schachar, R., Jadad, A. R., Gauld, M., Boyle, M., Booker, L., Snider, A., et al. (2002). Attention-deficit hyperactivity disorder: Critical appraisal of extended treatment studies. *Canadian Journal of Psychiatry, 47*, 337–348.

Schachter, S., & Latane, B. (1964). Crime, cognition, and the autonomic nervous system. In D. Levine (Ed.), *Nebraska Symposium on Motivation* (Vol. 12). Lincoln, NB: University of Nebraska Press.

Schacter, D. L., & Loftus, E. F. (2013). Memory and law: What can cognitive neuroscience contribute? *Nature Neuroscience, 16*(2), 119–123.

Schaler, J. A. (2004). *Szasz under fire: The psychiatric abolitionist faces his critics.* Chicago, IL: Open Court.

Schalock, R. L. (2002). What's in a name? *Mental Retardation, 40*, 57–59.

Schalock, R. L. (Ed.). (1996). *Quality of life. Vol. I: Conceptualization and measurement.* Washington, DC: American Association on Mental Retardation.

Schalock, R. L. (Ed.). (1997). *Quality of life. Vol. II: Application to persons with disabilities.* Washington, DC: American Association on Mental Retardation.

Schalock, R. L., Borthwick-Duffy, S. A., Bradley, V. J., Buntinx, W. H., Coulter, D. L., Craig, E. M., . . . & Shogren, K. A. (2010). *Intellectual disability: Definition, classification, and systems of supports.* Washington, DC: American Association on Intellectual and Developmental Disabilities.

Schalock, R. L., Luckasson, R. A., & Shogren, K. A. (2007). The renaming of mental retardation: Understanding the change to the term intellectual disability. *Intellectual and developmental disabilities, 45*(2), 116–124.

Schalock, R. L., Stark, J. A., Snell, M. E., Coulter, D. L., Polloway, E. A., Luckasson, R., et al. (1994). The changing conception of mental retardation: Implications for the field. *Mental Retardation, 32*, 181–193.

Scherk, H., Pajonk, F. G., & Leucht, S. (2007). Second-generation antipsychotic agents in the treatment of acute mania: A systematic review and meta-analysis of randomized controlled trials. *Archives of General Psychiatry, 64*, 442–455.

Schiffer, B., Peschel, T., Paul, T., Gizewski, E., Forsting, M., Leygraf, N., et al. (2007). Structural brain abnormalities in the frontostriatal system and cerebellum in pedophilia. *Journal of Psychiatric Research, 41*, 753–62.

Schildkraut, J. J. (1965). The catecholamine hypothesis of affective disorders: A review of supporting evidence. *American Journal of Psychiatry, 122*, 609–622.

Schiller, C. E., Meltzer-Brody, S., & Rubinow, D. R. (2015). The role of reproductive hormones in postpartum depression. *CNS Spectrum, 20*, 48–59.

Schiltz, K., Witzel, J., Northoff, G., Zierhut, K., Gubka, U., Fellmann, H., et al. (2007). Brain pathology in pedophilic offenders. *Archives of General Psychiatry, 64*, 737–46.

Schlam, T. R., & Baker, T. B. (2013). Interventions for tobacco smoking. *Annual Review of Clinical Psychology, 9*, 675–702.

Schmauk, F. J. (1970). Punishment, arousal, and avoidance learning in sociopaths. *Journal of Abnormal Psychology, 76*, 325–335.

Schneier, F. R. (2011). Pharmacotherapy of social anxiety disorder. *Expert Opinion on Pharmacotherapy, 12*, 1–11.

Schnell, K., & Herpertz, S. C. (2007). Effects of dialectic-behavioral-therapy on the neural correlates of affective hyperarousal in borderline personality disorder. *Journal of Psychiatric Research, 41*, 837–847.

Schnell, K., Dietrich, T., Schnitker, R., Daumann, J., & Herpertz, S. C. (2007). Processing of autobiographical memory retrieval cues in borderline personality disorder. *Journal of Affective Disorders, 97*, 253–259.

Schoenman, T. J. (1984). The mentally ill witch in textbooks of abnormal psychology: Current status and implications of a fallacy. *Professional Psychology, 15*, 299–314.

Schopp, R. F. (2001). *Competence, condemnation, and commitment: An integrated theory of mental health law.* Washington, DC: American Psychological Association.

Schreibman, L. (2000). Intensive behavioral/psychoeducational treatments for autism: Research needs and future directions. *Journal of Autism and Developmental Disorders, 30*, 373–376.

Schroeck, J. L., Ford, J., Conway, E. L., Kurtzhalts, K. E., Gee, M. E., Vollmer, K. A., & Mergenhagen, K. A. (2016). Review of safety and efficacy of sleep medicines in older adults. *Clinical Therapeutics, 38*(11), 2340–2372. doi:http://dx.doi.org.uml.idm.oclc.org/10.1016/j.clinthera.2016.09.010

Schuck, P. (1999, April 20). London psychiatric pioneer gets recognition at long last. *The London Free Press.* Retrieved from www.physicianscanada.net/article1.htm

Schulsinger, F., Kety, S. S., Rosenthal, D., & Wender, P. H. (1979). A family study of suicide. In M. Schou & E. Stromgren (Eds.), *Origin, prevention and treatment of affective disorders* (pp. 277–287). New York, NY: Academic Press.

Schultz, D. S., & Brabender, V. M. (2013). More challenges since Wikipedia: The effects of exposure to internet information about the Rorschach on selected Comprehensive System variables. *Journal of Personality Assessment, 95*(2), 149–158. https://doi.org/10.1080/00223891.2012.725438

Schultz, D. S., & Loving, J. L. (2012). Challenges since Wikipedia: The availability of Rorschach information online and internet users' reactions to online media coverage of the Rorschach–Wikipedia debate. *Journal of Personality Assessment, 94*(1), 73–81. https://doi.org/10.1080/00223891.2011.627963

Schulz, R., & Beach, S. R. H. (1999). Caregiving as a risk factor for mortality: Caregiver Health Effects Study. *Journal of the American Medical Association, 282*, 2215–2219.

Schulz, R., & Martire, L. M. (2004). Family caregiving of persons with dementia: Prevalence, health effects, and support strategies. *American Journal of Geriatric Psychiatry, 12*, 240–249.

Schutzman (Re), 2013 ONCA 48

Schwartz, J. B., & Nye, C. (2006). A systematic review, synthesis, and evaluation of the evidence for teaching sign language to children with autism. *Evidence Based Practice Briefs, 1*, 1–17.

Schwartz, J. S., & Maric, M. (2015). Negative cognitive errors in youth: Specificity to anxious and depressive symptoms and age differences. *Behavioural and Cognitive Psychotherapy, 43*, 526–537.

Schwarz, E., & Bahn, S. (2008). The utility of biomarker discovery approaches for the detection of disease mechanisms in psychiatric disorders. *British Journal of Pharmacology, 153*(Suppl. 1), 133–136.

Schweinhart, L. J., & Weikart, D. P. (1988). The High/Scope Perry Preschool Program. In R. H. Price, E. L. Cowen, R. P. Lorion, & J. Ramos-McKay (Eds.), *Fourteen ounces of prevention: A casebook for practitioners* (pp. 53–65). Washington, DC: American Psychological Association.

Schweinhart, L. J., Montie, J., Xiang, Z., Barnett, W. S., Belfield, C. R., & Nores, M. (2005). *Lifetime effects: The High/Scope Perry Preschool study through age 40.* (Monographs of the High/Scope Educational Research Foundation, 14). Ypsilanti, MI: High/Scope Press.

Scogin, F., Welsh, D., Hanson, A., Stump, J., & Coates, A. (2005). Evidence-based psychotherapies for depression in older adults. *Clinical Psychology: Science and Practice, 12*, 222–237.

Scorgie, K., & Sobsey, D. (2000). Transformational outcomes associated with parenting children who have disabilities. *Mental Retardation, 38*, 195–206.

Scorolli, C., Ghirlanda, S., Enquist, M., Zattoni, S., Jannini, E., Stockholms universitet, et al. (2007). Relative prevalence of different fetishes. *International Journal of Impotence Research, 19*, 432–437.

Scorsese, M. (Director). (2010). *Shutter Island* [Motion Picture]. USA: Paramount Pictures.

Scott, K. M., Lim, C., Al-Hamzawi, A., Alonso, J., Bruffaerts, R., Caldas-de-Almeida, J. M., Florescu, S., de Girolamo, G. . . . (2016). Association of mental disorders with subsequent chronic physical conditions: World mental health surveys from 17 countries. *JAMA Psychiatry, 73*(2), 150–158.

Scott, T., Mackenzie, C. S., Chipperfield, J., & Sareen, J. (2010). Mental health service use among Canadian older adults with anxiety disorders and high levels of anxiety symptoms. *Aging and Mental Health, 14*, 790–800.

Sealy, P., & Whitehead, P. C. (2004). Forty years of deinstitutionalization of psychiatric services in Canada: An empirical assessment. *Canadian Journal of Psychiatry, 49*, 249–257.

Sedvall, G. (1992). The current status of PET scanning with respect to schizophrenia. *Neuropsychopharmacology, 7*, 41–54.

Seeds, P. M., & Dozois, D. J. A. (2010). Prospective evaluation of a cognitive vulnerability-stress model for depression: The interaction of schema self-structure and negative life events. *Journal of Clinical Psychology, 66*, 1307–1323.

Seehusen, D. A., Baldwin, L. M., Runkle, G. P., & Clark, G. (2005). Are family physicians appropriately screening for postpartum depression? *Obstetrics Obstetrical & Gynecological Survey, 60*, 630–631.

Seeman, P., & Lee, T. (1975). Antipsychotic drugs: Direct correlation between clinical potency and presynaptic action on dopamine neurons. *Science, 188*, 1217–1219.

Seeman, P., Chau-Wong, M., Tedesco, J., & Wong, K. (1976). Dopamine receptors in human and calf brains, using [^{3}H] apomorphine and an antipsychotic drug. *Proceedings of the National Academy of Science USA, 73*, 4353–4358.

Segal, Z. V., & Shaw, B. F. (1996). Cognitive therapy. In L. J. Dickstein, J. M. Oldham, & M. B. Riba, *Annual Review of Psychiatry* (Vol. 15, pp. 69–90). Washington, DC: American Psychiatric Press.

Segal, Z. V., Bieling, P., Young, T., MacQueen, G., Cooke, R., Martin, L., et al. (2010). Antidepressant monotherapy vs sequential pharmacotherapy and mindfulness-based cognitive therapy, or placebo, for relapse prophylaxis in recurrent depression. *Archives of General Psychiatry, 67*, 1256–1264.

Segal, Z. V., Kennedy, S. H., & Cohen, N. L. (2001). Clinical guidelines for the treatment of depressive disorders. V. Combining psychotherapy and pharmacotherapy. *Canadian Journal of Psychiatry, 46*(Suppl. 91), 59–62.

Segal, Z. V., Kennedy, S., Gemar, M., Hood, K., Pedersen, R., & Buis, T. (2006). Cognitive reactivity to sad mood provocation and the prediction of depressive relapse. *Archives of General Psychiatry, 63*, 749–755.

Segal, Z. V., Williams, J. M. G., & Teasdale, J. D. (2002). *Mindfulness-based cognitive therapy for depression: A new approach to preventing relapse.* New York, NY: Guilford.

Segal, Z. V., Williams, J. M. G., & Teasdale, J. D. (2013). *Mindfulness-based cognitive therapy for depression* (2nd ed.). New York, NY: Guilford.

Séguin, M., Lesage, A., Chawky, N., Guy, A., Daigle, F., Girard, G., et al. (2006). Suicide cases in New Brunswick from April 2002 to May 2003: The importance of better recognizing substance and mood disorder comorbidity. *Canadian Journal of Psychiatry, 51*, 581–586.

Seibyl, J. P., Scanley, E., Krystal, J. H., & Innis, R. B. (2004). Neuroimaging methodologies: Utilizing radiotracers or nuclear magnetic resonance. In D. S. Charney & E. J. Nester (Eds.), *Neurobiology of mental illness* (2nd ed., pp. 190–209). Oxford, UK: Oxford University Press.

Seidman, B. T., Marshall, W. L., Hudson, S. M., & Robertson, P. J. (1994). An examination of intimacy and loneliness in sex offenders. *Journal of Interpersonal Violence, 9*, 518–534.

Seidman, L. J. (2006). Neuropsychological functioning in people with ADHD across the lifespan. *Clinical Psychology Review, 26*(4), 466–485.

Seidman, S. N., & Roose, S. P. (2000). The relationship between depression and erectile dysfunction. *Current Psychiatric Reports, 2*, 201–205.

Selby, E. A., Kranzler, A., Fehling, K. B., & Panza, E. (2015). Nonsuicidal self-injury disorder: The path to diagnostic validity and final obstacles. *Clinical Psychology Review, 38*, 79–91.

Seligman, M. E. P. (1971). Phobia and preparedness. *Behavior Therapy, 2*, 307–320.

Seligman, M. E. P. (1975). *Helplessness: On depression, development and death.* San Francisco, CA: Freeman.

Sellbom, M., & Bagby, R. M. (2010). Detection of overreported psychopathology with the MMPI-2 RF form validity scales. *Psychological Assessment, 22*(4), 757.

Selye, H. (1956). *The stress of life.* New York, NY: McGraw-Hill.

Semkovska, M. & McLoughlin, D. M. (2010). Objective cognitive performance associated with electroconvulsive therapy for depression: A systematic review and meta-analysis. *Biological Psychiatry, 68*, 568–577.

Semple, R. J., Lee, J., & Miller, L. F. (2014). Mindfulness-based cognitive therapy for children. In R. A. Baer (Ed.), *Mindfulness-based treatment approaches: Clinician's guide to evidence base and applications* (2nd ed., pp. 161–188). San Diego, CA: Elsevier Inc.

Semrud-Clikeman, M., & Fine, J. (2011). Presence of cysts on magnetic resonance images (MRIs) in children with Asperger disorder and nonverbal learning disabilities. *Journal of Child Neurology, 26*(4), 417–475.

Semrud-Clikeman, M., & Harder, L. (2011). Neuropsychological correlates of written expression in college students with ADHD. *Journal of Attention Disorders 15*(3), 215–223.

Semrud-Clikeman, M., & Hynd, G. W. (1990). Right hemispheric dysfunction in nonverbal learning disabilities: Social, academic, and adaptive functioning in adults and children. *Psychological Bulletin, 107*(2), 196–209.

Serban, G., Conte, H. R., & Plutchik, R. (1987). Borderline and schizotypal personality disorders: Mutually exclusive or overlapping? *Journal of Personality Assessment, 5*, 15–22.

Serin, R. C., & Amos, N. L. (1995). The role of psychopathy in the assessment of dangerousness. *International Journal of Law and Psychiatry, 18*, 231–238.

Serin, R. C., & Brown, S. L. (2000). The clinical use of the Hare Psychopathy Checklist–Revised in contemporary risk assessment. In C. Gacono (Ed.), *The clinical and forensic assessment of psychopathy: A practitioner's guide* (pp. 251–268). Hillsdale, NJ: Erlbaum.

Serin, R. C., & Kuriychuk, M. (1994). Social and cognitive processing deficits in violent offenders: Implications for treatment. *International Journal of Law and Psychiatry, 17*, 431–441.

Serin, R. C., & Preston, D. L. (2001). Managing and treating violent offenders. In J. B. Ashford, B. D. Sales, & W. Reid (Eds.), *Treating adult and juvenile offenders with special needs* (pp. 249–272). Washington, DC: American Psychological Association.

Seto, M. C., & Kuban, M. (1996). Criterion-related validity of a phallometric test for paraphilic rape and sadism. *Behaviour Research and Therapy, 34*, 175–183.

Seto, M.C., Hanson, R.K., & Babchishin, K.M. (2011). Contact sexual offending by men with online sexual offenses. *Sexual Abuse: A Journal of Research and Treatment, 23*, 124–45.

Seymour, A. (2006, August 17). Man who fought treatment ready to "get on with his life": Starson well enough to join community, psychiatrist tells panel. *The Ottawa Citizen,* p. B1.

Shadish, W. R., & Baldwin, S. A. (2005). Effects of behavioral marital therapy: A meta-analysis of randomized controlled trials. *Journal of Consulting and Clinical Psychology, 73*, 6–14.

Shadish, W. R., Matt, G. E., Navarro, A. M., Siegle, G., Crits-Christoph, P., Hazelrigg, M. D., et al. (1997). Evidence that therapy works in clinically representative conditions. *Journal of Consulting and Clinical Psychology, 65*, 355–365.

Shaffer, D., & Craft, L. (1999). Methods of adolescent suicide prevention. *Journal of Clinical Psychiatry, 60*(Suppl. 2), 70–74.

Shaffer, D., Fisher, P., Dulcan, M., Davies, M., Piacentini, J., Schwab-Stone, M. E., et al. (1996). The NIMH Diagnostic Interview Schedule for Children Version 2.3 (DISC–2.3): Description, acceptability, prevalence rates, and performance in the MECA study. *Journal of the American Academy of Child and Adolescent Psychiatry, 35*, 865–877.

Shaffer, D., Garland, A., Gould, M., Fisher, P., & Trautman, P. (1988). Preventing teenage suicide: A critical review. *Journal of the American Academy of Child & Adolescent Psychiatry, 27*, 675–686.

Shafran, R., & Rachman, S. (2004). Thought-action fusion: A review. *Journal of Behavior Therapy and Experimental Psychiatry, 35*, 87–107.

Shafran, R., Cooper, Z., & Fairburn, C. G. (2002). Clinical perfectionism: A cognitive–behavioural analysis. *Behaviour Research and Therapy, 40*(7), 773–791. http://doi.org/10.1016/S0005-7967(01)00059-6

Shamblen, S. R., & Derzon, J. H. (2009). A preliminary study of the population-adjusted effectiveness of substance abuse prevention programming: Towards making IOM program types comparable. *Journal of Primary Prevention, 30*, 89–107.

Shapiro, D. (1981). *Autonomy and rigid character.* New York, NY: Basic Books.

Shapiro, F. (2001). *Eye movement desensitization and reprocessing: Basic principles, protocols, and procedures* (2nd ed.). New York, NY: Guilford.

Sharma, A., Gokulchandran, N., Sane, H., Nagrajan, A., Paranjape, A., Kulkarni, P., . . . Biju, H. (2013). Autologous bone marrow mononuclear cell therapy for autism: An open label proof of concept study. *Stem Cells International, 2013*, 1–13.

Sharma, M., & Rush, S. E. (2014). Mindfulness-based stress reduction as a stress management intervention for healthy individuals: A systematic review. *Journal of Evidence-Based Complementary & Alternative Medicine, 19*(4), 271–286.

Shattell, M. M., Hamilton, D., Starr, S. S., Jenkins, C. J., & Hinderliter, N. A. (2008). Mental health service needs of a Latino population: A community-based participatory research project. *Issues in mental health nursing, 29*, 351–370.

Shaw, J., & Porter, S. (2012). Psychopathy and the criminal career trajectory. In H. Hakkanen-Nyholm & Nyholm, J. (Eds.), *Psychopathy and law.* West Sussex, UK: Wiley.

Shaw, P., Eckstrand, K., Sharp, W., Blumenthal, J., Lerch, J. P., Greenstein, D., et al. (2007). Attention-deficit/hyperactivity disorder is characterized by a delay in cortical maturation. *Proceedings of the National Academy of Sciences of the United States of America, 104*, 19649–19654. doi:10.1073/pnas.0707741104

Shaywitz, S. (2008). Why some smart people can't read. In M. H. Immordino-Yang (Ed.), *The Jossey-Bass reader on the brain and learning* (pp. 242–250). San Francisco, CA: Jossey-Bass.

Shaywitz, S. E., Morris, R., & Shaywitz, B.A. (2008). The education of dyslexic children from childhood to young adulthood. *Annual Review of Psychology, 59*, 451–475.

Shaywitz, S. E., Shaywitz, B. A., Fletcher, J., & Escobar, M. (1990). Prevalence of reading disability in boys and girls: Results of the Connecticut Longitudinal Study. *Journal of the American Medical Association, 254*, 998–1002.

Sheline, Y. I., Sanghavi, M., Mintun, M. A., & Gado, M. H. (1999). Depression duration but not age predicts hippocampal volume loss in medically healthy women with recurrent major depression. *Journal of Neuroscience, 19*, 5034–5043.

Shelton, D. (2006). A study of young offenders with learning disabilities. *Journal of Correctional Health Care, 12*(1), 36–44.

Shenton, M. E., Dickey, C. C., Frumin, M., & McCarley, R. W. (2001). A review of MRI findings in schizophrenia. *Schizophrenia Research, 49*, 1–52.

Sher, K. J., Trull, T. J., Bartholow, B. D., & Vieth, A. (1999). Personality and alcoholism: Issues, methods, and etiological processes. In K. E. Leonard & H. T. Blane (Eds.), *Psychological theories of drinking and alcoholism* (2nd ed., pp. 54–105). New York, NY: Guilford.

Shields, B. (2005). *Down Came the Rain.* New York, NY: Hyperion Books.

Shields, S. (2000). Enhanced surveillance of Canadian street youth—Phase II: Self-identified Aboriginal youth. Ottawa, ON: Bureau of HIV/AIDS, STD and TB.

Shimada-Sugmoto, M., Otowa, T., & Hettema, J. M. (2015). Genetics of anxiety disorders: Genetic epidemiological and molecular studies in humans. *Psychiatry and Clinical Neurosciences, 69*(7), 388–401.

Shingleton, R. M., Thompson-Brenner, H., Thompson, D. R., Pratt, E. M., & Franko, D. L. (2015). Gender differences in clinical trials of binge eating disorder: An analysis of aggregated data. *Journal of Consulting and Clinical Psychology, 83,* 382–386. doi: 10.1037/a0038849

Shinn, M., & Toohey, S. (2003). Community contexts of human welfare. *Annual Review of Psychology, 54,* 427–459.

Shneidman, E. S. (1993). *Suicide as psychache: A clinical approach to self-destructive behavior.* New York, NY: Rowman & Littlefield.

Shogren, K. A., & Broussard, R. (2011). Exploring the perceptions of self-determination of individuals with intellectual disability. *Intellectual and Developmental Disabilities, 49,* 86–102.

Shorter, E. (1997). *A history of psychiatry: From the era of the asylum to the age of Prozac.* New York, NY: Wiley.

Shrivastava, A., Johnston, M., Shah, N., & Burueau, Y. (2010). Redefining outcome measures in schizophrenia: Integrating social and clinical parameters. *Current Opinion in Psychiatry, 23,* 120–126.

Siegel, S. (2016). The heroin overdose mystery. *Current Directions in Psychological Science, 25*(6), 375–379.

Siegle, G. J., Steinhauer, S. R., Thase, M. E., Stenger, V. A., & Carter, C. S. (2002). Can't shake that feeling: fMRI assessment of sustained amygdala activity in response to emotional information in depressed individuals. *Biological Psychiatry, 51,* 693–707.

Sierra, M., Senior, C., Dalton, J., McDonough, M., Bond, A., Phillips, M. L., et al. (2002). Autonomic response in depersonalization disorder. *Archives of General Psychiatry, 59,* 833–838.

Siever, L. J. (1985). Biological markers in schizotypal personality disorders. *Schizophrenia Bulletin, 11,* 564–575.

Siever, L. J., & Davis, K. L. (1991). A psychobiological perspective on the personality disorders. *American Journal of Psychiatry, 148,* 1647–1658.

Sigelman, C. K., Schoenrock, C. J., Winer, J. L., Spanhel, C. L., Hromas, S. G., Martin, P. W., et al. (1981). Issues in interviewing mentally retarded persons: An empirical study. In R. H. Bruininks, C. E. Meyers, B. B. Sigford, & K. C. Lakin (Eds.), *Deinstitutionalization and community adjustment of mentally retarded people. Monograph of the American Association on Mental Deficiency,* No. 4 (pp. 114–132). Washington, DC: American Association on Mental Deficiency.

Sigman, M., & Mundy, P. (1989). Social attachments in autistic children. *Journal of Child Psychiatry, 28,* 74–81.

Silberg, J. L., Maes, H., & Eaves, L. J. (2010). Genetic and environmental influences on the transmission of parental depression to children's depression and conduct disturbance: An extended children of twins study. *Journal of Child Psychology and Psychiatry, 51*(6), 734–744. doi:10.1111/j.1469-7610.2010.02205.x

Silbersweig, D., Clarkin, J. F., Goldstein, M., Kernberg, O. F., Tuescher, O., Levy, K. N., et al. (2007). Failure of frontolimbic inhibitory function in the context of negative emotion in borderline personality disorder. *American Journal of Psychiatry, 164,* 1832–1841.

Silver, C. H., Ruff, R. M., Iverson, G. L., Barth, J. T., Broshek, D. K., Bush, S.S., et al. (2008). Learning disabilities: The need for neuropsychological evaluation. *Archives of Clinical Neuropsychology, 23,* 217–219.

Silverman, K. W., Ortiz, C. D., Viswesvaran, C., Burns, B. J., Kolko, D. J., Putnam, F. W., et al. (2008). Evidence-based psychosocial treatments for children and adolescents exposed to traumatic events. *Journal of Clinical Child and Adolescent Psychology, 37,* 156–183.

Simeon, D. (2009). Depersonalization disorder. In P. F. Dell & J. A. O'Neil (Eds.), *Dissociation and the dissociative disorders: DSM-V and beyond* (pp. 435–444). New York, NY: Routledge.

Simeon, D., Guralnik, O., Knutelska, M., Yehuda, R., & Schmeidler, J. (2003). Basal norepinephrine in depersonalization disorder. *Psychiatry Research, 121,* 93–97.

Simeon, D., Knutelska, M., Nelson, D., & Guralnik, O. (2003). Feeling unreal: A depersonalization disorder update of 117 cases. *Journal of Clinical Psychiatry, 64*(9), 990–997.

Simmons, H. G. (1987). Psychosurgery and the abuse of psychiatric authority in Ontario. *Journal of Health Politics, Policy and Law, 12,* 537–550.

Simon, G. E. (2002). Management of somatoform and factitious disorders. In P. Natham, & J. M. Gorman (Eds.), *A guide to treatments that work* (2nd ed., pp. 408–422). London, UK: Oxford University Press.

Simon, G. E., & Perlis, R. H. (2010). Personalized medicine for depression: Can we match patients with treatments? *American Journal of Psychiatry, 167,* 1445–1455. doi:10.1176/appi.ajp.2010.0911680

Simon, T. J., & Rivera, S. M. (2007). Neuroanatomical approaches to the study of mathematical ability and disability. In D. B. Berch & M. Mazzacco (Eds.), *Why is math so hard for some children? The nature and origins of mathematical learning difficulties and disabilities* (pp. 283–305). Baltimore, MD: Paul H. Brookes.

Simonoff, E., Pickles, A., Meyer, J. M., Silberg, J. L., Maes, H. H., Loeber, R., et al. (1997). The Virginia Study of Adolescent Behavioral Development: Influences of age, sex, and impairment on rates of disorder. *Archives of General Psychiatry, 54,* 801–808.

Simpson, T. L., Kivlahan, D. R., Bush, K. R., & McFall, M. E. (2005). Telephone self-monitoring among alcohol use disorder patients in early recovery: A randomized study of feasibility and measurement reactivity. *Drug and Alcohol Dependence, 79,* 241–250.

Sims, T., Hogan, C. L., & Carstensen, L. L. (2015). Selectivity as an emotion regulation strategy: Lessons from older adults. *Current Opinion in Psychology, 3,* 80–84.

Singh, J. P., Desmarais, S. L., Hurducas, C., Arbach-Lucioni, K., Condemarin, C., Dean, K., . . . & Ho, R. M. Y. (2014). International perspectives on the practical application of violence risk assessment: A global survey of 44 countries. *International Journal of Forensic Mental Health, 13,* 193–206.

Sirri, L., & Fava, G. A. (2013). Diagnostic criteria for psychosomatic research and somatic symptom disorders. *International Review of Psychiatry, 25,* 19–30.

Siu, A. L., Bibbins-Domingo, K., Grossman, D. C., Baumann, L. C., Davidson, K. W., Ebell, M., . . . & Krist, A. H. (2016). Screening for autism spectrum disorder in young children: US Preventive Services Task Force recommendation statement. *Jama, 315*(7), 691–696.

Sivertsen, B. (2007). Chronic primary insomnia among older individuals. *Geriatrics and Aging, 10*(6), 385–388.

Sivertsen, B., Omvik, S., Pallesen, S., Bjorvatn, B., Havik, O. E., Kvale, G., Nielsen, G. H., & Nordhus, I. H. (2006). Cognitive behavioral therapy vs zopiclone for treatment of chronic primary insomnia in older adults. *JAMA, 295*(24), 2851–2858.

Skeem, J., Johansson, P., Andershed, H., Kerr, M, & Louden, J. E. (2007). Two subtypes of psychopathic violent offenders that parallel primary and secondary variants. *Journal of Abnormal Psychology, 116,* 395–409.

Skeem, J. L., & Mulvey, E. P. (2001). Psychopathy and community violence among civil psychiatric patients: Results from the MacArthur Violence Risk Assessment Study. *Journal of Consulting and Clinical Psychology, 69,* 358–374.

Skeem, J. L., Monahan, J., & Mulvey, E. P. (2002). Psychopathy, treatment involvement, and subsequent violence among civil psychiatric patients. *Law and Human Behavior, 26,* 577–603.

Skinner, B. F. (1953). *Science and human behavior.* New York, NY: Macmillan.

Skinner, C. H., Freeland, J. T., & Shapiro, E. S. (2003). Procedural issues associated with the behavioral assessment of children. In C. R. Reynolds & R. W. Kamphaus (Eds.), *Handbook of psychological and educational assessment of children: Personality, behavior and context* (2nd ed., pp. 30–47). New York, NY: Guilford.

Skinner, M. E., & Lindstrom, B. D. (2003). Bridging the gap between high school and college: Strategies for the successful transition of students with learning disabilities. *Preventing School Failure, 47,* 132–137.

Sklar, L. S., & Anisman, H. (1979). Stress and coping factors influence tumor growth. *Science, 205,* 513–515.

Skodol, A. E., Gunderson, J. G., Shea, M. T., McGlashan, T. H., Morey, L. C., Sanislow, C. A., et al. (2005). The collaborative longitudinal personality disorders study (CLPS): Overview and implications. *Journal of Personality Disorders, 19,* 487–504.

Skrtic, T. M., Summers, J. A., Brotherson, M. J., & Turnbull, A. P. (1984). Severely handicapped children and their brothers and sisters. In J. Blacher (Ed.), *Severely handicapped young children and their families: Research in review* (pp. 215–246). New York, NY: Academic Press.

Skuse, D., Bruce, H., Dowdney, L., & Mrazek, D. (2011). *Child psychology and psychiatry: Frameworks for practice.* Oxford, UK: Wiley.

Slade, P. D. (1974). Psychometric studies of obsessional illness and obsessional personality. In H. R. Beech (Ed.), *Obsessional states* (pp. 95–112). London, UK: Methuen.

Slater, E., & Glithero, E. (1965). A follow-up of patients diagnosed as suffering from hysteria. *Journal of Psychosomatic Research, 9,* 9–13.

Slaunwhite, A. K. (2015). The role of gender and income in predicting barriers to mental health care in Canada. *Community Mental Health Journal, 51,* 621–627.

Slavich, G. M., & Irwin, M. R. (2014). From stress to inflammation and major depressive disorder: a social signal transduction theory of depression. *Psychological Bulletin, 140,* 774–815.

Slavich, G. M., O'Donovan, A., Epel, E. S., & Kemeny, M. E. (2010). Black sheep get the blues: a psychobiological model of social rejection and depression. *Neuroscience and Biobehavioral Reviews, 35*(1), 39–45.

Sloan, D. M., Gallagher, M. W., Feinstein, B. A., Lee, D. J., & Pruneau, G. M. (2011). Efficacy of telehealth treatments for posttraumatic stress-related symptoms: A meta-analysis. *Cognitive Behaviour Therapy, 40,* 111–125.

Slovenko, R. (2001). Aphrodisiacs—then and now. *Journal of Psychiatry and Law, 29*(1), 103–116.

Slutske, W., Heath, A. C., Dunne, M. P., Statham, D. J., Dinwiddie, S. H., Madden, P. A. F., et al. (1997). Modeling genetic and environmental influences on the etiology of conduct disorder: A study of 2,682 adult twin pairs. *Journal of Abnormal Psychology, 106*(2), 266–279.

Smetanin, P., Stiff, D., Briante, C., Adair, C., Ahmad, S. & Khan, M. (2011). *The life and economic impact of major mental illnesses in Canada: 2011 to 2041.* Retrieved from the Mental Health Commission of Canada www.mentalhealthcommission. ca/sites/default/files/MHCC_Report_Base_Case_FINAL_ENG_0_0.pdf

Smith, A., Stewart, D., Peled, M., Poon, C., Saewyc, E., & McCreary Centre Society. (2009). *A picture of health: Highlights from the 2008 British Columbia Adolescent Health Survey.* Vancouver, BC: McCreary Centre Society.

Smith, A. M., Gacono, C. B., & Kaufman, L. (1997). A Rorschach comparison of psychopathic and nonpsychopathic conduct disordered adolescents. *Journal of Clinical Psychology, 53,* 289–300.

Smith, D. F. (2014). Exploratory meta-analysis on deep brain stimulation in treatment-resistant depression. *Acta Neuropsychiatrica, 26,* 382–384.

Smith, G. T., Goldman, M., Greenbaum, P. E., & Christiansen, B. A. (1995). Expectancy for social facilitation from drinking: The divergent paths of high-expectancy and low-expectancy adolescents. *Journal of Abnormal Psychology, 104,* 32–40.

Smith, J. D. (2002). The myth of mental retardation: Paradigm shifts, disaggregation and developmental disabilities. *Mental Retardation, 40,* 62–64.

Smith, L., Onwumere, J., Craig, T., McManus, S., Bebbington, P., & Kuipers, E. (2014). Mental and physical illness in caregivers: results from an English national survey sample. *The British Journal of Psychiatry, 205*(3), 197–203.

Smith, M. L., Glass, G. V., & Miller, T. I. (1980). *The benefits of psychotherapy.* Baltimore, MD: Johns Hopkins University Press.

Smith, P. (2007). Have we made any progress? Including students with intellectual disabilities in regular education classrooms. *Intellectual and Developmental Disabilities, 45,* 297–309.

Smith, T., Groen, A. D., & Wynn, J. W. (2000). Randomized trial of intensive early intervention for children with pervasive developmental disorder. *American Journal on Mental Retardation, 105*(4), 269–285.

Smith, T. W. (1992). Hostility and health: Current status of a psychosomatic hypothesis. *Health Psychology, 11,* 139–150.

Smith, T. W., & Frohm, K. D. (1985). What's so unhealthy about hostility? Construct validity and psychosocial correlates of the Cook and Medley Ho scale. *Health Psychology, 4,* 503–520.

Smith, T. W., Uchino, B. N., Berg, C. A., Florsheim, P., Pearce, G., Hawkins, M., et al. (2008). Associations of self-reports versus spouse ratings of negative affectivity, dominance, and affiliation with coronary artery disease: Where should we look and who should we ask when studying personality and health? *Health Psychology, 27,* 676–684.

Smolak, L., Levine, M. P., & Schermer, F. (1999). Parental input and weight concerns among elementary school children. *International Journal of Eating Disorders, 25,* 263–271.

Smyer, M. A. (1995). Prevention and early intervention for mental disorders of the elderly. In M. Gatz (Ed.), *Emerging issues in mental health and aging* (pp. 163–182). Washington DC: American Psychological Association.

Smyth, J. M., Wonderlich, S. A., Heron, K. E., Sliwinski, M. J., Crosby, R. D., Mitchell, J. E., & Engel, S. G. (2007). Daily and momentary mood and stress are associated with binge eating and vomiting in bulimia nervosa patients in the natural environment. *Journal of Consulting and Clinical Psychology, 75,* 629. doi: 10.1037/0022-006X.75.4.629

Smyth, N., Siriwardhana, C., Hotopf, M., & Hatch, S. L. (2015). Social networks, social support *and psychiatric symptoms: Social determinants* and associations within a multicultural community population. *Social Psychiatry and Psychiatric Epidemiology, 50,* 1111–1120.

Snowling, M. J. (1996). Contemporary approaches to the teaching of reading. *Journal of Child Psychology and Psychiatry, 37,* 139–148.

Snowling, M. J. & Melby-Lervag, M. (2016). Oral language deficits in familial dyslexia: A meta-analysis and review. *Psychological Bulletin 142,* No. 5, 498–545.

Snyder, J. J. (1977). Reinforcement and analysis of interaction in problem and nonproblem families. *Journal of Abnormal Psychology, 86,* 528–535.

Snyder, S. M., Hall, J. R., Cornwell, S. L., & Quintana, H. (2006). Review of clinical validation of ADHD behavior rating scales. *Psychological Reports, 99*(2), 363–378.

Sobell, L. C., Toneatto, A., & Sobell, M. B. (1990). Behavior therapy. In A. S. Bellack & M. Hersen (Eds.), *Handbook of comparative treatments for adult disorders* (pp. 479–505). New York, NY: Brunner/Mazel.

Sobell, M. B., & Sobell, L. C. (1973). Alcoholics treated by individualized behavior therapy: One year treatment outcome. *Behaviour Research and Therapy, 11,* 599–618.

Sobell, M. B., & Sobell, L. C. (1976). Second year treatment outcome of alcoholics treated by individualized behavior therapy: Results. *Behaviour Research and Therapy, 14,* 195–215.

Sobsey, D., Gray, S., Wells, D., Pyper, D., & Reimer-Heck, B. (1991). *Disability, sexuality and abuse: An annotated bibliography.* Baltimore, MD: Paul H. Brookes.

Soderstrom, H., Blennow, K., Manhem, A., & Forsman, A. (2001). CSF studies in violent offenders: I. 5-HIAA as a negative and HVA as a positive predictor of psychopathy. *Journal of Neural Transmission, 108,* 869–878.

Softley, I. (Director). (2001). *K-Pax* [Motion Picture]. USA: Intermedia Films.

Solis, E., Antypa, N., Conijn, J. M., Kelderman, H., & Van der Does, W. (2016). Psychometric Properties of the Leiden Index of Depression Sensitivity (LEIDS). *Psychological Assessment, 29,* 158–171. https://doi.org/10.1037/pas0000326

Solish, A., Perry, A., & Minnes, P. (2010) Participation of Children with and without Disabilities in Social, Recreational and Leisure Activities. *Journal of Applied Research in Intellectual Disabilities, 23,* 226–236.

Solomon, D. A., Keller, M. B., Leon, A. C., Mueller, T. I., Lavori, P. W., Shea, M. T., et al. (2000). Multiple recurrences of major depressive disorder. *American Journal of Psychiatry, 157,* 229–233.

Somashekar, B., Jainer, A., & Wuntakal, B. (2013). Psychopharmacotherapy of somatic symptoms disorders. *International Review of Psychiatry, 25*(1), 107–115.

Somer, E., Amos-Williams, T., & Stein, D. J. (2013). Evidence-based treatment for depersonalisation-derealisation disorder (DPRD). *BMC Psychology, 1,* 1–13.

Sonn, C. C., & Fisher, A. T. (1998). Sense of community: Community resilient responses to oppression and change. *Journal of Community Psychology, 26*(5), 457–472.

Southam-Gerow, M., & Prinstein, M. J. (2014). Evidence base updates: The evolution of the evaluation of psychological treatments for children and adolescents. *Journal of Clinical Child and Adolescent Psychology, 43,* 1–6.

Spacarelli, S., Colter, S., & Penman, D. (1992). Problem solving skills training as a supplement to behavioural parent education. *Cognitive Therapy Research, 16,* 1–18.

Spanos, N. (1996). *Multiple identities and false memories: A sociocognitive perspective.* Washington, DC: American Psychiatric Press.

Spanos, N. P. (1994). Multiple identity enactments and multiple personality disorder: A socio-cognitive perspective. *Psychological Bulletin, 116*(1), 143–165.

Spape, J., Timmers, A., Yoon, S., Ponseti, J., & Chivers, M. L. (2014). Gender-specific genital and subjective sexual arousal to prepotent sexual features in heterosexual women and men. *Biological Psychology, 102,* 1–9.

Sparrow, S. S., Cicchetti, D., & Balla, D. A. (2005). *Vineland Adaptive Behavior Scales manual* (2nd ed.). Minneapolis, MN: Pearson Inc.

Sparrow, S. S., Cicchetti, D. V., & Balla, D. A. (2006). *Vineland Adaptive Behavior Scales Vineland II* (2nd ed.). Toronto, ON: Pearson Education.

Spector, I. P., & Carey, M. P. (1990). Incidence and prevalence of the sexual dysfunctions: A critical review of the literature. *Archives of Sexual Behavior, 19,* 389–408.

Speisman, J., Lazarus, R. S., Mordkoff, A., & Davidson, L. (1964). Experimental reduction of stress based on ego defense theory. *Journal of Abnormal and Social Psychology, 68,* 367–380.

Spence, S. H., Donovan, C. L., March, S., Gamble, A., Anderson, R. E., Prosser, S., & Kenardy, J. (2011). A randomized controlled trial of online versus clinic-based CBT for adolescent anxiety. *Journal of Consulting and Clinical Psychology, 79,* 629–642.

Spencer, T. J., Biederman, J., & Mick, E. (2007). Attention-deficit/hyperactivity disorder: Diagnosis, lifespan, comorbidities, and neurobiology. *Journal of Pediatric Psychology, 32*(6), 631–642.

Sperry, L. (2003). *Handbook of diagnosis and treatment of DSM-IV-TR personality disorders.* New York, NY: Brunner-Routledge.

Spicer, C. C., Stewart, D. N., & Winser, D. M. R. (1944). Perforated peptic ulcer during the period of heavy air raids. *The Lancet, January 1,* 14.

Spiegel, D., Loewenstein, R. J., Lewis-Fernández, R., Sar, V., Simeon, D., Vermetten, E., . . . & Dell, P. F. (2011). Dissociative disorders in DSM-5. *Depression and Anxiety, 28*(12), E17–E45.

Spielman, A. J., Caruso, L. S., & Glovinsky, P. B. (1987). A behavioral perspective on insomnia treatment. *Psychiatric Clinics of North America*, *10*(4), 541–553.

Spinath, B., Spinath, F. M., Harlaar, N., & Plomin, R. (2006). Predicting school achievement from general cognitive ability, self-perceived ability, and intrinsic value. *Intelligence*, *34*(4), 363–374. https://doi.org/10.1016/j.intell.2005.11.004

Spittal, P. M., Tyndall, M., Li, K., Laliberta, N., Wood, E., Craib, K., O'Shaughnessy, M. V., et al. (1998). *Vancouver injection drug study*. Vancouver, BC: British Columbia Centre for Excellence in HIV/AIDS.

Spitzer, B. L., Henderson, K. A., & Zivian, M. T. (1999). Gender differences in population versus media body sizes: A comparison over four decades. *Sex Roles*, *40*, 545–565.

Spitzer, R. L., Endicott, J., & Gibbon, M. (1979). Crossing the border into borderline personality and borderline schizophrenia. *Archives of General Psychiatry*, *36*, 17–24.

Spoth, R. L., Redmond, C., Trudeau, L., & Shin, C. (2002). Longitudinal substance initiation outcomes for a universal preventive intervention combining family and school programs. *Psychology of Addictive Behaviors*, *16*(2), 129–134.

Sprock, J., Blashfield, R. K., & Smith, B. (1990). Gender weighting of DSM-III-R personality disorder criteria. *American Journal of Psychiatry*, *147*, 586–590.

Srivastava, S., John, O. P., Gosling, S. D., & Potter, J. (2003). Development of personality in early and middle adulthood: Set like plaster or persistent change? *Journal of Personality and Social Psychology*, *84*(5), 1041–1053.

St. George-Hyslop, P. (2006). Genetics of dementia. *CONTINUUM Lifelong Learning in Neurology*, *14*(2), 29–48.

St. Pierre, E. S., & Melnyk, W. T. (2004). The prescription privilege debate in Canada: The voice of today's and tomorrow's psychologists. *Canadian Psychology*, *45*, 284–292.

Stallard, P., Richardson, T., Velleman, S., & Attwood, M. (2011). Computerized CBT (Think, Feel, Do) for depression and anxiety in children and adolescents: Outcomes and feedback from a pilot randomized controlled trial. *Behavioural and Cognitive Psychotherapy*, *39*, 273–284.

Stanford, M. S., Ebner, D., Patton, J. H., & Williams, J. (1994). Multi-impulsivity within an adolescent psychiatric population. *Personality and Individual Differences*, *16*, 395–402.

Stanton, B. R., David, A. S., Cleare, A. J., Sierra, M., Lambert, M. V., Phillips, M. L., . . . & Young, A. H. (2001). Basal activity of the hypothalamic–pituitary–adrenal axis in patients with depersonalization disorder. *Psychiatry Research*, *104*(1), 85–89.

Starson v. Swayze (2003), 1 S.C.R. 722.

Statistics Canada. (2006, October). Canada's population by age and sex. *The Daily*. Ottawa, ON: Author.

Statistics Canada. (2007). *Mortality: Summary list of causes, 2000, 2001, 2002, 2003*. Ottawa, ON: Author.

Statistics Canada. 2009. *Suicide rates: An overview*. Retrieved from www.statcan.gc.ca/pub/82-624-x/2012001/article/11696-eng.htm

Statistics Canada. (2012a). *Canadian Community Health Survey – mental health*. Retrieved from www.statcan.gc.ca/pub/82-624-x/2013001/article/11855-eng.htm#a6

Statistics Canada. (2012b). *Current smoking trends*. Retrieved from www.statcan.gc.ca/pub/82-624-x/2012001/article/11676-eng.htm

Statistics Canada. (2012c). The 2012 Canada Year Book (11-402-X). Retrieved from www.statcan.gc.ca/pub/11-402-x/2010000/chap/pop/pop02-eng.htm

Statistics Canada. 2013. Mental and substance use disorders in Canada. Statistics Canada Catalogue no. 82-624-X. Ottawa. Version updated September 2013. Ottawa, ON. pub/82-624-x/2013001/article/11855-eng (April 20, 2017).

Statistics Canada. (2014). Ranking, number and percentage of deaths for the 10 leading causes. Canada, 2000, 2010, and 2011. *The Daily*. Retrieved from www.statcan.gc.ca/daily-quotidien/140128/t140128b001-eng.htm

Statistics Canada. (2016). CANSIM table 105-0501 In Catalogue no 82-221-X. Retrieved from www.statcan.gc.ca/tables-tableaux/sum-som/l01/cst01/health110d-eng.htm

Steele, V. R., Staley, C., Fong, T., & Prause, N. (2013). Sexual desire, not hypersexuality, is related to neurophysiological responses elicited by sexual images. *Socioaffective Neuroscience & Psychology*, *3*, 20770.

Stefan, S. (2006). *Emergency department treatment of the psychiatric patient: Policy issues and legal requirements*. New York, NY: Oxford University Press.

Steffy, R. A., & Waldman, I. (1993). Schizophrenics' reaction time: North star or shooting star? In R. L. Cromwell & C. R. Snyder (Eds.), *Schizophrenia: Origins, processes, treatment, and outcome* (pp. 111–134). New York, NY: Oxford University Press.

Steffy, R. A., Asarnow, R. F., Asarnow, J. R., MacCrimmon, D. J., & Cleghorn, J. M. (1984). The McMaster-Waterloo High-Risk Project: Multifaceted strategy for high-risk research. In N. F. Watt, E. J. Anthony, L. C. Wynne, & J. E. Rolf (Eds.), *Children at risk for schizophrenia: A longitudinal perspective* (pp. 401–413). Cambridge UK: Cambridge University Press.

Steiger, H., Richardson, J., Israel, M., Ng Ying Kin, N. M. K., Bruce, K., Mansour, S., & Parent, A. M. (2005). Reduced density of platelet-binding sites for [^{3}H] paroxetine in remitted bulimic women. *Neuropsychopharmacology*, *30*, 1028–1032.

Stein, A., Woolley, H., Cooper, S., Winterbottom, J., Fairburn, C. G., & Cortina-Borja, M. (2006). Eating habits and attitudes among 10-year-old children of mothers with eating disorders: Longitudinal study. *British Journal of Psychiatry*, *189*, 324–329.

Stein, K. D., Goldman, M. S., & Del Boca, F. K. (2000). The influence of alcohol expectancy priming and mood manipulation on subsequent alcohol consumption. *Journal of Abnormal Psychology*, *109*(1), 106.

Stein, K. F., & Corte, C. (2007). Identity impairment and the eating disorders: Content and organization of the self-concept in women with anorexia nervosa and bulimia nervosa. *European Eating Disorders Review*, *15*, 58–69.

Stein, M. B., Goldin, P. R., Sareen, J., Zorrila, L. T. E., & Brown, G. G. (2002). Increased amygdala activation to angry and contemptuous faces in generalized social phobia. *Archives of General Psychiatry*, *59*, 1027–1034.

Stein, M. B., Roy-Byrne, P., Craske, M. G., Campbell-Sills, L., Lang, A. J., Golinelli, D., . . . Sherbourne, C. D. (2011). Quality of and patient satisfaction with primary health care for anxiety disorders. *The Journal of Clinical Psychiatry*, *72*, 970–976.

Stein, M. T., Klin, A., & Miller, K. (2004). When Asperger's syndrome and a nonverbal learning disability look alike. *Pediatrics*, *114*, 1458–1463.

Stein, R. M., & Ellinwood, E. H. (1993). Stimulant use: Cocaine and amphetamine. In D. L. Dunner (Ed.), *Current psychiatric therapy* (pp. 98–105). Philadelphia, PA: Saunders.

Steiner, M., Lepage, P., & Dunn, E. J. (1997). Serotonin and gender-specific psychiatric disorders. *International Journal of Psychiatry in Clinical Practice*, *1*, 3–13.

Stepanski, E., Rybarczyk, B., Lopez, M., & Stevens, S. (2003). Assessment and treatment of sleep disorders in older adults: A review for rehabilitation psychologists. *Rehabilitation Psychology*, *48*, 23–36.

Stephens, R. S., Roffman, R. A., & Curtin, L. (2000). Comparison of extended versus brief treatment for marijuana use. *Journal of Consulting and Clinical Psychology*, *61*, 1100–1104.

Stepp, S. D., Hallquist, M. N., Morse, J. Q., & Pilkonis, P. A. (2011). Multimethod investigation of interpersonal functioning in borderline personality disorder. *Personality Disorders: Theory, Research, and Treatment*, *2*, 175–192. doi:10.1037/a0020572

Steuwe, C., Daniels, J. K., Frewen, P. A., Densmore, M., Pannasch, S., Beblo, T., . . . Lanius, R. A. (2014). Effect of direct eye contact in PTSD related to interpersonal trauma: An fMRI study of activation of an innate alarm system. *Social Cognitive and Affective Neuroscience*, *9*, 88–97.

Stevens, D., Charman, R., & Blair, R. J. R. (2001). Recognition of emotion in facial expressions and vocal tones in children with psychopathic tendencies. *Journal of Genetic Psychology*, *162*, 201–211.

Stevenson, J., & Meares, R. (1992). An outcome study of psychotherapy for patients with borderline personality disorder. *American Journal of Psychiatry*, *149*, 358–362.

Stewart, J. G. & Harkness, K. L. (2015). The interpersonal toxicity of excessive reassurance-seeking: Evidence from a longitudinal study of romantic relationships. *Journal of Social and Clinical Psychology*, *34*, 392–410.

Stewart, J. G., & Harkness, K. L. (2017). Testing a revised interpersonal theory of depression using a laboratory measure of excessive reassurance-seeking. *Journal of Clinical Psychology*, *73*, 331–348.

Stewart, R., Besset, A., Bebbington, P., Brugha, T., Lindesay, J., Jenkins, R., Singleton, N., & Meltzer, H. (2006). Insomnia comorbidity and impact and hypnotic use by age group in a national survey population aged 16 to 74 years. *Sleep*, *29*(11), 1391–1397.

Stewart, R. E., & Chambless, D. L. (2009). Cognitive-behavioral therapy for adult anxiety disorders in clinical practice: A meta-analysis of effectiveness studies. *Journal of Consulting and Clinical Psychology*, *77*, 595–606.

Stewart, S. E., & Pauls, D. L. (2010). The genetics of obsessive-compulsive disorder. *Focus*, *8*, 350.

Stewart, S. H., Westra, H. A., Thompson, C. E., & Conrad, B. E. (2000). Effects of naturalistic benzodiazepine use on selective attention to threat cues among anxiety disorder patients. *Cognitive Therapy & Research*, *24*, 67–85.

Stice, E. (2002). Risk and maintenance factors for eating pathology: A meta-analytic review. *Psychological Bulletin*, *128*, 825. doi: 10.1037//0033-2909.128.5.825

Stice, E., & Shaw, H. (2004). Eating disorder prevention programs: A meta-analytic review. *Psychological Bulletin, 130*, 206–227.

Stichter, J. P., Herzog, M. J., Visovsky, K., Schmidt, C., Randolph, J., Schultz, T., & Gage, N. (2010). Social competence intervention for youth with Asperger syndrome and high-functioning autism: An initial investigation. *Journal of Autism and Developmental Disorders, 40*, 1067–1079.

Still, B. (1932). *The history of pediatrics: The progress of the study of diseases of children up to the end of the eighteenth century.* London, UK: Oxford University Press.

Stockings, E., Hall, W. D., Lynskey, M., Morley, K. I., Reavley, N., Strang, J., . . . & Degenhardt, L. (2016). Prevention, early intervention, harm reduction, and treatment of substance use in young people. *The Lancet Psychiatry, 3*(3), 280–296.

Stone, A. A., Schwartz, J. E., Broderick, J. E., & Deaton, A. (2010). A snapshot of the age distribution of psychological well-being in the United States. *Proceedings of the National Academy of Sciences, 107*, 9985–9990.

Stone, G. L. (1995). Review of the Hare Psychopathy Checklist—Revised. In J. C. Conoley & J. C. Impara (Eds.), *Twelfth mental measurements yearbook* (pp. 454–455). Lincoln, NE: Buros Institute.

Stone, J., Carson, A., Duncan, R., Coleman, R., Roberts, R., Warlow, C., . . . & Sharpe, M. (2009). Symptoms 'unexplained by organic disease' in 1144 new neurology out-patients: How often does the diagnosis change at follow-up? *Brain, 132*, 2878–2888.

Stone, J., Smyth, R., Carson, A., Lewis, S., Prescott, R., Warlow, C., & Sharpe, M. (2005). Systematic review of misdiagnosis of conversion symptoms and "hysteria." *British Medical Journal, 331*, 989.

Stone, J., Smyth, R., Carson, A., Warlow, C., & Sharpe, M. (2006). *La belle indifférence* in conversion symptoms and hysteria: Systematic review. *British Journal of Psychiatry, 188*, 204–209.

Stone, J., Warlow, C., & Sharpe, M. (2010). The symptom of functional weakness: A controlled study of 107 patients. *Brain, 133*, 1537–1551.

Stone, M. (1993). Long-term outcome in personality disorders. *British Journal of Psychiatry, 162*, 299–313.

Stone, W. L., Lemanek, K. L., Fishel, P. T., Fernandez, M. C., & Altemeier, W. A. (1990). Play and imitation skills in the diagnosis of autism in young children. *Pediatrics, 86*, 267–272.

Storebó, O. J., Krogh. H. B., Ramstad, E., Moreira-Maia, C. R., Holmskov, M., Skoog, M. . . & Gluud, C. (2015). Methylphenidate for attention-deficit/hyperactivity disorder in children and adolescents: Cochrane systematic review with meta-analyses and trial sequential analyses of randomised clinical trials. *British Medical Journal 351*, h5031. doi: 10.1136/bmj.h5203

Strand, J. E., & Nybäck, H. (2005). Tobacco use in schizophrenia: a study of cotinine concentrations in the saliva of patients and controls. *European Psychiatry, 20*, 50–54.

Strand, J.E., & Nybäck, H. (2005). Tobacco use in schizophrenia: A study of cotinine concentrations in the saliva of patients and controls. *European Psychiatry, 20*, 50-54.

Strauss, E., Sherman, E. M., & Spreen, O. (2006). *A compendium of neuropsychological tests: Administration, norms, and commentary* (3rd ed.). New York, NY: Oxford University Press.

Stravynski, A., Lesage, A., Marcouiller, M., & Elie, R. (1989). A test of the therapeutic mechanism in social skills training with avoidant personality disorder. *Journal of Nervous and Mental Disease, 177*, 739–744.

Streiner, D. L., Cairney, J., & Veldhuizen, S. (2006). The epidemiology of psychological problems in the elderly. *Canadian Journal of Psychiatry, 51*(3), 185–191.

Streissguth, A. P., & O'Malley, K. (2000). Neuropsychiatric implications and long-term consequences of fetal alcohol spectrum disorders. *Seminars in Clinical Neuropsychiatry 5*, 177–190.

Streissguth, A. P., Barr, H. M., & Sampson, P. D. (1990). Moderate prenatal alcohol exposure: Effects on child IQ and learning problems at age 7 1/2 years. *Alcoholism: Clinical and Experimental Research, 14*, 662–669.

Streissguth, A. P., Bookstein, F. L., & Barr, H. M. (1996). A dose-response study of the enduring effects of prenatal alcohol exposure: Birth to 14 years. In H. Spohn & H. Steinhausen (Eds.), *Alcohol, pregnancy and the developing child* (pp. 141–168). Cambridge, UK: Cambridge University Press.

Strenze, T. (2007). Intelligence and socioeconomic success: A meta-analytic review of longitudinal research. *Intelligence, 35*(5), 401–426. https://doi.org/10.1016/j.intell.2006.09.004

Striegel-Moore, R. H. (1993). Etiology of binge eating: A developmental perspective. In C. G. Fairburn & G. T. Wilson (Eds.), *Binge eating: Nature, assessment and treatment* (pp. 144–172). New York, NY: Guilford.

Striegel-Moore, R. H. (1997). Risk factors for eating disorders. *Annals of the New York Academy of Sciences: Adolescent nutritional disorders: Prevention and treatment, 817*, 98–109.

Striegel-Moore, R. H., & Bulik, C. M. (2007). Risk factors for eating disorders. *American Psychologist, 62*, 181. doi: 10.1037/0003-066X.62.3.181

Striegel-Moore, R. H., Franko, D. L., & Garcia, J. (2009). The validity and clinical utility of night eating syndrome. *International Journal of Eating Disorders, 42*, 720–738.

Stringaris, A., & Goodman, R. (2009). Longitudinal outcome of youth oppositionality: Irritable, headstrong, and hurtful behaviors have distinctive predictions. *Journal of the American Academy of Child and Adolescent Psychiatry, 48*, 404–412. doi:10.1097/CHI.0b013e3181984f30

Stringaris, A., Zavos, H., Leibenluft, E., Maughan, D., & Eley, T.C. (2012). Adolescent Irritability: Phenotypic Associations and Genetic Links with Depressed Mood. *American Journal of Psychiatry, 169*, 47–54.

Strober, M., Freeman, R., Lampert, C., Diamond, J., & Kaye, W. (2000). Controlled family study of anorexia nervosa and bulimia nervosa: Evidence of shared liability and transmission of partial syndromes. *American Journal of Psychiatry, 157*, 393–401.

Strober, M., Morrell, W., Burroughs, J., Lampert, C., Danforth, H., & Freeman, R. (1988). A family study of bipolar I disorder in adolescence: Early onset of symptoms linked to increased familial loading and lithium resistance. *Journal of Affective Disorders, 15*, 255–268.

Strong, S. M., Williamson, D. A, Netemeyer, R. G., & Geer, J. H. (2000). Eating disorder symptoms and concerns about body differ as a function of gender and sexual orientation. *Journal of Social and Clinical Psychology, 19*, 240–255.

Stuart, H., Arboleda-Florez, J., & Crisanti, A. S. (2001). Impact of legal reforms on length of forensic assessments in Alberta, Canada. *International Journal of Law and Psychiatry, 24*, 527–538.

Stunkard, A. J. (1959). Eating patterns and obesity. *Psychiatric Quarterly, 33*, 284–295.

Suarez, E., & Williams, R. B. (1989). Situational determinants of cardiovascular and emotional reactivity in high and low hostile men. *Psychosomatic Medicine, 51*, 404–418.

Sue, D. W., Capodilupo, C. M., Torino, G. C., Bucceri, J. M., Holder, A., Nadal, K. L., & Esquilin, M. (2007). Racial microaggressions in everyday life: Implications for clinical practice. *American Psychologist, 62*(4), 271.

Suedfeld, P., & Landon, P. B. (1978). Approaches to treatment. In R. D. Hare & D. Schalling (Eds.), *Psychopathic behavior: Approaches to research* (pp. 347–376). Chichester, UK: Wiley.

Sullivan, J. M., & Cross Jr, W. E. (Eds.). (2016). *Meaning-making, internalized racism, and African American identity.* New York, NY: SUNY Press.

Sullivan, P. F. (2008). Schizophrenia genetics: The search for a hard lead. *Current Opinion in Psychiatry, 21*, 157–160.

Sullivan, P. F., Neale, M. C., & Kendler, K. S. (2000). Genetic epidemiology of major depression: Review and meta-analysis. *American Journal of Psychiatry, 157*, 1552–1562.

Summerfeldt, L. J., Kloosterman, P. H., & Antony, M. M. (2010). Structured and semistructured diagnostic interviews. In M. M. Antony & D. H. Barlow (Eds.), *Handbook of assessment and treatment planning for psychological disorders* (2nd ed., pp. 95–137). New York, NY: Guilford.

Sunderland, A., & Findlay, L. C. (2013). Perceived need for mental health care in Canada: Results from the 2012 Canadian community health survey-mental health. *Health Reports, 24*(9), 3–9.

Sussman, S. (1998). The first asylums in Canada: A response to neglectful community care and current trends. *Canadian Journal of Psychiatry, 43*, 260–264.

Sutton, K. S., Stratton, N., Pytyck, J., Kolla, N. J., & Cantor, J. M. (2015). Patient characteristics by type of hypersexuality referral: A quantitative chart review of 115 consecutive male cases. *Journal of Sex & Marital Therapy, 41*, 563–580.

Svartberg, M., & Stiles, T. C. (1991). Comparative effects of short-term psychodynamic psychotherapy: A meta-analysis. *Journal of Consulting and Clinical Psychology, 59*, 704–714.

Swan, J. L., & Hodgins, D. C. (2015). Brief interventions for disordered gambling. *Canadian Journal of Addiction, 6*(2), 29-36.

Swann, W. B., Jr. (1990). To be adored or to be known: The interplay of self-enhancement and self-verification. In R. M. Sorrentino & E. T. Higgins (Eds.), *Foundations of social behavior* (Vol. 2, pp. 408–448). New York, NY: Guilford.

Swann, W. B., Jr., Wenzlaff, R. M., & Tafarodi, R. W. (1992). Depression and the search for negative evaluations: More evidence of the role of self-verification strivings. *Journal of Abnormal Psychology, 101*, 314–317.

Swann, W. B., Jr., Wenzlaff, R. M., Krull, D. S., & Pelham, B. W. (1992). The allure of negative feedback: Self-verification strivings among depressed persons. *Journal of Abnormal Psychology, 101*, 293–306.

Swanson, H. L. (2007). Cognitive aspects of math disabilities. In D.B. Berch & M. Mazzacco (Eds.), *Why is math so hard for some children? The nature and origins of mathematical learning difficulties and disabilities* (pp. 133–144). Baltimore, MD: Paul H. Brookes Publishing.

Swanson, J. M., Elliott, G. R., Greenhill, L. L., Wigal, T., Arnold, L. E., Vitiello, B., et al. (2007). Effects of stimulant medication on growth rates across 3 years in the MTA follow-up. *Journal of the American Academy of Child and Adolescent Psychiatry, 46*(8), 1015–1027.

Swartz, M. S., & Swanson, J. W. (2004). Involuntary outpatient commitment, community treatment orders, and assisted outpatient treatment: What's in the data? *Canadian Journal of Psychiatry, 49,* 585–591.

Swazey, J. P. (1974). *Chlorpromazine in psychiatry: A study of therapeutic innovation.* Cambridge, MA: MIT Press.

Sweet, M. A., & Applebaum, M. I. (2004). Is home visiting an effective strategy? A meta-analytic review of home visiting programs for families with young children. *Child Development, 75,* 1435–1456.

Swift, J. K., & Greenberg, R. P. (2012). Premature discontinuation in adult psychotherapy: A meta-analysis. *Journal of Consulting and Clinical Psychology, 80,* 547–559.

Swift, R. M. (2003). Medications. In R. K. Hester & W. R. Miller (Eds.), *Handbook of alcoholism treatment approaches: Effective alternatives* (3rd ed., pp. 259–281). Boston: Allyn and Bacon.

Symons, F. J., Byiers, B. J., Raspa, M., Bishop, E., & Bailey, D. B., Jr. (2010). Self-injurious behaviour and Fragile X syndrome: Findings from the National Fragile X survey. *American Journal on Intellectual and Developmental Disabilities, 115,* 473–481.

Sypeck, M. F., Gray, J. J., Etu, S. F., Ahrens, A. H., Mosimann, J. E., & Wiseman, C. V. (2006). Cultural representations of thinness in women, redux: *Playboy* magazine's depiction of beauty from 1979 to 1999. *Body Image 3,* 229–235.

Szabo, G., Tabakoff, B., & Hoffman, P. L. (1994). The NDMA receptor antagonist dizocilpine differentially affects environment-dependent and environment-independent ethanol tolerance. *Psychopharmacology, 113*(3–4), 511–517.

Szasz, T. S. (1961). *The myth of mental illness.* New York, NY: Harper & Row.

Szasz, T. S. (1970). *The manufacture of madness.* New York, NY: Harper & Row.

Szatmari, P., Boyle, M., & Offord, D. R. (1989). ADDH and conduct disorder: Degree of diagnostic overlap and differences among correlates. *Journal of the American Academy of Child and Adolescent Psychiatry, 28,* 865–872.

Szucs, D., Devine, A., Soltesz, F., Nobes, A., & Gabriel, F. (2013). Developmental dyscalculia is related to visuo-spatial memory and inhibition impairment. *Cortex, 49,* 2674–2688.

Tabakoff, B., & Hoffman, P. L. (1991). Neurochemical effects of alcohol. In R. J. Frances & S. I. Muller (Eds.), *Clinical textbook of addictive disorders* (pp. 501–525). New York, NY: Guilford.

TADS Team. (2007). The Treatment for Adolescents with Depression Study (TADS): Long-term effectiveness and safety outcomes. *Archives of General Psychiatry, 64*(10), 1132.

Taheri, A., Perry, A. & Minnes, P. (2016). Examining the social participation of children and adolescents with intellectual disabilities and autism spectrum disorder in relation to peers. *Journal of Intellectual Disability Research, 60,* 435–443

Tai, S., & Turkington, D. (2009). The evolution of cognitive behavior therapy for schizophrenia: Current practice and recent developments. *Schizophrenia Bulletin, 35*(5), 865–873.

Talge, N. M., Neal, C., Glover, V., & Early Stress, Translational Research and Prevention Science Network: Fetal and Neonatal Experience on Child and Adolescent Mental Health. (2007). Antenatal maternal stress and long-term effects on child neurodevelopment: How and why? *Journal of Child Psychology and Psychiatry, and Allied Disciplines, 48*(3–4), 245–261.

Tamminga, H. g. H., Reneman, L., Huizenga, H. M., & Geurts, H. M. (2016). Effects of methylphenidate on executive functioning in attention-deficit/hyperactivity disorder across the lifespan: A meta-regression. *Psychological Medicine, 46,* 1791–1807.

Tandon, R., Gaebel, W., Barch, D., Bustillo, J., Gur, R., Heckers, S., . . . Carpenter, W., (2013). Definition and description of schizophrenia in the DSM-5. *Schizophrenia Research, 150*(1), 3–10.

Tandon, R., Keshavan, M. S., & Nasrallah, H. A. (2008a). Schizophrenia, "just the facts": What we know in 2008: Part 1: Overview. *Schizophrenia Research, 100*(1), 419.

Tandon, R., Keshavan, M. S., & Nasrallah, H. A. (2008b). Schizophrenia, "just the facts": What we know in 2008. Part 2: Epidemiology and etiology. *Schizophrenia Research, 102,* 1–18.

Tandon, R., Nasrallah, H. A., & Keshavan, M. S. (2009). Shizophrenia, "just the facts" 4. Clinical features and conceptualization. *Schizophrenia Research, 110,* 1–23.

Tandon, R., Nasrallah, H. A., & Keshavan, M. S. (2010). Schizophrenia, "just the facts" 5: Treatment and prevention past, present, and future. *Schizophrenia Research, 122,* 1–23.

Task force on misogyny, sexism and homophobia in the faculty of dentistry (2015, June 26). Retrieved from www.dal.ca/content/dam/dalhousie/pdf/cultureofrespect/DalhousieDentistry-TaskForceReport-June2015.pdf

Tassé, M. J. (2006). Functional behavioural assessment in people with intellectual disabilities. *Current Opinion in Psychiatry, 19*(5), 475–480.

Tausig, H. B. (1962). Thalidomide: A lesson in remote effects of drugs. *American Journal of Diseases of Children, 104,* 111–113.

Tausk, V. (1948). On the origin of the "influencing machine" in schizophrenia. In R. Fleiss (Ed.), *The psychoanalytic reader* (pp. 31–64). New York, NY: International Universities Press.

Taylor, C. B., Bryson, S., Luce, K. H., Cunning, D., Doyle, A. C., Abascal, L. B., . . . Wilfley, D. E. (2006). Prevention of eating disorders in at-risk college-age women. *Archives of General Psychiatry, 63,* 881–888.

Taylor, J. L., Lindsay, W. R., Hastings, R. P., & Hatton, C. S. (Eds.). (2012). *Psychological therapies for adults with intellectual disabilities.* Chichester, UK: Wiley.

Taylor, S. (2014). *Anxiety sensitivity: Theory, research, and treatment of the fear of anxiety.* New York, NY: Routledge.

Taylor, S. E. (2006). Tend and befriend biobehavioral bases of affiliation under stress. *Current Directions in Psychological Science, 15*(6), 273–277.

Taylor, S. E., Klein, L. C., Lewis, B. P., Gruenewald, T. L., Gurung, R. A., & Updegraff, J. A. (2000). Biobehavioral responses to stress in females: tend-and-befriend, not fight-or-flight. *Psychological Review, 107*(3), 411–429.

Taylor, S., Afifi, T. O., Stein, M. B., Asmundson, G. J. G., & Jang, K. L. (2010). Etiology of obsessive beliefs: A behavioral-genetic analysis. *Journal of Cognitive Psychotherapy, 24,* 177–186.

Taylor, S., Zvolensky, M. J., Cox, B. J., Deacon, B., Heimberg, R. G., Ledley, D. R., et al. (2007). Robust dimensions of anxiety sensitivity: Development and initial validation of the Anxiety Sensitivity Index-3. *Psychological Assessment, 19,* 176–188.

Taylor, T. K., Schmidt, F., Pepler, D., & Hodgins, C. (1998). A comparison of eclectic treatment with Webster-Stratton's parents and children series in a children's mental health setting: A randomized controlled trial. *Behavior Therapy, 29,* 221–240.

Taylor, W. D. (2014). Depression in the elderly. *New England Journal of Medicine, 371*(13), 1228–1236. doi:10.1056/NEJMcp1402180

Teasdale, J. D., Segal, Z. V., Williams, J. M., Ridgeway, V. A., Soulsby, J. M., & Lau, M. A. (2000). Prevention of relapse/recurrence in major depression by mindfulness-based cognitive therapy. *Journal of Consulting & Clinical Psychology, 68,* 615–623.

Tellegen, A., Lykken, D. T., Bouchard, T. J., Wilcox, K. J., Segal, N. L., & Rich, S. (1988). Personality similarity in twins reared apart and together. *Journal of Personality and Social Psychology, 54,* 1031–1039.

Temple, E., Deutsch, G., Poldrack, R., Miller, S., & Tallal, P. (2003). Neural deficits in children with dyslexia ameliorated by behavioral remediation: Evidence from fMRI. *Proceedings of the National Academy of Sciences, 100,* 2860–2865.

Tennent, G., Tennent, D., Prins, H., & Bedford, A. (1993). Is psychopathic disorder a treatable condition? *Medicine, Science, and the Law, 33,* 63–66.

Teo, A. R., Lerrigo, R., & Rogers, M. A. M. (2013). The role of social isolation in social anxiety disorder: A systematic review and meta-analysis. *Journal of Anxiety Disorders, 27,* 353–364.

Teodorescu, M. C., & Husain, N. F. (2010). Nonpharmacologic approaches to insomnia in older adults. *Annals of Long Term Care, 18*(8), 36–42.

Terman, M., Terman, J. S., Quitkin, F. M., McGrath, P. J., Stewart, J. W., & Rafferty, B. (1989). Light therapy for seasonal affective disorder: A review of efficacy. *Neuropsychopharmacology, 2,* 1–22.

Test, D. W., Fowler, C. H., Wood, W. M., Brewer, M., & Eddy, S. (2005). A conceptual framework of self-advocacy for students with disabilities. *Remedial and Special Education, 26,* 43–54.

Thapar, A., Cooper, M., Eyre, O., & Langley, K. (2013). Practitioner Review: What have we learnt about the causes of ADHD? *Journal of Child Psychology and Psychiatry, 54,* 3–16. doi: 10.1111/j.1469-7610.2012.02611.x

Thaper, A., & McGuffin, P. (1995). Are anxiety symptoms in childhood heritable? *Journal of Child Psychology and Psychiatry, 36,* 439–447.

Thase, M. E., & Howland, R. H. (1995). Biological processes in depression: An updated review and integration. In E. E. Beckham & W. R. Leber (Eds.), *Handbook of depression* (2nd ed.). New York, NY: Guilford.

Thase, M. E., & Rush, A. J. (1997). When at first you don't succeed: Sequential strategies for antidepressant nonresponders. *Journal of Clinical Psychiatry, 58,* 23–29.

Thase, M. E., Greenhouse, J. B., Frank, E., Reynolds III, C. F., Pilkonis, P. A., Hurley, K., et al. (1997). Treatment of major depression with psychotherapy or psychotherapy-pharmacotherapy combinations. *Archives of General Psychiatry, 54,* 1009–1015.

Thase, M. E., Jindal, R., & Howland, R. H. (2002). Biological aspects of depression. In I. H. Gotlib & C. L. Hammen (Eds.), *Handbook of depression* (3rd ed., pp. 192–218). New York, NY: Guilford.

Thayer, J. F., Friedman, B. H., & Borkovec, T. D. (1996). Autonomic characteristics of generalized anxiety disorder and worry. *Biological Psychiatry, 39,* 255–266.

The Atlantic. (2016, June 17). Why the Stanford judge gave Brock Turner six months. Retrieved from www.theatlantic.com/news/archive/2016/06/stanford-rape-case-judge/487415/

The Toronto Star. (2011, February, 18). Cop apologizes for 'sluts' remark at law school. Retrieved from www.thestar.com/news/gta/2011/02/18/cop_apologizes_for_sluts_remark_at_law_school.html

Thibaut, F., Boutros, N. N., Jarema, M., Oranje, B., Hasan, A., Daskalakis, Z. J., … & Falkai, P. (2015). Consensus paper of the WFSBP Task Force on Biological Markers: Criteria for biomarkers and endophenotypes of schizophrenia part I: Neurophysiology. *The World Journal of Biological Psychiatry, 16*(5), 280–290.

Thigpen, C. H., & Cleckley, H. M. (1957). *The three faces of Eve.* New York, NY: McGraw Hill.

Thompson-Pope, S. K., & Turkat, I. D. (1988). Reactions to ambiguous stimuli among paranoid personalities. *Journal of Psychopathology and Behavioral Assessment, 10,* 21–32.

Thompson, J. K., & Stice, E. (2001). Thin-ideal internalization: Mounting evidence for a new risk factor for body-image disturbance and eating pathology. *Current Directions in Psychological Science, 10,* 181–183.

Thompson, J. R., Bradley, V. J., Buntinx, W. H. E., Schalock, R. L., Shogren, K. A., Snell, M. E., et al. (2009). Conceptualizing supports and the support needs of people with intellectual disabilities. *Intellectual Disability, 47,* 135–146.

Thompson, R. A. (2008). Early attachment and later development: Familiar questions, new answers. New York, NY: Guilford.

Thornicroft, G., Mehta, N., Clement, S., Evans-Lacko, S., Doherty, M., Rose, D., … & Henderson, C. (2016). Evidence for effective interventions to reduce mental-health-related stigma and discrimination. *The Lancet, 387,* 1123–1132.

Tiggemann, M., & Lynch, J. E. (2001). Body image across the life span in adult women: The role of self-objectification. *Developmental Psychology, 37,* 243. doi: 10.1037//0012-1649.37.2.243

Tiggemann, M., & Polivy, J. (2010). Upward and downward: Social comparison processing of thin idealized media images. *Psychology of Women Quarterly, 34,* 356–364.

Tiggemann, M., Martins, Y., & Kirkbride, A. (2007). Oh to be lean and muscular: Body image ideals in gay and heterosexual men. *Psychology of Men & Masculinity, 8,* 15. doi: 10.1037/1524-9220.8.1.15

Tiihonen, J., Haukka, J., Taylor, M., Haddad, P. M., Patel, M. X., & Korhonen, P. (2011). A nationwide cohort study of oral and depot antipsychotics after first hospitalization for schizophrenia. *American Journal of Psychiatry, 168,* 603–609.

Tillich, P. (1952). *The courage to be.* New Haven, CT: Yale University Press.

Timmons, K. A., & Joiner, T. E. (2008). Reassurance seeking and negative feedback seeking. In K. S. Dobson & D. J. A. Dozois (Eds.), *Risk factors in depression* (pp. 429–446). Oxford, UK: Elsevier/Academic Press.

Tiplady, B., Franklin, N., & Scholey, A. (2004). Effect of ethanol on judgments of performance. *British Journal of Psychology, 95*(1), 105–118.

Tiwari, A. K., Zai, C. C., Müller, D. J., & Kennedy, J. L. (2010). Genetics in schizophrenia: Where are we and what next? *Dialogues in Clinical Neuroscience, 12,* 289–303.

Tobler, N. S. (2000). Lessons learned. *Journal of Primary Prevention, 20,* 261–274.

Tobler, N. S., Roona, M. R., Ochshorn, P., Marshall, D. G., Streke, A. V., & Stackpole, K. M. (2000). School-based adolescent drug prevention programs: 1998 meta-analysis. *Journal of Primary Prevention, 20,* 275–336.

Toch, H. (1971). *The social psychology of social movements.* London, UK: Methuen.

Tolin, D. F., & Foa, E. B. (2006). Sex differences in trauma and posttraumatic stress disorder: A quantitative review of 25 years of research. *Psychological Bulletin, 132,* 959–992.

Tolmunen, T., Lehto, S.M., Heliste, M., Kurl, S. & Kauhanen, J. (2010). Alexithymia is associated with increased cardiovascular mortality in middle-aged Finnish men. *Psychosomatic Medicine, 72,* 187–191.

Tomasulo, D. (1994). Action techniques in group counseling: The double. *Habilitative Mental Healthcare Newsletter, 13,* 41–45.

Tomasulo, D., Keller, E., & Pfadt, A. (1995). The healing crowd: Process, content and technique issues in group counseling for people with mental retardation. *Habilitative Mental Healthcare Newsletter, 14,* 43–49.

Torgersen, S. (1984). Genetic and nosological aspects of schizotypal and borderline personality disorders. *Archives of General Psychiatry, 41,* 546–554.

Torgersen, S., & Alnaes, R. (1992). Differential perception of parental bonding in schizotypal and borderline personality disorder patients. *Comprehensive Psychiatry, 33,* 34–88.

Torresan, R. C., Ramos-Cerqueira, A. A., Shavitt, R. G., Conceicao do Rosario, M., de Mathis, M. A., Miguel, E. C., & Torres, A. R. (2013). Symptoms dimensions, clinical course and comorbidity in men and women with obsessive-compulsive disorder. *Psychiatry Research, 209,* 186–195.

Torrey, E. F. (1995). *Surviving schizophrenia: A family manual.* (3rd ed.) New York, NY: Harper & Row.

Torrey, E. F., & Miller, J. (2001). *The invisible plague: the rise of mental illness from 1750 to the present.* Camden, NJ: Rutgers University Press.

Tougas, G., Chen, Y., Hwang, P., Liu, M. M., & Eggleston, A. (1999). Prevalence and impact of upper gastrointestinal symptoms in the Canadian population: Findings from the DIGEST study. Domestic/International Gastroenterology Surveillance Study. *American Journal of Gastroenterology, 94,* 2845–2854.

Tourigny-Rivard, M. (1997). Pharmacotherapy of affective disorders in old age. *Canadian Journal of Psychiatry, 42,* 10S–18S.

Traffic Injury Foundation. (2014). *The road safety monitor 2014: drinking and driving in Canada.* Retrieved from http://tirf.ca/publications/PDF_publications/RSM_2014_Drinking_Driving_Eng_2.pdf

Tran, L., Sanchez, T., Arellano, B., & Swanson, H. L. (2011). A meta-analysis of the RTI literature for children at risk for reading disabilities. *Journal of Learning Disabilities, 44*(3), 283–295.

Treatment for Adolescent with Depression Study (TADS) Team. (2004). Fluoxetine, cognitive-behavioral therapy, and their combination for adolescents with depression. *Journal of the American Medical Association, 292,* 807–820.

Treatment for Adolescents with Depression Study (TADS) Team. (2003). Treatment for adolescents with depression study (TADS): Rationale, design, and methods. *Journal of the American Academy of Child & Adolescent Psychiatry, 42,* 531–542.

Tremblay, P., King, P., & Baines, G. (1994). Clinical and demographic characteristics of voluntary and involuntary psychiatric inpatients. *Canadian Journal of Psychiatry, 39,* 297–299.

Trent Jr., J. W. (1994). *Inventing the feeble mind: A history of mental retardation in the United States* (Vol. 6). Los Angeles, CA: University of California Press.

Trestrail, J. H. (1991). Mushroom poisoning in the United States—An analysis of 1989 United States poison center data. *Clinical Toxicology, 29,* 459–465.

Trottier, K., McFarlane, T., Olmsted, M. P., & McCabe, R. (2013). The Weight Influenced Self-Esteem Questionnaire (WISE-Q): Factor structure and psychometric properties. *Body Image, 10,* 112–120.

Trottier, K., Monson, C., Wonderlich, S., & Olmsted, M. P. (2017). Initial findings from Project Recover: Overcoming co-occurring eating disorders and posttraumatic stress disorder through integrated treatment. *Journal of Traumatic Stress, 30,* 173–177.

Trottier, K., Wonderlich, S. A., Monson, C. M., Crosby, R. D., & Olmsted, M. P. (2016). Investigating posttraumatic stress disorder as a psychological maintaining factor of eating disorders. *International Journal of Eating Disorders, 49,* 455–457. doi: 10.1002/eat.22516

Troyb, E., Knoch, K., & Barton, M. (2011). Phenomenology of ASD: Definition, syndromes and major features. In D. A. Fein (Ed.), *The neuropsychology of autism* (p. 17). New York, NY: Oxford University Press.

Trull, T. J., Widiger, T. A., & Frances, A. (1987). Covariation of criteria for avoidant, schizoid, and dependent personality disorders. *American Journal of Psychiatry, 144,* 767–771.

Truscott, D., & Crook, K. H. (2004). *Ethics for the practice of psychology in Canada.* Edmonton, AB: University of Alberta Press.

Trzaskowski, M., Zavos, H. M. S., Haworth, C. M. A., Plomin, R., & Eley, T. C. (2011). Stable genetic influence on anxiety-related behaviours across middle childhood. *Journal of Abnormal Child Psychology.* Advance online publication. doi:10.1007/s10802-011-9545-z

Tsang, A., Von Korff, M., Lee, S., Alonso, J., Karam, E., Angermeyer, M. C., … & Watanabe, M. (2008). Common chronic pain conditions in developed and developing countries: Gender and age differences and comorbidity with depression-anxiety disorders. *The Journal of Pain, 9*(10), 883–891.

Tsoi, W. F. (1990). Developmental profile of 200 male and 100 female transsexuals in Singapore. *Archives of Sexual Behavior, 19,* 595–605.

Tsuang, D. W., & Bird, T. D., (2002). Genetics of dementia. *Medical Clinics of North America, 86,* 591–614.

Tsuchiya, M., Kawakami, N., Ono, Y., Nakane, Y., Nakamura, Y., Tachimori, H., … Watanabe, M. (2009). Lifetime comorbidities between phobic disorders and major depression in Japan: Results from the world mental health Japan 2002–2004 survey. *Depression and Anxiety, 26,* 949–955.

Tuma, T. A. (2000). Outcome of hospital-treated depression at 4.5 years: An elderly and a younger adult cohort compared. *British Journal of Psychiatry, 176,* 224–228.

Turetsky, B. I., Moberg, P. J., & Mozley, L. H. (2002). Memory-delineated subtypes of schizophrenia: Relationship to clinical, neuroanatomical and neurophysiological measures. *Neuropsychology, 16,* 481–490.

Turkat, I. D., & Banks, D. (1987). Paranoid personality and its disorder. *Journal of Psychopathology and Behavioral Assessment, 9,* 295–304.

Turkat, I. D., & Levin, R. A. (1984). Formulation of personality disorders. In H. E. Adams & P. B. Sutker (Eds.), *Comprehensive handbook of psychotherapy* (pp. 495–522). New York, NY: Plenum.

Turkat, I. D., Keane, S. P., & Thompson-Pope, S. K. (1990). Social processing in paranoid personalities. *Journal of Psychopathology and Behavioral Assessment, 12,* 263–269.

Turkington, D., Dudley, R., Warman, D. M., & Beck, A. T. (2004). Cognitive-behavioral therapy for schizophrenia: A review. *Journal of Psychiatric Practice, 10,* 5–16.

Turnbull, A. P., Brown, I., & Turnbull, H. R., III. (Eds.). (2003). *Family quality of life: An introduction to conceptualization, measurement and application.* Washington, DC: American Association on Mental Retardation.

Turnbull, R., Turnbull, A., Warren, S., Eidelman, S., & Marchand, P. (2002). Shakespeare redux or Romeo and Juliet revisited: Embedding a terminology and name change in a new agenda for the field of mental retardation. *Mental Retardation, 40,* 65–70.

Turner, J. R. (1994). *Cardiovascular reactivity and stress: Patterns of physiological response.* New York, NY: Plenum.

Turner, S. M., Beidel, D. C., & Costello, A. (1987). Psychopathology in the off-spring of anxiety disorders patients. *Journal of Consulting and Clinical Psychology, 55,* 229–235.

Turner, S. M., Beidel, D. C., Dancu, C. V., & Keys, D. J. (1991). Social Phobia: Axis I and II correlates. *Journal of Abnormal Psychology, 100,* 102–106.

Turner, T. H. (1992). Schizophrenia as a permanent problem: Some aspects of historical evidence in the recency (new disease) hypothesis. *History of Psychiatry, 3,* 413–429.

Tyrer, P. (2009). Why borderline personality disorder is neither borderline nor a personality disorder. *Personality and Mental Health, 3*(2), 86–95.

Tyrer, P., Oliver-Africano, P. C., Ahmed, Z., Bouras, N., Cooray, S., Deb, S., . . . & Kramo, K. (2008). Risperidone, haloperidol, and placebo in the treatment of aggressive challenging behaviour in patients with intellectual disability: a randomised controlled trial. *The Lancet, 371*(9606), 57–63.

Üçok, A., Polat, A., Bozkurt, O., & Meteris, H. (2004). Cigarette smoking among patients with schizophrenia and bipolar disorders. *Psychiatry and clinical neurosciences, 58,* 434–437.

Udry, J. R. (1993). The politics of sex research. *Journal of Sex Research, 30,* 103–110.

UK ECT Review Group. (2003). Efficacy and safety of electroconvulsive therapy in depressive disorders: A systematic review and meta-analysis. *The Lancet, 361,* 799–808.

Ungar, M. (2004). A constructionist discourse on resilience multiple contexts, multiple realities among at-risk children and youth. *Youth & Society, 35*(3), 341–365.

Ungar, M. (2011). The social ecology of resilience: Addressing contextual and cultural ambiguity of a nascent construct. *American Journal of Orthopsychiatry, 81*(1), 1–17.

Ungar, M. (2015). Social ecological complexity and resilience processes. *Behavioral and Brain Sciences.* Published online www.cambridge.org/core/services/aop-cambridge-core/content/view/88733BFAEA2DA6FD0143BC6332FF9A33/S0140525X14001721a.pdf/social_ecological_complexity_and_resilience_processes.pdf

Ungar, M., Ghazinour, M., & Richter, J. (2013). Annual research review: What is resilience within the social ecology of human development? *Journal of Child Psychology and Psychiatry, 54*(4), 348–366.

United States Centers for Disease Control. (1992). *Youth suicide prevention program: A resource guide.* Atlanta, GA: Author.

United States Centers for Disease Control. (2011). Quitting smoking among adults: United States 2001–2010. *Morbidity and Mortality Weekly Report, 60,* 1513–1519.

United States Department of Health and Human Services. (2000). *Evidence-based findings on the efficacy of syringe exchange programs: An analysis prepared for the Assistant Secretary for Health and Surgeon General.* Washington, DC: US Department of Health and Human Services.

Unützer, J. (2007). Late-life depression. *New England Journal of Medicine, 357,* 2269–2276.

Upthegrove, R., Ives, J., Broome, M. R., Caldwell, K., Wood, S. J., & Oyebode, F. (2016). Auditory verbal hallucinations in first-episode psychosis: A phenomenological investigation. *British Journal of Psychiatry Open, 2*(1), 88–95.

Ussher, J. M. (2011). *The madness of women: Myth and experience.* London, UK: Routledge.

Uzzell, B. P., Ponton, M., & Ardila, A. (2007). *International handbook of cross-cultural neuropsychology.* Mahwah, NJ: Psychology Press.

Vaillancourt, T., & Haltigan, J. D. (2017). Joint trajectories of depression and perfectionism across adolescence and childhood risk factors. *Development and Psychopathology, 13* 1–17.

Vaillancourt, T., Brittain, H., Haltigan, J.D., Ostrov, J. M., & Muir, C. (2017). Cortisol moderates the relation between physical peer victimization and physical aggression in preschoolers attending high quality daycares: Evidence of differential susceptibility across informants. *Merrill-Palmer Quarterly.*

Vaillancourt, T., Duku, E., Becker, S., Schmidt, L., Nicol, J., Muir, C., & MacMillian, H. (2011). Peer victimization, depressive symptoms, and high salivary cortisol predict poor memory in children. *Brain and Cognition, 77,* 191–199. doi:10.1016/j.bandc.2011.06.012

Valas, H. (1999). Low achieving students: Peer acceptance, loneliness, self-esteem and depression. *Social Psychology of Education, 3,* 173–192.

Valenstein, E. S. (1986). Great and desperate cures: The rise and decline of psychosurgery and other radical treatments for mental illness. New York, NY: Basic Books.

Van Bockstaele, B., Verschuere, B., Tibboel, H., De Houwer, J., Crombez, G., & Koster, E. H. (2014). A review of current evidence for the causal impact of attentional bias on fear and anxiety. *Psychological Bulletin, 140*(3), 1–40.

Van Damme, J., Maes, L., Kuntsche, E., Crutzen, R., De Clercq, B., Van Lippevelde, W., & Hublet, A. (2015). The influence of parental drinking on offspring's drinking motives and drinking: A mediation analysis on 9 year follow-up data. *Drug and alcohol dependence, 149,* 63–70.

Van der Does, W. (2002). Cognitive reactivity to sad mood: Structure and validity of a new measure. *Behaviour Research and Therapy, 40*(1), 105–120. https://doi.org/10.1016/S0005-7967(00)00111-X

Van der Ham, T., Meulman, J. J., Van Strien, D. C., & Van Engeland, H. (1997). Empirically based subgrouping of eating disorders in adolescents: A longitudinal perspective. *British Journal of Psychiatry, 170,* 363–368.

van der Kolk, B. A., & Van der Hart, O. (1989). Pierre Janet and the breakdown of adaptation in psychological trauma. *American Journal of Psychiatry, 146,* 1530–1540.

van der Meer, L. A., & Rispoli, M. (2010). Communication interventions involving speech-generating devices for children with autism: A review of the literature. *Developmental Neurorehabilitation, 13*(4), 294–306.

Van Der Vorst, H., Krank, M., Engels, R. C., Pieters, S., Burk, W. J., & Mares, S. H. (2013). The mediating role of alcohol-related memory associations on the relation between perceived parental drinking and the onset of adolescents' alcohol use. *Addiction, 108*(3), 526–533.

van Elst, L. T., Woermann, F. G., Lemieux, L., Thompson, P. J., & Trimble, M. R. (2000). Affective aggression in patients with temporal lobe epilepsy: A quantitative MRI study of the amygdala. *Brain, 123,* 234–243.

van Erp, T. G. M., Hibar, D. P., Rasmussen, J. M., Glahn, D. C., Pearlson, G. D., Andreassen, O. A., . . . & Melle, I. (2016). Subcortical brain volume abnormalities in 2028 individuals with schizophrenia and 2540 healthy controls via the ENIGMA consortium. *Molecular Psychiatry, 21*(4), 547–553.

van Goozen, S. H. M., Matthys, W., Cohen-Kettenis, P. T., Gispen-de Wied, C., Wiegant, V. M., & Engeland, H. V. (1998). Salivary cortisol and cardiovascular activity during stress in oppositional-defiant disorder boys and normal controls. *Biological Psychiatry, 43,* 531–539.

van Grootheest, D. S., Bartels, M., Van Beijsterveldt, C. E. M., Cath, D. C., Beekman, A. T., Hudziak, J. J., & Boomsma, D. I. (2008). Genetic and environmental contributions to self-report obsessive-compulsive symptoms in Dutch adolescents at ages 12, 14, and 16. *Journal of the American Academy of Child & Adolescent Psychiatry, 47,* 1182–1188.

Van Orden, K. A., Witte, T. K., Cukrowicz, K. C., Braithwaite, S., Selby, E. A., & Joiner, T. E. Jr. (2010). The Interpersonal Theory of Suicide. *Psychological Review, 117,* 575–600.

Van Rooij, S. J. H., Kennis, M., Sjouwerman, R., Van Den Heuvel, M. P., Kahn, R. S., & Geuze, E. (2015). Smaller hippocampal volume as a vulnerability factor for the persistence of post-traumatic stress disorder. *Psychological Medicine, 45*(13), 2737–2746.

van't Veer-Tazelaar, P. J., van Marwijk, H. W., van Oppen, P., van Hout, H. P., van der Horst, H. E., Cuijpers, P., . . . Beekman, A. T. (2009). Stepped-care prevention of anxiety and depression in late life: A randomized controlled trial. *Archives of General Psychiatry, 66,* 297–304.

Vancouver Coastal Health. (2003). *Injection drug use in Downtown Eastside.* Vancouver, BC: Vancouver Coastal Health.

Varese, F., Smeets, F., Drukker, M., Lieverse, R., Lataster, T., Viechtbauer, W., . . . & Bentall, R. P. (2012). Childhood adversities increase the risk of psychosis: A meta-analysis of patient-control, prospective-and cross-sectional cohort studies. *Schizophrenia Bulletin*, 38(4), 661–671.

Vasiliadis, H. M., Tempier, R., Lesage, A., & Kates, N. (2009). General practice and mental health care: Determinants of outpatient service use. *Canadian Journal of Psychiatry*, 54, 468–476.

Vaskinn, A., Ueland, T., Melle, I., Agartz, I., Andreassen, O. A., & Sundet, K. (2014). Neurocognitive decrements are present in intellectually superior schizophrenia. *Frontiers in Psychiatry*, 5, 1–9.

Vaz, F. J., Guisado, J. A., & Peñas-Lledó, E. M. (2003). History of anorexia nervosa in bulimic patients: Its influence on body composition. *International Journal of Eating Disorders*, 34, 148–155.

Vedi, K., & Bernard, S. (2012). The mental health needs of children and adolescents with learning disabilities. *Current Opinion in Psychiatry*, 25(5) 353–358.

Veenker, H., & Paans, W. (2016). A dynamic approach to communication in health literacy education. *BMC Medical Education*, 16, 280. http://doi.org/10.1186/s12909-016-0785-z

Vellutino, F. R., Fletcher, J. M., Snowling, M. J., & Scanlon, D. M. (2004). Specific reading disability (dyslexia): What have we learned in the past four decades? *Journal of Child Psychology and Psychiatry*, 45(1), 2–40.

Venter, A., Lord, C., & Schopler, E. (1992). A follow-up study of high-functioning autistic children. *Journal of Child Psychology and Psychiatry*, 33, 489–507.

Verdoux, H., & Bégaud, B. (2004). Pharmaco-epidemiology: What do (and don't) we know about utilization and impact of psychotropic medications in real-life conditions? *British Journal of Psychiatry*, 185, 93–94.

Vermeulen-Smit, E., Koning, I. M., Verdurmen, J. E., Van der Vorst, H., Engels, R. C., & Vollebergh, W. A. (2012). The influence of paternal and maternal drinking patterns within two-partner families on the initiation and development of adolescent drinking. *Addictive Behaviors*, 37(11), 1248–1256.

Vernick, J. S., Burris, S., & Strathdee, S. A. (2003). Public opinion about syringe exchange programmes in the USA: An analysis of national surveys. *International Journal of Drug Policy*, 14, 431–435.

Vervoort, T., Goubert, L., Eccleston, C., Bijttebier, P., & Crombez, G. (2006). Catastrophic thinking about pain is independently associated with pain severity, disability, and somatic complaints in school children and children with chronic pain. *Journal of Pediatric Psychology*, 31(7), 674–683.

Vessey, J. T., & Howard, K. I. (1993). Who seeks psychotherapy? *Psychotherapy*, 30, 546–553.

Videnieks, M. (2003). Heroin deal ends health service for drug users. *The HEP C Review*, 42, 7.

Viding, E., Blair, R. J. R., Moffitt, T. E., & Plomin, R. (2005). Evidence for substantial genetic risk for psychopathy in 7-year-olds. *Journal of Child Psychology and Psychiatry*, 46, 592–597.

Viladrich, A., Yeh, M. C., Bruning, N., & Weiss, R. (2009). "Do real women have curves?" Paradoxical body images among Latinas in New York City. *Journal of Immigrant and Minority Health*, 11, 20–28. doi: 10.1007/s10903-008-9176-9

Viljoen, J. L., & Roesch, R. (2007). Assessing adolescents' adjudicative competence. In R. Jackson (Ed.), *Learning forensic assessment* (pp. 291–312). New York, NY: Taylor & Francis.

Viljoen, J. L., & Zapf, P. A. (2002). Fitness to stand trial evaluations: A comparison of referred and non-referred defendants. *International Journal of Forensic Mental Health*, 1, 127–138.

Viljoen, J. L., Roesch, R., Ogloff, J. R. P., & Zapf, P. A. (2003). The role of Canadian psychologists in conducting fitness and criminal responsibility evaluations. *Canadian Psychology*, 44, 369–381.

Villeneuve, M., Chatenoud, C., Hutchinson, N. L., Minnes, P., Perry, A., Dionne, C., . . . Weiss, J (2013). The experience of parents as their children with developmental disabilities transition from early intervention to kindergarten. *Canadian Journal of Education*, 36(1) 4–43.

Vissers, L. E. L. M., Gilissen, C., & Veltman, J. A. (2016). Genetic studies in intellectual disability and related disorders. *Nature Reviews. Genetics*, 17(1), 9–18. https://doi.org/10.1038/nrg3999

Vitacco, M. J., Rogers, R., Neumann, C. S., Durrant, S., & Collins, M. (2000, March). *Adolescent psychopathy: Contributions of sensation seeking, impulsivity, and externalizing disorders.* Paper presented at the biennial conference of the American Psychology and Law Society, New Orleans, United States.

Vitale, J. E., Smith, S. S., Brinkley, C. A., & Newman, J. P. (2002). The reliability and validity of the Psychopathy Checklist-Revised in a sample of female offenders. *Criminal Justice and Behavior*, 29(2), 202–231.

Vitaliano, P. P., Zhang, J., & Scanlan, J. M. (2003). Is caregiving hazardous to one's physical health? A meta-analysis. *Psychological Bulletin*, 129, 946–972.

Vitaro, F., Brendgen, M., & Tremblay, R. E. (2000). Influence of deviant friends on delinquency: Searching for moderator variables. *Journal of Abnormal Child Psychology*, 28(4), 313–325.

Vitaro, F., Tremblay, R. E., Kerr, M., Pagani, L., & Bukowski, W. M. (2007). Disruptiveness, friends' characteristics, and delinquency in early adolescence: A test of two competing models of development. *Child Development*, 68(4), 676–689.

Vitiello, M. V., & Prinz, P. N. (1994). Sleep disturbances in the elderly. In M. L. Albert & J. E. Knoefel (Eds.), *Clinical neurology of aging*, New York, NY: Oxford University Press.

Vo, M., Accurso, E. C., Goldschmidt, A. B., & Le Grange, D. (2016). The impact of DSM-5 on eating disorder diagnoses. *International Journal of Eating Disorders*, 50, 578-581. doi: 10.1002/eat.22628

Vogel, D. L., Bitman, R. L., Hammer, J. H., & Wade, N. G. (2013). Is stigma internalized? The longitudinal impact of public stigma on self-stigma. *Journal of Counseling Psychology*, 60(2), 311–316.

Vogel, D. L., Wade, N. G., & Haake, S. (2006). Measuring the self-stigma associated with seeking psychological help. *Journal of Counseling Psychology*, 53, 325–337.

Volkmar, F. R., & Schwab-Stone, M. (1996). Childhood disorders in DSM-IV. *Journal of Child Psychology and Psychiatry*, 37, 779–784.

Volkmar, F. R., Carter, A., Grossman, J., & Klin, A. (1997). Social development in autism. In D. J. Cohen & F. R. Volkmar (Eds.), *Handbook of autism and pervasive developmental disorders* (pp. 173–194). New York, NY: Wiley.

Volkow, N. D., Swanson, J. M., Evins, A. E., DeLisi, L. E., Meier, M. H., Gonzalez, R., . . . & Baler, R. (2016). Effects of cannabis use on human behavior, including cognition, motivation, and psychosis: a review. *JAMA psychiatry*, 73(3), 292–297.

Vortstenbosch, V., Newman, L., & Antony, M. M. (2014). Exposure techniques. In Dozois, D. J. A. (Vol. Ed.), S. G. Hofmann (Series Ed.), CBT: General strategies. *The Wiley handbook of cognitive-behavioral therapy* (Vol I, pp. 45–65). Oxford, UK: Wiley-Blackwell.

Waddell, C., McEwan, K., Peters, R. DeV., Hua, J. M., & Garland, O. (2007). Preventing mental disorders in children: A public health priority. *Canadian Journal of Public Health*, 98, 174–178.

Waddell, C., McEwan, K., Shepherd, C., Offord, D. R., & Hua, J. M. (2005). A public health strategy to improve the mental health of Canadian children. *Canadian Journal of Psychiatry*, 50, 226–233.

Waddell, C., Offord, D. R., Shepherd, C., Hua, J. M., & McEwan, K. (2002). Child psychiatric epidemiology and Canadian public policy-making: The state of the science and the art of the possible. *Canadian Journal of Psychiatry*, 47, 825–832.

Waddell, C., Shepherd, C. A., Schwartz, C., & Barican, J. (2014). *Child and youth mental disorders: Prevalence and evidence-based interventions.* Vancouver, BC: Children's Health Policy Centre, Simon Fraser University.

Wade, C., Llewellyn, G., & Matthews, J. (2008). Review of parent training interventions for parents with intellectual disability. *Journal of Applied Research in Intellectual Disabilities*, 21, 351–366.

Wagner, K. D., Berard, R., Stein, M. B., Wetherhold, E., Carpenter, D. J., Perera, P., et al. (2004). A multicenter, randomized, double-blind, placebo-controlled trial of paroxetine in children and adolescents with social anxiety disorder. *Archives of General Psychiatry*, 61(11), 1153–1162.

Wahlbeck, K., Cheine, M., Essali, A., & Adams, C. (1999). Evidence of clozapine's effectiveness in schizophrenia: A systematic review and meta-analysis of randomized trials. *American Journal of Psychiatry*, 156, 990–999.

Waite, J., & Easton, A. (Eds.). (2013). *The ECT handbook.* London, UK: RCPsych Publications.

Wakefield, J. C. (1993). Limits of operationalization: A critique of Spitzer and Endicott's (1978) proposed operational criteria for mental disorder. *Journal of Abnormal Psychology*, 102, 160–172.

Wakefield, J. C. (1997). Diagnosing DSM-IV—Part 1: DSM-IV and the concept of disorder. *Behaviour Research and Therapy*, 35, 633–649.

Wakefield, J. C. (1999). Evolutionary versus prototype analyses of the concept of disorder. *Journal of Abnormal Psychology*, 108, 374–399.

Wakefield, J. C. (2014). The biostatistical theory versus the harmful dysfunction analysis, part 1: is part-dysfunction a sufficient condition for medical disorder? *Journal of Medical Philosophy*, 39, 648–682.

Wakeling, A. (1996). Epidemiology of anorexia nervosa. *Psychiatry Research*, 62, 3–9.

Wakschlag, L. S., Lahey, B. B., Loeber, R., Green, S. M., Gordon, R. A., & Leventhal, B. L. (1997). Maternal smoking during pregnancy and the risk of conduct disorder in boys. *Archives of General Psychiatry*, 54, 670–676.

Wald, N. J., Kennard, A., Densem, J. W., Cuckle, H. S., Chard, T., & Butler, L. (1992). Antenatal maternal serum screening for Down's syndrome: Results of a demonstration project. *British Medical Journal, 305,* 391–394.

Waldinger, M. D. (2005). Relevance of an evidence-based ejaculation time cutoff point for neurobiological research of premature ejaculation. *The Journal of Comparative Neurology, 493,* 46–50.

Waldinger, M. D., Hengeveld, M. W., Zwinderman, A. H., & Olivier, B. (1998). An empirical operationalization study of DSM-IV diagnostic criteria for premature ejaculation. *International Journal of Psychiatry and Clinical Practice, 2,* 278–293.

Walker, E. F., & Diforio, D. (1997). Schizophrenia: A neural diathesis-stress model. *Psychological Review, 104,* 667–685.

Walker, E. F., Mittal, V., & Tessner, K. (2008). Stress and the hypothalamic pituitary adrenal axis in the developmental course of schizophrenia. *Annual Review of Clinical Psychology, 4,* 189–216.

Walker, E. F., Savoie, T., & Davis, D. (1994). Neuromotor precursors of schizophrenia. *Schizophrenia Bulletin, 20,* 441–451.

Walkup, J. T., Albano, A. M., Piacentini, J., Birmaher, B., Compton, S. N., Sherrill, J. T., et al. (2008). Cognitive behavioral therapy, sertraline, or a combination in childhood anxiety. *The New England Journal of Medicine,* doi:10.1056/NEJMoa0804633.

Walkup, J., Labellarte, M., Riddle, M. A., Pine, D. S., Greenhill, L., Fairbanks, J., et al. (2002). Treatment of pediatric anxiety disorders: An open-label extension of the research units on pediatric psychopharmacology anxiety study. *Journal of Child and Adolescent Psychopharmacology, 12*(3), 175–188.

Wallace, J., & Pfohl, B. (1995). Age-related differences in the symptomatic expression of major depression. *Journal of Nervous and Mental Disease, 183,* 99–102.

Wallace, J., Schneider, T., & McGuffin, P. (2002). Genetics of depression. In I. H. Gotlib & C. L. Hammen (Eds.), *Handbook of depression* (pp. 169–191). New York, NY: Guilford.

Wallace, J. F., Schmitt, W. A., Vitale, J. E., & Newman, J. P. (2000). Experimental investigations of information-processing deficiencies in psychopaths: Implications for diagnosis and treatment. In C. Gacono (Ed.), *The clinical and forensic assessment of psychopathy: A practitioner's guide* (pp. 87–109). Hillsdale, NJ: Erlbaum.

Wallach, H. S., Safir, M. P., & Bar-Zvi, M. (2009). Virtual reality cognitive behavior therapy for public speaking anxiety. *Behavior Modification, 33,* 314–338.

Waller, N. G., & Ross, C. A. (1997). The prevalence and biometric structure of pathological dissociation in the general population: Taxometric and behaviour genetic findings. *Journal of Abnormal Psychology, 106,* 499–510.

Waller, N. G., Putnam, F. W., & Carlson, E. B. (1996). Types of dissociation and dissociative types: A taxometric analysis of dissociative experiences. *Psychological Methods, 1,* 300–321.

Wallgren, H., & Barry, H. (1971). *Actions of alcohol.* Amsterdam, The Netherlands: Elsevier.

Walsh, A. E. S., Oldman, A. D., Franklin, M., Fairburn, C. G., & Cowen, P. J. (1995). Dieting decreases plasma tryptophan and increases the prolactin response to d-fenfluramine in women but not men. *Journal of Affective Disorders, 33,* 89–97.

Walsh, B. T., Seidman, S. N., Sysko, R., & Gould, M. (2002). Placebo response in studies of major depression. *Journal of the American Medical Association, 287,* 1840–1847.

Walsh, E., Buchanan, A., & Fahy, T. (2002). Violence and schizophrenia: Examining the evidence. *The British Journal of Psychiatry, 180,* 490–495.

Walsh, J. (1990). Assessment and treatment of the schizotypal personality disorder. *Journal of Independent Social Work, 4,* 41–59.

Walsh, K. (2002). Thoughts on changing the term *mental retardation. Mental Retardation, 40,* 70–75.

Walsh-Bowers, R. (1998). Community psychology in the Canadian psychological family. *Canadian Psychology, 37,* 281–287.

Walter, M., Witzel, J., Wiebking, C., Gubka, U., Rotte, M., Schiltz, K., et al. (2007). Pedophilia is linked to reduced activation in hypothalamus and lateral prefrontal cortex during erotic stimulation. *Biological Psychiatry, 62,* 698–701.

Walther, S. (2015). Psychomotor symptoms of schizophrenia map on the cerebral motor circuit. *Psychiatry Research: Neuroimaging, 233*(3), 293–298.

Wampold, B. E., Mondin, G. W., Moody, M., Stich, F., Benson, K., & Ahn, H. (1997). A meta-analysis of outcome studies comparing bona fide psychotherapies: Empirically, "All must have prizes." *Psychological Bulletin, 122,* 203–215.

Wandersman, A., Chien, V. H., & Katz, J. (2012). Toward an evidence-based system for innovation support for implementing innovations with quality: Tools, training, technical assistance, and quality assurance/quality improvement. *American Journal of Community Psychology, 50*(3–4), 445–459.

Wandersman, A., Duffy, J., Flaspohler, P., Noonan, R., Lubell, K., Stillman, L., et al. (2008). Bridging the gap between prevention research and practice: The interactive systems framework for dissemination and implementation. *American Journal of Community Psychology, 41,* 171–181.

Wang, J. L., Schmitz, N., & Dewa, C. S. (2010). Socioeconomic status and the risk of major depression: The Canadian National Population Health Survey. *Journal of Epidemiology and Community Health, 64,* 447–452.

Wang, T., Ren, X., Schweizer, K., & Xu, F. (2015). Schooling effects on intelligence development: Evidence based on national samples from urban and rural China. *Educational Psychology, 36*(5), 831–844. https://doi.org/10.1080/01443410.2015.1099618

Wang, W., Kumar, P., Minhas, S., & Ralph, D. (2005). Proposals or findings for a new approach about how to define and diagnose premature ejaculation. *European Urology, 48,* 418–423.

Ward, T., & Beech, A. (2006). An integrated theory of sexual offending. *Aggression and Violent Behavior, 11,* 44–63.

Ward, T. & Gannon, T. (2006). Rehabilitation, etiology, and self-regulation: The Good Lives Model of sexual offender treatment. *Aggression and Violent Behavior, 11,* 77–94.

Ward, T. & Stewart, C. (2003). Criminogenic needs and human needs: A theoretical model. *Psychology, Crime & Law, 9,* 125–143.

Warne, J. P., & Dallman, M. F. (2007). Stress, diet and abdominal obesity: Y? *Nature Medicine, 13,* 781–783.

Warner, R. (1978). The diagnosis of antisocial and hysterical personality disorders: An example of sex bias. *Journal of Nervous and Mental Disease, 166,* 839–845.

Warren, J. I., Burnette, M. L., South, S. C., Chauhan, P., Bale, R., Friend, R., et al. (2003). Psychopathy in women: Structural modeling and comorbidity. *International Journal of Law and Psychiatry, 26,* 233–242.

Warren, S. L., Huston, L., Egeland, B., & Sroufe, L. A. (1997). Child and adolescent anxiety disorders and early attachment. *Journal of the American of Child and Adolescent Psychiatry, 36,* 637–644.

Wasik, B. H., Ramey, C. T., Bryant, D. M., & Sparling, J. J. (1990). A longitudinal study of two early intervention strategies: Project CARE. *Child Development, 61,* 1682–1692.

Wass, R. S. (2008). Neuroanatomical and neurobehavioral effects of heavy prenatal alcohol exposure. In J. Brick (Ed.), *Handbook of the medical consequences of alcohol and drug abuse* (2nd ed., pp. 177–217). New York: Haworth Press.

Waterhouse, L., Morris, R., Allen, D., Dunn, M., Fein, D., Feinstein, C., et al. (1996). Diagnosis and classification in autism. *Journal of Autism and Developmental Disorders, 26,* 59–86.

Waters, A. M., & Craske, M. G. (2005). Generalized anxiety disorder. In M. M. Antony, D. R., Ledley, & R. G. Heimberg (Eds.), *Improving outcomes and preventing relapse in cognitive-behavioral therapy* (pp. 77–127). New York, NY: Guilford.

Waters, E. (1995). Let's not wait till it's broke: Interventions to maintain and enhance mental health in late life. In M. Gatz (Ed.), *Emerging issues in mental health and aging* (pp. 183–209). Washington DC: American Psychological Association.

Watling, R. L., & Dietz, J. (2007). Immediate effect of Ayres's sensory integration–based occupational therapy intervention on children with autism spectrum disorders. *American Journal of Occupational Therapy, 61*(5), 574–583.

Watson, J. B. (1913). Psychology as the behaviorist views it. *Psychological Review, 20,* 158–177.

Watson, J. B., & Rayner, R. (1920). Conditioned emotional reactions. *Journal of Experimental Psychology, 3,* 1–14.

Watson, T. L., & Andersen, A. E. (2003). A critical examination of the amenorrhea and weight criteria for diagnosing anorexia nervosa. *Acta Psychiatrica Scandinavica, 108,* 175–182.

Watts, B. V., Schnurr, P. P., Mayo, L., Young-Xu, Y., Weeks, W. B., & Friedman, M. J. (2013). Meta-analysis of the efficacy of treatments for posttraumatic stress disorder. *Journal of Clinical Psychiatry, 74,* 541–550.

Webster, C. D., Douglas, K. S., Eaves, D., & Hart, S. D. (1997). *HCR-20: Assessing risk for violence, version 2.* Burnaby, BC: Mental Health, Law, & Policy Institute, Simon Fraser University.

Webster-Stratton, C. H. (1996). *The incredible years: A guide for parents of children aged 2–8 years.* London, UK: Lavis.

Webster-Stratton, C., & Reid, J. M. (2008). Preventing and treating conduct disorders. In A. E. Kazdin & J. R. Weisz (Eds.), *The incredible years parents, teachers, and children training series: A multifaceted treatment approach for young children with conduct problems* (pp. 224–240). New York, NY: Guilford.

Wechsler, D. (1997). *Wechsler memory scale* (3rd ed.). San Antonio, TX: Psychological Corporation.

Wechsler, D. (2008). *Wechsler adult intelligence scale* (4th ed.). Bloomington, MN: Pearson Inc.

Wechsler, D. (2009). *Wechsler individual achievement test* (3rd ed.). San Antonio, TX: Psychological Corporation.

Wechsler, D. (2012). *Wechsler preschool and primary scale of intelligence* (4th ed.). San Antonio, TX: Psychological Corporation.

Wechsler, D. (2014). *Wechsler intelligence scale for children* (5th ed.). Bloomington, MN: Pearson Inc.

Weddington, W. W., Brown, B. S., Haertzen, M. H., Cone, E. J., Dax, E. M., Herning, R. I., & Michaelson, B. S. (1990). Changes in mood, craving, and sleep during short-term abstinence reported by male cocaine addicts. *Archives of General Psychiatry, 47*, 861–868.

Weems, C. F., Costa, N. M., Watts, S. E., Taylor, L. K., & Cannon, M. F. (2007). Cognitive errors, anxiety sensitivity, and anxiety control beliefs: Their unique and specific associations with childhood anxiety symptoms. *Behavior Modification, 31*, 174–201.

Weems, C. F., Silverman, W. K., & LaGreca, A. M. (2000). What do youth referred for anxiety problems worry about? Worry and its relation to anxiety and anxiety disorders in children and adolescents. *Journal of Abnormal Child Psychology, 28*(1), 63–72.

Wehmeyer, M. L., Palmer, S., Smith, S., Parent, W., Davies, D. K., & Stock, S. E. (2006). Technology use by people with intellectual and developmental disabilities to support employment activities: A single-subject design meta-analysis. *Journal of Vocational Rehabilitation, 24*, 81–86.

Weiler, B. L., & Widom, C. S. (1996). Psychopathy and violent behavior in abused and neglected young adults. *Criminal Behaviour and Mental Health, 6*, 253–271.

Weinberger, A.H., Funk, A.P. & Goodwin, R.D. (2016). A review of epidemiologic research on smoking behavior among persons with alcohol and illicit substance use disorders. *Preventive Medicine, 92*, 148–159.

Weinberger, D. R. (1987). Implications of normal brain development for the pathogenesis of schizophrenia. *Archives of General Psychiatry, 44*(7), 660–669.

Weinberger, D. R. (1995). From neuropathology to neurodevelopment. *The Lancet, 346*(8974), 552557.

Weinberger, D. R. (1995). Schizophrenia as a neurodevelopment disorder: A review of the concept. In S. R. Hirsch & D. R. Weinberger (Eds.), *Schizophrenia* (pp. 293–323). London, UK: Blackwood.

Weinberger, M., Hiner, S. L., & Tierney, W. M. (1987). In support of hassles as a measure of stress in predicting health outcomes. *Journal of Behavioral Medicine, 10*, 19–31.

Weiner, D. B. (1979). The apprenticeship of Philippe Pinel: A new document, "Observations of Citizen Pussin on the insane." *American Journal of Psychiatry, 136*, 1128–1134.

Weiner, H. (1996). Use of animal models in peptic ulcer disease. *Psychosomatic Medicine, 58*, 524–545.

Weiner. L, & Avery-Clark, C. (2014). Sensate focus: Clarifiying the Masters and Johnson's model. *Sexual and Relationhip Therapy, 29*, 307–319.

Weisberg, R. B., Brown, T. A., Wincze, J. P., & Barlow, D. H. (2001). Causal attributions and male sexual arousal. *Journal of Abnormal Psychology, 110*, 324–334.

Weiss, B., & Weisz, J. R. (1995). Relative effectiveness of behavioral and non-behavioral child psychotherapy. *Journal of Consulting and Clinical Psychology, 63*, 317–320.

Weiss, J. (1972). Psychological factors in stress and disease. *Scientific American, 226*, 104–113.

Weiss, J. A., Tint, A., Paquette-Smith, M., & Lunsky, Y. (2016). Perceived self-efficacy in parents of adolescents and adults with autism spectrum disorder. *Autism, 20*(4), 425–434.

Weiss, J. M. (1970). Somatic effects of predictable and unpredictable shock. *Psychosomatic Medicine, 32*, 397–408.

Weiss, J. M. (1971). Effects of coping behavior with and without a feedback signal on stress pathology in rats. *Journal of Comparative and Physiological Psychology, 77*, 22–30.

Weiss, L. G., Saklofske, D. H., Coalson, D., & Raiford, S. E. (Eds.). (2010). *WAIS-IV: Clinical use and interpretation.* San Diego, CA: Academic Press.

Weiss, P. A., & Weiss, W. U. (2010). Using the MMPI-2 in police psychological assessment. *Personality Assessment in Police Psychology: A 21st Century Perspective.* Springfield, IL: Charles C. Thomas.

Weissberg, R. P., & Greenberg, M. T. (1998). School and community competence-enhancement and prevention programs. In W. Damon (Series Ed.), I. E. Siegel & K. A. Renninger (Vol. Eds.), *Handbook of child psychology: Vol. 4. Child psychology in practice* (5th ed., pp. 877–954). New York, NY: Wiley.

Weissman, A. N., & Beck, A. T. (1978). Development and validation of the Dysfunctional Attitude Scale: A preliminary investigation. Proceedings of the Annual Meeting of the American Educational Research Association, Toronto, 27–31 March 1978, 1–13.

Weissman, M. M., Bland, R. C., Canino, G. J., Faravelli, C., Greenwald, S., Hwu, H. G., et al. (1997). The cross-national epidemiology of panic disorder. *Archives of General Psychiatry, 54*, 305–309.

Weissman, M. M., Leaf, P. J., Bruce, M. L., & Florio, L. (1988). The epidemiology of dysthymia in five communities: Rates, risks, comorbidity, and treatment. *American Journal of Psychiatry, 145*, 815–819.

Weissman, M. M., Prusoff, B. A., DiMascio, A., Neu, Goklaney, & Klerman, G. (1979). The efficacy of drugs and psychotherapy in the treatment of acute depressive episodes. *American Journal of Psychiatry, 136* (4B), 555–558.

Weisz, J. R., Kuppens, S., Eckshtain, D., Ugueto, A. M., Hawley, K. M., & Jensen-Doss, A. (2013). Performance of evidence-based youth psychotherapies compared with usual clinical care: A multilevel meta-analysis. *JAMA Psychiatry, 70*, 750–761.

Welch, S., Klassen, C., Borisova, O., & Clothier, H. (2013). The DSM-5 controversies: How should psychologists respond? *Canadian Psychology, 54*, 166–175.

Wenzlaff, R. M., & Wegner, D. M. (2000). Thought suppression. *Annual Review of Psychology, 51*, 59–91.

Wersebe, H., Sijbrandij, M., & Cuijpers, P. (2013). Psychological group-treatments of social anxiety disorder: A meta-analysis. *PLoS ONE, 8*(11), e79034. doi:10.1371/journal.pone.0079034

Wertheim, E. H., Paxton, S. J., Schutx, H. K., & Muir, S. L. (1997). Why do adolescent girls watch their weight? An interview study examining sociocultural pressures to be thin. *Journal of Psychosomatic Research, 42*, 345–355.

Wessing, I., Romer, G., & Junghöfer, M. (2017). Hypervigilance-avoidance in children with anxiety disorders: Magnetoencephalographic evidence. *Journal of Child Psychology and Psychiatry, 58*, 103–112. https://doi.org/10.1111/jcpp.12617

West, M., Keller, A., Links, P. S., & Patrick, J. (1993). Borderline disorder and attachment pathology. *Canadian Journal of Psychiatry, 38*, 16–22.

West, R. (2006). *Theory of addiction.* Oxford, UK: Blackwell.

West, S. L., & O'Neal, K. K. (2004). Project D.A.R.E. outcome effectiveness revisited. *American Journal of Public Health, 94*, 1027–1029.

Westen, D., & Morrison, K. (2001). A multidimensional meta-analysis of treatments for depression, panic, and generalized anxiety disorder: An empirical examination of the status of empirically supported therapies. *Journal of Consulting and Clinical Psychology, 69*, 875–899.

Westerhof, G. J., & Keyes, C. L. (2010). Mental illness and mental health: The two continua model across the lifespan. *Journal of Adult Development, 17*(2), 110–119.

Westra, H. A., & Stewart, S. H. (1998). Cognitive behavioural therapy and pharmacotherapy: Complementary or contradictory approaches to the treatment of anxiety? *Clinical Psychology Review, 18*, 307–340.

Westra, H.A., Constantino, M.J., & Antony, M.M. (2016). Integrating motivational interviewing with cognitive-behavioral therapy for severe generalized anxiety disorder: An allegiance-controlled randomized clinical trial. *Journal of Consulting and Clinical Psychology, 84*, 768–782.

Westra, H. A., Stewart, S. H., Teehan, M., Johl, K., Dozois, D. J. A., & Hill, T. (2004). Benzodiazepine use associated with decreased memory for psycho-education material in cognitive behavioral therapy for panic disorder. *Cognitive Therapy & Research, 28*, 193–208.

Wetherell, J. L., Afari, N., Ayers, C. R., Stoddard, J. A., Ruberg, J., Sorrell, J. T., et al. (2011). Acceptance and commitment therapy for generalized anxiety disorder in older adults: A preliminary report. *Behavior Therapy, 42*, 127–134.

Wetherell, J., Petkus AJ, White, K., Nguyen H, Kornblith, S., Andreescu, C., Zisook, S., & Lenze, E. (2013). Antidepressant medication augmented with cognitive-behavioral therapy for generalized anxiety disorder in older adults. *American Journal of Psychiatry, 170*(7), 782–789.

Wetherill, R. R. & Fromme, K. (2016), Alcohol-induced blackouts: A review of recent clinical research with practical implications and recommendations for future studies. *Alcoholism: Clinical and Experimenal Research, 40*, 922–935. doi:10.1111/acer.13051

Wheeler, D. L., Jacobson, J. W., Paglieri, R. A., & Schwartz, A. A. (1993). An experimental assessment of facilitated communication. *Mental Retardation, 31*, 49–60.

Wheeler, S., Book, A., & Costello, K. (2009). Psychopathic traits and perceptions of victim vulnerability. *Criminal Justice and Behavior, 36*, 635–648. doi:10.1177/0093854809333958

White, A. M., Jamieson-Drake, D. W., & Swartzwelder, H. S. (2002). Prevalence and correlates of alcohol-induced blackouts among college students: Results of an e-mail survey. *Journal of American College Health, 51*, 117–132.

White, C., Holland, E., Marsland, D., & Oakes, P. (2003). The identification of environments and cultures that promote the abuse of people with intellectual disabilities: A review of the literature. *Journal of Applied Research in Intellectual Disabilities, 16*, 1–9.

White, P. (2009, July 31). Rorschach and Wikipedia: The battle of the inkblots. *The Globe and Mail.* Retrieved from www.theglobeandmail.com

Whitehouse, M. A., & McCabe, M. P. (1997). Sex education programs for people with intellectual disability: How effective are they?. *Education and Training in Mental Retardation and Developmental Disabilities, 32,* 229–240.

Whitman, B. Y. (2008). Human behavior genetics: Implications for neurodevelopmental disorders. In P. J. Accardo (Ed.), *Capute and Accardo's neurodevelopmental disabilities in infancy and childhood: Vol 1: Neurodevelopmental diagnosis and treatment* (3rd ed., pp. 175–197). Baltimore, MD: Paul H. Brookes.

Whittal, M. L., Agras, W. S., & Gould, R. A. (1999). Bulimia nervosa: A meta-analysis of psychosocial and pharmacological treatments. *Behavior Therapy, 30,* 117–135.

Whittal, M. L., Thordarson, D. S., & McLean, P. D. (2005). Treatment of obsessive-compulsive disorder: Cognitive behavior therapy vs. exposure and response prevention. *Behaviour Research and Therapy, 43,* 1559–1576.

Whitton, A. E., Treadway, M. T., & Pizzagalli, D. A. (2016). Reward processing dysfunction in major depression, bipolar disorder and schizophrenia. *Current Opinion in Psychiatry, 28*(1), 7–12.

Whooley, M. A., & Wong, J. M. (2013). Depression and cardiovascular disorders. *Annual Review of Clinical Psychology, 9,* 327–354.

Whooley, M. A., de Jonge, P., Vittinghoff, E., Otte, C., Moos, R., Carney, R. M., ... & Schiller, N. B. (2008). Depressive symptoms, health behaviors, and risk of cardiovascular events in patients with coronary heart disease. *Journal of the American Medical Association, 300*(20), 2379–2388.

Widiger, T. A., & Boyd, S. E. (2009). Personality disorders: Assessment instruments. In J. N. Butcher (Ed.), *Oxford handbook of personality assessment* (pp. 336–363). New York, NY: Oxford University Press.

Widiger, T. A., & Frances, A. J. (1989). Epidemiology, diagnosis, and comorbidity of borderline personality disorder. In A. Tasman, R. E. Hales, & A. J. Frances (Eds.), *Review of Psychiatry* (Vol. 8, pp. 8–24). Washington, DC: American Psychiatric Press.

Widiger, T. A., & Lowe, J. R. (2010). Personality disorders. In M. M. Antony & D. H. Barlow (Eds.), *Handbook of assessment and treatment planning for psychological disorders* (2nd ed., pp. 571–605). New York, NY: Guilford.

Widiger, T. A., & Rogers, J. H. (1989). Prevalence and comorbidity of personality disorders. *Psychiatric Annals, 19,* 132–136.

Widiger, T. A., & Spitzer, R. L. (1991). Sex bias in the diagnosis of personality disorders: Conceptual and methodological issues. *Clinical Psychology Review, 11,* 1–22.

Widiger, T. A., & Trull, T. J. (1991). Diagnosis and clinical assessment. *Annual Review of Psychology, 41,* 109–135.

Widiger, T. A., & Trull, T. J. (1992). Personality and psychopathology: An application of the five-factor model. *Journal of Personality, 60,* 363–393.

Widiger, T. A., & Trull, T. J. (1993). Borderline and narcissistic personality disorders. In P. B. Sutker & H. E. Adams (Eds.), *Comprehensive handbook of psychopathology* (2nd ed., pp. 371–397). New York, NY: Plenum Press.

Widiger, T. A., Frances, A. J., & Trull, T. J. (1987). A psychometric analysis of the social-interpersonal and cognitive-perceptual items for the schizotypal personality disorder. *Archives of General Psychiatry, 44,* 741–745.

Widiger, T. A., Miele, G. M., & Tilly, S. M. (1992). Alternative perspectives on the diagnosis of borderline personality disorder. In J. F. Carkin, E. Marziali, & H. Munroe-Blum (Eds.), *Borderline personality disorder: Clinical and empirical perspectives* (pp. 89–115). New York, NY: Guilford.

Widmer, E. D., Tread, J., & Newcomb, R. (1998). Attitudes toward non-marital sex in 24 countries. *Journal of Sex Research, 35,* 349–358.

Wiech, K., & Tracey, I. (2009). The influence of negative emotions on pain: Behavioral effects and neural mechanisms. *Neuroimage, 47*(3), 987–994.

Wiederhold, B. K., & Wiederhold, M. D. (2004). *Virtual reality therapy for anxiety disorders: Advances in evaluation and treatment.* Washington, DC: American Psychological Association.

Wilde, J. (2003, November 8). More than skin deep. *The Guardian.* Retrieved from www.guardian.co.uk/film/2003/nov/08/features

Wilens, T., McBurnett, K., Stein, M., Lerner, M., Spencer, T., & Wolraich, M. (2005). ADHD treatment with once-daily OROS methylphenidate: Final results from a long-term open-label study. *Journal of the American Academy of Child and Adolescent Psychiatry, 44,* 1015–1023.

Wilhelm, S., & Steketee, G. S. (2006). *Cognitive therapy for obsessive-compulsive disorder: A guide for professionals.* New York, NY: New Harbinger.

Wilhelm, S., Phillips, K. A., & Steketee, G. (2013). *Cognitive-behavioral therapy for body dysmorphic disorder.* New York, New York: Guilford.

Willi, T. S., Barr, A. M., Gicas, K., Lang, D. J., Vila-Rodriguez, F., Su, W., ... Panenka, W. J. (2016). Characterization of white matter integrity deficits in cocaine-dependent individuals with substance-induced psychosis compared with non-psychotic cocaine users. *Addiction Biology,* ePub. https://doi.org/10.1111/adb.12363

Williams, J. H. G., & Ross, L. (2007). Consequences of prenatal toxin exposure for mental health in children and adolescents: A systematic review. *European Child and Adolescent Psychiatry, 16,* 243–253.

Williams, J. M. G. (1997). *Cry of pain.* London: Penguin.

Williams, J. M. G. (2008). Mindfulness, depression and modes of mind. *Cognitive Therapy and Research, 32,* 721–733.

Williams, J. M., & Kuyken, W. (2012). Mindfulness-based cognitive therapy: A promising new approach to preventing depressive relapse. *The British Journal of Psychiatry, 200,* 359–360.

Williams, J. M., Mathews, A., & MacLeod, C. (1996). The emotional Stroop task and psychopathology. *Psychological Bulletin, 120,* 3–24.

Williams, R. B., Barefoot, J. C., Califf, R. M., Haney, T. L., Saunders, W. B., Pryor, D. B., et al. (1992). Prognostic importance of social and economic resources among medically treated patients with angiographically documented coronary artery disease. *Journal of the American Medical Association, 267,* 520–524.

Williamson, H. J. & Perkins E. A. (2014). Family caregivers of adults with intellectual and developmental disabilities: Outcomes asssociated with U.S. services and supports. *Intellectual and Developmental Disabilities, 52,* 147–159.

Williamson, S., Hare, R. D., & Wong, S. (1987). Violence: Criminal psychopaths and their victims. *Canadian Journal of Behavioral Science, 19,* 454–462.

Williamson, S., Harpur, T. J., & Hare, R. D. (1991). Abnormal processing of affective words by psychopaths. *Psychophysiology, 28,* 260–273.

Willner, P., & Hatton, C. (2006). CBT for people with intellectual disabilities. *Journal of Applied Research in Intellectual Disabilities, 19*(1), 1–3.

Willner, P., Jones, J., Tams, R., & Green, G. (2002). A randomized controlled trial of the efficacy of a cognitive-behavioural anger management group for clients with learning disabilities. *Journal of Applied Research in Intellectual Disabilities, 15*(3), 224–235.

Willner, P., Rose, J., Jahoda, A., Kroese, B. S., Felce, D., Cohen, D., ... & Shead, J. (2013). Group-based cognitive-behavioural anger management for people with mild to moderate intellectual disabilities: cluster randomised controlled trial. *The British Journal of Psychiatry, 203,* 288–296.

Willoughby, M. T. (2003). Developmental course of ADHD symptomatology during the transition from childhood to adolescence: A review with recommendations. *Journal of Child Psychology and Psychiatry, and Allied Disciplines, 44*(1), 88–106.

Wilson, A.M., Armstrong, CD., Furrie, A. & Walcot, E. (2009). The mental health of Canadians with self reported learning disabilities. *Journal of Learning Disabilities 42,* 24–40.

Wilson, D., Peters, R., Ritchie, K., & Ritchie, C. W. (2011). Latest advances on interventions that may prevent, delay or ameliorate dementia. *Therapeutic Advances in Chronic Disease, 2* (3), 161–173.

Wilson, D. S., Near, D., & Miller, R. R. (1996). Machiavellianism: A synthesis of the evolutionary and psychological literatures. *Psychological Bulletin, 119,* 285–299.

Wilson, G. T., & Lawson, D. M. (1976). Effects of alcohol on sexual arousal in women. *Journal of Abnormal Psychology, 85,* 489–497.

Wilson, K., Demetrioff, S., & Porter, S. (2008). A pawn by any other name? Social information processing as a function of psychopathic traits. *Journal of Research in Personality, 42,* 1651–1656. doi:10.1016/j.jrp.2008.07.006

Wilson, L. M., Avila Tang, E., Chander, G., Hutton, H. E., Odelola, O. A., Elf, J. L., ... & Apelberg, B. J. (2012). Impact of tobacco control interventions on smoking initiation, cessation, and prevalence: a systematic review. *Journal of Environmental and Public Health.* Published online www.ncbi.nlm.nih.gov/pubmed/22719777

Wilson, M., Joffe, R. T., & Wilkerson, B. (2000). The unheralded business crisis in Canada: Depression at work. Business and Economic Roundtable on Mental Health. Retrieved from www.mentalhealthroundtable.ca/aug_round_pdfs/Roundtable%20report_Jul20.pdf

Wilson, R. J., Abracen, J., Picheca, J. E., Malcolm, P. B., & Prinzo, M. (2003, October). Pedophilia: An evaluation of diagnostic and risk management methods. Paper presented at the 22nd Annual Research and Treatment Conference of the Association for the Treatment of Sexual Abusers, St Louis, MO.

Wilson, T. G. (1993). Psychological and pharmacological treatments of bulimia nervosa: A research update. *Applied and Preventative Psychology, 2,* 35–42.

Wilson, W. H., Ellinwood, E. H., Mathew, R. J., & Johnson, K. (1994). Effects of marijuana on performance of a computerized cognitive-neurological test battery. *Psychiatry Research, 51,* 115–125.

Wilson-Bates, F. (2008). *Lost in transition: How a lack of capacity in the mental health system is failing Vancouver's mentally ill and draining police resources.* Vancouver, BC: Vancouver Police Department.

Win, S., Parakh, K., Eze-Nliam, C. M., Gottdiener, J. S., Kop, W. J., & Ziegelstein, R. C. (2011). Depressive symptoms, physical inactivity and risk of cardiovascular mortality in older adults: the Cardiovascular Health Study. *Heart, 97,* 500–505.

Wincze, J. P., & Carey, M. P. (2001). *Sexual dysfunction: A guide for assessment and treatment* (2nd ed.). New York, NY: Guilford.

Wincze, J. P., Bach, A. K., & Barlow, D. H. (2008). Sexual dysfunction. In D. H. Barlow (Ed.), *Clinical handbook of psychological disorders: A step-by-step treatment manual* (pp. 615–661). New York, NY: Guilford.

Wing, L. (1996). Autistic spectrum disorders. *BMJ: British Medical Journal, 312*(7027), 327.

Wing, L., & Potter, D. (2002). The epidemiology of autistic spectrum disorders: Is the prevalence rising? *Mental Retardation and Developmental Disabilities Research Reviews, 8,* 151–161.

Wing, L., & Potter, D. (2009). The epidemiology of autism spectrum disorders: Is the prevalence rising? In S. Goldstein, J. Naglieri, & S. Ozonoff (Eds.), *Assessment of autism spectrum disorders* (pp. 18–54). New York, NY: Guilford.

Wing, V. C., Bacher, I., Sacco, K. A., & George, T. P. (2011). Neuropsychological performance in patients with schizophrenia and controls as a function of cigarette smoking status. *Psychiatry research, 188*(3), 320–326.

Winko v. British Columbia (Forensic Psychiatric Institute), [1999] 2 S.C.R. 625

Winzer-Serhan, U. H. (2008). Long term consequences of maternal smoking and developmental chronic nicotine exposure. *Frontiers in Bioscience, 13,* 636–649.

Wise, J. (2014). Only half of patients referred for talking therapies enter treatment. *British Medical Journal, 348.* doi: 10.1136/bmj.g295.

Wise, T. N., & Birket-Smith, M. (2002). The somatoform disorders for DSM-V: The need for changes in process and content. *Psychosomatics, 43,* 437–440.

Wiseman, C. V., Gray, J. J., Mosimann, J. E., & Ahrens, A. H. (1992). Cultural expectations of thinness in women: An update. *International Journal of Eating Disorders, 11,* 85–89.

Witkiewitz, K., & Marlatt, G. A. (2004). Relapse prevention for alcohol and drug problems. *American Psychologist, 59,* 224–235.

Wolery, M., & Bailey, D. B. (2002). Early childhood special education research. *Journal of Early Intervention, 25,* 88–99.

Wolfe, B. E., Metzger, E. D., & Jimerson, D. C. (1997). Research update on serotonin function in bulimia nervosa and anorexia nervosa. *Psychopharmacology Bulletin, 33,* 345–354.

Wolfensberger, W. (1972). *The principle of normalization in human services.* Toronto, ON: Leonard Crainford.

Wolfensberger, W. (1975). *The origin and nature of our institutional models.* Syracuse, NY: Human Policy Press.

Wolfensberger, W. (2002). Needed or at least wanted: Sanity in the language wars. *Mental Retardation, 40,* 75–80.

Wolitzky-Taylor, K. B., Castriotta, N., Lenze, E. J., Stanley, M. A., & Craske, M. G. (2010). Anxiety disorders in older adults: A comprehensive review. *Depression and Anxiety, 27,* 190–211.

Wolpe, J. (1958). *Psychotherapy by reciprocal inhibition.* Stanford, CA: Stanford University Press.

Wolpe, J., & Rachman, S. (1960). Psychoanalytic evidence: A critique based on Freud's case of Little Hans. *Journal of Nervous and Mental Disease, 131,* 135–145.

Wonderlich, S. A., Gordon, K. H., Mitchell, J. E., Crosby, R. D., & Engel, S. G. (2009). The validity and clinical utility of binge eating disorder. *International Journal of Eating Disorders, 42,* 687–705.

Wong, D. F., Wagner, H. N., Jr., Tune, L. E., Dannals, R. F., Pearlson, G. D., Links, J. M., et al. (1986). Positron emission tomography reveals elevated D$_2$ dopamine receptors in drug-naive schizophrenics. *Science, 234,* 1558–1562.

Wong, G., Derthick, A. O., David, E. J. R., Saw, A., & Okazaki, S. (2014). The what, the why, and the how: A review of racial microaggressions research in psychology. *Race and Social Problems, 6*(2), 181–200.

Wong, S. (1984). *The criminal and institutional behaviors of psychopaths.* Programs Branch Users Report. Ottawa, ON: Ministry of the Solicitor General of Canada.

Wong, S., & Hare, R. D. (2005). *Guidelines for a psychopathy treatment program.* Toronto, ON: Multi-Health Systems.

Wong, T., Ho, C.S., & Tang, J. (2017). Defective number sense or impaired access? differential impairments in different subgroups of children with mathematics difficulties. *Journal of Learning Disabilities, 50*(1) 49–61.

Wood, J. M., Lilienfeld, S. O., Nezworski, M. T., Garb, H. N., Allen, K. H., & Wildermuth, J. L. (2010). Validity of Rorschach Inkblot scores for discriminating psychopaths from nonpsychopaths in forensic populations: A meta-analysis. *Psychological Assessment, 22*(2), 336.

Woodhouse, K. W. (1993). Sleep disorders in the elderly. In R. Levy, R. Howard, & A. Burns (Eds.), *Treatment and care in old age psychiatry.* Petersfield, UK: Wrightson Biomedical Publishing.

Woodruff, S. C., Arnkoff, D. B., Glass, C. R., & Hindman, R. K. (2014). Mindfulness and anxiety. In A. Ie, C. T. Ngnoumen, & E. J. Langer, (Eds.), *The Wiley Blackwell handbook of mindfulness* (Vols I & II, pp. 732–754). Oxford: Wiley-Blackwell.

Woodside, D. B., & Kaplan, A. S. (1994). Day hospital treatment in males with eating disorders—Response and comparison to females. *Journal of Psychosomatic Research, 38,* 471–475.

Woodworth, M., & Porter, S. (2002). In cold blood: Characteristics of criminal homicides as a function of psychopathy. *Journal of Abnormal Psychology, 111,* 436–445.

Woody, S. R., & Tolin, D. F. (2002). The relationship between disgust sensitivity and avoidant behaviour: Studies of clinical and nonclinical samples. *Anxiety Disorders, 16,* 543–559.

Woolfolk, R. L., & Allen, L. A. (2007). *Treating somatization: A cognitive-behavioral approach.* New York, NY: Guilford.

Woolfolk, R. L., & Allen, L. A. (2010). Affective-cognitive behavioral therapy for somatization disorder. *Journal of Cognitive Psychotherapy, 24,* 116–131.

World Health Organization. (1992a). *International classification of diseases and related health problems* (10th rev. ed.). Geneva: WHO.

World Health Organization. (1992b). *ICD-10 Classifications of Mental and Behavioural Disorders: Clinical Descriptions and Diagnostic Guidelines.* Geneva: WHO.

World Health Organization. (2000). Cross-national comparisons of the prevalences and correlates of mental disorders. WHO International Consortium in Psychiatric Epidemiology. *Bulletin of the World Health Organization, 78*(4), 413–426.

World Health Organization. (2008). *Depression.* Retrieved from www.who.int/mental_health/management/depression/definition/en

World Health Organization. (2014a). *Global status report on alcohol and health 2014.* World Health Organization.

World Health Organization (Calouste Gulbenkian Foundation) (2014b). *Social determinants of mental health.* Retrieved from www.who.int/mental_health/publications/gulbenkian_paper_social_determinants_of_mental_health/en/.

World Health Organization. (2015). Global Mental Health. Retrieved from www.who.int/mental_health/evidence/atlas/interactive_infographic_2015.pdf

World Health Organization. (2016a). Classifications of Diseases (ICD). Retrieved from www.who.int/classifications/icd/revision/en

World Health Organization. (2016b). Depression Fact Sheet. Retrieved from www.who.int/mediacentre/factsheets/fs369/en/

WPATH, Standards of Care V7. (2011). Retrieved from www.wpath.org/site_page.cfm?pk_association_webpage_menu=1351&pk_association_webpage=3926

Wright, D., Moran, J., & Gouglas, S. (2003). The confinement of the insane in Victorian Canada: The Hamilton and Toronto asylums. In R. Porter & D. Wright (Eds.). *The confinement of the insane: International perspectives, 1800–1965* (pp. 100–128). New York, NY: Cambridge University Press.

Wrightsman, L. S., & Porter, S. (2005). *Forensic psychology* (1st Canadian ed.). Toronto: Thomson Nelson.

Wu, J. C., & Bunney, W. E. (1990). Sleep deprivation and relapse. *American Journal of Psychiatry, 147,* 14–21.

Wulsin, L. R., & Singal, B. M. (2003). Do depressive symptoms increase the risk for the onset of coronary disease? A systematic, quantitative review. *Psychosomatic Medicine, 65,* 201–210.

Wyatt Kaminski, J., Valle, L. A., Filene, J. H., & Boyle, C. L. (2008). A meta-analytic review of componets associated with parent training program effectiveness. *Journal of Abnormal Child Psychology, 36,* 567–589. doi:10.1007/s10802-007-9201-9

Wykes, T., Huddy, V., Cellard, C., McGurk, S. R., & Czobor, P. (2011). A meta-analysis of cognitive remediation for schizophrenia: Methodology and effect sizes. *American Journal of Psychiatry, 168*(5), 472–485.

Wyngaarden, M. (1981). Interviewing mentally retarded persons: Issues and strategies. In R. Bruininks, C. E. Meyers, B. B. Sigford, & K. C. Lakin (Eds.), *Deinstitutionalization and community adjustment of mentally retarded people.* Monograph No. 4 (pp. 107–113). Washington, DC: American Association on Mental Deficiency.

Yaffe, K., Falvey, C. M., & Hoang, T. (2014). Connections between sleep and cognition in older adults. *The Lancet Neurology, 13*(10), 1017–1028. doi:http://dx.doi.org/10.1016/S1474-4422(14)70172-3

Yang, Y., Raine, A., Lencz, T., Bihrle, S., LaCasse, L., & Colletti, P. (2005). Volume reduction in prefrontal gray matter in unsuccessful criminal psychopaths. *Biological Psychiatry, 57,* 1103–1108.

Yates, G. P., & Feldman, M. D. (2016). Factitious disorder: A systematic review of 455 cases in the professional literature. *General Hospital Psychiatry, 41,* 20–28.

Yates, P. M., Goguen, B. C., Nicholaichuk, T. P., Williams, S. M., Long, C. A., Jeglic, E., et al. (2000). *National sex offender programs (moderate, low, and maintenance intensity levels)*. Ottawa, ON: Correctional Service of Canada.

Yatham, L. N., Kennedy, S. H., Parikh, S. V., Schaffer, A., Beaulieu, S., Alda, M., . . .Berk, M. (2013). Canadian Network for Mood and Anxiety Treatment (CANMAT) and Internation Society for Bipolar Disorders (ISBD) collaborative update of CANMAT guidelines for the management of patients with bipolar disorder: Update 2013. *Bipolar Disorders, 15,* 1–44.

Yayla, S., Bakım, B., Tankaya, O., Ozer, O. A., Karamustafalioglu, O., Ertekin, H., & Tekin, A. (2015). Psychiatric comorbidity in patients with conversion disorder and prevalence of dissociative symptoms. *Journal of Trauma & Dissociation, 16*(1), 29–38.

Yehuda, R., Golier, J. A., Halligan, S. L., Meaney, M., & Bierer, L. M. (2004). The ACTH response to dexamethasone in PTSD. *American Journal of Psychiatry, 161,* 1397–1403.

Yehuda, R., Halligan, S. L., Golier, J. A., Grossman, R., & Bierer, L. M. (2004). Effects of trauma exposure on the cortisol response to dexamethazone administration in PTSD and major depressive disorder. *Psychoneuroendocrinology, 29,* 389–404.

Yin, L., Wang, J., Klein, P. S., & Lazar, M. A. (2006). Nuclear receptor Rev-ErbA alpha is a critical lithium-sensitive component of the circadian clock. *Science, 311,* 1002–1005.

Young, A. H., & Hammond, J. M. (2007). Lithium in mood disorders: Increasing evidence base, declining use? *British Journal of Psychiatry, 191,* 474–476.

Young, J. E. (1994). *Cognitive therapy for personality disorders: A schema-focused approach* (rev. ed.). Sarasota, FL: Professional Resource Press.

Young, J. E. (1999). *Cognitive therapy for personality disorders: A schema-focused approach* (3rd ed.). Sarasota, FL: Professional Resource Press.

Young, J. E., Klosko, J. S., & Weishaar, M. E. (2003). *Schema therapy: A practitioner's guide.* New York, NY: Guilford.

Young, M. M., & Jesseman, R. (2014). *The impact of substance use disorders on hospital use.* Ottawa, ON: Canadian Centre on Substance Abuse.

Young, R., Oei, T. P., & Knight, R. G. (1990). The tension reduction hypothesis revisited: An alcohol expectancy perspective. *British Journal of Addiction, 85*(1), 31–40.

Young, T. K. (1998). *Population health.* New York, NY: Oxford University Press.

Youngren, M. A., & Lewinsohn, P. M. (1980). The functional relationship between depressed and problematic interpersonal behavior. *Journal of Abnormal Psychology, 89,* 333–341.

Youth Criminal Justice Act, R.S.C. 2002, c. 1.

Yu, S., Pritchard, M. D., Kremer, E., Lynch, M., Nancarrow, J., Baker, E., et al. (1991). Fragile X genotype characterized by an unstable region of DNA. *Science, 252,* 1179–1181.

Yusuf, S., Hawken, S., Ounpuu, S., Dans, T., Avezum, A., Lanas, F., McQueen, M., Budaj, A., Pais, P., Varigos, J., Lisheng, L., & the INTERHEART Study Investigators (2004). Effect of potentially modifiable risk factors associated with myocardial infarction in 52 countries (the INTERHEART study): Case-control study. *The Lancet, 364,* 937–952.

Zakowski, S. G., McAllister, C. G., Deal, M., & Baum, A. (1992). Stress, reactivity, and immune function in healthy men. *Health Psychology, 11,* 223–232.

Zammit, S., & Owen, M. J. (2006). Stressful live events, 5-HTT genotype and risk of depression. *British Journal of Psychiatry, 188,* 199–201.

Zanarini, M. C., Frankenburg, F. R., Hennen, J., Reich, B., & Silk, K. R. (2005). The McLean study of adult development (MSAD): Overview and implications of the first six years of prospective follow-up. *Journal of Personality Disorders, 19,* 505–523.

Zanarini, M., Skodol, A., Bender, D., Dolan, R., Sanislow, C., Schaefer, E., et al. (2000). The Collaborative Longitudinal Personality Disorders Study: Reliability of Axis I and II diagnoses. *Journal of Personality Disorders, 14*(4), 291–299.

Zang, Y., Hunt, N., & Cox, T. (2013). A randomized controlled pilot study: The effectiveness of narrative exposure therapy with adult survivors of the Sichuan earthquake. *BMC Psychiatry, 31,* 13–41. doi:10. 1186/1471-244X-13-41

Zapf, P. A., & Roesch, R. (1997). Assessing fitness to stand trial: A comparison of institution-based evaluations and a brief screening interview. *Canadian Journal of Community Mental Health, 16,* 53–66.

Zapf, P. A., & Roesch, R. (1998). Fitness to stand trial: Characteristics of remands since the 1992 criminal code amendments. *Canadian Journal of Psychiatry, 43,* 287–293.

Zapf, P. A., & Roesch, R. (2009). *Best practices in forensic mental health assessments: Evaluation of competence to stand trial.* New York, NY: Oxford University Press.

Zapf, P. A., Golding, S. L., & Roesch, R. (2005). Criminal responsibility and the insanity defense. In I. B. Weiner & A. K. Hess (Eds.), *Handbook of forensic psychology* (3rd ed., pp. 332–363). New York, NY: Wiley.

Zapf, P. A., Roesch, R., & Viljoen, J. L. (2001). Assessing fitness to stand trial: The utility of the Fitness Interview Test (rev. ed.). *Canadian Journal of Psychiatry, 46,* 426–432e.

Zarit, S. H., & Zarit, J. M. (1998). *Mental disorders in older adults: Fundamentals of assessment and treatment.* New York, NY: Guilford.

Zemishlany, Z., Siever, L. J., & Coccaro, E. F. (1988). Biological factors in personality disorders. *Israel Journal of Psychiatry and Related Sciences, 25,* 12–23.

Zetterqvist M. (2015). The DSM-5 diagnosis of nonsuicidal self-injury disorder: a review of the empirical literature. *Child and Adolescent Psychiatry and Mental Health, 28,* 9–31.

Zhou, X., Hetrick, S. E., Cuijpers, P., Qin, B., Barth, J., Whittington, C. J. . . . Xie, P. (2015). Comparative efficacy and acceptability of psychotherapies for depression in children and adolescents: a systematic review and network meta-analysis. *World Psychiatry, 14,* 207–222.

Ziats, M. N., & Rennert, O. M. (2016). The Evolving Diagnostic and Genetic Landscapes of Autism Spectrum Disorder. *Frontiers in Genetics, 7,* 65. https://doi.org/10.3389/fgene.2016.00065

Zigler, E. (1967). Familial mental retardation: A continuing dilemma. *Science, 155,* 292–298.

Zigler, E., & Hodapp, R. M. (1991). *Understanding mental retardation.* Cambridge, UK: Cambridge University Press.

Zigler, E., Hodapp, R. M., & Edison, M. (1990). From theory to practice in the care and education of mentally retarded individuals. *American Journal on Mental Retardation, 95,* 1–12.

Zigman, W. B., Schupf, N., Lubin, R. A., & Silverman, W. P. (1987). Premature regression of adults with Down syndrome. *American Journal of Mental Deficiency, 92,* 161–168.

Zilboorg, G., & Henry, G. W. (1941). *A history of medical psychology.* New York, NY: Norton.

Zimmerman, M. (1994). Diagnosing personality disorders: A review of issues and research methods. *Archives of General Psychiatry, 51,* 225–245.

Zimmerman, M., & Coryell, W. H. (1990). Diagnosing personality disorders in the community: A comparison of self-report and interview measures. *Archives of General Psychiatry, 47,* 527–531.

Zimmerman, M., Mattia, J. I., & Posternak, M. A. (2002). Are subjects in pharmacological treatment trials of depression representative of patients in routine clinical practice? *American Journal of Psychiatry, 159,* 469–473.

Zipursky, R. B., Meyer, J. H., & Verhoeff, N. P. (2007). PET and SPECT imaging in psychiatric disorders. *Canadian Journal of Psychiatry, 52*(3), 146.

Zisook, S., & Kendler, K. S. (2007). Is bereavement-related depression different than non-bereavement-related depression? *Psychological Medicine, 37,* 779–794.

Zivian, M. T., Larsen, W., Knox, V. J., Gekoski, W. L., & Hatchette, V. (1992). Psychotherapy for the elderly: Psychotherapists' preferences. *Psychotherapy, 29,* 668–674.

Zlotnick, C. (1999). Antisocial personality disorder, affect dysregulation and childhood abuse among incarcerated women. *Journal of Personality Disorders, 13,* 90–95.

Zoccolillo, M. (1993). Gender and the development of conduct disorder. *Development and Psychopathology, 5,* 65–78.

Zoccolillo, M., & Rogers, K. (1991). Characteristics and outcome of hospitalized adolescent girls with conduct disorder. *Journal of the American Academy of Child & Adolescent Psychiatry, 30*(6), 973–981.

Zorn, J. V., Schür, R. R., Boks, M. P., Kahn, R. S., Joëls, M., & Vinkers, C. H. (2016). Cortisol stress reactivity across psychiatric disorders: A systematic review and meta-analysis. *Psychoneuroendocrinology, 77,* 25–36.

Zucker, K. J. (1990). Gender identity disorders in children. In R. Blanchard & B. W. Steiner (Eds.), *Clinical management of gender identity disorders in children and adults* (pp. 27–45). Washington, DC: American Psychiatry Press.

Zucker, K. J. (2005). Gender identity disorder in children and adolescence. *Annual Review of Clinical Psychology, 1,* 467–492.

Zucker, K. J., & Bradley, S. J. (1995). Gender identity disorder and psychosexual problems in children and adolescents. New York, NY: Guilford.

Zucker, K. J., Beaulieu, N., Bradley, S. J., Grimshaw, G. M., & Wilcox, A. (2001). Handedness in boys with gender identity disorder. *Journal of Child Psychology and Psychiatry, 42,* 767–776.

Zunhammer, M., Eberle, H., Eichhammer, P., & Busch, V. (2013). Somatic symptoms evoked by exam stress in university students: The role of alexithymia, neuroticism, anxiety and depression. *PLOS ONE, 8*(12), 1–11.

Zürcher, N. R., Bhanot, A., McDougle, C. J., & Hooker, J. M. (2015). A systematic review of molecular imaging (PET and SPECT) in autism spectrum disorder: Current state and future research opportunities. *Neuroscience & Biobehavioral Reviews, 52,* 56–73.

Name Index

Subject Index